HANDBOOK OF RESEARCH ON SCIENCE TEACHER EDUCATION

This groundbreaking handbook offers a contemporary and thorough review of research relating directly to the preparation, induction, and career long professional learning of K–12 science teachers.

Through critical and concise chapters, this volume provides essential insights into science teacher education that range from their learning as individuals to the programs that cultivate their knowledge and practices. Each chapter is a current review of research that depicts the area and then points to empirically based conclusions or suggestions for science teacher educators or educational researchers. Issues associated with equity are embedded within each chapter. Drawing on the work of over 100 contributors from across the globe, this handbook has 35 chapters that cover established, emergent, diverse, and pioneering areas of research, including:

- Research methods and methodologies in science teacher education, including discussions of the purpose of science teacher education research and equitable perspectives;
- Formal and informal teacher education programs that span from early childhood educators to the complexity of preparation, to the role of informal settings such as museums;
- Continuous professional learning of science teachers that supports building cultural responsiveness and teacher leadership;
- Core topics in science teacher education that focus on teacher knowledge, educative curricula, and working with all students; and
- Emerging areas in science teacher education such as STEM education, global education, and identity development.

This comprehensive, in-depth text will be central to the work of science teacher educators, researchers in the field of science education, and all those who work closely with science teachers.

Julie A. Luft is Distinguished Research Professor, Athletic Association Professor of Mathematics and Science Education, and Adjunct Professor of Biochemistry and Molecular Biology at the University of Georgia, USA.

M. Gail Jones is Alumni Distinguished Graduate Professor of Science Education and Senior Research Fellow at the Friday Institute for Educational Innovation at North Carolina State University, USA.

HANDBOOK OF RESEARCH ON SCIENCE TEACHER EDUCATION

Edited by
Julie A. Luft and M. Gail Jones

Routledge
Taylor & Francis Group

NEW YORK AND LONDON

Cover image: © Getty Images

First published 2022
by Routledge
605 Third Avenue, New York, NY 10158

and by Routledge
4 Park Square, Milton Park, Abingdon, Oxon, OX14 4RN

Routledge is an imprint of the Taylor & Francis Group, an informa business

Library of Congress Cataloging-in-Publication Data
Names: Luft, Julie, editor. | Jones, M. Gail, 1955- editor.
Title: Handbook of research on science teacher education / edited by Julie A. Luft and M. Gail Jones.
Description: New York, NY : Routledge, 2022. | Includes bibliographical references and index.
Identifiers: LCCN 2021050930 | ISBN 9780367565831 (hardcover) | ISBN 9780367565824 (paperback) | ISBN 9781003098478 (ebook)
Subjects: LCSH: Science teachers—Tranining of. | Science—Study and teaching.
Classification: LCC Q181 .H1495 2022 | DDC 507.1/2—dc23/eng/20211217
LC record available at https://lccn.loc.gov/2021050930

ISBN: 9780367565831 (hbk)
ISBN: 9780367565824 (pbk)
ISBN: 9781003098478 (ebk)

DOI: 10.4324/9781003098478

Typeset in Bembo
by Apex CoVantage, LLC

This book is dedicated to science teachers who graciously opened and open their classrooms to collaborate with science teacher educators and researchers. Every time we work together, we learn together.

Advisory Committee for the
Handbook of Research on Science Teacher Education

Lucy Avraamidou – University of Groningen, Netherlands
Julie A. Bianchini – University of California at Santa Barbara, USA
Elizabeth A. Davis – University of Michigan, USA
Linda Hobbs – Deakin University, Australia
Carla C. Johnson – North Carolina State University, USA
Jing Lin – Beijing Normal University, China
Aik-Ling Tan – National Institute of Education, Nanyang Technological University, Singapore
Fred Lubben – The University of York, UK and South Africa
Dana Vedder-Weiss – Ben Gurion University of the Negev, Israel

Project Assistants

José Manuel Pavez, Lead Assistant, University of Georgia, USA
Joe DeLuca, University of Georgia, USA
Kayla Flanagan, University of Georgia, USA

CONTENTS

List of Contributors	*xi*
Preface	*xxxvi*
Acknowledgments	*xxxix*

SECTION 1

Research in Science Teacher Education   **1**

Section Editor: Julie A. Luft

1   The Importance of Research in Science Teacher Education   5
Sibel Erduran and Liam Guilfoyle

2   The Contribution of Large Educational Surveys to Science Teacher
Education Research   16
Robert H. Tai, Joseph A. Taylor, Vijay Reddy,
and Eric R. Banilower

3   Qualitatively Conducting Teacher Education Research   28
Felicia Moore Mensah and Jessica L. Chen

4   Mixed Methods Research on Science Teacher Education   41
Gayle A. Buck and Francesca A. Williamson

5   Towards Justice: Designing for a Rightful Presence as a Lens for
Science Teacher Education Research   52
Angela Calabrese-Barton, Edna Tan, Kathleen Schenkel,
and Aerin W. Benavides

SECTION 2
Initial Science Teacher Education – Core Areas   **65**
Section Editor: Sarah J. Carrier

6   Preparing Early Childhood Teachers to Support Young Children's
Equitable Science Sensemaking   69
Carla Zembal-Saul, Christina Siry, Sabela F. Monteira,
and Frances Nebus Bose

7   Well-Started Beginners: Preparing Elementary Teachers for Rigorous,
Consequential, Just, and Equitable Science Teaching   83
Elizabeth A. Davis and Christa Haverly

8   Research on Secondary Science Teacher Preparation   97
Todd Campbell, Ron Gray, Xavier Fazio, and Jan van Driel

9   Understanding the Role of Field Experiences in Preservice Science
Teacher Preparation   119
David Stroupe

10   Recent Trends in Science Education Research on Mentoring
Preservice Teachers   132
Leslie U. Bradbury

11   Alternative Pathways to Science Teaching: Approaches and Impacts   145
Elizabeth Edmondson, Alison Dossick, Smadar Donitsa-Schmidt,
Yehudit Judy Dori, Christine Ure, and Christel Balck

SECTION 3
Initial Teacher Preparation – Situated Aspects   **159**
Section Editor: David F. Jackson

12   Preservice Science Teachers Education Around the Globe: Trends,
Challenges, and Future Directions   163
Hernán Cofré, Claudia Vergara, David Santibáñez, and José Manuel Pavez

13   Partnerships in K–12 Preservice Science Teacher Education   178
Andrew Gilbert and Linda Hobbs

14   The Magic of Informal Settings: A Literature Review of Partnerships
and Collaborations that Support Preservice Science Teacher
Education Across the Globe   189
Natasha Cooke-Nieves, Jamie Wallace, Preeti Gupta,
and Elaine Howes

Contents

15 Discursive Practices in Initial Science Teacher Education   203
    Mercè Izquierdo, Ainoa Marzábal, Cristian Merino, Valeria Cabello,
    Patricia Moreira, Luigi Cuellar, Virginia Delgado,
    Franklin Manrique, and Macarena Soto

16 The Role of Emerging Technologies in Science Teacher Preparation   218
    Gina Childers and Rebecca Hite

17 Policy in K–12 Science Teacher Preparation: Uniformity
    and Diversity from International Perspectives   231
    Cheng Liu, Wenyuan Yang, and Enshan Liu

SECTION 4
Science Teacher Continuing Professional Development   243
Section Editor: Lauren Madden

18 The Learning Opportunities of Newly Hired Teachers of Science   245
    Shannon L. Navy, Julie A. Luft, and Audrey Msimanga

19 Science Teacher Leadership: The Current Landscape and Paths Forward   257
    Brooke A. Whitworth, Julianne A. Wenner, and Dorit Tubin

20 Professional Development of Science Teachers for Inquiry Instruction   273
    Umesh Ramnarain, Daniel Capps, and Ying-Shao Hsu

21 A Literature Review of Global Perspectives on the Professional
    Development of Culturally Responsive Science Teachers   287
    Julie C. Brown, Rose M. Pringle, and Nihat Kotluk

22 Professional Learning Communities Across Science Teachers' Careers:
    The Importance of Differentiating Learning   300
    Ron Blonder and Vicki Vescio

23 Digital Technologies and Professional Learning of Science Teachers:
    A Technological Pedagogical Content Knowledge (TPACK) Perspective   313
    Seng Chee Tan, Tang Wee Teo, and Chin-Chung Tsai

SECTION 5
Science Teacher Education – Central Tenets   325
Section Editor: Soonhye Park

24 Science Teacher Professional Knowledge and Its Relationship to
    High-Quality Science Instruction   329
    Vanessa Kind, Soonhye Park, and Kennedy Kam Ho Chan

Contents

25　Indigenous Knowledge in Science Education: Implications for Teacher
　　Education　　　　　　　　　　　　　　　　　　　　　　　　　340
　　Josef de Beer, Neal Petersen, and Meshach Ogunniyi

26　Action Research: A Promising Strategy for Science Teacher Education　352
　　Allan Feldman, Nadja Belova, Ingo Eilks, Marika Kapanadze,
　　Rachel Mamlok-Naaman, Franz Rauch, and Mehmet Fatih Taşar

27　Including All Learners Through Science Teacher Education　　　　363
　　Michele Hollingsworth Koomen, Sami Kahn, and Teresa Shume

28　The Role of Teacher Education in Teaching Science to Emergent
　　Bilingual Learners　　　　　　　　　　　　　　　　　　　376
　　Edward G. Lyon and Sara Tolbert

29　Educative Curriculum Materials and Their Role in the Learning
　　of Science Teachers　　　　　　　　　　　　　　　　　　388
　　Melina Furman, Mariana Luzuriaga, Margarita Gómez,
　　and Mauricio Duque

SECTION 6
Science Teacher Education – Emerging Areas　　　　　　　　**399**
Section Editor: Rachel Mamlok-Naaman

30　Learning to Teach Controversial Topics　　　　　　　　　403
　　Michael J. Reiss

31　Professional Identity as a Framework for Science Teacher Education
　　and Professional Development　　　　　　　　　　　　　414
　　Dana Vedder-Weiss

32　Emotion and Science Teacher Education　　　　　　　　　426
　　Alberto Bellocchi and Arnau Amat

33　Learning to Teach Science From a Contextualized Stance　　　439
　　Michael Giamellaro, Kassandra L'Heureux, Cory Buxton,
　　Marie-Claude Beaudry, Jean-Philippe Ayotte-Beaudet, and Talal Alajmi

34　Learning in and Through Researcher-Teacher Collaboration　　452
　　Eve Manz, Sara C. Heredia, Carrie D. Allen, and William R. Penuel

35　Integrated STEM Teacher Education: An Opportunity for Promoting Equity　465
　　Erin E. Peters-Burton and Kelly L. Knight

Index　　　　　　　　　　　　　　　　　　　　　　　　477

CONTRIBUTORS

Talal Alajmi is a doctoral student in the Science and Mathematics Education Program at Oregon State University, USA. Prior to OSU, Talal completed two graduate degrees: one from the University of Edinburgh in science (biochemistry) communication and public engagement, and the most recent one from the University of Oregon in educational leadership. Talal's focus is in exploring science education through authenticity and context and utilizing this framework to enhance and improve students' knowledge and interest in science. Since enrolling at OSU in 2018, Talal has worked with an array of students from different backgrounds and believes that each learner is unique and deserves an engaging and collaborative environment to grow intellectually and socially. In addition to his obligations as a PhD student, Talal teaches several courses at OSU, including Inquiry in Science Education, Designing Learning Environments: Physical Dimensions of Informal Learning, and Examining Learner's Own Ideas: Personal Dimensions of Informal Learning.

Carrie D. Allen is Assistant Professor of Learning Sciences at the University of North Texas, USA. Her research aims to develop understanding of the various processes through which equity- and justice-oriented reform efforts within STEM education become understood, experienced, responded to, and enacted in order to inform the approach to designing learning opportunities for both teachers and students. She considers how espoused commitments to equity and instructional reform take on meaning and become consequential for youth, families, and educators in local practice. Toward these ends, she employs research designs that center the perspectives of youth and educators toward bringing about transformative learning and institutional change within the education system. Some of her current work explores the relationships among local policy, educators' organizational contexts, and their efforts to implement reform-based and equity-oriented pedagogies.

Arnau Amat is Professor of Education and Coordinator of the Master's Degree in Innovation in Specific Didactics at the Universitat de Vic – Universitat Central de Catalunya, Catalonia, Spain. His research focuses on sociocultural approaches in three different areas: involving the community in the school through science education, environmental education, and science teacher education. Prior to that he worked as environmental educator for various private companies and education authorities and as a science teacher in high school.

Jean-Philippe Ayotte-Beaudet is Director of, and an instructor in, the Research Center on Science Teaching and Learning in the Department of PreSchool and Primary Education at the

University of Sherbrooke, Canada. His research focuses on contextualization of science learning and currently explores the impact of learning science in the context of the transfer of learning to everyday life. He is also interested in outdoor teaching and learning in schools' immediate surroundings, conducting research on the impact of outdoor education in schools' immediate surroundings on learning and on the implementation of more physically active behaviors. Ayotte-Beaudet has examined the role of situational interest in science learning.

Christel Balck is a lecturer and researcher in physics, technology, and STEM education at Odisee University of Applied Sciences in Flanders, Belgium. She obtained a master's degree in Physics at Antwerp University, Belgium, and taught secondary science and math from 1990 to 2000. From 2013 to 2015 she was a lecturer at the Erasmus Mundus program STETTIN (Science and Technology Education Teacher Training International Network). Her research interests include using preconceptions in science and technology to facilitate learning (Factory of Ideas research project), the implementation of thinking strategies in the didactics of STEM projects (STEM3D, from thinking to doing through dialogue in STEM projects) and culturally responsive teaching in STEM (Dialogo project). Through intense cooperation with in-service teachers , she aims to guarantee the transfer of research results in the practice of STEM teaching. She presented research results at national and international conferences VLHORA, VELON, VELOV ESERA, and NARST.

Eric R. Banilower is Vice President of Horizon Research, Inc., USA. Mr. Banilower has been part of the science education system in the United States for over 30 years, starting as a high school science teacher. Since 1998, he has worked at Horizon Research on a wide variety of evaluation and research projects focused on STEM education. He has particular expertise in teacher professional learning, research design, and measurement. His work has also included numerous large-scale science education program evaluations. He has also led the 2012 and 2018 iterations of the National Survey of Science and Mathematics Education which periodically gathers data about key aspects of the K–12 science and mathematics education system in the United States.

Marie-Claude Beaudry is a graduate student at the University of Sherbrooke, Canada. Beaudry is interested in the contextualization of outdoor teaching and learning in schools. Her research aims to better understand how teachers contextualize their teaching of outdoor science near the school. By studying different practices, she hopes to develop an approach that would help teacher candidates and teachers contextualize science learning in the immediate school environment. Her work is supervised by Professor Jean-Philippe Ayotte-Beaudet. She worked for about 10 years as an elementary school teacher and is now a lecturer at the University of Sherbrooke in didactics of science (BSc) and in outdoor science education (MSc).

Alberto Bellocchi is Associate Professor of Education at the Queensland University of Technology, Australia. He has established and leads the Studies of Emotion and Affect in Education Laboratory (SEAELs), a group of international education scholars interested in understanding the role of emotions, social bonds, and affect in school and university educational contexts. Alberto has published widely about emotions and social bonds in school and preservice teacher education and on methods and theories for understanding emotions during interactions. He is the lead editor of the collection *Exploring Emotions, Aesthetics, and Wellbeing in Science Education Research* (Springer) and co-editor of the collection *Emotions in Late Modernity* (Routledge).

Nadja Belova is a postdoctoral researcher at the Institute for Science Education (Chemistry Education Group) at the University of Bremen, Germany. Dr. Belova's doctoral work focused on advertising in science education. After her PhD, she worked as a grammar school teacher for two years before rejoining the science education group. Her main research focus is media literacy in the science classroom. In this context, she explicitly addresses modern media types such as social media and has designed and published a number of curricular innovations involving different types of media using action research.

Aerin W. Benavides is an Adjunct Research Assistant Professor at the University of North Carolina at Greensboro, USA. She is also a certified environmental educator and a bilingual STEM teacher educator. Dr. Benavides's environmental sustainability-minded STEM education inter-institutional research focuses on seeking social justice in education for marginalized learners by incorporating community-based issues and solutions into science education. Dr. Benavides's collaborative work with communities, on projects funded by the National Science Foundation, include investigating youth-engagement in outdoor environmental science activities and middle-school teachers and students taking up engineering for sustainable communities in classrooms. Her research has been published in *Science Education*, among others.

Ron Blonder is Professor in the Department of Science Teaching at the Weizmann Institute of Science, Israel. She is Head of the chemistry group and Head of the Rothschild-Weizmann Master's Program for Excellence in Mathematics and Science Teaching. Her research focuses on chemistry teachers' professional development in the context of contemporary science using innovative technological tools and environments. She has published over 100 peer-reviewed and invited papers and book chapters in which she has explored chemistry teachers' self-efficacy beliefs and knowledge development when teachers learn contemporary research in chemistry (mainly nanochemistry) and when they incorporate innovative pedagogies in their chemistry teaching. She has also investigated differentiated instruction in heterogeneous chemistry classes with and without the aid of technology to promote personalization in chemistry teaching. Professor Blonder has applied the results of her educational research to chemistry teachers' professional development in different frameworks including PLCs.

Frances Nebus Bose is a postdoctoral research associate and educator in the College of Education at the Pennsylvania State University, USA, where she also received a PhD in curriculum and instruction. Her research and teaching center on the advocacy of young bilingual/multilingual children for whom English is an additional language in the context of US schools. She is particularly interested in how science, technology, and engineering interactions offer unique opportunities for engaging and connecting within linguistically and culturally diverse classrooms and schools. Frances is a former bilingual preschool and elementary English as a Second language teacher and has taught in the mainland United States, Puerto Rico, China, and Italy.

Leslie U. Bradbury is Professor in the Department of Curriculum and Instruction at Appalachian State University, USA. Dr. Bradbury earned her PhD in science education at the University of Georgia. Her research interests include the use of multiple modes of learning in science, the integration of science with other content areas, and new teacher mentoring. She has published articles related to mentoring in the journals *Science Education*, *Journal of Science Teacher Education*, and *Teaching and Teacher Education*. Dr. Bradbury has received an Outstanding Teaching Award from the Reich College of Education and the Appalachian State University College Excellence in Teaching Award.

Julie C. Brown is Associate Professor in Science Education in the School of Teaching and Learning at the University of Florida, USA. Her work focuses on advancing equitable STEM learning environments by preparing culturally responsive science educators and designing equitable STEM instructional tools. Dr. Brown's research examines how science educators learn to enact cultural responsiveness for the students they serve through their attitudes, classroom practices, and designed curricula. She employs design-based research methods to devise, assess, and revise theoretically grounded interventions that are responsive to specific, contextualized problems. As a design researcher, Dr. Brown has produced theoretical insights for promoting equitable science teaching and positive impacts for partnering communities.

Gayle A. Buck is Associate Dean for Research and Professor in the School of Education, Indiana University, Bloomington, USA. Dr. Buck's scholarship focuses on relationships between learners, teachers, communities, and science. Her research objective is to further enhance our understanding of the complexity of teaching science to an increasingly diverse student population. To that end, she has developed a research agenda that focuses on: (1) student populations traditionally underserved by science education; (2) neglected epistemological assumptions in science teaching; and (3) pragmatic, participatory, and mixed approaches to educational research. She has published and presented many research studies on science teaching and learning in venues such as *Journal of Science Teacher Education, Studying Teacher Education, Science Education*, and *Journal of Research in Science Teaching*, as well as in books such as *Enhancing Professional Knowledge of Pre-Service Science Teacher Education by Self-Study Research, Moving the Equity Agenda Forward*, and *Research Based Undergraduate Science Teaching*.

Cory Buxton is Program Chair for Science and Mathematics Education at Oregon State University, USA. His research fosters more equitable science learning opportunities for all students, and especially for multilingual learners, by bringing together teacher professional learning and family engagement experiences in both school-based and out-of-school settings. His most recent research is on creating culturally and linguistically sustaining learning spaces where students, parents, teachers, and researchers can engage together as co-learners while strengthening their academic relationships, cultural connections, cumulative science knowledge building, and ownership of the language and practices of science. Buxton's research has been funded by the National Science Foundation, the U.S. Department of Education, and several private foundations.

Valeria Cabello is Assistant Professor in the Department of Learning and Development, of the Faculty of Education at the Pontificia Universidad Católica de Chile. She is a psychologist and holds a MPhil in educational psychology from Pontificia Universidad Católica de Chile, Chile. She obtained her PhD in educational psychology at the University of Dundee (Scotland, United Kingdom). Currently, her research focuses on science learning with two emphases: how student teachers learn to explain in the science classroom, and how students develop thinking processes in context-based STEAM education. She collaborates with two research centers of excellence: the Center for Policies and Practices in Education (CEPPE UC), and the Research Center for Integrated Disaster Risk Management (CIGIDEN).

Angela Calabrese-Barton is Professor in the Educational Studies Department at the University of Michigan, USA. Dr. Calabrese-Barton's research focuses on issues of equity and justice in STEM education in school and community settings. A former chemistry teacher, she takes an historicized and future-oriented ecological and participatory approach to give witness to and learn with school and community partners. She studies approaches to teaching and learning that center on what matters to people in the here-and-now and towards imagined social futures; and that disrupt/transform injustices that operate in classrooms. Current funded projects include collaborative co-design of justice-oriented science pedagogies, the design of equitable and consequential STEM-rich making programs, and youths' STEM learning and action-taking in everyday living in a multi-pandemic. She has served as a WT Grant Foundation Distinguished Fellow and is a Fellow of the American

Education Research Association. She is an Editor of the *American Educational Research Journal* and former Editor of the *Journal of Research in Science Teaching*.

Todd Campbell is Department Head of Curriculum and Instruction and Professor of Science Education in the Neag School of Education at the University of Connecticut, USA. His research focuses on cultivating imaginative and equitable representations of STEM activity. This is accomplished in formal science learning environments through partnering with preservice and in-service science teachers and leaders to collaboratively focus on supporting student use of modeling as an anchoring epistemic practice to reason about events that happen in the natural world. Currently, he is Co-Editor in Chief of the *Journal of Science Teacher Education*.

Daniel Capps is Associate Professor of Science Education at the University of Georgia, USA. His research focuses on supporting K–12 teachers and students in understanding more about what science is and the many ways it is practiced. Related strands of his research program investigate teacher learning and teacher change connected with reform-based educational practices and the design of instructional experiences to support students in learning about inquiry and the nature of science. More recently, he has become interested in designing instructional experiences around modeling in order to position big ideas in the curriculum as tools for understanding challenging science content.

Sarah J. Carrier is Distinguished Graduate Professor of Science Education in the Department of Teacher Education and Learning Sciences at North Carolina State University, USA. She has been involved in elementary science education initially as an elementary school teacher and as a teacher educator and mentor for undergraduate and graduate students. Her research goals have focused on elementary teachers and students learning about the wonders of science and the natural world in formal and informal settings. Her research on environmental education and outdoor learning complements her examinations of teachers' developing identities as teachers of science and using the language of science for communication and sensemaking. She is an Editor for the *International Journal of Science Education* and has served on editorial review boards for several journals, including the *Journal of Science Teacher Education*, and as an Associate Editor for the *Electronic Journal of Science Education*. She has been honored to serve as a section editor for *Handbook of Research on Science Teacher Education*.

Kennedy Kam Ho Chan is Assistant Professor at the University of Hong Kong. Dr. Chan's research interests include science teacher expertise and the use of video in teacher education. He has been an invited participant of the second PCK summit in the Netherlands and a recipient of various research awards and fellowships, including the East-Asian Association for Science Education Young Scholar Award and the Doris Zimmern HKU-Cambridge Hughes Hall Fellowship (2019–2020). He practices research-led teaching and is a recognized exemplary instructor. He is a Fellow of The Higher Education Academy and has won multiple teaching awards, including the 2017 University Early Career Teaching Award and the 2017 Student-Led University Teaching Feedback Award.

Jessica L. Chen is a postdoctoral fellow at Teachers College, Columbia University, New York, USA. Dr. Chen's research focuses on issues of equity, diversity, and social justice in science teacher education. Her work examines the science teacher identity and agency of elementary teachers as they participate in professional development and preservice teacher preparation programs. Her research has been published in the *Journal of Science Teacher Education*, and she has contributed several book chapters. She has been invited to present her research at AERA and NARST conferences. She currently teaches elementary preservice science methods courses. She received the Teachers College Doctoral Fellowship and Doctoral Dissertation Grant during her graduate studies.

Gina Childers is Assistant Professor of STEM Education in the Department of Curriculum and Instruction at Texas Tech University, USA. Her research interests include the investigation of remote and virtual technologies utilization in science education as well as the exploration of STEM within informal, nonformal, and community-based learning environments such as science cafés, science fiction conventions, and science festivals. Dr. Childers currently serves on the leadership team for the Southeastern Association for Science Teacher Education (SASTE) and on the *International Journal of Science Education* editorial board.

Hernán Cofré is Professor of Science Education in the Institute of Biology at Pontificia Universidad Católica de Valparaíso, Valparaíso, Chile. He obtained the degree of doctor of biological sciences in 2004 at the Pontificia Universidad Católica of Chile and has a postdoctoral experience in science education in the Department of Mathematics and Science Education at the Illinois Institute of Technology, Chicago, USA (2012). He is an Editor for *Journal of Science Teacher Education* and *Studies in Science Education*. His research interests focus on teaching and understanding the nature of science and the theory of evolution, and the professional development of biology teachers. He has been a guest presenter in a plenary session at NARST (2015) and has published more than 30 scientific articles in national and international journals. He is currently engaged in two funded projects about pedagogical content knowledge, nature of science, scientific argumentation, and climate change education.

Natasha Cooke-Nieves is Senior Specialist in Science and Teacher Education at the American Museum of Natural History, USA. Dr. Cooke-Nieves serves as Clinical Supervisor and Professor in the Masters of Arts in Teaching program for earth science teachers at the Richard Gilder Graduate School. Prior to this, she served as Instructional Specialist for Math and Science for a network of 27 New York City public schools, where she provided professional development for principals, administrators, and teachers in high-needs schools on differentiation and exemplary teaching practices. She also held positions as a science coach and science teacher in an elementary school. She holds a bachelor's degree in biopsychology from Vassar College and a master's degree in education from Brooklyn College at the City University of New York, and she earned a doctoral degree in science education from Columbia University Teacher's College.

Luigi Cuellar is Associate Professor in the Faculty of Education at the Universidad Católica de la Santísima Concepción, Chile. He obtained a degree of chemistry teacher at the Universidad Distrital de Bogotá (Colombia) and a PhD in science education at the Pontificia Universidad Católica de Chile. His research interests are science education at the school level, with special emphasis on the history of science, and teacher education for the development of scientific competences in secondary education. He is currently Coordinator of the Scientific Inquiry Program for Science Education (ICEC) of the Chilean Ministry of Education, in the Biobío Region.

Elizabeth A. Davis is Professor at the University of Michigan School of Education, USA. Her research focuses on beginning and experienced elementary teachers, teachers learning to engage in rigorous, consequential, and equitable science teaching, and the roles of curriculum materials and practice-based teacher education in promoting teacher learning. She was Chair of the Elementary Teacher Education Program at the University of Michigan for 4 years and helped lead a major redesign of this practice-based program. Davis received the Presidential Early Career Award for Scientists and Engineers at the White House in 2002. She has served on National Research Council committees focused on teacher learning and instructional materials, and she currently chairs the National Academies of Sciences, Engineering, and Medicine committee on enhancing science and engineering in preschool through elementary education. Davis earned her PhD in education in mathematics, science, and technology from the University of California, Berkeley.

Josef de Beer is Research Professor at North-West University, South Africa. His main research focus is on the affordances of indigenous knowledge to enhance self-directed learning in the natural sciences. Accolades include the National Research Foundation "Excellence in Science Engagement" Award that Josef received in 2019, and the Education Association of South Africa's Medal of Honour in 2020. Josef is the principal investigator in a Fuchs Foundation funded project, "Teachers without Borders." He has published at national and international levels and acts as a supervisor for postgraduate students. His most recent publication, "The Decolonization of the Curriculum Project: The Affordances of Indigenous Knowledge for Self-Directed Learning," was published by AOSIS.

Virginia Delgado is Assistant Professor at the Faculty of Chemistry and Pharmacy, Pontificia Universidad Católica de Chile, Chile. She obtained a chemistry degree at the Universidad Nacional de San Agustín (Perú), and a PhD in chemistry at the Pontificia Universidad Católica de Chile. Her research interests are focused on medical chemistry, specifically on quinones chemistry and natural products (synthesis and anticancer activity). At present, she is focused on chemistry education, specifically in preservice science teacher education. She has been co-investigator in three research projects in chemistry and two in education. She has also worked as an advisor with two undergraduate students, and she is Director of Program in Chemistry in Context for Science and Chemistry Teachers.

Smadar Donitsa-Schmidt is Associate Professor in the Kibbutzim College of Education in Israel. Since 2013 she has served as the Dean of the Faculty of Humanities and Social Sciences. Her previous roles in the college were Head of the Research Authority, Head of the Post Graduate Training Program, and Head of the English Department. Her PhD from Ontario Institute for Studies in Education (OISE) at Toronto University is in educational linguistics. Her current areas of research are initial teacher education with a particular emphasis on alternative pathways to teaching, teacher professional development, policy in education and higher education, and teaching in multicultural and multilingual contexts.

Yehudit Judy Dori is Professor of Science Education in the Faculty of Education in Science and Technology, Technion – Israel Institute of Technology, Israel. She was Dean of Faculty during 2015–2020 and Dean of Continuing Education and External Studies at the Technion during 2009–2013. She is Senior Researcher at the Samuel Neaman Institute for National Policy Research, Haifa, Israel. She has been intermittently Visiting Professor or Visiting Scholar at Massachusetts Institute of Technology between 2000 and 2014 and during 2020. Professor Dori research interests encompass educational technology, teacher education, assessment, 21st-century STEM skills, and metacognition at the high school and university levels. Professor Dori co-edited two books on cognition and metacognition in STEM education, published by Springer in 2012 and 2018. Professor Dori received the 2020 NARST Distinguished Contributions to Science Education through Research Award (DCRA) for her exceptional research contributions and strong national and international community engagements.

Alison Dossick is a doctoral student at Virginia Commonwealth University, USA. She has a bachelor's degree in biology from Virginia Tech and a Master's of Education from Marymount University. She taught middle school science for 18 years before pursuing her doctorate. In 2020, she served as a Research Fellow at the Bay Area Museum in San Francisco, working on STEM content delivery for PreK children. In 2021, she was a Fellow with the Smithsonian Science Education Center working on their Zero Barriers in STEM program. This professional development pilot study provided curriculum and training for teachers to meet the needs of special education students in the general education classroom. Her research interests involve creating more equitable spaces for all learners in the science classroom.

Mauricio Duque is the Scientific and Academic Coordinator of the Stem-Academia Program at the Colombian Academy of Sciences, Colombia. In 2020 he created the program Young Scientists (*Pequeños Científicos*) to promote science education in public primary schools in Colombia. He designed and performed dozens of teacher training sessions and coordinated the evaluation of the project. He has been an advisor to various ministries of education in Latin America as well as to the IDB and WB. His work includes curriculum development, public policy recommendations, rural education programs in science and mathematics, and, more recently, computational education projects. He has written several papers and books concerning engineering education and is also a member of editorial committees of magazines and congresses on engineering education. He has worked for 25 years in teacher professional development, instructional material development, and evaluation of STEM education programs.

Elizabeth Edmondson is Program Coordinator for the Secondary Science and Mathematics Program at the Virginia Commonwealth School of Education, USA. She is also the principal investigator for a Robert Noyce Grant Phase I and NIH NIDA grant Hero-T. She is the Co-PI on BEST in Bay Watershed, a NOAA B-Wet grant; VCU SEED, a US Department of Education SEED grant; and Investigating Effective Teaching through a Culturally Responsive Lens, a Noyce Track 4 grant. Her research interests include classroom discourse, supporting novice teachers, initial teacher preparation (through licensing programs and provisional licensure efforts), and teacher professional development.

Ingo Eilks is a Full Professor in Chemistry Education at the University of Bremen, Germany. Dr. Eilks holds a full teacher qualification in secondary chemistry and mathematics teaching, a PhD (University of Oldenburg) and Habilitation (University of Dortmund), both in chemistry education. For many years he has been involved in research and development projects in science education both nationally and internationally, many of which are based in different modes of action research. He is one of the founding editors of the *Action Research and Innovation in Science Education* journal and serves on editorial boards of numerous journals. His areas of research encompass, among others, action research in science education, education for sustainable development, and science teacher professional development.

Sibel Erduran is Professor of Science Education and Fellow of St. Cross College at University of Oxford, United Kingdom. Dr. Erduran is also Professor II at University of Oslo, Norway. She is President of the European Science Education Research Association; Editor in Chief of *Science and Education* and an Editor for *International Journal of Science*. Her work experience includes positions in the USA, Ireland, and the UK. Her research interests focus on the infusion of epistemic practices of science in science education and the professional development of science teachers. Her work on argumentation has received international recognition through awards from NARST and EASE. She is currently engaged in three funded projects, including the FEDORA Project (European Union Horizon 2020). Her recent books are *Argumentation in Chemistry Education: Research, Policy and Practice* (Royal Society of Chemistry) and *Transforming Teacher Education Through the Epistemic Core of Chemistry: Empirical Evidence and Practical Strategies* (Springer).

Xavier Fazio is Professor of Science and Environmental Sustainability Education in the Department of Educational Studies at Brock University in Ontario, Canada. He holds a doctorate in curriculum and instruction with a focus on science teacher education. Dr. Fazio is also a member of the Environmental Sustainability Research Centre at Brock University. His research focuses on science and environmental sustainability education, teacher education and professional development, and curriculum innovation. Dr. Fazio's research has been supported by the Social Sciences and Humanities Research Council of Canada and various government agencies and educational associations, and he has collaborated with school districts and not-for-profit organizations. As principal investigator, he currently leads a multi-year project connecting school science to local communities using place-based perspectives. Dr. Fazio is presently Associate Editor for the *Journal of Science Teacher Education*.

Allan Feldman is a Professor of Science Education and Associate Director for Educational Innovation of the David C. Anchin Center at the University of South Florida, USA. Dr. Feldman's scholarship focuses on science teacher education, and in particular how in-service science teachers learn from their practice in a variety of subjects including physics, environmental education, and education for sustainability in formal and informal settings. In addition, he studies the ways in which people learn to engage in science and engineering practices in apprenticeship situations. He has been PI and co-PI of a number of funded projects, many of which have been in collaboration with colleagues in the sciences and engineering. These include environmental studies of acid mine drainage, arsenic in the environment, algal biofuels, and water and wastewater treatment. He is one of the editors of *Educational Action Research Journal*.

Melina Furman is Associate Professor at the University of San Andrés, Argentina, and Researcher at the National Council of Science and Technology, Argentina. She holds a PhD in education from Columbia University, USA, and a BA in biology from the University of Buenos Aires, Argentina. Her research focuses on science teaching and the development of scientific thinking across educational levels and contexts, and on educational innovation in schools and community settings. She has extensively worked with schools, nonprofit organizations, international agencies, and governments on innovative programs aimed to spark lifelong learning in students of all ages. She has authored books, academic papers, curriculum materials, and other dissemination materials. Melina directs the science education postgraduate degree and is a professor in the bachelor's and master's degrees in education at the University of San Andrés.

Michael Giamellaro is Associate Professor of Science Education at Oregon State University, USA. Dr. Giamellaro studies the role of contextualization in the teaching and learning of science. His work, funded by the NSF and others, examines how learning in authentic contexts or with contextual supports impacts learning processes and outcomes. This includes field learning experiences, whole-school STEM initiatives, teacher-scientist partnerships, and immersive technologies. Dr. Giamellaro is also invested in developing innovative approaches to mixed methods research. He is a former middle and high school science teacher and earned his PhD at the University of Colorado. Giamellaro's current teaching is focused on preparing future science teachers through the OSU-Cascades Masters in Teaching Program in Bend, Oregon.

Andrew Gilbert is Associate Professor at George Mason University in Fairfax County, Virginia, USA. He has taught in a variety of K–12 settings across the United States. He also has two decades' experience with school university partnerships as a science teacher educator across the United States and Australia. His two main research strands include developing inquiry practice with both in-service and preservice teachers as well as investigating the potential of wonder as a means to build interest and understanding within science.

Margarita Gómez is Professional Development Coordinator of the STEM-Academia Program at the Colombian Academy of Sciences, Colombia. She has worked in teacher training for more than 10 years and has contributed to the elaboration of educational materials for science and mathematics in primary education. At this moment she coordinates professional development actions at

STEM-Academia, a program of the Colombian Academy of Science that aims to promote science, mathematics, and engineering education in the region, and is also in charge of the implementation of a climate change education project with the office for climate education in Paris.

Ron Gray is Associate Professor of Science Education in the Department of STEM Education at Northern Arizona University, USA. His work focuses on providing secondary science teachers with the tools to design and implement learning experiences for their students that are effective and authentic to the discipline. Much of this work has been centered on model-based inquiry and the integration of scientific practices in a supportive and structured way. In addition, he examines the science studies literature and its potential impact on science education. A former middle school science teacher, Dr. Gray received his PhD in science education from Oregon State University.

Liam Guilfoyle is Departmental Lecturer in Science Education in the Department of Education at the University of Oxford, United Kingdom. Dr. Guilfoyle has also worked on the Oxford Argumentation in Religion and Science (OARS) project, funded by the Templeton World Charity Foundation. His PhD from the University of Limerick focused on teachers' epistemic beliefs and perceptions of their teacher education. He has been involved in a range of other research projects including an FP7-funded in-service teacher education project on inquiry-based science education and a National Forum for Teaching and Learning-commissioned exploration of nonaccredited CPD for those who teach in higher education. Liam is particularly motivated by exploring the challenges and possibilities for teachers drawing on educational research for classroom practice. To this end, he is a member of the Teaching Council's Research Engagement Group in Ireland, which works to promote teachers' engagement with and in research.

Preeti Gupta is Director for Youth Learning and Research at the American Museum of Natural History, USA. Dr. Gupta is responsible for strategic planning, program development, human capital development and research and evaluation for out-of-school time youth initiatives. Her portfolio also includes leading the summer museum residency components of the master of arts in teaching program for earth science teachers. Prior to this she served as Senior Vice President for Education and Family Programs at the New York Hall of Science. In that role, she led the internationally replicated Science Career Ladder Program, key initiatives in school change, teacher professional development, and family programs. She has a bachelor's degree in bioengineering from Columbia University, a master's degree in education from George Washington University, and a doctoral degree in urban education from the City University of New York Graduate Center.

Christa Haverly is a postdoctoral researcher at Northwestern University, USA. Her research focuses on supporting elementary teachers in science instruction both from a practice-based approach, considering students' sensemaking and teachers' responsiveness, as well as from a systems-building approach, considering how school systems can organize to support instructional improvements in elementary science. She is particularly interested in examining these issues through an equity lens that moves beyond access and opportunities for student learning to consider the ways that school systems, schools, and teachers make space for students to claim epistemic agency in the elementary science classroom. Haverly has published in *Cognition and Instruction* and *Journal of Teacher Education*, among other venues.

Sara C. Heredia is Assistant Professor of Science Education in the School of Education at the University of North Carolina at Greensboro, USA. Her research focuses on the design of professional learning opportunities that engage secondary science teachers in experiences that support them in facilitating student sensemaking in their classrooms. In particular, she focuses on the ways in which teachers' school and district contexts matter for how they make decisions about reform implementation. She works in partnership with teachers, schools, and informal science institutions to create a network of support for implementation of science education reform. Her work has been published in research journals including *Science Education* and the *Journal of Science Teacher Education*, as well as practitioner journals such as *Science Scope* and *Connected Science Learning*.

Rebecca Hite is Assistant Professor of Science Education in the Department of Curriculum and Instruction at Texas Tech University, USA. Her research studies focus on curricular and instructional interventions, augmented by emerging technologies, that occur within in/formal learning spaces as well as professional pathways for K–12 STEM teacher leadership in policy-advocacy. Hite is on the editorial board for the *Journal of Interdisciplinary Teacher Leadership* (2015–present), the *Journal for Research in Science Teaching* (2019–22), and the *Journal of Science Teacher Education* (2020–23).

Linda Hobbs is Associate Professor of Education at Deakin University, Australia. Hobbs's research focuses on teaching out-of-field, partnerships in science teacher education, STEM, and science education, and she works with schools and teachers in a range of capacities through professional development, student programs, and research. Her most recent work has focused heavily on the various aspects of the out-of-field teaching phenomenon, particularly on the experiences of teachers who teach mathematics and science out-of-field. Her recent research funded internally is exploring the subject-specific nature of teaching out-of-field, the pedagogy of STEM professional development, and evaluation in education research.

Elaine Howes is a faculty member in education in the American Natural History Museum's (AMNH) Master of Arts in Teaching (MAT) Earth Science Residency Program, USA. Dr. Howes's work includes studying her own teaching, and teaching and collaborating with preservice and in-service science teachers, has led to publications about teachers' practices in working with English-language learners in science, and the challenges involved in developing environmentally and culturally relevant science curriculum for urban K–12 classrooms. Her current research examines how teacher education programs support new teachers in learning about their students' ideas, communities, and cultures, and how they use what they learn to inform their science teaching. As a member of the AMNH MAT faculty, she is continuing her commitment to working with teachers to develop science education that supports all students in succeeding in science in high-need schools.

Ying-Shao Hsu is Professor in the Graduate Institute of Science Education and the Department of Earth Sciences, as well as Chair Professor of National Taiwan Normal University, Taiwan. She received her PhD degree in 1997 from the Department of Curriculum and Instruction at Iowa State University. Her research focuses on e-learning and teaching, inquiry learning, science curriculum design, metacognition, social-scientific issues, and STEM education. Professor Hsu's research work has been recognized with Outstanding Research Awards by the Minister of Science Technology (MOST) in Taiwan (2011, 2015), National Science Council Reward Special Talents (2010, 2011), National Taiwan Normal University Research Awards (2005, 2006, 2007, 2008, 2012, 2015), and the Wu Da-Yu Memorial Award (2005).

Mercè Izquierdo is an Emeritus Professor at Universitat Autònoma de Barcelona, Spain. She obtained a bachelor's degree in chemistry at the Universitat de Barcelona, and a PhD in science at the Universitat Autònoma de Barcelona. She worked as a secondary chemistry teacher and also as a chemistry university lecturer before being involved in science teacher education and science education research. Her current research interests are history and philosophy of science, modeling and language, and chemistry education within the contexts of secondary education and science teacher education. During her career, she has contributed to incorporating science education as part of primary and secondary teachers' education, and to consolidating science education as a research field in Spain and Latin America. She has also made significant theoretical contributions to models and modeling as a science learning perspective, and regarding the contributions of history and philosophy of science-to-science education.

David F. Jackson is Associate Professor of Science Education at the University of Georgia, USA, where he teaches in the Secondary Science teacher certification program, has been in charge of the science aspects of the Middle Grades teacher certification program for 32 years, and previously served as Graduate Coordinator for 13 years and as Associate Department Head for 3 years. He teaches a preservice course held in middle school classrooms and planned in cooperation with practicing middle school teachers, most often at the 8th-grade level. He recently designed and developed UGA's online MEd in science education program. The primary foci of his research efforts have been the use of electronic technologies and simulations in science teaching; cognitive, cultural, and political issues in the teaching of biological evolution and historical geology; and all aspects of middle-grades science teaching and teacher education.

M. Gail Jones is Alumni Distinguished Graduate Professor of Science Education and Senior Research Fellow, Friday Institute for Educational Innovation at North Carolina State University, Raleigh, North Carolina, USA. Dr. Jones teaches preservice and in-service teachers and conducts research on teaching and learning science, concepts of size and scale, and the development of science career aspirations. She serves as Co-Editor in Chief of the *International Journal of Science Education*. Dr. Jones's scholarship has been recognized for excellence, with awards that include the Jackson Distinguished Service for Outstanding Science Education Leadership, the Association of Supervision and Curriculum Development, the Educational Innovation for NC Science Mathematics and Technology Education Center Partnership Award, the Academy of Outstanding Faculty Engaged in Extension, and the Alumni Outstanding Research Award. Dr. Jones's research group is currently identifying factors and strategies to enhance science career aspirations and studying new approaches to convergence science education.

Sami Kahn is Executive Director of the Council on Science and Technology at Princeton University, USA. Dr. Kahn uses her background in science education and law to inform her research on inclusive science practices, socioscientific issues (SSI), argumentation, and social justice. An award-winning science educator, teacher educator, and author, she currently serves as Chair of the Inclusive Science Education Forum for the Association for Science Teacher Education (ASTE) and Co-Editor of the *Journal of Science Education for Students with Disabilities*. Her former posts include serving as Chair of the National Science Teaching Association's (NSTA) Special Needs Advisory Board and President of NSTA's associated group, Science Education for Students with Disabilities (SESD). Dr. Kahn holds an MS in ecology and evolutionary biology from Rutgers University, a JD in law from Rutgers School of Law, and a PhD in curriculum and instruction with a specialization in science education from the University of South Florida, where she served as a Presidential Doctoral Fellow.

Marika Kapanadze is Head of the Science Education Research Centre SALiS and PhD program in education at Ilia State University, Georgia. She develops training and learning programs for preservice and in-service science teachers and cooperates with the universities of different countries in the world. Her research interests are teacher professional development, science curriculum development, and investigation of teachers' attitudes/students' interest in science. She has long experience in implementing and coordinating international programs in education in Georgia. Dr. Kapanadze is the author of many scientific papers published in international journals and is Joint Founding Editor of the online science journal *Action Research and Innovation in Science Education* (ARISE).

Vanessa Kind is Professor of Education and Head of the School of Education at Leeds University, UK. Previously she held a personal Chair in Education in the School of Education at Durham University, United Kingdom, and held the position of Deputy Executive Dean in Social Sciences and Health at Durham from 2015 to 2020 with responsibility for postgraduate students. She became a Principal Fellow of the Higher Education Academy in July 2021. Vanessa's research explores teacher professional knowledge, particularly teachers' science subject knowledge, beliefs and orientations, views about science, instructional strategies, self-confidence, attitudes, and the impact of these on student learning outcomes. She contributes to international debate on teacher knowledge and connections between science teacher education policy and practice. Vanessa has directed funded projects in teacher development and aspects of science education, including a nationwide survey of practical work in science and an interdisciplinary project on students' understandings of scientific issues in medical ethics. Trained initially as a chemistry teacher, Vanessa has held teaching positions as principal of an international school in Norway and taught chemistry in London and Hull in the UK.

Kelly L. Knight is Associate Professor with the George Mason University Forensic Science Program and a STEM Accelerator, USA. As a STEM Accelerator, she mentors STEM students and leads K–12 STEM outreach programs. She is the co-founder and director of Females of Color and those Underrepresented in STEM (FOCUS), a program which makes STEM exciting and accessible for BIPOC (Black, Indigenous, and people of color) girls. Professor Knight is also currently working on her doctorate in science education research at George Mason. Her research examines how out-of-school STEM programs impact BIPOC girls, particularly in the area of STEM identity. Through her advisory roles and participation in various diversity, equity, and inclusion committees across campus, such as the President's Anti-Racism and Inclusive Excellence taskforce, Professor Knight's work in higher education centers on the development and implementation of equitable practices for both STEM students and faculty. She recently received the 2020 University Teaching Excellence Award.

Michele Hollingsworth Koomen is a Research Professor in Science Education at Gustavus Adolphus College in St. Peter, Minnesota, USA. Dr. Koomen's scholarship focuses on the intersection of inclusion and equity across citizen science, disciplinary literacy, the practices of science, and professional development. Her publications can be found in *Science Education, Journal of Research in Science Teaching, Cultural Studies in Science Education, Science and Children*, and the *American Biology Teacher*, to name just a few. She has been an invited speaker at NSTA and many state teacher association conferences and presented research at AERA, ASTE, CSA, EARLI, NARST, and NSTA. Koomen served as lead editor for the Brill-edited book *Towards Inclusion of All Learners Through Science Teacher Education* (2018). She is the former president of the Minnesota Science Teachers Association and a current co-editor of the *Journal of Science Education for Students with Disabilities*.

Nihat Kotluk is a postdoctoral researcher in the College des Humanities, The École Polytechnique Fédérale de Lausanne (EPFL), Switzerland. He has mainly focused on equality and diversity issues in engineering education. Nihat started his academic career as a physics teacher in Turkey in 2008 and received a PhD degree in educational science in 2018. In his thesis, Nihat studied the perceptions and practices of teachers in culturally relevant pedagogy and developed recommendations to put greater emphasis on inclusion in preservice teacher education. Nihat has published several articles in academic and international peer-reviewed journals. In his more recent work, he focused on the challenges teachers faced while implementing the culturally relevant pedagogy principles with Syrian students in Turkey. His teaching and research interests include educational psychology, culturally relevant pedagogy, culturally responsive science/STEM education, equity, and diversity in education.

Kassandra L'Heureux is a graduate student at Université de Sherbrooke, Canada. She is interested in the contextualization of science learning and teaching inside and outdoor teaching and learning in schools' immediate surroundings. She is also interested in the development of critical thinking in the context of socioscientific topics, including the context of the pandemic. Her master's project focuses on the methods and strategies used to contextualize learning for future elementary and secondary science teachers. Her work is supervised by Professor Jean-Philippe Ayotte-Beaudet and Professor Abdelkrim Hasni. She used to work in orthopedagogy in high school. She is a lecturer at the Université de Sherbrooke, Canada, in Didactics of Science where she teaches to 1st- and 3rd-year undergrad students.

Cheng Liu is Associate Professor of Biology Education at the College of Life Sciences, Beijing Normal University, China. He received his PhD in curriculum and pedagogy from Beijing Normal University in 2011 and did postdoctoral research in mathematics and science education at the Illinois Institute of Technology during 2011–2012. His areas of research include teaching and learning scientific conceptions, nature of science, scientific inquiry, and science teacher professional development. He has authored or co-authored more than 20 articles and chapters in Chinese and English journals and books. He also has experience designing and implementing professional development programs for elementary and secondary science teachers.

Enshan Liu is Professor of Biology Education at the College of Life Sciences, Beijing Normal University, China. For over 30 years, he has studied the high school biology curriculum standards and the professional learning of biology teachers. His expertise resides in the areas of professional development programming and biology curriculum reform. He has led more than 15 national research projects and has authored or co-authored more than 200 papers in both Chinese and international journals and conferences. His commitment to the biology education community is extensive and includes being a member of the Basic Education Teaching Guidance Committee and Chairman of the Biology Teaching Guidance Committee of the Ministry of Education.

Julie A. Luft is a Distinguished Research Professor, Athletic Association Professor of Mathematics and Science Education, and Adjunct Professor of Biochemical and Molecular Biology at the University of Georgia, USA. Dr. Luft's studies have explored science teacher development, professional development, and recently leadership. She has awards for her research and practitioner studies and for her teaching and mentoring of graduate and undergraduate students. She is a Fellow of the National Science Teaching Association (NSTA), American Association for the Advancement of Science and the University of Georgia Owens Institute of Behavioral Research. She has been an Associate Editor of several journals including the *Journal of Research in Science Teaching*, President of the Association of Science Teacher Education, an NSTA scholar-in-residence, and a Fulbright Specialist. She has testified about inquiry instruction to a US congressional subcommittee and served on the National Academies of Sciences, Engineering, and Medicine committee on the professional learning of science teachers.

Mariana Luzuriaga is a research assistant and Assistant Professor at the University of San Andrés, Argentina. She has a bachelor's degree and a postgraduate teaching qualification in education, and is currently a PhD candidate at the University of San Andrés, Argentina. Since 2014 she has been a member of the Science Education Program at the same university, participating in various research and professional development projects related to science teaching at all educational levels. She has co-authored books, academic papers, and curriculum materials in the field, including the design of science teacher professional development courses within the National Teacher Training Program in Argentina. Her current research interests revolve around the planning and decision-making processes of primary-level teachers, and the ways in which these relate to curriculum policies and materials.

Edward G. Lyon is Associate Professor of Science Education at Sonoma State University, USA. Dr. Lyon researches how science teachers learn and enact core instructional and assessment practices that integrate inquiry-based science with language and literacy development for emergent bilinguals. He also co-directs the Sonoma State STEM Teacher Education Pathways Center. He has published in leading science education journals, authored the book *Secondary Science Teaching for English Learners: Developing Supportive and Responsive Learning Contexts for Sense-Making and Language Development*, and co-led the NSF-funded Secondary Science Teaching with English Language and Literacy Acquisition (SSTELLA) Project. He has served as an editorial board member for the *Journal of Research in Science Teaching and the Journal of Science Teacher Educator*. He earned his PhD in science education from the University of California, Santa Cruz and received the UC/ACCORD Dissertation Fellowship, the CCTE Outstanding Dissertation Award, and the NARST Outstanding Paper Award in 2012.

Lauren Madden is a Professor of Elementary Science Education at The College of New Jersey, USA, where she also coordinates the Environmental Sustainability Minor and Graduate Certificate programs. Her mission is to advocate for scientific literacy and the health of our planet through teaching and learning. She has published more than 40 peer-reviewed articles and book chapters, and has a textbook on science teaching methods due out in 2022. Her current research focus is on developing teachers' content knowledge and confidence in marine science, climate change, and the effective use of the NGSS. Her work has been funded by the New Jersey Sea-Grant Consortium, the US Environmental Protection Agency, and the National Science Foundation. In 2021, she was recognized as the Association for Science Teacher Education's Outstanding Science Teacher Educator of the Year and NJ STEM Pathways' inaugural iCAN STEM role model.

Rachel Mamlok-Naaman served as Head of the National Center for Chemistry Teachers until September 2020, and until June 2016 she was the Coordinator of the chemistry group at the Weizmann Institute, Israel. Dr. Mamlok-Naaman was the coordinator of a special master's program for chemistry teachers, and of projects in the framework of the European Union in Israel. In addition, she is the chair of EuCheMS DivCED, an ACS titular member, and serves on editorial and advisory boards of science education journals and organizations. Her publications focus on topics related to curriculum development, student learning, and teachers' professional development.

Franklin Manrique is a chemistry teacher from the Universidad Pedagógica Nacional de Bogotá, Colombia. He has a MSc in science education from the Pontificia Universidad Católica de Valparaíso (Chile). He has experience as a chemistry teacher in secondary education and is currently working as a science teacher educator in Chile. He also collaborates with the Mirador Interactive Museum (MIM), a space for informal science education, through practicing science teachers' education. His professional interests focus on science for citizenship, chemical education and initial science teacher education. His research has special emphasis on science teachers' formulation of productive questions in the classroom.

Eve Manz is an Assistant Professor of science education at Boston University Wheelock College of Education and Human Development, USA. Her research focuses on the development of epistemic practices in mathematics and science; that is, supporting students to participate in making and using knowledge in powerful, disciplinary ways. She seeks to understand how to design learning environments so that practices such as modeling, experimentation, and argumentation are meaningful and useful for elementary school students. She is the 2019 recipient of the Early Career Research Award from the National Association for Research in Science Teaching and recently served on the National Academies of Science and Engineering Committee on *Enhancing Science and Engineering in Prekindergarten through Fifth Grade.*

Ainoa Marzábal is an Associate Professor at the Faculty of Education of the Pontificia Universidad Católica de Chile, Chile. She obtained a bachelor's degree in Chemistry and a PhD in Science Education (2011) at the Universitat Autònoma de Barcelona (Spain). Her research interests are science education at the school level with a special emphasis on model-based teaching and learning, and science teacher education that focuses on the transformation of science teachers' disciplinary teaching practices. In addition, she currently leads the impact assessment of a teacher education program for science teachers in public schools of the Chilean Ministry of Education. She also coordinated the team that proposed the Standards of Chemistry Teachers Education programs in Chile and collaborates permanently with schools and educational institutions.

Felicia Moore Mensah is a Professor of science education, and Department Chair of Mathematics, Science, and Technology at Teachers College, Columbia University, New York, USA. Dr. Mensah has published extensively, where her work addresses issues of diversity, equity, and identity in science education. Her most recent research utilizes critical race theory and intersectionality to transform teacher education research and practice. Her work on the experiences of Teachers of Color and preparing future teacher educators for racial literacy combines years of teaching, mentoring, and outreach. Dr. Mensah was the recipient of the 2017 Outstanding Science Teacher Educator of the Year (ASTE); the 2012 Early Career Award, Division K Teaching and Teacher Education (AERA); and an Equity and Ethics Scholar in 2005 (NARST). Dr. Mensah is a Past President of Sisters of the Academy Institute, or SOTA, an organization that supports the success of Black women in higher education. Among other activities, she is co-editor of the *Journal of Research in Science Teaching (JRST).*

Cristian Merino is an Adjunct Professor in Chemistry Teaching at different educational levels, at the Institute of Chemistry of the Pontificia Universidad Católica de Valparaíso, Chile. He has a bachelor's degree in Chemistry Education at the Pontificia Universidad Católica de Valparaíso (Chile), and a PhD in science education at the Universitat Autònoma de Barcelona (Spain). His research interests focus on the characterization of school chemical activity for the development and analysis of innovation activities that favor the construction of school-scientific explanations, with an emphasis on the transition between phenomenon and theory under a modeling approach for initial science teacher preparation (especially in chemistry), as well as experimental work and the teaching of chemistry through technological mediations.

Sabela F. Monteira is an educational researcher at the SciTeach Center at the University of Luxembourg, Luxembourg. Her work focuses on the collaborative creation of resources for promoting science teaching and learning during the early ages, as well as for supporting the development of creative spaces for engaging in science. She is also a preservice teacher educator (PhD, ed., Universidade de Santiago de Compostela, Spain) and former chemist (BSc, chemistry, University of Glasgow, Scotland). Her research uses ethnographic methods in order to investigate the multiple ways through which young children and their teachers collectively engage in inquiry along the first 3 years of formal schooling. Her work focuses on how children's engagement in the disciplinary practices of science evolves from 3 to 6 years of age and on how teachers foster the development of children's communication and representational skills, as well as cognitive and affective scaffolding strategies that promote increasing children's autonomy.

Patricia Moreira is a natural science and chemistry teacher in Chile. She received her PhD in science education at the Pontificia Universidad Católica de Chile (Chile) in 2019. Moreira has 6 years of experience teaching at both middle and high school levels in Chile, and the last 6 years as a teacher educator at Pontificia Universidad Católica de Chile. The principal goal of her research is to provide evidence to understand and enhance the teaching and learning processes in science education through the characterization of the expressed scientific reasoning of middle school and high school students, and by identifying how classroom interactions shape students' expressed reasoning.

Audrey Msimanga is Associate Professor of Science Education and Head of the School of Education at the University of the Witwatersrand, South Africa. Audrey has worked in biology research, science education research, and teacher education for over 30 years. Audrey's research seeks to understand the challenges and affordances of access to science and success in science education for English second-language students in sub-Saharan Africa. Audrey is currently Associate Editor for the *Journal for Research in Science Teaching* (JRST), a member of the Editorial Board of the European Science Education Research Association (ESERA) Book Series, and President-Elect of the Southern African Association for Research in Mathematics, Science and Technology Education (SAARMSTE).

Shannon L. Navy is Assistant Professor of Science Education at Kent State University, USA. Dr. Navy's research pertains to STEM teacher education, teacher induction, and the professional development of teachers. Her work is published in leading journals in the field, and she recently co-edited a book on newly hired science teachers. She completed her postdoctoral studies at the University of Virginia, and was Assistant Professor and Director of the Woodrow Wilson Teaching Fellowship and Induction Program at Valparaiso University. As a graduate student she attended the Sandra K. Abell Summer Research Institute and won the Dissertation Award in the AERA SIG Research on Teacher Induction.

Meshach Ogunniyi is Emeritus Professor at the University of the Western Cape, South Africa. His research interests straddle NOS, IKS, and the integration of the two using an argumentation instructional model. He has written over a dozen books and published over 200 articles in refereed journals, conference proceedings, and book chapters. He has supervised over 80 master's and doctoral theses and has conducted several large-scale studies. He retired first in 2009 and finally in 2014. He has served as an editor and member of editorial boards of several journals. He received the Vice-Chancellor Best Teacher Award in 2008, a Life-time Research Award of SAARMSTE in 2014, and the NARST Distinguished Research Award in 2015.

Soonhye Park is Professor in Science Education at North Carolina State University, USA. Dr. Park's research centers on teacher Pedagogical Content Knowledge (PCK) and teacher professional development. She has led various federal, state, and internally funded grant projects on teacher professional development that explicitly seek effective ways to advance teachers' knowledge, skills, and practices that promote students' engagement in scientific practices, critical thinking skills, and science achievement, especially in the context of rural and low SES schools. She also served on the Editorial Board for the *Journal of Research in Science Teaching* and the *Journal of Science Teacher Education*. The impact and quality of her scholarship has been recognized by several awards, including PCK Summit invitee (2012, 2016), NARST Outstanding Paper Award (2014), David P. Butts Award for Contributions to Science Education (2014), and University Faculty Scholar (2017–2018).

José Manuel Pavez is a doctoral student at the University of Georgia, USA. Originally from Chile, he graduated from the Metropolitan University of Educational Sciences, Santiago, Chile. He has over 10 years of teaching experience from 5th grade to the graduate level in Chile and the USA. He has been actively involved in educational research since 2012. His research interest has been around science teacher education, nature of science, and science methods courses. He has participated in different research projects funded by NSF and FONDECYT (Chilean state funds). He has served multiple local and international organizations like NARST, ASTE, and SCHEC, as well as many journals in science education, like the *Journal of Science Teacher Education* (JSTE), where he is part of the editorial review board. His efforts were recognized by the ethics and equity panel of NARST, who named him a Jhumki Basu fellow in 2021.

William (Bill) Penuel is Professor of Learning Sciences and Human Development in the School of Education and Institute of Cognitive Science at the University of Colorado, Boulder, USA. His research focuses on interest-related learning across settings, classroom assessment in science, teacher learning, and promoting the equitable implementation of reforms in STEM education. As Principal Investigator for a U.S. Department of Education knowledge utilization center, the National Center for Research in Policy and Practice, he studies how school, district, and state education leaders use research evidence in decision-making. He has been involved in research-practice partnerships at the district and state levels, focused on supporting implementation of the Next Generation Science Standards through co-design of curriculum and assessment resources that connect to students' interests, identities, and experiences. He is a Fellow of the International Society of the Learning Sciences, American Educational Research Association, the International Society for Design and Development in Education, and the National Education Policy Center. He is also an elected member of the National Academy of Education and member of the Board on Science Education at the National Academy of Sciences, Engineering, and Medicine.

Erin E. Peters-Burton is the Donna R. and David E. Sterling Endowed Professor in Science Education and Founder and Director of the Center for Social Equity through Science Education at George Mason University in Fairfax, Virginia, USA. Dr. Peters-Burton's research agenda is based in social justice, and she pursues projects that help students who feel excluded in science classes become more aware of the scientific enterprise and how scientific knowledge is generated. She is PI for an NSF-funded research project entitled *Fostering Student Computational Thinking with Self-Regulated Learning*, which is developing an electronic notebook that prompts students to think computationally with self-regulated learning strategies while collecting analytics on student learning (SPIN; Science Practices Innovation Notebook). In addition, Dr. Peters-Burton is an editor of the *STEM Roadmap Curriculum Series* published by NSTA Press, a K–12 curriculum that integrates STEM, English-language arts, and social studies concepts and practices.

Neal Petersen is Deputy Director in the School of Mathematics, Science, and Technology Education at North-West University, South Africa. His research interests focus on using engaging pedagogies to contextualize science teaching including indigenous knowledge, STEAM education, cooperative learning, self-directed learning, and teacher professional development. He was the principal investigator of a project on using engaging pedagogies and is currently a co-investigator in a Fuchs Foundation-funded project, "Teachers without Borders," with a focus on empowering in-service science teachers to use engaging pedagogies. He acts as supervisor and co-supervisor for various postgraduate students, has published in national and international publications, is the co-editor of a AOSIS book, and has presented papers at national and international conferences.

Rose M. Pringle is Associate Professor in Science Education in the School of Teaching and Learning at the University of Florida, USA. Her research agenda extends into two parallel yet related areas in science education. In one line, she focuses on the development of science teachers' disciplinary content knowledge and their response to professional development. In her other line of research, Rose investigates inquiry-based pedagogical content knowledge as a framework for shifting practices and heightening science teachers' stance toward issues of social justice and cultural competence. She therefore operates at the nexus between teachers' knowledge and its transformation into culturally relevant and appropriate science teaching practices – that is, teaching in a manner that challenges assumptions and the status quo and leads to increased science achievement among minoritized populations.

Umesh Ramnarain is Professor in Science Education and Head of the Department in Science and Technology Education at the University of Johannesburg, South Africa. His main research interest is on inquiry-based science education, with a particular focus on its uptake in South African classrooms. His research has been published in top-tier journals such as the *International Journal of Science Education, Research in Science Education, Journal of Research in Science Teaching, Chemistry Education Research and Practice*, and *Teaching and Teacher Education*. His work has also been disseminated at prominent international conferences such as NARST, ESERA, and IOSTE. He is associate editor of *Research in Science Education* and has served on the editorial board of *Journal of Research in Science Teaching*.

Franz Rauch is Professor for School Pedagogy and Environmental Education at the University of Klagenfurt, Austria. Dr. Rauch holds a master's degree in natural sciences (teaching certification), a PhD in education at Graz University, Austria, and a Habilitation in education (with a focus on environmental education). He has been involved in research and development projects internationally and nationally for many years. He is one of the editors of *Educational Action Research Journal* and the ARISE journal (*Action Research in Science Education*) and serves on editorial boards of other journals. His areas of research, teaching, and publication are education for sustainable development/environmental education, networks in education, school development, science education, continuing education for teachers, and action research.

Vijay Reddy is Distinguished Research Specialist at the Human Sciences Research Council (HSRC), South Africa, in the Inclusive Economic Development (IED) research division. Dr. Reddy assumed this position after serving as Executive Director at the HSRC from 2006 to 2018. The three major thrusts of her research are large-scale achievement studies, skills planning, and public understanding of science. She has extensive experience in social scientific research, especially in science and mathematics education. Her work has included the application of large-scale surveys, life history research, and research contributing to setting up a skills planning mechanism. Earlier in her career, she worked as a high school teacher as well as a university chemistry and science education lecturer.

Michael J. Reiss is Professor of Science Education at IOE, UCL's Faculty of Education and Society, University College London, a Fellow of the Academy of Social Sciences, and Visiting Professor at the Royal Veterinary College, United Kingdom. The former director of education at the Royal Society, he is a member of the Nuffield Council on Bioethics and has written extensively about curricula, pedagogy, and assessment in science education and has directed a very large number of research, evaluation and consultancy projects over the past 25 years funded by UK research councils, government departments, charities, and international agencies.

David Santibáñez is Professor of Science Education at Finis Terrae University. He is Public Policy Director of the Chilean Society of Scientific Education (SChEC), of which he is one of its founders. He has vast experience as a biology teacher in elementary, middle, and university education. He is the author and advisor of numerous textbooks and a consultant for national teacher evaluation agencies in the area of science. He is a researcher in FONDECYT (Chilean state funds) projects related to the training of science teachers, the nature of science, and pedagogical knowledge content (PCK). He has recently participated in the publication of the book *Teaching Evolution and Genetics for Scientific Literacy*. David's main interest is related to the training of elementary teachers, especially the process that allows them to develop their PCK in science.

Kathleen Schenkel is Assistant Professor in the School of Teacher Education at San Diego State University, USA. Dr. Schenkel is a former middle school science teacher, and her scholarship draws on critical sociocultural and consequential theories of learning and utilizes participatory research methodologies with teachers and students. She explores with students and their teachers how to redress systems of power and oppression operating within science learning spaces. One area of focus is the role of participatory pedagogies in disrupting systems of power. Her research has been published in *Science Education*, *Science Scope*, and the *Journal of Research in Science Teaching*, among other places.

Teresa Shume is an Associate Professor in the School of Education at North Dakota State University in Fargo, USA. Dr. Shume's research explores equity, inclusion, and environmental sustainability within the realms of science education and teacher preparation. Dr. Shume's scholarship has appeared in journals such as the *International Journal of Inclusive Education*, *Cultural Studies in Science Education*, and *Environmental Education Research* and has been presented to the National Association for Research in Science Teaching (NARST), the Association for Science Teacher Education (ASTE), and the American Educational Studies Association (AESA), among many others. An award-winning educator of science and teacher education for over 25 years, she holds a PhD in teaching and learning from the University of North Dakota, an MEd from the University of Utah, and undergraduate degrees in biology and education completed in French at Collège Universitaire de St.-Boniface in Canada.

Christina Siry is Professor of Learning and Instruction at the University of Luxembourg, Luxembourg. She has several lines of research that focus on the intertwined areas of science learning and learning to teach science, particularly at the primary and early childhood levels. Together with her research team, she investigates the ways in which plurilingual young children interact with peers, teachers, and materials as they engage in science lessons. Grounded in critical perspectives, her work focuses on the necessity of incorporating multiple perspectives in research, and she draws upon collaborative pedagogies and participatory methodologies as tools for transforming science teacher education and science education. One of her current projects is the SciTeach Center at the University of Luxembourg, which provides resources and continuing education opportunities to support primary school teachers in teaching science. Using a foundation of sociocultural theories, she and her team work with teachers to explore the emerging possibilities for drawing on the many diverse resources plurilingual students bring to the classroom.

Macarena Soto is Assistant Adjunct Professor at Pontificia Universidad Católica de Chile, Chile. She obtained her degree in physics and mathematics pedagogy at Universidad de Santiago de Chile and a PhD in science education at the Universitat Autònoma de Barcelona (Spain). She worked as a physics and mathematics teacher in the Chilean school system, and also as a teacher in the Physics and Mathematics Teacher Education Program at the Universidad de Santiago de Chile. Her research interest is focused on science education at the school level and on preservice physics teachers. Her research has a special emphasis on the development of scientific practices and scholar scientific models through research-based design, focusing on learning and teaching sequences.

David Stroupe is Associate Professor of Teacher Education and Science Education and Associate Director of STEM Teacher Education at the CREATE for STEM Institute at Michigan State University, USA. He has three overlapping areas of research interests anchored around ambitious and equitable teaching. First, he frames classrooms as science practice communities. Using lenses from science, technology, and society (STS) and the history and philosophy of science (HPS), he examines how teachers and students disrupt epistemic injustice through the negotiation of power, knowledge, and epistemic agency. Second, he examines how beginning teachers learn from practice in and across their varied contexts. Third, he studies how teacher preparation programs can provide support and opportunities for beginning teachers to learn from practice. David has a background in biology and taught secondary life science for 4 years.

Robert H. Tai is Associate Professor at the University of Virginia, USA. Dr. Tai's research has primarily focused on the use of large-scale, nationally representative survey data to address a variety of research topics including science and mathematics teacher retention, youth science engagement, and out-of-school time science program impact. His work applying these types of data resources was recognized with the 2008 Council of Scientific Society Presidents Award for Educational Research Leadership. He is Co-Editor in Chief of the *Science Educator*, official peer-reviewed research journal of the National Science Education Leadership Association. He currently teaches elementary science teaching methods to preservice teachers at the School of Education and Human Development at the University of Virginia.

Edna Tan is Professor of Science Education at the University of North Carolina at Greensboro, USA. Dr. Tan's collaborative research investigates the design, support, and outcomes of equitable and consequential STEM learning for historically minoritized youth across learning contexts and over time. Current National Science Foundation-funded projects include longitudinal, community-engaged research with minoritized and refugee youth engaging in makerspace work, focused on identifying the elements of an authentic, community-owned, and youth-centered making space; and working with middle school teachers in co-developing and enacting an engineering for sustainable communities curriculum that attends to students' identity work and engineering toward justice-oriented ends. Her research has been published in the *American Educational Research Journal*, *Teachers College Record*, the *Journal of the Learning Sciences*, *Journal of Research in Science Education*, and *Science Education*, among others. In 2020, Dr. Tan was elected as a Fellow of the American Association for the Advancement of Science.

Seng Chee Tan is Associate Professor with the Learning Sciences and Assessment Academic Group and Associate Dean with the Office of Graduate Studies and Professional Learning, National Institute of Education, Nanyang Technological University, Singapore. He obtained his PhD (instructional systems) from the Pennsylvania State University in 2000. His research interests include integration of technologies in education, computer-supported collaborative learning, knowledge building, and adult learning. As a trained chemist and chemistry educator, many of his research studies were conducted in science classrooms. His recent research works include the use of learning analytics to analyze students' ideas in online forums and using eye-tracking glasses to study teacher noticing in science classrooms.

Mehmet Faith Taşar is Professor of Mathematics and Science Education at Gazi University, Turkey. Dr. Taşar earned his PhD from the Pennsylvania State University in 2001 in curriculum and instruction with emphasis on science education. His research focuses on qualitative methodologies, learning process studies, and science teacher education. Dr. Taşar has supervised 12 doctoral students and eight master's students to the successful completion of their degrees. He has published numerous journal articles, delivered keynote speeches, and presented scholarly works at the conferences of professional organizations around the world. He has served as an editor, editorial board member, and reviewer for international journals. Currently Dr. Taşar is Co-Editor of the *International Journal of Physics & Chemistry Education* and *Action Research and Innovation in Science Education* (ARISE).

Joseph A. Taylor is Assistant Professor of Educational Leadership, Research, and Foundations at the University of Colorado, Colorado Springs, USA. Dr. Taylor teaches courses in intermediate and advanced quantitative research methods as well as program evaluation. Formerly, he served as Director of Research and Development at BSCS Science Learning. Focusing primarily on STEM education contexts, his research focuses on issues of knowledge accumulation from intervention studies, including effect size reporting, study replication, and synthesis methods. Dr. Taylor also studies the use of research evidence by education practitioners. His publications have appeared in numerous research journals, including *American Educational Research Journal, Journal Research in Science Teaching*, and *International Journal of Science Education*.

Tang Wee Teo is Associate Professor in the Natural Sciences and Science Education – Academic Group, in the National Institute of Education, Singapore. She is also Co-Head of the Multi-centric Education, Research and Industry STEM Centre. Tang Wee is a social equity scholar in science education. She applies a critical lens to examine diverse equity issues in science education that affect learners (e.g., science learners with special education needs, lower track students, children aged 6–8, and international students) who are underrepresented in the local and international literature. She has more than a decade of teaching and research experience in STEM teaching and learning, specifically critical studies of STEM education. Her current work focuses on special education-needs science learners and lower-track science students. As a trained chemist and chemistry education professor, she also actively publishes in chemistry education journals.

Sara Tolbert is Associate Professor of Science and Environmental Education at the University of Canterbury, New Zealand. Dr. Tolbert has an extensive teaching and research background in science and ESOL education and teacher education. She has contributed to multiple federally funded projects, including as co-lead for the NSF-funded Secondary Science Teaching with English Language and Literacy Acquisition (SSTELLA) Project, recognized as a Hispanic Bright Spot for Education under the Obama administration; and consulted on the recent National Academies of Sciences, Engineering, and Medicine's *STEM Education for English Learners* report. She was awarded a National Academy of Education/Spencer Postdoctoral Fellowship in 2015 to investigate how teachers enact social justice in school science. Her current work explores how science teachers can engage in justice-oriented praxis within the complex sociopolitical dimensions of teaching with/for emergent bilingual students.

Chin-Chung Tsai is currently Chair Professor and Dean for School of Learning Informatics, National Taiwan Normal University, Taipei, Taiwan. He received a master of education degree from

Harvard University and completed his doctoral study at Teachers College, Columbia University, in 1996. He is also Director of the Institute for Research Excellence in Learning Sciences, National Taiwan Normal University. Since July 2009, he has been appointed as the Co-Editor of Computers and Education (SSCI, IF = 8.538, rank 3/264). He also currently serves as Editor of the *International Journal of Science Education* (indexed in SSCI, one among the three core journals in science education). His research interests deal largely with constructivism, epistemic beliefs, and various types of technology-enhanced (such as VR, AR, game) instruction. He has a Google Scholar citation of more than 36,000 and an h-index of above 100.

Dorit Tubin is Head of the Masters of Arts Program for Educational Administration, Policy, and Society, and the Principal Preparation Program Head at Ben Gurion University, Israel. Dr. Tubin's main research interests are educational leadership and professional development, school success, and the relations between structure and interactions. She has published more than 50 papers, and her work is published in leading journals such as *Educational Administration Quarterly* and *School Effectiveness and School Improvement*. She also collaborates with the international research group as ISSPP (International Successful School Principal Project) and the OECD/CERI innovative learning environments project.

Christine Ure is Alfred Deakin Professor of School Education at the Faculty of Arts and Education, Deakin University, Australia. She was Executive Dean of the Faculty from 2018 to 2020 and Head of School of Education from 2012 to 2018, and she represented the tertiary sector in government forums on teacher supply and quality schooling. During 2017–2021 she was an expert panel member to the Australian Institute of Teaching and School Leadership for graduate teacher performance assessment, and in 2015 she established a National Network of Associate Deans of Professional Experience to lead a national review of practicum in ITE. During 2014–2017 she led the project for Successful Students – STEM Program, to improve teaching capability in secondary schools and promote student engagement with STEM disciplines. She currently advises the review of the Tech Schools Initiative in Victoria, which is designed to increase student and teacher engagement with STEM capabilities and link education with emerging industries.

Jan van Driel is Professor of Science Education and Leader of the Mathematics, Science and Technology Education Group in the Melbourne Graduate School of Education at the University of Melbourne, Australia. His research interests include science teacher knowledge, teacher education and professional learning, science and gender, and interdisciplinary science and STEM education. He has supervised 25 doctoral students to successful completion. He has served on the boards of a number of associations for educational research in the Netherlands and the USA. Currently, he is Co-Editor in Chief of the *International Journal of Science Education* and a member of the Education Committee of Council of the Australian Academy of Science and the executive board of the Australasian Science Education Research Association (ASERA).

Dana Vedder-Weiss serves as the Chair of Teacher Education Program and leads the Informal Learning Environments Research Group as a faculty member in the Department of Education at Ben-Gurion University of the Negev, Israel. She was a science teacher and curriculum developer and earned her PhD in science education from the Weizmann Institute of Science. She is interested in the socio-emotional dimensions of learning, including, for example, identity, emotions, motivation, agency, and face management. Her research studies examine teacher and student learning in science (and other domains) in formal and informal settings. In recent years, she has been involved in a design-based implementation research, aiming to advance on-the-job professional learning and to cultivate pedagogical discourse and teacher leadership. Additionally, she has been exploring learning processes in family everyday life. She has received the NARST 2020 Early Career Research Award and serves as Associate Editor for the *Journal of Research in Science Teaching*.

Claudia Vergara is Professor of Science Education in the Faculty of Philosophy and Humanities at the Alberto Hurtado University, Santiago, Chile. She earned a bachelor's degree in biology (1996) and a PhD in education from the Pontifical Catholic University of Chile (2006). She had a postdoctoral experience in science education at the Illinois Institute of Technology, USA (2012). She served as a biology and natural sciences teacher in secondary and middle school for five years. She is the author or co-author of 20 scientific articles in national and international journals and of five national and international book chapters. She is a founding member of the Chilean Society of Scientific Education, of which she is past president (2014–2015). Her current line of research is pedagogical knowledge content, geoscience education, nature of science, and the professional development of primary school teachers. She is a member of the editorial staff of the *Journal of Science Teacher Education*. She is currently engaged in two funded projects about pedagogical content knowledge, nature of science, scientific argumentation, and climate change education.

Vicki Vescio is Clinical Associate Professor in the School of Teaching and Learning at the University of Florida, USA. She teaches master's and doctoral courses in curriculum, social justice, qualitative research, and culturally responsive pedagogy. She specifically works with pre- and in-service educators to support endeavors designed to make schools more equitable. She is the lead author of *A Review of Research on the Impact of Professional Learning Communities on Teaching Practice and Student Learning*, a publication that has been cited 3,000 times since 2008. Her current research interests include advancing teachers' understandings of social justice as it relates to classroom practices, examining teacher professional development in collaborative groups, and exploring the experiences of educators enrolled in an online professional practice doctoral program focused on equity. Dr. Vescio is also an active member of professional organizations including the American Educational Research Association (AERA) and the National Association for Multicultural Education (NAME), where she engages in service that both advances and gives back to education as a profession.

Jamie Wallace works in educational research and evaluation at the American Museum of Natural History (AMNH), USA. She is a member of the research and evaluation team for the Master of Arts in Teaching Earth Science Residency Program. Some of her current research projects focus on culturally responsive science education and conceptions of mentoring practice. Her background is in cultural and material anthropology and museum ethnography. She has worked at AMNH for more than 10 years and has worked as an evaluator, researcher, and educator in a variety of learning settings in the United States and internationally.

Julianne A. Wenner is Associate Professor at Clemson University, USA. She was Program Coordinator for the MiT in Elementary Education as well as the MA in curriculum and instruction at Boise State University, USA. Dr. Wenner's research focuses on teacher leadership, elementary/early childhood science education, and science teacher education. Wenner also collaborates with interdisciplinary projects to assist with educational research and qualitative data collection and analysis. Her work has been published in *Review of Educational Research*, *Journal of Research in Science Teaching*, and *Journal of Science Teacher Education*. Wenner currently serves on the Editorial Board for the *International Journal of Teacher Leadership*.

Brooke A. Whitworth is Associate Professor and Doctoral Program Coordinator in Teaching and Learning at Clemson University, USA. Dr. Whitworth's research focuses on teacher leadership, district science coordinators, and more broadly on professional development. Whitworth has received a teaching award and recognition for her work with undergraduate and graduate students. She currently serves as an Executive Director on the National Association of Research in Science Teaching (NARST) Board of Directors and as Program Coordinator for the Association for Science Teacher Education (ASTE). Whitworth also serves on the Editorial Review Boards for the *Journal of Research in Science Teaching* and *Journal of Science Teacher Education*.

Francesca A. Williamson is Assistant Professor at Indiana University School of Medicine, USA. Dr. Williamson earned her PhD in science education and inquiry methodology. Her research is interdisciplinary and focuses on three main areas: (1) equity work in STEMM education, (2) STEMM future faculty development and socialization, and (3) qualitative and multimethod research in education. She is a research associate for several NSF-funded multimethod and mixed methods projects, including the I CAN PERSIST STEM Initiative for Girls and Women of Color and Cultivating Scientific Literacy and Action through Place-Based Experiential Learning at Butler University. Dr. Williamson was the 2017–2019 Graduate Student Representative to the NARST Executive Board, a 2019 Sandra K. Abell Scholar, and is currently a member of the NARST External Policy and Relations Committee.

Wenyuan Yang is Associate Professor of the College of Teacher Education, Capital Normal University, China. Her areas of research include pre- and in-service teacher education, assessment on scientific literacy, teaching, and learning about scientific conceptions, scientific inquiry, and evaluation and policy of textbooks. She has published more than 20 articles in Chinese and English journals. She is currently completing a book manuscript in Chinese that addresses the policy of schoolbooks in the USA and explores the historical development process of the publishing and adoption of textbooks in the United States. She feels it is enjoyable and joyful to work in this field, appreciates the broad world and wonderful views of this field, and perceives the improvement of her personal thinking style since entering into this field.

Carla Zembal-Saul holds the Kahn Endowed Professorship of STEM Education at the Pennsylvania State University, USA. She is an educational researcher, science teacher educator, and biologist. Dr. Zembal-Saul's work is situated in school–university–community partnerships in the United States and abroad. Her research investigates how preservice and practicing elementary teachers learn to support children's equitable sensemaking in science through participation in disciplinary discourses and practices. Her most recent work is situated in a semi-urban community undergoing rapid demographic shifts with teachers and other education professionals who work with emergent bilingual students and their families. Dr. Zembal-Saul is committed to collaborating with teachers and families to provide opportunities for children from under-resourced communities to experience authentic science and engineering investigations and design.

PREFACE

The idea for this book began with a friend, Patricia (Pat) Friedrichsen. In discussing our final years in science teacher education, we shared the important contributions we hoped to make in the field. Our discussion meandered through research contributions, our work with graduate students, and our work on behalf of different professional organizations. It was an easy conversation that gave us a moment to reflect on the work we had done and the work we planned to conclude in the upcoming years.

We talked about compilations of research that could guide the field, leading us to the topic of handbooks. Both Pat and I have always appreciated handbooks for teacher educators. Clandinin and Husu's (2017) *Handbook of Research on Teacher Education* and Loughran and Hamilton's (2016) *International Handbook of Teacher Education* were two that we found useful in our own work. These handbooks reviewed established and emerging research in teacher education in general, yet they offered insights to the field of science teacher education.

We found that the unique qualities, attributes, and challenges in science teacher education could intersect with the topics in these handbooks. However, the time seemed right for a handbook focused on science teacher education. We understood the potential and the need for such a handbook. Excited in our vision, within two days we had an outline for a *Handbook of Research on Science Teacher Education* and the name of a person at Taylor and Francis.

Our plan for the *Handbook* clipped along. We wanted it to capture essential areas in the field, as well as new areas in need of review. Established science teacher educators with a solid understanding of the field and emerging science teacher education researchers with fresh ideas would be the authors. We envisioned chapters that were concise reviews and that would suggest future research which would be important in years to come. Most importantly, we wanted the *Handbook* to have global appeal. We would ask authors to partner with their colleagues in different countries and attend to research across the globe. It was a lofty vision.

As the *Handbook* started to take shape, Pat was asked to take on new responsibilities at her institution. The university needed her administrative expertise. Pat felt the *Handbook* was in a good position, but she would not have the time needed to review and shape the chapters. It was a difficult decision for Pat, and I wanted to be supportive. I agreed to continue moving the *Handbook* forward, while Pat focused on a new role at her university. This was ultimately a good decision for Pat. During the writing and editing of the *Handbook*, Pat was diagnosed with an aggressive form of lymphoma, underwent chemotherapy, and recovered from a stem cell transplant. Pat reminds me often that she is forever grateful for the power of science and science education. I am too.

Pat and I discussed potential co-editors, and we agreed that Gail Jones's experience in publishing would be a tremendous asset to this project. In just a few days, Gail and I were talking about the *Handbook*. Gail needed time to think about joining the project. The workload, the reading, and the necessary comments on chapters would add to her already busy schedule. Needless to say, Gail joined the project because it sounded novel and brought her back to her passion of science teacher education.

Taking on this project was a huge leap of faith for Gail. While Pat had contributed to the conceptualization of the project, the procedural part would now rest with Gail and me. We had never worked on a project together before, but Gail's experience as an editor would be an ongoing asset. She could see how to move the chapters along and point out ways to make the chapters stronger. She was ultimately the perfect person for this stage of the project. It was clear Gail and I were like the experimentalists on a physics experiment – charged with enacting the vision of the theorists. We were constantly figuring out how to enhance the chapters in ways that could best present the field of science teacher education.

One of our first tasks was meeting with our global advisory team and our section editors. These two groups had different purposes on this project. Our intent was to make the *Handbook* global. Thus, we convened a global advisory team who suggested authors and occasionally provided reviews of the different chapters. The section editors were important in doing first- or second-level reviews that could guide the authors. In preparing for these meetings, Gail and I identified different documents that needed to be created and shared with the advisory team and editors. Gail's documents were usually completed before mine and always stated what was needed in the final product.

In working with Gail, I have learned that she is organized and procedural. We were a good team for this part of the project. We divided the chapters for review, worked with section editors, discussed the different chapters repeatedly, and decided how to bolster the ideas that were being advanced. Our Tuesday afternoon meetings were good discussions about the topics in the *Handbook*, and they resulted in suggestions that could guide the chapter authors.

As Gail and I worked with the chapters, we were always aware of the challenges our authors were facing. COVID had moved many of our authors to home offices, and many of our authors were navigating the virtual working environment. We had to strike a balance between what we could ask for and what was reasonable to request. Gail was exceptional in this area. She could see good ways to move the different chapters forward, and she could help find new authors when an author or team had to drop out.

In looking over the *Handbook*, I can see that we have achieved a global document that summarizes the research in the field. Across the 35 chapters, the *Handbook* has 111 authors, who come from 22 countries. Most of the authors are from the United States, with a good number from Chile. Authors from South Africa, Israel, Canada, and Australia also have a good presence in the *Handbook*. There are authors from Argentina, Austria, Belgium, China, Colombia, England, Georgia, Germany, Hong Kong, Luxembourg, New Zealand, Singapore, Spain, Switzerland, Taiwan, and Turkey, as well.

As this project comes to fruition, I have a few thoughts. First, I hope the *Handbook* continues to remind us that teachers are not our subjects, but partners in our research work. Each day I spend in a science classroom, I learn something new, and I realize the tremendous knowledge that science teachers hold.

Second, I hope the *Handbook* sees a second edition. I learned quite a bit during this project. Most importantly, I learned that many more areas worth examination are not included in the *Handbook*. So much more empirical work is available to be shared to guide science teacher education.

Finally, we are truly a community of science teacher educators. The individuals comprising the chapter authors in the *Handbook* include people who are new to the field and who will guide our future. Some authors are experienced science teacher education researchers who have made significant contributions over time and who have something to say. These individuals reside across the globe, and they easily associate with one another. These authors came together to create an intergenerational and globally oriented *Handbook* that will guide many educators and researchers in the field.

– Julie A. Luft, Distinguished Research Professor,
Athletic Association Professor of Mathematics and
Science Education, University of Georgia

ACKNOWLEDGMENTS

The list consists of many people who have supported and contributed to this project. To begin with, this project would not have happened without the team at Routledge/Taylor and Francis. Simon Jacobs saw the importance of this project from the beginning. As the COVID pandemic became more pronounced, Simon was still optimistic that we could manage the *Handbook*. As the *Handbook* started to take shape, AnnaMary Goodall was vital. She answered every question asked about formatting and the submission process.

Three University of Georgia students also joined the project. Kayla Prichard, who graduated with her doctorate after we started the project, and José Manuel Pavez, a doctoral candidate, willingly offered to help with the project in the beginning. They were a perfect team in the early part of the project. As time went on, José shifted to a more central role in the project. Joe DeLuca joined José in preparing the final document for Taylor and Francis. Their attention to detail was essential during this phase. I am forever indebted to José for his connections to collaborators across the globe (many in the *Handbook*) and for his attention to detail in organizing the *Handbook* for submission to Taylor and Francis. The *Handbook* would not be possible without Kayla, José, and Joe.

The *Handbook* came into its own because of the section editors. The team was great to work with from the beginning through to the final stages. Each section editor was diligent in communicating with authors and focused on having each chapter in its best state. As in all endeavors, these editors brought their own skills to this project. It was an outstanding team. Thank you, Sarah J. Carrier, Lauren Madden, David F. Jackson, Soonhye Park, and Rachel Mamlok-Naaman.

Finally, this project was made possible, in part, through funding from the University of Georgia Office of the Vice President for Research and the Athletic Association Professorship in Mathematics and Science Education. The findings or conclusions offered in the *Handbook* do not necessarily reflect the views of the people at these organizations.

SECTION 1

Research in Science Teacher Education

Section Editor: Julie A. Luft

Science teacher education relies on empirical work to advance the field. Through investigations of science teaching, science learning, and teacher learning, knowledge accumulates that provides insights into ways science teachers should be supported throughout their careers. Investigations in the field of science teacher education can use different theories, methodologies, or methods to contribute to the knowledge base. Of course, the methodological, theoretical, and conceptual orientation also entails a sound understanding of the studied area. As many researchers know, these considerations are only a few that are important for empirical work that contributes to the field.

The chapters in this section represent a few areas associated with empirical work in science teacher education. They were initially envisioned to be educative and directive for those in science teacher education and science teacher education research. With a broad charge, the authors of these chapters offer science teacher education researchers insights into different dimensions of educational research. They conceptualize science teacher education research, contemplate methodological approaches, and illustrate how a theoretical orientation can contribute to the field of science teacher education.

This section begins with a chapter by Erduran and Guilfoyle, who take a broad view of the nature of research in science teacher education. In their conceptualization of the research, they describe the space existing between science teachers and science teacher educators. The complex nature of this research space is evident in the examples they provide. They describe a continuum of teacher learning that reaches from preservice teachers to experienced teachers to knowledgeable veterans. Science teacher educators engage in the process of research in different ways. These groups are essential in shaping the space of science teacher education research.

Erduran and Guilfoyle's chapter is to be appreciated for the way in which they attempt to portray this space. Like a painting that is the result of both subject and artist, the activity of science teacher education research is varied. Within this activity is a topic of study that associates with an area and that can have an orientation that ranges from broad, macro, or general to refined, micro, or specific. The varied positioning becomes evident in the examples later in the chapter. However, Erduran and Guilfoyle leave the door open for different configurations or descriptions that comprise the activity of science teacher education, and future science teacher educators are left to contemplate these configurations.

Within science teacher education research are different methodologies and methods that contribute to the variability of contributions. The next chapters broadly contemplate these areas. Tai, Taylor, Reddy, and Banilower provide an overview regarding large data sets that are used in education. The data sets they focus on are the Trends in International Mathematics and Science Surveys (TIMSS), the National Teachers and Principals Survey, the National Assessment of Education Progress, the National Survey of Science and Mathematics Education, and the High School Longitudinal Study of 2009. In their examination of these data sets, they suggest how the data can be used to inform science teacher education and add to the field's knowledge in various science teacher education research areas.

Their overview provides science teacher educators and researchers with some important considerations related to using these data sets. As experienced researchers who work with large data sets, Tai et al. are the right people to distill the important considerations that should be made when working with these and similar data sets. They also provide a solid example from South Africa about how an analysis of TIMSS data can guide science teacher educators in their work with teachers.

Moore Mensah and Chen, in contrast to analyzing large data sets, explore how science teacher education researchers utilize qualitative or interpretivist research methods. Their analysis of published articles reveals that general qualitative studies and case studies were the most prevalent methods, followed by grounded theory, ethnography, phenomenology, narrative, action research, and self-study. To frame these areas, spotlight studies are selected and described in a way that provides insights about these types of studies to both new and experienced researchers.

The descriptions provided by Moore Mensah and Chen illustrate the manner in which these studies are designed and enacted. These descriptions also provide guidance to those who engage in qualitative research. The authors point out the complex nature of qualitative work and the importance of qualitative research in understanding the varied nature of science teacher education. They also reiterate the need for the purposeful selection and discussion of the research process, especially in areas needing understanding. Qualitative research, they posit, is well-positioned to explore and address many topics that are underexplored – most notably, issues of power/knowledge, diversity, equity, and inclusion.

Buck and Williamson's chapter on mixed methods research is focused on ways mixed methods studies can and do contribute to the knowledge base in science teacher education. They begin their overview by defining mixed methods research, which is followed by a discussion of the purposes and questions associated with mixed methods research. The rest of the chapter describes the ways mixed methods approaches are used in science teacher education, what has been learned from mixed methods work, and what mixed methods researchers should look toward in the future.

The important contribution of this chapter resides in two areas: the discussion of ways mixed methods research is used in the science teacher education community and the knowledge obtained through mixed methods approaches. Not surprisingly, much of the mixed methods research in science teacher education is evaluative in nature. Buck and Williamson suggest that science teacher education researchers should move beyond this evaluative stance and use mixed methods approaches to understand the more nuanced how-and-why aspect of a study. This methodological orientation will help build a knowledge base with utility in science teacher education.

The final chapter in this section, by Calabrese-Barton, Tan, Schenkel, and Benavides, focuses on the equity-oriented research framework referred to as "rightful presence." According to Calabrese-Barton et al., this emerging framework pushes equity beyond the notions of inclusion and focuses on high-quality learning experiences that allow students to address their experiences and redress systemic inequities. In this section, they describe the framework, link it to science teacher education, and suggest ways science educators and science teachers can support the enactment of this framework.

The contribution of the chapter to this section is significant. It illustrates how an emerging framework focused on students can be used to guide research in science teacher education. Descriptions in this chapter are drawn from their work in the field with teachers, and they suggest how teachers can create this type of instructional space. The focus on the enactment of a rightful presence framework certainly leaves room for research that explores how science teachers move (or not) toward this approach. The space between the framework and the actions of the teachers and students is ripe for exploring how to support science teacher learning. This opportunity for research occurs with so many other frameworks that are important in science teacher education.

As a collection, the chapters in this section provide a characterization of science teacher education research, an overview of a few research approaches, and an example of ways in which a framework can guide research and implications for science teaching. While several other chapters could have been included in this section, these chapters serve as a beginning point. As researchers review these chapters, they may engage in generative discussions that contemplate how science teacher education researchers engage in their investigations, how they situate their work within a framework, and how their work contributes to the knowledge base in the field of science teacher education. We hope these discussions result in new characterizations, overviews, or examples, and potential chapters for the next handbook.

1

THE IMPORTANCE OF RESEARCH IN SCIENCE TEACHER EDUCATION

Sibel Erduran and Liam Guilfoyle

Introduction

Research in STE is a complex area that involves a range of theoretical perspectives (e.g., sociocultural theories, cognitive psychological frameworks), methodological approaches (e.g., action research, experimental studies, ethnographies, case studies) and actors (e.g., teacher educators, student teachers, in-service teachers). Not all research is STE is empirical in nature. In fact, very important research involves conceptual, theoretical, philosophical, or other non-empirical approaches. For example, there are systematic reviews (e.g., Rushton & Reiss, 2021) and meta-analyses on STE (Kraft et al., 2018). Often, theoretical studies challenge the community to think about what key issues need to be the focus of investigation, problematizing the function, purpose, or direction of STE in research, policy, and practice (e.g., Luehmann, 2007). In this chapter, we trace the scope and breadth of recent research in STE by raising three questions: (a) What are the purposes of research in STE? (b) What are the key concepts and methods underpinning research in STE? and (c) What are some example areas of research in STE? Given that STE is a very rich and complex domain as evidenced by the remit of this handbook itself, it is beyond the scope of a single chapter to cover all aspects of research in STE. Hence, the chapter is intended to provide a meta-perspective on a set of example areas of research to illustrate the rationale for carrying out research in STE and to illustrate some indicative areas of work for advancing the field.

Many international curriculum reform efforts have placed new and emerging demands on science teachers, making it necessary to develop teachers' knowledge about a whole range of issues (Reiser, 2013). For example, in the USA, the Next Generation Science Standards (NGSS) (NGSS, Lead States, 2013) have recently prompted a shift in the emphasis away from the breadth of too much content to a focus on the in-depth development of core explanatory ideas. Similar shifts in curricula in other parts of the world have been observed, for instance in the case of the inclusion of argumentation in the science curriculum in South Africa (Erduran & Msimanga, 2014). Another dimension of recent science curriculum reform includes the emphasis on integrated science, technology, engineering, and mathematics (STEM) in education when, traditionally, these subjects are taught separately in schools. However, research has illustrated that there may be a lack of coherence in how different aspects of STEM are represented in curriculum documents. For example, by tracing the disciplinary aims, values, methods, and practices of STEM disciplines in science curriculum standards from Korea and Taiwan as well as the USA, Park et al. (2020) demonstrated that mathematics is underemphasized in science curriculum statements.

DOI: 10.4324/9781003098478-2

In light of recent developments in science curriculum reform, we review a set of themes that highlight the significance of research in STE. Researching the experiences of teachers as they navigate their developmental journey is helpful for teacher educators to better understand so that they can respond to teachers' needs. Likewise, teacher educators' research into their own practice can potentially improve the quality of their teaching. The discussion will identify (a) the purposes of doing research in STE, (b) the key constructs that frame research in STE, and (c) some example areas of research in STE. As we survey research in STE, we will often use the generic term "teacher" rather than the specific terms preservice teacher (PST) or in-service teacher. This is in recognition of the continuum of teacher education, which extends beyond the initial phase focusing on preservice teachers (Kahle & Kronebusch, 2003).

Key Constructs in Research in Science Teacher Education

Teacher education can be highly contested and variable in different jurisdictions around the world (Kitchen & Petrarca, 2016). Over the past decade, there have been increasing calls for teacher education to become more "evidence informed" and for research to become a more integral part of teacher education (Menter & Flores, 2020). The role of research in teacher education programmes was discussed in broad and inclusive terms by the BERA-RSA report (2014). The report cited purposes such as (a) informing the content of teacher education, (b) informing the designing and structure of teacher education, (c) equipping teachers and teacher educators to engage with and be discerning consumers of research, and (d) to equip teachers and teacher educators to conduct their own research investigating the impact of particular interventions or to explore the positive and negative effects of educational practice. It has also been argued that teacher educators' understandings and experiences of research can influence their teaching approaches in initial teacher education (Brew & Saunders, 2020). Therefore, it appears important to develop research programmes in teacher education where teacher educators investigate their own practices and "engage in collaborative research-based partnerships with school mentors, student teachers and teachers" (Menter & Flores, 2020, p. 9).

As a research field, STE literature presents a plethora of theoretical and empirically derived constructs such as "Pedagogical Content Knowledge" (PCK) and "Metacognition" which are also prominent in generic teacher education literature. These constructs often frame researchers' discussions about how teachers learn to teach as well as the nature of their pedagogical and subject knowledge. Numerous theoretical orientations, thus, inform such constructs including cognitive psychological accounts in the case of "metacognition" and epistemological perspectives, including the nature of subject knowledge (Schwab, 1962). PCK, a concept proposed by Lee Shulman (1986), has framed much research in STE. PCK has provided a powerful framework to illustrate a central feature of teachers' knowledge. Shulman described PCK as "The most useful forms of content representation . . . the most powerful analogies, illustrations, examples, explanations, and demonstrations – in a word, the ways of representing and formulating the subject that makes it comprehensible for others" (p. 9). Various iterations of PCK have been proposed by other researchers, often complemented with other aspects of science teaching including subject knowledge (Berry et al., 2015; Hume et al., 2019).

Grossman (1990) added two other components to Shulman's original PCK components: knowledge of curriculum, and knowledge of purposes for teaching. A further account was proposed by Magnusson et al. (1999). This model added three components to Shulman's original ones: orientation to teaching science (i.e., knowledge and beliefs about purposes and goals for teaching), knowledge of science curricula, and knowledge of assessment of scientific literacy. A recent perspective on teacher knowledge uses a transformative yet structured model of teacher professional knowledge and skills. A model proposed by Gess-Newsom (2015) incorporates ideas from Shulman (1986), such as PCK, as well as other concepts such as Teacher Professional Knowledge Bases (TPKB) and Topic Specific Professional Knowledge (TSPK). The model makes explicit that content for teaching occurs at the topic levels (i.e., chromatography) and not at the disciplinary level (e.g., chemistry). Furthermore, authors have argued that subject matter, pedagogy, and context can be considered in unison.

"Metacognition" is another widely and broadly used concept in teacher education. It is often considered as knowledge about cognition which refers to one's knowledge about her/his own cognition (Schraw & Moshman, 1995). It consists of three sub-components: (a) declarative, (b) procedural, and (c) conditional knowledge. Declarative knowledge is defined as one's knowledge about oneself as a cognitive processor. Procedural knowledge involves knowledge about execution of procedures for a specific cognitive task. The conditional knowledge refers to knowledge of why and when to use a particular strategy for a particular cognitive task. Accounts of science teachers' cognition include domain-specific aspects of science teaching, such as the teaching of scientific inquiry. Examples of metacognition articulated in the work of STE researchers include Zohar's (2012) framework that distinguishes meta-strategic knowledge or MSK as a sub-component of metacognition. MSK is the "thinking behind the thinking" (meta-level of thinking) rather than the "thinking behind the doing" (Zohar & Ben-David, 2008).

Research in STE is conducted through a range of methodological approaches. The sorts of knowledge claims that these audiences are interested in may differ, and so the sorts of evidence or method of generating evidence that they value may also differ. More generally, there are noticeable trends towards valuing forms of evidence in education, and efforts to make educational research "more scientific" (Wrigley, 2018). Researchers in STE often use experimental methods and randomised control trial (RCT) approaches to study the impact of interventions. While there is perhaps a heightened value on RCTs or experimental studies in some spheres, researchers in STE recognise value in wider forms of evidence for informing practice. There are a broad range of frequently used research approaches beyond the experimental designs, including action research, ethnographies, and case studies. Quantitative (Ronald, 2012) and mixed methods (Luft et al., 2011) studies that seek to explore and explain relationships between variables, such as between teacher competence, quality, and student outcomes (e.g., Fauth et al., 2019). Further examples include investigations about how individuals in particular contexts respond in given research instruments for beliefs or understanding at points in time, or developmentally over periods of time (e.g., Herman & Clough, 2016).

Areas of Research in Science Teacher Education

Research in STE often differentiates the issues related to beginning and in-service teachers (Cochran et al., 1993; Friedrichsen et al., 2010). The needs of beginning and experienced teachers can vary significantly. For example, while experienced teachers can benefit from professional development on higher-order thinking skills, novice teachers tend to focus on more basic matters such as classroom management (Luft et al., 2011). Regardless of the career trajectories of teachers, studies on teacher education draw from a range of foundational disciplines that frame science teaching and teacher education. Some areas are guided by theoretical constructs from diverse fields such as cognitive psychology – for instance, those focusing on teachers' cognition (Borko & Putnam, 1996) – and sociology of the teaching profession – for instance, those focusing on teaching in the broader societal norms and institutional imperatives (Ferfolja et al., 2015). Figure 1.1 provides an illustration of the areas of research in STE and the ways in which these areas relate to each other.

Any such illustration will necessarily be limited insofar as it is a reduction of the true complexity of teacher education. However, such representations can help summarise some of the key constituents of teacher education where research efforts are placed. In the center of Figure 1.1 lies the activity of STE. This activity is flanked by the primary actors involved in the activity, namely teachers and teacher educators. Research in STE will be related to all three of these elements, but some research is associated with one more than the others. A wide range of research is undertaken pertaining to the actors involved in teacher education (i.e., their beliefs, their background profiles and journeys, or

Figure 1.1   Areas of research in science teacher education

other characteristics) as well as systemic elements including the broader policy landscape of teacher education and accountability measures.

There are a variety of different areas and levels of research on the activity of STE, and some of the most pertinent of these are represented around the outside of the activity. Many of these are unpacked in greater detail in the body of the chapter but are briefly introduced here as a way to think about the breath of research in STE. *Landscape* refers to the kinds of research that are most concerned with understanding the "current state" of STE, particularly in light of policies in national as well as international comparative contexts (Scherr & Chasteen, 2020). For example, research can focus on who is entering STE (Roloff Henoch et al., 2015) or the policies relating to STE more generally (Olson et al., 2015). *Orientations* refers to the forms of research which are related to the overarching principles of STE, often informed by philosophies of education or other underpinning values. These principles and values guide the decision-making of STE and even the fundamental structure or approach to teacher preparation that is adopted (Craig, 2016). *Accountability* as a term in this representation includes a reasonably wide range of research interests. It differs from *Landscape* in that it is less about providing an account of the current state (the who, what, and how of current provision) and more about the measures and outcomes of the process.

The most familiar area of research is related to how teacher education programmes are evaluated for their outcomes such as teacher retention (Zhang & Zeller, 2016) or student achievement (Boyd et al., 2009). Subsumed in such evaluations, there is also the assessment and certification of teachers that many teacher education providers are accredited to undertake (Richmond et al., 2019). An area of research involves teacher competencies and how to assess that such competencies are adequately developed in STE. *Strategies and self-study* are closely related in that they can both be concerned with the practices of teacher educators (Bullock & Russell, 2012; Hordvik et al., 2020; Loughran et al., 2004). Research on pedagogical strategies used in STE can be subjected to a wide range of forms of empirical study, some of which are on a large scale (Ronald, 2012) while others are investigated and usefully described in rich detail through an individual teacher educators' own self-study (Russell & Berry, 2014). Teacher self-studies can be concerned with their own developmental journeys as actors in the activity of teacher education, and not just about the impact of their strategies. In the rest of this section, we focus on some example areas of research that are subsumed under each aspect of the broad characterisation in Figure 1.1.

Teacher beliefs, attitudes, dispositions, and identities

Research on beliefs, attitudes, and dispositions of teachers, both preservice and in-service, has been a long-standing strand in STE (Bryan, 2012). Much of this research has been motivated by the need to identify the thought processes that drive teacher behavior, paralleled with the idea that changes in such mental constructs could yield changes in teaching practices (Cochrane-Smith & Fries, 2005). Approaches in research shifted towards considering teacher education as learning experience where it was necessary to understand how teachers' knowledge and beliefs develop, and how teachers ultimately translate these beliefs into practice (Bryan, 2012). The task of defining the construct of teacher beliefs is a challenging one (Pajares, 1992), and despite a growing literature on the topic, it continues to be "murky" and lacking consensus (Fives & Buehl, 2012). Nonetheless, it has been argued that preservice teachers come to teacher education with pre-existing beliefs (Yesil-Dagli et al., 2012) and these beliefs act as filters for the information encountered in their education (Fives & Buehl, 2017). It is therefore important for teacher educators to investigate and understand the beliefs of preservice teachers to establish how their learning progression can be supported (Guilfoyle et al., 2020).

A range of beliefs, attitudes, and dispositions have been examined as important and influential in teacher education, including instructional beliefs (Rubie-Davies, 2015), goal-orientation beliefs (Anderman et al., 2002), self-efficacy beliefs (Cakiroglu et al., 2012), as well as beliefs about assessment (Barnes et al., 2015), technology (Hermans et al., 2008) and diversity (Gay, 2010). Among the wide range of beliefs that are relevant for teaching in general, beliefs about the nature of the subject/ discipline are clearly of particular importance to STE. Shulman (1986) argued that teachers need to be able to guide students not only in learning the "accepted truths in a domain" but also in why these truths are deemed warranted in the domain (p. 9). For science teachers to be able to do so, STE must consider understanding of the nature of the discipline as part of the subject matter preparation of teachers (Ball & McDiarmid, 1990). Indeed, the science education community has long focused on this issue of students' and teachers' beliefs about the nature of science (e.g., Erduran & Dagher, 2014; Lederman, 1992).

Some researchers have taken particular interest in the beliefs about the epistemic nature of the discipline and considered how these play a role in learning (Peng & Fitzgerald, 2006), teaching (Kang, 2008), and learning to teach (Buehl & Fives, 2016). Researchers are often interested in how such themes develop over time. Consequently, longitudinal studies have been designed and implemented to trace teachers' development over the course of teacher education and into their careers (Buldur, 2017; Herman & Clough, 2016). A relatively recent area of research in STE focuses on science teachers' identities (Avraamidou, 2014), and here, too, there is growing interest in identity development through the life cycle of the teacher (Hong et al., 2017). Although this is a recent emphasis in science education research, preservice science teachers' identities have been investigated from a developmental and social psychological perspective in the broader teacher education for a number of years (Friesen & Besley, 2013).

Pedagogy of Teacher Education

Being concerned with the development of teachers, STE researchers take particular interest in understanding the aspects and activities of teacher education that can support teachers' professional development. Studies of the content and processes of teacher education take a number of forms. At the broadest level, studies can be conducted which aim to generate an understanding of the landscape of STE provision at any given point in time. For example, the Research on Science Education Survey (ROSES) report in the USA (Newton & Watson, 1968), provided insight into, amongst other things, the particular practices of teacher education employed in various institutions (e.g., the use of class discussion, student laboratories, student demonstrations, mock teaching, construction of teaching units, and lecturing). Other studies about the pedagogy of STE can focus on the level of the overarching orientation to programme construction. More recently, Olson (2017) explained how STE programmes can be differently constructed depending on the conceptual orientation of "construction," "resolution," "discrimination," or "assimilation."

Korthagen (2016) argued that the pedagogy of teacher education should be different from other areas of higher education and that teacher educators need to "show exemplary pedagogical behaviour" (p. 313). Thus, the development and study of specific pedagogical practices in teacher education has been an important and growing area of research. Korthagen reviews illustrative examples of specific pedagogical practices and techniques that have been studied in the context of teacher education, including workplace learning, case methods, the use of video, approximations of practice, reflective practice, learning communities, narratives, teacher research, portfolios, and modeling (2016, pp. 320–331). In the specific case of STE, Berry and Loughran (2012) documented how science teacher educators developed their personal pedagogies for STE, and how they articulate these pedagogies in ways that can impact the work of others. They describe a series of self-studies where science teacher educators explore tensions in their practice to build upon and communicate their pedagogies. However, science teacher educators can investigate pedagogies in other ways as well. For example, Scantlebury et al. (2008) conducted a longitudinal ethnographic study of the implementation of co-teaching in an undergraduate science education course. In doing so, they evaluate their own practice and share both the affordances and challenges of the pedagogical strategy for preservice teachers and teacher educators.

Siry and Martin (2014) used case study approaches to examine the role of video analysis in supporting preservice science teachers to reflect on their classroom teacher, in tandem with cogenerative dialogue, to make reflexive changes to their practice. They argue that while the pedagogy of using video-based media in STE has received attention in literature, there is less reporting of the impact resulting from such practices for teachers. Siry and Martin's research suggests that their dialogic video analysis can be transformative for preservice teachers' practice. Hetherington and Wegerif (2018) use a large-scale international teacher survey and teacher interviews in a case study school to argue how dialogic pedagogy in STE needs to be cognisant of the material-dialogic relationships (i.e., not just focusing on words, but also how material resources used in the science classroom are linked to the dialogue). In this case, the research advocates for a pedagogy of teacher education by identifying a gap, rather than evaluating the implementation of the pedagogy. In summary, the scope of research on the pedagogy of STE is vast and diverse, ranging from the macro levels of ascertaining the landscape of provision and categorisation of approaches to programme construction, to micro levels of measuring and articulating pedagogical strategies.

Teacher Educators' Professional Development

An important yet still growing focus of research in teacher education has been on teacher educators themselves, including their journeys, identities, beliefs, practices, and competencies (Korthagen et al., 2005; Lunenberg et al., 2011). However, there is still much left to do in this area, particularly in the specific cases of science teacher educators (Berry & Van Driel, 2012). Research studies on teacher educators address the questions of "Who teaches teachers?" "How do they become teacher educators?" "How can teacher educators be supported in their development?" These studies can focus on the personal experiences and professional journeys to becoming a teacher educator, including the challenges and opportunities along the way. Some focus on pathways through various career roles, such as from classroom teacher to cooperating teacher or from school-based mentor to university teacher educator (e.g., Zeichner, 2005). Others focus on the implications of the academic expectations of teacher educators, whose identities and backgrounds do not always match the "academic scholar" of other disciplines in the academy (e.g., Murray & Male, 2005; Loughran, 2011). Such research on teacher educators can help to better understand how STE works in practice and how best to support science teacher educators' own professional journeys.

An example of a study that homed in on the case of subject discipline teacher educators is that of Johnston and Purcell (2020). These authors explored the profiles and practices of those involved in initial teacher education programmes who provide disciplinary content knowledge to preservice teachers (e.g., a physics lecturer on a teacher education course). Johnston and Purcell argued that although undergraduate preservice teachers would spend a significant portion of their initial teacher education course with such subject discipline teacher educators, little attention has been paid to them in teacher education research or policy. Erduran and Kaya (2019) reflected on their own journeys as science teacher educators as they collaboratively designed and taught a preservice science teacher education course about nature of science. The authors remarked about their own exposure to the foundational disciplines of history, philosophy, and sociology of science that help frame nature of science in science education. Research accounts of science teacher educators thus help to identify the opportunities as well as constraints to teacher educators' own knowledge base in what they are including in their teaching. Berry & Van Driel (2012), in their study of science teacher educators' expertise and practices, suggest that this form of research can contribute not only to a better understanding of science teacher educators' work but also to "the development of a pedagogy of STE" (p. 117).

Teacher Education Communities, Institutions, and Accountability

Some researchers argue that a systemic approach that considers teacher education communities, institutions, and accountability mechanisms is necessary for significant and lasting changes to reforming science teacher education (Bryk et al., 2015; Coburn & Penuel, 2016). However, research investigating STE through frameworks focusing on a systems approach are scarce. Based on a review of literature, Allen and Heredia (2021) specify four practices that can aid in designing professional learning to facilitate science teachers' organizational sensemaking of science reform. These practices are intended to complement and expand upon existing best practices for teacher professional learning, including active learning opportunities for teachers. The authors recommend practices that are aimed at intentionally surfacing organizational sensemaking: (a) anticipating sources of uncertainty and ambiguity teachers may experience due to their organizational context and (b) triggering sensemaking during professional learning meetings. These practices are then followed by opportunities to reduce ambiguity and uncertainty through (c) collective meaning-making and materials development and (d) sustained professional development and iteration around perceived barriers to implementation.

Organisations that provide teacher education are governed by accountability for quality and performance (Gitomer, 2003). For example, in many parts of the world, there are government-based standards for being qualified to teach, and teacher training programmes are periodically inspected for quality assurance purposes. Research on such matters of accountability is often conducted within organisational settings and commissioned by the relevant organisation. For instance, in the United Kingdom, Ofsted has published research evidence underpinning the education inspection framework. Ofsted stands for Office for Standards in Education, Children's Services and Skills, and it is a non-ministerial department of the UK government, reporting to Parliament. Ofsted is responsible for inspecting a range of educational institutions, including initial teacher training. Ofsted regularly conducts research drawing on a range of sources, including both Ofsted's own research programme and a review of the existing evidence base. Ofsted subsequently used their research report to justify the key judgements for a proposed new framework on inspection of schools, including quality of education, leadership, and management (Ofsted, 2019). When research is conducted within the institutional settings of accountability, particular biases may potentially arise guided by ideological stances (e.g., Murray & Wittaker, 2018). Nevertheless, it can also be argued that the research-policy gap is narrowed when organisations that govern and lead STE provisions engage in research.

Discussion and Conclusion

The chapter outlined an overview of research in STE, including some key constructs and areas of research. The discussion raises numerous questions, some of which pertain to long-standing problems. For example, questions about the theory-practice gap (Kortkagen & Kessels, 1999) and scaling up of research outcomes involving a small number of teachers to the system level of teacher education (Schalock et al., 2006) persist. As the research base in STE continues to build, a significant concern is the extent to which congruence in evidence is established across the various methods, agents, concepts, and contexts of research. At times, the interpretations in evidence may potentially include biases of researchers imposing meanings on teachers, teaching, and teacher education not necessarily matching those of the participants of research. Convergence in collaboration and dialogue among the stakeholders of STE is likely to improve the credibility of evidence generated through multiplicity of approaches to research in STE. Some examples of spaces that are aiming to create platforms for such interaction are beginning to emerge. For instance, there are now websites that build connections, mediate the development of research projects, and enable sharing of research findings as exemplified by the *Teachers' Research Exchange (T-Rex)* in Ireland (McGann et al., 2020). Such initiatives are already extending the more traditional School-University Partnerships for research collaboration in STE, such as the Oxford Deanery situated at our own institution (Fancourt et al., 2015) and research briefs generated by organisations such as the NSTA in the USA that are intended to communicate outcomes of research. Ultimately, effective incorporation of robust research evidence in STE will ensure that science teachers are well prepared for the demands of teaching.

References

Allen, C. D., & Heredia, S. C. (2021). Reframing organizational contexts from barriers to levers for teacher learning in science education reform. *Journal of Science Teacher Education, 32*(2), 148–166.

Anderman, L. H., Patrick, H., Hruda, L. Z., & Linnenbrink, E. A. (2002). Observing classroom goal structures to clarify and expand goal theory. In C. Midgley (Ed.), *Goals, goal structures, and patterns of adaptive learning* (pp. 243–294). Mahwah, NJ: Lawrence Erlbaum.

Avraamidou, L. (2014). Studying science teacher identity: Current insights and future research directions. *Studies in Science Education, 50*(2), 145–179.

Ball, D. L., & McDiarmid, G. W. (1990). The subject-matter preparation of teachers. In W. R. Houston, M. Haberman, & J. Sikula (Eds.), *Handbook of research on teacher education* (pp. 437–449). New York: Palgrave Macmillan.

Barnes, N., Fives, H., & Dacey, C. (2015). Teachers' beliefs about assessment. In H. Fives & M. G. Gill (Eds.), *International handbook of research on teacher beliefs* (pp. 284–300). Oxon: Routledge.

BERA-RSA. (2014). Research and the teaching profession: Building the capacity for a self-improving education system. *Final Report of the BERA-RSA Inquiry into the Role of Research in Teacher Education.* London. www.thersa.org/discover/publications-and-articles/reports/researchand-the-teaching-profession-building-the-capacity-for-a-self-improving-education-system

Berry, A., Friedrichsen, P., & Loughran, J. (2015). *Re-examining pedagogical content knowledge in science education.* New York: Routledge.

Berry, A., & Loughran, J. (2012). Developing science teacher educators' pedagogy of teacher education. In B. J. Fraser, K. Tobin, & C. J. McRobbie (Eds.), *Second international handbook of science education* (pp. 401–415). Dordrecht: Springer Netherlands.

Berry, A., & Van Driel, J. H. (2012). Teaching about teaching science: Aims, strategies, and backgrounds of science teacher educators. *Journal of Teacher Education, 64*(2), 117–128.

Borko, H., & Putnam, R. T. (1996). Learning to teach. In D. C. Berliner & R. C. Calfee (Eds.), *Handbook of educational psychology* (p. 673–708). Macmillan Library Reference USA; Prentice Hall International.

Boyd, D. J., Grossman, P. L., Lankford, H., Loeb, S., & Wyckoff, J. (2009). Teacher preparation and student achievement. *Educational Evaluation and Policy Analysis, 31*(4), 416–440. https://doi.org/10.3102/0162373709353129

Brew, A., & Saunders, C. (2020). Making sense of research-based learning in teacher education. *Teaching and Teacher Education, 87*(January), 1–11. https://doi.org/10.1016/j.tate.2019.102935

Bryan, L. A. (2012). Research on science teacher beliefs. In B. Fraser, K. Tobin, & C. McRobbie (Eds.), *Second International Handbook of Science Education*. Springer. https://doi.org/https://doi.org/10.1007/978-1-4020-9041-7_33

Bryk, A. S., Gomez, L. M., Grunow, A., & LeMahieu, P. G. (2015). *Learning to improve: How America's Schools can get better at getting better*. Cambridge, MA: Harvard Education Press.

Buehl, M. M., & Fives, H. (2016). The role of epistemic cognition in teacher learning and praxis. In J. A. Greene, W. A. Sandoval, & I. Bråten (Eds.), *Handbook of epistemic cognition* (pp. 247–264). New York: Routledge.

Buldur, S. (2017). A longitudinal investigation of the preservice science teachers' beliefs about science teaching during a science teacher training programme. *International Journal of Science Education, 39*(1), 1–19.

Bullock, S., & Russell, T. (Eds.). (2012). *Self-studies of science teacher education practices*. Springer: Dordrecht.

Cakiroglu, J., Capa-Aydin, Y., & Hoy, A. W. (2012). Science teaching efficacy beliefs. In B. J. Fraser, K. Tobin, & C. J. McRobbie (Eds.), *Second international handbook of science education* (pp. 449–461). Dordrecht: Springer Netherlands.

Coburn, C. E., & Penuel, W. R. (2016). Research – practice partnerships in education: Outcomes, dynamics, and open questions. *Educational Researcher, 45*(1), 48–54.

Cochran, K. F., DeRuiter, J. A., & King, R. A. (1993). Pedagogical content knowing: An integrative model for teacher preparation. *Journal of Teacher Education, 44*, 263–272.

Cochran-Smith, M., & Fries, K. (2005). Researching teacher education in changing times: Politics and paradigms. In M. Cochran-Smith & K. M. Zeichner (Eds.), *Studying teacher education: The report of the AERA Panel on research and teacher education* (pp. 69–110). Mahwah, NJ: Lawrence Erlbaum.

Craig, C. (2016). Structure of teacher education. In J. Loughran & M. L. Hamilton (Eds.), *International handbook of teacher education* (Vol. 1, pp. 69–135). Singapore: Springer.

Erduran, S., & Dagher, Z. R. (2014). *Reconceptualizing the nature of science for science education: Scientific knowledge, practices and other family categories*. Netherlands: Springer.

Erduran, S., & Kaya, E. (2019). *Transforming teacher education through the epistemic core of chemistry*. Switzerland: Springer.

Erduran, S., & Msimanga, A. (2014). Science curriculum reform in South Africa: Lessons for professional development from research on argumentation in science education. *Education as Change, 18*(S1), S33–S46.

Fancourt, N., Edwards, A., & Menter, I. (2015). Reimagining a school – university partnership: The development of the oxford education deanery narrative. *Education Inquiry, 6*(3), 27724.

Fauth, B., Decristan, J., Decker, A.-T., Büttner, G., Hardy, I., Klieme, E., & Kunter, M. (2019). The effects of teacher competence on student outcomes in elementary science education: The mediating role of teaching quality. *Teaching and Teacher Education, 86*, 102882.

Ferfolja, T., Jones Díaz, C., & Ullman, J. (2015). *Understanding sociological theory for educational practices*. Cambridge: Cambridge University Press. https://doi.org/10.1017/CBO9781316151167

Fives, H., & Buehl, M. M. (2012). Spring cleaning for the "messy" construct of teachers' beliefs: What are they? Which have been examined? What can they tell us? In K. Harris, S. Graham, T. Urdan, C. McCormick, G. Sinatra, & J. Sweller (Eds.), *APA educational psychology handbook: Theories, constructs, and critical issues* (Vol. 1, pp. 471–499). Washington, DC: American Psychological Association. https://doi.org/doi:10.1037/13273-008

Fives, H., & Buehl, M. M. (2017). The functions of teachers' beliefs: Personal epistemology on the pinning block. In G. Schraw, J. Lunn, L. Olafson, & M. VenderVeldt (Eds.), *Teachers' personal epistemologies: Evolving models for transforming practice* (pp. 25–54). Charlotte, NC: Information Ag.

Friedrichsen, P., Van Driel, J. H., & Abell, S. K. (2010). Taking a closer look at science teaching orientations. *Science Education, 95*, 358–376.

Friesen, M. D., & Besley, S. C. (2013). Teacher identity development in the first year of teacher education: A developmental and social psychological perspective. *Teaching and Teacher Education, 36*, 23–32.

Gay, G. (2010). Acting on beliefs in teacher education for cultural diversity. *Journal of Teacher Education, 61*(1–2), 143–152. https://doi.org/10.1177/0022487109347320

Gess-Newsome, J. (2015). A model of teacher professional knowledge and skill including PCK: Results of the thinking from the PCK summit. In A. Berry, P. Friedrichsen, & J. Loughran (Eds.), *Re-examining pedagogical content knowledge in Science Education* (pp. 28–42). New York, NY: Routledge.

Gitomer, D. (2003). *Preparing teachers around the world. Policy information report*. Princeton, NJ: Educational Testing Service.

Grossman, P. L. (1990). *The making of a teacher: Teacher knowledge and teacher education*. New York: Teachers College Press.

Guilfoyle, L., McCormack, O., & Erduran, S. (2020, April). The "tipping point" for educational research: The role of pre-service science teachers' epistemic beliefs in evaluating the professional utility of educational research. *Teaching and Teacher Education, 90*.

Herman, B. C., & Clough, M. P. (2016). Teachers' longitudinal NOS understanding after having completed a science teacher education program. *International Journal of Science and Mathematics Education, 14*(1), 207–227. https://doi.org/10.1007/s10763-014-9594-1

Hermans, R., Tondeur, J., van Braak, J., & Valcke, M. (2008). The impact of primary school teachers' educational beliefs on classroom use of computers. *Computers & Education, 51*, 1499–1509.

Hetherington, L., & Wegerif, R. (2018). Developing a material-dialogic approach to pedagogy to guide science teacher education. *Journal of Education for Teaching, 44*(1), 27–43. https://doi.org/10.1080/02607476.2018.1422611

Hong, J., Greene, B., & Lowery, J. (2017). Multiple dimensions of teacher identity development from preservice to early years of teaching: A longitudinal study. *Journal of Education for Teaching, 43*(1), 84–98. https://doi.org/10.1080/02607476.2017.1251111

Hordvik, M., MacPhail, A., & Ronglan, L. T. (2020). Developing a pedagogy of teacher education using self-study: A rhizomatic examination of negotiating learning and practice. *Teaching and Teacher Education, 88*. https://doi.org/10.1016/j.tate.2019.102969.

Hume, A., Cooper, R., & Borowski, A. (2019). *Repositioning pedagogical content knowledge in teachers' knowledge for teaching science*. Singapore: Springer.

Johnston, J., & Purcell, R. (2020). Who else is teaching the teachers? The subject discipline teacher educator in initial teacher education. *European Journal of Teacher Education*, 1–14. https://doi.org/10.1080/02619768.2020.1803267

Kahle, J. B., & Kronebusch, M. (2003). Science teacher education: From a fractured system to a seamless continuum. *Review of Policy Research, 20*(4), 585–602.

Kang, N. H. (2008). Learning to teach science: Personal epistemologies, teaching goals, and practices of teaching. *Teaching and Teacher Education, 24*(2), 478–498.

Kitchen, J., & Petrarca, D. (2016). Approaches to teacher education. In J. Loughran & M. L. Hamilton (Eds.), *International handbook of teacher education* (Vol. 1, pp. 127–186). Singapore: Springer.

Korthagen, F., & Kessels, J. (1999). Linking theory and practice: Changing the pedagogy of teacher education. *Educational Researcher, 28*(4), 4–17.

Korthagen, F., Loughran, J., & Lunenberg, M. (2005). Teaching teachers – studies into the expertise of teacher educators: An introduction to this theme issue. *Teaching and Teacher Education, 21*(2), 107–115. https://doi.org/10.1016/j.tate.2004.12.007

Korthagen, F. A. J. (2016). Pedagogy of teacher education. In J. Loughran & M. L. Hamilton (Eds.), *International handbook of teacher education* (Vol. 1, pp. 311–346). Singapore: Springer.

Kraft, M. A., Blazar, D., & Hogan, D. (2018). The effect of teacher coaching on instruction and achievement: A meta-analysis of the causal evidence. *Review of Educational Research, 88*(4), 547–588.

Lederman, N. G. (1992). Students' and teachers' conceptions of the nature of science: A review of the research. *Journal of Research in Science Teaching, 29*, 331–359.

Loughran, J. (2011). On becoming a teacher educator. *Journal of Education for Teaching, 37*(3), 279–291.

Loughran, J. J., Hamilton, M. L., LaBoskey, V. K., & Russell, T. L. (Eds.). (2004). *International handbook of self-study of teaching and teacher education practices*. Dordrecht, The Netherlands: Kluwer Academic Publishers.

Luehmann, A. L. (2007). Identity development as a lens to science teacher preparation. *Science Education, 91*(5), 822–839.

Luft, J. A., Firestone, J. B., Wong, S. S., Ortega, I., Adams, K., & Bang, E. (2011). Beginning secondary science teacher induction: A two-year mixed methods study. *Journal of Research in Science Teaching, 48*(10), 1199–1224.

Lunenberg, M., Korthagen, F., & Zwart, R. (2011). Self-study research and the development of teacher educators' professional identities. *European Educational Research Journal, 10*(3), 407–420. https://doi.org/10.2304/eerj.2011.10.3.407

Magnusson, S., Krajcik, J., & Borko, H. (1999). Nature, sources and development of pedagogical content knowledge for science teaching. In, J. Gess-Newsome & N. G. Lederman (Eds.), *Examining pedagogical content knowledge: The construct and its implication for science education* (pp. 95–132). Dordrecht, the Netherlands: Kluwer Academic.

Menter, I., & Flores, M. A. (2020). Connecting research and professionalism in teacher education. *European Journal of Teacher Education*, 1–13.

McGann, M., Ryan, M., McMahon, J., & Hall, T. (2020). T-REX: The teachers' research exchange. Overcoming the research-practice gap in education. *TechTrends*. https://doi.org/10.1007/s11528-020-00486-4

Murray, J., & Male, T. (2005). Becoming a teacher educator: Evidence from the field. *Teacher and Teacher Education, 21*(2), 124–142.

Murray, C., & Wittaker, F. (2018, October 11). *Ofsted chief 'horrified' by accusations of knowledge bias in curriculum review*. Retrieved March 31, 2021, from https://schoolsweek.co.uk/ofsted-chief-horrified-by-accusations-of-knowledge-bias-in-curriculum-review/

Newton, D. E., & Watson, F. G. (1968). *The research on science education survey*. Cambridge, MA: Harvard Graduate School of Education.

NGSS Lead States (2013). *Next generation science standards: For states, by states*. Washington, DC; National Academies Press.

Ofsted (2019, January). *Education inspection framework: Overview of research*. No: 180045.

Olson, J. K. (2017). Teacher preparation for science education. In K. S. Taber & B. Akpan (Eds.), *Science education: An international course companion* (pp. 523–537). Rotterdam: Sense Publishers.

Olson, J. K., Tippett, C. D., Milford, T. M., Ohana, C., & Clough, M. P. (2015). Science Teacher Preparation in a North American Context. *Journal of Science Teacher Education, 26*(1), 7–28.

Park, W., Wu, J., & Erduran, S. (2020). The nature of STEM disciplines in the science education standards documents from the United States, Korea and Taiwan: Focusing on disciplinary aims, values and practices, Science & Education. *Science & Education* 29(4), 899–927.

Pajares, F. (1992). Teachers' beliefs and educational research: Cleaning up a messy construct. *Review of Educational Research, 62*(3), 307–332. http://rer.sagepub.com/content/62/3/307.short

Peng, H., & Fitzgerald, G. (2006). Relationships between teacher education students' epistemological beliefs and their learning outcomes in a case-based hypermedia learning environment. *Journal of Technology and Teacher Education. 14*(2). 255–285.

Reiser, B. (2013). *What professional development strategies are needed for successful implementation of the Next Generation Science Standards*. K-12 Centre at ETS: International Research Symposium on Science Assessment.

Richmond, G., Salazar, M. d. C., & Jones, N. (2019). Assessment and the Future of Teacher Education. *Journal of Teacher Education, 70*(2), 86–89. https://doi.org/10.1177/0022487118824331

Ronald, M. (2012). Large-scale interventions in science education: The road to utopia? *Journal of Research in Science Teaching, 49*, 420–427.

Rubie-Davies, C. (2015). Teachers' instructional beliefs and classroom climate: Connections and conundrums. In H. Fives & M. Gill (Eds.), *International handbook of research on teachers' beliefs* (pp. 266–283). New York, NY: Routledge.

Rushton, E. A. C., & Reiss, M. J. (2021). Middle and high school science teacher identity considered through the lens of the social identity approach: A systematic review of the literature. *Studies in Science Education, 57*(2), 141–203. https://doi.org/10.1080/03057267.2020.1799621

Russell, T., & Berry, A. (2014). Self-study of teacher education practices promotes self-understanding. *Studying Teacher Education, 10*(1), 1–2. https://doi.org/10.1080/17425964.2014.878988

Scantlebury, K., Gallo-Fox, J., & Wassell, B. (2008). Coteaching as a model for preservice secondary science teacher education. *Teaching and Teacher Education, 24*(4), 967–981.

Schalock, H. D., Schalock, M. D., & Ayres, R. (2006). Scaling up research in teacher education: New demands on theory, measurement, and design. *Journal of Teacher Education, 57*(2), 102–119.

Scherr, R. E., & Chasteen, S. V. (2020). Initial findings of the Physics Teacher Education Program Analysis rubric: What do thriving programs do? *Physical Review Physics Education Research, 16*(1), 010116.

Schraw, G., & Moshman, D. (1995). Metacognitive theories. *Educational Psychology Review, 7*(4), 351–371.

Schwab, J. J. (1962). *The teaching of science as enquiry*. Cambridge, MA: Harvard University Press.

Shulman, L. S. (1986). Those who understand: Knowledge growth in teaching. *Educational Researcher, 15*(2), 4–14.

Siry, C., & Martin, S. N. (2014). Facilitating reflexivity in preservice science teacher education using video analysis and cogenerative dialogue in field-based methods courses. *Eurasia Journal of Mathematics, Science and Technology Education, 10*(5), 481–508.

Wrigley, T. (2018). The power of 'evidence': Reliable science or a set of blunt tools? *British Educational Research Journal, 44*(3), 359–376.

Yesil-Dagli, U., Lake, V. E., & Jones, I. (2012). Preservice teachers' perceptions towards mathematics and science. *Journal of Research in Education, 20*(2), 32–48.

Zeichner, K. (2005). Becoming a teacher educator: A personal perspective. *Teaching and Teacher Education, 21*(2), 117–124.

Zhang, G., & Zeller, N. (2016). A longitudinal investigation of the relationship between teacher preparation and teacher retention. *Teacher Education Quarterly, 43*(2), 73–92.

Zohar, A. (2012). Explicit teaching of metastrategic knowledge: Definitions, students' learning, and teachers' professional development. In A. Zohar & Y. J. Dori (Eds.), *Metacognition in science education: Trends in current research* (pp. 197–223). Dordrecht: Springer.

Zohar, A., & Ben-David, A. (2008). Explicit teaching of meta-strategic knowledge in authentic classroom situations. *Metacognition Learning, 3*, 59–82.

2

THE CONTRIBUTION OF LARGE EDUCATIONAL SURVEYS TO SCIENCE TEACHER EDUCATION RESEARCH

Robert H. Tai, Joseph A. Taylor, Vijay Reddy, and Eric R. Banilower

Introduction

The importance of large-scale data sets in educational research is grounded in the necessity to account for representativeness, inclusiveness, and diversity in a population in order to enact the proper recommendations for and implementation of policies and standardization of educational practices. With respect to science teacher education research, differences in access to educational resources, among other factors, may have a profound impact on the effectiveness of particular pedagogical approaches. Large-scale nationally representative data can be used to uncover trends that elucidate disparities that might otherwise go undocumented. At times, the analysis of these types of data sets is the only means to offer convincing evidence of the existence of broad-based inequities that might influence policy makers to effect change.

Large-scale data set analyses are not a replacement for other research approaches, but rather, have a synergetic relationship with them, each extending the reach of the other when used in concert. Findings from analyses of large-scale nationally representative data sets offer insights that may serve as a guide for further investigation using qualitative methods. Other times, findings from studies using other methods, including qualitative approaches, may be examined using large-scale data sets to determine the pervasiveness of these findings within a population. While this chapter focuses on large-scale educational surveys implemented by institutional organizations, surveys developed and implemented by independent researchers also play important roles. Indeed, large-scale educational surveys and independent researcher-developed surveys each have different roles that may inform and enlighten the other, and overall push the boundaries of our understanding of impactful pedagogical practices to inform science teacher education.

This chapter will discuss nationally representative studies carried out under the auspices of governmental agencies or organizations. The chapter begins with an overview of some large-scale data sets that are currently available for secondary analysis. This discussion will provide examples of the types of data that are collected and explore questions relevant to science teacher education research. Next, the chapter will provide an overview of five existing large educational surveys available to researchers. These selected data resources serve as exemplars of large-scale nationally representative data sets both through both sample size and through robustness and comprehensiveness of data collection. The chapter will conclude with an example of an analysis from the South African educational context. The aim of this example is to give readers some sense of the potential for large-scale data analysis as a research approach.

DOI: 10.4324/9781003098478-3

Large-Scale Nationally Representative Data Sets

This section provides descriptions of some broadly useful large-scale data sets available to researchers interested in studying science teacher education. Five large-scale nationally representative data sets were selected as exemplars. They include: Trends in International Mathematics and Science Surveys (TIMSS); National Teachers and Principals Survey (NTPS); National Assessment of Education Progress (NAEP); National Survey of Science and Mathematics Education (NSSME); and High School Longitudinal Study of 2009 (HSLS:2009). Each of these data sets offers unique characteristics. TIMSS is a multi-national study that offers researchers the opportunity to focus on a specific nation or to perform an international comparison. TIMSS national data sets are all designed to be nationally representative for each participating nation and are designed to provide trend measures. NTPS is a national survey that specifically focuses on teachers and principals in United States (US) schools. NAEP is a cross sectional data set that focuses on science and mathematics indicators of attainment in US schools that allows for multi-year comparisons. NSSME surveys schools and teachers in multiple years in elementary, middle, and high schools in the US. HSLS:2009 is a US longitudinal study that tracks youth over time with follow-up surveys in 2012 and 2016. NTPS is a US survey specific to teachers and principals. While most surveys focus mainly on student outcomes, all include specific teacher questionnaires. While only HSLS:2009 is longitudinal in design, the other four surveys have multi-year cross sectional data.

TIMSS, NTPS, NAEP, NSSME, and HSLS:2009 are exemplar data resources for a number of reasons. They offer the sample size and sample diversity to give researchers the statistical power and flexibility to apply many different analytical approaches and reach robust results. These data resources also collect data at different levels, many times from students to teachers to principals/schools to parents. This array of different surveyed subgroups widens the research options of science teacher education researchers. Finally, these data resources have the backing of the wider research community, having been vetted through peer review.

Table 2.1 displays some questionnaire items from the teacher surveys from each of the five data sets used as exemplars in this chapter. The survey items displayed in Table 2.1 offer readers a glimpse of the variety of potential research topics that these data sets may be used to examine. The questionnaire items span five topics: teacher educational background and training, professional development experiences, curriculum and instruction practices, teachers' attitudes and opinions, and teachers' views on school environment. Yet, there are many more topics in addition to these listed here.

Variations for many specific questionnaire items may appear across a number of data sets. An example is the item from HSLS:2009, "How much emphasis are you placing on each of the following objectives? Increasing students' interest in science." This also appears in NSSME as "Think about your plans for this class for the entire course/year. By the end of the course/year, how much emphasis will each of the following student objectives receive? Increasing students' interest in science." Both items have identical four-choice response options. While there is some overlap in questionnaire items, these data sets are far from identical. The overlap gives researchers multiple analysis options for pursuing their research questions. If a specific combination of variables or respondent characteristics for addressing a researcher's questions is not available in a given data set, a different data set may contain the necessary combination. For example, the HSLS:2009 survey item was administered to teachers at the 9th-grade level in 2009, while the NSSME survey was administered in 2018 to K–12th-grade teachers.

The structure of the large-scale nationally representative data resources and the breadth of their surveys allow researchers to answer a variety of different questions. The structures of these types of data resources are typically consistent over a time span of years. For example, the same form and format of many questions are used in different surveys from year to year. This characteristic allows for the study of educational trends over time. Science teacher education researchers have the capacity to compare and contrast differences across spans of time, which opens up numerous options for

Table 2.1 Examples of science teacher survey topics and questionnaire items

Topics	Questionnaire Item	Source Survey
Educational Background and Training	BEFORE your first year of teaching, did you take any graduate or undergraduate courses which taught you – • Classroom management techniques? • How to assess learning? • How to use student performance data to inform instruction? • How to serve students from diverse economic backgrounds?	NTPS 2020–2021
Professional Development	How frequently, if at all, did you collaborate with other teachers on issues of instruction excluding administrative meetings?	NTPS 2017–2018
	Did you receive the following kinds of support in your first year of teaching? • Reduced teaching schedule or number of preparations. • Release time to participate in support activities for new or beginning teachers.	NTPS 2020–2021
Curriculum and Instructional Practice	How often do you ask your students to interpret data from experiments or investigations?	TIMSS 2019
	How often do your science students work with other students on a science project or activity?	NAEP 2018 Pilot
	How often do your science students figure out different ways to solve a science problem?	NAEP 2018 Pilot
	Think about your plans for this class for the entire course/year. By the end of the course/year, how much emphasis will each of the following student objectives receive? • Learning science vocabulary and/or facts • Understanding science concepts • Learning about real-life applications of science/engineering	NSSME 2018
	How much control do you have over each of the following aspects of science instruction in this class? • Determining course goals and objectives • Selecting content, topics, and skills to be taught • Selecting teaching techniques	NSSME 2018
	How much emphasis are you placing on each of the following objectives? • Increasing students' interest in science • Teaching students basic science concepts • Preparing students for further study in science	HSLS 2009
Attitudes and Opinions	To what extent do you agree or disagree with each of the following statements as it applies to your instruction? • If you really try hard, you can get through to even the most difficult or unmotivated students. • When it comes right down to it, you really cannot do much because most of a student's motivation and performance depends on their home environment.	HSLS 2009
	How often do you feel the following way about being a teacher? • I find my work full of meaning and purpose • I am enthusiastic about my job	TIMSS 2019

Topics	Questionnaire Item	Source Survey
Views on School Environment	Thinking about your current school, indicate the extent to which you agree or disagree with each of the following statements. • This school's security policies and practices are sufficient • I feel safe at this school	TIMSS 2019
	How would you characterize each of the following within your school? • Parental support for student achievement • Collaboration between school leadership (including master teachers) and teachers to plan instruction	TIMSS 2019

Note: While source surveys are cited, many times similar questionnaire items appear in the other surveys.

Sources: Trends in International Mathematics and Science Surveys (IEA, 2019); National Teachers and Principals Survey (NCES, 2017a, 2017b); National Assessment of Education Progress (NAEP, 2018a, 2018b, 2018c, 2018d, 2020); High School Longitudinal Study of 2009 (NCES, 2020); National Survey of Science and Mathematics Education (NSSME).

analysis. These data resources are also designed to be broadly inclusive of various subpopulations. For researchers interested in examining differences between rural and suburban science teacher classroom experiences, or for researchers with questions about regional and national differences in science teacher professional development, large-scale data resources contain the information to make these comparisons. These data resources also have sample weights that allow researchers to produce findings that are nationally representative. Sample weighting allows the statistical analysis to account for each subgroup within the large-scale data set in a manner that reflects its share of the national population. This capacity means that research findings have the robustness necessary to allow researchers to compare differences in educational policies and practices, and to claim that significant findings represent national trends.

Trends in International Mathematics and Science Surveys (TIMSS)

TIMSS contains data on students, teachers, school principals, and parents. Initiated in 1995 as the Third International Mathematics and Science Survey, TIMSS has collected data through surveys in 1995, 1999, 2003, 2007, 2011, 2015, and 2019. The 2019 survey collected data from 64 participating countries primarily in grades 4 and 8, though some countries surveyed students in grades 5 and 9.

While much focus has been placed on TIMSS Student Questionnaire data, TIMSS also includes teacher surveys about school resources and educational approaches, including curriculum and instructional practices, as well as parent surveys about home learning contexts and school surveys. Additional surveyed topics include teacher preparation and experience, instructional practices and strategies, instructional clarity, classroom climate, use of technology in instruction, and challenges faced by teachers. The most recently available data came from the TIMSS 2019 Teacher Questionnaires.

The data collection approaches used in TIMSS follow a study-wide data collection protocol that is designed to obtain nationally representative samplings of students from all participating nations. Data collected from teachers and schools are associated with the participating students. Users should closely examine the technical details of data collection for each nation available in the *Methods and Procedures: TIMSS 2019 Technical Report* (Martin et al., 2020). The capacity for producing nationally representative analyses is generally good, but users should examine the sampling methods and procedures for each country as relevant to their specific analyses.

National Teacher and Principal Survey (NTPS)

The NTPS describes the national context of elementary and secondary education in the United States. Formally known as the Schools and Staffing Survey, the NTPS is administered and scored by the National Center for Education Statistics (NCES) every 2 to 3 years (NCES, 2020a). The NTPS sample is a nationally representative sample of teachers and principals. While sample sizes vary by administration year, samples of over 4000 randomly selected teachers or principals is typical. The 2015–16 administration of the NTPS had approximately 8,300 respondents according to a publicly available suite of data analysis tools called *DataLab* (NCES, 2020b). This suite of tools has an integrated capacity to handle weighting and allows for basic inferential statistical analysis (logistic or linear regression analyses) for testing multiple main effects.

However, there are some drawbacks. The reader should note that for all the NCES data sets, analyses must employ the provided sample weights. Additionally, for restricted-use or public-use raw data, appropriate use of weights is the responsibility of the researcher, although NCES's *DataLab* and its associated tools have an integrated capacity to handle weighting and allow for basic inferential statistical analysis (logistic or linear regression analyses) for testing multiple main effects. However, *DataLab* lacks the capacity for testing interaction effects or centering variables for enhanced interpretation, and analyzes only public access data, which may not contain all of the researcher's desired variables.

The NTPS queries teachers on their preparation, teaching assignments, and demographic characteristics. Some administrations of NTPS include questions about teachers' working conditions, professional development opportunities, and evaluation experiences. Specifically, teachers provide information about their race, sex, age, teaching experience, degree attainment, undergraduate and graduate preparation, class sizes, salary, evaluation frequency and perceptions of the evaluation process, and the frequency and nature of their professional development opportunities.

NTPS data support both descriptive analyses (e.g., proportions, central tendency) and associational (e.g., correlation, chi-squared, regression) analyses of teacher variables. These analyses leverage the two-stage (school, then teacher) random sampling process that results in a nationally representative sample of teachers.

National Assessment of Educational Progress (NAEP)

NAEP is a nationally representative, continuing evaluation of the US education system. Within NAEP, science assessment data are collected and used to measure student achievement in Earth and space science, physical science, and life science topics. In 2015, the most recent science assessment was administered to a nationally representative sample consisting of 115,400 students in grade 4, 110,900 students in grade 8, and 11,000 students in grade 12. Data and results are now available for the 2015 administration of NAEP Science.

Data from each of the achievement tests (for grades 4, 8, and 12) are accompanied by voluntary questionnaires administered to students, teachers, and school administrators. These additional surveys provide information on students' education background and demographic characteristics, school contextual information, and information on the nature of students' formal and informal learning experiences.

The NAEP teacher questionnaires collect helpful information about teachers and their teaching practices. This information falls in several key categories, including demographics, experience teaching and teaching science, certification level, degree attainment, disciplinary emphasis of undergraduate and graduate major/minor, nature and focus of professional development opportunities, available teaching resources, frequency with which they use selected instructional practices, and the extent to they emphasize selected instructional objectives.

NAEP analyses support correlation/regression-based analyses that examine the strength and direction of relationships between teacher characteristics or practices and student achievement. These analyses leverage the two-stage (school, then student) random sampling process that results in a nationally representative sample of students. Note that the teachers associated with these students are not randomly sampled within randomly selected schools. As such, researchers may report descriptive statistics on the available teacher variables but should not refer to those statistics as nationally representative.

High School Longitudinal Study of 2009 (HSLS:2009)

HSLS:2009 is a longitudinal study of a nationally representative sample of US students who were 9th graders in 2009. The sample includes over 23,000 students from 944 schools, their teachers, school administrators, and parents. Follow-up data collection occurred with these students in 2012 and 2016, assessing, among other things, post-secondary enrollment and career outcomes (e.g., STEM occupational intentions, employment/earnings expectations), respectively. Post-secondary transcripts for these students are now available. For most students, HSLS:2009 includes an achievement measure related to algebraic skills, reasoning, and problem solving at both 9th and 11th grades.

The HSLS:2009 student data are accompanied by questionnaire responses from science teachers. The teacher questionnaire collected data on teacher background characteristics including demographics (i.e., sex, race/ethnicity), degrees earned, certification, and post-secondary coursework. Other questionnaire sections queried teachers on their beliefs about teaching and their current school, as well as their beliefs about instruction and their science department. Teacher beliefs about their school or department include those about their current working conditions. Teacher beliefs about instruction include those pertaining to students and student learning.

HSLS:2009 data support correlation/regression-based analyses that examine the strength and direction of relationships between science teacher characteristics, or beliefs and student achievement in high school mathematics or other subsequent outcomes (e.g., post-secondary enrollment, career intentions). These analyses leverage the two-stage (school, then student) random sampling process that results in a nationally representative sample of students. Note that the teachers associated with HSLS:2009 students are not randomly sampled within randomly selected schools. Therefore, as with NAEP, researchers may report descriptive statistics on the available teacher variables but should not refer to those statistics as nationally representative.

National Survey of Science and Mathematics Education (NSSME)

The NSSME has periodically collected data about the status of the US K–12 science and mathematics education system, beginning in 1977, and then again in 1985–86, 1993, 2000, 2012, and 2018.[1] The 2018 iteration expanded the scope of the study to include a focus on computer science education, particularly at the high school level. The NSSME provides nationally representative information about the status of the system in the areas of teacher background and experience, instructional practices, the availability and use of instructional resources, and school policies and practices.

The 2018 NSSME+ (the plus symbol reflects the inclusion of computer science in the study) used a stratified two-stage random sampling approach. In the first stage, 2,000 elementary and secondary schools, public and private, were selected within strata (defined by grades served) with probability proportional to size. At the second stage, approximately 10,000 science and mathematics teachers were sampled at predetermined rates to ensure a sufficient sample size for domain estimates, such as region or community type. Computer science teachers were sampled with certainty to allow for national estimates, as their prevalence in secondary schools was much lower than science and mathematics teachers.

In 2018, the study collected data from 1,273 schools and 7,600 teachers (3,497 teachers of science, 3,814 teachers of mathematics, and 289 teachers of high school computer science). In addition to teacher questionnaires, program questionnaires (asking about subject-specific school practices and policies) were administered to each participating school – typically completed by a department chair, lead teacher, or school administrator.

De-identified data from the 2000, 2012, and 2018 iterations of the study are available for secondary analysis. The materials for each year include data from each questionnaire, a data dictionary, and guidance on how to compute standard errors for estimates given the sample design.

The NSSME program questionnaires collect data about several school-level factors, including courses offered, resources provided for instruction, programs and practices to encourage student interest and achievement, and school/district professional development practices. The school coordinator questionnaire collects data about the students served by the school, and, in 2018, included a series of items about induction supports offered for new teachers.

The NSSME teacher questionnaires collect a wide range of information about teachers, their teaching practices, and factors that may affect their teaching. The questionnaires ask about their preparation for teaching, beliefs about teaching and learning, perceptions of preparedness, and professional development experiences. For a randomly sampled class, teachers are also asked the extent to which instruction emphasizes various objectives, instructional strategies used, and homework and assessment practices. Lastly, the questionnaire asks about factors that may affect instruction, including the availability and use of different types of instructional materials and resources and the supportiveness of the school context.

The NSSME data allow researchers to examine many issues related to teacher education. For example, the data about classroom instruction could be used to identify areas of strength and need in the preservice preparation and in-service support of science teachers. The NSSME also provides a great deal of data about teacher professional development, including extent of participation and the nature of these experiences. Further, the NSSME allows researchers to examine relationships among a variety of factors such as teachers' preparation for teaching, their teaching practices, and the characteristics of the schools they work in. Because of the sampling method used, school, teacher, and classroom data are nationally representative when analyzed with the complex sample replicate weights included in the data sets.

Table 2.2 shows a summary of the data access and analytical software options for the five data resources discussed in this chapter.

An Example of Analysis: Using TIMSS Data from South Africa to Explore Science Teacher Education Research

In this section an analysis of TIMSS data is presented to illustrate how the analyzed data was used to inform South African science teacher education programs. South Africa has a national school curriculum, and all students are expected to achieve the same outcomes. Yet, students start school with vastly different levels of school readiness. It is these differences that heavily impact educational outcomes, and in particular, science teacher education. South Africa is one of 39 countries that participated in TIMSS 2019 at the grade 9 level. Established in 1994, South Africa is a young and diverse democracy in terms of its people, ethnicity and racial backgrounds, languages, politics, religions, social stratifications, and histories. The historical legacy of apartheid and racial discrimination has left South Africa with stubbornly high levels of inequity that mirror its deeply polarized society, with a small elite class (4%), a relatively small middle class (20%), and three-quarters of the population characterized as poor according to the World Bank (Sulla & Zikhali, 2018).

Table 2.2 Summary of data access and analysis software options for several large-scale data sets

Data Set	Data Access		Commonly Used Analysis Software
	Public-Use Data	Restricted-Use Data	
Trends in International Mathematics and Science Surveys	Available	Permission required	IDB Analyzer, R (R Core Team, 2020), SPSS® (IBM, 2020), Stata® (STATA, 2020), SAS®
National Teacher and Principal Survey	Available	Permission required	NCES Datalab, R, SPSS®, Stata®, SAS®
National Assessment of Educational Progress	Available	Permission required	NAEP Data Explorer, SPSS®, Stata®, SAS®, Ed*Survey* (AIR, 2020a), *AM* (AIR, 2020b)
High School Longitudinal Study of 2009	Available	Permission required	R, SPSS®, Stata®, SAS®
National Survey of Science and Mathematics Education	Available with term of use agreement	Not available	Wesvar, R, Stata®, SAS®

It is clear that education, and specifically science education, offers a path forward for the growth and development of a technically proficient workforce, as well as through the proliferation of scientific knowledge important to daily life. The South African educational aspiration is to improve the educational level of all students in schools and to decrease the achievement gaps between different groups. The 4-year TIMSS cycle offers a credible and trusted measure of science and mathematics achievements over time.

"Know your student" is an age-old maxim in teaching. Using the nationally representative TIMSS data, a picture is painted of students' current science achievement, and information regarding the resources and pedagogical practices of grade 9 South African science teachers is distilled.

Unequal Science Achievement

To address high levels of poverty and socioeconomic inequality, the South African state abolished school fees for students in poorer communities. These schools are known as "no-fee" schools, while schools where students pay fees are designated as "fee-paying" schools. Two-thirds of South African students attend no-fee schools and one-third attend fee-paying schools. Figure 2.1 compares grade 9 science achievement score averages and distribution in no-fee versus fee-paying schools. The comparison shows a 107-point gap in average science achievement. Considering that science proficiency is qualified by a score of 400, about two in three students in fee-paying schools, versus only one in four students in no-fee schools, demonstrated attainment of science proficiency. The challenge in preparing new teachers for these starkly different circumstances is immense, and it is critical that science teacher educators understand existing inequities and prepare their students accordingly. For full details of South African TIMSS 2019 achievement and the context of learning see Reddy et al. (2020).

Inequalities at Home Carry Over to Classrooms

Existing literature has shown that access to resources at home (e.g., Sirin, 2005) and school (e.g., van der Berg, 2008) are predictors of achievement. To better understand the underlying causes of these

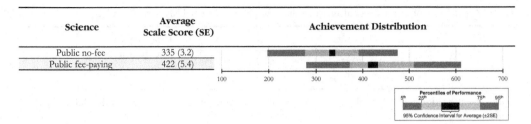

Science	Average Scale Score (SE)	Achievement Distribution
Public no-fee	335 (3.2)	
Public fee-paying	422 (5.4)	

Figure 2.1 Science achievement scores for fee and no-fee schools and the corresponding achievement distribution

achievement differences, the conditions at home for students from fee-paying versus no-fee schools are examined. Figure 2.2 juxtaposes home conditions of students in the two types of South African schools to offer some insight into the differences in their lived experiences. The lack of running water in the home for more than one-third of no-fee school students presents a stark contrast to fee-paying school students and defines a clear difference in the educational focus of science teachers in these two educational environments.

The higher levels of parental education for students in fee-paying schools mean better parental support for learning than in no-fee schools. While the South African constitution protects the rights of the 11 official languages, schools have chosen the language of learning and teaching as either English or Afrikaans. The proficiency in the language of the test continues to be an epistemic barrier for the majority of students. Half the students in fee-paying schools, while only 16% in no-fee schools, say they frequently speak the language of the test at home (a proxy for test language proficiency). Data from the TIMSS 2019 Grade 8 Teacher Survey shows that among teachers, only 26% reported no students have difficulty understanding the language of instruction, while 74% reported at least "some" to "a lot."

These findings regarding language proficiency illustrate the power of large-scale data sets for identifying issues of equity in science education. In addition, while students develop knowledge about topics, they are also learning a new language; e.g., see National Academies of Sciences, Engineering, and Medicine (2018). Large-scale surveys can help track the diffusion of this knowledge through the education system. For example, a large-scale survey can assess teachers' access to and participation in professional learning on a topic, their preparedness to use and beliefs about the efficacy of instructional practices to support language learners, and their implementation of these practices. Further, with a study like TIMSS, large-scale studies can help track changes in student outcomes over time.

Figure 2.2 also shows student access to digital assets at home (69% for fee-paying versus 37% for no-fee students). The TIMSS Grade 8 Teacher Questionnaire data showed that only 10% of learners had access to computers or tablets in their science lessons (8% in no-fee schools and 15% in fee-paying schools). The lack of digital assets poses immense limitations on the pedagogical choices of science teachers. Yet the challenges facing science teachers and researchers are broader in scope than educating South Africa's youth without resources common in other countries. The larger issue is providing these youth with the requisite educational experiences necessary for them to participate in the modern global economy.

In the context of high-poverty levels, parents and society in general often view schools as institutions that can provide opportunities for students from poorer homes, and they attempt to level the playing field of educational success. Inequalities experienced by students at home continue to schools, with students in no-fee schools facing multiple inequalities.

Teaching and learning will be affected by the school conditions and the resources they have. On average, the class size for no-fee schools is 56 students compared to fee-paying schools at

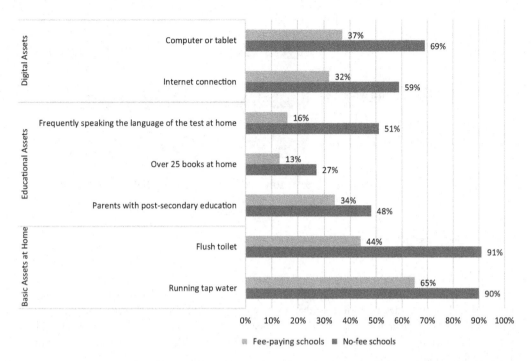

Figure 2.2   Percentage of students, in fee-paying and no-fee schools, having basic, educational, and digital assets at home

41 students (TIMSS 2019 data set). This 37% difference in class size from fee-paying classrooms to no-fee schools creates immense challenges for teachers. Inequalities in the two school types extend to the availability of science textbooks and workbooks as well, which is a key policy intervention from the state to equalize educational opportunities. Yet, there are still differences in students' access to science textbooks and workbooks in fee-paying and no-fee schools (Figure 2.3). Fewer than half the students in no-fee schools have a workbook or a textbook, compared with close to two-thirds of students in fee-paying schools.

The availability of laboratories and science equipment in a school is critical to conduct science experiments and investigations, an essential ingredient for the successful teaching and learning of the sciences. These are expensive resources, and only one-third of students in no-fee schools, compared to three-quarters of students in fee-paying schools, have access to a laboratory. The lessons given by teachers with and without a science laboratory space and equipment will be vastly different. This situation presents a challenge for science teacher education programs to determine how to prepare the next generation of new teachers to adapt and overcome a lack of resources. It is apparent from this analysis that science teacher education in South Africa should include pedagogy applying advanced technology, as well as pedagogy with no technology access. Recognizing this inequality of opportunity, and the impact it has, must be a serious consideration for teacher education programs.

Summary

Collectively, large-scale nationally representative data sets provide a wealth of analysis options for science teacher education research that may offer findings generalizable to the population. It is the responsibility of researchers to make candid assessments of the condition of science education. This type of data allows researchers to make assessments at a national level, as well as disaggregate data for

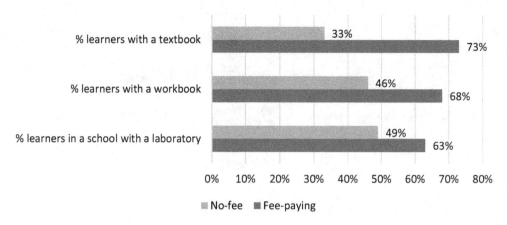

Figure 2.3   Resources in fee-paying and no-fee schools

important subgroup analyses. The aim of the example provided in this chapter speaks to this result. Data sets such as these described in this chapter may cast light on numerous topics, such as use and effectiveness of particular teaching practices, equity of common teaching practices, diversity in a nation's students and teaching workforce, typical working conditions for teachers, and resources available for teaching, among others.

Each data resource has its own focus and primary approach. For example, NTPS and NSSME provide descriptive information on teachers, their professional development experiences, teaching practices, and working conditions, while HSLS:2009 and NAEP Science offer more information linking teachers' and students' reported experiences. As a result, researchers seeking answers to research questions would be well served to examine a number of different data resources.

For some researchers, a lack of experience or training inhibits their engagement with these types of data resources. Professional development options are available. For example, in the United States, the National Center for Education Statistics (NCES) has developed a comprehensive *Distance Learning Dataset Training* (DLDT) system (NCES, 2021). This resource is an online tool that allows researchers to learn about NCES data products and assess the fit with their research needs. The modules in the DLDT cover each survey's design and specific analysis considerations. The International Association for the Evaluation of Educational Achievement (IEA) provides training and tutorials on the use of the TIMSS data.

Other researchers may be concerned about the shelf life of these data sets with release dates sometimes as many as 3 years after data collection. The fact remains that large-scale data sets focus on national-level trends, and these trends are more like the climate and less like the weather. While there may be local shifts, the climate of educational practice and policy outcomes remain stable and shift only slowly with time. In the years following publication of this volume, more data sets will follow, each holding important findings patiently waiting to be discovered by imaginative and determined researchers.

Note

1. The NSSME has been conducted under the National Science Foundation grant numbers DGE-1642413, DRL-1008228, and REC-9814246. Any opinions, findings, and conclusions or recommendations expressed in this material are those of the authors and do not necessarily reflect the views of the National Science Foundation.

References

American Institute of Research. (2020a). *NCES data R project – EdSurvey*. Retrieved June 17, 2021, from www.air.org/project/nces-data-r-project-edsurvey

American Institute of Research. (2020b). *Am statistical software*. Retrieved June 17, 2021, from https://am.air.org/default.asp

IBM. (2020). *SPSS Statistics*. Retrieved June 17, 2021, from www.ibm.com/products/spss-statistics

IEA. (2019). *TIMSS 2019 teacher questionnaire science*. https://nces.ed.gov/timss/pdf/T19_Gr8 _SciTchQ_USA_Questionnaire.pdf.

Martin, M. O., von Davier, M., & Mullis, I. V. S. (Eds.). (2020). *Methods and procedures: TIMSS 2019 technical report*. TIMSS & PIRLS International Study Center. https://timssandpirls.bc.edu/timss2019/methods/pdf/TIMSS-2019-MP-Technical-Report.pdf

National Academies of Science, Engineering, and Medicine. (2018). *English learners in STEM subjects: Transforming classrooms, schools, and lives*. Washington, DC: The National Academies Press. https://doi.org/10.17226/25182.

National Assessment of Educational Progress. (2018a). *Teacher questionnaire – Science classroom organization and instruction 4th grade*. National Center for Educational Statistics.https://nces.ed.gov/nationsreportcard/subject/about/pdf/bgq/teacher/2018_sq_teacher_science_class_org_g4_pilot.pdf

National Assessment of Educational Progress. (2018b). *Teacher questionnaire – Science classroom organization and instruction 8th grade*. National Center for Educational Statistics. https://nces.ed.gov/nationsreportcard/subject/about/pdf/bgq/teacher/2018_sq_teacher_science_class_org_g8_pilot.pdf

National Assessment of Educational Progress. (2018c). *Teacher questionnaire – Science background education and training 4th grade*. National Center for Educational Statistics.https://nces.ed.gov/nationsreportcard/subject/about/pdf/bgq/teacher/2018_sq_teacher_science_core_g4_pilot.pdf

National Assessment of Educational Progress. (2018d). *Teacher questionnaire – Science background education and training 8th grade*. National Center for Educational Statistics. https://nces.ed.gov/nationsreportcard/subject/about/pdf/bgq/teacher/2018_sq_teacher_science_core_g8_pilot.pdf

National Assessment of Educational Progress. (2020). *Nation's report card*. Retrieved June 17, 2021, from www.nationsreportcard.gov/.

National Center for Educational Statistics. (2017a). *National teacher and principal survey teacher questionnaire 2017–2018*. US Department of Education. https://nces.ed.gov/surveys/ntps/pdf/1718/Teacher_Questionnaire_2017-18.pdf.

National Center for Educational Statistics. (2017b). *National teacher and principal survey teacher questionnaire 2020–2021*. US Department of Education. https://nces.ed.gov/surveys/ntps/pdf/2021/Teacher_Questionnaire_2020_21.pdf.

National Center for Educational Statistics (2020). *Online codebook*. Retrieved June 17, 2021, from https://nces.ed.gov/onlinecodebook.

National Center for Educational Statistics (2021). *Distance learning dataset training*. https://nces.ed.gov/training/datauser/#/

R Core Team (2020). *R: A language and environment for statistical computing*. Vienna, Austria: R Foundation for Statistical Computing. Retrieved June 17, 2021, from www.R-project.org/

Reddy, V., Winnaar, L., Juan, A., Arends, F., Harvey, J., Hannan, S., . . . Zulu, N. (2020). *TIMSS 2019: Highlights of South African grade 9 results in mathematics and science*. Pretoria, South Africa: Human Sciences Research Council. www.hsrc.ac.za/uploads/pageContent/1044991/TIMSS%202019_Grade9_HSRC_FinalReport.pdf

Sirin, S. (2005). Socioeconomic status and academic achievement: A meta-analytic review of research. *Review of Educational Research*, *75*, 417–453. https://doi.org/10.3102/00346543075003417

STATA. (2020). Retrieved June 17, 2021, from www.stata.com/

Sulla, V., & Zikhali, P. (2018). *Overcoming poverty and inequality in South Africa: An assessment of drivers, constraints and opportunities*. The World Bank. https://documents1.worldbank.org/curated/en/530481521735906534/pdf/124521-REV-OUO-South-Africa-Poverty-and-Inequality-Assessment-Report-2018-FINAL-WEB.pdf

Van der Berg, S. (2008). How effective are poor schools? Poverty and educational outcomes in South Africa. *Studies in Educational Evaluation, 34*, 145–154.

WesVar [Computer software]. (2015). Retrieved June 17, 2021, from www.westat.com/capability/information-technology/wesvar.

3

QUALITATIVELY CONDUCTING TEACHER EDUCATION RESEARCH

Felicia Moore Mensah and Jessica L. Chen

Introduction

The questions, methods, and methodologies in science teacher education vary and add much to the field's evolving understanding of research and what is gained in understanding issues and questions to promote science teaching and learning. For instance, qualitative research is an approach that seeks to answer questions to problems that people have about the social world. Various researchers have defined qualitative research in the following ways: "By the term qualitative research, we mean any kind of research that produces findings not arrived at employing statistical procedures or other means of quantification" (Strauss & Corbin, 1990, p. 17). Qualitative research "seeks to understand phenomena via induction; to emphasize process, contracts, and interpretation in the construction of meaning and concept; and to report in narrative form" (Goodwin & Goodwin, 1996, p. 19).

Even as a research paradigm, qualitative research has evolved over the years. For example, Denzin and Lincoln (2011) have contributed a definition that has evolved as the nature of qualitative research shifts from social construction to interpretivism and then to social justice orientations (Creswell & Poth, 2018). The methods of data collection have expanded as well. A commonly referred definition includes the orientation, methods, and design of qualitative research:

> Qualitative research is a situated activity that locates the observer in the world. Qualitative research consists of a set of interpretive, material practices that make the world visible. These practices transform the world. They turn the world into a series of representations, including field notes, interviews, conversations, photographs, recordings, and memos to the self. At this level, qualitative research involves an interpretive, naturalistic approach to the world. This means that qualitative researchers study things in their natural settings, attempting to make sense of, or interpret, phenomena in terms of the meanings people bring to them.
>
> (Denzin & Lincoln, 2011, p. 3)

The attraction of qualitative research is that it allows researchers to conduct in-depth studies along with a broad range of contemporary topics of interest, and it holds many opportunities for developing new concepts, ideas, and meanings in science teacher education (Yin, 2016). Instead of research on teacher education conducted by an outside party, practitioner research examines practice from

DOI: 10.4324/9781003098478-4

the inside; it is research by teacher educators about their practice and most frequently utilizes qualitative research. Therefore, the process of documentation and analysis of science education through qualitative research approaches is made public and accessible to improve our teaching and increase the likelihood that our work will be useful to our professional peers engaged in similar practices and to policymakers who have an invested interest in the findings and implications garnered from our research.

Borko et al. (2007), however, noted a couple of limiting factors in doing interpretivist or qualitative research: first, the lack of shared conceptual frameworks and designs, which make it challenging to aggregate findings and to make comparisons across studies, even with studies looking at similar phenomena. Second, the body of teacher education research has focused primarily on the perspectives of teacher candidates, teacher educators, and school-based personnel involved in teacher preparation. Researchers advise that broadening our empirical eye to include other stakeholders, such as university administrators, legislators, school board members, district administrators, departments of education, parents, and K–12 learners may provide important findings that speak to the current policy demands to link teacher preparation with student learning (Borko et al., 2007).

Qualitative Research Approaches

Science teacher educators ask a range of questions that pertain to various contexts and constituents when conducting research, as well as different ways that problems are conceptualized. The methods, methodologies, and analyses vary also in how science teacher educators choose to conduct qualitative research. Research design decisions are made based on the questions asked and the approaches taken. For example, Creswell and Poth (2018) have outlined five approaches to conducting qualitative research – narrative, phenomenology, grounded theory, ethnography, and case study. These are the most commonly used qualitative or interpretivist approaches availed in the social, behavioral, and health science literature, with Merriam and Grenier (2019) including arts-based and qualitative action research, and Yin (2016) adding autoethnography, critical theory, discourse analysis, ethnomethodology, and oral history to the list. These approaches utilize a variety of research strategies and methods of collecting, analyzing, interpreting, and evaluating data, as well as writing and presenting qualitative research findings. While each qualitative approach has unique features, they also share common philosophical assumptions or characteristics (Figure 3.1). Even with a few common elements, there is no single method or methodological approach for doing qualitative research. In fact, "given the complexity of [science] teacher education" and "its connections to various aspects of teacher quality and student learning, no single methodological or theoretical approach will be able to provide all that is needed to understand how and why [science] teacher education influences educational outcomes" (Zeichner, 2005, p. 743).

In this chapter, we conducted a review of the literature of qualitative research methods utilized in science teacher education research. We were curious to learn about the various ways that science educators conducted qualitative or interpretivist research, noting the types of questions, methods, methodologies, and analyses they employed. Though the chapter is not an exhaustive search of the field, we note some general and specific characteristics of qualitative research in science teacher education that qualitatively represent the field, and we offer recommendations to expand the field to address additional questions that could transform qualitative research design.

Methodology

We first performed a broad search using the *Education Full Text* database to identify the qualitative research that was published in the field of science teacher education globally and in the United States within the past 10 years. We used the search terms "qualitative research," "mixed methods"

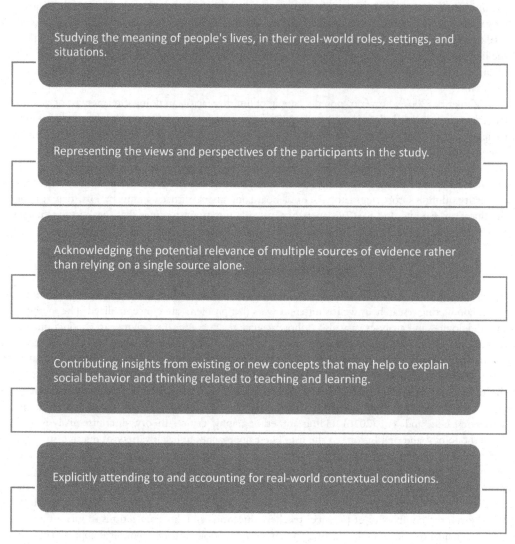

Figure 3.1 Characteristics of qualitative research.

Source: Adapted from Yin (2016, p. 9).

(to capture diverse methodological approaches of data), and "science teacher education," without quotation marks, and set the year range for 2010 to 2020. We hoped in this decade of research to capture trends addressing both the research and practice dichotomy of science teacher education (Lederman & Abell, 2014). This search returned a total of 221 articles related to qualitative and mixed methods research in science teacher education. These articles were mostly published in the *Journal of Science Teacher Education*, *International Journal of Science and Mathematics*, *Cultural Studies in Science Education*, and *School Science and Mathematics*. Because the *Education Full Text* database included only articles published before 2018 for the *Journal of Science Teacher Education*, an additional search was performed in this journal between the years 2018 and 2020 using the same search terms. This search produced 101 additional articles. Together, the searches in the *Education Full Text* and *Journal of Science Teacher Education* produced a total of 322 articles.

We read the methodology section of all 322 articles and excluded 162 of them; these were conceptual papers, editorials, or mixed methods studies, or they focused on K–12 students or teachers who taught subjects other than science. However, studies with both science and mathematics teachers were not excluded. After applying these exclusion criteria, 160 articles remained and were included in this literature review (Table 3.1). We uploaded them into Zotero, an online management database, and read the methodology sections in more detail. While going through this process, we notated and grouped the articles by the qualitative methodology and created a table, identifying the author(s) name, year of publication, method(s) of research and research design, name of the journal, and content of the research article for our initial round of organizing the studies as data. From reading the abstract and methods sections of the articles, we added the research questions, including analytical and descriptive notes within Zotero.

While organizing the 160 articles by qualitative methodology into a second data table, we read and discussed in greater detail the research questions, methodologies, participants, collected data, analyses, and areas of research among these articles, and identified 70 articles to potentially spotlight. We also paid attention to international studies to ensure equitable representation of studies done in and outside of the United States. Where appropriate, we selected two articles as exemplars that represent the current field in terms of qualitative approaches and methodologies in science teacher education. This review is less about the findings and implications of the studies, though we mention this, and more about the use of the qualitative methods and analyses. We conclude this review by offering ideas on expanding qualitative research to address questions through critical methodologies that might contribute more to the maturing and evolving field of science teacher education.

Conducting Qualitative Studies

We start with general qualitative studies and case studies, as these were the most common approaches from the literature review, followed by grounded theory, ethnography, phenomenology, narrative, action research, and self-study. We use Creswell and Poth (2018), Merriam and Grenier (2019), and Yin (2016) in describing and categorizing the qualitative approaches. The spotlight studies are exemplars of the types of methods, methodologies, and analyses. We also note the kinds of questions being asked and how they were addressed qualitatively.

Spotlight Studies: General Qualitative

In qualitative research, researchers are interested in knowing how people understand and experience their world at a particular point in time and in a particular context. The contexts, questions,

Table 3.1 Qualitative/Interpretivist Approaches

Qualitative/Interpretivist Approaches	Number of Studies
General qualitative	85
Case study	54
Phenomenology	9
Action research	4
Grounded theory	3
Self-study	2
Ethnography	2
Narrative	1
Total	160

and overall research design differ in as many ways as there are questions to be addressed. Researchers gather data to build concepts, hypotheses, or theories, and the product is "richly descriptive" (Merriam & Grenier, 2019, p. 6). The majority of articles we reviewed were identified as general qualitative, meaning no specific qualitative approach, like a case study, ethnography, or narrative, was mentioned. However, the two spotlight articles used a variety of data sources and analytical methods to address their research questions about national educational policy and reform in Taiwan and teaching practices, and the nature of student teachers' field trip pedagogy in informal settings using drawings and other methods.

First, the qualitative study conducted by Huang and Asghar (2018) was situated within the context of science education reform initiated by the Taiwanese government in the 1990s. The study looked at the secondary science (grades 7–9) teachers' perspectives on the implementation of the new science curriculum, as certain Confucian learning traditions created obstacles for developing innovation and critical-thinking skills in students. Ten inservice teachers participated in individual interviews to focus on their understanding of Taiwan's reform policies and the new curriculum goals. A reflective journal with responses from four open-ended questions was collected. In their journals, teachers expressed their thoughts and perspectives on Confucianism and its role in Taiwan's educational system. Huang, one of the researchers, also maintained a reflective diary to record and examine her biases and assumptive interpretations of participants' meaning-making during the data collection process. The interviews and written reflections were collected in Mandarin Chinese and transcribed into English for data analysis. The researchers used several qualitative analysis tools and techniques, such as thematic analysis, with categorizing and clustering salient themes emerging from the data, concept maps, and thematic matrices to explore relationships among the different categories and themes. The authors also performed constant comparative analysis to compare the policy documents with the science teachers' vision for science education reform.

In the second spotlighted article, Subramaniam et al. (2018) used three stages of conceptualization of pre-, during-, and post-field trip pedagogy as quality learning experiences for 72 student teachers (75% White female student teachers, 20% Hispanic female student teachers, and 5% African American and Asian student teachers). The study focused on the images the student teachers drew and the pedagogy of learning within informal settings. In addition to the drawings, narratives were collected as qualitative data to provide text balance and allow participants to describe and interpret their drawings in their own words. The researchers used a holistic coding process for depictions of products (animals, trees, scientific equipment, etc.), emergent analytic coding for specific features within the holistic coding process to match the narratives from the drawings, and trait coding for a higher level of abstraction of the drawings for uniqueness, identification, and quantification (Haney et al., 2003). They also used intercoder agreement (Kurasaki, 2000). The narratives were analyzed using a deductive thematic analysis approach (Braun & Clarke, 2006). With predetermined constructs to guide the analysis, the narratives were used to corroborate the processes, products, features, and traits depicted in the preservice teachers' drawings. In sum, these two studies are exemplars of using multiple sources of evidence rather than relying on a single source alone in addressing their research questions (Figure 3.1). They use diverse analytical approaches for analyses of interviews, narratives, and drawings, but did not indicate a specific qualitative approach.

Spotlight Studies: Case Study

Yin (2016) described that the value of a case study is that it is situated within the actual context and allows the researchers to get close to the participants by direct observation in natural settings. The case is the center for understanding and not so much the variables. Thus, the spotlight studies for case study show the collection and analysis of multiple data sources with data collection in different contexts and from different participants. Both are professional development studies.

For this first professional development case study, Ceven McNally (2016) used video-recorded classroom observations within an established distance e-Mentoring for Student Success program. This online professional development for teachers used several qualitative methods, such as observations and cycles of activities with the collaboration of the mentor-mentee pair, pre-observation discussions, the sharing of a video recording of a short classroom episode, and a post-observation discussion in which mentor and mentee analyzed evidence from the video to determine an action plan of next steps for the new teacher. Each mentor-mentee pair was treated as a case study, and trends between the first and second cycle of observations for each pair or case were shared. For the case studies, multiple sources of data were collected and corroborated to establish the validity of the findings. For instance, data triangulation was achieved by collecting evidence from observation discussions, interviews, and reflections from the participants.

In their qualitative case study of 20 teachers enrolled in a 2-year fellowship, Gunning and colleagues (2020) collected data from the teachers' participation in a monthly professional learning community. Their vertical professional learning community (V-PLC) PD model was constructed as teaming teachers from elementary, middle, and high school levels to examine the progression of science content knowledge in K–12 classrooms. Qualitative data collection and analysis of five data sets took place from each of the five V-PLC (i.e., documents, videos, reflections, observations, and pre/post questionnaires). The four data sets collected from the five vertical teams as well as observation data, student exemplars, anecdotes, activities, and feedback from audience presentations were collected and analyzed. Overall, the researchers collected an array of data and utilized numerous analytical tools to address teacher professional development discussed as cases of teachers learning together.

Spotlight Studies: Grounded Theory

Similar to other qualitative research designs, grounded theory is "the study of experience from the standpoint of those who live it" (Charmaz, 2006, p. 522). However, what distinguishes a grounded theory approach from other qualitative research designs is that the goal of a grounded theory study is the "building of a substantive theory – theory that emerges from and is 'grounded' in the data collected" (p. 185). Data collection can come from a variety of sources, with interviews and observation being the primary sources (Merriam & Grenier, 2019). Another feature of grounded theory is its process of data analysis; grounded theory research is guided by the constant comparative method (Strauss & Corbin, 1998). Units of data deemed meaningful by the researcher are compared with each other to generate tentative categories or themes and properties, the basic elements of a grounded theory study. The two spotlight articles contribute new insights to explain social behavior and thinking related to teaching and learning in the use of grounded theory.

Borgerding and Caniglia (2017) chose grounded theory because it allowed for "an inductive approach grounded in data without constraint by a theoretical framework" (p. 67), and it provided a systematic way to guide emerging findings, subsequent data collection, and analysis. During their 3-year study, the researchers followed seven mathematics and science Noyce preservice teachers. They were interested in knowing the preservice teachers' views of their science service learning teaching experiences throughout their master's teacher preparation program and first years of teaching and the impact of service learning on their preparation for teaching in high-need schools. Data sources included semi-structured interviews with each preservice teacher throughout the length of the study, a focus group occurring before the semester of their student teaching, and a survey administered during the participants' second year of teaching. Theoretical memoing guided the organization of codes into categories, and three key categories were organized into a working theory on the impact of service learning teaching and teacher development. Member-checking and prolonged engagement were used to support the credibility of the findings.

Informed by the theoretical underpinnings of sociocultural and sociolinguistic perspectives, Sezen-Barrie et al. (2020) combined grounded theory and discourse analysis methodologies in their qualitative research design. They were interested in the teachers' sources of ambiguities and uncertainties and how teachers' contextualized goals shaped their pedagogical strategies for scaffolding students' engagement in epistemic practices. The teachers' sensemaking of their scaffolding was accomplished through interactions with colleagues in Professional Learning Environments (PLEs) and with students in their classrooms. The PLEs, developed by scientists, teacher educators, and science education researchers, included activities and workshops on three climate change topics and emphasized scaffolding scientific practices, epistemic tools, and pedagogical strategies. A total of 58 secondary science teachers participated in one to three of the PLEs and implemented the activities in their classrooms between 2015 and 2017. The results of the constant-comparative analysis of teachers' scaffolding process were used to organize responses to the two research questions of the study. For both studies, developing codes and categories and conducting the constant comparative methods are defining processes of grounded theory. Findings from the two studies contributed deeper theoretical ideas on teachers and student learners.

Spotlight Studies: Ethnography

An ethnographic research design takes "an emic (or insider) approach" to describe and interpret the culture of a group (Merriam & Grenier, 2019, p. 135). Ethnography is also concerned with understanding the cultural context of a setting. Ethnography is historically associated with the field of anthropology and has come to be viewed as both the approach to conducting research as well as the product of doing research. The two spotlight studies selected for ethnography exemplify studying the meaning of people's lives, in their real-world roles, settings, and situations.

For example, Rinchen et al. (2016) explored 28 secondary preservice teachers' perceptions of classroom emotional climate in the context of the Bhutanese macro-social policy of Gross National Happiness to boost the nation's emotional well-being and prosperity. Over five months, the researchers collected data, such as observations and videos of 16 lessons of 1-hour duration each, and student perceptions of classroom emotional climate. The students recorded their perceptions for each lesson at 3-minute intervals using keypads (clickers), which produced a graph of the highs and lows of the emotional climate of the classroom. The video recordings were placed in a fixed position on students, as was a hand-held camera to capture group activity. The videos were also used in the interviews with students, stimulated recall interviews with the tutor, and the instructor's researcher diary. From the analyses of multiple data sources, the researchers addressed their question that the emotional climate of the class depended on the type of learning activities the participants engaged with.

In Kang et al.'s (2013) ethnographic study, researchers investigated the successes and struggles in moving back and forth across the cultural border between science and inquiry-oriented science teaching. The eight preservice secondary science teachers enrolled in a post-baccalaureate teacher education program were the participants. They first engaged in a toxicology investigation in pairs as science students and then designed an inquiry lesson plan as science teachers in different pairs. Four types of data were collected: (1) 14.5 hours of videotape of small group and whole-class interactions over eight class sessions; (2) the preservice teachers' drafts and final reports, and peer reviews of their toxicology investigation; (3) inquiry lesson plans designed in pairs; and (4) interviews done in pairs with preservice teachers about their understanding of toxicology, inquiry, and how they might incorporate inquiry into their science classrooms. The authors performed two qualitative analyses. For each analysis, the authors looked for patterns by gender, undergraduate degree, and intended science teaching credential. The two studies in ethnography focused on the classroom environment and learning among students within their specific context as it relates to teaching and learning. Moreover, two additional advantages of doing ethnography are the amount of time spent in the context, with 5 months for the Rinchen et al. (2016) study and 1 year for the Kang et al. (2013) study. The second advantage is the opportunity to observe individual and group behavior in its natural context (Guest et al., 2013).

Spotlight Studies: Phenomenology

Phenomenology has roots in philosophy and psychology and focuses on the subjective experience of the participants where the individual and the person are interrelated to capture "the essence of the meaning of this interaction" (Merriam & Grenier, 2019, p. 87). When conducting, analyzing, and writing the findings of a phenomenological study, the final step is "to construct a synthesis of textual and structural descriptions of the phenomenon such that the essence or meaning of the experience can be conveyed to others" (p. 88). Phenomenology as a qualitative approach for science teacher education was not commonly conducted; however, we selected two spotlight studies that used this approach that highlight shared experiences of participants in informal settings.

Peters-Burton and Hiller's (2013) phenomenological study strived to understand the shared experience of preparing and implementing a weeklong summer science camp for six undergraduate students working towards a minor in education. The students worked as camp counselors, which was part of a course that provided science teaching theory and experiential learning for the students who had no prior science teaching experience. Data sources included a written assignment asking students to explain what they thought was fun and motivating about science for children at the beginning of the course; field notes during the camp implementation; students' reflective portfolios; interviews conducted after the completion of the course; and a pre- and post-test survey of Science Teaching Efficacy Beliefs Inventory–Preservice (Enochs & Riggs, 1990). Along with this survey, the students completed an open-ended writing assignment focusing on their perceptions of what motivated students, their childhood science learning experiences, and their confidence in teaching science. The authors used line-by-line analysis and constant comparative process (Strauss & Corbin, 1998) to analyze the qualitative data and developed categories and descriptions of how the students found meaning in the experience of teaching science in the summer camp.

While many studies focused on teacher education, preservice teachers, and inservice teachers, the Underwood and Mensah (2018) study examined 33 science teacher educators' understanding of culturally relevant pedagogy. For part 1 of the study, the researchers used a yes/no qualitative online survey to determine the selection of participants for interviews. The researchers used both deductive and inductive phenomenological approaches to analyze the qualitative survey that asked questions about teaching style, race, and culture. For part 2 of the study, interviews were collected to gain rich information about the participants' perceptions of their teaching beliefs and practices. Using the three tenets of culturally relevant pedagogy, the data were categorized and coded as academic success, cultural competence, and critical consciousness. Thus, capturing the essence of an experience of phenomenology has broad applicability to denote the study of individuals' perceptions, feelings, and lived experiences (Guest et al., 2013), and allows participants to talk about a topic in their own words. The two spotlights are representative of this experiential lens.

Spotlight Studies: Narrative

Studies that use a narrative inquiry approach are accounts of the experiences of people's lives and how they come to understand their world. Narrative studies are written in story format. They are used to communicate and make meaning of a particular human experience. Beyond just capturing the story, the narrative is an analysis of the story that involves interpretation within the cultural context of the story (Merriam & Grenier, 2019). Considering the interpretivist paradigm of qualitative research, researchers writing narrative studies construct and, in a sense, co-author others' stories through representing and transforming their texts and discourses (Merriam & Grenier, 2019).

Only one narrative study met the inclusion criteria. Napier et al. (2020) constructed narratives of 17 newly hired science teachers who were teaching both in-field and out-of-field in secondary physics, chemistry, and physical science in public schools located in urban areas. The authors collected data that consisted of 4 yearly observations (total of 12), yearly interviews (total of 4), and monthly interviews (total of 24). Semi-structured interviews were collected before and after the participants' first, second, and third year of teaching. The observations of classroom practices data were collected, along with corresponding materials and artifacts. Data in the participants' files were coded in two cycles: first, structural coding and analytical memos (Saldaña, 2013), which had an emphasis on content and instructional practices with labeling and indexing the data for emergent codes; and second, creating the teacher narratives with descriptions and a storyline that outlined the changes in teacher practices. For the final analysis, the researchers created a case dynamics matrix (Miles et al., 2014) for showing how out-of-field teaching interacted with the teachers' classroom instruction. Narratives were constructed of the new teachers teaching over time, and comparisons were made for in-field and out-of-field subject teaching across the novices.

Spotlight Studies: Action Research

Action research is an approach to qualitative research oftentimes used by practitioners to solve a problem of practice within the workplace (Merriam & Grenier, 2019). The problem is identified within a local context and based on collaborative problem-solving between the researcher and the participants that result in action to change policy, programs, and practices. It is a cyclical process that involves identifying a problem, planning and gathering data, taking action to address the problem, and then analyzing the results of the action to plan and take further action. Generally, action research studies are unique in that they include participatory designs and connect theory to practice by seeking practical solutions to a specific, localized problem (Merriam & Grenier, 2019).

In the first spotlight study of action research and professional development, Goodnough (2016) examined the experiences and changes of K-6 teachers' engagement in collaborative action research. The goals of the professional development were to assist the teachers in adopting inquiry-based approaches to teaching STEM and becoming more confident in teaching STEM subjects. Goodnough specifically examined how contradictions or tensions became sources of change in teachers' objectives. The teachers completed two action research cycles over 2 years in their small, urban K-6 school in Newfoundland. Over the 2 years, the teachers created two action research projects that involved attending and maintaining a school-based garden. The data collected included a pre-implementation inquiry brief, teacher reflections, post-implementation semi-structured interviews, a multimedia presentation by the teachers, and researcher notes. The data were coded deductively for teacher change and contradictions in their activity system using the key elements of the Cultural Historical Activity Theory framework: subject, object, tools, community, norms, and division of labor.

Thirteen secondary preservice teachers participated in an integrated action research study conducted by Mawyer and Johnson (2019). This approach allowed the teacher participants to design and "try out" a lesson on tacit reading strategies on different genres of science texts – popular science texts (a newspaper), science texts for education (a section of a textbook), and scientific texts (a journal article). The study took place in a 15-week secondary science methods seminar course that was co-developed by the instructors at two universities. The preservice teachers wrote focused analytical field notes from their time in their field placements observing teachers' use of texts in their teaching. During one session of their methods course, the preservice teachers read three text examples on global warming, completed a questionnaire after reading, and participated in small groups to share personal reading strategies. Following these activities, the preservice teachers designed and implemented a lesson incorporating a science text. The qualitative data collection for the study consisted of annotated packets of readings, written responses to the questionnaire, group posters, and field notes from the whole-class discussion. The data were analyzed using a two-part coding methods strategy that incorporated eight metacognitive strategies. The researchers used genre-specific text structures and features to create genre-specific codes which then produced seven dimensions across the different texts. Both action research studies were reflective accounts of instructors and students improving teaching and learning in science classrooms.

Spotlight Studies: Self-Study

Action research and self-study are similar; however, Feldman et al. (2004) presented three methodological features: (1) a self-study would bring to the forefront the importance of self; (2) self-study would make the experience of teacher educators a resource for research; and (3) self-study would urge those who engage in self-study to be critical of themselves and their roles as researchers and teacher educators. Self-study may incorporate other methods, such as arts-based methods, memory work, narrative inquiry, personal history, or reflective portfolios (Lassonde et al., 2009). Nonetheless, researchers who conduct self-study research use their experiences as a resource for conducting research and problematize themselves in their research context.

As with narrative, only one self-study met the inclusion criteria. Garbett (2011), an elementary science teacher educator, did a systematic self-study in her elementary science methods course to deepen an understanding of her pedagogy and the factors that enhanced and hindered her confidence and competence to teach student teachers. The focus of the self-study was a collaborative assessment task she designed that consisted of eight questions that asked the student teachers to support explanations of fundamental science concepts taught in the New Zealand science curriculum and activities to engage learners in learning these concepts. One data source for Garbett's self-study was 41 electronic journal entries, which recorded her impressions and description of events, circumstances, experiences, discussions, and reflections. Other data sources included three Likert scale questionnaires, open-ended questions, and peer evaluations of the student teachers' learning. Lastly, Garbett held informal focus group interviews to share and discuss the findings of the self-study with her student teachers. Data collection and analysis occurred hermeneutically, reading and re-reading the data and jotting notes until the author recognized emergent themes. She also shared her interpretations of the data with two critical friends, which enabled her to gather a sense of her changing practice and greater awareness and understanding of the efficacy of her pedagogy.

Discussion

Qualitative research is "the most fundamentally constructivist research method available to us" (Erickson, 2012, p. 1468). In this chapter, numerous studies fit squarely within the qualitative or interpretivist paradigm. We identified, read, notated, and organized 160 articles for review, and offered exemplary spotlights of qualitative research approaches in science teacher education that attend to general characteristics of qualitative research as well as specific interpretivist approaches. An interpretivist perspective is based on the idea that qualitative research is concerned with "revealing multiple realities" as opposed to research from "one *objective* reality" (Guest et al., 2013, p. 6). There is no single method or distinct interpretivist approach that can address the varied, complex, relevant, and interesting questions in science teacher education.

Traditional qualitative research is critiqued for not being rigorous and not attending to power dynamics in research (Erickson, 2012). However, there are opportunities for greater transparency in doing and reporting qualitative research. For instance, many studies were categorized as "general qualitative" and did not use a specific approach. In another way, few studies were categorized as narrative, ethnography, phenomenology, or self-study. Engaging more fully with approaches may build a stronger base for qualitative research in the field. Doing more participatory action research and practitioner research are attempts to address the power/knowledge issues involved in science teacher education research. Though we note a few of these studies in our review, the field would benefit from more of them.

Studies focusing on the positionalities of science teachers (Teachers of Color), career stages (mid-career and veteran), as well as the experiences and teaching of science in diverse settings (international, informal, online) are welcomed. These topics relate to issues of diversity, equity, and inclusion and can be addressed by many of the qualitative approaches mentioned in this review; yet as a field, questions, methods, and methodologies on these topics are not addressed substantially. Additionally, trajectories of science teachers and more longitudinal studies are needed. This might allow for additional stakeholders and participatory methods across various settings to be engaged in science teacher education research. This would require teacher educators and researchers to build alliances to think differently about doing qualitative research and who is invited to participate in the research process.

Expanding Qualitatively

From the review, there is much potential for blurring the boundaries between the two paradigms of qualitative and quantitative for mixed methods, or integrated methods research for science teacher education. For example, Zeichner (2007) argued that teacher educators and teacher education research must "build upon each other's work conceptually, theoretically, and methodologically" (p. 40) so that research programs, self-studies, and teacher education research can have a greater impact on policy debates within the field. As a fairly nascent field, science teacher education must take advantage of methodological advances to design and conduct more complex and critical research studies, which could fare well across the different qualitative approaches. For example, expanding data methods to include the creative arts, where participants engage in artistic processes, such as music, visual art, dance, poetry, or multimedia pieces to express their experiences in different forms (Merriam & Grenier, 2019) may also provide new ways for researchers to conduct, capture, think about, analyze, and communicate science teacher education research through critical and more inclusive perspectives.

Furthermore, critical race methodology and narrative studies (Mensah, 2019) as well as arts-based ethnodance methodology (Chappell & Varelas, 2020) are examples that expand the qualitative repertoires in science teacher education research. Moreover, new technologies and digital innovation for gathering, recording, storing, and analyzing high-quality digital records, such as audio and video of teaching and learning activities, with computer software and applications for coding and reporting, would allow for larger data sets to be available for qualitative research and analysis. As the field grows, the qualitative researcher can take a few more methodological risks and take advantage of the many opportunities provided by new technologies, such as social media, websites, blogs, graphic novels, and multimedia for doing qualitative research and analyses (Flick, 2014). Likewise, as researchers involve research participants and partners in the knowledge-production process of participatory research (Bergold & Thomas, 2012), we challenge notions of what qualitative research is within and outside the common approaches that are familiar.

Conclusion

We acknowledge the value of qualitatively conducting teacher education research and encourage expansion in methods, methodologies, and participants while also blurring the lines and tightening the reins, depending upon how researchers choose to answer questions of inquiry in science teacher education. Researchers can help to ensure the advancement and growth of the field by recognizing both the affordances and limitations of various qualitative or interpretivist approaches in pursuing the enduring questions the field has to address. The methodological contributions and findings in the field of science teacher education are commendable. We note, however, that more inclusive, critical, emancipatory, and liberatory research approaches done qualitatively would advance the field.

References

*Bergold, J., & Thomas, S. (2012). Participatory research methods: A methodological approach in motion. *Historical Social Research, 37*(4), 191–222. https://doi.org/10.12759/hsr.37.2012.4.191-222

Bogdan, R. C., & Biklen, S. K. (1998). *Qualitative research for education: An introduction to theory and methods* (3rd ed.). Boston, MA: Allyn & Bacon.

*Borgerding, L. A., & Caniglia, J. (2017). Service learning within a secondary math and science teacher education program: Preservice MAT teachers' perspectives. *School Science & Mathematics, 117*(2), 63–75. https://doi.org/10.1111/ssm.12210

Borko, H., Liston, D., & Whitcomb, J. A. (2007). Genres of empirical research in teacher education. *Journal of Teacher Education, 58*(1), 3–11. https://doi.org/10.1177/0022487106296220

Braun, V., & Clarke, V. (2006). Using thematic analysis in psychology. *Qualitative Research in Psychology, 3*, 77–101. https://doi.org/10.1191/1478088706qp063oa

*Ceven McNally, J. (2016). Learning from one's own teaching: New science teachers analyzing their practice through classroom observation cycles. *Journal of Research in Science Teaching, 53*(3), 473–501. https://doi.org/10.1002/tea.21253

Chappell, M. J., & Varelas, M. (2020). Ethnodance and identity: Black students representing science identities in the making. *Science Education, 104*(2), 193–221. https://doi.org/10.1002/sce.21558

Charmaz, K. (2006). *Constructing grounded theory: A practical guide through qualitative analysis*. Thousand Oaks, CA: Sage.

Creswell, J. W., & Poth, C. P. (2018). *Qualitative inquiry and research design: Choosing among five approaches* (4th ed.). Thousand Oaks, CA: Sage.

Denzin, N. K., & Lincoln, Y. S. (2011). Introduction: The discipline and practice of qualitative research. In N. K. Denzin & Y. S. Lincoln (Eds.), *The Sage handbook of qualitative research* (4th ed.). Thousand Oaks, CA: Sage.

Emerson, R. M., Fretz, R. I., & Shaw, L. L. (2011). *Writing ethnographic fieldnotes*. Chicago, IL: University of Chicago Press.

Enochs, L., & Riggs, I. (1990). Towards the development of an elementary teacher's science teaching efficacy belief instrument. *Science Education, 74*, 625–638. https://doi.org/10.1002/sce.3730740605

Erickson, F. (2012). Qualitative research methods for science education. In B. J. Fraser, K. Tobin, & C. McRobbie (Eds.), *Second international handbook of science education* (pp. 1451–1469). Dordrecht, Switzerland: Springer. https://doi.org/10.1007/978-1-4020-9041-7_93

Feldman, A., Paugh, P., & Mills, G. (2004). Self-study through action research. In J. J. Loughran, M. L. Hamilton., V. K. LaBoskey, & T. Russell (Eds.), *International handbook of self-study of teaching and teacher education practices* (pp. 943–978). Dordrecht, Switzerland: Springer.

Flick, U. (2014). Mapping the field. In U. Flick (Ed.), *The SAGE handbook of qualitative data analysis* (pp. 3–18). London: Sage. https://doi-org.10.4135/9781446282243

*Garbett, D. (2011). Developing pedagogical practices to enhance confidence and competence in science teacher education. *Journal of Science Teacher Education, 22*(8), 729–743. https://doi.org/10.1007/s10972-011-9258-8

*Goodnough, K. (2016). Professional learning of K-6 teachers in science through collaborative action research: An activity theory analysis. *Journal of Science Teacher Education, 27*(7), 747–767. https://doi.org/10.1007/s10972-016-9485-0

Goodwin, W. L., & Goodwin, L. D. (1996). *Understanding quantitative and qualitative research in early childhood education*. New York, NY: Teachers College Press.

Guest, G., Namey, E., & Mitchell, M. (2013). Qualitative research: Defining and designing. In *Collecting qualitative data: A field manual for applied research*, online version (pp. 1–43). Thousand Oaks, CA: Sage.

*Gunning, A. M., Marrero, M. E., Hillman, P. C., & Brandon, L. T. (2020). How K-12 teachers of science experience a vertically articulated professional learning community. *Journal of Science Teacher Education, 31*(6), 705–718. https://doi.org/10.1080/1046560X.2020.1758419

Haney, W., Russell, M., & Bebell, D. (2003). Drawing on education: Using drawings to document schooling and support change. *Harvard Educational Review, 74*(3), 241–271. https://doi.org/10.17763/haer.74.3.w0817u84w7452011

*Huang, Y., & Asghar, A. (2018). Science education reform in Confucian learning cultures: Teachers' perspectives on policy and practice in Taiwan. *Cultural Studies in Science Education, 13*(1), 101–131. https://doi.org/101007/s11422-016-9762-4

*Kang, E., Bianchini, J., & Kelly, G. (2013). Crossing the border from science student to science teacher: Preservice teachers' views and experiences learning to teach inquiry. *Journal of Science Teacher Education, 24*(3), 427–447. https://10.1007/s10972-012-9317-9

Kurasaki, K. S. (2000). Intercoder reliability for validating conclusions drawn from open-ended interview data. *Field Methods, 12*(3), 179–194. https://doi.org/10.1177/1525822X0001200301

Lassonde, C. A., Galman, S., & Kosnik, C. (2009). *Self-study research methodologies for teacher educators*. Rotterdam, Netherlands: Sense Publishers.

Lederman, N. G., & Abell, S. K. (2014). *Handbook of research on science education* (Vol. II). New York, NY: Routledge. https://doi.org/10.4324/9780203097267

*Mawyer, K. N. N., & Johnson, H. J. (2019). Eliciting preservice teachers' reading strategies through structured literacy activities. *Journal of Science Teacher Education, 30*(6), 583–600. https://doi.org/10.1080/1046560X.2019.1589848

Mensah, F. M. (2019). Finding voice and passion: Critical race theory methodology in science teacher education. *American Educational Research Journal, 56*(4), 1412–1456. https://doi.org/10.3102/0002831218818093

Merriam, S. B., & Grenier, R. S. (2019). *Qualitative research in practice: Examples for discussion and analysis* (2nd ed.). San Francisco, CA: Jossey-Bass.

Miles, M. B., Huberman, A. M., & Saldaña, J. (2014). *Qualitative data analysis: A method sourcebook* (3rd ed.). Thousand Oaks, CA: Sage.

*Napier, J. B., Luft, J. A., & Singh, H. (2020). In the classrooms of newly hired secondary science teachers: The consequences of teaching in-field or out-of-field. *Journal of Science Teacher Education, 31*(7), 802–820. www.doi.org/10.1080/1046560X.2020.1800195

*Peters-Burton, E., & Hiller, S. (2013). Fun science: The use of variable manipulation to avoid content instruction. *Journal of Science Teacher Education, 24*(1), 199–217. www.doi.org/10.1007/s10972-012-9269-0

*Rinchen, E., Ritchie, S., & Bellocchi, A. (2016). Emotional climate of a pre-service science teacher education class in Bhutan. *Cultural Studies in Science Education, 11*(3), 603–628. www.doi.org/10.1007/s11422-014-9658-0

Saldaña, J. (2013). *The coding manual for qualitative researchers* (2nd ed.). Thousand Oaks, CA: Sage.

*Sezen-Barrie, A., Stapleton, M. K., & Marbach-Ad, G. (2020). Science teacher" sensemaking of the use of epistemic tools to scaffold students' knowledge (re)construction in classrooms. *Journal of Research in Science Teaching, 57*(7), 1058–1092. https://doi.org/10.1002/tea.21621

Strauss, A., & Corbin, J. (1990). *Basics of qualitative research*. Thousand Oaks, CA: Sage.

Strauss, A., & Corbin, J. (1998). *Basics of qualitative research: Techniques and procedures for developing grounded theory* (2nd ed.). Thousand Oaks, CA: Sage.

*Subramaniam, K., Asim, S., Lee, E. U., & Koo, Y. (2018). Student teachers' images of science instruction in informal settings: A focus on field trip pedagogy. *Journal of Science Teacher Education, 29*(4), 307–325. https://doi.org/10.1080/1046560X.2018.1452531

*Underwood, J., B., & Mensah, F. M. (2018). An investigation of science teacher educators' perspectives of culturally relevant pedagogy. *Journal of Science Teacher Education, 29*(1), 46–64. www.doi.org/10.1080/1046560X.2017.1423457

Yin, R. K. (2016). *Qualitative research from start to finish* (2nd ed.). Guilford Press.

Zeichner, K. (2005). A research agenda for teacher education. In M. Cochran-Smith & K. M. Zeichner (Eds.), *Studying teacher education: The report of the AERA Panel on research and teacher education* (pp. 737–759). Mahwah, NJ: Lawrence Erlbaum.

Zeichner, K. (2007). Accumulating knowledge across self-studies in teacher education. *Journal of Teacher Education, 58*(1), 36–46. https://doi.org/10.1177/0022487106296219

4

MIXED METHODS RESEARCH ON SCIENCE TEACHER EDUCATION

Gayle A. Buck and Francesca A. Williamson

Educational researchers are increasingly using mixed methods approaches to address the expectations of various stakeholder audiences, to design and evaluate innovative practices, to secure federal and state funding, and to meet the local needs of teachers, learners, and school administrators (Greene, 2008; Johnson & Onwuegbuzie, 2004). Science education researchers, specifically, are similarly leveraging mixed methods with the aim of improving teaching and learning science across contexts. As a result, mixed methods inquiries are becoming more common in the field of science teacher education. The time is right to explore the contemporary use of mixed methods research in science teacher education and consider ways to strengthen its usefulness and effectiveness.

Building a sound mixed methods research culture in science teacher education requires understanding the current use of this research paradigm. This understanding can come from a strategic review of the mixed methods studies in science teacher education, revealing how researchers use mixed methods and the potential affordances and constraints for science teacher education research. While this review would seem to be straightforward, it is complicated by the variability in how researchers label combined qualitative and quantitative methods in research publications (e.g., mixed methods, multiple methods) and how these types of studies draw on the different mixed methods traditions. Underlying these explicit decisions are debates about whether combining qualitative and quantitative methods is, or should be, considered a distinctive paradigm, community of practice, methodology, or approach (see Greene, 2008; Lederman & Lederman, 2013). Nonetheless, the recent years' upward trend of mixed methods warrants an interrogation of the underlying rationales, affordances, and constraints of combining quantitative and qualitative methods for science teacher education research.

This chapter is an overview of the current use of mixed methods research in science teacher education. The historical and methodological contexts of the development of mixed methods approaches situate this discussion. It is grounded in the mixed methods orientation of Hesse-Biber (2015) and literature on the methodological development of mixed methods (Creswell & Plano Clark, 2007; Greene, 2008; Johnson & Onwuegbuzie, 2004; Morse & Niehaus, 2009; Teddlie & Tashakkori, 2009). Using this foundation, a sample of 45 science teacher education mixed methods research articles published in peer-reviewed research journals was contemplated. The parameters for the collection of the studies were: (a) mixed methods research design, as identified by the researchers given an intent to learn field-specific practices for and orientations to mixed methods; (b) focus on science teacher education; and (c) a publication date between 2010 and 2020. This narrative was developed and guided by the understandings that resulted from this contemplation. Examples from

DOI: 10.4324/9781003098478-5

individual studies provide support for critical points. A summary of the overview and considerations for strengthening mixed methods inquiry in science teacher education research concludes the chapter.

Defining Mixed Methods Research

Researchers have combined quantitative and qualitative research methods in natural and social sciences since as early as the 17th century. According to Maxwell (2016), astronomer Galileo and geologist Charles Lyell both used a combination of observational description (qualitative) and measurement (quantitative) to generate scientific knowledge about the natural world. Similarly, researchers have combined quantitative and quantitative methods (e.g., data collection and analysis) in social and behavioral sciences since the 19th and 20th centuries (Denscombe, 2008). Sociologist W. E. B. Du Bois's *The Philadelphia Negro* (1899) study combined ethnography, social history, and descriptive statistics. Du Bois's study was likely one of the earliest documented mixed methods studies in the social sciences (Maxwell, 2016). Historically, these earlier practices of combining qualitative and quantitative methods were not described as mixed methods, nor were these practices documented as a distinctive methodological approach (see Maxwell et al., 2015, for further discussion). Nevertheless, these examples indicate that researchers have combined qualitative and quantitative methods since natural and social scientific endeavors began.

It was not until the 1980s and 1990s that mixed methods became recognized as a distinctive research approach. Since that time, mixed methods approaches have been conceptualized in diverse ways. Scholars have described mixed methods research as a third paradigm or middle ground between quantitative and qualitative approaches (Johnson &, Onwuegbuzie, 2004), a community of practice (Denscombe, 2008), a way of thinking (Greene, 2008), or simply the combined use of qualitative and quantitative methods (Lederman & Lederman, 2013). Within this process of conceptualization, there have been ongoing debates about what constitutes integration of methods (e.g., Lyman et al., 2020), standards for rigor (e.g., Harrison et al., 2020), and the relationship between mixed methods and multimethod approaches to research (Anguera et al., 2018). A complete discussion of the debates surrounding mixed methods is beyond the scope of this chapter. However, it is essential to note that the conceptualization and use of mixed methods are varied and still in development (Harrison et al., 2020).

In addition to varied conceptualizations of mixed methods, scholars vary in their approaches. According to Hesse-Biber (2015), researchers most commonly use a *pragmatic approach* in mixed methods inquiries. This approach involves adopting the best methods suited to answer research questions and the principle of praxis – implementing actions and experiencing results. Johnson and Onwuegbuzie (2004) argue that mixed methods approaches can become more effective and produce the most helpful result by adopting "epistemological and methodological pluralism" (p. 15). By contrast, Hesse-Biber characterized a *dialectical approach* to mixed methods espoused by Greene (2008) and colleagues. The dialectical approach involves interaction between and across quantitative and qualitative methodologies to account for what is gained or lost using contrasting perspectives. A third possible approach is the combined use of qualitative and quantitative methods absent from philosophical or theoretical considerations. Despite this variation, Hesse-Biber (2015) suggested that the main commonality across articulations of mixed methods includes at least one quantitative and one qualitative research method within a single study or across sets of research projects. Mixed methods research is distinct in that it involves mixing or integrating methods within or across studies (Greene, 2008; Johnson & Onwuegbuzie, 2004). Furthermore, mixed methods researchers often pursue similar goals, such as social change and justice, improving practice, increasing research quality, and meeting various stakeholder audiences' needs and requests.

Proponents of mixed methods research have drawn attention to the benefits of combining qualitative and quantitative approaches. The combination allows researchers to capitalize on the strengths of the different approaches in a manner that compensates for the weaknesses, provides a level of flexibility and rigor (Almalki, 2016), and allows researchers to understand the phenomenon deeply and accurately (McKim, 2017). Researchers often note the usefulness of mixed methods to address diverse stakeholders' concerns within sociopolitical contexts that demand evidence for generality and particularity (Greene, 2008). The increase in mixed methods research resulted from practitioners, educators, and evaluation researchers seeking to generate research that could effectively address practical concerns (Denscombe, 2008; Johnson & Onwuegbuzie, 2004).

Hesse-Biber (2015) argued that disciplinary practices, cultures, norms, and skills shape how scholars and novice researchers orient to mixed methods research. Thus, the fundamental problems and topics of inquiry in science teacher education inevitably shape how researchers use mixed methods. In their review of research paradigms in science education research, Treagust et al. (2014) suggested that mixed methods approaches were most often investigations or evaluations of interventions. However, an analysis of the rationales, conceptualizations, methods, and uses of mixed methods inquiries found in science teacher education literature has not been completed. A close examination of how researchers use mixed methods research approaches in science teacher education over the past decade serves as the foundation for this chapter. This discussion aims to illuminate the benefits and opportunities for strengthening mixed methods research in science teacher education.

Purposes and Research Questions Motivating the Use of Mixed Methods

All aspects of research, especially methodological approaches, flow from the purpose (Creswell, 2003). Purpose statements and research questions reveal the underlying reasons science teacher researchers are selecting mixed methods to address their inquiries. In light of this, the purposes and research questions of mixed methods research in science teacher education are critical components of this discussion.

The purpose of most of the mixed methods research in science teacher education is to measure the effectiveness of programs or initiatives aimed at preservice and in-service science teacher education (e.g., Feldman & Pirog, 2011; Menon & Sadler, 2016; Mintzes et al., 2013). Specifically, researchers select mixed methods approaches to determine if initiatives or programs meet the goals (quantitative) while exploring specific experiences within the enterprises' impacts (qualitative). For example, Feldman and Pirog (2011) used a mixed methods approach to evaluate an initiative to engage 27 teachers and their students in scientific research in collaboration with scientists. They sought to determine whether the teachers gained the intellectual and methodological proficiencies they believed were needed to engage in scientific activities legitimately and, if so, whether they could effectively use this expertise to guide students in authentic scientific research. Similarly, Mintzes et al. (2013) used a mixed methods approach to explore changes in personal self-efficacy and outcome expectancy among 116 teachers engaged in a grant-funded program that established professional learning communities that featured demonstration laboratories, lesson study, and annual summer institutes. In studies such as these, the intent was to measure and explore the impacts of a specific initiative. Across most of the evaluation studies reviewed, the purposes focused on single initiatives, although implications to the field of practice – most notably providing an example of a program that successfully addresses a need in teacher education – were made.

The evaluative purposes of mixed methods research on preservice teacher education often differ from those on in-service teacher education, such as the examples previously noted. The preservice inquiries often focus on evaluating existing programs or course activities (e.g., Bautista & Boone,

2015; Seung et al., 2019; Forbes, 2013; Menon, 2020). For example, Seung et al. (2019) used a mixed methods approach to examine the effectiveness of their K-6 camp-based practicum for 55 preservice teachers in their summer methods course. They sought to answer:

1) How does an inquiry-based science methods course combined with a summer camp influence elementary preservice teachers' self-efficacy in teaching science as inquiry?
2) What experiences from the course are identified as sources of their self-efficacy?
3) What experiences from the course are perceived to be more significant sources of self-efficacy? (p. 874).

Similarly, Bautista and Boone used a mixed methods approach to investigate their mixed-reality teaching activity's impact on 64 early childhood education majors' science teaching self-efficacy beliefs. Like the studies noted earlier, they sought to determine if the action met the stated goals and explain or expand on understandings of the effectiveness of various components. They asked: (1) How does participation in the TMI impact ECE PSTs' self-efficacy beliefs in the context of science over a semester? (2) What sources of efficacy does the TML experience provide? Similarly, Akerson et al. (2011) explored 17 preservice teachers' views of their cultural values, the cultural values they believed scientists hold, and the overall relationship between these views and their conceptions of the nature of science. Their research questions focused on the impacts of their methods courses on preservice teachers' views. The purpose was grounded in a pragmatic approach like the in-service examples previously noted.

Although the purpose of most contemporary mixed methods studies in science teacher education is to evaluate the impact of a program, some researchers are also using this methodological approach to address research questions about the participants in a program. The results of these studies are often used to guide, rather than evaluate, the initiative (e.g., Capobianco et al., 2020; Milford & Tippett, 2013; Tao et al., 2013). For example, Milford and Tippett (2013) explored 165 preservice teachers' beliefs about scientists. The purpose of their inquiry was to identify the extent to which preservice teachers hold stereotypical images of scientists and how previous formal and informal science experiences may have influenced those images. Their research questions focused on the differences in the visual representations of scientists among preservice teachers and how those representations related to prior science experiences. They studied the students in the class but did not evaluate the course or specific activities. Similarly, Capobianco and colleagues (2020) sought to explore four elementary teachers' sensemaking with learning to implement engineering design in a university-school partnership. Like other researchers in this category, these authors embedded their study within a specific program that provided the context (e.g., teachers learning how to implement engineering design) but were not seeking to evaluate the course or initiative.

A comparatively smaller number of researchers use mixed methods approaches for purposes other than studying specific initiatives or programs (e.g., Milner et al., 2012; Palmberg et al., 2015). For example, Milner and her colleagues (2012) conducted a mixed methods study to explore the dynamics that impact in-service teacher practices pre ($n = 502$) and post ($n = 170$) implementation of state testing required by No Child Left Behind (NCLB). Their research questions were:

1. What are elementary teachers' belief-based affects (before and after NCLB science testing requirement) concerning their science teaching?
2. Do elementary teachers' belief-based affects influence their intent to teach science in their own classrooms (both before and after NCLB state science testing requirements)?

3. Do elementary teachers believe NCLB required science testing has impacted their science teaching? If so, how?
4. What influence did NCLB required science testing have on elementary teachers' classroom practices? (p. 116).

Similarly, Ramnarain (2016) sought to understand 186 South African high school teachers' perceptions of intrinsic factors (personal attributes of the teacher) and extrinsic factors (environmental) influencing the implementation of inquiry-based science learning. The research questions for this study focused on identifying the perceptions of intrinsic and extrinsic factors related to the implementation of inquiry-based learning and teachers' explanations of the influences.

In general, this review of the current use of mixed methods approaches in science teacher education supports Treagust and colleagues' (2014) statement about mixed methods research in the larger field of science education: the purposes of most are for the evaluation of teacher education interventions or programs. Specifically, the purpose statements often focused on determining if the researchers' programs met the stated goals (quantitative) and explored or expanded on understanding the effectiveness of various initiative components (qualitative). Consequently, the inquiries often had practical purposes. Furthermore, most of the studies exclusively focused on the participants who took part in the initiative or program – with extraordinarily little evidence sought to make generalizable claims. However, there were some examples of researchers using mixed methods research to produced generalizable findings.

Mixed Methods Approaches in Science Teacher Education Research

Science teacher researchers select mixed methods approaches for a wide variety of reasons. Most aligned with Hesse-Biber's (2015) definition of mixed methods: combining at least one qualitative and one quantitative method within a single study or set of projects. Very few explicitly note a pragmatic approach as the basis for the mixed methods approach (e.g., Boda & Brown, 2019; Luft et al., 2011; Ramnarain, 2016; Steele et al., 2013); and even fewer convey precise alignment with Greene and colleagues' dialectical approach (Wong & Luft, 2015). Most of the current mixed methods research does not include a description of the underlying philosophical, epistemological, methodological, or theoretical perspectives that informed mixed approaches. In addition, only about one-third of the studies are citing specific mixed methods designs. Examples include concurrent (e.g., Boda & Brown, 2019), convergent (e.g., Cutucache et al., 2017), and sequential-explanatory (e.g., Ramnarain, 2016) designs.

Science teacher researchers emphasize the benefits of combining qualitative and quantitative methods at the level of data collection. Most are often described as using contrasting methods for triangulation (e.g., Menon, 2020), to improve the rigor of a study (Tao et al., 2013), to minimize the weaknesses of singular approaches (e.g., Steele et al., 2013), to enhance or expand understanding of phenomena (e.g., Wong & Luft, 2015), or to gain a more holistic picture of the practice under study (e.g., Cutucache et al., 2017). In some cases, researchers believed that combining qualitative and quantitative methods improves the quality of an investigation. For example, Tao et al. (2013) referred to the triangulation of data sources as a strategy for enhancing the rigor of their study. Similarly, Steele et al. (2013) suggested that a mixed methods approach maximizes the strengths and minimizes the weaknesses of the individual approaches. They stated that by "using multiple data sources concerning a focus of interest, the aim is to eclipse the weaknesses inherent in singular methods" (p. 119). In both cases, researchers combined methods to reduce threats to research rigor or quality. By contrast, some researchers draw attention to how combining methods could expand or add nuance to the findings. For example, Wong and Luft (2015) argued that complementary methods offer opportunities to expand, explain, and clarify findings. They noted that "qualitative methods were useful for exploring the intricacies and complexities of the quantitative results" (p. 625). Similarly, Cutucache and colleagues (2017) claimed that using qualitative and quantitative methods provided them with a holistic picture of the impact of professional development. Most contemporary studies emphasize the complementary nature of the methodological approaches.

The type of data sources and analytical approach vary across the studies. The most common combination is surveys and interviews. For example, in their study of the professional development with preservice teachers, Urbani et al. (2017) used quantitative data collections to measure participants' perceptions and focus group interviews to gain insights into their experience with the professional development activities. In a similar study, Grimberg and Gummer (2013) used various methods to comprehensively understand the impact of professional development activities on culturally congruent science instruction. In addition to a survey, the authors collected multiple qualitative data sources, including classroom observations, teacher portfolios, and student work. In only a few cases was a single approach to data collection and analysis done quantitatively and qualitatively. Seung et al. (2011), for example, collected qualitative data sources and pre- and post-examples of metaphor writing, to study changes in preservice teachers' beliefs as an outcome of activities in a science methods course. They used a combination of qualitative and quantitative data analysis methods to represent, compare, and interpret the findings. These articles most often cited Creswell and colleagues (e.g., Creswell & Plano Clark, 2007) to justify the methods, strategies, and approaches used in their mixed methods studies. The other key contributors to the methodological development of mixed methods approaches (e.g., Greene, 2008; Johnson & Onwuegbuzie, 2004; Morse & Niehaus, 2009; Teddlie & Tashakkori, 2009) were cited less often.

To summarize, we found that mixed methods approaches vary in research on science teacher education. Most researchers align with the commonsense definition of mixed methods – a combination of qualitative and quantitative methods within one study (Hesse-Biber, 2015). Notably, very few explicitly mention the distinct approaches to mixed methods described in the methodological literature (Greene, 2008; Hesse-Biber, 2015; Johnson & Onwuegbuzie, 2004; Morse & Niehaus, 2009). Hesse-Biber (2015) noted research practices and engagement are shaped by numerous factors, such as disciplinary norms, stakeholder pressures, peer review, publication processes, research skills, and research competencies. Because of this, Hesse-Biber warned that what counts as mixed methods research and its markers of quality *should not be* narrowly defined. Nevertheless, the sample of articles in this review underscores the need for more in-depth engagement with the methodological literature to maintain the standards for depth, quality, and rigor in mixed methods research in the field.

Understandings of Science Teacher Education Resulting from Mixed Methods Approaches

Many empirically based models for teacher preparation and development have resulted from the use of mixed methods approaches. For example, Shanahan and Shea (2012) provide a research-based professional development model that embeds language learning strategies in inquiry-based science lessons. Teachers experiencing this professional development internalized the learning, successfully implemented the strategies, and transferred learning to other subject areas. The levels of teachers' participation significantly impacted outcomes. Instruction and academic year support were critical components of this model. Similarly, Menon (2020) effectively demonstrated how adding a field-based component into methods courses increased the self-efficacy of 121 preservice teachers while also providing qualitative evidence on how various sources of science efficacy contributed to positive changes for four of the participants. The authors noted that multiple teaching opportunities and additional mentoring and support as the participants negotiated their teaching identities might improve the initiative.

The aforementioned examples are only two of a substantial number of empirically based models supported by data from mixed methods research. Generalizable statements about the myriad of studies are difficult if not impossible to make, as most of the research exclusively focuses on narrowly defined initiatives. As the research approach is evaluative, it makes sense that they are initiative-specific. The quantitative aspects of the studies are often descriptive and cannot be generalized. However, a closer look reveals that common quantitative outcomes are being sought and measured. For example, many different initiatives focus on increasing preservice or in-service science teachers' self-efficacy in teaching. Mintzes et al. (2013) showed that the teachers who took part in their professional learning communities increased their self-efficacy in teaching by inquiry and reported changes in classroom teaching practices. Bautista (2011) showed that the preservice elementary teachers who took part in a science methods course that contained effective instructional practices and provided mastery experiences through these practices resulted in increased science teaching self-efficacy. Researchers are also studying such initiatives as community-based learning (Flores et al., 2015), field-based teaching (Menon, 2020; Seung et al., 2019), mixed-reality teaching (Bautista & Boone, 2015), and specialized content courses (Menon & Sadler, 2016) to increase self-efficacy for science teaching. For the most part, common outcomes (e.g., self-efficacy) were measured quantitatively and often used the same or similar instruments. Several of these studies noted connections to larger data sets in the implication sections. Yet, these connections went largely untapped, and researchers did not take the opportunity to use mixed methods to move beyond the particularity and provide greater generality (Greene, 2008).

The well-studied concepts, combined with validated quantitative instruments that drill down into the specifics of those concepts, could allow for more complex understandings of the strategies and offer the potential for generalizable knowledge. But most science teacher researchers are not capitalizing on what the quantitative paradigm provides in this area. The quantitative component is often limited to a small number of participants in a specific intervention, with little connection to the research base on the concepts (e.g., teaching self-efficacy). The survey data is often utilized only as descriptive data pre- and post-intervention. Thus, the mixed methods approach is primarily in the qualitative paradigm. Some researchers, however, do expand on the quantitative aspects of their mixed methods approaches. For example, Ramnarain (2016) provided findings on 186 teachers' perceptions of intrinsic and extrinsic factors influencing the implementation of inquiry-based science learning in townships in South Africa. The quantitative and qualitative results supported five assertions. The broad quantitative and narrowly focused qualitative components provided deep understandings of the factors that impact the implementation of inquiry-based teaching in undeveloped urban areas in South Africa. Their findings revealed that teachers from township schools perceived (a) a need for more professional development on inquiry, (b) township schools as lacking adequate resources to teach by inquiry, (c) a lack of sufficient time to planning and teaching by inquiry, (d) their school management as not recognizing the importance of teaching by inquiry, and (e) teachers having a positive attitude and interest in teaching by inquiry despite deficits. Tao et al. (2013) provided findings on six Chinese and Australian teachers' curricular and teaching experiences and 245 students' perceived experiences in learning. Their results included evidence that the teachers had greater autonomy regarding the implementation of the curriculum; however, low SES students had fewer opportunities to participate in inquiry-based instruction than their high SES peers. Milford and Tippett's (2013) study on preservice teachers' stereotypical understandings of science, Zangori and colleagues' (2013) study on in-service teachers' priorities when teaching scientific explanations, and Wong and colleagues' (2015) study on science teacher persistence over time are more examples of mixed methods studies with strong quantitative components.

In sum, as a result of mixed methods research on science teacher education, the professional community has an impressive number of research-based models. Although there are studies that provide understanding about general populations of teachers or students, there is room for growth.

A possible direction is to look beyond the specific initiative to the outcomes being sought and measured – such as self-efficacy in science teaching. Exploring the nuances of the initiatives' impacts in these areas and further maximizing the benefits of the quantitative research paradigm could provide opportunities for growth in mixed methods research in science teacher education.

Discussions and Future Directions

Not long ago, science teacher researchers were discouraged and often prevented from pushing the boundaries of the paradigms and practices guiding education research. Research studies tended to adhere to strict distinctions of either quantitative or qualitative. The acceptance and growing importance of mixed methods research on science teacher education has opened the door for utilizing the specific methods and associated paradigms. One of the noted advantages of this methodological approach is that it allows researchers to address diverse stakeholder audiences' concerns. Our review revealed that science education teacher researchers are taking full advantage of the flexibility and affordances of mixed methods research and answering the questions asked by various stakeholders associated with their teaching initiatives. They use this approach to triangulate their data, improve the rigor of their studies, and gain more holistic pictures of practice. They emphasize the quantitative components, the qualitative components, or both. The outcomes of this work suggest that their efforts in this regard are providing the professional community with valuable understandings and models.

However, as a body of research, the full benefit of what this methodological approach can provide those seeking to understand their initiatives is not being fully realized. Most studies in this review did not explicitly link the underlying philosophical, epistemological, methodological, or theoretical perspectives that guide researchers' decisions to use mixed methods approaches. Denscombe (2008) noted that mixed methods researchers risk implying that "anything goes" when they do not account for the underlying principles and standards for quality that guide their research practice (p. 274). Thus, as evidenced in this review, the disconnect from the methodological literature base limits the quality, rigor, and usefulness of the insights we can gain from mixed methods research on science teacher education. Furthermore, most of the mixed methods studies in this review were evaluations of educational initiatives or programs with very pragmatic purposes. Only a few studies fully maximized the potential of mixed methods, particularly the quantitative component. For example, these studies focused on singular initiatives or interventions, limiting the possibility of generalizations. Many studies limited the use of quantitative data to descriptive purposes. Indeed, the future direction of this body of research still has room to grow and expand.

The findings of this review are consistent with broader concerns about research quality and the impact of mixed methods research. This research approach is becoming increasingly complex and specialized, creating difficulties with establishing standards and supporting the next generation of researchers to conduct high-quality mixed methods studies (Ivankova & Plano Clark, 2018). Guetterman (2017) suggested strengthening and expanding opportunities to develop mixed methods research skills to improve quality during graduate education (and beyond). Moreover, methodologists consistently advocate for situating mixed methods research skills development within the disciplinary norms that inform how researchers carry out their studies (Hesse-Biber, 2015; Ivankova & Plano Clark, 2018). A reflexive stance toward methodological practice must be taken. The professional field should examine how science teacher education researchers develop the methodological skill set for conducting mixed methods research to identify growth opportunities and maximize the benefits of this approach for understanding science teacher preparation and practice.

This chapter provided an overview of how science teacher education researchers use mixed methods to study teacher preparation and practice. Mixed methods research, though still developing, offers many advantages for science teacher education researchers. It affords science teacher educators opportunities to generate findings that effectively improve science teaching and learning. We imagine that the future direction of this body of research continues to hold promises not yet fully realized. Given the complex nature of science teacher education, this is a wonderfully dynamic and challenging task necessary for science teacher education to be truly viable. We hope this review can contribute to fruitful discussions about mixed methods research and methodological practices in science teacher education.

References

Akerson, V. L., Buzzelli, C. A., & Eastwood, J. L. (2011). Bridging the gap between pre-service early childhood teachers' cultural values, perceptions of values held by scientists, and the relationships of these values to conceptions of nature of science. *Journal of Science Teacher Education, 23*, 133–157. https://doi.org/10.1007/s10972-011-9244-1

Almalki, S. (2016). Integrating quantitative and qualitative data in mixed methods research: Challenges and benefits. *Journal of Education and Learning, 5*(3), 288–296. https://doi.org/10.5539/jel.v5n3p288

Anguera, M. T., Blanco-Villaseñor, A., Losada, J. L., Sánchez-Algarra, P., & Onwuegbuzie, A. J. (2018). Revisiting the difference between mixed methods and multimethods: Is it all in the name? *Quality & Quantity, 52*, 2757–2770. https://doi.org/10.1007/s11135-018-0700-2

Bautista, N. U. (2011). Investigating the use of vicarious and mastery experiences in influencing early childhood education majors' self-efficacy beliefs. *Journal of Science Teacher Education, 22*(4), 333–349. https://doi.org/10.1007/s10972-011-9232-5

Bautista, N. U., & Boone, W. J. (2015). Exploring the impact of TeachME lab virtual Classroom teaching simulation on early childhood education majors' self-efficacy beliefs. *Journal of Science Teacher Education, 26*(3), 237–262. https://doi.org/10.1007/s10972-014-9418-8

Boda, P. A., & Brown, B. (2019). Priming urban learner's attitudes toward the relevancy of science: A mixed-methods study testing the importance of context. *Journal of Research in Science Teaching, 57*, 567–596. https://doi.org/10.1002/tea.21604

Capobianco, B. M., Radloff, J., & Lehman, J. D. (2021). Elementary science teachers' sense-making with learning to implement engineering design and its impact on students' science achievement. *Journal of Science Teacher Education, 32*(1), 39–61. https://doi.org/10.1080/1046560X.2020.1789267

Creswell, J. W. (2003). *Research design: Qualitative, quantitative, and mixed methods approaches*. Thousand Oaks, CA: Sage Publications.

Creswell, J. W., & Plano Clark, V. (2007). *Designing and conducting mixed methods research*. Thousand Oaks, CA: Sage Publications.

Cutucache, C. E., Leas, H. D., Grandgenett, N. F., Nelson, K. L., Rodie, S., Shuster, R., . . . Tapprich, W. E. (2017). Genuine faculty-mentored research experiences for In-Service science teachers: Increases in science knowledge, perception, and confidence levels. *Journal of Science Teacher Education, 28*(8), 724–744. https://doi.org/10.1080/1046560X.2017.1415615

Denscombe, M. (2008). Communities of practice: A research paradigm for the mixed methods approach. *Journal of Mixed Methods Research, 2*(3), 270–283. http://doi.org/10.1177/1558689808316807

Du Bois, W. E. B. (1899). *The Philadelphia Negro: A social study*. Philadelphia, PA: University of Pennsylvania Press.

Feldman, A., & Pirog, K. (2011). Authentic science research in elementary school after-school science clubs. *Journal of Science Education and Technology, 20*(5), 494–507. https://doi.org/10.1007/s10956-011-9305-4

Flores, B. B., Claeys, L., Gist, C. D., Clark, E. R., & Villarreal, A. (2015). Culturally efficacious mathematics and science teacher preparation for working with English learners. *Science Teacher Education Quarterly, 42*(4), 3–31. www.jstor.org/stable/10.2307/teaceducquar.42.4.3

Forbes, C. T. (2013). Curriculum-dependent and curriculum-independent factors in pre-service elementary teachers' adaptation of science curriculum materials for inquiry-based science. *Journal of Science Teacher Education, 24*(1), 179–197. https://doi.org/10.1007/s10972-011-9245-0

Greene, J. C. (2008). Is mixed methods social inquiry a distinctive methodology? *Journal of Mixed Methods Research, 2*(1), 7–22. https://doi.org/10.1177/1558689807309969

Grimberg, B. I., & Gummer, E. (2013). Teaching science from cultural points of intersection. *Journal of Research in Science Teaching, 50*(1), 12–32. https://doi.org/10.1002/tea.21066

Guetterman, T. C. (2017). What distinguishes a novice from an expert mixed methods researcher?. *Quality & Quantity, 51*, 377–398. https://doi.org/10.1007/s11135-016-0310-9

Harrison, R. L., Reilly, T. M., & Creswell, J. W. (2020). Methodological rigor in mixed methods: An application in management studies. *Journal of Mixed Methods Research, 14*(4), 473–495. https://doi.org/10.1177/1558689819900585

Hesse-Biber, S. (2015). Introduction: Navigating a turbulent research landscaper: Working the boundaries, tensions, diversity, and contradictions of multi-method and mixed-methods inquiry. In S. Hesse-Biber & R. Burke Johnson (Eds.), *The Oxford handbook of multimethod and mixed methods research inquiry* (pp. xxxiii–liii). New York, NY: Oxford University Press.

Ivankova, N. V., & Plano Clark, V. L. (2018). Teaching mixed methods research: Using a socioecological framework as a pedagogical approach for addressing the complexity of the field. *International Journal of Social Research Methodology, 21*(4), 409–424. https://doi.org/10.1080/13645579.2018.1427604

Johnson, R. B., & Onwuegbuzie, A. J. (2004). Mixed methods research: A research paradigm whose time has come. *Educational Researcher, 33*(7), 14–26. https://doi.org/10.3102/0013189X033007014

Lederman, N. G., & Lederman, J. S. (2013). Mixed up about mixed methods. *Journal of Science Teacher Education, 24*(7), 1073–1076. https://doi.org/10.1007/s10972-013-9367-7

Luft, J. A., Firestone, J. B., Wong, S. S., Ortega, I., Adams, K., & Bang, E. (2011). Beginning secondary science teacher induction: A two-year mixed-methods study. *Journal of Research in Science Teaching, 48*(10), 1199–1224. https://doi.org/10.1002/tea.20444

Lynam, T., Damayanti, R., Rialine Titaley, C., Suharno, N., Bradley, M., & Krentel, A. (2020). Reframing integration for mixed methods research. *Journal of Mixed Methods Research, 14*(3), 336–357. https://doi.org/10.1177/1558689819879352

Maxwell, J. A. (2016). Expanding the history and range of mixed methods research. *Journal of Mixed Methods Research, 10*(1), 12–27. https://doi.org/10.1177/1558689815571132

Maxwell, J. A., Chmiel, M., & Rogers, S. (2015). Designing integration in multimethod and mixed methods research. In Hesse-Bieber, S. & Johnson, R. B. (Eds.), *Oxford handbook of multimethod and mixed methods research inquiry* (pp. 688–706). New York, NY: Oxford University Press.

McKim, C. (2017). The value of mixed methods research: A mixed methods study. *Journal of Mixed Methods Research, 11*(2), 202–222. https://doi.org/10.1177/1558689815607096

Menon, D. (2020). Influence of the sources of science teaching self-efficacy in pre-service elementary teachers' identity development. *Journal of Science Teacher Education, 31*(4), 460–481. https://doi.org/10.1080/1046560X.2020.1718863

Menon, D., & Sadler, T. D. (2016). Pre-service elementary teachers' science self-efficacy beliefs and science content knowledge. *Journal of Science Teacher Education, 27*(6), 649–673. https://doi.org/10.1007/s10972-016-9479-y

Milford, T. M., & Tippett, C. D. (2013). Pre-service teachers' images of scientists: Do prior science experiences make a difference? *Journal of Science Teacher Education, 24*, 745–762.

Milner, A. R., Sondergeld, T. A., Demir, A., Johnson, C. C., & Czerniak, C. M. (2012). Elementary teachers' beliefs about teaching science and classroom practice: An examination of pre/post NCLB testing in science. *Journal of Science Teacher Education, 23*(2), 111–132. https://doi.org/10.1007/s10972-011-9230-7

Mintzes, J. J., Marcum, V., Messerschmidt-Yates, C., & Mark, A. (2013). Enhancing self-efficacy in elementary science teaching with professional learning communities. *Journal of Science Teacher Education, 24*(7), 1201–1218. https://doi.org/10.1007/s10972-012-9320-1

Morse, J. M., & Niehaus, L. (2009). *Mixed method design: Principles and procedures.* Walnut Creek, CA: Left Coast Press Inc.

Palmberg, I., Berg, I., Jeronen, E., Kärkkäinen, S., Norrgård-Sillanpää, P., Persson, C., . . . Yli-Panula, E. (2015). Nordic-Baltic student teachers' identification of and interest in plant and animal species: The importance of species identification and biodiversity for sustainable development. *Journal of Science Teacher Education, 26*(6), 549–571. https://doi.org/10.1007/s10972-015-9438-z

Ramnarain, U. (2016). Understanding the influence of intrinsic and extrinsic factors on inquiry-based science education at township schools in South Africa. *Journal of Research in Science Teaching, 53*(4), 598–619. https://doi.org/10.1002/tea.21315

Seung, E., Park, S., & Lee, M. (2019). The impact of a summer camp-based science methods course on pre-service teachers' self-efficacy in teaching science as inquiry. *Journal of Science Teacher Education, 30*(8), 872–889. https://doi.org/10.1080/1046560X.2019.1635848

Seung, E., Park, S., & Narayan, R. (2011). Exploring elementary pre-service teachers' beliefs about science teaching and learning as revealed in their metaphor writing. *Journal of Science Education and Technology, 20*(6), 703–714. https://doi.org/10.1007/s10956-010-9263-2

Shanahan, T., & Shea, L. M. (2012). Incorporating English language teaching through science for K-12 teachers. *Journal of Science Teacher Education, 23*(4), 407–428. https://doi.org/10.1007/s10972-012-9276-1

Steele, A., Brew, C., Rees, C., & Ibrahim-Khan, S. (2013). Our practice, their readiness: Teacher educators collaborate to explore and improve pre-service teacher readiness for science and math instruction. *Journal of Science Teacher Education, 24*(1), 111–131. https://doi.org/10.1007/s10972-012-9311-2

Tao, Y., Oliver, M., & Venville, G. (2013). A comparison of approaches to the teaching and learning of science in Chinese and Australian elementary classrooms: Cultural and socioeconomic complexities. *Journal of Research in Science Teaching, 50*(1), 33–61. https://doi.org/10.1002/tea.21064

Teddlie, C., & Tashakkori, A. (2009). *Foundations of mixed methods research: Integrating quantitative and qualitative approaches in the social and behavioral sciences.* London: Sage Publications.

Treagust, D. F., Won, M., & Duit, R. (2014). Paradigms in science education research. In N. G. Lederman & S. K. Abell (Eds.), *Handbook of science education research* (Vol. II, pp. 3–17). New York: Routledge.

Urbani, J. M., Roshandel, S., Michaels, R., & Truesdell, E. (2017). Developing and modeling 21st-century skills with pre-service teachers. *Teacher Education Quarterly, 44*(4), 27–50. www.jstor.org/stable/90014088

Wong, S. S., & Luft, J. A. (2015). Secondary science teachers' beliefs and persistence: A longitudinal mixed-methods study. *Journal of Science Teacher Education, 26*(7), 619–645. https://doi.org/10.1007/s10972-015-9441-4

Zangori, L., Forbes, C. T., & Biggers, M. (2013). Fostering students' sense-making in elementary science learning environments: Elementary teachers' use of science curriculum materials to promote explanation construction. *Journal of Research in Science Teaching, 50*(8), 989–1017. https://doi.org/10.1002/tea.21104

5

TOWARDS JUSTICE

Designing for a Rightful Presence as a Lens for Science Teacher Education Research

*Angela Calabrese-Barton, Edna Tan, Kathleen Schenkel,
and Aerin W. Benavides*

Introduction

Inequities in educational opportunity in science persist globally, privileging children and youth from white, middle and upper-class families, with Eurocentric and English-speaking histories. In current turbulent times, where health, race, climate, and economic crises converge, educational inequities have only exacerbated. The growing focus on justice-oriented science education has pointed towards the need for new frameworks to guide science teacher education. Beginning teachers are both capable of and responsible for addressing inequities in science education. However, they need the tools to do so (Madkins & Morton, 2021). This chapter focuses on the *rightful presence framework* as one approach to supporting science teachers in learning to teach in justice-oriented ways.

Consider the following quote from 15-year-old Jazmyn:

> The racist stereotype is that Black people are not listening to science. That is not true. Maybe it's the other way around, like science is not listening to us. I wish that people could see what I could do, like what I am doing at home. Making homemade hand sanitizer, making masks, caring for my elders. I don't want to act White. I don't want people to tell me I'm not white enough. I want you to know how I feel as a young, Black girl in America and in STEM. I want to feel like I can be me in STEM and have that celebrated.

Jazmyn is asking for recognition for who she is: A bright, caring Black girl. She is also critiquing a system that has made her invisible despite her embodied presence. Jazmyn's experiences are not unique. Many youth want to be legitimately welcomed in science as whole people with valuable knowledge, practices, and experiences that matter. Jazmyn's comment speaks to the importance of youths' rightful presence in science education.

Like Jazmyn, many youth are discouraged from having *their* powerful cultural experiences and expertise legitimized as integral to meaningful learning and engagement in science. This is denying youth a rightful presence in science (Calabrese Barton & Tan, 2020). Rightful presence refers to youth having legitimate membership in their science learning community because of who they are, and not because of who they should be. Rightful presence is a critical mode for *making present* those who have been made *missing* by intersectional racism and other forms of oppression manifest in science and in schooling.

DOI: 10.4324/9781003098478-6

Why Equity as Inclusion Is Not Enough

A review of the literature in science education indicates a growing, robust interest in issues of equity (Asowayan et al., 2017). With attention on promoting standards-based learning, research has focused on how to provide students with access to high-quality science learning opportunities. Equity as inclusion focuses on redressing systemic inequities by supporting high-quality learning opportunities through innovative approaches such as ambitious science teaching (Windschitl et al., 2018), and culturally relevant pedagogies (Johnson & Atwater, 2014).

Research on equity as inclusion in science teacher education has been instrumental in advancing the field, and supporting children and youth's opportunities to learn. However, access and inclusion are based upon extending the rights to participate in science education as it is, even when access is bridged through cultural connections. For example, the US-based Next Generation Science Standards states that, "All individuals can engage in and learn complex subject matter . . . when supportive conditions and feedback mechanisms are in place and the learner makes a sustained effort" (p. 280). While the intent of such policy statements is to suggest that all people can learn, it neglects to address how *what* people learn is grounded in cultural systems of knowledge and practice. In science education, the very system itself, made up of pedagogies, curriculum, and assessments, reflects Whiteness and heteropatriarchy (Bang et al., 2012). As Madkins and Morton (2021) remind us, teaching is, and has always been, a political act.

When science is taught as separate from the livelihood of minoritized communities, youth of Color can be positioned as deficient, delimiting their agency to leverage the power of science alongside other ways of knowing to take action on the questions and concerns they care about (Morales-Doyle, 2017). When youths' knowledge, practices, and already-present forms of expertise they bring to science learning are made *invisible*, they, too, are made invisible (Tedesco & Bagelman, 2017) and denied a "rightful presence" in their learning community.

An equity agenda focused on inclusion may formalize rights students should have in science classrooms and provide opportunities otherwise denied. However, this stance does not account for whose values undergird these rights and how they are enacted in practice in science classrooms. It is imperative to critically examine what it means to have such rights. What rights are extended and how in science teaching can make a difference in whether or not a student, like Jazmyn, is welcomed as a fully legitimate member of the learning community. In science education, these rights, as they have historically been constructed, reflect Whiteness and heteropatriarchy.

This chapter is focused on new work on justice-oriented approaches to science teacher education. However, few studies in science teacher education move beyond the equity focus towards justice. There has been powerful recent work focused on critical race theory and science teacher education (e.g., Madkins & Morton, 2021; Mensah & Jackson, 2018), and which also explicitly address systemic racism and anti-blackness (e.g., Nxumalo & Gitari, 2021), epistemologies (e.g., Bang et al., 2012), and justice-oriented pedagogies (Calabrese Barton & Tan, 2009, 2019; Calabrese Barton et al., 2020; Morales-Doyle, 2017). This chapter builds on the literature in justice-oriented science teacher education to provide a backdrop to the rightful presence framework. Most germane to this chapter, however, is the literature on rightful presence in education. Though limited, given the recent introduction of this framework, studies of rightful presence in educational studies and contexts broadly are included.

Rightful Presence Framework

Rightful presence asserts that legitimately being welcomed in a community requires the student/ teacher-powered relationship to change (Calabrese Barton & Tan, 2020). Teaching shifts from having the power to dictate norms for others, to having the responsibility to make sense of and value the cultural knowledge and experiences of newcomers as powerful contributions to society (Shirazi, 2018). It also involves the responsibility to acknowledge the injustices newcomers have experienced historically and in their new lives, as they seek to build a new present and future in their new home (Squire & Darling, 2013). Thus, legitimately belonging means more than expanding who has a right to participate within the community. It means understanding and seeing children and youths' political struggle to belong in science, and that often arise contentiously in science teaching and learning interactions, as forms of legitimate presence and as integral to learning.

Working towards a more rightful presence involves a process of renegotiating what the rights to being and learning in science are or could be. This renegotiation is a fraught process. It focuses on how the current set of rights to science learning – that is, what it means to know, do, and become in science – are grounded in systems of privilege and oppression. This involves a process of perturbing these underpinning hierarchies of White supremacy and patriarchy which benefit already privileged groups.

Who youth are and want to be would look different from normative practices in classrooms if youth were more than guests – if they had a rightful presence in their learning communities. However, the challenge is in supporting teachers in imagining and enacting what this may look like. There are rich ideas in the literature which give texture to what teaching towards rightful presence may look like. For example, when teachers enact a rightful presence approach, youth and community knowledge and experiences would be amplified, disrupting whose voices are typically erased (Morales-Doyle, 2017). It would also foreground the political dimensions of teaching and learning, including how teachers can support students' agency to leverage science knowledge and practice in conjunction with one's cultural repertoires towards individual/community empowerment and social transformation (Calabrese Barton & Tan, 2009; Bang et al., 2012). In enacting practice towards rightful presence, teachers support students in developing critical awareness of and strategies for navigating the sociohistorical and political dimensions of learning science (Madkins & Morton, 2021).

Rightful presence in teaching and learning is enacted through a set of three tenets (Calabrese Barton & Tan, 2020):

- Tenet 1: Allied political struggle is integral to science learning: the right to reauthor rights
- Tenet 2: Rightfulness is claimed through presence: making justice/injustice visible
- Tenet 3: Collective disruption of guest/host relationalities: amplifying the sociopolitical

First, allied political struggle is integral to science learning. This means that teachers and students work together to challenge and transform what participation in science entails or what meaningful representations of learning look like in ways that humanize participation and value students as cultural and whole people. This is referred to as reauthoring rights because these disruptions and transformations change whose knowledge, practices, and experiences matter. This requires reconfiguring established classroom norms that include relinquishing some and adding new ones. Reconfiguring classroom norms and practices has to be sanctioned by teachers. Teachers need to be attuned to what youth bring to the classroom and to design in ways that allow for this to emerge.

Second, rightfulness is claimed through presence. This means that youths' whole lives – and that which makes participation in science empowering and/or marginalizing – becomes a visible part of teaching and learning. Jazmyn's identity as a Black girl and her community's experiences helping each other make homemade sanitizers because none could be bought from the stores during the early stages of the COVID-19 pandemic is a part of their engagement with socioscientific issues and science, implicated with immediate and weighty consequences. Having a rightful presence in science means making the work of justice happen in the here-and-now – in this moment in this classroom or other science learning settings, rather than in some abstracted future. A common science teacher refrain to students goes along the line of "if you learn what I am telling you know you could be a scientist one day." While orienting towards the future is important, so is attending to the present if youth are to build a rightful presence in science.

Lastly, guest/host classroom relationalities are disrupted collectively. The responsibility for disruption and transformation is borne by all members of the learning community, teachers and students alike, not just by those who have been marginalized. This kind of power sharing is important because it helps to create new and different spaces for making visible youths' lives.

Teaching Towards Rightful Presence

In this section two brief vignettes are offered that describe partner teacher efforts to teach towards a rightful presence in their classrooms. What teachers learn through engaging in this process, and its implications for students, are discussed. The first vignette explores how one teacher noticed and responded into youth's bids for rightful presence. The second explores how teachers purposefully designed for rightful presence in their teaching.

Noticing Student Bids for Rightful Presence

This vignette illustrates how one 6th-grade science teacher, Mr. M, a relatively new teacher in his first 5 years of teaching, noticed and responded to his students' bid for a more rightful presence in his classroom. His students attend school in one of the lowest-income districts in the country; 100% of the students receive free breakfast, lunch, and after-school snacks. Access to such food is important given the economic challenges of families and the fact that the communities served by the school have limited access to quality grocery stores. Many students shunned the school food because of its quality and stigma. This became an issue for youth in their investigation of food, energy, and the human body.

Making Bids for Rightful Presence: What Constitutes Rights?

Prior to the required unit focused on energy, food, and the human biological system/health, Mr. M met with a group of students to co-design lesson adaptations as part of a larger study on learning about students' funds of knowledge (Calabrese Barton & Tan, 2009). Mr. M wished to actively make space for his students' lived experiences and expertise to be a part of their science learning. One co-designed lesson was the "$2 snack competition." Students were each given two dollars to go to the corner store and buy the healthiest snack they could for that amount or less. After they had done so, students returned to the classroom, analyzed the snacks, and built a scientific argument for why their snack was the healthiest. In Mr. M's words, his students were "animated," and this activity was a "huge success."

After the weekend, Mr. M began class by using the snack competition to review the unit's key ideas. However, he struggled to get student participation, surprising him, given how engaged they were the week before. Mr. M tried to make this conversation enjoyable and relevant by insisting students compete with each other for having purchased the healthiest snack. Yet, as the following transcript illustrates, student participation was sluggish and followed a traditional teacher-student response pattern:

Mr. M: Jessica. Do you think your team was the best? Came up with the best snacks? For two dollars?
Jess: No.
Mr. M: You don't? Does anyone disagree with her?
Silence

Mr. M:	Jana, do you think your team had the best snacks? Maybe not everyone there. [waits] Jana, what are your thoughts? [waits] Jana, refresh our memories, what did you buy for two dollars?
Jana:	Cheese cracker and peanut butter.
Mr. M:	Yup.
Jana:	Cereal and orange juice.
Mr. M:	Cereal and orange juice. That all sounds pretty good. Jim, what did your team get?
Jim:	Orange juice. And bananas.
Mr. M:	Bananas. Alright. Nadia. What did your team buy?
Silence	
Mr. M:	[waiting a minute] Nadia, do you remember?
Nadia:	Sun Chips.
Mr. M:	Sun Chips. What else was that?

Mr. M used many powerful teacher moves, including encouraging students to disagree with each other, offering encouragement, and re-voicing ideas. As shown in the preceding exchange, he first asked if students agree with Jess ("Does anyone disagree with her?"), but no students responded. He then called on Jana, one of the more talkative girls, and asked her if her team had the best snacks ("Jana, do you think your team had the best snacks?"). After waiting several seconds, he asked her to remind the class on what her team bought. Mr. M then offered an encouraging response ("Yup") and revoiced her ideas.

Mr. M felt like he was "pulling teeth" to facilitate the conversation. Students gave one-word responses, not delving into the detailed notes they took the previous week.

Moving from Personal to Legitimized, Shared Epistemic Resources (Linking Tenets 1 and 2)

Mr. M shifted from reviewing the snack competition to ask if any students had gone back to the store. Mr. M hoped students would offer stories about how they applied their scientific thinking in choice-making over the weekend. However, Shernice responded in a way that Mr. M did not anticipate:

Mr. M:	Shernice, what did you get there?
Shernice:	I got . . . two bags of chips and a candy? [Class laughs, including Mr. M]
Mr. M:	Ok, why?
Shernice:	Because I like to eat them.
Mr. M:	[matter of factly, non-judgmentally] Because you like your junk food, ok. Now is that replacing a meal, or is that one of your two snacks? Was that going to be your lunch?
Shernice:	It was actually my breakfast. [students nodding in agreement, making exclamations such as "Wow," etc.]
Mr. M:	For this morning? Ok . . . anyone else? Go back to those stores? I like the honesty and you're probably not alone.

When Shernice responded that she bought "two bags of chips and a candy," everyone laughed. Instead of shutting her down, he asked, "Why"? When she said she likes chips, Mr. M responded with another question about whether this snack was a meal, and thanked Shernice for her honesty.

When Shernice responded, "It was actually my breakfast," others chimed in with their own stories about the chips and candy they too purchased for breakfast. After soliciting several stories and revoicing some of the key points students raised, Mr. M asked the students to compare what they bought over the weekend to what they bought in the competition:

Mr. M:	Mabel, what did you buy for two dollars last Friday, you and your team?
Mabel:	We got granolas and some orange juice.
Mr. M:	Did you think about what you did on Friday when you went in there to buy those? What was your thought process? Why did you take what you learned and make a different choice? Was it purely taste? That it was something you were craving?
Mabel:	Yes . . .
Cindy:	I . . .
Mr. M:	Ok, that's honest . . . yes, Cindy?
Cindy:	I only bought ONE bag of chips . . . but, I was going to buy more, I felt bad, so I just bought one.
Mr. M:	Why didn't you buy more?
Cindy:	Because, I know it's not healthy. . .
Mr. M:	Ok, what could you buy in place of another bag of chips? I'm OKAY with one bag of chips 'cause it's small enough for a nice little snack . . . but what could you add to that to get a balanced snack?
Cindy's teammate:	[whispers to Cindy] Orange juice!
Cindy:	[nods at teammate] Yeah, a small container of orange juice. [Two of Cindy's teammates, including the one who whispered to her, high-five each other.]

As noted in the preceding transcript and reflecting Tenets 1 and 2, Mr. M's moves, in-the-moment, actively valued students' historicized lives in support of making sense of energy and nutrition needed for healthy eating. When students confined themselves to canonical "textbook" discourse, conversation was stilted. This led Mr. M to shift his "review and report out" activity to one inviting and centering students' lived experiences, opening up the range of sanctioned "texts" relevant to the teaching and learning of nutrition (Tenet 1). When Mr. M made visible Shernice's efforts to position her choice inside the historicized experiences of living in a food desert, and the social challenges middle school youth face by eating the school's free food (Tenet 2). Mr. M's response, by welcoming the rush of new stories, further supported the reauthoring of rights (Tenet 1) because it redefined *what* was allowed/legitimized as a useful resource for learning in the classroom space. This move allowed these personal stories to shift from serving as private resource to public resources, and together, with Mr. M, a *shared responsibility for* knowledge building and sharing using a wide range of resources emerges.

Collective Disruption and Engagement (Tenet 3)

Mr. M also shifted in his content story line. Instead of using the warmup discussion to remind students of what they learned the previous week about healthy food choices, he used their weekend stories to expand that storyline, with the students, to acknowledge the daily tensions that young people, living in a food desert, experience when they are hungry and have limited food choice options. He subtly shifted from the stance of "Here is what science tells us is good eating" to "Here are some good choices you can make given what you know scientifically and your realities of the moment."

This shift redirected the rest of the class period. When Mr. M asked the class if they went to the store that morning, instead of teacher call and student response, students began calling out. They began talking to each other, offering suggestions for what to say, and commenting on each other's experiences and ideas. They were laughing. After soliciting a few more ideas, he had students work in groups to prepare a healthy snack menu, using their nutrition guide and their weekend experiences. He asked them to write out appetizer ideas on the back of the menu so that they could plan and cook a healthy appetizer breakfast together in the classroom.

The students' accounts, while personal, also included scientific talk, leveraging practices such as obtaining, evaluating, and communicating information and thinking around the ideas of energy and the human body they had covered in the previous week. They raised questions and insights into the complexity of understanding healthy food choices and dynamic equilibrium in the human body. The students were quick to support their peers' "wrong answers" – their seemingly bad choice of snacks – by emphasizing their experiences outside of school science. For example, Shernice's snack choices were cast in more complex shades of a limited budget, undesirable school lunch, and teenage preferences instead of a right or wrong application of a school science lesson to everyday decision-making. What students were learning in science – what constitutes a healthy snack and why – became a visible and important part of the larger mosaic for how students made sense of their choices.

Designing for Rightful Presence: "What Is Community Ethnography? Paper Circuits Are Hard!"

This vignette illustrates how 6th-grade science teachers incorporated community ethnography into their teaching of a unit focused on Engineering for Sustainable Communities (EfSC). The goal in supporting students in engaging in community ethnography was to foster new possibilities for youth to bring their lived lives and community wisdom into science class, and to see these powerful forms of knowledge refracted into the design process. This vignette zooms into the practices of three teachers at Sage Middle School that serves a diverse population of students with 43% Black, 38% White, 11% Latinx, 5% Biracial, 3% Asian, and <1% each Native American. While the school displays overt signs of solidarity and friendship for all, such as "This school serves ALL students" posters prominently in the building, incidences of bullying regularly occur. The school also reported a disproportionate data of disciplining African American boys.

These teachers took on the role of political allies as they listened and learned from youths' insights gleaned from community ethnography. They collaborated with youth to trouble and expand upon what had been a static set of rights dictating how both teachers and students participate in science class (Tenet 1). When thinking about the right to reauthor rights, it is important to consider teachers' rights in tandem with students', since they are inextricably linked. At Sage, teachers typically engage in tightly scripted curriculum organized around pacing guides, with minimal room for teacher adaptations. For the EfSC unit, community ethnography was a core component of the curriculum. A key principle of the curriculum is integrating social elements with technical elements in the two main engineering principles – define a community problem, and design a community solution. To elicit community data as part of the EfSC curriculum, students learned how to craft survey questions, conduct interviews and analyze survey data from the tool SurveyMonkey.

Teachers Authoring New Curricular and Pedagogical Rights

Due to how the EfSC curriculum was set up, teachers were afforded greater leeway to try out and take up new curricular and pedagogical decisions. In terms of authoring new curricular rights, teachers were supported in introducing, through enacting community ethnography with students, new texts through community data into the science classroom. Beyond pre-set curricular resources in the form of textbooks or web-based packaged resources that were the norm, all three teachers discussed what engaging students in community ethnography would entail at Sage.

Teacher discussions spanned what counted as community and how to facilitate student interviews within the structural constraints of the school day – all related to the nature of the rights teachers have when they design for particular teaching and learning activities. Unpacking the idea of community ethnography led teachers to perturb how bounded their individual science class was, in terms of people, texts, material resources, and activities that were sanctioned. What mattered as relevant and necessary curricular resources expanded beyond the usual ready-made curricular resources, a marked departure from the limited curricular choices teachers usually adhered to.

On considering who and what constitutes community in the school context, teachers looked with new eyes on what and who stakeholders were and could be, in middle school engineering. Mr. K wondered about who and how to define community when he stated, "I was also thinking what would constitute community in our school . . . is it level-wide? School wide? . . . how do we know . . . about community knowledge? Do we survey? Interview?"

Discussions also included how to facilitate the logistics for student interviews. Teachers looked at their timetables with one another and considered different scenarios of rotating different combinations of students from one class to another, which physical locations might work for student interviewing, how to use the school laptops as a tool to input survey data via SurveyMonkey, something that school laptops have not been used for. Planning involved making curricular decisions on how the lessons on soliciting community data would play out in the local context of their school, with the particulars of their timetables and students.

When teachers and students analyzed survey results using pie charts, graphs, and descriptive statistics such as percentages on responses, teachers expanded on their right to relinquish being the repository of knowledge and instead became co-learners with students in unpacking community data. By choosing to spend classroom time on collective meaning-making of community data, teachers exercised new rights in their pedagogical decisions. They solicited and validated new texts – community data and students' embodied experiences related to these data – as relevant material for middle school engineering. During the lesson focused on community survey data analysis, Ms. D and her students perused all the open-ended responses carefully and shared aloud the ones that resonated with them, such as: "We don't always do fun stuff in our class with our classmates. And usually when we're in groups we are only doing a lab and not talking." And, "We need to have more opportunities to have fun and spend time with our friends. We need to feel safe at Sage."

Ms. D and her students unpacked what "fun" might entail at their school and why students felt as stressed as they did. Students discussed the possible connections between two prominent themes in the data – "fun" and "safety." Students commented that "kids have bad days too" and it makes it worse when "teachers just give silent lunch, and they don't tell you positive things." Ms. D's students stressed to her that middle schoolers are "human too" and should be allowed to have bad days. They further asserted that school should actively help students who are feeling down, instead of berating or disciplining them for having "an attitude."

Across their classes, teachers facilitated discussions on community concerns reflected in the data, including bathroom bullying, low school morale, unfair disciplinary measures meted out along racial lines, and boring book work being the norm in science, among others. These classroom discussions, based on analyzing community survey data, informed and refined the engineering problem-space for students. Their workable prototypes that were made to respond to these community issues included a light-up positive messaging "Happy Box" mailbox and a "celebratory light-up basketball hoop" installed in a corner of the classroom where students could toss a ball into the hoop as a way to take a break during class.

Reauthoring Rights as a Part of Science Learning

Since engaging in community ethnography is integral to providing the social data to inform engineering design, teachers' reauthoring of curricular and pedagogical rights was in service of rigorous disciplinary learning. None of the teachers had much experience in teaching engineering in middle school and so were co-learners alongside their students. A positioning as a co-learner also reauthored teachers' and students' rights in the classroom space as power hierarchies were less acute. Teachers positioned as co-learners were also helped by the focus on collective sensemaking of community data on what issues concerned the community for which students could engineer a sustainable solution.

Ms. D and Ms. J decided to make a video of themselves figuring out (and making mistakes along the way) circuits with copper tape, LED lights, and a coin-cell battery during the first engineering design challenge, which was to make an electric art card for someone they love. The teachers wanted to show students how they struggled through the design process when considering technical and social elements in dialogue. Both teachers shared this video as part of the curriculum to show the students that they, too, were learners who struggled to build paper circuits and that they learned through *doing*. Making this video is another example of reauthoring curricular and pedagogical rights. The video itself also helped make visible the possibilities for social change as teachers themselves became learners (connecting Tenet 1 to Tenet 2). Having a colleague to partner with to make this video supported teachers in feeling unsure about themselves as teachers new to teaching middle school engineering.

Students Reauthored Rights in Expanding Sanctioned Forms of Participation

Students also reauthored their rights in what counts as science participation. Instead of reading packets or texts on the laptop and answering worksheets, students interviewed, analyzed community data, and used materials to engage in iterative design to produce prototypes that addressed a range of issues important to them and to their community. Some of the working prototypes students created include a light-up desk system for locating items under the desk, light-up board games to build in fun moments for use in the class, an extendable slide that attaches to too-short bathroom cubicles to curb bathroom bullying, to name a few. Beyond a test where students demonstrated knowledge gains, they were involved in identifying, constraining, and designing a solution for a community issue they cared about shifted the form and function of the rights students had as science learners. As 6th grader Naomi described about how she experienced EfSC, where her project was a light-up celebration board to celebrate students and friends who are kind, and who excel in areas *apart from test scores*:

> It is pretty incredible that we actually built something . . . like with our own hands. And that it works. It is pretty incredible that we actually solved a community problem . . . this is real. Regular science class is just . . . you know, like school stuff. This is real.

This quote shows how student reauthoring of rights was contingent on teachers' reauthoring of rights, where teachers acted as political allies to students who shared the burden of challenging and disrupting the acceptance of a static set of rights contoured to the teaching and learning of traditional school science. However, Naomi's comment also shows how the very construction of an artifact changed how the classroom operated – in this case by creating a new space to celebrate students – and became a visible reminder of the social change that youth and their teachers collectively engineered.

Discussion

Working towards rightful presence is a collective, sociopolitical endeavor. One starting point is the recognition that traditional ways of teaching and learning science – the norm of the equity as inclusion model – reproduces inequities through the continued buttressing of power differentials.

Working towards rightful presence necessitates taking disruptive actions. While disruption may evoke dramatic, far-flung gestures, it need not be so. A seemingly mundane pedagogical decision can be powerfully disruptive. Mr. M making the decision to pause and ask his students what they bought at the corner store over the weekend is one example. Ms. G and Ms. J making the decision to be vulnerable and playful through making their "paper circuit mistakes video" is another example of how pedagogical and curricular decisions by both teachers disrupted well-entrenched beliefs that the science teacher is the repository of knowledge and that teachers do not have the luxury to prioritize making mistakes and iteration in science teaching and learning.

Even as the three tenets undergirding rightful presence are presented separately for clarity, in practice, these tenets are imbricated, contingent on and in dialogue with one another. Through collective, sociopolitical struggle where the more-powered teacher took on risks alongside the lesser-powered students, new norms that were productive seeding and nurturing rightful presence emerged. These new norms wrought through disruptive moves brought new texts (including social texts) and resources into the classroom, expanded how students participate in middle school science through new activities (community ethnography, youth design lesson extensions, and engineering designs to be used over time in classrooms), and physically expanded the boundaries relevant to school science to be inclusive of other spaces, such as hallways, bathrooms, and lunch rooms, and beyond school spaces into the community.

Two directions for research and practice that support a focus repertoires for rightful presence for teacher education are discussed next.

Supporting Teachers in Noticing Student Bids for Rightful Presence

Learning to notice and respond to youth bids for rightful presence is a powerful direction for teacher education research (Calabrese Barton et al., 2020). Youth are in a constant process of taking actions to be recognized for who they are and how their lives matter in science. When youth make such bids, they seek to disrupt the ways in which everyday knowledge and practice of science position them without power and authority. They also seek to amplify their already-present brilliant and agentic acts of everyday knowing and practice and have their transformative potential made visible. These bids happen even when teachers engage in pedagogical practices that value students, as was the case with Mr. M. When teachers recognize their students' actions as bids rather than disruptions, they can better respond in ways that made space for their lives to be more visible in their classrooms, and as integral to science learning.

Questions that need to be asked are "What do these bids look like in practice?" and "How can I understand what meanings these bids have for students and in relation to teaching practice?"

Research and development can focus on how teachers may be supported in taking a student-focused lens to reflecting on practice. For example, teaching tools can support teachers in thinking about which students may be struggling for a more rightful presence in their classroom, when, and how so. As teachers think deeply about individual students, they may begin to re-see their students' actions, which they may have previously thought of as off-task or disruptive, as powerful bids for recognition. The field requires new knowledge on what student bids look like (what happens in these moments, how, and why), what productive pedagogical responses may be, and their impacts on individual and collective students.

Engaging in Pedagogical Practices to Make Space for Enactments of Rightful Presence

A second area of needed research focuses on pedagogical approaches which support students in navigating both vertical (e.g., disciplinary defined movement from novice to expert) and horizontal dimensions of learning through social activity (e.g., across communities, with the recontextualization/hybridization of what counts as resources, ideas, and processes related to science). This is a critical mode for *making present* youth who have been made *missing* by intersectional racism and other forms of oppression manifest in science and schooling. As noted in Tenet 2, rightfulness is claimed through presence, in the sense that power relations shift so that youths' whole lives become integral to learning, and the outcomes of learning focus not only on individual gains but also the kinds of social transformations that allow for presence to thrive.

In our second vignette, the design approach of Pedagogies of Community Ethnography or PCEs is discussed. PCEs are pedagogies that support teachers not just in noticing students' lived lives but in doing so differently – shifting not only *what* they see, but *where* they see, and to see the seen anew. These pedagogies involve: a *stance* that community knowledge/practice is a valuable part of science knowing/doing; new *roles* for students and teachers as co-learners of the intersections of community wisdom with science; and *instructional* moves that create spaces for eliciting and making visible community wisdom, and which refract these forms of knowing/being into science learning, disrupting settled expectations for who/what it means to learn science.

Further work on PCEs and related pedagogies are needed to support youths' lived experiences and community insider status in becoming public epistemic resources for supporting youths' lives and the possibilities for social change visible and important. When students modeled their data through charts, graphs, and bubble maps, it created space for new science/community hybrid discourses to emerge as they talked about what these representations meant. Both students and teachers leveraged these discourses, and these discourses integrated science knowledge and knowledge of the needs of communities.

Conclusions

Designing for rightful presence is an important approach to remediating the science education infrastructure that limits participation in science among historically marginalized youth. These processes involve flattening knowledge and power hierarchies through centering and legitimizing the discourses, practices, and forms of representation that reflect the lives of those made missing by historicized oppressions in science and schooling. It was through the practices and stance oriented to rightful presence that enabled the teachers – as allies – to navigate emerging tensions and disrupt norms and practices towards social transformation. This process is collective and ongoing, as rightful presence does not happen in a moment. Sustained efforts are required to make present and center youth's lives, communities, histories, presents, and hoped-for futures as integral to reimagine what engaging with science is and could be.

References

Asowayan, A., Ashreef, S., & Omar, S. (2017). A systematic review: NGSS and the increased cultural diversity. *English Language Teaching, 10*(10), 63.

Bang, M., Warren, B., Rosebery, A., & Medin, D. (2012). Desettling expectations in science education. *Human Development, 55*(5–6), 302–318. https://doi.org/10.1159/000345322.

Calabrese Barton, A., & Tan, E. (2009). Funds of knowledge and discourses and hybrid space. *Journal of Research in Science Teaching, 46*(1), 50–73.

Calabrese Barton, A., & Tan, E. (2019). Designing for rightful presence in STEM: The role of making present practices. *Journal of the Learning Sciences, 28*(4–5), 616–658. https://doi.org/10.1080/10508406.2019.1591411

Calabrese Barton, A., & Tan, E. (2020). Beyond equity as inclusion: A framework of "rightful presence" for guiding justice-oriented studies in teaching and learning. *Educational Researcher, 49*(6), 433–440. https://doi.org/10.3102/0013189X20927363

Calabrese Barton, A., Tan, E., & Birmingham, D. (2020). Rethinking high leverage practices in justice-oriented ways. *Journal of Teacher Education.* https://doi.org/10.1177/0022487119900209

Johnson, N., & Atwater, M. (2014). Impact of beliefs and actions on the infusion of culturally relevant pedagogy in science teacher education. In *Multicultural science education* (pp. 81–102). Dordrecht: Springer.

Madkins, T., & Morton, K. (2021). Disrupting anti-Blackness with young learners in STEM: Strategies for elementary science and mathematics teacher education. *CJSMTE*, 1–18.

Mensah, F., & Jackson, I. (2018). Whiteness as property in science teacher education. *Teachers College Record, 120*(1), 1–38.

Morales-Doyle, D. (2017). Justice-centered science pedagogy: A catalyst for academic achievement and social transformation. *Science Education, 101*(6), 1034–1060. https://doi.org/10.1002/sce.21305.

Nxumalo, F., & Gitari, W. (2021). Introduction to the special theme on responding to anti-blackness in science, mathematics, technology and STEM education. *CJSMTE*, 1–6.

Shirazi, R. (2018). Between hosts and guests: Conditional hospitality and citizenship in an American suburban school. *Curriculum Inquiry, 48*(1), 95–114. https://doi.org/10.1080/03626784.2017.1409592

Squire, V., & Darling, J. (2013). The 'minor' politics of rightful presence: Justice and relationality in City of Sanctuary. *International Political Sociology, 7*(1), 59–74. https://doi.org/10.1111/ips.12009

Tedesco, D., & Bagelman, J. (2017). The 'missing' politics of whiteness and rightful presence in settler-colonial city. *Millennium, 45*(3), 380–402 https://doi.org/10.1177/0305829817712075

Windschitl, M., Thompson, J., & Braaten, M. (2018). *Ambitious science teaching*. Cambridge: Harvard Education Press.

SECTION 2

Initial Science Teacher Education – Core Areas

Section Editor: Sarah J. Carrier

The chapters in this section provide science educators with in-depth reviews of research literature on science teacher preparation. In addition to the authors' thorough reviews of research, the chapters' authors have added their critical insights as they examine how research has informed teacher preparation. The authors' presentations reveal issues that contribute to, or inhibit, effective science instruction and ultimately student learning.

In Chapter 6, Zembal-Saul, Siry, Monteira, and Bose focus on preparation for teachers of children from ages three to seven years old, reviewing 41 studies of early childhood teacher preparation in three countries: Spain, the United States, and Lithuania. The authors begin by positioning young children as capable learners to situate research that identifies young children's capacity for learning science and for science sense-making.

The review of studies in this chapter highlights the complexities of preparing early childhood educators to teach science, and one significant theme in this chapter is the relationship of early childhood preservice teachers' knowledge, attitudes, and field experiences with teachers' knowledge and beliefs about learners and practice. The authors recommend a shared vision for science in early childhood education with whole-child approaches that allow children to explore the science in their daily lives, positioned in sociocultural approaches to learning. Zembal-Saul and colleagues recommend that early childhood teacher educators attend to equitable sense-making, child-centered approaches to children's own inquiry, attention to the whole child by moving beyond learning content, and that teacher educators recognize the assets and affordances of early childhood preservice teachers to support children's equitable sense-making.

Chapter 7 by Davis and Haverly presents research that focuses on teacher educators' efforts to prepare elementary science teachers who will provide their students with rigorous, consequential, and – as in Chapter 6 – equitable science teaching. This review is organized around three key structures in teacher education: content courses, methods courses, and field experiences. In addition to the content courses section's examination of preservice teachers' knowledge of subject matter, the authors also present research that examines how these courses influence preservice teachers' self-efficacy, attitudes, beliefs, practices, and offer models for effective science instruction.

In Chapter 7, the research on science methods courses is organized by the relationship of the methods courses with preservice teachers' characteristics. Studies include interventions to support preservice teachers' content knowledge, inquiry, practices, literacy, and curriculum and planning. Davis and Haverly further document research on how field experiences, including the role of mentor teachers, influence preservice teacher characteristics, self-efficacy, identity, beliefs, knowledge, and practice; these studies reinforce the importance of coherence across experiences to help preservice teachers become "well started beginners."

In Chapter 8, Campbell, Gray, Fazio, and van Driel review research on secondary science teacher preparation. The authors present research on secondary preservice teacher characteristics, their abilities to engage students and support their science learning, and they identify features of teacher preparation programs that support secondary preservice teachers' learning. As in other chapters in this section, this chapter includes research on the role of field experiences for secondary science teacher preparation, including important connections of science teacher education program support for secondary preservice teachers during their field experiences. Research in this chapter identifies challenges of secondary science teacher preparation, such as the influence of secondary preservice teachers' own experiences as students on their science teaching practices, reform-based science teaching practices such as engaging students in investigations, facilitating student discourse and sense-making, and assessing student thinking. Relatedly, researchers identify the need to situate learning in authentic classroom practices and reflections.

In Chapter 8, the authors identify studies on pedagogies to improve secondary science preservice teacher knowledge, pedagogical content knowledge, or knowledge on the nature of science. There are a number of studies that examine reflective practices, such as using models or videos to support reflections. Another set of studies in this chapter examines research pedagogies designed to approximate practices include microteaching, macroteaching, and rehearsals. Teacher education pedagogies that support teaching diverse learners highlight facilitating student talk and interaction and the important role of language and science literacies.

In Chapter 9, Stroupe focuses on the role of field experiences in science teacher preparation. While research on field experiences is touched on in previous chapters, Stroupe describes this as a surprisingly underexplored area for teacher educators. Stroupe begins by providing an historical background of field experiences from the 1970s. This review provides the following themes for preservice teacher preparation: pedagogical rehearsals with K–12 students, linking planned pedagogical actions with student outcomes, influencing preservice teachers' attitudes through interactions with schools and children, and conceptual consistency between theories of student and preservice teacher learning.

Stroupe synthesizes this research by asking us to consider a number of ideas related to field experience in education. These "wonderings" ask: How do we best design field experiences? How can field experiences support preservice teacher learning? How do we promote congruence between field experiences and methods courses? And, how can field experiences from other professions such as medicine inform science teacher preparation?

In Chapter 10, Bradbury reviews research on recent trends in mentoring preservice teachers as positioned in the context of NGSS and the related reforms over the last decade. Bradbury identifies themes: new lenses for framing the work of mentors, tools to support mentoring work, alternative models for mentoring, and context in mentoring relationships. By identifying problems with traditional mentoring models of an expert guiding a novice that minimize novice opportunities and discourage new approaches to teaching, Bradbury identifies new forms of mentoring that offer cooperative/reciprocal relationships and focus on student learning rather than teaching practices. Other new mentoring trends examine various frameworks and timing that include "co-inquiry" models of shared interactions of mentor and preservice teacher at all stages of the learning cycle: planning, instruction, and after lessons have occurred. Further, mentoring experiences are impacted by the different cultures and policies in different countries, and these influence the experiences for preservice and novice teachers.

Bradbury presents a range of professional development opportunities to support teacher mentors, and she recommends future directions for mentoring and research that explores the shifting role of mentor from didactic to educative. She also recommends consideration of newer research methods to study mentoring, such as audio recordings that can capture spontaneous conversations and social media postings. She encourages science teacher education programs to continue to explore alternative models for mentoring and for researchers to consider creative examinations of mentoring that investigate the role of context, asking: What types of mentoring contexts support the development of effective science instruction? And, what role does national or state policy play in mentoring experiences?

In Chapter 11, Edmondson, Dossick, Donitsa-Schmidt, Dori, Ure, and Balck share research on alternative teacher preparation programs around the globe. This chapter begins by presenting a range of definitions for alternative programs and frames the research in themes: reasons for the occurrence of alternative pathways to science teaching, comparisons of programs and their components, and measures of success of these programs for science teachers and their students. Some reasons behind the alternative pathways to teacher preparation in many countries around the globe include a shortage of science teachers and goals to expand the diversity of teachers and to enhance teacher retention. A range of program designs from Israel, the United States, Belgium, and Australia highlight the different routes to preparing science teachers. The chapter presents research rating the effectiveness of alternative teacher preparation by examining teacher quality, retention, job placement of alternative preparation program graduates, and student achievement.

Critiques of the research on alternative licensure programs include challenges controlling variables such as teacher characteristics, the varied preparation designs, and places of employment of teachers. Such confounding variables limit comparisons of traditional and alternative teacher preparation. Areas that require further research include comparing program designs from different countries, comparing program designs of traditional and alternative programs, and strategies for attracting teachers to the profession and teacher retention.

Each of the chapters in this section presents key areas of research beginning with chapters on preparing teachers of young learners to provide their students with science education early and effectively. The chapter on secondary science teacher preparation continues with identifying characteristics of effective science teaching, and two chapters dig deeply into features of teacher preparation: field experiences and mentoring. As in all the chapters, the examination of alternative pathways to science teacher preparation provides a global picture of key issues in science teacher preparation and recommendations for future research.

6
PREPARING EARLY CHILDHOOD TEACHERS TO SUPPORT YOUNG CHILDREN'S EQUITABLE SCIENCE SENSEMAKING

Carla Zembal-Saul, Christina Siry, Sabela F. Monteira,
and Frances Nebus Bose

In this chapter, the authors set out to review the research literature on the preparation of early child-hood preservice teachers (EC-PSTs) for teaching science, with a goal of drawing implications for future research and practice. In recent years, there has been mounting interest among researchers and practitioners regarding young children and science, a focus also reflected in contemporary early childhood education (ECE)[1] reform globally. Science in ECE emphasizes the integrated nature of science learning for young children, presenting a holistic view of children and their proficiencies for investigation and embodied sensemaking practices (Siry & Gorges, 2020). Support for science in the early years is grounded in children's innate curiosity about how the world works and their drive to "figure it out" (National Research Council [NRC], 2007). A growing body of research indicates young children are capable of reasoning that reflects the work of the scientific community (Kirch, 2009; Metz, 1995; Monteira & Jiménez-Aleixandre, 2016; Trundle & Saçkes, 2012). Children who are exposed to science instruction early develop positive attitudes and interest in science (Eshach & Fried, 2005); when this does not happen, interest in science may drop off (Mullis & Jenkins, 1988). However, children from communities that experience unequal distribution of resources and power, or who are part of groups that have been historically marginalized in science, tend not to have access to equitable science instruction (see Haverly et al., 2020). Gaps in opportunities that begin early are amplified later in schooling and career choice (Mbamalu, 2001), creating an urgent need to attend to inequities embedded in science for ECE.

The authors of this chapter position children as capable learners with multiple ways of knowing, who have the right to experience the natural world, make sense of it, and have their ideas taken seriously (UN General Assembly, 1989). Children's learning in science is as much about the process of inquiry as it is about developing meaningful understanding of science concepts. Haverly and col-leagues (2020) extend sensemaking in science to include classroom interactions that disrupt domi-nant epistemological orientations and normative ways of knowing and expressing understanding. Equitable sensemaking in science is conceptualized as a co-construction of knowledge incorporating students' epistemic resources – including language practices, discursive forms, and cultural practices (Nasir et al., 2006) – not always traditionally legitimized in classroom spaces (Haverly et al., 2020, pp. 65–66). Engaging with children in science in ways that cultivate their multiple and embodied

DOI: 10.4324/9781003098478-8

ways of knowing can be challenging for teachers of young children, who have themselves been characterized as lacking confidence and knowledge for science teaching.

The authors here assert that teachers of young children are uniquely equipped to support their science sensemaking (Zembal-Saul et al., 2020). Given EC classrooms are often self-contained and emphasize socio-emotional development, EC teachers are positioned to notice, explore, and connect with children's differing cultural and linguistic resources, lived experiences, and value systems. This relational work can support a classroom community in which children feel safe and valued, shifting historicized positions of power (Haverly et al., 2020). Further, EC teachers' proficiency in literacy instruction can be reimagined as an asset to facilitate science sensemaking – a collective discourse-rich endeavor (NRC, 2007). As such, the authors encourage readers to consider how teacher preparation experiences might be designed to build upon these overlooked assets.

In sum, when EC teachers prioritize children's equitable science sensemaking, they position young children as capable of asking and investigating scientific questions as part of developing science knowledge and practices, as well as reaching their full potential as human beings. *Given these uniquely favorable features of the EC profession more generally, what is known from the literature about preparing EC-PSTs to support young children's equitable science sensemaking?* It is this question that frames the chapter, which continues with a description of the search methods, findings from the literature review, and discussion of emergent questions and future directions for the design and study of EC teacher preparation for science.

Literature Review Methods

This chapter builds from a review of literature published in journals between 2010 and 2020 to reflect the current state of the art regarding EC teacher preparation for science. Given our central aim of working toward an understanding of the literature from a *global* perspective, two issues needed to first be resolved regarding the selection of keywords: (a) the age range and related schooling level terms referred to as ECE; and (b) the terms for those professionals educating children at the EC levels.

What Is Meant by EC-PST in This Review, and Why Does It Matter?

The authors use the term EC-PST to refer to individuals in their initial preparation, learning to teach children in "programmes that have an intentional education component and aim to develop cognitive, physical and socio-emotional skills necessary for participation in school and society" (Organization for Economic Co-operation and Development [OECD], 2020, p. 20). Determining how to define the parameters for a globally inclusive review was complex given vastly different conceptualizations of the relationship between education and care, who is responsible for children, how education and care is institutionally organized, and what ages correspond to these categories. Even more complex is that these differences exist not only across countries, but also within countries at state, regional, and local levels. Varying terminologies represent these differences, many of which have nuanced translations and localized significance. Even across the three countries where the authors' work is situated (see Figure 6.1), differences exist.

Given these complexities, the authors adopted a definition of early childhood encompassing birth to age eight, as specified by the National Association for the Education of Young Children in the United States. The literature search retrieved no studies focusing on teacher preparation for working with children under 2 years old in science; teacher preparation studies for children at the upper end of the boundary (age 8) overlapped heavily with elementary. As a result, the review attends to those working with children 3 to 7 years old, grouped broadly in the literature as preschool, PreK, kindergarten, and early elementary.

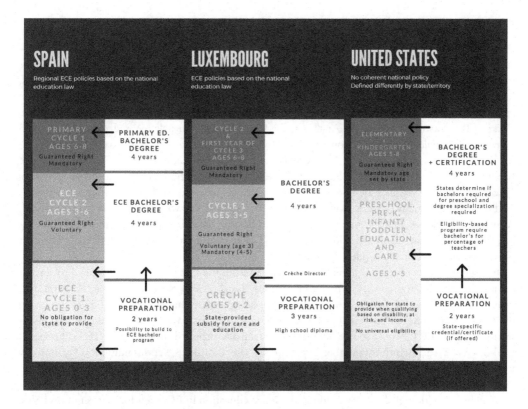

Figure 6.1   ECE complexities across three countries

Variations extend to the preparation of EC professionals, with considerable differences in regional requirements. For example, in the United States, criteria for teaching children prior to elementary school are not national, but location-specific, involving different preparation pathways ranging from no specified preparation, a secondary school diploma, or a bachelor's degree in ECE. In Spain, regional policies are developed according to the national educational law, and just as in Luxembourg, teachers across the country have national requirements for preparation. The intent in comparing ECE teacher preparation across contexts is threefold: to represent diversity across contexts; to illustrate that in attempting to represent such diversity, oversimplifying through decontextualization is a risk; and to suggest that despite these differences, considering the broader context of ECE reveals significant similarities (Neuman et al., 2015). Awareness of global variation in the preparation of EC-PSTs was reflected in the keyword search, which included (a) the diverse routes to becoming an EC teacher internationally (e.g., ECE bachelor's and master's degrees, vocational programs, and certificates in ECE and care), and (b) the terms used in publications focusing on EC and teacher education (TE), together with considering those used by the European Science Education Research Association and NARST, a global organization for improving science education through research.

The range of terms and diverse pathways for becoming an EC teacher is significant because it creates challenging parameters in which to inclusively frame EC-PST preparation for science. Further, although the pathways to becoming an EC teacher vary, the majority of studies reviewed are situated in university programs. This portrayal of EC-PST preparation as based largely in university programs suggests that the literature may not be representative of other routes by which many EC teachers worldwide are prepared.

Search Terms and Two-Phase Methods

From the process of identifying what is meant by ECE, coupled with what is meant by teacher preparation for ECE, the following keywords emerged: *teacher preparation, teacher education science, preservice teacher, science, early childhood education, preschool, kindergarten, PreK, infant and toddler, primary school, elementary school, pre-primary,* and *early years*. In a first phase, high-impact journals in English were identified from the education and educational research category of most recently available Journal Citation Reports (JCR, Clarivate Analytics, 2019). Identified journals focused on *science* (SE, 13 journals), *early childhood* (ECE, 8 journals), and/or *teacher education* (TE, 6 journals). *Journal of Science Teacher Education* and *Journal of Early Childhood Teacher Education*, both in the Emergent Science Citation Index (ESCI), were also included because of their specific focus. Additionally, *Review of Educational Research* was included because it is the highest-ranked journal in the education category.

The journals' archives were manually searched for each keyword and results were merged. A majority of papers focused on EC classroom studies or in-service teacher professional development; only those that specifically addressed EC-PST preparation for science were retained. This first phase of review retrieved a modest 32 studies.

In a second phase of review, publications retrieved from the first phase were examined to further identify journals referenced that were not included in initial review. New keywords were also added, including *nature of science (NOS), conceptual change, gender, identity,* and *environmental education*. Using the expanded list of keywords, journals (see Table 6.1[2]), the databases Education Resources Information Center (ERIC) and Google Scholar were manually searched over several cycles. The search methods retrieved a significant number of potentially relevant studies, yet this number was drastically reduced after closer examination due to only nine papers pertaining to both science in ECE and teacher preparation. For example, the journal *Science Education* initially retrieved 76 articles, yet none were included. Although 10 studies addressed science education in EC, their focus was not on PSTs; relatedly, although 19 publications addressed PSTs, their focus was not on EC.

Identifying Trends Across the Literature

Aligning with EC teacher workforce data worldwide (Neuman et al., 2015), the 41 studies examining EC-PST preparation for science were from OECD countries, focusing primarily on bachelor's degree programs. Despite the small number of articles, the findings mapped onto themes in elementary teacher preparation (Davis & Haverly, Chapter 7, this volume).

Studies Confirm the Relationship Between Knowledge, Beliefs, and Attitudes

Studies confirmed the relationship between EC-PSTs' knowledge, beliefs, and attitudes, as also represented in a model by Wu et al. (2020). While attending methods courses, PSTs' attitudes and shifting knowledge interacted. Thus, instruction played a positive role in PSTs' attitudes regarding the inclusion of science in ECE, either because EC-PSTs observed EC teachers implementing science during field experiences in schools (e.g., Reinoso et al., 2019; Sundberg & Ottander, 2013) or due to pedagogical practices facilitated through methods courses. For instance, pre- and posttests in Bulunuz's studies (2012a, 2012b) showed a positive influence from PSTs' engagement in playful science activities. Additionally, PSTs in Çiftçi and colleagues' (2020) study engaged in inquiry with peers using the 5E model, and later expressed the value of STEM. EC-PSTs' views of science and its role in ECE were the foci of Thulin and Redfors's (2016) investigation of a methods course. This study found that integrating science with theories of learning led to more developed explanations and higher complexity in EC-PSTs' views on science, and the use of expansive language regarding children's learning and the role of the teacher. EC-PSTs referred to the relevance of science for society, and for children, as the main reason for including science in ECE. These authors argue for an intertwining of subject knowledge with theories of early learning.

Four studies used STEBI-B (Science Teaching Efficacy Belief Instrument-B) questionnaires (Enochs & Riggs, 1990), together with data such as journals, interviews, class assignments, and productions, and found that EC-PSTs held more positive science teaching self-efficacy beliefs after engaging in methods courses (Bautista, 2011; Bautista & Boone, 2015; Giallousi et al., 2014; Saçkes et al., 2012). Further aspects examined through instruction and related to attitudes were EC-PSTs' willingness to take action for sustainability and address it in the classroom (O'Gorman & Davis, 2013); and acceptance of the "more-than-human" (Tsevreni, 2020).

EC-PSTs' ideas and attitudes about science and science teaching were also rooted in their personal beliefs and previous experiences. For instance, EC-PSTs' interactions with elements of the natural world influenced their willingness to use natural resources as pedagogical tools (Ernst & Tornabene, 2012; Torkar, 2015; Yılmaz et al., 2016) and religious faith influenced PSTs' scientific explanations (Kotaman, 2016). EC-PSTs' prior knowledge about science has been examined through the use of data collection tools targeting particular aspects of EC science education. Moseley et al . (2010) used a tool that showed EC-PSTs' models of the environment were mostly incomplete, as these rarely included humans. Similarly, EC-PSTs in Torres-Porras and Alcántara-Manzanares's (2019) study did not include plants when asked to identify living organisms during a park excursion. Ärlemalm-Hagsér and Sandberg (2011) found that EC-PSTs defined sustainable development both as an attitude and as conscious thinking, with themes emerging around fundamental values, nature, learning, and children's physical needs. In sum, methods courses have been successful for supporting EC-PST learning objectives.

Only two studies discussed the design of methods courses. Lippard et al. (2018) reported the research-based redesign of an EC program based on course instructors' professional development in EC science and alignment of the pedagogic perspectives of the courses with policy documents. These decisions improved comfort with science teaching for both instructors and EC-PSTs, highlighting how a case study in the context of a program can be useful for improving EC-PST preparation. Science education in EC teacher preparation programs was often integrated with mathematics in a single methods course. Kalchman and Kozoll (2016) argued that separating disciplines would increase EC-PSTs' awareness of each subject's epistemology, promoting understanding of the content and thus allowing for developing better instructional practices. More often, the research was focused on the outcomes of methods courses, and studies showed that these generally have a positive influence on EC-PSTs and desired outcomes were achieved.

The elementary literature has documented that teachers' subject matter knowledge (SMK) influences science teaching. Numerous studies also focused on changes in EC-PSTs' SMK and teaching strategies that supported such changes. Instruction targeting conceptual change has been shown to promote EC-PSTs SMK (Saçkes & Cabe-Trundle, 2014/2016; Trundle & Bell, 2010), and learning-by-design approaches (Sancar Tokmak, 2014) have been shown to support the development of EC-PSTs' technological pedagogical content knowledge (TPACK). A project focusing on 3D printing (Novak & Wisdom, 2018) showed how firsthand experiences helped EC-PSTs see how they could integrate technology into instruction. Three publications by Akerson and colleagues focused on EC-PSTs' understanding of NOS in science methods and ECE foundations courses. The exploratory study by Akerson et al. (2010) revealed that EC-PSTs whose cooperating teachers understood NOS, and could modify the curriculum to include NOS, were in turn able to explicitly teach NOS. Relatedly, Akerson et al. (2012) investigated changes taking place during an ECE course and a science methods course with a NOS focus. Using an identity formation frame, it was found that EC-PSTs' understanding about NOS improved during the course, and their perception of differences between their own views and scientists' views decreased. In a later study (Akerson et al., 2019), EC-PSTs designed children's books to teach aspects of NOS to children during field-placements, which supported EC-PSTs' understanding of NOS and related pedagogical content knowledge (PCK). Relatedly, positive relationships were found between the number of learning opportunities with a focus on science instruction for EC and PSTs' PCK and self-efficacy (Barenthien et al., 2020), suggesting a link between EC-PST science methods courses and improved knowledge and self-efficacy for teaching science.

Field Experiences Influence Knowledge and Beliefs About Learners and Practice

Several studies focused on how field experiences influenced knowledge and beliefs about learners and teaching practices. Siry and colleagues examined how EC-PSTs enacted inquiry-based practices together with children in field-based methods courses, exploring how these experiences mediated EC-PST approaches to teaching. In Siry and Lang (2010), EC-PSTs engaged in dialogue with children, expanding both children's agentic actions during science investigations and EC-PSTs' awareness of children's learning. Siry and Lara's (2012) related paper explored an EC-PST's identity formation, finding that dialogue with peers, co-teaching, and interaction with children all played essential roles for her development as a teacher of science. The EC-PST combined her expectations before teaching – how she *imagined* the science class would be – with lived experiences – how the class *was*. In a response article, Fleer (2011) proposed the dialectical concepts of imagination and creativity as a complementary framework to examine EC-PST identity construction in science. EC-PSTs in Eckhoff's (2017) study similarly engaged in collaborative inquiry with children during school placements in a kindergarten classroom. As a result, EC-PSTs improved their understandings of science inquiry and reflected on assessment possibilities of different types of children's documentation, such as pictures and drawings. All four papers underscore the value of EC teacher educators working toward opportunities for PSTs to experience the process of developing and teaching inquiry-based science experiences in supportive environments.

Classroom observation as well as video cases can serve as alternative experiences for EC-PSTs to learn about practice, particularly in contexts lacking structural opportunities to gain direct experience teaching children. Several authors have investigated how observation-based assignments influence EC-PSTs' knowledge and beliefs. Olson et al. (2016) examined the impact of two different class assignments: analysis of videos of science teaching and creation of a unit plan. EC-PST end-of-semester oral defenses revealed that those who completed the video-based assignment showed higher awareness of children's learning in comparison with the ones who did not. Relatedly, Gullberg et al. (2017) examined how reflective classroom observations in student teaching placements impacted EC-PSTs' views of children and science pedagogies. Both studies emphasized the value of connecting course assignments with field experiences for EC-PST growth.

A Focus on Diversity, Equity, and Inclusion Can Make a Positive Difference in PST Preparation

EC-PSTs' views of children and their perspectives on teaching science are deeply interwoven, and several studies explored the ways these come together to position EC-PSTs' sociocultural responsiveness. Several articles explored how EC-PST awareness and action regarding sociocultural biases shaped science teaching and learning. Gullberg et al. (2017) analyzed EC-PSTs' field notes and written reflections on student teaching placements for dominant discourses related to gender and emergent science. Their analysis led to a model for gender-aware teaching based on three actions related to gendered situations: detect, counteract, and self-reflect. Relatedly, Andersson et al. (2020) examined EC-PSTs' assignments and conversations for emerging tensions between two coexisting cultures – preschool culture, often identified with a culture of care and feminine values; and the culture of science, identified with masculine values and considered more hierarchical. The authors coined the term *chafing borderlands* to describe the boundaries between these cultures, and they emphasized how feelings pertaining to school culture can inhibit science teaching. Boundary objects, such as children and care, can reduce these tensions.

Several U.S. studies addressed cultural diversity. Martínez-Álvarez (2019) focused on EC-PSTs participating in an after-school program at a public bilingual school and examined approaches to connect everyday science with school science in culturally relevant ways. The study provided implications for EC-PSTs to engage in science in informal settings in order to experience first-hand learning with children. Yoon and Martin (2019) used a culturally responsive curriculum aligned with science curricula from South Korea and the United States. EC-PSTs developed culturally responsive lesson plans and experienced an increase in confidence for teaching science. Similarly, a methods course in Bravo et al.'s (2014) study was based on a model for diversity pedagogy to support EC-PSTs who were placed with children from cultural and linguistic minority groups. EC-PSTs showed gains in using purposeful grouping, sharing authority, addressing the language and literacy involved in science, questioning children, and providing scaffolds. This approach demonstrated how EC-PSTs strengthened their beliefs about diversity pedagogy when practices were highlighted and modeled, and when feedback on enactment of such practices was provided.

Longitudinal Studies Reveal the Complexities Involved in EC-PST Development

The limited literature has underscored the complex and longitudinal nature of becoming and being an EC teacher of science. One exploratory study (Sundberg & Ottander, 2013) examined the interplay of EC-PST perspectives on the role of the teacher, and how their attitudes toward science and science teaching developed. The purpose was to explore how this in turn influenced the teaching of science. They found that as EC-PSTs' view of the profession became more complex over time, PSTs' initial perspectives on science and science teaching remained similar but were expanded. More specifically, EC-PSTs' attitudes about science grew more positive with increasing competence and confidence, yet PSTs continued to express hesitation regarding the teaching of science.

Two central themes emerged when looking across the 41 papers. The first addresses connections between teacher preparation experiences and teaching praxis. Multiple authors stressed the different ways that EC-PST attitudes, beliefs, and knowledge can *expand* with different teacher preparation initiatives; however, when looking across the studies, it is evident that even when knowledge increases, concerns about practice remain (Eckhoff, 2017; Gullberg et al., 2017). Second, a central question that emerged across the different studies relates to the notion of science itself, as several authors asked, *What is science in early childhood?* These themes are taken up in the discussion that follows.

Discussion: Emergent Questions and Future Directions

Although fewer studies pertaining to teacher preparation of science in ECE were identified than anticipated, much of what was located aligns with findings for preparing elementary teachers for science (Davis & Haverly, Chapter 7, this volume). In addition, throughout the process, the authors recognized that issues of language and power, as well as nuances across ECE contexts, added complexities that contributed to the small number of studies that surfaced. In the following sections, questions that emerged from the review are used to propose future directions for EC-PST preparation for science.

How Can This Small Collection of Studies Inform EC Teacher Preparation Moving Forward?

A question raised by multiple authors was, *What is science in ECE?* The design of powerful EC teacher preparation experiences calls for coherence, not only across coursework and field experiences but more broadly across anticipated outcomes of children's learning, instructional practices that support such learning, repeated opportunities to work with conceptual ideas, and professional and instructional practices (Darling-Hammond & Oakes, 2019). Designing coherent teacher preparation experiences requires a shared vision for science in ECE. The authors argue that such a vision be inclusive of multiple voices and grounded in research and practice. A number of frameworks for integrating science with ECE have been proposed. Larimore (2020), for example, articulates a unified vision for integrating the strengths of ECE and science education advanced by current scholarship and reform. Starting with the premise that all children have the right to make sense of their worlds, the following features round out a future perspective for science in ECE (p. 705):

- Whole-child approaches that go beyond an emphasis on learning content to address a range of non-cognitive facets, such as identity development and socio-emotional learning;
- Rich disciplinary practices of science, which map well to holistic EC practices;
- Playful exploration and investigation of everyday phenomena that are interesting to children and relevant to their lives; and
- Sociocultural approaches to learning that promote interactions with peers as part of sensemaking.

A compelling vision for science education in EC serves as a useful starting point for designing teacher preparation programs and research agendas. Still, there remains an important need to examine the kinds of experiences necessary to shape EC-PSTs' knowledge, beliefs, and practices for supporting children's science sensemaking.

The review revealed considerations that require attention on the part of EC teacher educators. First, the perspective on EC science in this chapter emphasizes young children's *equitable* sensemaking (Haverly et al., 2020), which underscores that children do not explore and investigate everyday phenomena equally (Cannella, 1997) – varied ways of knowing and being shape participation in science practices and learning differently. Teaching to children's resources rather than to the dominant culture can disrupt inequities in classroom science interactions. *How, then, do teacher educators prepare EC-PSTs to notice and build upon the rich cultural, linguistic, and investigative resources of children from diverse cultural and linguistic backgrounds? In addition, how do teacher educators prepare EC-PSTs to recognize and disrupt the uneven classroom interactions that children experience when engaging with science in school settings?*

Second, the authors advocate for responsive approaches that encourage inquiry into children's questions, ideas, thinking, and interests. In addition to leveraging teacher inquiry as a process for addressing problems of practice, inquiry can also be conceptualized as stance (Cochran-Smith & Lytle, 2009). EC teachers engaging in inquiry alongside children shift emphasis from evaluating whether answers are right or wrong to genuine curiosity and excitement about figuring out what and how children are making meaning. Dahlberg and Moss (2005) refer to this as the pedagogy of listening, explaining that "as a teacher you have to participate together with the child, entering a space together where both teacher and child are actively listening and trying to construct meaning out of the situation" (p. 101). Learning to listen to children's voices, as well as to recognize and honor their multiple ways of knowing, being, and becoming, requires EC-PSTs to have authentic, extended, and in-depth interactions with children that in turn also shape PSTs' learning. The promise of preparing EC-PSTs to inquire alongside children can further promote the aim of noticing and responding to children's questions and interests in ways that are culturally sustaining and contextually responsive. *How can extended field experiences be structured so that they promote an inquiry stance and equip EC-PSTs to elicit, listen, and respond to children's ideas with interest and excitement?*

Third, just as a holistic perspective presses beyond a focus on learning content, so too should teacher preparation include serious attention to non-cognitive factors. In recent years, there has been a groundswell of research on teacher identity, which is conceptualized as socially constructed, fluid, dynamic, complex, and multifaceted (Avraamidou, 2016). Teacher identity formation occurs in different contexts and within moment-to-moment classroom interactions. This is of particular importance for science in ECE given that many teachers of young children see themselves as "literacy people" more so than as "science people" (Kane & Varelas, 2016). Additionally, EC teachers need to be able to navigate the "chafing borderlands" between the cultures of science and care (Andersson et al., 2020). It takes intentional effort on the part of teacher educators to ensure the initial and ongoing formation of EC-PST identities as capable of supporting children's equitable science sensemaking. *What kinds of opportunities contribute to EC-PSTs' coming to see themselves as capable of nurturing children's curiosity, supporting their investigating and sensemaking, and advocating for their right to be heard and taken seriously?*

Finally, as mentioned at the start of the chapter, EC teachers themselves have under- recognized assets and affordances of context that position them as uniquely capable to support young children's equitable science sensemaking (Zembal-Saul et al., 2020). Evidence from the review demonstrates EC-PSTs are able to develop deeper understandings of science, NOS, and science teaching, as well as positive attitudes and beliefs, through their preparation coursework and field experiences. The authors here assert that explicit attention to assets and affordances in designing and studying EC teacher preparation programs is needed to realize the full potential of EC-PSTs' capabilities for supporting young children's equitable science sensemaking. *What does it look like to design teacher preparation experiences that value and build upon the assets of EC-PSTs?*

Where Does Expertise for EC Teacher Preparation for Science Reside?

Despite multiple cycles of increasingly refined searches, the authors identified only a modest number of studies focused on EC-PST for science. Globally, colleagues are known to be doing important work, yet much was not surfaced by this process. In the review of literature, an alarming parallel surfaced across representation of children, EC-PSTs, and the geographic situatedness of scholarship. First, the prevalent trend in Europe and the United States of EC-PSTs representing dominant racial, linguistic, and more privileged social class backgrounds, as well as having fewer experiences of immigration in comparison to the children they teach (American Association of Colleges for Teacher Education, 2019; Donlevy et al., 2016; Yoon & Martin, 2019), is also reflected in this review (see Moseley et al. , 2010, as the exception). Furthermore, since all studies in the review are situated in OECD countries and more widely represent the United States in this distribution, EC-PSTs worldwide are minimally represented. This parallel of underrepresentation of EC-PSTs and children continues to the professionals that write about the preparation of EC-PSTs. Just as in the case of children and EC-PSTs, there are voices of professionals at the periphery that may hold important insights to the questions we raise in this review. Inclusive representation of professionals and scholarship in the field are needed in order to advocate for the children and EC-PSTs whose voices must be heard.

Concluding Thoughts

While the findings of the review map readily to themes in studies of elementary teacher preparation for science, it does not mean that this work should be applied to the preparation of EC-PSTs without careful consideration. The goals and purposes of ECE and elementary education differ considerably, as do the policies, professional organizations, and systems in which ECE is situated. Moreover, pathways for professional preparation are multiple and diverse within and across countries. Much of the existing literature focuses on interventions that shape EC (and elementary) teachers' knowledge and beliefs about science, the nature of science, and science teaching. The authors were particularly interested in studies that examined how *authentic interactions with children* in EC settings inform the development of instructional practices for science, and those that focused on learning to teach science in ways that are equitable and just. Preparing EC teachers who are equipped to participate in and continue to learn from the ambitious and complex practices necessary to engage *with* children in science sensemaking requires holistic and contextualized approaches to professional learning within and beyond university-based teacher preparation experiences. Such approaches take into account more than teacher knowledge and include the development of a science identity, a pedagogy of listening and responsiveness, an inquiry stance toward teaching and learning, and a strong orientation toward social justice. While there is much work to do in EC teacher preparation for science, practice-based approaches with significant and repeated opportunities to interact with children are promising.

In closing, the question *What is science in ECE?* is left for readers to contemplate as new lines of research and practice unfold. Teacher educators and researchers must address this question locally and continually if there is to be a transformation of learning opportunities in EC science – one that builds from children's cultural and linguistic resources, their innate sense of wonder about the world, and their multiple and perceptive ways of investigating and sensemaking.

Notes

1. Science education in Early childhood (EC) encompasses both education and care. In this review, the authors address teacher preparation for contexts with an education focus, while still recognizing children's social, emotional, and physical care as integral to high-quality education. As such, the term Early Childhood Education (ECE) is the acronym used throughout rather than the broader term Early Childhood Education and Care (ECEC).
2. Table 6.1 List of journals examined: JCR-indexed journals are shown according to their position in the ranking, out of the 266 in the Educational Research category.

Rank	Journal (N = 37)	Theme*	No. Studies and Country
1	*Review of Educational Research*	E	0
4	*Computers and Education*	E	1 United States
10	*Journal of Research in Science Teaching*	SE	2 United States
12	*Studies in Science Education*	SE	0
15	*Journal of Teacher Education*	TE	0
19	*Science Education*	SE	0
38	*Teaching and Teacher Education*	TE	0
55	*Teachers and Teaching*	TE	0
57	*Early Childhood Research Quarterly*	ECE	0
61	*Environmental Education Research*	EE	4 total: – 1 from Australia – 1 from Sweden – 2 from the United States
65	*European Journal of Teacher Education*	TE	0
66	*Research in Science Education*	SE	3 total: – 1 from Sweden – 2 from the United States
81	*Journal of Environmental Education*	EE	1 Greece
100	*International Journal of STEM Education*	SE	0
124	*Journal of Science Education and Technology*	SE	1 United States
133	*International Journal of Science and Mathematics Education*	SE	0

Rank	Journal (N = 37)	Theme*	No. Studies and Country
143	Early Education and Development	ECE	1 China
146	International Journal of Science Education	SE	2 total: – 1 Germany – 1 United States
149	Journal of Education for Teaching	TE	1 Turkey
171	Elementary School Journal	ECE	0
179	Science and Education	SE	0
188	Early Childhood Education Journal	ECE	2 total: – 1 Sweden – 1 United States
189	Asia-Pacific Journal of Teacher Education	TE	1 Turkey
191	Research in Science and Technological Education	SE	1 Turkey
195	European Early Childhood Education Research Journal	ECE	1 Spain
207	Early Child Development and Care	ECE	0
212	Journal of Baltic Science Education	SE	1 Slovenia
223	Journal of Biological Education	SE	1 Spain
226	Early Years	ECE	0
236	Australasian Journal of Early Childhood	ECE	0
248	Cultural Studies of Science Education	SE	4 total: – 1 Luxembourg and 1, response – 1 Sweden – 1 United States
ESCI	Contemporary Issues in Early Childhood	ECE	0
ESCI	Journal of Science Teacher Education	SE & TE	6 United States
ESCI	Journal of Early Childhood Teacher Education	ECE & TE	5 total: – 1 Greece – 1 Sweden – 3 United States
Scopus	Eurasia Journal of Mathematics, Science and Technology Education	SE	1 Turkey
–	International Journal of Early Childhood Environmental Education	ECE & EE	0
–	International Journal of Environmental and Science Education (continued as Interdisciplinary Journal of Environmental and Science Education)	EE & SE	2 Turkey

* E = Education; ECE = Early Childhood Education; EE = Environmental Education; SE = Science E = Education; ECE = Early Childhood Education; EE = Environmental Education; SE = Science Education; TE= Teacher Education

References

(*= articles that are part of the review)

*Akerson, V., Buzzelli, C., & Borgerding, L. (2010). On the nature of teaching nature of science: Preservice early childhood teachers' Instruction in preschool and elementary settings. *Journal of Research in Science Teaching, 47*(2), 213–233. http://dx.doi.org/10.1002/tea.20323

*Akerson, V., Buzzelli, C., & Eastwood, J. (2012). Bridging the gap between preservice early childhood teachers' cultural values, perceptions of values held by scientists, and the relationships of these values to conceptions of nature of science. *Journal of Science Teacher Education, 23*(2), 133–157. http://dx.doi.org/10.1007/s10972-011-9244-1

*Akerson, V., Erumit, B. A., & Kaynak, N. E. (2019). Teaching Nature of Science through children's literature: An early childhood preservice teacher study. *International Journal of Science Education, 41*(18), 1–23. http://dx.doi.org/10.1080/09500693.2019.1698785

American Association of Colleges for Teacher Education (2019). *Education students and diversity: A review of New Evidence.* https://aacte.org/resources/research-reports-and-briefs/education-students-and-diversity-a-review-of-new-evidence/

★Andersson, K., Gullberg, A., Danielsson, A., Scantlebury, K., & Hussenius, A. (2020). Chafing borderlands: Obstacles for science teaching and learning in preschool teacher education. *Cultural Studies of Science Education, 15*, 1–20. http://dx.doi.org/10.1007/s11422-019-09934-x

★Ärlemalm-Hagsér, E., & Sandberg, A. (2011). Sustainable development in early childhood education: In-service students' comprehension of the concept. *Environmental Education Research, 17*(2), 187–200. http://dx.doi.org/10.1080/13504622.2010.522704

Avraamidou, L. (2016). *Studying science teacher identity: Theoretical, methodological, and empirical explorations.* Rotterdam, Netherlands: Sense Publishers.

★Barenthien, J., Oppermann, E., Anders, Y., & Steffensky, M. (2020). Preschool teachers' learning opportunities in their initial teacher education and in-service professional development – do they have an influence on preschool teachers' science-specific professional knowledge and motivation? *International Journal of Science Education, 42*(5), 744–763. http://dx.doi.org/10.1080/09500693.2020.1727586

★Bautista, N. U. (2011). Investigating the use of vicarious and mastery experiences in influencing early childhood education majors' self-efficacy beliefs. *Journal of Science Teacher Education, 22*, 333–349. http://dx.doi.org/10.1007/s10972-011-9232-5

★Bautista, N. U., & Boone, W. J. (2015). Exploring the impact of TeachME™ lab virtual classroom teaching simulation on early childhood education majors' self-efficacy beliefs. *Journal of Science Teacher Education, 26*(2), 237–262. http://dx.doi.org/10.1007/s10972-014-9418-8

★Bravo, M. A., Mosqueda, E., Solís, J. L., & Stoddart, T. (2014). Possibilities and limits of integrating science and diversity education in preservice elementary teacher preparation. *Journal of Science Teacher Education, 25*(5), 601–619. http://dx.doi.org/10.1007/s10972-013-9374-8

★Bulunuz, M. (2012a). Developing Turkish preservice preschool teachers' attitudes and understanding about teaching science through play. *International Journal of Environmental and Science Education, 7*(2), 141–166.

★Bulunuz, M. (2012b). Motivational qualities of hands-on science activities for Turkish preservice kindergarten teachers. *Eurasia Journal of Mathematics, Science & Technology Education, 8*(2), 73–82. http://dx.doi.org/10.12973/eurasia.2012.821a

Cannella, G. S. (1997). *Deconstructing early childhood education: Social justice and revolution.* New York, NY: Peter Lang.

★Çiftçi, A., Topçu, M. S., & Foulk, J. A. (2020). Pre-service early childhood teachers' views on STEM education and their STEM teaching practices. *Research in Science & Technological Education*, 1–27. http://dx.doi.org/10.1080/02635143.2020.1784125

Cochran-Smith, M., & Lytle, S. (2009). *Inquiry as stance: Practitioner research for the next generation.* New York, NY: Teachers College Press.

Dahlberg, G., & Moss, P. (2005). *Ethics and politics in early childhood education.* Abingdon, UK: Routledge.

Darling-Hammond, L., & Oakes, J. (2019). *Preparing teachers for deeper learning.* Cambridge, MA: Harvard Education Press.

Donlevy, V., Meierkord, A., & Rajania, A. (2016). *Study on the diversity within the teaching profession with particular focus on migrant and/or minority background: Final report to DG education and culture of the European commission.* https://op.europa.eu/en/publication-detail/-/publication/e478082d-0a81-11e7-8a35-01aa75ed71a1

★Eckhoff, A. (2017). Partners in inquiry: A collaborative life science investigation with preservice teachers and kindergarten students. *Early Childhood Education Journal, 45*(2), 219–227. http://dx.doi.org/10.1007/s10643-015-0769-3

★Enochs, L. G., & Riggs, I. M. (1990). Further development of an elementary science teaching efficacy belief instrument: A preservice elementary scale. *School Science and Mathematics, 90*(8), 694–706. http://dx.doi.org/10.1111/j.1949-8594.1990.tb12048.x

★Ernst, J., & Tornabene, L. (2012). Preservice early childhood educators' perceptions of outdoor settings as learning environments. *Environmental Education Research, 18*(5), 643–664. http://dx.doi.org/10.1080/13504622.2011.640749

Eshach, H., & Fried, M. N. (2005). Should science be taught in early childhood? *Journal of Science Education and Technology, 14*(3), 315–336. https://doi.org/10.1007/s10956-005-7198-9

★Fleer, M. (2011). Imagination, emotions and scientific thinking: What matters in the being and becoming of a teacher of elementary science? *Cultural Studies of Science Education, 7*(1), 31–39. http://dx.doi.org/10.1007/s11422-011-9365-z

★Giallousi, M., Tselfes, V., & Gialamas, V. (2014). Using student-teachers' reports of self-efficacy to evaluate an early childhood science course. *Journal of Early Childhood Teacher Education, 35*(4), 337–356. http://dx.doi.org/10.1080/10901027.2014.968298

★Gullberg, A., Andersson, K., Danielsson, A., Scantlebury, K., & Hussenius, A. (2017). Pre-service teachers' views of the child – reproducing or challenging gender stereotypes in science in preschool. *Research in Science Education, 48*, 691–715. http://dx.doi.org/10.1007/s11165-016-9593-z

Haverly, C., Calabrese Barton, A., Schwarz, C. V., & Braaten, M. (2020). "Making space": How novice teachers create opportunities for equitable sense-making in elementary science. *Journal of Teacher Education, 71*(1), 63–79. http://dx.doi.org/10.1177/0022487118800706

★Kalchman, M., & Kozoll, R. (2016). Dis-integrating mathematics and science in early childhood methods courses: Encouraging discrete content area proficiency. *Journal of Early Childhood Teacher Education, 37*(1), 61–75. http://dx.doi.org/10.1080/10901027.2015.1131210

Kane, J. M., & Varelas, M. (2016). Elementary school teachers constructing teacher-of-science identities: Two communities of practice coming together. In L. Avraamidou (Ed.), *Studying science teacher identity: Theoretical, methodological, and empirical explorations* (pp. 177–195). Rotterdam, Netherlands: Sense Publishers.

Kirch, S. A. (2009). Identifying and resolving uncertainty as a mediated action in science: A comparative analysis of the cultural tools used by scientists and elementary science students at work. *Science Studies and Science Education*, 308–335. https://doi.org/10.1002/sce.20362

★Kotaman, H. (2016). Impact of religion on Turkish prospective early childhood teachers' judgments of fact. *Journal of Education for Teaching, 42*(2), 163–172. http://dx.doi.org/10.1080/02607476.2016.1143140

Larimore, R. A. (2020). Preschool science education: A vision for the future. *Early Childhood Education Journal, 48*, 703–714. http://dx.doi.org/10.1007/s10643-020-01033-9

★Lippard, C. N., Tank, K., Walter, M. C., Krogh, J., & Colbert, K. (2018). Preparing early childhood preservice teachers for science teaching: Aligning across a teacher preparation program. *Journal of Early Childhood Teacher Education, 39*(3), 193–212. http://dx.doi.org/10.1080/10901027.2018.1457578

★Martínez-Álvarez, P. (2019). What counts as science? Expansive learning actions for teaching and learning science with bilingual children. *Cultural Studies of Science Education, 14*, 799–837. http://dx.doi.org/10.1007/s11422-019-09909-y

Mbamalu, G. E. (2001). Teaching science to academically underprepared Students. *Journal of Science Education and Technology, 10*, 267–272. https://doi.org/10.1023/A:1016642717633

Metz, K. E. (1995). Reassessment of developmental constraints on children's science instruction. *Review of Educational Research, 65*(2), 93–127. http://dx.doi.org/10.3102/00346543065002093

Monteira, S. F., & Jiménez-Aleixandre, M. P. (2016). The practice of using evidence in kindergarten: The role of purposeful observation. *Journal of Research in Science Teaching, 53*(8), 1232–1258. http://dx.doi.org/10.1002/tea.21259

★Moseley, C., Desjean-Perrotta, B., & Utley, J. (2010). The Draw-An-Environment Test Rubric (DAET-R): Exploring pre-service teachers' mental models of the environment. *Environmental Education Research, 16*(2), 189–208. http://dx.doi.org/10.1080/13504620903548674

Mullis, I. V. S., & Jenkins, L. B. (1988). *The science report card.* Report No. 17–5–01. Educational Testing Service.

Nasir, N. S., Rosebery, A. S., Warren, B., & Lee, C. D. (2006). Learning as a cultural process: Achieving equity through diversity. In R. K. Sawyer (Ed.), *The Cambridge handbook of the learning sciences* (pp. 489–504). New York, NY: Cambridge University Press.

National Research Council (2007). *Taking science to school: Learning and teaching science in grades K-8.* The National Academies Press. https://doi.org/10.17226/11625

Neuman, M. J., Josephson, K., & Chua, P. G. (2015). *A review of the literature: Early childhood care and education (ECCE) personnel in low-and middle-income countries.* Paris, France: United Nations Educational, Scientific and Cultural Organization (UNESCO).

★Novak, E., & Wisdom, S. (2018). Effects of a 3D printing project on preservice elementary teachers' science attitudes, science content knowledge, and anxiety about teaching science. *Journal of Science Education and Technology, 27*(7), 412–432. http://dx.doi.org/10.1007/s10956-018-9733-5

★O'Gorman, L., & Davis, J. (2013). Ecological footprinting: Its potential as a tool for change in preservice teacher education, *Environmental Education Research, 19*(6), 779–791. http://dx.doi.org/10.1080/13504622.2012.749979

★Olson, J. K., Bruxvoort, C. N., & Vande Haar, A. J. (2016). The impact of video case content on preservice elementary teachers' decision-making and conceptions of effective science teaching. *Journal of Research in Science Teaching, 53*, 1–24. http://dx.doi.org/10.1002/tea.21335

Organization for Economic Co-operation and Development (2020). *Education at a glance: OECD indicators.* https://doi.org/10.1787/69096873-en

★Reinoso, R., Delgado-Iglesias, J., & Fernández, I. (2019). Preservice teachers' views on science teaching in Early Childhood Education in Spain. *European Early Childhood Education Research Journal, 27*(6), 801–820. http://dx.doi.org/10.1080/1350293X.2019.1678720

*Saçkes, M., & Cabe-Trundle, K. (2014). Preservice early childhood teachers' learning of science in a methods course: Examining the predictive ability of an intentional learning model. *Journal of Science Teacher Education*, *25*(4), 413–444. http://dx.doi.org/10.1007/s10972-013-9355-y

*Saçkes, M., & Cabe-Trundle, K. (2016). Change or durability? The contribution of metaconceptual awareness in preservice early childhood teachers' learning of science concepts. *Research in Science Education*, *47*, 655–671. http://dx.doi.org/10.1007/s11165-016-9522-1

*Saçkes, M., Flevares, L. M., Gonya, J., & Cabe Trundle, K. (2012). Preservice early childhood teachers' sense of efficacy for integrating mathematics and science: Impact of a methods course. *Journal of Early Childhood Teacher Education*, *33*(4), 349–364. http://dx.doi.org/10.1080/10901027.2012.732666

*Sancar Tokmak, H. (2014). Pre-service teachers' perceptions on TPACK development after designing educational games. *Asia-Pacific Journal of Teacher Education*, *43*(5), 1–19. http://dx.doi.org/10.1080/1359866X.2014.939611

Siry, C., & Gorges, A. (2020). Young students' diverse resources for meaning making in science: Learning from multilingual contexts. *International Journal of Science Education*, *42*(14), 2364–2386. http://dx.doi.org/10.1080/09500693.2019.1625495

*Siry, C., & Lang, D. (2010). Creating participatory discourse for teaching and research in early childhood science. *Journal of Science Teacher Education*, *21*, 149–160. http://dx.doi.org/10.1007/s10972-009-9162-7.

*Siry, C., & Lara, J. (2012). "I didn't know water could be so messy": Coteaching in elementary teacher education and the production of identity for a new teacher of science. *Cultural Studies of Science Education*, *7*(1), 1–30. http://dx.doi.org/10.1007/s11422-011-9339-1

*Sundberg, B., & Ottander, C. (2013). The conflict within the role: A longitudinal study of preschool student teachers' developing competence in and attitudes towards science teaching in relation to developing a professional role. *Journal of Early Childhood Teacher Education*, *34*(1), 80–94. http://dx.doi.org/10.1080/10901027.2013.758540

*Thulin, S., & Redfors, A. (2016). Student preschool teachers' experiences of science and its role in preschool. *Early Childhood Education Journal*, *45*, 509–520. http://dx.doi.org/10.1007/s10643-016-0783-0

*Torkar, G. (2015). Pre-service teachers' fear of snakes, conservation attitudes, and likelihood of incorporating animals into the future science curriculum. *Journal of Baltic Science Education*, *14*, 401–410.

*Torres-Porras, J., & Alcántara-Manzanares, J. (2019). Are plants living beings? Biases in the interpretation of landscape features by pre-service teachers. *Journal of Biological Education*, *55*(2), 1–11. http://dx.doi.org/10.1080/00219266.2019.1667405

*Trundle, K. C., & Bell, R. L. (2010). The use of a computer simulation to promote conceptual change: A quasi-experimental study. *Computers and Education*, *54*(4), 1078–1088. http://dx.doi.org/10.1016/j.compedu.2009.10.012

Trundle, K. C., & Saçkes, M. (2012). Science and early education. In R. C. Pianta, W. S. Barnett, L. M. Justice, & S. M. Sheridan (Eds.), *Handbook of early childhood education* (pp. 240–258). New York, NY: Guilford Press.

*Tsevreni, I. (2020). Nature journaling as a holistic pedagogical experience with the more-than-human world. *The Journal of Environmental Education*, *52*(1), 14–24. http://dx.doi.org/10.1080/00958964.2020.1724854

UN General Assembly (1989). *Convention on the rights of the child*. United Nations, Treaty Series, vol. 1577, p. 3. https://f/www.refworld.org/docid/3ae6b38f0.html

*Wu, D., Liao, T., Yang, W., & Li, H. (2020). Exploring the relationships between scientific epistemic beliefs, science teaching beliefs and science-specific PCK among pre-service kindergarten teachers in China. *Early Education and Development*, *32*(1), 82–97. http://dx.doi.org/10.1080/10409289.2020.1771971

*Yılmaz, S., Olgan, R., & Yılmaztekin, E. (2016). Nature connectedness and landscape preferences of Turkish preservice preschool teachers. *International Journal of Environmental and Science Education*, *11*(15), 8120–8142.

*Yoon, J., & Martin, L. (2019). Infusing culturally responsive science curriculum into early childhood teacher preparation. *Research in Science Education*, *49*, 697–710. http://dx.doi.org/10.1007/s11165-017-9647-x

Zembal-Saul, C., Carlone, H., & Brown, M. (2020). Flipping the script: A possibility-centric vision of elementary teachers and ambitious science teaching. In D. Stroupe, K. Hammerness, & S. McDonald (Eds.), *Preparing science teachers through practice-based teacher education.* (pp. 117–132). Cambridge, MA: Harvard Education Press.

7

WELL-STARTED BEGINNERS

Preparing Elementary Teachers for Rigorous, Consequential, Just, and Equitable Science Teaching

Elizabeth A. Davis and Christa Haverly

Introduction and Theoretical Framework

This chapter addresses the overarching research question, *How can elementary science teacher education work toward a next-generation vision of rigorous, consequential, just, and equitable science teaching?* Inspired in part by Windschitl and Calabrese Barton's (2016) focus on rigor and equity, this question is used to address a fundamental question Roth (2014) raised in her recent review on elementary science teaching: *What does it take to help teachers to be well-started beginners with regard to elementary science?*

By *rigorous and consequential elementary science teaching*, the authors mean teaching that investigates phenomena, integrates science content with science practice, and is grounded in children's lived experiences. By *just and equitable elementary science teaching*, the authors mean, further, teaching that: sets and maintains high expectations for all children; works to overcome opportunity gaps manifested by systemic racism and other forms of oppression; affords opportunities for every child to be a doer of science and a knowledge generator in science, and to see themselves in science; and works to overcome systemic inequities in science instruction in elementary schools. This is a tall order, and elementary science teacher education must work toward this "next-generation vision." Being *well-started beginners* includes *both* working toward the vision of rigorous and consequential science learning laid out in current reforms worldwide *and* working toward equity- and justice-oriented science teaching.

The authors bring a situated and sociocultural perspective to the conceptualization of elementary science teacher education. This kind of rigorous, consequential, just, and equitable science teaching hinges on teachers having knowledge, beliefs, and practices that allow them to engage in this kind of work, as well as supportive contexts for learning and teaching. Teacher education experiences within methods classes, field experiences, science content classes, and other structures provide situated and social opportunities to learn, allowing novices to develop the knowledge, beliefs, and practices needed for effective teaching (Putnam & Borko, 2000). These experiences can support the visions for reform-oriented teaching put forward globally (e.g., Australian Curriculum Assessment and Reporting Authority (ACARA), 2014; NAE, 2018; National Research Council, 2012), making big ideas and disciplinary practices central, engaging students over time with natural phenomena and authentic problems, and working toward justice in and outside of classrooms. To reach these visions, the work must begin in the youngest grades – and therefore, these visions have important implications for primary or elementary science teacher education.

DOI: 10.4324/9781003098478-9

Methods

In conducting this review, the authors searched 12 top journals in education research, teacher education, and science education, looking at every paper published between 2010 and March 2020, identifying empirical studies that focused on elementary science teacher education. Papers from any country, using any methodological approach or theoretical stance, were included. Through this process, 229 papers were identified as potentially relevant. Culling the papers based on more systematic application of these criteria yielded 185 unique papers. Further culling to remove papers that focused only on preservice elementary *teachers* of science (as opposed to their teacher education experiences) brought the total number of potential papers down to 125.

From there, further choices about inclusion were still needed due to space limitations within this handbook. Papers were excluded if they did not *directly and empirically address the research question*, even if they focused on ways of improving self-efficacy, beliefs, attitudes, or knowledge for science or science teaching with implied outcomes towards rigorous, consequential, just, and/or equitable science teaching. Despite being excluded here, such studies make an important contribution to the field because they provide design insights for getting preservice elementary teachers to the point of being *able* to work on this kind of next-generation science teaching. (The authors review the literature on preservice elementary teachers of science themselves in Haverly & Davis, in progress.)

In reporting on the findings of the resulting 78 empirical studies, the authors:

- Present at a high level the overarching findings related to particular foci and provide relevant citations
- Elaborate on a few of these papers based on how they inform the research question.

Most of the papers were studies based in US contexts, and most of those studies focused on participants who are typical of US elementary teachers – namely white, middle-class, English-speaking women. Despite this skew in the available research, the authors highlight some studies from across the globe and with participants less typical of US elementary teachers.

Review of the Literature: Elementary Science Teacher Education Experiences

The review is organized around three key structures in teacher education – content courses, methods courses, and field experiences – and a section focused on programmatic designs.

Content Courses and Content-Focused Experiences

The fundamental role of content courses and other content-focused experiences is to build preservice teachers' subject matter knowledge. These courses can also, however, serve other roles, including developing preservice teachers' self-efficacy, attitudes, beliefs, and practice, and providing innovative models of science instruction. Here, the focus is on how such courses can support engagement in science practices and the development of preservice teachers' instructional practices, as well as providing models of innovative designs for such courses.

Two studies explore how content courses and experiences support preservice teachers' engagement in science practices (Kim et al., 2014; Saribas & Akdemir, 2019). Saribas and Akdemir looked at how an environmental education course in Turkey supported preservice teachers' development of scientific models, and Kim and colleagues looked at how a science, technology, and society course in Canada supported preservice teachers' argumentation.

One study examined how a content course supported preservice teachers' own teaching practice (Sabel et al., 2015). Sabel and colleagues looked at 49 preservice elementary teachers in a life science course designed for elementary teacher education students in the US; the course had a focus on formative assessment and lesson planning. The authors found that preservice teachers' subject matter knowledge increased across the course. The preservice teachers improved in their ability to anticipate and assess students' ideas, but they did not improve in knowing what to do instructionally with that information. The authors looked at nuances of the relationships between how preservice teachers' own life science subject matter knowledge related to their abilities to anticipate and assess students' ideas – and how they developed strategies for accounting for gaps in their subject matter knowledge to allow them to engage in these practices effectively. Preservice elementary teachers leveraged their content understandings *and* accommodated their weaknesses through leveraging their other strengths and resources.

A few innovative designs provide "images of the possible," showing how designers of content coursework aimed at preservice elementary teachers might push the boundaries of the typical course design. These studies described:

- A physics course in the US with a focus on learning about learning and analyzing children's thinking (Harlow et al., 2014)
- A physics course in the US with a "friends and family" focus that – among other things – supported preservice teachers in collaborating around science using language and tools (Crowl et al., 2013)
- A physical science course in the US with an emphasis on using educative curriculum materials (Donna & Hick, 2017)
- A multi-content course in Australia with a focus on engaging students in innovative and unusual instructional experiences to support engagement and interest (Palmer et al., 2016).

In sum, content course instructors are experimenting with innovative course designs to meet the needs of elementary preservice teachers, supporting their subject matter knowledge but also a broader range of outcomes related to their abilities around rigorous, consequential, equitable, and just science teaching. More research is needed to characterize the influence of these course designs on preservice teachers' engagement in science practices and their instructional practices.

Science Methods Courses

Science methods courses are another key part of preservice teachers' preparation. These papers are organized around (a) the relationship of methods courses with preservice teachers' characteristics (beliefs, attitudes, identities, knowledge) as well as (b) the foci of interventions (science content, science inquiry and/or practices, science and literacy, and curriculum and planning) and their relationship with preservice teachers' characteristics and performances.

Supporting Beliefs, Attitudes, and Identities in Science Methods Courses

Two studies that focused on beliefs and attitudes did so from an equity or justice lens (Bravo et al., 2014; Mensah & Jackson, 2018). Mensah and Jackson (2018) investigated the beliefs about science and science teaching of seven preservice elementary teachers of color in an elementary science methods course in New York City. Over the semester-long course, teachers' beliefs shifted to science as being for them and their students of color. This was largely attributed to having an instructor who was also a woman of color, in addition to curriculum and pedagogy that was explicitly multicultural.

Bravo and colleagues (2014) studied 110 preservice elementary teachers at two US universities, 65 of whom were enrolled in an innovative elementary science methods course (the intervention group) that aligned with a set of standards for linguistic and cultural diversity, and 45 who were taught about those ideas separately (the control group). The quantitative study connected beliefs, practice, and a teacher education experience focused on linguistic and cultural diversity. The study demonstrates the complexity of the work of supporting preservice elementary teachers to engage in justice-oriented science teaching. The findings suggested that the preservice teachers who experienced the intervention developed a slightly stronger belief in the need for teachers and students to engage in joint productive activity (though both groups had initially strong beliefs along these justice dimensions). On the post-observation measure, the intervention group also scored higher than the control group in teaching practices along three dimensions: language and literacy, instructional conversations, and challenging activities. Despite these positive effects, the preservice teachers had stronger beliefs about science teaching for justice than they had the ability to enact such teaching.

Some studies reported on preservice elementary teachers' identity development through experiences in elementary science methods courses (Naidoo, 2017; Settlage, 2011). For example, Settlage (2011) investigated identity development with regard to multicultural education. Conducted in a predominantly white institution in the United States, Settlage used qualitative data analysis with five preservice teachers who were students in an elective elementary science methods course with culture as a focus. The results suggest that preservice elementary teachers who have not had culturally, racially, or linguistically diverse experiences can nonetheless make some positive shifts in their identities.

Supporting Knowledge in Science Methods Courses

Several papers explored how science methods courses shaped preservice elementary teachers' knowledge for science teaching. Some focused on pedagogical content knowledge (PCK) and/or subject matter knowledge in the context of science methods courses (Hoban et al., 2011; Hume, 2012; Nilsson & Loughran, 2012). One focused on knowledge of assessments (Buck et al., 2010). Two focused on knowledge and beliefs related to multicultural and culturally relevant science education (Mensah et al., 2018; Yoon & Martin, 2019).

Some studies explored the effects of explicit instruction on preservice teachers' views of the nature of science (NOS; Akerson, Buzellii, et al., 2012; Bell et al., 2011; Valente et al., 2018). For example, in an elementary science methods course in the US, Bell and colleagues (2011) designed a mixed methods, experimental design testing explicit versus implicit NOS instruction and contextualized versus non-contextualized NOS instruction. The study involved 75 preservice elementary teachers. Explicit instruction in NOS was more successful at changing the preservice teachers' views than was implicit instruction in NOS. While whether the instruction was contextualized (in the context of global warming and climate change) did not affect the preservice teachers' views of NOS, contextualization did support the preservice teachers in being able to *use* their knowledge of the nature of science in decision-making. Valente and colleagues' study, taking place in Portugal, also suggested some positive effects of explicit instruction in NOS, and, perhaps, some delayed effects of research experiences.

Supporting Performance in Science Methods Courses

Several papers explored the relationship between science methods courses and preservice elementary teachers' engagement in, beliefs about, or understanding of inquiry and/or science practices. Two papers tackled this topic by studying specific science or inquiry practices in elementary science methods courses: Kaya (2013) around argumentation, and Cruz-Guzman and colleagues (2017) around researchable questions. Other papers looked at interventions and their relationship more broadly with teachers' knowledge and/or beliefs about inquiry (Biggers & Forbes, 2012; Greca, 2016; Kazempour, 2018; Wang & Sneed, 2019). As an example, in the Kazempour case study, four preservice elementary teachers engaged in a semester-long home inquiry project as part of their elementary science methods course in the US. The participants improved in their understanding of the inquiry process and showed increased readiness and interest in incorporating inquiry practices into their own science teaching.

A few studies looked at the role of elementary science methods courses in supporting preservice elementary teachers' engagement with science and literacy. Two focused on teachers' improved facility with science vocabulary (Carrier, 2013; Carrier & Grifenhagen, 2020). A third, focused on the integration of science and literacy, analyzed lesson plans from 45 preservice elementary teachers enrolled in an elementary science methods course in the US (Wallace & Coffey, 2019). Preservice teachers were directed to create a lesson plan to teach complementary skills for reading and science. Findings demonstrated preservice teachers' abilities to integrate and pair inquiry skills with reading skills, and to devise pedagogical strategies for engaging students in these skills towards deeper conceptual understandings.

Several papers explored curriculum and planning. One from Australia focused on preservice elementary teachers' use of curriculum materials that positively shaped their interest in and readiness for teaching science (Cooper et al., 2012). Two studies used preservice teachers' curriculum materials produced for their elementary science methods course to draw conclusions about their ideas and beliefs regarding students' funds of knowledge (McLaughlin & Calabrese Barton, 2013) and their beliefs about the role of the teacher (Olson et al., 2016). Finally, others considered the effect of interventions on preservice teachers' lesson planning (Gunckel, 2011; Patrick et al., 2013; Plummer & Ozcelik, 2015; Zangori et al., 2017). In Plummer and Ozcelik's (2015) US-based study, the intervention was an immersive experience in a 5-week inquiry investigation in astronomy. Thirty preservice elementary teachers later planned and taught a 5-week inquiry sequence on the same astronomy topic to children. Results from the mixed methods study showed that about one-third of participants successfully planned coherent inquiry investigations that also focused on student sensemaking. The other two-thirds planned inquiry experiences for students that involved some key practices like collecting data. The authors found that participants' reliance on curriculum materials did not support them in developing coherent inquiry investigations. This finding contrasts with Cooper and colleagues' (2012) study, which showed increased confidence and interest in teaching science when provided with inquiry-based curriculum materials, as well as other work in this review that generally suggests a positive effect of using curriculum materials.

Another group of studies explored how approximations of practice and other features of practice-based teacher education might shape preservice teachers' characteristics (Bautista & Boone, 2015; Bottoms et al., 2015; d'Alessio, 2018; Ruiz-Gallardo & Reavey, 2019; Wenner & Kittleson, 2018). Practice-based teacher education uses representations, decompositions, and approximations of practice to support learning a set of core or high-leverage teaching practices or moves (Grossman et al., 2009). Approximations of practice can be facilitated virtually (e.g., Bautista & Boone, 2015) or in person, and many take place in the context of a science methods course connected to a field experience. As an example of in-person approximations of practice, Wenner and Kittleson (2018) studied nine preservice teachers in an elementary science methods class in the US. The class was designed using a supported collaborative teaching model, and the qualitative study was designed to look at how the structure of a sequence of approximations of practice involving small-group teaching, along with a framework for teaching, supported the preservice teachers' learning. Examining the preservice teachers' reflections, the authors suggest that the preservice teachers demonstrated sophisticated understandings of some aspects of teaching, such as what constitutes a good question. The preservice teachers attributed the shifts in their thinking to the instructional framework as well as the scaffolded reflection process and structured teaching model.

In a study leveraging a somewhat similar instructional approach, Bottoms and colleagues (2015) engaged 19 preservice elementary teachers in an elementary science methods course in the US. The science methods course was connected to an after-school, Spanish/English dual immersion STEM club in which the preservice teachers worked on core instructional practices with small groups of children with diverse cultural and linguistic backgrounds. The authors drew on the preservice teachers' written analyses of their teaching (i.e., what the preservice teachers noticed, not their actual enacted practice). The authors identified themes such as how the preservice teachers were able to draw on resources to inform their practice (e.g., taking up ideas from readings to incorporate into their instruction), how they renegotiated their roles in teaching (e.g., repositioning themselves as co-inquirers with the children), and how they shifted from having deficit perspectives of emergent multilingual learners to recognizing the need for changes to their own instructional approaches. As one of few papers in the data set that reflected purposeful work with culturally and linguistically diverse children, this study suggests the importance of engaging preservice teachers in supportive justice-oriented field placements, to move their thinking forward about teaching for equity. Similar to Wenner and Kittleson's (2018) study, it also shows the ways in which structured science teaching experiences could support new ways of thinking about science teaching.

The literature reviewed shows that elementary science methods courses shape preservice elementary teachers' knowledge, beliefs, identities, and performances related to science teaching. This theme underscores the key role elementary science methods courses can play in reversing the global trend of elementary teachers feeling ill-equipped to teach science. For example, structured – and sometimes small-scale or even virtual – teaching experiences as approximations of practice support preservice teachers. They also benefit when programs diversify the pool of teacher educators themselves and connect methods classes to field sites with children from a range of cultural and linguistic backgrounds. Some under-researched areas also surfaced, including the need for more studies that explore (a) how elementary science methods courses can shift preservice teachers' beliefs, attitudes, knowledge, and practice of culturally sustaining pedagogies, and (b) the impact of using curriculum materials on preservice teachers' readiness for and ability to plan and enact inquiry-based (and justice-oriented) instruction.

Field Experiences

Papers about the role of the practicum or student teaching focused on how these field experiences shaped preservice teachers' characteristics, such as their beliefs, identities, or knowledge; their practice or performance, including how they planned and enacted lessons; or both.

Several studies looked at the role of mentor teachers (Abed & Abd-El-Khalick, 2015; Chen & Mensah, 2018; Miller et al., 2019; Siry & Lara, 2012). For example, Chen and Mensah (2018) examined the role of the cooperating teacher in supporting the identity development of three preservice teachers in a social justice-focused elementary teacher education program in the US. Multiple factors mediated how identities as science teachers and as social justice teachers developed; their cooperating teachers had an important role in shaping that identity development. Overall, these studies suggest that the mentor teachers working with the preservice teachers in the field shape preservice teachers' self-efficacy, as well as other aspects of their beliefs, their knowledge, and their identities as science teachers.

Another set of papers looked at how field experiences shaped what preservice teachers were able to do – that is, their practice or performance of practice-related tasks (Canipe & Gunckel, 2020; Forbes, 2013; Gunckel & Wood, 2016; Plonczak, 2010; Subramaniam, 2013). Two of these studies, based in the US, looked at co-learning tasks between preservice and mentor teachers working together (Canipe & Gunckel, 2020; Gunckel & Wood, 2016). The co-learning tasks required the preservice and mentor teachers to collaboratively apply principles related to science inquiry and equitable science learning as they engaged in instructional design. Gunckel and Wood (2016), looking at 11 preservice elementary teachers and 18 mentor teachers, found that the tasks seemed to help the preservice teachers make connections between their science methods course and their field placements. While conversations about inquiry were frequent between preservice and mentor teachers, the study also highlighted how rare conversations about equity were.

Extending other work (Biggers & Forbes, 2012; Forbes, 2011; Forbes & Davis, 2010; Zangori & Forbes, 2013), Forbes (2013) examined the characteristics of field placements and the curriculum materials used in those placements, and the study connected those characteristics to how the preservice teachers engaged in lesson planning. Forbes conducted a mixed methods study involving 46 preservice elementary teachers in a science methods course in an elementary teacher education program in the US. Features of the science curriculum materials accounted for some of the variance in the preservice teachers' curricular adaptations, but the field placement played a stronger role in how the preservice teachers adapted these curriculum materials.

Several papers looked at the relationship between field experiences and the characteristics *and* practice of preservice teachers (Akerson, Donnelly, et al., 2012; Cartwright & Hallar, 2018; Gunckel, 2013; Hawkins & Park Rogers, 2016; Nilsson & van Driel, 2010; Smith & Jang, 2011; Sullivan-Watts et al., 2013; Tsybulsky & Oz, 2019). For example, Sullivan-Watts and colleagues (2013) followed 27 preservice teachers from their science methods class in the US into student teaching. In this mixed methods study, exploring similar territory to the Forbes studies noted earlier (Biggers & Forbes, 2012; Forbes, 2011, 2013; Forbes & Davis, 2010; Zangori & Forbes, 2013), the authors found that most of the preservice teachers' lessons involved inquiry in some way. Initially, however, many of these lessons focused only on observation or classifying with limited opportunities for sensemaking with data. The authors found that science subject matter knowledge and preference for science teaching were both strong predictors of the quality of science lessons. The authors also took up the apparent effects of using kit-based curricula and found that kits did seem to support structuring questions and investigations; the kits did not, however, seem to support sensemaking around data. In one of this review's most comprehensive studies, this paper explores and makes connections among many of the dimensions that shape elementary science teaching for preservice teachers.

Other work explored particular characteristics of the practicum experience, including the role of service learning (Cone, 2012; Trauth-Nare, 2015; Wilson et al., 2015), informal science teaching experiences (Bottoms et al., 2015; Harlow, 2012; Katz et al., 2011; Kisiel, 2013; Seung et al., 2019; Wallace & Brooks, 2015), or other kinds of characteristics (Rivera Maulucci, 2011; Weller, 2019).

As an example, Rivera Maulucci (2011) studied one preservice teacher in a teacher education program in the US, looking at the preservice teacher's identity as an urban science teacher. The practicum experiences were based in two dual-language elementary classrooms. Atypical for this review, the preservice teacher herself was bilingual and was an immigrant. The study focused on how her own language experiences shaped how she approached language learning and science learning and teaching. The author found that the preservice teacher's early experiences as a Spanish speaker and as a learner of English shaped how she viewed the intersections of language learning and science learning. Through the dual-language program's practicum experiences, she developed more sophisticated understandings; she also became an advocate for dual-language models for children.

Taken together, these studies from the field reflect much of the complexity of learning to teach and show the important roles that field-based experiences, mentor teachers, and curriculum materials can play in supporting that learning. Some of these studies show how specific characteristics of these field experiences (e.g., linguistic diversity, supportive mentor teachers) may play important roles in supporting novices in learning to teach toward equity and justice. One study looked for a focus on equity in collaborations between preservice and mentor teachers and found it lacking.

Other work explores the ways that curriculum materials and characteristics of the field setting (e.g., the mentor teacher) synergistically shape how preservice teachers may be able to engage in rigorous and consequential science teaching, though there is need for more support in engaging children in sensemaking. Further research is needed to better understand how the field can support justice-oriented teaching practice and teaching toward sensemaking, two key aspects of next-generation science teaching.

Teacher Education Programs

Studies that focus at the level of the teacher education program sometimes take the unit of analysis to be the program as a whole, and sometimes it is more fine-grained (e.g., coordination across science and math methods classes). This kind of work is relatively rare despite its potential for being important for the field given the multi-subject nature of elementary teaching and elementary teacher preparation. Much of this work focuses on self-efficacy, identity, beliefs, and knowledge, with a few studies looking at practice.

Hernandez and Shroyer (2017) conducted a qualitative study in the US involving 12 Latinx preservice teachers. Participants were generally bilingual, non-traditional (i.e., older), first-generation students. The participants were enrolled in a teacher education program with a purposeful pipeline design intended to diversify the teaching force. The study connected the preservice teachers' knowledge and practice related to science teaching with their field experiences within this innovative program structure; the authors looked at the participants' use of culturally responsive teaching strategies in their science (and math) instruction when teaching students from a range of cultural and linguistic backgrounds. The preservice teachers were mostly successful with certain dimensions of culturally responsive teaching (e.g., connecting content to students' lives and cultural backgrounds; building relationships with children; holding high expectations for children; using native language supports), though they struggled with teaching for social justice, facilitating knowledge construction, and supporting academic development.

Avraamidou's (2014) study, located in a southern European country, qualitatively analyzed longitudinal data for one elementary teacher from her first year in university through her first year of teaching. Avraamidou found that this teacher's positive experiences with science and methods for teaching science inquiry in university positively shaped her identity for science teaching. Central to this positive identity development were the relationships formed with her female university instructors as contrasted with her male instructors in her high school courses – like Mensah and Jackson's (2018) study, Avraamidou's shows the importance of diversifying the instructors in higher education.

Hanuscin (2013) worked with one preservice elementary teacher across an elementary science methods course focused on the nature of science, an informal science teaching experience, and student teaching, within an elementary teacher education program. In this US-based longitudinal case study drawing on extensive data, Hanuscin focused on the preservice teacher's knowledge and beliefs through an examination of critical incidents across the experiences. Hanuscin found that the preservice teacher portrayed science as a human endeavor, considered multiple "scientific methods," and valued evidence in science. She also desired to empower students. Hanuscin found that the preservice teacher's informal science teaching experiences were important for developing her PCK for teaching NOS, complementing the explicit work done in the methods class. Hanuscin highlighted the importance of the mentoring the preservice teacher experienced as well as her analysis of student work.

Another set of papers looks at the role of practice-based teacher education programs (Arias & Davis, 2017; Benedict-Chambers, 2016; Benedict-Chambers & Aram, 2017; Kademian & Davis, 2018; Lewis, 2019). For example, Arias and Davis (2017) used a case study approach to longitudinally study four preservice teachers across a 2-year practice-based teacher education program in the US. The authors found that the preservice teachers experienced growth in their enactment of the high-leverage science teaching practice of supporting children in making evidence-based claims. The authors suggested that variation in this growth was related to multiple factors, including the preservice teachers' prior experiences and backgrounds, and that growth was supported by the representations, decompositions, and approximations of practice incorporated across the design of the program. Despite the strengths in the preservice teachers' enactment of the practice, the authors also identified areas for further growth, including a tendency toward doing the intellectual work for children. In a second example, based in the same setting, Kademian and Davis (2018) explored related terrain for the high-leverage science teaching practice of leading a discussion. Besides showing a range of strengths of the preservice teachers' practice, the authors also highlighted the importance of conceptual tools and frameworks in learning to teach.

In sum, these papers that look at programmatic efforts demonstrate how coherence across multiple experiences (e.g., multiple subject areas' methods courses; a series of pedagogies of practice or tools across an entire program) can support preservice teachers' learning and development. Particularly for preservice *elementary* teachers, seeing coherence across experiences seems important, as they will typically be teaching all academic subject areas.

Conclusion

In the current times of a global pandemic, environmental collapse, and debilitating racial injustices and other forms of systemic oppression, scientific literacy and justice are critical for even the youngest learners. This review has begun to answer the question, *How can elementary science teacher education work toward a next-generation vision of rigorous, consequential, just, and equitable science teaching?* with the goal of helping teachers become well-started beginners (Roth, 2014). The review provides evidence of the important roles that science content courses, science methods courses, field experiences, and teacher education programs writ large can play in supporting the kind of next-generation science teaching needed in the elementary grades. The review points to some potentially supportive characteristics of these structures, as summarized in Table 7.1.

When looking at the big picture, this review shines a light on the need for more work that directly informs how beginning elementary teachers learn to teach science in rigorous, consequential, equitable, *and* just ways. This review highlights the relative dearth of scholarship that centrally focuses on learning to engage in equitable and just elementary science teaching (e.g., how methods courses can prepare elementary science teachers for enacting culturally sustaining pedagogies), particularly with regard to looking at teachers' actual practice. It also highlights the near absence of scholarship that works at the *intersection* of the two dimensions that were of interest here: rigorous and consequential (e.g., phenomena-driven, oriented around the integration of content and practice) *and* just and equitable (e.g., providing opportunities for every child to see themselves as a knowledge generator and doer of science). An example of such work might be research on how preservice elementary teachers' practice of this kind of next-generation science teaching develops in a field setting with children from a range of cultural and linguistic backgrounds and curriculum materials that support students in sensemaking around phenomena.

In conclusion, this review identifies that experiences in teacher education can and do support the development of preservice teachers' knowledge, beliefs, identities, and practice as elementary teachers of science. Overall, experiences in teacher education can help preservice elementary teachers develop into effective and efficacious – competent and confident – well-started beginners in the complex but crucial work of supporting every child in being able to experience science teaching that is rigorous, consequential, equitable, and just.

Table 7.1 Potentially supportive design features of elementary science teacher education experiences

Teacher Education Structure	Examples of Potentially Supportive Design Features
Content courses	Diversifying content course instructors
	Engaging in science practices
	Planning lessons and formative assessments
	Analyzing children's thinking
	Collaborating in doing science
	Supporting use of curriculum materials
Methods courses	Diversifying science methods instructors
	Learning about leveraging children's linguistic and cultural diversity
	Focusing (extensively) on multicultural science education
	Explicitly teaching about NOS and contextualizing this instruction
	Engaging in science practices
	Integrating science and literacy
	Working with science curriculum materials (mixed results)
	Engaging in approximations of practice
	Connecting to culturally and linguistically diverse field sites
Field experiences	Ensuring supportive mentor teachers
	Engaging in co-learning between preservice and mentor teachers
	Working with science curriculum materials
	Connecting to culturally and linguistically diverse field sites
Programmatic characteristics	Coordinating across methods courses
	Diversifying the preservice teacher pipeline
	Diversifying teacher educators
	Coordinating across a teacher education program
	Engaging in coordinated representations, decompositions, and approximations of practice

Acknowledgments

Work on this paper was funded in part by the National Science Foundation (NSF Core Grant number 1761129). However, any opinions, findings, and conclusions or recommendations expressed here are those of the authors. We thank the editors and reviewers who helped to strengthen this manuscript, including Julie A. Luft, M. Gail Jones, Sarah Carrier, and Jan van Driel.

References

Abed, O., & Abd-El-Khalick, F. (2015). Jordanian preservice primary teachers' perceptions of mentoring in science teaching. *International Journal of Science Education, 37*(4), 703–726.

Akerson, V., Buzellii, C., & Eastwood, J. (2012). Bridging the gap between preservice early childhood teachers' cultural values, perceptions of values held by scientists, and the relationships of these values to conceptions of nature of science. *Journal of Science Teacher Education, 23*(2), 133–157.

Akerson, V., Donnelly, L., Riggs, M., & Eastwood, J. (2012). Developing a community of practice to support preservice elementary teachers' nature of science instruction. *International Journal of Science Education, 34*(9), 1371–1392.

Arias, A., & Davis, E. A. (2017). Supporting children to construct evidence-based claims in science: Individual learning trajectories in a practice-based program. *Teaching and Teacher Education, 66*, 204–218.

Australian Curriculum Assessment and Reporting Authority (ACARA). (2014). *The Australian curriculum: Science.* Sydney: Australian Curriculum Assessment and Reporting Authority. www.australiancurriculum.edu.au/science/curriculum/f-10?layout=1

Avraamidou, L. (2014). Tracing a beginning elementary teacher's development of identity for science teaching. *Journal of Teacher Education, 65*(3), 223–240.

Bautista, N., & Boone, W. (2015). Exploring the impact of TeachME™ Lab virtual classroom teaching simulation on early childhood education majors' self-efficacy beliefs. *Journal of Science Teacher Education, 26*(3), 237–262.

Bell, R., Matkins, J., & Gansneder, B. (2011). Impacts of contextual and explicit instruction on preservice elementary teachers' understandings of the nature of science. *Journal of Research in Science Teaching, 48*(4), 414–436.

Benedict-Chambers, A. (2016). Using tools to promote novice teacher noticing of science teaching practices in post-rehearsal discussions. *Teaching and Teacher Education, 59*, 28–44.

Benedict-Chambers, A., & Aram, R. (2017). Tools for teacher noticing: Helping preservice teachers notice and analyze student thinking and scientific practice use. *Journal of Science Teacher Education, 28*(3), 294–318.

Biggers, M., & Forbes, C. (2012). Balancing teacher and student roles in elementary classrooms: Preservice elementary teachers' learning about the inquiry continuum. *International Journal of Science Education, 34*(14), 2205–2229.

Bottoms, S., Ciechanowski, K., & Hartman, B. (2015). Learning to teach elementary science through iterative cycles of enactment in culturally and linguistically diverse contexts. *Journal of Science Teacher Education, 26*(8), 715–742.

Bravo, M., Mosqueda, E., Solís, J., & Stoddart, T. (2014). Possibilities and limits of integrating science and diversity education in preservice elementary teacher preparation. *Journal of Science Teacher Education, 25*(5), 601–619.

Buck, G., Trauth-Nare, A., & Kaftan, J. (2010). Making formative assessment discernable to pre-service teachers of science. *Journal of Research in Science Teaching, 47*(4), 402–421.

Canipe, M., & Gunckel, K. (2020). Imagination, brokers, and boundary objects: Interrupting the mentor – preservice teacher hierarchy when negotiating meanings. *Journal of Teacher Education, 71*(1), 80–93.

Carrier, S. (2013). Elementary preservice teachers' science vocabulary: Knowledge and application. *Journal of Science Teacher Education, 24*(2), 405–425.

Carrier, S., & Grifenhagen, J. (2020). Academic vocabulary support for elementary science pre-service teachers. *Journal of Science Teacher Education, 31*(2), 115–133.

Cartwright, T. J., & Hallar, B. (2018). Taking risks with a growth mindset: Longterm influence of an elementary pre-service after school science practicum. *International Journal of Science Education, 40*(3), 348–370.

Chen, J., & Mensah, F. M. (2018). Teaching contexts that influence elementary preservice teachers' teacher and science teacher identity development. *Journal of Science Teacher Education, 29*(5), 420–439.

Cone, N. (2012). The effects of community-based service learning on preservice teachers' beliefs about the characteristics of effective science teachers of diverse students. *Journal of Science Teacher Education, 23*(8), 889–907.

Cooper, G., Kenny, J., & Fraser, S. (2012). Influencing intended teaching practice: Exploring pre-service teachers' perceptions of science teaching resources. *International Journal of Science Education, 34*(12), 1883–1908.

Crowl, M., Devitt, A., Jansen, H., van Zee, E., & Winograd, K. (2013). Encouraging prospective teachers to engage friends and family in exploring physical phenomena. *Journal of Science Teacher Education, 24*(1), 93–110.

Cruz-Guzmán, M., García-Carmona, A., & Criado, A. (2017). An analysis of the questions proposed by elementary pre-service teachers when designing experimental activities as inquiry. *International Journal of Science Education, 39*(13), 1755–1774.

d'Alessio, M. (2018). The effect of microteaching on science teaching self-efficacy beliefs in preservice elementary teachers. *Journal of Science Teacher Education, 29*(6), 441–467.

Donna, J., & Hick, S. (2017). Developing elementary preservice teacher subject matter knowledge through the use of educative science curriculum materials. *Journal of Science Teacher Education, 28*(1), 92–110.

Forbes, C. (2011). Preservice elementary teachers' adaptation of science curriculum materials for inquiry-based elementary science. *Science Education, 95*, 927–955.

Forbes, C. (2013). Curriculum-dependent and curriculum-independent factors in preservice elementary teachers' adaptation of science curriculum materials for inquiry-based science. *Journal of Science Teacher Education, 24*(1), 179–197.

Forbes, C., & Davis, E. A. (2010). Curriculum design for inquiry: Preservice elementary teachers' mobilization and adaptation of science curriculum materials. *Journal of Research in Science Teaching, 47*(7), 820–839.

Greca, I. (2016). Supporting pre-service elementary teachers in their understanding of inquiry teaching through the construction of a third discursive space. *International Journal of Science Education, 38*(5), 791–813.

Grossman, P., Compton, C., Igra, D., Ronfeldt, M., Shahan, E., & Williamson, P. W. (2009). Teaching practice: A cross-professional perspective. *Teachers College Record, 111*(9), 2055–2100.

Gunckel, K. (2011). Mediators of a preservice teacher's use of the inquiry-application instructional model. *Journal of Science Teacher Education, 22*(1), 79–100.

Gunckel, K. (2013). Fulfilling multiple obligations: Preservice elementary teachers' use of an instructional model while learning to plan and teach science. *Science Education, 97*, 139–162.

Gunckel, K., & Wood, M. (2016). The principle – practical discourse edge: Elementary preservice and mentor teachers working together on colearning tasks. *Science Education, 100*, 96–121.

Hanuscin, D. (2013). Critical incidents in the development of pedagogical content knowledge for teaching the nature of science: A prospective elementary teacher's journey. *Journal of Science Teacher Education, 24*(6), 933–956.

Harlow, D. (2012). The excitement and wonder of teaching science: What pre-service teachers learn from facilitating family science night centers. *Journal of Science Teacher Education, 23*(2), 199–220.

Harlow, D., Swanson, L., & Otero, V. (2014). Prospective elementary teachers' analysis of children's science talk in an undergraduate physics course. *Journal of Science Teacher Education, 25*(1), 97–117.

Haverly, C., & Davis, E. A. (in progress). Unpacking readiness for elementary science teaching: What preservice teachers bring and how that can be shaped through teacher education.

Hawkins, S., & Park Rogers, M. (2016). Tools for reflection: Video-based reflection within a preservice community of practice. *Journal of Science Teacher Education, 27*(4), 415–437.

Hernandez, C., & Shroyer, M. G. (2017). The use of culturally responsive teaching strategies among Latina/o student teaching interns during science and mathematics instruction of CLD students. *Journal of Science Teacher Education, 28*(4), 367–387.

Hoban, G., Loughran, J., & Nielsen, W. (2011). Slowmation: Preservice elementary teachers representing science knowledge through creating multimodal digital animations. *Journal of Research in Science Teaching, 48*(9), 985–1009.

Hume, A. (2012). Primary connections: Simulating the classroom in initial teacher education. *Research in Science Education, 42*, 551–565.

Kademian, S., & Davis, E. A. (2018). Supporting beginning teacher planning of investigation-based science discussions. *Journal of Science Teacher Education, 29*(8), 712–740.

Katz, P., McGinnis, R., Hestness, E., Riedinger, K., Marbach-Ad, G., Dai, A., & Pease, R. (2011). Professional identity development of teacher candidates participating in an informal science education internship: A focus on drawings as evidence. *International Journal of Science Education, 33*(9), 1169–1197.

Kaya, E. (2013). Argumentation practices in classroom: Pre-service teachers' conceptual understanding of chemical equilibrium. *International Journal of Science Education, 35*(7), 1139–1158.

Kazempour, M. (2018). Elementary preservice teachers' authentic inquiry experiences and reflections: A multicase study. *Journal of Science Teacher Education, 29*(7), 644–663.

Kim, M., Anthony, R., & Blades, D. (2014). Decision making through dialogue: A case study of analyzing preservice teachers' argumentation on socioscientific issues. *Research in Science Education, 44*, 903–926.

Kisiel, J. (2013). Introducing future teachers to science beyond the classroom. *Journal of Science Teacher Education, 24*(1), 67–91.

Lewis, A. (2019). Practice what you teach: How experiencing elementary school science teaching practices helps prepare teacher candidates. *Teaching and Teacher Education, 86*, 1–10.

McLaughlin, D., & Calabrese Barton, A. (2013). Preservice teachers' uptake and understanding of funds of knowledge in elementary science. *Journal of Science Teacher Education, 24*(1), 13–36.

Mensah, F. M., Brown, J., Titu, P., Rozowa, P., Sivaraj, R., & Heydari, R. (2018). Preservice and inservice teachers' ideas of multiculturalism: Explorations across two science methods courses in two different contexts. *Journal of Science Teacher Education, 29*(2), 128–147.

Mensah, F. M., & Jackson, I. (2018). Whiteness as property in science teacher education. *Teachers College Record, 120*, 1–38.

Miller, M., Hanley, D., & Brobst, J. (2019). The impacts of a research-based model for mentoring elementary preservice teachers in science. *Journal of Science Teacher Education, 30*(4), 357–378.

NAE. (2018). *Curriculum for the compulsory school, preschool class and school-age educare.* Stockholm: The Swedish National Agency for Education.

Naidoo, K. (2017). Capturing the transformation and dynamic nature of an elementary teacher candidate's identity development as a teacher of science. *Research in Science Education, 47*, 1331–1355.

National Research Council. (2012). *A framework for K-12 science education: Practices, crosscutting concepts, and core ideas.* Washington, DC: The National Academies Press.

Nilsson, P., & Loughran, J. (2012). Exploring the development of pre-service science elementary teachers' pedagogical content knowledge. *Journal of Science Teacher Education, 23*(7), 699–721.

Nilsson, P., & van Driel, J. (2010). Teaching together and learning together – Primary science student teachers' and their mentors' joint teaching and learning in the primary classroom. *Teaching and Teacher Education, 26,* 1309–1318.

Olson, J., Bruxvoort, C., & Vande Haar, A. (2016). The impact of video case content on preservice elementary teachers' decision-making and conceptions of effective science teaching. *Journal of Research in Science Teaching, 53*(10), 1500–1523.

Palmer, D., Dixon, J., & Archer, J. (2016). Identifying underlying causes of situational interest in a science course for preservice elementary teachers. *Science Education, 100,* 1039–1061.

Patrick, P., Mathews, C., & Tunnicliffe, S. (2013). Using a field trip inventory to determine if listening to elementary school students' conversations, while on a zoo field trip, enhances preservice teachers' abilities to plan zoo field trips. *International Journal of Science Education, 35*(15), 2645–2669.

Plonczak, I. (2010). Videoconferencing in math and science preservice elementary teachers' field placements. *Journal of Science Teacher Education, 21*(2), 241–254.

Plummer, J., & Ozcelik, A. (2015). Preservice teachers developing coherent inquiry investigations in elementary astronomy. *Science Education, 99,* 932–957.

Putnam, R., & Borko, H. (2000). What do new views of knowledge and thinking have to say about research on teacher learning? *Educational Researcher, 29*(1), 4–15.

Rivera Maulucci, M. (2011). Language experience narratives and the role of autobiographical reasoning in becoming an urban science teacher. *Cultural Studies of Science Education, 6,* 413–434.

Roth, K. (2014). Elementary science teaching. In N. Lederman & S. Abell (Eds.), *Handbook of research on science teaching* (Vol. II). New York: Routledge.

Ruiz-Gallardo, J.-R., & Reavey, D. (2019). Learning science concepts by teaching peers in a cooperative environment: A longitudinal study of preservice teachers. *Journal of the Learning Sciences, 28*(1), 73–107.

Sabel, J., Forbes, C., & Zangori, L. (2015). Promoting prospective elementary teachers' learning to use formative assessment for life science instruction. *Journal of Science Teacher Education, 26*(4), 419–445.

Saribas, D., & Akdemir, Z. (2019). Using an innovative tool in science education: Examining pre-service elementary teachers' evaluation levels on the topic of wetlands. *International Journal of Science Education, 41*(1), 123–138.

Settlage, J. (2011). Counterstories from White mainstream preservice teachers: Resisting the master narrative of deficit by default. *Cultural Studies of Science Education, 6,* 803–836.

Seung, E., Park, S., & Lee, M.-A. (2019). The impact of a summer camp-based science methods course on preservice teachers' self-efficacy in teaching science as inquiry. *Journal of Science Teacher Education, 30*(8), 872–889.

Siry, C., & Lara, J. (2012). "I didn't know water could be so messy": Coteaching in elementary teacher education and the production of identity for a new teacher of science. *Cultural Studies of Science Education, 7,* 1–30.

Smith, D., & Jang, S. (2011). Pathways in learning to teach elementary science: Navigating contexts, roles, affordances and constraints. *Journal of Science Teacher Education, 22*(8), 745–768.

Subramaniam, K. (2013). Examining the content of preservice teachers' reflections of early field experiences. *Research in Science Education, 43,* 1851–1872.

Sullivan-Watts, B., Nowicki, B., Shim, M., & Young, B. (2013). Sustaining reform-based science teaching of preservice and inservice elementary school teachers. *Journal of Science Teacher Education, 24*(5), 879–905.

Trauth-Nare, A. (2015). Influence of an intensive, field-based life science course on preservice teachers' self-efficacy for environmental science teaching. *Journal of Science Teacher Education, 26*(5), 497–519.

Tsybulsky, D., & Oz, A. (2019). From frustration to insights: Experiences, attitudes, and pedagogical practices of preservice science teachers implementing PBL in elementary school. *Journal of Science Teacher Education, 30*(3), 259–279.

Valente, B., Mauricio, P., & Faria, C. (2018). Understanding the process and conditions that improve preservice teachers' conceptions of nature of science in real contexts. *Journal of Science Teacher Education, 29*(7), 620–643.

Wallace, C., & Brooks, L. (2015). Learning to teach elementary science in an experiential, informal context: Culture, learning, and identity. *Science Education, 99,* 174–198.

Wallace, C., & Coffey, D. (2019). Investigating elementary preservice teachers' designs for integrated science/literacy instruction highlighting similar cognitive processes. *Journal of Science Teacher Education, 30*(5), 507–527.

Wang, J., & Sneed, S. (2019). Exploring the design of scaffolding pedagogical instruction for elementary preservice teacher education. *Journal of Science Teacher Education, 30*(5), 483–506.

Weller, J. (2019). Primary science preservice teacher (PST) online publishing: Is it recognized as valuable? *Journal of Science Teacher Education, 30*(7), 716–736.

Wenner, J., & Kittleson, J. (2018). Focused video reflections in concert with practice-based structures to support elementary teacher candidates in learning to teach science. *Journal of Science Teacher Education, 29*(8), 741–759.

Wilson, R., Bradbury, L., & McGlasson, M. (2015). Integrating service-learning pedagogy for preservice elementary teachers' science identity development. *Journal of Science Teacher Education, 26*(3), 319–340.

Windschitl, M., & Calabrese Barton, A. (2016). Rigor and equity by design: Locating a set of core teaching practices for the science education community. In D. Gitomer & C. Bell (Eds.), *Handbook of research on teaching* (5th ed., pp. 1099–1158). Washington, DC: American Educational Research Association.

Yoon, J., & Martin, L. (2019). Infusing culturally responsive science curriculum into early childhood teacher preparation. *Research in Science Education, 49*, 697–710.

Zangori, L., & Forbes, C. (2013). Preservice elementary teachers and explanation construction: Knowledge-for-practice and knowledge-in-practice. *Science Education, 97*, 310–330.

Zangori, L., Friedrichsen, P., Wulff, E., & Womack, A. (2017). Using the practice of modeling to support preservice teachers' reflection on the process of teaching and learning. *Journal of Science Teacher Education, 28*(7), 590–608.

8

RESEARCH ON SECONDARY SCIENCE TEACHER PREPARATION

Todd Campbell, Ron Gray, Xavier Fazio, and Jan van Driel

The variability in contexts, programmatic structures, and the organization of initial secondary science teacher preparation programs are almost as vast as the numbers of programs found within and across countries around the world (Abell, 2006; Cochran-Smith & Zeichner, 2005). In many instances, these variations in programs are outgrowths of the unique contexts within which each program is situated and necessitated by the differences in policies and contexts at local or national levels. Given this, research on secondary science teacher preparation at the programmatic level is limited, and any ambitions of standardizing initial science teacher preparation at this global level are neither desirable nor feasible. Therefore, this chapter builds on previous handbook chapters (e.g., Russell & Martin, 2007, 2014) to synthesize at a more fine-grained level what we know about secondary science teacher preparation

Our aim is to synthesize what we know about secondary preservice science teachers (S-PSTs) in relation to their characteristics (e.g., conceptions, beliefs about teaching and learning), their facility to engage students using teaching practices consequential for supporting science learning (e.g., attending to, analyzing, and responding to student thinking), and the pedagogies employed in teacher education programs (e.g., video reflection to support teacher noticing, rehearsals) that have shown promise in supporting S-PST learning. Recommendations are made in the discussion section about what we see as potential directions for the field of secondary preservice science teacher education moving forward.

Methods

Given the focus of our chapter, we searched the Web of Science academic database for research included in peer-reviewed journals in science education or teacher education. To do this, we compiled the following list of primary search terms to aggregate articles that described secondary preservice science teacher learning: "science" and "preservice" or "candidate" or "pre-service" or "intern" or "student teach" and "secondary" or "middle school" or "high school" not "induction" or "professional development." The search was also refined to English-language articles and research commentaries published between 2010 and 2020. We conducted the database search in August 2020, which led to 235 articles. After the 235 articles were identified, the authors completed an abstract analysis to sort the articles into our categories of interest. As a result of the sorting process and abstract analysis, 124 articles were excluded from our database for various reasons (e.g., focused on elementary preservice science teachers or in-service science teachers). Finally, based on research pointing to the

DOI: 10.4324/9781003098478-10

benefits of combining formal and informal literature review sampling methodologies (Niaz, 2015), a snowballing literature review sampling approach was also used to identify any additional important research or summaries as relevant articles emerged as a result of the in-depth review and analysis of our initial article pool. This led to a final pool of 115 total articles, as well as the following final number and percentage of each category of papers: S-PST characteristics (*n* = 52), S-PST practices (*n* = 26), and pedagogies supportive of S-PST learning (*n* = 40). It should be noted that some articles (*n* = 3) were categorized into two or more categories because the conceptual overlap of the articles deemed it appropriate. An in-depth review and analysis of each article in each category was completed and used as the basis for each of the sections discussed in our findings. We included all articles we referenced as part of our review in Figures 8.1 and 8.2, instead of in our reference list at the end of the chapter. Additionally, for each article reviewed, we referenced the country where the research or article summaries were conducted in the citation to illustrate the international nature of the studies included.

Findings

The Characteristics of Secondary Preservice Science Teachers in and Across Preservice Programs

For this section, 52 articles were selected and analyzed. The characteristics were defined in two broad categories in the following section headings: cognitive and non-cognitive.

Cognitive Characteristics of S-PSTs

The first category primarily included studies on the content knowledge or conceptions related to specific science topics of S-PSTs at certain moments in their program. These studies applied both quantitative (e.g., surveys, tests) and qualitative (e.g., interviews) methods and were conducted in a variety of countries. Typically, the authors of these studies took a deficit perspective (Gray et al., 2021) and reported weaknesses or misconceptions concerning PSTs' understanding of specific science topics, or concluded that S-PSTs did not perform at the expected level.

In some studies, content knowledge of S-PSTs was investigated in relation to other characteristics. To give an example of this type of study, Cebesoy and Öztekin (2016, Turkey) developed and administered a survey among a sample of S-PSTs (*n* = 355) and found that self-perceived interest in and the importance of genetics literacy issues was positively associated with participants' genetics literacy levels, as well as their attitudes towards the use of genetic information, gene therapy, and gene therapy applications.

Other studies focused on S-PSTs' knowledge and understanding of student learning and thinking in science. For example, Larkin (2012, USA) examined how S-PSTs (*n* = 14) interpreted the rationale for eliciting student ideas and found five different orientations, including viewing student ideas as evidence of content coverage; as obstacles to understanding; as tools to prime students' thinking, interest, and activity; as elements of a positive classroom environment; and as the raw material of learning.

A specific group of studies focused on S-PSTs' knowledge and views about controversial topics, most notably evolution. Studies report strong positive correlations between understanding and acceptance of evolution and understanding of the nature of science (e.g., Glaze et al., 2014, USA). However, acceptance of the theory of evolution as established scientific knowledge does not guarantee S-PSTs' understanding of it (Cofre et al., 2016, Chile). Also, S-PSTs with strong religious views tend to reject the theory of evolution and its teaching in schools (e.g., Losh & Nzekwe, 2011, USA).

S-PST Characteristics

Abrie, A. L. (2010). Student teachers' attitudes towards and willingness to teach evolution in a changing South African environment. *Journal of Biological Education, 44*(3), 102–107. https://doi.org/10.1080/00219266.2010.9656205

Akbas, A. (2010). Attitudes, self-efficacy and science processing skills of teaching certificate master's program (OFMAE) students. *Eurasian Journal of Educational Research, 10*(39), 1–12.

Akkus, H. (2013). Pre-service secondary science teachers' images about themselves as science teachers. *Journal of Baltic Science Education, 12*(2), 249–260.

Al Amoush, S., Markic, S., Muhammet, U., Erdogan, M., & Eilks, I. (2014). Beliefs about chemistry teaching and learning – A comparison of teachers' and student teachers' beliefs from Jordan, Turkey, and Germany. *International Journal of Science and Mathematics Education, 12*, 767–792. https://doi.org/10.1007/s10763-013-9435-7

Arigbabu, A. A., & Oludipe, D. I. (2010). Perceived efficacy beliefs of prospective Nigerian science teachers. *Journal of Science Education and Technology, 19*, 27–31.

Arsian, H. O., Clgdemoglu, C., & Moseley, C. (2012). A three-tiered diagnostic test to assess pre-service teachers' misconceptions about global warming, greenhouse effect, ozone layer depletion, and acid rain. *International Journal of Science Education, 34*(11), 1667–1686. https://doi.org/10.1080/09500693.2012.680618

Aydeniz, M., & Gurcay, D. (2013). Assessing quality of pre-service physics teachers' written arguments. *Research in Science & Technological Education, 31*(3), 269–287. https://doi.org/10.1080/02635143.2013.834883

Baptiste, D. J., Archer, J., & Palmer, D. (2019). Preservice teachers' ideas about how to enhance pupils' long-term interest in science. *Research in Science & Technological Education, 37*(3), 279–296. https://doi.org/10.1080/02635143.2018.1543186

Barrett, S. E., & Nieswandt, M. (2010). Teaching about ethics through socioscientific issues in physics and chemistry: Teacher candidates' beliefs. *Journal of Research in Science Teaching, 47*(4), 380–401. https://doi.org/10.1002/tea.20343

Borgerding, L. A., & Dagistan, M. (2018). Preservice science teachers' concerns and approaches for teaching socioscientific and controversial issues. *Journal of Science Teacher Education, 29*(4), 283–306. https://doi.org/10.1080/1046560X.2018.1440860

Borrachero, A. B., Brigido, M., Mellado, L., Costillo, E., & Mellado, V. (2014). Emotions in prospective secondary teachers when teaching science content, distinguishing by gender. *Research in Science & Technological Education, 32*(2), 182–215. https://doi.org/10.1080/02635143.2014.909800

Britton, S. A., & Tippins, D. J. (2015). Practice or theory: Situating science teacher preparation within a context of ecojustice philosophy. *Research in Science Education, 45*, 425–443. https://doi.org/10.1007/s11165-014-9430-1

Cansiz, N., & Cansiz, M. (2020). Profiling preservice science teachers' early experiences, beliefs about teaching, and teaching practices. *Research in Science & Technological Education*, 1–19. https://doi.org/10.1080/02635143.2020.1780207

Carpenter, S. L., Iveland, A., Moon, S., Hansen, A. K., Harlow, D. B., & Bianchini, J. A. (2019). Models are a metaphor in your brain: How potential and preservice teachers understand the science and engineering practice of modeling. *School Science and Mathematics, 119*(5), 275–286. https://doi.org/10.1111/ssm.12340

Figure 8.1 *S-PST characteristics*: Summary of the research on characteristics of secondary preservice science teachers

Cebesoy, U. B., & Oztekin, C. (2016). Relationships among Turkish pre-service science teachers' genetics literacy levels and their attitudes towards issues in genetics literacy. *Journal of Baltic Science Education, 15*(2), 159–172.

Chung-Parsons, R., & Bailey, J. M. (2019). The hierarchical (not fluid) nature of preservice secondary science teachers' perceptions of their science teacher identity. *Teaching and Teacher Education, 78*, 39–48. https://doi.org/10.1016/j.tate.2018.11.007

Çiçek, Ö., & Ilhan, N. (2017). Evaluating interest in acids–bases: Development of an acid–base interest scale (ABIS) and assessment of pre-service science teachers' interest. *Chemical Education Research and Practice, 18*, 630–640. https://doi.org/10.1039/C6RP00238B

Cofre, H., Jimenez, J., Santibanez, D., & Vergara, C. (2016). Chilean pre-service and in-service teachers and undergraduate students' understandings of evolutionary theory. *Journal of Biological Education, 50*(1), 10–23. https://doi.org/10.1080/00219266.2014.967278

Demirci, N. (2015). Prospective high school physics teachers' beliefs about teaching practices: From traditionalist to constructivist. *EURASIA Journal of Mathematics, Science, & Technology Education, 11*(3), 693–711.

Gardner, G., & Jones, G. (2011). Pedagogical preparation of the science graduate teaching assistant: Challenges and implications. *Science Educator, 20*(2), 31–41.

Glaze, A. L. Goldston, M. J., & Dantzler, J. (2014). Evolution in the southeastern USA: Factors influencing acceptance and rejection in pre-service science teachers. *International Journal of Science and Mathematics Education, 13*, 1189–1209.

Hrin, T., Milenkovic, D., & Segedinac, M. (2018). Diagnosing the quality of high school students' and pre-service chemistry teachers' cognitive structures in organic chemistry by using students' generated systemic synthesis questions. *Chemical Education Research and Practice, 19*(1), 305–318.

Hudson, P., Usak, M., Fancovicova, J., Erdogan, M., & Prokop, P. (2010). Preservice teachers' memories of their secondary science education experiences. *Journal of Science Education and Technology, 19*(6), 546–552.

Ilhan, N., Yilmaz, Z. A., & Dede, H. (2015). Attitudes of pre-service science teachers towards educational research and their science teaching efficacy beliefs in Turkey. *Journal of Baltic Science Education, 14*(2), 183–193.

Kara, Y. (2012). Pre-service biology teachers' perceptions on the instruction of socio-scientific issues in the curriculum. *European Journal of Teacher Education, 35*(1), 111–129.

Kilinc, A., Watt, H. M. G., & Richardson, P. (2012). Factors affecting teaching choice in Turkey. *Asia-Pacific Journal of Teacher Education, 40*(3):199–226.

Kim, S. Y., & Nehm, R. H. (2011). A cross-cultural comparison of Korean and American science teachers' views of evolution and the nature of science. *International Journal of Science Education, 33*(2), 197–227. https://doi.org/10.1080/09500690903563819

Kiray, S. A., & Simsek, S. (2020). Determination and evaluation of the science teacher candidates' misconceptions about density by using four-tier diagnostic test. *International Journal of Science and Mathematics Education,* https://link.springer.com/article/10.1007/s10763-020-10087-5

Krause, M., Pietzner, V., Dori, Y. J., & Eilks, I. (2017). Differences and developments in attitudes and self-efficacy of prospective chemistry teachers concerning the use of ICT in education. *Eurasia Journal of Mathematics, Science and Technology Education, 13*(8), 4405–4417. https://doi.org/10.12973/eurasia.2017.00935a

Figure 8.1 Continued

Kurt, H. (2013). Determining biology teacher candidates' conceptual structures about energy and attitudes towards energy. *Journal of Baltic Science Education*, *12*(4), 399.

Larkin, D. (2012). Misconceptions about "misconceptions": Preservice secondary science teachers' views on the value and role of student ideas. *Science Education*, *96*(5), 927–959. https://doi.org/10.1002/sce.21022

Losh, S. C., & Nzekwe, B. (2011). Creatures in the classroom: Preservice teacher beliefs about fantastic beasts, magic, extraterrestrials, evolution and creationism. *Science & Education*, *20*(5–6), 473–489. https://doi.org/10.1007/s11191-010-9268-5

Mark, S., Id-Deen, L., & Thomas, S. (2020). Getting to the root of the matter: Pre-service teachers' experiences and positionalities with learning to teach in culturally diverse contexts. *Cultural Studies of Science Education*, 1–31. https://doi.org/10.1007/s11422-019-09956-5

Markic, S., & Eilks, I. (2012). A comparison of student teachers' beliefs from four different science teaching domains using a mixed methods design. *International Journal of Science Education*, *34*(4), 589–608. https://doi.org/10.1080/09500693.2011.608092

Marshall, J. A., Petrosino, A. J., & Martin, T. (2010). Preservice teachers' conceptions and enactments of project-based instruction. *Journal of Science Education and Technology*, *19*(4), 370–386. https://doi.org/10.1007/s10956-010-9206-y

Mawyer, K. K., & Johnson, H. J. (2019). Eliciting preservice teachers' reading strategies through structured literacy activities. *Journal of Science Teacher Education*, *30*(6), 583–600. https://doi.org/10.1080/1046560X.2019.1589848

Melville, W., Campbell, T., Fazio, X., Stefanile, A., & Tkaczyk, N. (2014). Problematizing the practicum to integrate practical knowledge. *Research in Science Education*, *44*(5), 751–775. https://doi.org/10.1007/s11165-014-9404-3

Mutlu, A., & Şeşen, B. A. (2016). Evaluating of pre-service science teachers' understanding of general chemistry concepts by using two tier diagnostic test. *Journal of Baltic Science Education*, *15*(1), 79.

Oh, J. Y. (2014). Understanding the alternative conceptions of pre-service secondary science teachers about tidal phenomena based on Toulmin's argumentation. *International Journal of Science and Mathematics Education*, *12*(2), 353–370. https://doi.org/10.1007/s10763-013-9403-2

Paulick, I., Großschedl, J., Harms, U., & Möller, J. (2016). Preservice teachers' professional knowledge and its relation to academic self-concept. *Journal of Teacher Education*, *67*(3), 173–182. https://doi.org/10.1177%2F0022487116639263

Rinke, C. R., Mawhinney, L., & Park, G. (2014). The apprenticeship of observation in career contexts: A typology for the role of modeling in teachers' career paths. *Teachers and Teaching*, *20*(1), 92–107. https://doi.org/10.1080/13540602.2013.848517

Roychoudhury, A., & Rice, D. (2013). Preservice secondary science teachers' teaching and reflections during a teacher education program. *International Journal of Science Education*, *35*(13), 2198–2225. https://doi.org/10.1080/09500693.2012.678907

Rusek, M., Stárková, D., Chytrý, V., & Bílek, M. (2017). Adoption of ICT innovations by secondary school teachers and pre-service teachers within chemistry education. *Journal of Baltic Science Education*, *16*(4), 510.

Sesen, B. A. (2013). Diagnosing pre-service science teachers' understanding of chemistry concepts by using computer-mediated predict–observe–explain tasks. *Chemistry Education Research and Practice*, *14*(3), 239–246. https://doi.org/10.1039/C3RP20143K

Figure 8.1 Continued

Subramaniam, K. (2014). Student teachers' conceptions of teaching biology. *Journal of Biological Education, 48*(2), 91–97. https://doi.org/10.1080/00219266.2013.837405

Taber, K. S., & Tan, K. C. D. (2011). The insidious nature of "hard-core" alternative conceptions: Implications for the constructivist research programme of patterns in high school students' and pre-service teachers' thinking about onization energy. *International Journal of Science Education, 33*(2), 259–297. https://doi.org/10.1080/09500691003709880

Tomažič, I., & Vidic, T. (2012). Future science teachers' understandings of diffusion and osmosis concepts. *Journal of Biological Education, 46*(2), 66–71. https://doi.org/10.1080/00219266.2011.617765

Usak, M., Ozden, M., & Eilks, I. (2011). A case study of beginning science teachers' subject matter (SMK) and pedagogical content knowledge (PCK) of teaching chemical reaction in Turkey. *European Journal of Teacher Education, 34*(4), 407–429. https://doi.org/10.1080/02619768.2011.592977

Varelas, M., Morales-Doyle, D., Raza, S., Segura, D., Canales, K., & Mitchener, C. (2018). Community organizations' programming and the development of community science teachers. *Science Education, 102*(1), 60–84. https://doi.org/10.1002/sce.21321

Vázquez-Alonso, Á., García-Carmona, A., Manassero-Mas, M. A., & Bennassar-Roig, A. (2013). Spanish secondary-school science teachers' beliefs about Science-Technology-Society (STS) Issues. *Science & Education, 22*(5), 1191–1218. https://doi.org/10.1007/s11191-012-9440-1

Wheeldon, R. (2012). Examining pre-service teachers' use of atomic models in explaining subsequent onization energy values. *Journal of Science Education and Technology, 21*(3), 403–422. https://doi.org/10.1007/s10956-011-9333-0

Zhou, S., Wang, Y., & Zhang, C. (2016). Pre-service science teachers' PCK: Inconsistency of pre-service teachers' predictions and student learning difficulties in Newton's Third Law. *EURASIA Journal of Mathematics, Science and Technology Education, 12*(3), 373–385. https://doi.org/10.12973/eurasia.2016.1203a

Figure 8.1 Continued

Non-Cognitive Characteristics of S-PSTs

The second category of articles focused on non-cognitive characteristics, such as the beliefs, views, attitudes, and emotions of S-PSTs. Whereas some studies focused on teaching and learning broadly, others were focused more specifically (e.g., on acids and bases).

A group of studies focused on S-PSTs' beliefs about teaching and learning, either generally or related to the teaching of science. These studies typically report that S-PSTs tend to hold traditional, teacher-centered, or transmission-oriented beliefs (e.g., Markic et al., 2012, Germany). Other studies found a variation in S-PSTs' beliefs, for example, ranging from traditionalist to constructivist (Demirci, 2015, Turkey), or that S-PSTs from Jordan held more traditional beliefs compared to those from Germany (Al Amoush et al., 2014).

Some studies investigated S-PSTs' beliefs before and after a placement or practicum, typically reporting discrepancies between S-PSTs' expressed beliefs and their observed teaching practices (e.g., Cansiz & Cansiz, 2020, Turkey). To account for such discrepancies, Melville et al. (2017, Canada) suggested that S-PSTs' prior experiences as science learners may outweigh the impact of their teacher education program. Related to this, other studies explored how S-PSTs' personal histories influence their ideas about teaching science and becoming a science teacher. Rinke et al.

S-PST Practices

Arias, A., Criswell, B., Ellis, J. A., Escalada, L., Forsythe, M., Johnson, H., Mahar, D., Palmeri, A., Parker, M., & Riccio, J. (2020). The framework for analyzing video in science teacher education and examples of its broad applicability. *Innovations in Science Teacher Education*, *5*(4). https://innovations.theaste.org/the-framework-for-analyzing-video-in-science-teacher-education-and-examples-of-its-broad-applicability/

Borgerding, L. A., Klein, V. A., Ghosh, R., & Eibel, A. (2015). Student teachers' approaches to teaching biological evolution. *Journal of Science Teacher Education*, *26*(4), 371–392. https://doi.org/10.1007/s10972-015-9428-1

Braaten, M. (2019). Persistence of the two-worlds pitfall: Learning to teach within and across settings. *Science Education*, *103*(1), 61–91. https://doi.org/10.1002/sce.21460

Chan, K. K. H., & Yau, K. W. (2020). Using video-based interviews to investigate pre-service secondary science teachers' situation-specific skills for informal formative assessment. *International Journal of Science and Mathematics Education*. https://doi.org/10.1007/s10763-020-10056-y

Cian, H., & Cook, M. (2020). Secondary science student teachers' use of verbal discourse to communicate scientific ideas in their field placement classrooms. *Research in Science Education*, *50*(4), 1389–1416. https://doi.org/10.1007/s11165-018-9737-4

Corrigan, D. (2015). Chemistry teacher education. In R. Gunstone (Ed.), *Encyclopedia of Science Education*. Springer, Dordrecht. https://doi-org.proxy.library.brocku.ca/10.1007/978-94-007-2150-0_214

Davis, E. A., Kloser, M., Wells, A., Windschitl, M., Carlson, J., & Marino, J.-C. (2017). Teaching the practice of leading sense-making discussions in science: Science teacher educators using rehearsals. *Journal of Science Teacher Education*, *28*(3), 275–293. https://doi.org/10.1080/1046560X.2017.1302729

Fazio, X., & Volante, L. (2011). Preservice science teachers' perceptions of their practicum classrooms. *The Teacher Educator*, *46*(2), 126–144. https://doi.org/10.1080/08878730.2011.553028

Fazio, X., & Volante, L. (2015). Practicum/school experience/fieldwork. In R. Gunstone (Ed.), *Encyclopedia of Science Education*. Springer, Dordrecht. https://doi.org/10.1007/978-94-007-6165-0_401-3

Gotwals, A. W., & Birmingham, D. (2016). Eliciting, identifying, interpreting, and responding to students' ideas: Teacher candidates' growth in formative assessment practices. *Research in Science Education*, *46*(3), 365–388. https://doi.org/10.1007/s11165-015-9461-2

Kang, H. (2017). Preservice teachers' learning to plan intellectually challenging tasks. *Journal of Teacher Education*, *68*(1), 55–68. https://doi.org/10.1177/0022487116676313

Kloser, M. (2014). Identifying a core set of science teaching practices: A Delphi expert panel approach. *Journal of Research in Science Teaching*, *51*(9), 1185–1217. https://doi.org/10.1002/tea.21171

Kloser, M., Wilsey, M., Madkins, T. C., & Windschitl, M. (2019). Connecting the dots: Secondary science teacher candidates' uptake of the core practice of facilitating sensemaking discussions from teacher education experiences. *Teaching and Teacher Education*, *80*, 115–127. https://doi.org/10.1016/j.tate.2019.01.006

Lam, D. S. H., & Chan, K. K. H. (2020). Characterising pre-service secondary science teachers' noticing of different forms of evidence of student thinking. *International Journal of Science Education*, *42*(4), 576–597. https://doi.org/10.1080/09500693.2020.1717672

Figure 8.2   S-PST practices and pedagogies: Summary of secondary science teacher education pedagogies

Larkin, D. B., & Perry-Ryder, G. M. (2015). Without the light of evolution: A case study of resistance and avoidance in learning to teach high school biology. *Science Education, 99*(3), 549–576. https://doi.org/10.1002/sce.21149

Loughran, J. J. (2014). Developing understandings of practice: Science teacher learning. In N. G. Lederman & S. K. Abell (Eds.), *Handbook of Research on Science Education* (Vol. II, pp. 811–829). UK: Routledge.

Lyon, E. G. (2013). What about language while equitably assessing science? Case studies of preservice teachers' evolving expertise. *Teaching and Teacher Education, 32*, 1–11. https://doi.org/10.1016/j.tate.2012.12.006

Marshall, J. A., Petrosino, A. J., & Martin, T. (2010). Preservice teachers' conceptions and enactments of project-based instruction. *Journal of Science Education and Technology, 19*(4), 370–386. https://doi.org/10.1007/s10956-010-9206-y

Mitton-Kukner, J., & Murray Orr, A. (2015). Inquiring into pre-service content area teachers' development of literacy practices and pedagogical content knowledge. *Australian Journal of Teacher Education, 40*(5). https://doi.org/10.14221/ajte.2015v40n5.3

Mulhall, P. (2015). Physics teacher education. In R. Gunstone (Ed.), *Encyclopedia of Science Education*. Springer, Dordrecht. https://doi-org.proxy.library.brock.ca/10.1007/978-94-007-2150-0_231

Oh, P. S. (2010). How can teachers help students formulate scientific hypotheses? Some strategies found in abductive inquiry activities of earth science. *International Journal of Science Education, 32*(4), 541–560. https://doi.org/10.1080/09500690903104457

Russell, T. (2015). Secondary science teacher education. In R. Gunstone (Ed.), *Encyclopedia of Science Education*. Springer, Dordrecht. https://doi.org/10.1007/978-94-007-2150-0_248

Stroupe, D. (2016). Beginning teachers' use of resources to enact and learn from ambitious instruction. *Cognition and Instruction, 34*(1), 51–77. https://doi.org/10.1080/07370008.2015.1129337

Thompson, J., Hagenah, S., Kang, H., Stroupe, D., Braaten, M., Colley, C., & Windschitl, M. (2016). Rigor and responsiveness in classroom activity. *Teachers College Record, 118*(5), 1–58.

Yakmaci-Guzel, B. (2013). Preservice chemistry teachers in action: An evaluation of attempts for changing high school students' chemistry misconceptions into more scientific conceptions. *Chemistry Education Research and Practice, 14*(1), 95–104. https://doi.org/10.1039/C2RP20109G

Yeung, Y. Y. (2015). General science teacher education. In R. Gunstone (Ed.), *Encyclopedia of Science Education*. Springer, Dordrecht. https://doi-org.proxy.library.brock.ca/10.1007/978-94-007-2150-0_219

Pedagogies for S-PSTs

Bagdonas, A., & Silva, C. C. (2015). Enhancing teachers' awareness about relations between science and religion. *Science & Education, 24*(9–10), 1173–1199. https://doi.org/10.1007/s11191-015-9781-7

Bailie, A. L. (2017). Developing preservice secondary science teachers' pedagogical content knowledge through subject area methods courses: A content analysis. *Journal of Science Teacher Education, 28*(7), 631–649. https://doi.org/10.1080/1046560X.2017.1394773

Barnhart, T., & van Es, E. (2015). Studying teacher noticing: Examining the relationship among pre-service science teachers' ability to attend, analyze and respond to student thinking. *Teaching and Teacher Education, 45*, 83–93. https://doi.org/10.1016/j.tate.2014.09.005

Figure 8.2 Continued

Barth-Cohen, L. A., Little, A. J., & Abrahamson, D. (2018). Building reflective practices in a pre-service math and science teacher education course that focuses on qualitative video analysis. *Journal of Science Teacher Education, 29*(2), 83–101. https://doi.org/10.1080/104 6560X.2018.1423837

Casanoves, M., Salvadó, Z., González, Á., Valls, C., & Novo, M. T. (2017). Learning genetics through a scientific inquiry game. *Journal of Biological Education, 51*(2), 99–106. https://doi.org/10.1080/00219266.2016.1177569

Cetin, P. S. (2014). Explicit argumentation instruction to facilitate conceptual understanding and argumentation skills. *Research in Science & Technological Education, 32*(1), 1–20. https://doi.org/10.1080/02635143.2013.850071

Danday, B. A., & Monterola, S. L. C. (2019). Effects of microteaching multiple-representation physics lesson study on pre-service teachers' critical thinking. *Journal of Baltic Science Education, 18*(5), 692. https://doi.org/10.33225/jbse/19.18.692

Danielowich, R. M. (2014). Shifting the reflective focus: Encouraging student teacher learning in video-framed and peer-sharing contexts. *Teachers and Teaching, 20*(3), 264–288. https://doi.org/10.1080/13540602.2013.848522

Davis, E. A., Kloser, M., Wells, A., Windschitl, M., Carlson, J., & Marino, J. C. (2017). Teaching the practice of leading sense-making discussions in science: Science teacher educators using rehearsals. *Journal of Science Teacher Education, 28*(3), 275–293. https://doi.org/10.1080/1046560X.2017.1302729

Eshach, H. (2010). Using photographs to probe students' understanding of physical concepts: The case of Newton's 3rd law. *Research in Science Education, 40*(4), 589–603. https://doi.org/10.1007/s11165-009-9135-z

Feez, S., & Quinn, F. (2017). Teaching the distinctive language of science: An integrated and scaffolded approach for pre-service teachers. *Teaching and Teacher Education, 65*, 192–204. https://doi.org/10.1016/j.tate.2017.03.019

García-Carmona, A., & Acevedo-Díaz, J. A. (2017). Understanding the nature of science through a critical and reflective analysis of the controversy between Pasteur and Liebig on fermentation. *Science & Education, 26*(1–2), 65–91. https://doi.org/10.1007/s11191-017-9876-4

Janssen, F., Westbroek, H., & Doyle, W. (2014). The practical turn in teacher education: Designing a preparation sequence for core practice frames. *Journal of Teacher Education, 65*(3), 195–206. https://doi.org/10.1177%2F0022487113518584

Johnson, H. J., & Cotterman, M. E. (2015). Developing preservice teachers' knowledge of science teaching through video clubs. *Journal of Science Teacher Education, 26*(4), 393–417. https://doi.org/10.1007/s10972-015-9429-0

Johnson, H. J., & Mawyer, K. K. (2019). Teacher candidate tool-supported video analysis of students' science thinking. *Journal of Science Teacher Education, 30*(5), 528–547. https://doi.org/10.1080/1046560X.2019.1588630

Karlström, M., & Hamza, K. (2019). Preservice science teachers' opportunities for learning through reflection when planning a microteaching unit. *Journal of Science Teacher Education, 30*(1), 44–62. https://doi.org/10.1080/1046560X.2018.1531345

Karpudewan, M., Ismail, Z., & Roth, W. M. (2012). Ensuring sustainability of tomorrow through green chemistry integrated with sustainable development concepts (SDCs). *Chemistry Education Research and Practice, 13*(2), 120–127.

Figure 8.2 Continued

Kaya, E. (2013). Argumentation practices in classroom: Pre-service teachers' conceptual understanding of chemical equilibrium. *International Journal of Science Education*, *35*(7), 1139–1158. https://doi.org/10.1080/09500693.2013.770935

Kloser, M., Wilsey, M., Madkins, T. C., & Windschitl, M. (2019). Connecting the dots: Secondary science teacher candidates' uptake of the core practice of facilitating sensemaking discussions from teacher education experiences. *Teaching and Teacher Education*, *80*, 115. https://doi.org/10.1016/j.tate.2019.01.006

Küçükaydin, M., & Gökbulut, Y. (2020). The impact of a research methods course on teacher candidates' epistemological beliefs. *Australian Journal of Teacher Education*, *45*(3), 2.

Lyon, E. G., Stoddart, T., Bunch, G. C., Tolbert, S., Salinas, I., & Solis, J. (2018). Improving the preparation of novice secondary science teachers for English learners: A proof of concept study. *Science Education*, *102*(6), 1288–1318. https://doi.org/10.1002/sce.21473

Masters, H. (2020). Using teaching rehearsals to prepare preservice teachers for explanation-driven science instruction. *Journal of Science Teacher Education*, *31*(4), 414–434. https://doi.org/10.1080/1046560X.2020.1712047

McDonald, M., Kazemi, E., & Kavanagh, S. S. (2013). Core practices and pedagogies of teacher education: A call for a common language and collective activity. *Journal of Teacher Education*, *64*(5), 378–386. https://doi.org/10.1177%2F0022487113493807

Namdar, B., & Shen, J. (2016). Intersection of argumentation and the use of multiple representations in the context of socioscientific issues. *International Journal of Science Education*, *38*(7), 1100–1132. https://doi.org/10.1080/09500693.2016.1183265

Nilsson, P., & Karlsson, G. (2019). Capturing student teachers' pedagogical content knowledge (PCK) using CoRes and digital technology. *International Journal of Science Education*, *41*(4), 419–447. https://doi.org/10.1080/09500693.2018.1551642

Rutt, A., & Mumba, F. (2019). Developing preservice teachers' understanding of and pedagogical content knowledge for history of science – Integrated science instruction. *Science & Education*, *28*(9–10), 1153–1179. https://doi.org/10.1007/s11191-019-00089-3

Rutt, A. A., & Mumba, F. M. (2020). Developing secondary pre-service science teachers' instructional planning abilities for language- and literacy-integrated science instruction in linguistically diverse classrooms. *Journal of Science Teacher Education*. Advance online publication. https://doi.org/10.1080/1046560X.2020.1760431

Scharfenberg, F. J., & Bogner, F. X. (2016). A new role change approach in pre-service teacher education for developing pedagogical content knowledge in the context of a student outreach lab. *Research in Science Education*, *46*(5), 743–766. https://doi.org/10.1007/s11165-015-9478-6

Sherin, M. G., & van Es, E. A. (2005). Using video to support teachers' ability to interpret classroom interactions. *Journal of Technology and Teacher Education*, *13*, 475–491.

Sorensen, P., Newton, L., & McCarthy, S. (2012). Developing a science teacher education course that supports student teachers' thinking and teaching about the nature of science. *Research in Science & Technological Education*, *30*(1), 29–47. https://doi.org/10.1080/02635143.2012.671767

Stroupe, D., & Gotwals, A. W. (2018). "It's 1000 degrees in here when I teach": Providing preservice teachers with an extended opportunity to approximate ambitious instruction. *Journal of Teacher Education*, *69*(3), 294–306. https://doi.org/10.1177%2F0022487117709742

Figure 8.2 Continued

Thompson, J., Hagenah, S., Lohwasser, K., & Laxton, K. (2015). Problems without ceilings: How mentors and novices frame and work on problems-of-practice. *Journal of Teacher Education, 66*(4), 363–381. https://doi.org/10.1177%2F0022487115592462

Thompson, J., Windschitl, M., & Braaten, M. (2013). Developing a theory of ambitious early-career teacher practice. *American Educational Research Journal, 50*(3), 574–615. https://doi.org/10.3102%2F0002831213476334

Tolbert, S., Knox, C., & Salinas, I. (2019). Framing, adapting, and applying: Learning to contextualize science activity in multilingual science classrooms. *Research in Science Education, 49*(4), 1069–1085. https://doi.org/10.1007/s11165-019-9854-8

Tural, G., Akdeniz, A. R., & Alev, N. (2010). Effect of 5E teaching model on student teachers' understanding of weightlessness. *Journal of Science Education and Technology, 19*(5), 470–488. https://doi.org/10.1007/s10956-010-9214-y

Ucar, S., Trundle, K. C., & Krissek, L. (2011). Inquiry-based instruction with archived, online data: An intervention study with preservice teachers. *Research in Science Education, 41*(2), 261–282. https://doi.org/10.1007/s11165-009-9164-7

Walan, S. (2020). Pre-service teachers' reflections when drama was integrated in a science teacher education program. *Journal of Biological Education.* Advanced online publication. https://doi.org/10.1080/00219266.2020.1776751

Wheeldon, R. (2017). Improving preservice chemistry teachers' content knowledge through intervention activities. *International Journal of Science Education, 39*(9), 1238–1261. https://doi.org/10.1080/09500693.2017.1333655

Windschitl, M., Thompson, J., & Braaten, M. (2020). *Ambitious science teaching.* Cambridge, MA: Harvard Education Press.

Zangori, L., Friedrichsen, P. J., Wulff, E., & Womack, A. J. (2017). Using the practice of modeling to support preservice teachers' reflection on the process of teaching and learning. *Journal of Science Teacher Education, 28*(7), 590–608. https://doi.org/10.1080/104656 0X.2017.1389223

Figure 8.2 Continued

(2014, USA) found that past educational experiences are strongly connected with career choice, intended professional path, and pedagogical focus. Hudson (2010, USA) studied what S-PSTs found memorable about the characteristics of their own secondary science teachers, that is, enthusiasm and a positive attitude towards science.

A group of studies focused on S-PSTs' beliefs about teaching socioscientific issues (SSI) or science, technology, and society (STS), sometimes in relation to other issues (e.g., nature of science, social justice, or ethics). Typically, these studies report misunderstanding and confusion (e.g., between SSI and controversial topics; Borgerding & Dagistan, 2018, USA) or a gap between the need to teach SSI and feeling able to teach it (Kara, 2012, USA). Barrett and Nieswandt (2010, Canada) reported that S-PSTs' beliefs about teaching physics and chemistry using SSI originate from a range of fundamental beliefs exemplified by four archetypes representing subject-specific identities. Here, the four archetypes were identified in relation to what the S-PSTs saw as their role in (1) developing their students' science knowledge, (2) character, (3) capacity for informed citizenship, and/or (4) preparation as an ethical scientist. Mark et al. (2020, USA) studied the experiences of a group of S-PSTs during a practicum in a large, urban, culturally diverse public high school. The S-PSTs were characterized in terms of particular positionalities as indicators of more deeply held beliefs about cultural diversity and how these beliefs may influence teaching urban and culturally diverse students.

Three studies focused on how S-PSTs see themselves as science teachers. As an example, Chung-Parsons and Bailey (2019, USA) investigated the conceptions of three S-PSTs in regard to their science teacher identities, finding that they saw themselves primarily as teachers but drew upon their science identity when teaching science content and analyzing student work to facilitate learning.

Finally, a couple of studies focused on S-PSTs' emotions, motivation, and interest. For instance, Kilinc et al. (2012, Turkey) conducted a survey among a large sample of preservice teachers about their motivation to become a teacher, finding that, compared to preservice teachers of other subjects, science teacher candidates were less intrinsically motivated to become a teacher and less motivated by job security.

The studies in this section represent a remarkable distribution across countries as diverse as Nigeria, Czech Republic, China, and Canada, with Turkey and the US being most present. Most studies reviewed in this section applied a survey design, typically using existing instruments to probe the beliefs or attitudes of a cohort of S-PSTs, sometimes using two instruments to explore possible relationships between variables (such as self-efficacy beliefs and attitudes towards educational research – Ilhan et al., 2015) and very often using a convenient sample (i.e., a cohort of their own S-PSTs).

The review is dominated by deficit framed studies that conclude that the participating S-PSTs have limited knowledge of, or misconceptions about, the science topics under consideration, or that S-PSTs hold traditional views about teaching and learning science. A few studies investigated how S-PSTs' teaching beliefs or attitudes changed after a practicum, typically finding discrepancies between S-PSTs' beliefs and practice, or only minor changes in beliefs or attitudes before and after the practicum (e.g., Krause et al., 2017). Similar to the conclusion drawn by Gray et al. (2021), this leads us to the critical question of what, from a research perspective, can be learned from studies that focus on the deficiencies of S-PSTs, or that reveal that after an intervention (e.g., a practicum) S-PTSs fail to implement practices that align with their expressed beliefs, given how the literature in science teacher education we reviewed is rife with such research already (see Dillon & Avraamidou, 2020).

Studies that investigate science S-PSTs' content knowledge in relation to other variables tend to be more insightful. Most of these studies seek to relate content knowledge (measured either by a content test or through self-reports) to affective variables, such as attitudes, confidence, or self-efficacy (typically measured through questionnaires). These studies tend to report more nuanced findings, for instance, by demonstrating that the relationships between these characteristics are not straightforward but depend on the context of the study or the topic under consideration (e.g., evolution). Other studies in this selection show how S-PSTs' characteristics are influenced by their biographies and their own science education. Studies that reveal relationships between the characteristics of S-PSTs and provide insight in their origins or sources are generally more helpful to inform the design of teacher education programs than those that are limited to highlighting the deficiencies or inconsistencies of S-PSTs.

Secondary Preservice Science Teachers' Practices

S-PSTs are at the beginning of their science teaching career. As such, learning context-specific practices associated with effective science teaching, which include pre-instructional planning (e.g., deciding on grouping and science equipment organization; lesson planning), classroom enactment (e.g., time spent with hands-on vs. sensemaking discourses), and post-instruction reflection (e.g., student feedback; instructional alignment), is a daunting endeavor. What becomes clear early in their teacher education program is that S-PSTs' content background in the sciences, while important, is insufficient to refine all their science teaching practices (Loughran, 2014). What is necessary for S-PSTs is to connect their current science teaching practices learned in science teacher education programs to authentic classroom contexts. This bridging of "theory-to-practice" by S-PSTs must take into account science students' engagement, cultural characteristics, and the school environment. Thus, a relationship can be described between science teaching practice and students' outcomes (Mostafa et al., 2018). These science teaching practices can be organized broadly into inquiry, experiential, science teacher-directed, feedback, and adaptive based practices that support science students' cognitive and emotional engagement, sensemaking and discourse activities, and conceptual understanding of scientific concepts and disciplinary practices (Mostafa, 2018; OECD, 2020; Peterson, 2018). Current research on secondary science teacher education showcases this reciprocal and important relationship.

S-PST Practices and Field Experiences

Practicum experiences with students are widely recognized as vital to any science teacher education program. Although practicum experiences can vary in terms of activities and duration, ultimately these experiences consist of a period of observation, modeling, teaching, reflection, and critique with the supervision of a practicing science teacher (i.e., associate or cooperating teacher) (Fazio & Volante, 2015, Canada). When courses (science methods courses) are aligned with practice or associated field experiences, pedagogical opportunities emerge that support and enhance S-PSTs' learning and implementing teaching practices in science classrooms.

In a study of secondary science student teachers' use of verbal discourse to communicate scientific ideas during their field placement classrooms, Cian and Cook (2020, USA) identified the ubiquitous reality of student teachers' struggles during their student teaching field placement. Their detailed observations and debrief activities with S-PSTs over this period revealed that the ability to communicate their knowledge of science to their field placement students was negatively impacted by their recent science learning experiences in their university programs, with some struggling to use lectures effectively or engage students in meaningful conversation or questioning.

Braaten's (2019, USA) investigation explored the learning opportunities in field experiences for S-PSTs' uptake of ambitious science teaching (AST) practices (Thompson et al., 2016, USA). Themes in the findings included how the participation and activity structures used in the S-PSTs' science practicum classrooms presented affordances and limitations for their efforts to negotiate the practices learned during their secondary teacher program. Further, the study highlighted how the cooperating (a.k.a., associate or mentor) teacher mediated these experiences and subsequent enacting of AST practices in practicum settings. Often referred to as the "rhetoric-practice" gap, this finding can be found in many studies of secondary science teacher education programs. For instance, Fazio and Volante's (2011, Canada) mixed methods study of S-PSTs' perceptions of their science practicum classrooms using an adapted version of a well-known *Constructivist Learning Environment Survey* (Taylor et al., 1997) discovered that the S-PSTs perceived their practicum science classrooms to have limited constructivist learning elements. Further, when they attempted to implement constructivist-based science teaching practices learned during their methods course, many of the innovative constructivist teaching practices were not supported by their cooperating teachers.

With respect to planning practices, few studies address these important practices with S-PSTs during their student teaching. One example is Kang's (2017, USA) study of effective planning practices that incorporate intellectually challenging tasks into lessons, using a situative perspective on learning, examined throughout their student teaching. This analysis showed how the S-PSTs' planning practices produced artifacts of lessons that linked to the ways in which they engaged with three interrelated processes: (a) framing instructional goals, (b) constructing a lesson scenario, and (c) addressing problems encountered in practicum.

The consistencies and changes observed in the S-PSTs' trajectories of planning practices can reveal the dynamic, responsive, and contentious nature of planning found in practicum school contexts. In Marshall and colleagues' (2010, USA) study, enactment of innovative practices such as project-based instruction (PBI) by S-PSTs during their practicum, even having cogent views of reform-based instructional practices, reported time and curriculum restrictions as major barriers in their practicum schools. However, it was found that S-PSTs were more likely to enact authentic implementation regardless of their previous views about PBI if they were supported by a cooperating teacher for whom enactment of PBI was an important instructional goal.

Stroupe (2016, USA) utilized a multi-case study approach examining the practicum practices of five S-PSTs, all of whom were engaged in a secondary science methods course focused on AST practices and the provision of aligned instructional resources (Windschitl et al., 2012). When examining how these learned practices were integrated with their planning and instruction encountered in their student teaching schools where science pedagogy was considered "traditional" (i.e., lectures, confirmatory activities), the S-PSTs engaged in varied cycles of resource-driven learning based on the instructional framework they enacted. The findings point to the commitment of instructional approaches that valued students' science ideas and reasoning. While individual S-PST characteristics mediated the pedagogical reasoning and uptake of this ambitious instruction, the school contexts, which included associate teacher and science department norms and knowledge-embedded artifacts (textbooks and prescribed curricula), mediated their implementation of AST core practices in their respective practicum classroom.

These studies collectively highlight the necessity of science teacher education programs to actively support S-PSTs' knowledge construction and practices during their field experiences. This can involve co-planning and co-teaching with the cooperating teacher during field placements, and effective science teacher education methods course alignment to increase the permeability between the "two worlds" of science teacher education programs and science practicum classrooms.

Challenges Implementing Practices Because of S-PSTs Science Disciplinary Characteristics

Secondary science teacher education programs need to carefully develop specific instructional strategies for assisting S-PSTs to adapt their current teaching habits acquired by observing their own science teachers over many years, and their current views of science topics. As they change their science teaching views, the ways they typically think about how students learn science can also change along with their related practices (Russell, 2015, Canada). However, this process can take time to accomplish in methods courses, leading to challenges for implementing current disciplinary ideas and practices associated with life, physical, and earth/space sciences. This may be especially relevant with S-PSTs who are considered science disciplinary "experts" in the eyes of secondary science students.

Larkin and Perry-Ryder's (2015, USA) detailed case study of a S-PST biology teacher's resistance and avoidance of learning to teach secondary school biology, due to their own biology education, led to disengagement with evolution in the methods coursework and student teaching. In a similar way, Borgerding and colleagues' (2015, USA) study of pedagogical recommendations focused on pedagogical content knowledge for teaching evolution during methods courses and found that support of cooperative teachers for the teaching of evolution was critical in secondary science classrooms. These findings remind us of the importance of explicit teaching supports that provide strategies for teaching important and sometimes contentious topic such as evolution and other topics taught in science classrooms.

An important practice for S-PSTs is to identify scientific preconceptions of secondary science students. This helps science teachers to productively engage students with scientific phenomena and scientific practices to constructively learn disciplinary core ideas. Yakmaci-Guzel's (2013, Turkey) study of chemistry S-PSTs highlights the importance of an explicit, collaborative, and reflective approach to provide S-PSTs with experiences and the confidence to capably implement these practices during their student teaching. Without these experiences and guidance, S-PSTs are often challenged to perform these complex practices during student teaching. Indeed, the big ideas of chemistry should be clearly identified based on learning progressions, which requires careful S-PSTs' planning and decision-making practices that need to be addressed in chemistry teacher education programs (Corrigan, 2015, Australia).

For physics S-PSTs, the challenge often involves balancing conceptual understanding in physics using both quantitative and qualitative problem-solving approaches. As with most science disciplines, this balanced approach typically differs from their undergraduate physics education, which tends to focus on quantitative approaches (Mulhall, 2015, Australia).

When considering general science teacher education courses (also known as integrated science teacher education courses) for secondary schools, these courses tend to differ considerably by institution. Many times, these programs reflect the education policy context of teacher programs in terms of certification for secondary school science, or even middle grade science curriculum standards or programming (Yeung, 2015, Hong Kong). More often, general science S-PSTs do not have the undergraduate breadth of disciplinary competency or know how to effectively address multiple scientific disciplines (e.g., biology, chemistry, physics, earth and environmental sciences) under the auspices of a "general science" curriculum found in secondary schools. This has implications for the curriculum and pedagogy of disciplinary secondary teacher preparation programs.

Improving S-PSTs' Core Practices

To support S-PSTs' developing science teaching practices over the duration of their secondary teacher education programs, it is important to recognize S-PSTs' prior knowledge, views, past school experiences, and identities that impact their practices. These specific science teaching practices should be cogent to educational reforms and thus require specific science teacher preparation experiences. Many of these core practices have been identified based on expert examination of the research on science teaching practices (Kloser, 2014, USA). Topmost of these core practices include engaging students in investigations, facilitating classroom discourse and sensemaking, and eliciting and assessing student thinking and providing feedback. For S-PSTs, the performative nature of these practices can be best understood in the context of science teacher education programs.

The importance of facilitating classroom discourse and assessing student thinking equitably requires S-PSTs to develop expertise in these practices, especially for linguistically diverse students. Lyon's (2013, USA) study of S-PSTs illustrates how they became more knowledgeable about the role of language in assessment, and incorporated scientific discourse practices while assessing science students during their teaching practicum. In a related study, Mitton-Kukner and Murray (2015, Canada) investigated the development of disciplinary pedagogical content and literacy practices. While not exclusively focused on preservice science teachers, their multi-year study demonstrated S-PSTs' ability to integrate language considerations within their PCK development to facilitate classroom discourse. In a similar vein, Mawyer and Johnson (2019, USA) investigated the tacit reading strategies that preservice science teachers use to understand science texts, finding – among others – that S-PSTs employ reading strategies that attend to genre-specific text features to understand texts. These findings are relevant to inform the design of science methods and disciplinary literacy courses that scaffold the development of pedagogical content knowledge (PCK) necessary to teach reading as a disciplinary practice.

Gotwals and Birmingham's (2016, USA) study showcased themes and patterns in S-PSTs' practices to elicit, identify, interpret, and respond to secondary science students' ideas over time across a yearlong course. Specifically, they found that those S-PSTs who grew in the ways in which they elicited students' ideas for formative feedback purposes were able to adopt a more balanced, reflective approach that considered both science teacher instructional moves and student learning activities.

However, even this growth was tempered in that S-PSTs who grew in these practices did not move toward seeing students' ideas as nuanced; rather, they saw students' ideas in a dichotomous right or wrong perspective.

With respect to practices for engaging students in scientific investigations, Oh's (2010, South Korea) study revealed practical ideas of what kinds of teaching strategies can be employed in order to help science students generate scientific hypotheses and representations of their thinking. This detailed identification of these science teacher practices in a S-PST program using a combined microteaching and authentic classroom context approach is important to creating pedagogical approaches that support development of core S-PST practices.

Summary of the Research on Secondary Preservice Science Teachers' Practices

Studies in this section highlight the central importance of supporting S-PSTs' facility with the teaching practices that will be paramount to their support of learners in secondary science classrooms. Central to S-PSTs' learning to enact teaching practices in authentic classrooms in secondary schools, are the extent to which program foci and aims align with the pragmatic goals that unfold in the authentic classroom contexts of practicum science classrooms, since the "two worlds" problem of science teacher education highlights the research in this area. What came out most clearly in these studies was the need for science teacher educators to situate learning in authentic classroom contexts, while ensuring that an explicit, practice-focused, and reflective approach prompted and supported the development of S-PSTs' teaching practices.

The Pedagogies Supportive of Secondary Preservice Science Teacher Learning

The third set of articles found during the literature review involves studies of secondary science teacher education pedagogies, or the strategies, structures, and routines teacher educators use to support and scaffold secondary preservice science teacher (S-PST) learning. We see from the previous section the significant work done to characterize S-PSTs' knowledge and practice. In response, secondary science teacher educators have developed or adapted teacher education pedagogies to prepare S-PSTs toward certain goals. In the 40 identified studies on teacher education pedagogies, we identified four distinct patterns, including pedagogies aimed at S-PSTs' knowledge, reflective practices, approximations of practice, and abilities to support diverse learners.

S-PST Knowledge

The most significant number of studies in our review focused on specific pedagogies to improve S-PSTs' content knowledge, pedagogical content knowledge (PCK), and/or knowledge of the nature of science (NOS). In the domain of chemistry, for example, these included studies of short intervention sessions (Wheeldon, 2017, UK), the role of argumentation-based chemistry lessons (Cetin, 2014, Turkey; Kaya, 2013, Turkey), and a green chemistry course (Karpudewan et al., 2012, Malaysia). In biology, studies examined pedagogies such as role change activities (Scharfenberg & Bogner, 2016, Germany), the use of drama (Walan, 2020, Sweden), and simulation games (Casanoves et al., 2017, Spain) to impact S-PSTs' biological content knowledge. In the earth sciences, Ucar et al. (2011, USA) provided evidence of the effectiveness of web-based activities using archived data on S-PSTs' knowledge of tides. In physics teacher education, studies included explorations of the role of argumentation and multiple representations on S-PSTs' knowledge of nuclear energy

(Namdar & Shen, 2016, USA), 5E teaching models on the topic of weightlessness (Tural et al., 2010, Turkey), and the use of photographs to identify misconceptions (Eshach, 2010, Israel). Bailie (2017, Ethiopia) examined changes in S-PSTs' PCK after taking either a subject-specific or a general methods course, finding no distinct difference.

Scholars added to the significant history of studies on S-PSTs' knowledge of NOS over the past decade as well, largely through examining pedagogical interventions such as the role of specific courses in NOS (Sorensen et al., 2012, UK), history of science (Rutt & Mumba, 2019, USA), and research methods (Küçükaydin & Gökbulut, 2020, Turkey). Specific types of activities and pedagogies, including historical controversy activities (Garcia-Carmona & Acevedo-Diaz, 2017, Spain) and didactic sequences centered on science and religion (Bagdonas & Silva, 2015, Brazil), were included as well.

Reflective Practice

The second pattern involves studies of pedagogies to improve S-PSTs' reflective practice. Reflective practices are essential to learning, as S-PSTs are able to make sense and draw meaning from their classroom experiences as they question their own values and assumptions of student learning (Loughran, 2002). Zangori and colleagues (2017, USA), for example, used the practice of modeling to support S-PSTs' reflective practice. S-PSTs drew initial and final models of the process of teaching and learning that included what occurred before, during, and after teaching. Through constructing models of their practice, secondary S-PSTs were shown to link ideas about teaching and learning with their own reflections on practice as well as see individual growth in teacher knowledge during the semester.

Most studies of S-PST reflective practices centered on the use of video. For example, Danielowich (2014, USA) examined the types of reflections six S-PSTs responded to after using scaffolds to analyze videos of their own or peers' teaching. He concludes that "more open-ended video-framed resources provide unique opportunities for preservice teachers to reflect at varying distances from their practices that their educators can adjust to help them cultivate and integrate change-directed thinking into those practices" (p. 285). Similarly, Barnhart and van Es (2015, USA) investigated S-PSTs' capacities to attend to, analyze, and respond to student thinking throughout a course built around the use of video cases and structured frameworks to scaffold the S-PSTs into reflective work. Framed by research on teacher noticing (Erickson, 2011), they found that students enrolled in the video-based course demonstrated higher sophistication overall in their attention, analysis, and response to student thinking than those in a traditional course. This was found to be true 3 months after the course as well. They noted, however, that many students did not consistently demonstrate high levels of sophistication across the three skills in tandem, which they refer to as "mixed" noticing. Finally, Barth-Cohen, Little, and Abrahamson (2018, USA) engaged S-PSTs in research-level qualitative video analysis to foster reflective practice, finding examples of S-PSTs learning to "identify subject differences in student understanding and reflection on their growth as a teacher" (p. 14).

Other studies focused on video clubs, a well-established teacher education pedagogy in mathematics education (Sharin & van Es, 2005, USA). In a video club, a small group of participants video-record their own teaching and then meet together to view and discuss this video. Video club "invites others into classrooms they may not get the chance to observe and allows for multiple perspectives to discuss and analyze the events of the clip" (Johnson & Cotterman, 2015, p. 296, USA). To explore how S-PSTs used video clubs to restructure their overall science knowledge into science knowledge for teaching, Johnson and Cotterman (2015, USA) paired video clubs with student teaching experiences. Their findings suggest that "video clubs allowed preservice teachers to access and leverage student thinking and instructional resources to deepen their understanding of science content and trajectories for science learning" (p. 393). In a later study, Johnson and Mawyer (2019, USA) framed the use of video clubs around practice-based approaches to teacher education by engaging S-PSTs in tool-supported analysis of student thinking in their own teaching practice. They reported examples of high levels of sophisticated analysis of student thinking which led to modification of instruction based on evidence from video clips.

Approximations of Practice

Another pattern of studies centers around the ways in which teacher educators work with S-PSTs to approximate practice in the controlled setting of the teacher education program. These approximations can take many forms as S-PSTs try out various pedagogical routines, often in methods courses, and receive feedback from instructors and peers (Grossman et al., 2009). Traditionally, the well-studied pedagogy of microteaching has been used in which S-PSTs briefly rehearse specific teaching strategies in a controlled setting and reflect on these experiences (MacLeod, 1987). More recent studies of the microteaching pedagogy have looked at the role of reflection (Karlström & Hamza, 2019, Sweden) and the use of multiple representations (Danday & Monterola, 2019, Philippines) within the practice.

Rehearsals differ from microteaching in that they place a more active role for the teacher educator to provide in-the-moment guidance and feedback. Scholars of elementary science teacher education have conducted a number of important studies of rehearsals that have provided evidence that rehearsals do influence PSTs' classroom practice (e.g., Arias & Davis, 2017; Benedict-Chambers, 2016). These studies have been influential to those in secondary teacher education. Kloser et al. (2019, USA), for example, studied eight secondary S-PSTs' abilities to facilitate sensemaking discussions within their classroom instruction after engaging in a rehearsal of this practice within their science methods course. They discovered the rehearsals served as a bridge between the implicit and explicit ideas presented in the methods courses to S-PST classroom practice. They also documented the importance of discursive and representational tools on practice in supporting S-PST rehearsals. Similarly, Masters (2020, USA) studied the role of rehearsals in preparing S-PSTs to enact explanation-driven science instruction through a comparison of groups of S-PSTs who did and did not engage in rehearsals. She found that S-PSTs that engaged in rehearsals were "able to successfully engage S-PSTs [in peer instruction] in a sensemaking discussion to identify patterns in the data, introduce the claim-evidence-reasoning framework, and support students in collaboratively forming a claim as well as multiple pieces of evidence" (p. 414).

Another study focused on the use of pauses, or moments in which the teacher educator suspends the rehearsal to interact with the S-PST to address issues of practice, during rehearsals to support the facilitation of sensemaking discussions (Davis et al., 2017, USA). Rehearsals led by three teacher educators revealed that the most common purposes for pausing a rehearsal were to provide feedback and to problem-solve with the S-PST, most often about attending to student thinking and the use of language (e.g., talk moves).

Finally, Stroupe and Gotwals (2018, USA) provided a rich description of a type of extended pedagogical rehearsal they called "macroteaching." In their design experiment, S-PSTs were placed into disciplinary teaching teams of four to plan and fully enact an instructional unit over days or weeks within a methods course. In this model, the teacher educators and S-PSTs became co-designers of the methods course. In addition to "pauses" as in the previous study, a number of teacher educator-mediated learning opportunities emerged, including, among others, in-the-moment consultations, instructor highlights, "rewinds," and post-rehearsal question-and-answer sessions. The results suggest that extended rehearsals provide S-PSTs and the course instructors with opportunities to advance their teaching and vision of the profession in a methods class.

Supporting Diverse Learners

The final pattern involves studies focused on preparing S-PSTs for teaching in diverse classrooms. In a large, multi-institution study, teacher educators at six university-based programs in the United States collaboratively restructured existing science methods courses around a set of classroom instructional practices designed to, among other things, create contextualized spaces for language and literacy development targeted to English learners (Lyon et al., 2018, USA). The group identified common teacher education pedagogies and activities implemented across the sites. Researchers examined the fidelity of implementation of these pedagogies across programs as well as the ways in which S-PSTs implemented the classroom practices in field placements. While variation was found across programs, the strongest evidence of S-PST fidelity to the intervention was found for two classroom practices: facilitating student talk, and increasing student interaction. Other pedagogies in this area include science methods course activities on language- and literacy-integrated science practices in lesson planning (Rutt & Mumba, 2020, USA), the integration of a context-based instructional framework into teacher education programs (Tolbert et al., 2019, USA), and a transdisciplinary model designed to demonstrate the teaching of specialized science literacies (Feez & Quinn, 2017, Australia).

Much of the work highlighted in Figure 8.2 has occurred within traditional teacher education frameworks. However, we note a growing focus on core practices amongst scholars of teacher education (Grossman, 2018). As part of a larger movement across initial teacher education generally, secondary science teacher educators have begun aligning teacher education work with core practices in a number of different ways, as can be seen throughout the previous sections (e.g., Janssen et al., 2014, the Netherlands). This shift from specifying the necessary knowledge for teaching toward specifying teaching practices that entail knowledge-in-use has important implications for the teacher education pedagogies we employ. For example, pedagogies in a core practices framework are shaped by the pedagogical cycles described by McDonald and colleagues (2013). These cycles include specific pedagogies aimed at (1) introducing and learning about core practices (e.g., learning from video), (2) sheltered planning and practice (e.g., rehearsals), (3) analysis and moving forward (e.g., reflections), and (4) enacting practice in the field (e.g., co-teaching). It is interesting to note that a number of common teacher education pedagogies did not appear in our review, including instructor modeling and co-teaching.

An important instantiation of the core practices framework in secondary science teacher preparation has been Ambitious Science Teaching (AST) in the USA (Stroupe et al., 2020). In 2013, Thompson and colleagues proposed the AST theory of ambitious early-career practice that has been taken up and utilized in numerous contexts. The AST framework consists of a series of core practices (i.e., planning for engagement with important science ideas, eliciting students' ideas, supporting ongoing changes in thinking, and pressing for evidence-based explanations) and associated tools to inform science teaching generally, and with implications for science teacher preparation. This early theory and its more current form (Windschitl et al., 2018) have been used in studies of rehearsals (Stoupe & Gotwals, 2018, USA), S-PSTs learning with mentors (Thompson et al., 2015, USA), and the role of videos in S-PST learning (Johnson & Mawyer, 2019, USA), among others.

Discussion and Conclusion

In this chapter we worked to identify and outline what we know about initial secondary science teacher preparation, especially in relation to the characteristics of S-PSTs, their facility with science teaching practices, and the pedagogies supportive of S-PST learning. While we believe our review provides a fairly comprehensive snapshot of research related to secondary science teacher preparation, we caution that our criteria for establishing our database may not have captured all articles during the time period, especially since articles included were only in English, potentially introducing an English-language bias connected to the research that was conducted. In this context, cumulatively from what we laid out in the preceding sections in our review, we believe the following three salient themes emerged that we think should be further considered as we seek to move the field of S-PST education forward: (a) a shift from a deficit framing to an asset framing, (b) recognition of the importance of core practices in science teacher education, and (c) a need for cohesive instructional and programmatic frameworks around which knowledge of S-PST can be built. We describe each, in turn, in this section.

Consequential in our review over the last decade, comparable to science education research focused on student learning in science (see Smith et al., 1993), was how much of the S-PST research was framed from a deficit perspective. We believe that S-PST knowledge and experiences can be used as stepping stones on which to build teacher knowledge and practices. Instead, much research has focused on S-PST's deficiencies in relation to their knowledge and practices or on an intervention that might serve to remedy their deficiencies. This was seen in the research on characteristics, where we noted how our review leads us to the critical question of whether there is a need for more studies that conclude that the participating S-PSTs have limited knowledge of, or have misconceptions about, the science topics under consideration, or that S-PSTs hold traditional views about teaching and learning science. Our conclusion coincides with that of Gray et al. (2021) in their recent systematic review of preservice science teacher knowledge studies, as well as with Dillon and Avraamidou (2020), who ask, "Do we really need another study that pre-service teachers don't know much about anything?" (p. 4).

In our conclusion of the pedagogies supportive of S-PST learning, we noted how a growing focus on core practices amongst scholars on teacher education (Grossman, 2018) has begun to influence the pedagogies employed by science teacher educators, especially in the USA. Here, a focus on core practices can be understood as a focus on practices that can "equip beginners with capabilities for the fundamental elements of professional work and that are unlikely to be learned on one's own through experience" (Ball et al., 2009, p. 460). Facility with these core practices can assist preservice teachers in engaging students in the complex moments of sensemaking as they try to apply knowledge (Grossman et al., 2009; Lampert & Graziani, 2009) by providing strategies and techniques that are exercised with sound judgment in context-specific ways (Ball & Forzani, 2007; Grossman et al., 2009; Zeichner, 2012).

Connected to the great potential of a shift toward core practices, we also noted the emergence and promise of overarching frameworks supportive of S-PST learning like Ambitious Science Teaching (AST) (Thompson et al., 2013; Windschitl et al., 2018), or those identified like that from Janssen and colleagues who have proposed a repertoire for teaching biology with accompanying tools (see Janssen & Van Driel, 2017; De Boer et al., 2016, 2019). In this, we believe overarching frameworks supportive of science teacher education are necessary, since Glazer and Peurach (2015) note how without some level of collegial forms of collaboration, common language, and pursuits, there is a danger of continued struggle to develop knowledge of teaching in the field of education. Here, as Campbell et al. (2019) noted, AST and other frameworks, like those proposed by Janssen and colleagues, can support geographically dispersed groups of science teacher educators to engage in common forms of language and performances in the development of knowledge and effective practices in science teaching, while concurrently leading to the development of tools capable of anchoring collaborative work and knowledge building in the field of science teacher education.

In the end, we believe the research we examined over the last decade is important, as it helps us better understand the S-PST characteristics, practices, and pedagogies supportive of S-PST learning, while also providing the field with a sense of the collective promise of the work that is not often considered as researchers undertake individual research projects. We also believe this opportunity to pause and survey the field of S-PST research literature was productive and needed, as it provided us a chance to consider and propose potentially productive directions for the field moving forward that we hope are pursued by our community of S-PST scholars.

References

Abell, S. K. (Ed.). (2006). *Science teacher education: An international perspective* (Vol. 10). New York, NY: Kluwer Academic Publishers. https://link.springer.com/content/pdf/bfm%3A978-0-306-47222-0%2F1.pdf

Arias, A. M., & Davis, E. A. (2017). Supporting children to construct evidence-based claims in science: Individual learning trajectories in a practice-based program. *Teaching and Teacher Education, 66*, 204–218. https://doi.org/10.1016/j.tate.2017.04.011

Ball, D. L., & Forzani, F. M. (2007). What makes education research "educational"? *Educational Researcher, 36*(9), 529–540.

Ball, D. L., Sleep, L., Boerst, T. A., & Bass, H. (2009). Combining the development of practice and the practice of development in teacher education. *The Elementary School Journal, 109*(5), 458–474.

Benedict-Chambers, A. (2016). Using tools to promote novice teacher noticing of science teaching practices in post-rehearsal discussions. *Teaching and Teacher Education, 59*, 28–44. https://doi.org/10.1016/j.tate.2016.05.009

Campbell, T., Verma, G., Melville, W., & Park, B. (2019). JSTE as a forum for engaging in knowledge generation and discourses in science teacher education, equity and justice-focused science teacher education, and professional learning for science teacher education scholars. *Journal of Science Teacher Education, 30*(5), 429–433.

Cochran-Smith, M., & Zeichner, K. M. (Eds.). (2005). *Studying teacher education: The report of the AERA panel on research and teacher education*. Mahwah, NJ: Lawrence Erlbaum Associates

De Boer, E., Dam, M., Janssen, F. J. J. M., & Van Driel, J. H. (2019). Perspective-based generic questions as a tool to promote student biology teacher questioning. *Research in Science Education*. https://doi.org/10.1007/s11165-019-9853-9

De Boer, E., Janssen, F. J. J. M., & Van Driel, J. H. (2016). Using an attribution support tool to enhance the teacher efficacy of student science teachers. *Journal of Science Teacher Education, 27*, 303–324. https://doi.org/10.1007/s10972-016-9461-8

Dillon, J., & Avraamidou, L. (2020). Towards a viable response to COVID-19 from the science education community. *Journal for Activist Science & Technology Education, 11*(2), 1–6. https://doi.org/10.33137/jaste.v11i2.34531

Erickson, F. (2011). On noticing teacher noticing. In M. G. Sherin, V. R. Jacobs, & R. A. Philipp (Eds.), *Mathematics teacher noticing: Seeing through teachers' eyes* (pp. 17–34). New York, NY: Routledge.

Glazer, J. L., & Peurach, D. J. (2015). Occupational control in education: The logic and leverage of epistemic communities. *Harvard Educational Review, 85*(2), 172–202.

Gray, R. E., McDonald, S., & Stroupe, D. (2021). What you find depends on how you see: Examining asset and deficit perspectives of preservice science teachers' knowledge and learning. *Studies of Science Education*. Advance online publication. https://doi.org/10.1080/03057267.2021.1897932

Grossman, P. (2018). *Teaching core practices in teacher education*. Cambridge, MA: Harvard Education Press.

Grossman, P., Compton, C., Igra, D., Ronfeldt, M., Shahan, E., & Williamson, P. (2009). Teaching practice: A cross-professional perspective. *Teachers College Record, 111*(9), 2055–2100.

Grossman, P., Hammerness, K., & McDonald, M. (2009). Redefining teaching, re-imagining teacher education. *Teachers and Teaching, Theory and Practice, 15*(2), 273–289.

Janssen, F. J. J. M., & Van Driel, J. H. (2017). Developing a repertoire for teaching biology. In A. Sickel & S. Witzig (Eds.), *Designing and teaching the secondary science methods course: An international perspective* (pp. 91–107). Rotterdam: Sense Publishers.

Lampert, M., & Graziani, F. (2009). Instructional activities as a tool for teachers' and teacher educators' learning in and for practice. *Elementary School Journal, 109*(5), 491–509.

Loughran, J. J. (2002). Effective reflective practice in search of meaning in learning about teaching. *Journal of Teacher Education, 53*(1), 33–43. https://doi.org/10.14221/ajte.2020v45n3.2

Macleod, G. (1987). Microteaching: End of a research era? *International Journal of Educational Research, 11*(5), 531–541.

McDonald, M., Kazemi, E., & Kavanagh, S. S. (2013). Core practices and pedagogies of teacher education: A call for a common language and collective activity. *Journal of Teacher Education, 64*(5), 378–386. https://doi.org/10.1177%2F0022487113493807

Mostafa, T., Echazarra, A., & Guillou, H. (2018). *The science of teaching science: An exploration of science teaching practices in PISA 2015.* OECD Education Working Papers, No. 188, OECD Publishing, Paris, https://doi.org/10.1787/f5bd9e57-en.

Niazi, M. (2015). Do systematic literature reviews outperform informal literature reviews in the software engineering domain? An initial case study. *Arabic Journal of Science and Engineering, 40*(3), 845–855. https://doi.org/10.1007/s13369-015-1586-0

OECD (2020). *Global teaching InSights.* Paris: OECD Publishing. https://doi.org/10.1787/20d6f36b-en

Peterson, A., Dumont, H., Lafuente, M., & Law, N. (2018). *Understanding innovative pedagogies: Key themes to analyse new approaches to teaching and learning.* OECD Education Working Paper No. 172. https://doi.org/10.1787/9f843a6e-en

Russell, T., & Martin, A. K. (2007). Learning to teach science. In S. Abell & N. Lederman (Eds.), *Handbook of research on science education* (pp. 1151–1178). Mahwah, NJ: Lawrence Erlbaum Associates.

Russell, T., & Martin, A. K. (2014). Learning to teach science. In S. Abell & N. Lederman (Eds.), *Handbook of research on science education* (pp. 1151–1176). Mahwah, NJ: Lawrence Erlbaum Associates.

Smith, J., diSessa, A., & Rochelle, J. (1993). Misconceptions reconceived: A constructivist analysis of knowledge in transition. *Journal of Learning Sciences, 3*, 115–163.

Stroupe, D., Hammerness, K., & McDonald, S. (2020). *Preparing science teachers through practice-based teacher education.* Boston, MA: Harvard University Press.

Taylor, P. C., Fraser, B. J., & Fisher, D. L. (1997). Monitoring constructivist classroom learning environments. *International Journal of Educational Research, 27*(4), 293–302.

Thompson, J., Windschitl, M., & Braaten, M. (2013). Developing a theory of ambitious early-career teacher practice. *American Educational Research Journal, 50*(3), 574–615. https://doi.org/10.3102%2F0002831213476334

Windschitl, M., Thompson, J., & Braaten, M. (2018). *Ambitious science teaching.* Cambridge, MA: Harvard Education Press.

Windschitl, M., Thompson, J., Braaten, M., & Stroupe, D. (2012). Proposing a core set of instructional practices and tools for teachers of science. *Science Education, 96*(5), 878–903.

Zeichner, K. (2012). The turn once again toward practice-based teacher education. *Journal of Teacher Education, 63*, 376–382.

9

UNDERSTANDING THE ROLE OF FIELD EXPERIENCES IN PRESERVICE SCIENCE TEACHER PREPARATION

David Stroupe

Where should preservice science teachers (PSTs) learn to teach? Science teacher educators agree on part of the answer to this question – PSTs should have opportunities to interact with K–12 children in various community-based locations. This chapter focuses on a particular category of opportunities for PSTs to interact with K–12 children that is built into many teacher preparation programs, but that is surprisingly underexamined and idiosyncratic: field experiences. While most teacher preparation programs design and enact some version of field experiences for PSTs, there is little agreement about the timing, duration, structure, effectiveness, or purpose of such experiences. In this chapter, field experiences are defined and distinguished from other learning opportunities. Next, given an examination of relevant international literature – 58 peer-reviewed articles examining field experiences in 10 different countries – three assertions are made about such research, concluding with recommendations and lingering questions for the field.

Identifying Literature to Review

Relevant articles were initially identified by searching three academic databases (Web of Science, Scopus, and Mendeley), focusing on peer-reviewed journals and handbooks. Using the keywords "field experience" and "field placement," I searched from the years 1900–2020 and generated an initial list of 300 initial manuscripts. Initially, I examined the abstracts of each manuscript, looking for the location, purpose, and study participants. After an initial examination, I narrowed the list of studies to 58 for a final review, which are international in scope.

Defining Field Experiences

The term "field experience" is frequently used as an umbrella term to describe a range of learning opportunities for PSTs, including:

- Clinical experiences in which PSTs are placed with a school-based mentor teacher for a predetermined duration of time to serve as lead instructors for one or more classes (clinical experiences might also be considered "student teaching");
- A partnership in which PSTs enter a site of learning, with or without K–12 children present – at the behest of researchers for the purpose of collecting data that may or may not pertain to the PSTs' teacher preparation program;

DOI: 10.4324/9781003098478-11

- Opportunities for PSTs to engage in field-based science research;
- Field trips to sites outside of classrooms, such as museums and outdoor education centers;
- "Discovery days" in which potential science majors learn about various science disciplines in efforts to recruit them into science teaching;
- Demonstration days in which future teachers enact entertaining demonstrations of STEM-based activities and phenomena for (often) elementary-aged students.

Each of these opportunities – described as a "field experience" by various researchers – illustrates the range of which the term has been applied. However, none of the opportunities listed above captures how many preparation programs help PSTs interact with K–12 children prior to a clinical experience.

Given the range of uses by researchers, the necessary task of identifying characteristics of "field experiences" can provide clarity about this distinct niche of learning opportunities and research. Across the 58 reviewed articles, Subramaniam (2013) helps to clarify the distinctiveness of field experiences for science PSTs that aid in defining the term, all of which are described further in the chapter. Field experiences are part of a teacher preparation program that occur prior to clinical (student teaching) opportunities. Often, field experiences are connected to PSTs' specific coursework. A primary purpose of field experiences seems to be for PSTs to interact with K–12 children, ideally while engaged in some form of instruction. Field experiences can occur in K–12 classrooms for a few hours each week but can also take place in informal settings. Often, teacher education programs, and individual course instructors, collect data about PSTs' participation in field experiences. Such data might be used for accreditation purposes, and for research about PSTs' learning (Wilson et al., 2001). These general characteristics help situate field experiences as a distinct learning opportunity for PSTs during their teacher preparation experience.

Field Experiences for Preservice Teachers

Given the seeming ubiquity of field experiences in elementary and secondary teacher preparation programs, there are rich opportunities for research about PSTs and their learning. While initial research provides a baseline for understanding the potential successes and challenges of field experiences, I propose that field experiences are an underexplored area for teacher educators to design and examine how PSTs might learn in settings with K–12 students.

Showcasing 1970s Field Experiences

Before examining more current research about field experiences, note that the 1970s saw a rise in the quantity and description of field experiences in major science education journals. Multiple scholars, including Frankel (1972) and Collea (1974), argued that field experiences might be an important avenue for PSTs to have improved and enriched attitudes about children and teaching, especially at the elementary level. Given such calls for field experiences and for research about such experiences, the prominent journal *Science Education* featured teacher educators' descriptions of programmatic field experiences, as well as methods used to collect and analyze data about PST learning. Several examples are highlighted here.

Capie (1973) reported on the University of Georgia's (UGA) connection with "portal schools" in which PSTs experience "life situations rather than life like situations" (p. 71). UGA's program developed three goals for PSTs in field experiences: (1) understanding science as an enterprise of building knowledge, (2) understanding children and learning processes, and (3) gaining familiarity with philosophies and resources available for teaching. To accomplish such goals, UGA attempted to link a learning stance for K–12 students – that students should pick topics to investigate at their own pace – to the methods course structure by allowing PSTs to complete course modules at their own pace. While there is little description of the data collected, Capie notes that the program was documenting positive changes in attitudes about teaching among elementary PSTs.

The University of Florida was featured twice, in 1973 and 1974, as program faculty presented two features of the preparation program. First, Oberlin and Sanders (1973) compared PSTs in a newly developed field experience-based route and PSTs who remained solely within the university during methods courses. Using a measure of PSTs' science knowledge (the Stanford Achievement Test of science knowledge), the authors found that content knowledge between comparison groups was both similar and "weak," noting that although "all of the students have taken 15 or more term hours of content science, some scored lower than the children they would be teaching. According to the norm tables, 33% of the New Elementary Program students and 47% of the regular program students scored lower than the top 10% of sixth grade students" (pp. 333–334). Oberlin and Sanders thus wondered about the value of field experiences in terms of PST learning. Second, Rowe (1974) advocated for a different purpose of the University of Florida field experiences from that of her colleagues – that PSTs should become good decision-makers who think ethically about how to respond to student thinking (Rowe is also famous for describing "wait time" in classroom interactions). Similar to Capie and UGA, Rowe worked in conjunction with mentor teachers at placement schools to create a plan for completion of methods coursework and field teaching for each PST. Thus, PSTs would learn to become "self-directed people" (p. 375) who could take responsibility for their actions, especially with regards to talking with students in classrooms. Interestingly, Rowe described how the program considered the "feedback loop" of PSTs' experiences, noting that PST success in the teacher preparation program depended on their well-being in all avenues of life.

Lunetta (1975) described the "field-based clinical experiences" at the University of Iowa in which they purposefully designed opportunities for PSTs to encounter the theories of pedagogy and to immediately put those theories into practice in classrooms. Lunetta noted that teacher preparation programs can only simulate classroom experiences, yet interacting with students is a crucial skill for PSTs to learn. Therefore, beginning in their sophomore year, PSTs enter into "self-paced" secondary school classes so that they could have opportunities to rehearse individualized instruction techniques. In the classrooms, PSTs enacted mini-lessons, engaged in "case studies" of two students to better understand their lives and needs, video-recorded their teaching for analysis in methods class, and used computer simulations to understand how teachers can serve as a pedagogical authority while developing empathy for students. (Remember – this is 1975!) Researchers collected various forms of data, including the video recordings, classroom artifacts, lesson plans and reflections, audio recordings of PST conversations with students, and questionnaires. Overall, the University of Iowa program reported positive outcomes for most PSTs in the program.

Finally, while most articles described programs from large research-orientated universities, several small teacher preparation programs received space in *Science Education*. For example, Battaglini et al. (1975) taught at the College of Saint Teresa (which closed in 1989). Battaglini and colleagues articulated three program principles, in which PSTs should: (1) have opportunities to unify methods of scientific investigation with methods of teaching; (2) experience the joy of discovery, similar to what scientists feel, and what we hope students experience in elementary classrooms; and (3) have freedom to select science and pedagogical content they wish to investigate because such freedom matches what we know about student learning. Such goals began during the PSTs' junior year in college, in which they engaged in outdoor investigations with a focus on environmental ethics. The investigations helped the PSTs prepare micro-lessons of 10–15 minutes several days per week for elementary school students. Impressively, the faculty allowed PSTs open access to college-based laboratory equipment that the PSTs were free to borrow and use with children. Across measures of PSTs, which included attitude testing and classroom observations, the faculty reported positive results in terms of PSTs' changing attitudes about teaching, students, and learning outdoors, as well as better use of time in classrooms with regard to interacting with students.

There are four shared themes across the field experiences highlighted in the 1970s in *Science Education* that might be worth revisiting today. First, each teacher preparation program called for PSTs to enact pedagogical rehearsals with K–12 students rather than rehearse teaching in methods courses alone in order to bridge divides between pedagogical theories and actual instruction. Second, programs pushed PSTs to link pedagogical actions they planned and enacted with student outcomes, which were more immediately visible in classrooms. Third, each program hoped PSTs' attitudes about teaching and students might shift if given opportunities to interact with the realities of schooling and to build relationships with children. Finally, most programs aimed to achieve conceptual consistency between theories of student and PST learning; specifically, multiple articles noted that if K–12 students learn best with "freedom" and "choice" of activities and topics, then teacher education programs should also allow "freedom" and "choice" for PSTs to complete their preparation process.

Examining PSTs in Field Experiences

While more teacher preparation programs designed field experiences after the 1970s, research about their potential and effectiveness remains limited. Here, three assertions are described based on a review of literature regarding field experiences for PSTs.

Assertion 1: The Location and Duration of Field Experiences Varies

While science education assumes that field experiences might be important for PSTs, a review of the literature shows that there is no consensus either about how long field experiences should last or about the ideal location in which field experiences should occur. Across the reviewed studies, field experiences occurred in six locations.

Location 1: Schools. Schools served as the most popular site of field experiences for PSTs. All school-based field experiences had a similar structure on an organizational level – PSTs spent some time in university-based methods courses, and then entered school-based classrooms to interact with children and teachers. The duration of such field experiences, however, varied greatly (see Table 9.1 for examples).

Table 9.1 Examples of the varied duration of school-based field experiences

Duration	Study
1 day per week for 3 hours	Min et al. (2020)
15 hours in 1 semester	Fitzgerald (2020)
1 full day per week for 15 weeks	Kinskey (2018)
2 full days during a semester	Perkins (2019)
3–4 days per semester	Hanuscin and Zangori (2016)
60 hours during 1 academic year	Coddington and Swanson (2019)
Observing a classroom all semester, PSTs planned and taught 3 lessons	Brown and Crippen (2016)
PSTs plan and teach 2 lessons to students	Forbes (2013)
2 full days per week	Settlage et al. (2009)
7 weeks, 2 hours per week	Ohana (2004)
70 hours in one semester	Hancock and Gallard (2004)
PSTs plan and teach 1 lesson per week	Nelson (2008)
PSTs teach science to 3 different grade levels 3 times throughout the semester	Wenner and Kittleson (2018)

Location 2: Summer camp. While most field experiences occurred in classrooms, three studies designed field experiences for PSTs in summer camps. First, Wallace and Brooks (2015) worked with a summer camp for grades K-7, which was open to the general public. Eighteen PSTs – who were enrolled in a summer methods course – spent 40 hours of time in the camp (alongside 35 hours of methods class time). The PSTs split into groups of six to plan, teach, and evaluate informal science lessons to the camp children. Second, Franks and Mcglamery (2016) wanted White PSTs to engage in culturally responsive teaching with African-American girls in a summer STEM camp. In conjunction with summer methods courses, the PSTs taught four 90-minute sessions to two to three children in the STEM camp. Third, Seung et al. (2019) examined how a summer camp-based science methods course impacted elementary PSTs' teaching by providing PSTs with a 4-week-long methods course that included teaching (two to three 50-minute lessons) during a 10-day summer science camp for grades K-6 students.

Location 3: After-school clubs. Two studies featured examples of PSTs participating in after-school clubs. Lux et al. (2017) examined PSTs' participation in "Tech Club," an after-school program aimed at helping students better understand and use technology. PSTs attended and taught in Tech Club approximately 1 day per week for 1 hour each visit during a 6-week period. Cartwright and Hallar (2018) utilized an after-school club for PSTs to teach 15 lessons (1 hour each lesson) to examine how PSTs developed a "growth mindset" about teaching.

Location 4: Community-based placements. Beyond school-based camps and clubs, PSTs also had opportunities to interact with students in community-based field experiences. Harlow (2012) examined PSTs' interactions with people during "family science nights," while Heineke and colleagues' (2019) "In Teaching for Change" program placed PSTs in community sites for 80% of their time while learning to teach. Similarly, Calabrese Barton (2000) conducted a summer methods course in which PSTs spent 4 hours per week in a homeless shelter, attempting to link ideas about multicultural education to students' lived experiences.

Location 5. Undergraduate laboratory courses. While most field experiences focused on placing PSTs in locations with K–12 students, Weld and French (2001) asked PSTs to observe undergraduate laboratory courses taught by graduate students, who themselves were learning about inquiry-based teaching. For this field experience, PSTs helped plan and teach 3 hours per week for undergraduate biology laboratory courses.

Location 6. Videoconference. While all other field experiences sites required the physical presence of PSTs to interact with children, Plonczak (2010) used videoconference technology to engage in virtual instruction, beaming PSTs in Boston to a school in Queens, New York. Placed in groups of two or three, 15 PSTs virtually planned and taught several science lessons (each lesson lasted 30–45 minutes), and was followed by collective discussion and reflection between PSTs, the host teacher, and the methods course instructor.

Looking across all five locations, there is little consensus about how long and where field experiences should occur. However, there is general agreement that PSTs should have opportunities to teach students in a community-based location (schools or informal sites), in conjunction with a methods course, prior to their clinical experience.

Assertion 2: Framing, Data Collection, and Data Analysis Varies

Similar to the different locations and durations of field experiences, the researchers' theoretical and methodological framing, data collection, and data analysis of PSTs during field experiences vary greatly.

Theoretical and methodological framing. Given the range of perspectives on PST thinking and learning among science educators, there is a wide continuum of how researchers framed and designed studies of PSTs in field experiences. The majority of research reviewed for this chapter utilized cognitive learning perspectives to frame PSTs' experiences. Cognitive perspectives view learning as an individual process in which information is acquired from local contexts and environments, is organized into internal structures such as concepts or schema, and changes states over time (Danish & Gresalfi, 2018). Of the literature reviewed for this chapter, researchers examined various domains of PSTs' knowledge, their shifting attitudes, beliefs, perceptions, and conceptions (see Assertion 3 for details), as well as one study using a "growth mindset" lens (Cartwright & Hallar, 2018). Several studies utilized "hybrid" lenses between cognitive and sociocultural perspectives, such as situated perspectives (Wallace & Brooks, 2015) and situative perspectives (Carrier et al., 2017). Finally, multiple articles used sociocultural theories. Sociocultural perspectives generally view learning in terms of ongoing changes in practice. Such perspectives see knowledge and participation as inextricably linked to the context in which individuals interact with actors, practices, and tools whose roles have been negotiated over time and thus are both historical and cultural (Danish & Gresalfi, 2018). Of the literature reviewed for this chapter, researchers examined how PSTs participated in communities of practice (Coddington & Swanson, 2019), and investigated PSTs' thinking and actions given their participation in specific contexts (Heineke et al., 2019).

Since theoretical framing shapes a study's methodology, researchers used a range of data collection and analysis techniques to examine PSTs in field experiences. Some researchers utilized quantitative measures aimed at determining relationships between field experiences and PSTs' thinking and actions, often through the lens of cognitive learning theories. For example, Forbes (2013) examined PST artifacts using regression modeling. Several studies used extra treatment groups in which some PSTs received additional resources and experiences that other peer PSTs were denied (e.g., Ohana, 2004; Sunal, 1982; Weaver et al., 1979). Other researchers utilized mixed methods (Fitzgerald, 2020; Lux et al., 2017; Seung et al., 2019) and qualitative approaches, which included:

- Case studies (Heineke et al., 2019; Kinskey, 2018);
- Ethnographies (Wallace & Brooks, 2015);
- Design-based research (Brown & Crippen, 2016);
- Phenomenological analysis (Varma & Hanuscin, 2008);
- Community-based service learning (Calabrese Barton, 2000; Cone, 2012);
- Lesson study with PST physics teachers in Norway (Juhler, 2016);
- Grounded theory (Ohana, 2004).

Each theoretical and methodological framing offered different perspectives on PSTs' field experiences (see Assertion 3).

Data collection and analysis. Given the varied framings of PSTs in field experiences, researchers employed multiple techniques for data collection and analysis. For example, studies utilizing cognitive perspectives often examined how some feature of PSTs changed, including attitudes, beliefs, knowledge, perceptions, and conceptions, To measure such changes, researchers created or used at least 14 different instruments (see Table 9.2).

Such a range of instruments simultaneously illustrates the suite of resources available for researchers to examine changing features of PSTs in field experiences, and the complexity of creating a shared understanding of how to investigate PSTs given the multitude of means to examine their changes.

Beyond instruments designed to capture changing PST features, researchers created many opportunities to examine PSTs in field experiences, as well as collected and analyzed an array of data (see Table 9.3).

Looking across the theoretical and methodological framing, as well as data collection and data analysis of PSTs during field experiences, there is a wide range of how and why researchers examined

Table 9.2 Instrument types

Instrument type	Purpose
Semantic Differential Instrument for Science Teaching (SDIS; Sunal, 1982)	To measure attitudes about science and pedagogical concepts
Science Teaching Efficacy Belief Instrument (STEBI-B; Cannon & Scharmann, 1996; Wilson, 1996)	To measure science teaching self-efficacy and outcome expectancy in preservice elementary teachers.
Perceptions of teaching instruments (Faikhamta et al., 2011)	To gauge shifts in PSTs' perceptions of teaching.
Pedagogical Content Knowledge measures (Perkins, 2019)	A series of instruments aiming to quantify PSTs' pedagogical content knowledge
Growing Awareness Inventory (GAIN; Brown & Crippen, 2016)	A structured observation protocol for building the awareness of PSTs for resources in mathematics and science classrooms that can be used for culturally responsive pedagogy
Professional Environment for Teaching Survey (PETS; Şahin & White, 2015)	This checklist consists of items generated from the analysis of qualitative and quantitative data gathered from teachers' written responses to open-ended questions and to formal and informal interview and debriefing sessions
The Science Attitude Scale for Preservice Elementary Teachers (Weaver et al., 1979)	To measure PSTs' attitudes about science and science concepts
The Science Teaching Attitude Scales (Weaver et al., 1979)	To measure PSTs' attitudes about pedagogical concepts
Sixteen Personality Factor Questionnaire (Weaver et al., 1979)	A "comprehensive" measure of normal-range personality
Rokeach Dogmatism Scale Form E (Weaver et al., 1979)	To measure PSTs' open or closed-mindedness about science
Shrigley-Johnson Science Attitude Scale (Harty et al., 1984)	To measure PSTs' changing attitudes towards science teaching
PMT Questionnaire (Horak, 1981)	A survey aimed at capturing PSTs' attitudes about classroom management and control, use of punishment in the classroom, and trust of students
Views of Scientific Inquiry (VOSI) questionnaire (Lotter et al., 2009)	An open-ended instrument that assesses views of scientific inquiry
Reactions to a Field Experience Evaluation Form (FEEF; Wilson, 1996)	To gauge PSTs' perceptions of the ability of field experiences to address prestated field experience outcomes

PSTs' experiences, which data to collect, and how the data should be analyzed. Such a range exemplifies how theoretical framing and methodologies shape the ways in which researchers decide how to ask questions, hope to make an impact on practices and policies, and select target audiences for the dissemination of their work.

Assertion 3: Field Experiences May Help PSTs Change Internally and Externally

While there is variability among durations and locations of field experiences and methodologies for analysis, there is general agreement that the ideal outcome of field experiences is that PSTs change internally (for example, beliefs and perceptions) and externally (pedagogical actions). Looking across studies, four categories of such changes emerged.

Table 9.3 Data collection and analysis of PSTs in field experiences

Data collection/analysis technique	Study examples
Classroom/site observations	Boyer (2016); Cartwright and Hallar (2018); Faikhamta et al. (2011); Forbes (2013); Min et al. (2020); Ohana (2004); Settlage et al. (2009); Varma and Hanuscin (2008)
Interviews (includes structured, semi-structured, and focus group)	Bulunuz (2012); Calabrese Barton (2000); Carrier et al. (2017); Cartwright and Hallar (2018); Cone (2012); Faikhamta et al. (2011); Fletcher and Luft (2011); Fitzgerald (2020); Matkins et al. (2014); Settlage et al. (2009); Varma and Hanuscin (2008); Weld and French (2001)
Reflections on teaching/journals	Calabrese Barton (2000); Chen and Mensah (2018); Coddington and Swanson (2019); Danielowich (2012); Harlow (2012); Lux et al. (2017); Min et al. (2020); Ohana (2004); Subramaniam (2013)
Survey/questionnaire	Bulunuz (2012); Lux et al. (2017); Weld and French (2001)
PST analyzing videos of their interactions with children	Boyer (2016); Nelson (2008); Wenner and Kittleson (2018)
PSTs describing noticing students' funds of knowledge	McLaughlin and Calabrese Barton (2013)
Teaching artifacts (such as lesson plans, assessments, and tasks)	Hanuscin and Zangori (2016)
PSTs drawing a picture of themselves as a teacher and of someone learning science	Hancock and Gallard (2004)
PSTs creating podcasts about field experiences	Heineke et al. (2019)

Category 1: Changing PSTs' internal features. The first category of changes researchers hope that PSTs might undergo is that of internal changes. Such changes, summarized in Table 9.4, involve shifts in how PSTs see and understand various features of teaching and learning.

While many researchers claimed that PSTs' changed internally, Settlage et al. (2009) found no discernible influence upon the teacher candidates' perceptions of themselves that could be attributed to the demographics of their field placements, and the authors call into question the tendency to use heightened teaching self-efficacy as an indicator of individual or programmatic success.

Category 2: Helping PSTs shift understanding of science knowledge and practices. The second category of changes involves PSTs' shifting understanding of science knowledge and practices. For example, Boyer (2016) examined how PSTs' understanding of argumentation shifted as they attempted to help students engage in such practices. Similarly, Boyle et al. (2013) found that PSTs needed to participate in classrooms in which the teacher and students engaged in science practices in order to understand how such practices might unfold in their future classrooms. Lotter et al. (2009) also found that PSTs' understanding of the nature of science (NOS) improved as they engaged in "low stakes" field experiences with support from a cooperating teacher and analytic self-reflection.

Category 3: Helping PSTs develop various pedagogical knowledge domains and practices. The third category of changes involves PSTs' shifting understanding of teaching and, ideally, their pedagogical actions. For example, in Thailand, Faikhamta et al. (2011) found that PSTs appreciated opportunities to interact with students to see how routines from methods courses might be enacted. However, PSTs still needed to improve on lesson planning, questioning, and classroom management. Similarly, Juhler (2016) argues that PSTs need opportunities to increase various pedagogical knowledge domains, and that in Norway, field experiences might help in such knowledge acquisition.

Table 9.4 Summary of internal PST changes in field experiences

Internal change	Study examples
Increased or decreased attitude about teaching science	Calabrese Barton (2000); Fitzgerald (2020); Sunal (1982); Weaver et al. (1979)
Increased or decreased self-efficacy about teaching science and engineering	Cannon and Scharmann (1996): Faikhamta et al. (2011); Franks and Mcglamery (2016), Kinskey (2018); Matkins et al. (2014); Perkins (2019); Seung et al. (2019); Wilson (1996)
Changing perceptions about teaching, students, and teaching environments	Brown and Crippen (2016); Bulunuz (2012); Lux et al. (2017); Plonczak (2010); Şahin and White (2015)
Changing beliefs about science teaching and/or students	Calabrese Barton (2000); Cone (2012); Fletcher and Luft (2011); Hancock and Gallard (2004); Horak (1981); Min et al. (2020); Nelson (2008)
Changing identity as future science teacher	Birmingham et al. (2019); Carrier et al. (2017); Coddington and Swanson (2019); Danielowich (2012); Fitzgerald (2020); Wallace and Brooks (2015)

Field experiences might also help PSTs develop a better sense of classroom realities. For example, Weld and French (2001), and Subramaniam (2013) noted that field experiences provided PSTs with opportunities to see how their cooperating teacher organized classrooms for learning, and engaged in the daily work of teaching (such as constructing lesson plans and creating instructional activities). Forbes (2013) also found that given opportunities, PSTs could rehearse adapting curricula for students' engagement in inquiry-based science. Similarly, Varma and Hanuscin (2008), as well as Wenner and Kittleson (2018), found that with supports from cooperating teachers and from Wenner and Kittleson's specific teaching model (Supported, Collaborative Teaching Model – SCTM), PSTs could plan, teach, and reflect about teaching and learning in ways that might not be possible without a field experience setting in which they interact with children.

Category 4: Helping PSTs understand communities and students' lived experiences. The fourth category of changes involves helping PSTs see and understand students' communities and lived experiences as important for their pedagogy. For example, Heineke et al. (2019) found that as PSTs visited community-based settings with students (such as the children's museum, science museum, history museum, planetarium, and zoo), they began to see new dimensions to students that are invisible in classrooms. Similarly, McLaughlin and Calabrese Barton (2013) argue that field experiences helped PSTs recognize and value students' funds of knowledge, and used such knowledge when planning lessons. Harlow (2012) also found that including science nights as a field experiences helped PSTs see children, and their community-based ideas, as crucial to consider when planning and teaching.

Across categories of research, field experiences served as sites in which researchers hoped that PSTs might change internally and externally, especially as they interacted with children in classrooms and informal settings.

Wonderings and Lingering Questions

Science teacher educators clearly hope that PSTs might change their ideas and actions around teaching and learning through field experiences. However, there is little agreement about the location, duration, framing, and methodologies of such field experiences. Given the research, and the explicit and implicit assumptions about field experiences, I provide six areas of wonderment and lingering questions for the field to consider.

First, given the lack of consensus about the duration and location of field experiences, there is little understanding about when and where PSTs should have opportunities to interact with children. Might differences exist between PSTs' thinking and actions in brief or extended field experiences? Is there a minimum threshold for quantity or location of field experiences that provides a better foundation for PSTs than other experiences? Could multiple field experiences be combined or sequenced to contribute to PST learning? If so, what trajectory of experiences might provide a powerful foundation for PST learning?

Second, research rests on the assumption, and hope, that field experiences might help PSTs learn about teaching. Thus far, the majority of studies about field experiences use cognitive learning perspectives to frame studies of features, traits, or knowledge of PSTs that they acquire or change over time. More recent studies use sociocultural learning theory perspectives to examine PSTs as situated in, and in conversation with, the multiple contexts of participation; however, such framing is not as common as cognitive learning theories. In addition, there are few, if any, studies of field experiences that use critical perspectives about PSTs' participation. Moving forward, researchers should unearth assumptions about field experiences and ask questions such as: What counts as PST learning? What are "good" field experiences? What evidence might the researchers compile to illustrate PST learning from field experiences?

Third, as seen in reports of field experiences in the 1970s, PSTs were allowed to choose modules, placement sites, classrooms, activities, and coursework in a teacher preparation program. Such agency is much less visible in many current projects and programs. Moving forward, how can PSTs advocate for learning opportunities during field experiences? What experiences would they like to have, and how can they be supported in asking for such experiences?

Fourth, there is a lack of congruence between teaching and learning expectations in field experiences and methods courses. However, there is little research about how to create better congruence across such sites. Across studies, there was rarely a mention of other actors involved in PST learning yet who clearly exist in field experiences, such as cooperating teachers, district administrators (including instructional coaches), parents, and students. In addition, researchers often superficially mentioned the planning and design of field experiences – how did such experiences come into existence? Moving forward, researchers should consider: Who is served by field placement experiences? Who is not served? Who decides what counts as a field placement? What are the roles of other actors involved in creating and supporting field experiences?

Fifth, none of the 58 studies reviewed for this chapter investigated the impact of PSTs' participation in field experiences on the children in such settings. Such a lack of perspective from the children with whom PSTs interact is both unsurprising (after all, PSTs are often the main unit of analysis) and troubling. Multiple studies reviewed for this chapter explicitly placed PSTs in underserved schools and marginalized communities, yet the lack of reported voices from people who inhabit such settings could indicate that their needs may not be considered when researchers establish field experiences. Brown (1973) elevated this exact gap of research in hopes that teacher educators might further examine the relationship between PSTs and children in field experiences. Given the lack of children's voices, some difficult and necessary questions emerge, such as: How can teacher educators help position K–12 children and their communities crucial for PST learning rather than sites into which PSTs are inserted by people with power? Are field experiences designed with partner schools and communities, or imposed upon them? How can PSTs and students build meaningful relationships during field experiences? How can field experiences serve as sites for PSTs to begin equitable and socially just instruction? Such questions are particularly important given a changing climate, impending global migrations, and systemic inequities built into systems of schooling around the world, which force PSTs to confront their biases and assumptions about ever-changing student populations.

Sixth, teacher education is not alone in providing field experiences to pre-professionals. Professions such as medicine, law, and clergy all provide opportunities for pre-professionals to interact with those whom they serve in the future as part of the preparation programs. While no profession is "perfect" in terms of preparation, given that multiple professions provide field experiences as part of the novice preparation, perhaps conversations across disciplines might generate shared language, tools, and pedagogies for future generations of pre-professionals. What lessons can various educators co-learn when engaged in conversations across pre-professional education programs about field experiences?

Moving Forward

Given the ubiquity of field experiences, and the need for more research about designing opportunities for PSTs to interact with children and their communities, I remind science educators about Cobb and colleagues' (2009) recommendations from their work with mathematics teachers. First, we must situate the activity of the teachers with whom we collaborate within the setting of the schools in which they teach. Second, researchers must develop and use interpretative frameworks that capture the complexity of PST learning in and across settings, rather than reducing PSTs to individual traits or decisions that are context-free. Third, researchers must be explicit about how they conceptualize the relations between PSTs' activities in and across different settings, especially given the different power structures in place across the settings. Given such recommendations, our field is poised to reimagine possibilities for PSTs in field experiences.

References

Battaglini, Sr., D., Pirkl, M., & Horner, O. (1975). Developing a humanistic, competency-based curriculum for preservice elementary science teachers – two years' experience. *Science Education, 59*(3), 357–271.

Birmingham, D., Smetana, L., & Coleman, E. (2019). "From the beginning, I felt empowered": Incorporating an ecological approach to learning in elementary science teacher education. *Research in Science Education, 49*, 1493–1521.

Boyer, E. (2016). Preservice elementary teachers' instructional practices and the teaching science as argument framework. *Science & Education, 25*, 1011–1047.

Boyle, J. D., Svihla, V., Tyson, K., Bowers, H., Buntjer, J., Garcia-Olp, M., . . . Sample, S. (2013). Preparing teachers for new standards: From content in core disciplines to disciplinary practices. *Teacher Education and Practice, 26*(2), 199–220.

Brown, J. C., & Crippen, K. J. (2016). The growing awareness inventory: Building capacity for culturally responsive science and mathematics with a structured observation protocol. *School Science and Mathematics, 116*, 127–138.

Brown, W. R. (1973). Experience-based science and mathematics preservice teacher education program. *Science Education, 57*(4), 453–466.

Bulunuz, M. (2012). Developing Turkish preservice preschool teachers' attitudes and understanding about teaching science through play. *International Journal of Environmental & Science Education, 7*(2), 141–166.

Calabrese Barton, A. (2000). Crafting multicultural science education with preservice teachers through service-learning. *Journal of Curriculum Studies, 32*(6), 797–820.

Cannon, J. R., & Scharmann, L. C. (1996). Influence of a cooperative early field experience on preservice elementary teachers' science self-efficacy. *Science Education, 80*(4), 419–436.

Capie, W. (1973). A modular methods course in conjunction with portal schools. *Science Education, 57*(1), 71–75.

Carrier, S. J., Whitehead, A. N., Walkowiak, T. A., Luginbuhl, S. C., & Thomson, M. M. (2017). The development of elementary teacher identities as teachers of science. *International Journal of Science Education, 39*, 1733–1754.

Cartwright, T. J., & Hallar, B. (2018). Taking risks with a growth mindset: Long-term influence of an elementary pre-service after school science practicum. *International Journal of Science Education, 40*(3), 348–370.

Chen, J., & Mensah, F. M. (2018). Teaching contexts that influence elementary preservice teachers' teacher and science teacher identity development. *Journal of Science Teacher Education, 29*(5), 420–439.

Cobb, P., Zhao, Q., & Dean, C. (2009). Conducting design experiments to support teachers' learning: A reflection from the field. *Journal of the Learning Sciences, 18*(2), 165–199.

Coddington, L. R., & Swanson, L. H. (2019). Exploring identity of prospective math and science teachers through reflections in early field contexts. *Journal of Teacher Education and Educators, 8*(3), 207–228.

Collea, F. P. (1974). A model for pre-service training of science teachers based on the intentions, perceptions, and verbal behaviors of first year science teachers. *Science Education, 58*, 363–367.

Cone, N. (2012). The effects of community-based service learning on preservice teachers' beliefs about the characteristics of effective science teachers of diverse students. *Journal of Science Teacher Education, 23*(8), 889–907.

Danielowich, R. M. (2012). Looking through different lenses: How preservice science teachers use practice-oriented reflections to negotiate more reform-minded identities. *Journal of Science Teacher Education, 23*, 323–346.

Danish, J. A., & Gresalfi, M. (2018). Cognitive and sociocultural perspective on learning: Tensions and synergy in the learning sciences. In F. Fischer, C. E. Hmelo-Silver, S. R. Goldman, & P. Reimann (Eds.), *International handbook of the learning sciences* (pp. 34–43). New York, NY: Routledge.

Faikhamta, C., Jantarakantee, E., & Roadrangka, V. (2011). The current situation of field experience in a five-year science teacher education program in Thailand. *US-China Education Review, B*(6), 829–839.

Fitzgerald, A. (2020). Out in the field: Examining the role of school-based experiences in preparing primary pre-service teachers as confident and competent teachers of science. *International Journal of Science Education, 42*(2), 290–309.

Fletcher, S. S., & Luft, J. (2011). Early career secondary science teachers: A longitudinal study of beliefs in relation to field experiences. *Science Education, 95*(6), 1124–1146.

Forbes, C. T. (2013). Curriculum-dependent and curriculum-independent factors in preservice elementary teachers' adaptation of science curriculum materials for inquiry-based science, *Journal of Science Teacher Education, 24*(1), 179–197.

Frankel, E. (1972). Teacher training in elementary science education. *Science Education, 56*, 57–63.

Franks, B., & Mcglamery, S. (2016). Effects of teaching in a science summer camp on preservice teachers' science self-efficacy. *Delta Kappa Gamma Bulletin, 82*(3), 63–73.

Hancock, E. S., & Gallard, A. J. (2004). Preservice science teachers' beliefs about teaching and learning: The influence of K-12 field experiences. *Journal of Science Teacher Education, 15*(4), 281–291.

Hanuscin, D. L., & Zangori, L. (2016). Developing practical knowledge of the *Next Generation Science Standards* in elementary science teacher education. *Journal of Science Teacher Education, 27*(8), 799–818.

Harlow, D. B. (2012). The excitement and wonder of teaching science: What pre-service teachers learn from facilitating family science night centers. *Journal of Science Teacher Education, 23*, 199–220.

Harty, H., Andersen, H. O., & Enochs, L. G. (1984). Science teaching attitudes and class control ideologies of preservice elementary teachers with and without early field experience. *Science Education, 68*(1), 53–59.

Heineke, A. J., Smetana, L., & Sanei, J. C. (2019). A qualitative case study of field-based teacher education: One candidate's evolving expertise of science teaching for emergent bilinguals. *Journal of Science Teacher Education, 30*(1), 80–100.

Horak, W. J. (1981). Field experiences: Their effects on beliefs of preservice elementary teachers. *Science Education, 65*(3), 277–284.

Juhler, M. V. (2016). The use of lesson study combined with content representation in the planning of physics lessons during field practice to develop pedagogical content knowledge. *Journal of Science Teacher Education, 27*, 533–553.

Kinskey, M. (2018). Using action research to improve science teaching self-efficacy. *International Journal of Science Education, 40*(15), 1795–1811.

Lotter, C., Singer, J., & Godley, J. (2009). The influence of repeated teaching and reflection on preservice teachers' views of inquiry and nature of science. *Journal of Science Teacher Education, 20*, 553–582.

Lunetta, V. N. (1975). Field-based clinical experiences in science teacher education. *Science Education, 59*(4), 517–520.

Lux, N., Obery, A., Cornish, J., Grimberg, B. I., & Hartshorn, A. (2017). Reflecting on the challenges of informal contexts: Early field experiences with technology in teacher education. *Contemporary Issues in Technology and Teacher Education, 17*(2), 250–267.

Matkins, J. J., McDonnough, J., & Goff, K. (2014). Preparing science teachers for teaching in high-need schools: A comparison of two science education programs. *Teacher Education and Practice, 27*(2–3), 297–315.

McLaughlin, D. S., & Calabrese Barton, A. (2013). Preservice teachers' uptake and understanding of funds of knowledge in elementary science. *Journal of Science Teacher Education, 24*, 13–36.

Min, M., Akerson, V., & Aydeniz, F. (2020). Exploring preservice teachers' beliefs about effective science teaching through their collaborative oral reflections. *Journal of Science Teacher Education, 31*(3), 245–263.

Nelson, T. H. (2008). Making the hidden explicit: Learning about equity in K-8 preservice science education. *Journal of Science Teacher Education, 19*(3), 235–254.

Oberlin, L., & Sanders, B. (1973). A comparison of the science content knowledge of graduates from Florida's new elementary program and graduates who had their science education in a traditional course. *Science Education, 57*(3), 331–334.

Ohana, C. (2004). Extended field experiences and cohorts with elementary science methods: Some unintended consequences. *Journal of Science Teacher Education, 15*(3), 233–254.

Perkins, C. M. (2019). Preparing preservice elementary teachers to teach engineering: Impact on self-efficacy and outcome expectancy. *School Science and Mathematics, 119*, 161–170.

Plonczak, I. (2010). Videoconferencing in math and science preservice elementary teachers' field placements. *Journal of Science Teacher Education, 21*(2), 241–254.

Rowe, M. B. (1974). A Humanistic intent: The program of preservice elementary education at the University of Florida. *Science Education, 58*(3), 369–376.

Şahin, M., & White, A. L. (2015). Teachers' perceptions related to characteristics of a professional environment for teaching. *Eurasia Journal of Mathematics, Science and Technology Education, 11*(3), 559–575.

Settlage, J., Southerland, S. A., Smith, L. K., & Ceglie, R. (2009). Constructing a doubt-free teaching self: Self-efficacy, teacher identity, and science instruction within diverse settings. *Journal of Research in Science Teaching, 46*(1), 102–125.

Seung, E., Park, S., & Lee, M-A. (2019). The impact of a summer camp-based science methods course on preservice teachers' self-efficacy in teaching science as inquiry. *Journal of Science Teacher Education, 30*(8), 872–889.

Subramaniam, K. (2013). Examining the content of preservice teachers' reflections of early field experiences. *Research in Science Education, 43*, 1851–1872.

Sunal, D. W. (1982). Affective predictors of preservice science teaching behavior. *Journal of Research in Science Teaching, 19*(2), 167–175.

Varma, T., & Hanuscin, D. L. (2008). Pre-service elementary teachers' field experiences in classrooms led by science specialists. *Journal of Science Teacher Education, 19*, 593–614.

Wallace, C. S., & Brooks, L. (2015). Learning to teach elementary science in an experiential, informal context: Culture, learning, and identity. *Science Education, 99*(1), 174–198.

Weaver, H. M., Hounshell, P. B., & Coble, C. B. (1979). Effects of science methods courses with and without field experience on attitudes of preservice elementary teachers. *Science Education, 63*(5), 655–664.

Weld, J. D., & French, D. P. (2001). An undergraduate science laboratory field experience for pre-service science teachers. *Journal of Science Teacher Education, 12*(2), 133–142.

Wenner, J. A., & Kittleson, J. (2018). Focused video reflections in concert with practice-based structures to support elementary teacher candidates in learning to teach science. *Journal of Science Teacher Education, 29*(8), 741–759.

Wilson, J. D. (1996). An evaluation of the field experiences of the innovative model for the preparation of elementary teachers for Science, mathematics, and technology. *Journal of Teacher Education, 47*(1), 53–59.

Wilson, S. M., Floden, R. E., & Ferrini-Mundy, J. (2001). *Teacher preparation research: Current knowledge, gaps, and recommendations.* Seattle: Center for the Study of Teaching and Policy, University of Washington.

10

RECENT TRENDS IN SCIENCE EDUCATION RESEARCH ON MENTORING PRESERVICE TEACHERS

Leslie U. Bradbury

In the *Second International Handbook of Science Education* (2012), the chapter on mentoring focused on the notion of mentoring to support reform-based practices in science education (Koballa & Bradbury, 2012). In that chapter, the authors discussed the possibility of effective mentoring providing a vehicle by which inquiry-based teaching could be increased in school settings. In the ensuing years, the Next Generation Science Standards were published and changed the conversation about what effective science teaching looks like (NGSS Lead States, 2013). Along with that significant shift in science education, the nature of what is expected of mentors has continued to evolve. The purpose of this chapter is to review more recent trends within the mentoring literature, concluding with recommendations for future research.

To find the research published on mentoring in science education since the previous version of the *Handbook*, the terms "mentoring" and "science education" were searched together in both Google Scholar and a university library search tool with a beginning date of 2013. This date was chosen because it was the year after the publication of the last *International Handbook of Science Education* (2012). Each of the articles was then read to determine whether the focus was on induction of novice science teachers or mentoring of preservice teachers. Those that focused on preservice teachers were then re-read to determine whether the article focused on an empirical study of mentoring within a science education context. References meeting those criteria were included in the review. Their reference lists were scanned to determine whether they cited any relevant articles that had not been found in the initial search. Additionally, each article related to preservice teacher mentoring was coded to determine which topics were discussed in the findings of the articles. These codes were grouped into themes which became the core trends reported on in this chapter. Additional references were included that focused on preservice teacher mentoring in international contexts, even when those articles were not specific to science education. These international articles cited, or were cited in, the science education-specific literature.

One noticeable trend since the previous version of the *Handbook* is the relatively small number of mentoring articles published that focus explicitly on science education. While there are a few groups (i.e., Melton et al., 2019; Thompson et al., 2018) exploring mentoring within the context of science education, those remain the exception compared with the proliferation of mentoring articles in other areas of teacher education (i.e. Ellis et al., 2020; Yuan, 2018). Though there have been a small number of science-specific studies since 2012, mentoring literature related to teaching more generally has been prevalent, with several literature reviews from prominent mentoring scholars

DOI: 10.4324/9781003098478-12

focusing on topics such as the theoretical foundations of different mentoring approaches (Orland-Barak & Wang, 2020), as well as the characteristics of effective mentors (Ellis et al., 2020). For this reason, the approach taken in this chapter is to describe themes within the recent science education literature with supplements from the descriptions of those trends with citations from the literature more broadly. These trends include the use of: new lenses for framing the work of mentors, tools to support mentoring work, and alternative models for mentoring, as well as the recognition of the importance of context in mentoring relationships.

New Lenses for Framing the Work of Mentors

Traditional views of a mentor's role focus on the pairing of an experienced expert teacher with a novice so that the veteran can share their knowledge and skills with the new teacher (Aspfors & Fransson, 2015). These relationships often focused on the provision of emotional support, introduction into the profession of teaching, and practical tips for success (Clarke et al., 2014; Kelchetermans & Deketelaere, 2016). Researchers have noted many problems with this approach to mentoring, including the tendency for mentoring to reproduce the status quo rather than supporting new approaches to teaching (Thompson et al., 2018), and the possibility for mentoring relationships to minimize novices' opportunities for learning, since they are not engaged in critical thinking and problem solving but are simply being asked to emulate the mentor (Miller et al., 2019).

While there are different terms that have become popular, such as "educative mentoring" (Barnett & Friedrichsen, 2015; Bradbury, 2010; Feiman-Nemser, 2001; Goodwin et al., 2016) or "collaborative mentoring" (Nam et al., 2011), no matter the name that is given, there is a trend towards more cooperative and equal mentoring relationships with an emphasis on supporting student science learning rather than tips or "tricks of the trade" (Ellis et al., 2020). Many of these approaches are grounded in the work of Feiman-Nemser (2001), who coined the term "educative mentoring" and promoted mentoring relationships based on strategies such as probing novices' thinking, focusing on students, and modeling wondering about teaching. This model of mentoring changes the emphasis from simply sharing advice to the mentor encouraging the novice to be "inquiry-oriented, critical, reflexive, and reflective" (Ellis et al., 2020, p. 7). These more contemporary views are documented in both US (Barnett & Friedrichsen, 2015; Thompson et al., 2018) and international contexts (Hume & Berry, 2013). This collaborative approach fosters relationships that are more egalitarian and less hierarchical in nature (Thompson et al., 2018). Rather than a one-way communication of opinions from the mentor to the novice, newer models emphasize a reciprocal sharing of ideas, and a mutual construction of new knowledge (Ellis et al., 2020). These types of interactions can lead to changes in the practice of the mentor teachers as well as the novice (Braaten, 2018).

One interesting trend in newer frameworks for mentoring is the timing of the interactions between participants. Instead of mentoring happening after a mentor observes a lesson or when a novice asks for help, these more ambitious approaches advocate for mentoring that occurs during all phases of the teaching cycle – including during planning, while instruction is occurring, and after lessons, in order to make adjustments to future lessons (Braaten, 2018). For example, the mentor and preservice teacher in Barnett and Friedrichsen's (2015) case study discussed common student misunderstandings and worked together during the planning stage to consider when to introduce the concept of adaptations within a unit on evolution to minimize student confusion. The mentor also helped the student teacher think about strategies he could use to determine which misconceptions the students held. In Braaten's (2018) study, sidebar conversations between mentors and novices during a lesson enabled them to make quick changes as the lesson occurred. In each of these studies, the focus of the conversation is on student learning rather than novice performance. According to Ellis et al. (2020), mentors who excel at this type of mentoring should be excellent teachers who are both empathetic and progressive in their ideas about teaching and learning.

For studies that focus specifically on science contexts, these newer types of mentoring relationships provide opportunities for student teachers to think about how students learn science (Barnett & Friedrichsen, 2015; Thompson et al., 2018), and which aspects of instruction helped to support their understanding. Mentor teachers use strategies such as modeling critical reflection about their own teaching and asking novices to do the same, rather than simply telling the novice teacher what they should do (Barnett & Friedrichsen, 2015). Mentors in Barnett and Friedrichsen's (2015) study attempted to meet student teachers' "immediate and long-term needs" (p. 664) by reflecting with the student teachers about their teacher-thinking in planning lessons and analyzing student performance. Conversations focused on why particular pedagogical approaches to teaching specific content might work, rather than simply sharing a particular activity or idea for teaching. The mentor asked the student teacher to consider his own beliefs about student- and teacher-focused approaches to instruction, the alignment between those beliefs and the instruction he enacted with students. Further, the mentor asked the student teacher to specifically consider how their instruction impacted student learning (Barnett & Friedrichsen, 2015).

Student work provided an important opening for discussion in several of the science-specific studies. For example, in studying the experience of secondary science preservice teacher candidates, Braaten (2018) found that mentoring conversations that focused on student work allowed teacher candidates to think about how students were understanding the science content so that they could plan effectively for future science lessons. Melton and colleagues' (2019) research indicated that the focus on analyzing student work and student learning rather than the performance of the novice teacher opened up a "safe space" where productive conversations could occur. Discussions then centered on "strengths and problematic aspects of students' thinking and the aspects of the lesson that supported or inhibited students' learning" (Miller et al., 2019, p. 360). Changes to future lessons could then be framed around teaching practices that supported student learning. Similarly, Thompson et al. (2018) observed that conversations that emphasized how students learned helped novices focus on students' ideas and how future teaching could be structured to improve teaching and learning. Rather than just changing the behaviors of preservice teachers, these dialogs served as openings for "co-inquiry" where mentors and novices were working together on problems of practice. One benefit of a more "educative" approach is that novice teachers were less resistant to changes in their practice when they were more equal partners in mentoring conversations (Bradley-Levine et al., 2016), and there was less tension in mentor conversations with their preservice teachers (Thompson et al., 2018).

While there is a great deal of support for the idea of "educative" mentoring practices, researchers did find barriers to successful implementation (i.e., Bradley-Levine et al., 2016; Goodwin et al., 2016). Because novices had many basic issues that they needed help with, such as classroom management, there was less time for more ambitious conversations about science teaching (Bradley-Levine et al., 2016). In some cases, mentors were not certain about how to provide feedback, given the new expectations for mentoring conversations, and reverted back to discussion of issues like lesson pacing that they were more familiar with (Hume & Berry, 2013). When mentors were not able to transition from traditional views of the role of the mentor to more contemporary approaches, they focused on providing answers and solutions more than on developing the novices' problem-solving skills (Miller et al., 2019).

Tools to Support Mentoring Work

One interesting development since the publication of the previous *Handbook* chapter is the increased use of tools to support the work of mentors and novices within science education (i.e., Hume & Berry, 2013; Melton et al., 2019). Though there are a few examples from other disciplines such as

English language arts (McDonald et al., 2014), this trend towards tool use seems to be more prevalent in science education-specific studies.

Thompson et al. (2018, p. 365) define a tool in this context as "a material object that enables (and constrains) actors to interpret and attend to a particular feature of an activity such as planning, teaching, debriefing." The tools are "objects of mediation" that can support the work of mentor pairs as they collaborate together to identify and solve problems. Tools can include items such as templates, models, or handbooks (Hegevold et al., 2015; Hume & Berry, 2013; Melton et al., 2019).

In the context of a preservice teacher education program in New Zealand, Hume and Berry (2013) reported on the use of CoRes to support Pedagogical Content Knowledge (PCK) development with preservice chemistry teachers during student teaching. The CoRes provided a graphic organizer or template for preservice teachers to use to organize their thinking. Using the CoRe, preservice teachers identified the "big ideas" for a particular content topic. Once those ideas were identified, preservice teachers filled in additional information for each idea such as why it was important for students to know that information, difficulties with teaching that idea, and teaching procedures for each idea along with the rationales for using them. Student teachers in the study reported that they felt more prepared to have meaningful conversations with their mentors as a result of the groundwork necessary to complete the CoRe (Hume & Berry, 2013). The preservice teachers discussed the document with their mentor teacher and made adjustments to their plans based on that conversation. Novices perceived the CoRes to be a useful tool in that they supported "authentic professional discussion" with their mentors and helped to develop their PCK in areas such as knowledge of curriculum, assessment, and instructional strategies.

Another tool developed in the United States that has been used in two studies is the "Stoplight Model for Reflection" (Melton et al., 2019; Miller et al., 2019). The tool includes a visual model of a stoplight that was shared with mentors during online professional development (PD), and was used to encourage a coaching stance on the part of the mentor (Melton et al., 2019; Miller et al., 2019). This coaching stance incorporated many aspects of educative mentoring. The red of the stoplight was chosen to encourage mentors to stop and make sure that their conversations were focused on student learning, rather than more traditional topics such as classroom management. Once mentors were certain that they were emphasizing student learning, they could "slow down" and discuss factors that supported or constrained student learning, and then "go" on to topics such as what instructional strategies should be used to further student knowledge in future lessons. When the researchers compared mentoring conversations from before the PD, to mentoring conversations after, they found that there were more conversations afterward that focused on elements of effective science instruction, and that student data was used more frequently as a part of that discussion (Melton et al., 2019).

In their work to promote ambitious science teaching, Thompson et al. (2018) introduced multiple tools to "build a shared language of practice, and support principled risk-taking together" (p. 363). The tools were categorized into planning, face-to-face, and reflection tools. According to Thompson et al. (2018), the "Big Idea Tool" was used most frequently during planning. The tool was printed on an 11 x 17 sheet of paper, and provided a graphic organizer with prompts so that teachers planning a unit could identify a phenomenon for study, an essential question, an explanatory model, and activities to support learning about the science topic. Face-to-face tools, such as sentence stems, were used by teachers during planning and reflection, and by students during the lessons. Tools were also an important aspect of reflection. For example, the Rapid Survey of Student Thinking document provided a scaffold for thinking about student understanding and language use during a lesson. Based on their observations in these areas, preservice teachers were asked to consider instructional decisions and options for future lessons. Mentors and preservice teachers created additional tools when they felt that they were needed (Thompson et al., 2018). For example, one pair developed a "How it All Connects Tool" to help the students see connections across the activities in a unit. As in the other studies which focused on tool use, the tools used throughout the process of planning, teaching, and reflecting supported mentors and preservice teachers to address complex problems through the lens of improving teaching and student learning rather than "fixing novices" (Thompson et al., 2018).

Tools have been used in other disciplines in international contexts. For example, in Norway, Hegevold et al. (2015) considered a handbook developed to support mentor teachers' work with preservice teachers, and student teacher observation notes and lesson plans as mediating tools. The handbook contained lists of questions that focused on student learning that mentors could consult as they engaged in conversations with their student interns. When they compared the interactions of mentors and preservice teachers who used the handbook, observation notes, and lesson plans with those that did not, they found that those who used the tools had more conversations about student learning. However, those who did not use the tools had more discussion of topics such as how much time to spend on different activities or which instructions to give during the lesson. Similarly, in a project that investigated mentoring practices in both Sweden and Australia, Windsor et al. (2020) found that the use of focused observation protocols helped mentors and preservice teachers emphasize evidence-based decision-making about student learning in their post-lesson conferences.

While they do not necessarily fit the definition of tools used in the preceding paragraphs, electronic forms of communication such as emails, texts, and social media platforms have also become important for facilitating sustained interactions between mentors and novices (Surrette, 2020). Rather than relying solely on face-to-face conversations in a school setting, mentors are using a number of different formats to communicate with novice teachers even after the school day has ended (Goodwin et al., 2016). Teachers in Thompson and colleagues' (2018) study participated in a closed Facebook group. Interactions in this space provided just-in-time support where participants shared resources and held discussions about relevant topics related to their science teaching.

Alternative Models for Mentoring

As mentioned previously, mentoring has traditionally been viewed as one expert and one novice working together as a pair. While there are still many examples of this model being used (Ochi & Isozaki, 2016; Orland-Barak & Wang, 2020), different types of models such as pairing two novices with an experienced teacher are also being explored (Braaten, 2018). In a secondary science teacher preparation program, Braaten (2018) placed two preservice teachers with one mentor. The mentoring triads had authority to negotiate the roles within the group. Braaten (2018) found that within the teams there was co-teaching and co-planning with the preservice teachers able to take the lead without being expected to follow the mentor's teaching. Members of the groups were able to allocate work across the team, which left more time for the group to engage in "ambitious and responsive science teaching" (Braaten, 2018, p. 81). The discussions between student teachers, which sometimes occurred as side conversations during a teaching episode, were useful for supporting learning even when their relationship with the mentor teacher was difficult.

In another model situated in a high school science teaching context, Gallo-Fox and Scantlebury (2015, 2016) investigated the interactions between mentors and preservice teachers who were co-teaching, but who switched classes throughout the day. In this arrangement, student teachers were paired with another student teacher, but they moved between different mentor teacher classrooms throughout the day. While there were some difficult personal interactions that had to be addressed (Gallo-Fox & Scantlebury, 2015), there were multiple benefits to the structure, including opportunities for rejuvenation for mentor teachers, and increased opportunities for reflection for both mentors and student teachers (Gallo-Fox & Scantlebury, 2016).

In the context of an initial elementary science teacher preparation program in England, Blackmore (2019) investigated the outcomes of placing a pair of student teachers with a more experienced mentor teacher. The goal was for the student teachers to learn from each other with support from the mentor that was not overly directive. Blackmore found that the student teachers had positive attitudes to the co-coaching model and felt that it helped them set goals for their own development, reflect effectively on lessons, and develop solutions to issues that arose in their teaching practice.

Another alternative model for mentoring relationships is the use of mentors who are not placed at the same school site as a novice. In a study of early career mathematics and science teachers with a large number of career changers, Surrette (2020) used semi-structured interviews to investigate how participants experienced the process of working with mentors and negotiating within professional communities. Findings indicated that the novice teachers felt that they gained the largest amount of support from mentors that were not based in their own schools. Rather, mentors from a university-based fellowship program and professional communities such as the cohort of other novices participating in the fellowship provided more opportunities for reflection and development according to study participants (Surrette, 2020).

Mentors and preservice teachers in Thompson and colleagues' (2018) study participated in mentor-novice dyads. However, university coaches engaged in three cycles of planning, teaching, and reflecting during the internship. In addition, dyads had monthly meetings with other pairs and interacted via social media platforms. Participants in the study built community that extended beyond just the mentor-novice partners. Thompson et al. (2018) found that mentors who framed their interactions around the idea of improving student learning worked to build relationships with other mentors who used this same frame. The authors found value in this approach, as "knowledge of practice and tools became distributed and advanced across individuals and across settings" (Thompson et al., 2018, p. 377) which helped to build teachers' knowledge across multiple contexts and contributed to the enactment of reform-based practices.

The studies reported on in this section highlight the opportunities for support and teacher learning when mentors, university teacher educators, preservice, and novice teachers participate in mentoring communities that go beyond the traditional mentoring pairs. Given the complexity of learning to teach science, it is not surprising that novice teachers see the benefit of interacting with a range of different people who can act in the role of a mentor as they develop their pedagogical content knowledge for science teaching (Blackmore, 2019).

Recognition of the Importance of Context on Mentoring Relationships

In both the literature specific to science education and the literature related to mentoring more broadly, there is an increased recognition of the importance of context on influencing what happens in mentoring relationships. These contexts can impact everything from the frequency of interactions between mentors and novices (Surrette, 2020), to the types of conversations that mentoring pairs engage in (Hume & Berry, 2013).

Several authors noted that when student teachers are partnered with teachers in public schools, they are expected to work across the different cultures of university and school settings (i.e., Anderson & Stillman, 2013; Blackmore, 2019). Authors describe the difficulty that preservice teachers encounter when they have to move between "two worlds" (Braaten, 2018, p. 64). As they move between the different contexts, novices may experience different expectations related to what effective science instruction looks like, as well as what should be discussed in mentoring conversations (Melton et al., 2019). These tensions can constrain what preservice teachers are able to gain from their mentoring experiences (Miller et al., 2019).

In a meta-analysis of research on mentor preparation, Aspfors and Fransson (2015) described the ways that school context could impact the work of mentors. Resources such as time to work together, flexible scheduling to promote mentoring conversations, and level of principal support varied in different school settings (Aspfors & Fransson, 2015). Goodwin et al. (2016) noted that when there was not structural support to allow time for mentors and novices to meet, the lack of time became a significant barrier to the mentors' ability to engage in educative mentoring practices. Hume and Berry (2013) described the experiences of one preservice chemistry teacher who could not enact the instructional strategies that he had planned at the university in his actual teaching practice because of the external testing pressures exerted on his mentor teacher.

Goodwin et al. (2016) noted the importance of the increased significance of standardized tests and accountability measures on the work of mentors, particularly in urban settings. They described how the working environment pressured mentors to engage in more traditional mentoring behaviors rather than the more educative approaches favored by the university. Though not specific to science education, there is growing evidence from studies across the globe that contextual factors influence the work of mentors. For example, a group of researchers in Australia investigated the mentoring practices of teachers after a significant change in governmental policy related to teacher education (Allen et al., 2017). They found that the increasing emphasis on standardized testing and a mandate for closer collaboration between schools and universities had led mentors to have to engage in multiple roles, including assessing and providing support in a highly structured and regulated environment. Anderson and Stillman (2013) explain that student teachers' placements in specific school and community contexts mediate what student teachers are able to learn during their field placements. Additionally, Aspfors and Fransson (2015) discussed the importance of the cultural context of the country that mentors were operating in and how the policies and directives of the country could impact the everyday practices of mentors and novices because the cultural expectations of mentors varied in different countries. In a comparison of teacher education programs across several countries, Darling-Hammond (2017) reported on how policies in different countries impact the experiences of preservice and novice teachers. For example, in Singapore, there is a career ladder for teachers which supports master teachers to become mentors in the teacher preparation process, providing opportunities for preservice teachers to work with recognized experts. In countries such as Finland and Singapore, there are national policies in place to provide systemic support for the development of novice teachers (Darling-Hammond, 2017).

Studies in this section underline the crucial role that context can play in mediating the interactions between mentors and preservice teachers. Anderson and Stillman (2013) assert that given the growing recognition of the influence of context, it is important for researchers to thoroughly describe the context in which their study takes place and recognize its significance in describing the learning opportunities of preservice teachers.

Impacts of Professional Development on Mentoring Practice

The previous *Handbook* chapter discussed the importance of professional development (PD) for science teacher mentors. At that time the focus was on meeting the needs of beginning teachers and the needs of the mentors as adult learners, as well as introducing mentor teachers to the key characteristics of reform-based science teaching (Koballa & Bradbury, 2012). More recent discussions of PD for mentors reflect a more complex view of the content and structure of these professional learning opportunities. As teacher educators design PD for mentors, it is important to consider that being a master teacher does not necessarily translate to possessing the competencies needed to be an effective mentor; therefore, it is necessary for mentors to gain experience and knowledge of the skills required for effective mentoring (Aspfors & Fransson, 2015).

One reason to emphasize the content of mentor PD is because it has been found to have an impact on interactions between mentors and novices (Aspfors & Fransson, 2015). After a PD intervention that included both general content such as effective mentoring strategies to support conversation and provide feedback, as well as specific instruction on effective science instruction, Melton et al. (2019) found that mentors significantly increased their understanding of the core principles of effective science instruction and were able to incorporate those topics in their mentoring conversations. Thompson et al. (2018) observed that mentors who had attended a summer institute were able to institute routines that meant that they engaged in co-planning with student teachers prior to their lesson, rather than waiting until after lessons to provide feedback. They were also able to successfully use tools to support preservice teachers in using ambitious science teaching practices.

Researchers have included suggestions for ideas and strategies that might be helpful for promoting more contemporary views of mentoring. These approaches might be included in PDs for science teacher mentors. Barnett and Friedrichsen (2015) proposed sharing cases that included teachers engaging in educative mentoring practice so that they might see strategies that could be effective in their own work with novice teachers. These cases could serve as an opening to help expert teachers expand their notions of what it means to be a mentor so that the emphasis is on collaboration and moving the novice towards self-reliance (Bradley-Levine et al., 2016). Embedded in this notion of co-inquiry as a step in the process of reaching autonomy is the importance of helping mentors learn to reflect on their own teaching and mentoring practices, so that they can support those habits of mind with the preservice teachers with whom they work (Aspfors & Fransson, 2015). Melton et al. (2019) proposed sharing a framework for topics that might be included in conversations so that the emphasis is on science instruction instead of other topics. Braaten (2018, p. 87) suggested communicating examples of tools that could be used to promote, "co-planning, co-teaching, co-assessment, and interpretation of student contributions." While there are many ideas for the content for mentor PD, given the emphasis on supporting mentors to engage in more contemporary views of mentoring, all of the suggestions included here are rooted in the idea that mentors have to be aware of issues of power, negotiation, and identity formation as they prepare for their role as a mentor (Aspfors & Fransson, 2015).

In addition to activities that ask mentors to reframe their notions of mentoring practice, it may be necessary to include activities that ask them to reconsider their notions of what science teaching looks like. Melton et al. (2019) wanted mentors within their program to engage in what they called effective science instruction (ESI). In this view, ESI consists of opportunities for students to share their initial ideas about science topics, engage in meaningful investigations, use evidence to develop and evaluate scientific claims, and make sense of their developing science ideas. During PD activities, Melton et al. (2019) shared a video of typical science instruction as a grounding to discuss elements of effective science instruction and what those might look like in the context of an elementary classroom. Thompson et al. (2018) advocate that in conversations with preservice teachers, mentors and teacher educators focus, "first and foremost on teaching practices known to support intellectual engagement and equity," (p. 378). Mentor teachers need assistance and encouragement to develop their own understandings of these practices, and PD sessions are a likely place for that support to occur.

Science educators who work with mentors continue to explore different formats for delivering PD for experienced teachers. For example, Melton et al. (2019) combined online and in-person sessions in their program for elementary teachers. Program developers used online modules that included case studies and animations to deliver more generalized information related to mentoring, while reserving in-person sessions for addressing the components of what was intended in mentoring to promote ESI. Thompson et al. (2018) included a summer institute as part of their PD for mentors. However, participants included a team of people including school-based instructional leaders, university coaches, and university researchers working together in a collaborative manner to develop and modify resources to use in mentoring interactions with preservice teachers. Team members participated in monthly follow-up sessions as they interacted with preservice teachers during their field placements. Similarly, in their review of the literature related to mentor education, Aspfors and Fransson (2015) reported that in order for PD to reach its full potential, the "theory" from the PD sessions needed to happen at a time when mentors could put what they were learning into practice working with a novice teacher. For example, as mentors learn about more collaborative views of mentoring, it is helpful for them to be able to put those ideas immediately into use with novices. Even though there is much for mentors to learn through PD, it is important for developers to consider the workload that they are asking of mentor teachers because the burden of the time required is frequently given as a reason for abandoning the mentoring role (Aspfors & Fransson, 2015).

Future Directions: Implementation of Mentoring Practice and Research on Mentoring

Reflecting on the trends in the mentoring literature described in this chapter, it is interesting to consider the connections between the themes and what those might mean for the future of mentoring practice for preservice teachers. For example, the studies reviewed here point to a changing understanding of the role of a mentor from a primarily didactic perspective to one that is more educative in nature. Tools to aid in reflective mentoring conversations focused on student learning can be an important support for promoting these new types of mentoring relationships (Windsor et al., 2020). Tools can also provide affordances for promoting reflective conversations in new types of mentoring arrangements that include multiple preservice teachers working with several mentors (Gallo-Fox & Scantlebury, 2016), or paired interns working with one mentor (Braaten, 2018). In addition, non-traditional types of mentoring relationships may lead to a continued evolution of the lenses and theoretical perspectives that we are using to frame our understanding of mentoring relationships. New technology-based tools for communication provide opportunities to facilitate new types of mentoring relationships. Given the significant changes in mentoring since the previous *Handbook* chapter, it is exciting to consider future directions in the field.

While much has been learned from the studies conducted since the publication of the previous *Handbook*, there are still many areas in need of further attention. One area for consideration is the methods used to study mentoring in science education. Several studies reported in this chapter include novel methods that go beyond traditional techniques for studying mentoring such as interviews or analysis of written reflections. These newer methods provide possibilities to uncover additional insights about our evolving understanding of mentoring. Barnett and Friedrichsen (2015) advocate for the use of audio recordings in which the researcher is not necessarily present. These recordings enable mentors and novices to record the conversations that happen spontaneously throughout the day without the influence of the researcher's presence. Braaten (2018) also argues that the examination of interactions as they happen will yield important insights into how mentoring impacts the opportunities for preservice teachers to learn during their field experiences in both positive and negative ways. Thompson et al. (2018) used participants' posts on Facebook as a key source of data in their study because the posts provided a unique opportunity to investigate interactions that went beyond traditional mentor pairs. These researchers were able to gain insights into how members of a larger mentoring community interacted and shared ideas and resources. Photographs of the tools that mentors and preservice teachers completed together also informed the findings of Thompson et al. (2018). Newer methods of data collection that go beyond traditional interviews or observations provide unique opportunities for additional insights into the interactions that occur between mentors and novices in their school settings.

Newer visions of what mentoring relationships should look like that incorporate more collaborative views with an emphasis on student learning lead to new opportunities for additional research. We are just beginning to understand the potential of these relationships as evidenced by positive outcomes in studies such as Barnett and Friedrichsen (2015) and Thompson et al. (2018). Additional studies are needed to learn more about the conditions and tools that support these types of relationships. Current studies that emphasize a view of educative mentoring have primarily been conducted in the US. The science education community would be well-served by additional studies that investigate the use of these mentoring lenses in the contexts of other countries. We also need to know more about what happens when preservice teachers are able to participate in these types of mentoring relationships over the course of a number of field experiences rather than just one semester (Gallo-Fox & Scantlebury, 2016). Finally, investigations that look at the impact of educative mentoring on the learning of students in K–12 classrooms, rather than just the learning of mentors or preservice teachers, would help to increase our understanding of the potential for effective mentoring relationships to change what is happening in science classrooms (Barnett & Friedrichsen, 2015). Questions for investigation could include: What conditions support the work of mentors and preservice teachers as they engage in relationships founded on a more contemporary view of mentoring? What barriers or difficulties constrain the work of mentoring pairs? How is the science learning of students impacted when they are in classrooms where educative mentoring is occurring?

The proliferation of tools to support the work of mentors as they engage with new approaches to mentoring is an exciting development in recent studies of mentoring practice. The work of Thompson et al. (2018) where science educators reflected on effective ways to support mentors and novices in their joint work, and the research of Hume and Berry (2013) provide evidence that carefully crafted tools can serve as affordances to support co-inquiry and deep thinking about student learning as mentors and preservice teachers interact. The work of these groups on the use of tools provides an important avenue for new research. Potential questions for future research are: Which additional tools could be used to promote reflective conversations about student science learning? What types of support do mentors need in order to engage in effective tool use? Are different types of tools appropriate for use with preservice teachers in varying stages of their teacher preparation program?

Teacher education programs continue to explore alternative models for mentoring student teachers, including pairing preservice teachers with one mentor (Braaten, 2018). These models provide unique opportunities for preservice teachers to support and learn from each other in addition to their more experienced mentor. However, we still know relatively little about the learning opportunities provided by these relationships. For example: What types of supports do preservice teachers need in order to engage productively in alternative models of mentoring? What types of scaffolds do mentors need to navigate the complexities of working with more than one novice at a time? What other types of mentoring models might be effective in fostering preservice science teacher growth? How can the idea of multiple mentors be leveraged to support development of preservice teachers?

The influence of context in impacting mentoring relationships is an important idea for consideration within the field of science education. Aspfors and Fransson (2015) call for increased research into how "contextual and systemic factors" impact the work of mentors and the type of education that they need. Included in their call is additional investigation of the differences between mentoring preservice versus newly qualified teachers and whether different supports and knowledge are needed by mentors in those differing contexts. Thus far, studies that have incorporated a discussion of how contextual factors influence mentoring relationships have included that topic as part of a study focused on other research questions (Braaten, 2018; Hume & Berry, 2013). We are currently lacking studies that directly investigate the role of context as a central feature of the investigations. Questions worthy of consideration include: What types of mentoring contexts support the development of effective science instruction or ambitious science teaching practices? What role does national or state education policy play in the mentoring experiences of preservice science teachers in different contexts? What contexts enhance the opportunities for preservice teachers and their mentors to engage in educative mentoring?

Though there are researchers who have made suggestions about important considerations for mentor PD, we need to know more about the knowledge and needs of mentors (Aspfors & Fransson, 2015). Bullough (2012) argues that little is known about mentor PD, such as which aspects are effective and how mentors' skills develop over time as they work with preservice teachers. The studies specific to science included in this review provided clear and detailed descriptions of the PD that the mentors participating in their studies engaged in (i.e., Melton et al., 2019; Thompson et al., 2018). A further step for future researchers is to investigate how elements of the mentor PD impact their interactions with preservice teachers. What types of PD experiences enable mentors to engage in educative practice with preservice teachers? What different types of experiences are more appropriate for building mentors' knowledge of certain skills and practices? How can newer forms of communication such as social media be leveraged to provide long-term support for mentors as they work with preservice teachers?

While the topics listed here are important, there are other issues that warrant further research. In their review of literature related to student teaching in urban schools, Anderson and Stillman (2013) point out that many studies related to student teaching focus on students' experiences during one semester. Lacking in the current science education literature are studies that investigate the impact of mentoring experiences for preservice teachers across longer time frames. How does the combination of mentoring experiences across several field experiences impact the science instruction of preservice teachers? How are the ideas that preservice teachers develop during their field experiences with the support of mentors enacted once they have their own classrooms? If preservice teachers develop habits of mind connected to critically examining their practice through the lens of student learning, how do those habits manifest once they are on their own?

Finally, recent studies in science education (Barnett & Friedrichsen, 2015; Thompson et al., 2018) and in the research base more broadly (Aspfors & Fransson, 2015) highlight the possibilities for mentors' work with novice teachers to influence their own teaching practices. While this finding is promising, additional research is needed to determine how this is occurring and how this idea can be promoted as a way to change what is happening in science classrooms. How does working with a preservice teacher change the teaching practices of the mentor? What is the impact for the mentor of working with preservice teachers over several semesters?

Conclusion

Newer views on the nature of mentoring show much promise for reframing what happens in our science classrooms. However, science educators must ensure that the time that preservice teachers spend in field placements does not lead to a replication of ineffective practices if novices mimic the actions of their mentors and do not develop the skills to effectively analyze their own teaching as it relates to student learning (Goodwin et al., 2016). The evolving focus in science education to a view of mentoring that includes collaborative conversations during planning, implementation, and reflection on science lessons has been a positive development within our field. Preservice teachers, mentors, and teacher educators all benefit from the transition to a view of mentoring that is more collaborative in nature with an emphasis on thinking critically about what happens in lessons to support and constrain student learning. Our science education community should continue on with the important work of enhancing mentoring relationships and research and not continue the alarming trend of a diminishing number of reported studies on this important topic.

References

Allen, J. M., White, S., & Sim, C. (2017). Project evidence: Responding to the changing professional learning needs of mentors in initial teacher education. *Australian Journal of Teacher Education, 42*(7). https://doi.org/10.14221/ajte.2017v42n7.2

Anderson, L., & Stillman, J. (2013). Student teachings' contribution to preservice teacher development: A review of research focused on the preparation of teachers for urban and high-needs contexts. *Review of Educational Research, 83*(1), 3–69. https://doi.org/10.3102/0034654312468619

Aspfors, J., & Fransson, G. (2015). Research on mentor education for mentors of newly qualified teachers: A qualitative meta-synthesis. *Teaching and Teacher Education, 48*, 75–86.

Barnett, E., & Friedrichsen, P. (2015). Educative mentoring: How a mentor supported a preservice biology teacher's pedagogical content knowledge development. *Journal of Science Teacher Education, 26*(7), 647–668. https://doi.org/10.1007/s10972-015-9442-3

Blackmore, K. (2019). Asking the right questions: An exploration into the introduction of co-coaching within initial teacher science education. *International Journal of Mentoring and Coaching in Education, 8*(3), 163–181. https://doi.org/10.1108/IJMCE-09-2018-0052

Braaten, M. (2018). Persistence of the two-worlds pitfall: Learning to teach within and across settings. *Science Education, 103*(1), 61–91. https://doi.org/10.1002/sce.21460

Bradbury, L. (2010). Educative mentoring: Promoting reform-based science teaching through mentoring relationships, *Science Education, 94*(6), 1049–1071.

Bradley-Levine, J., Lee, J., & Mosier, G. (2016). Teacher mentoring as a community effort. *School Science and Mathematics, 116*(2), 71–86.

Bullough, R. V., Jr. (2012). Mentoring and new teacher induction in the United States: A review and analysis of current practices. *Mentoring & Tutoring: Partnership in Learning, 20*(1), 57–74. http://dx.doi.org/10.1080/13611267.2012.645600.

Clarke, A., Triggs, V., & Nielsen, W. (2014). Cooperating teacher participation in teacher education: A review in literature. *Review of Educational Research, 84*(2), 163–202. https://doi.org/10.3102/0034654313499618

Darling-Hammond, L. (2017). Teacher education around the world: What can we learn from international practice? *European Journal of Teacher Education, 40*(3), 291–309. https://doi.org/10.1080/02619768.2017.1315399

Ellis, N., Alonzo, D., & Nguyen, H. (2020). Elements of a quality pre-service teacher mentor: A literature review. *Teaching and Teacher Education, 92*, 1–13.

Feiman-Nemser, S. (2001). Helping novices learn to teach: Lessons from an exemplary support teacher. *Journal of Teacher Education, 52*(1), 17–30.

Gallo-Fox, J., & Scantlebury, K. (2015). "It isn't necessarily sunshine and daisies every time": Coplanning opportunities and challenges when student teaching. *Asia-Pacific Journal of Teacher Education, 43*(4), 324–337. dx.doi.org/10.1080/1359866X.2015.1060294

Gallo-Fox, J., & Scantlebury, K. (2016). Coteaching as professional development for cooperating teachers. *Teaching and Teacher Education, 60*, 191–202.

Goodwin, A., Roegman, R., & Reagan, E. (2016). Is experience the best teacher? Extensive clinical practice and mentor teachers' perspectives on effective teaching. *Urban Education, 51*(10), 1198–1225. https://doi.org/10.1177/0042085915618720

Hegevold, N., Naeshiem-Bjorkvik, G., & Ostrem, S. (2015). Key focus areas and use of tools in mentoring conversations in initial teacher education. *Teaching and Teacher Education, 49*, 128–137.

Hume, A., & Berry, A. (2013). Enhancing the practicum experience for pre-service chemistry teachers through collaborative CoRe design with mentor teachers. *Research in Science Education, 43*(5), 2107–2136. https://doi.org/10.1007/s11165-012-9346-6

Kelchetermans, G., & Deketelaere, A. (2016). The emotional dimension in becoming a teacher. In J. Loughran & M. L. Hamilton (Eds.), *International handbook on teacher education* (pp. 429–469). Singapore: Springer.

Koballa, T. R., & Bradbury, L. U. (2012). Mentoring in support of reform-based science teaching. In B. Frasier & K. Tobin (Eds.), *Second international handbook of science education* (pp. 361–372). New York, NY: Springer.

McDonald, M., Kazemi, E., Kelley-Petersen, M., Mikolasy, K., Thompson, J., Valencia, S., & Windschitl, M. (2014). Practice makes practice: Learning to teach in teacher education. *Peabody Journal of Education, 89*(4), 500–515. https://doi.org/10.1080/0161956X.2014.938997

Melton, J., Miller, M., & Brobst, J. (2019). Mentoring the mentors: Hybridizing professional development to support cooperating teachers' mentoring practice in science. *Contemporary Issues in Technology and Teacher Education, 19*(1), 23–44.

Miller, M., Hanley, D., & Brobst, J. (2019). The impacts of a research-based model for mentoring elementary preservice teachers in science. *Journal of Science Teacher Education, 30*(4), 357–378. https://doi.org/10.1080/1046560X.2019.1573127

Nam, J., Seung, E., & Go, M. (2011). The effect of a collaborative mentoring program on beginning science teachers' inquiry-based teaching practice, *International Journal of Science Education.* https://doi.org/10.1080/09500693.2011.584329

NGSS Lead States. (2013). *Next generation science standards: For states, by states.* Washington, DC: The National Academies Press.

Ochi, T., & Isozaki, T. (2016). How do pre-service science teachers develop their teacher knowledge? A qualitative study focusing on teaching practice in schools. *Theory and Research for Developing Learning Systems, 2,* 23–33.

Orland-Barak, L., & Wang, J. (2020). Teacher mentoring in service of preservice teacher's learning to teach: Conceptual bases, characteristics, and challenges for teacher education reform. *Journal of Teacher Education, 0,* 1–14. https://doi.org/10.117/0022487119894230

Surrette, T. (2020). Influence of mentoring and professional communities on the professional development of a cohort of early career secondary mathematics and science teachers. *School Science and Mathematics, 120,* 175–188. https://doi.org/10.1111/ssm.12392

Thompson, J., Hagenah, S., Lohwasser, K., & Laxton, K. (2018). Problems without ceilings: How mentors and novices frame and work on problems-of-practice. *Journal of Teacher Education, 66*(4), 363–381. https://doi.org/10.1177/0022487115592462

Windsor, S., Kriewaldt, J., Nash, M., Lilja, A., & Thornton, J. (2020). Developing teachers: Adopting observation tools that suspend judgment to evidence-informed dialogue during the teaching practicum to enrich teacher professional development. *Professional Development in Education.* https://doi.org/10.1080/19415257.2020.1712452

Yuan, E. (2018). The dark side of mentoring on pre-service language teachers' identity formation. *Teaching and Teacher Education, 55,* 188–197.

11

ALTERNATIVE PATHWAYS TO SCIENCE TEACHING: APPROACHES AND IMPACTS

Elizabeth Edmondson, Alison Dossick, Smadar Donitsa-Schmidt, Yehudit Judy Dori, Christine Ure, and Christel Balck

Introduction

Alternative pathways into science teaching evolved globally in response to a growing demand for teachers who could inspire and prepare the next generation of students for careers in scientific innovation and development. In the 1980s, many countries began creating programs to fill a shortage of science teachers and attract science graduates into teaching, many of whom remained unemployed following graduation (Charette, 2013; Pennington & Stanford, 2019).

The research reviewed here included numerous and varied definitions of what constituted an alternative certification program (Miller et al., 1998; Tozer et al., 2006; Whitford et al., 2018). An examination of the research literature showed that a unified definition for alternative certification programs did not exist. The following list is a sampling of characteristics included:

1. Post-baccalaureate programs that award candidates a master's degree (Abell et al., 2006);
2. Career switcher programs, some of which required 5 years of experience in another career (Schwartz & Dori, 2020);
3. Programs with reduced coursework (Ng et al., 2010);
4. Programs run by nonprofit organizations (e.g., Teach for America; Carver-Thomas, 2018);
5. Programs with individuals serving as the teacher of record while they worked to gain the credentials for licensure in that country (Abell et al., 2006; Bowe et al., 2011).

Darling-Hammond and Youngs (2002) presented a succinct definition of alternative programs:

> Alternative programs vary from short summer programs that place candidates in teaching assignments with full responsibility for students after a few weeks of training to those that offer 1- or 2-year post-baccalaureate programs with ongoing support, integrated coursework, close mentoring, and supervision.
>
> (p. 287)

This definition, however, did not address all of the variations seen in the literature. Alternative certification programs (ACPs) examined in current research reports were often not the traditional 4- or 5-year baccalaureate or master's of teaching programs offered by universities that included coursework, practical experiences, and unpaid internships (e.g., student teaching). Thus, this chapter included literature on ACPs with one or more of the following parameters:

1. Programs for career switchers who were at least 1 year past graduation from college;
2. Shorter programs of study when compared to traditional programs;
3. Programs that supported teachers of record needing coursework to fulfill credentialing requirements;
4. Programs designed to prepare individuals for a long-term commitment to teaching.

The authors excluded programs such as Teach for America (TFA) and Teach For programs in other countries designed to fill teaching gaps for the short term (5 years or less), as they did not meet the criteria for commitment. In several studies, TFA was one of several programs examined, and these studies were not excluded from consideration in this review.

Within this framework, three research themes emerged: the reasons for the alternative pathways to science teaching; comparisons of the program designs and components; and the outcomes and measures of success for science teachers and their students. Finally, the authors considered areas not addressed in the current science education literature and offered recommendations for policy, practice, and future research.

Identification of Studies

The studies included in this review came from international online databases, such as the Educational Resources Information Clearinghouse (ERIC), EBSCO, Google Scholar, and ProQuest. Additional databases consulted were the US National Center for Education Statistics, UNESCO, and Organizations for Economic Cooperation and Development (OECD). The review used reports, dissertations, books, journals, and conference proceedings published between 1990 and 2020 but gave preference to research conducted between 2005 and 2020.

The search utilized various methods to find relevant research on programs for certifying teachers worldwide. Because the terminology for ACP differed worldwide, searches included "alternative" and "certification" OR "licensure" as keywords, combined with "STEM," "science," and "mathematics." In ERIC, the search string "alternative licensure" resulted in 259 titles. Additionally, the search terms "attrition" and "alternative" yielded 640 results, so the terms "science" and "teacher" limited the results to 631. "Alternative AND STEM" was another search string used, which resulted in 310 results. These results led to narrowing the search further to include only those addressing the certification of second-career teachers. Google Scholar yielded far more results (60,000+).

Selected articles discussed alternative licensing procedures and requirements internationally. Inclusion criteria also identified studies that focused on the outcomes of ACPs for either teacher retention or student achievement. Articles were included that compared the coursework requirements for ACPs. The snowball technique of scouring article references produced even more results. Chapters 11 and 18 of this *Handbook* examine mentoring and induction procedures in greater detail, so those studies were excluded from consideration.

Reasons for Alternative Pathways

The literature revealed multiple reasons for the development of alternative pathways to teaching, which included teacher shortages, as well as diversification in both experience and cultural backgrounds.

The Shortage of Science Teachers

Several research studies identified the shortage of science teachers as a reason for alternative pathways to science teaching (Diekman & Benson-Greenwald, 2018; Ingersoll & Perda, 2010; Nixon et al., 2017; Shwartz & Dori, 2020). Shortages were due, for example, to the increasing number of students that arose as developing countries like Africa opened up secondary education to more students (Chudgar et al., 2014; UNESCO, 2016), or to the fact that individuals with science degrees often had career paths more appealing than teaching (Avargil et al., 2020). Cowan et al. (2016) found that the need for increasing the science teaching pool, particularly in urban, rural, and hard-to-staff schools, drove the development of ACPs.

Teacher attrition also contributed significantly to the shortage of science teachers. Many researchers found that low wages and high-stress working conditions for teachers in the US, Australia, Israel, China, and India, coupled with the lack of student discipline or administrative support, contributed to low retention rates (Darling-Hammond et al., 2017; Goldring et al., 2014; Goss et al., 2019; Singh, 2017; Yin et al., 2019). The criticism of education, in general, and teachers, specifically, by the news media and other agencies negatively impact teacher morale and their desire to remain in the profession (Hargreaves & Flutter, 2019). The difficulty in recruiting science teachers was exacerbated by the retention issue (Wright et al., 2019), discussed later in this chapter.

Diversification of the Teaching Workforce: Talented and Experienced Professionals

ACPs sought to attract academically talented students into the teaching profession (Carver-Thomas, 2018; Feistritzer, 1998). In Israel, the country's low performance in the international comparative tests of student performance in science drove this recruitment effort (Dori et al., 2019; Weinberger & Donitsa-Schmidt, 2016). Researchers found that global programs such as Teach for All and China's Exceptional Graduates as Rural Teachers programs actively recruited academically talented candidates (Friedrich et al., 2015; Mayer, 2019; Yin et al., 2019). Belgium sought to attract academically talented individuals by ensuring that every teacher education institute provided a postgraduate pathway into teaching from other professions (Flemish Government, 2019).

Diversification of the Teaching Workforce: Cultural Backgrounds

The goal of some ACP programs, such as one in China, was to diversify the teaching force (Yin et al., 2019). Feistritzer (2011) and Shen (1998) found that ACP teachers in the United States were more culturally diverse than traditional certification program (TCP) teachers, thus better mirroring the heterogeneity in the student population. TCPs in the United States attract predominantly White and female candidates, according to findings by Whitford et al. (2019), while ACPs attract more males, Latinx, and Black teachers. African American candidates specifically came to the profession to be role models for students (Morrettini, 2014).

Program Design and Components

Academic institutions and other institutions, such as school systems, across the globe have designed ACPs to bring postbaccalaureate individuals and career changers into the classroom. In examining the research and other documents from ACP programs, six themes emerged around program design: science professionals' reasons for teaching; preferences for ACPs; recruitment of other education professionals; organizations providing the program; program coursework; and additional support for ACP science teachers (see Table 11.1).

Table 11.1 A comparison of program designs

	Who Offers Courses	Coursework Required	Coursework Parallels Traditional	Teaching Experience Begins	State or National Exams	Citation
Australia	NP with U Or U	Y	A	D 1st-year paraprofessional, 2nd year PTT	No state or national exam, authorities accredit programs	Dadvand and Dawborn-Gundlach (2020)
Belgium	U	Y	A	D	Y	Beleidsdomein Onderwijs en Vorming (2019)
Israel	NP U M 0	Y	A S	D	Y	Dori et al. (2019); Ramat & Donitsa-Schmidt (2021)
US	NP U S	Y	A S	B D A	Y	Mentzer et al. (2019); Morrison & Lightner (2017)
African Countries	NP U M 0	Y	S	B D A	NA	Chudgar et al. (2014); UNESCO (2016)
India	NP U M 0	Y	S	B D A	NA	Chudgar et al. (2014); Pugatch (2017); UNESCO (2016)

Who offers: NP = Non-profits, U = Universities or Colleges, S = Schools or Districts, O = Other Government Agencies;
Coursework Required: Y = Yes, N = No;
Coursework Parallels Traditional Program: A = All of the same courses, S = Some of the same courses, N = None of the same courses;
Teaching Begins: B = Before Courses, D = During or Simultaneous with Courses, A = After Course, PTT = Permission to Teach;
State or National Test: Y = Yes, N = No
NA = Not available

Reasons that Science Professionals Want to Teach K–12

Many reasons exist for why people decide to teach in either a TCP or ACP program. For individuals selecting ACPs, dissatisfaction with current career options and greater professional purpose were among those found by Proweller and Mitchener (2004) and Morettini (2014). Morettini did indicate that individuals in ACPs or TCPs have more similar reasons than differences for entering the profession. Morettini (2014) also noted that ACP teachers felt their previous careers limited their work to isolated areas of their discipline and they wanted to work more broadly in the discipline. Teaching, they believed, gave them this opportunity.

Preference for ACPs over TCPs

A 2009 research study conducted on the first Israeli alternative programs (Donitsa-Schmidt & Weinberger, 2014) showed that ACPs were more attractive to a far greater number of applicants than were traditional TCPs. The Israel ACPs recruited candidates with diverse demographic, academic, and occupational profiles that varied considerably from the profiles of candidates in the TCPs. A higher percentage of the students in ACPs had master's and even doctoral degrees in their content areas and had more occupational experience than did their counterparts from TCPs. While not examined in this study, research from the US indicates that graduate-level programs or fast-track programs are more attractive to professionals changing careers (Woods, 2016).

In comparison to many TCP candidates, Bowe et al. (2011) found that US science majors preferred earning their content degree and did not want to change their major to education. They were content with seeking licensure or certification afterwards. Some ACPs were successful at recruiting undergraduates while they were still finishing their undergraduate studies (Bowe et al., 2011). These students identified themselves as career changers.

Recruiting Other Education Professionals Into Teaching

Another approach used to bring individuals into the classroom in recent years was recruiting paraprofessionals (teaching assistants and unlicensed support staff) into licensed teaching positions. Recruitment of classroom paraprofessionals into ACPs suffers from limited research. No studies focused on science-specific content certification. Studies from other content areas highlighted several challenges for paraprofessionals in ACPs.

Morrison and Lightner's (2017) research identified low GPAs as limiting or preventing the admission of paraprofessionals into ACP graduate programs. Their research also showed high stress levels for these candidates, due to concurrently teaching and being in an academic degree program. Burbank et al. (2009) engaged paraprofessionals in a yearlong three-credit class to help them understand the profession and licensure requirements while acknowledging their voices and experiences. This study noted that successful recruitment of these individuals requires program leaders to listen to the candidates. While not specifically addressing paraprofessionals in science, the successes and challenges of these programs highlighted critical considerations for further research on best practices when recruiting from within schools.

Organizations Involved in Program Design

School districts were one example of the variety of organizations and collaborative efforts that delivered ACPs (see Table 11.1). Nonprofits, universities, and other governmental organizations, such as the Israeli Defense Force in Israel, ran other programs (Dori et al., 2019). In contrast, Australia requires all teachers graduating from ACPs to complete a university program accredited against the nationally approved standards. ACPs that include an employment-based pathway to certification were conducted in collaboration with Teach For Australia or a university in partnership with employers (Dadvand & Dawborn-Gundlach, 2020).

Program Coursework Comparisons

Most ACPs were fast-tracked and provided condensed coursework when compared to TCPs (Ingersoll et al., 2014; McConney et al., 2012). An analysis of various international studies indicated that participants took at least some educational coursework prior to or during their initial teaching experiences (Abell et al., 2006; Ingersoll et al., 2014). Two notable exceptions were Australia and Belgium, where teachers transitioned into the classroom while continuing a TCP program of study for teacher certification. The courses ranged from traditional offerings (i.e., educational psychology or classroom management) to only a few of these pedagogical courses. In the United States, the required pedagogical coursework in ACPs ranged from one or two courses on adolescent development and teaching methods to complete programs of study (e.g., 12–15 courses, or approximately 33 credit hours; Mentzer et al., 2019). The Commonwealth of Virginia provided an intermediate example of required courses for ACPs by requiring six courses (18 credit hours; Alternate Routes to Licensure, 2021). Within the coursework requirements, the level of teaching responsibility was found to vary from full control (e.g., requiring a teacher of record) to coteaching or working as a paraprofessional (Dadvand & Dawborn-Gundlach, 2020; Dori et al., 2019; Kyriakides & Houssart, 2016). Boone et al. (2011) found that ACP teachers' self-efficacy improved as they progressed through their program. They linked this increase to feeling better prepared to teach with time and viewing themself as a teacher.

Program Supports for Science Teachers

Several studies noted that ACPs did not address the specific needs of these teachers, such as tempering their idealistic visions of teaching as they entered the classroom (Morettini, 2014; Schwartz & Dori, 2020; Tigchelaar et al., 2010). Many ACPs provided mentoring and induction support for this reason (Koballa et al., 2006; Unruh & Holt, 2010). In 2011, Bowe et al. (2011) reported more mentoring experiences for ACP teachers than for TCP teachers. This situation may have changed in recent years, as many US states have added mentoring requirements for all new teachers. Research by Akiri and Dori (2019) and Richmond et al. (2020) found that a supportive community for ACP teachers allowed both novice and experienced teachers to grow successfully together in the teaching professions.

Measures of the Effectiveness of ACPs

Researchers rated the effectiveness of ACPs using several factors. Some used the vague term "quality" as a measure of effectiveness. Researchers have also examined teacher job placement, teacher retention, and student achievement.

Teacher Quality

Researchers have characterized teacher quality differently. Boyd et al. (2007) defined quality as student achievement. Rosenholtz's (1989) definition of quality was how "teachers make meaningful contributions" to the school (p. 422). Mentzer et al. (2019) defined a quality educator by their abilities in the classroom, including these attributes: "teaching self-efficacy," "instructional practices," and "student behavior" (p. 37). They also compared practical with theoretical approaches to teaching as well as knowledge and application. Ultimately, these researchers concluded that quality was indicated when the teacher used inquiry-based methods of teaching. Defining "quality" was a complex process for researchers and represented the researchers' priorities for a given project.

Teacher Job Placement

While requirements to obtain certification or registration differed across countries, alternative programs served to fill schools with immediate staffing needs. Because teacher shortages were more likely to occur in hard-to-staff and high-poverty schools (Ludlow et al., 2005) or schools in rural, remote, and isolated areas (García & Weiss, 2019; Organization for Economic Cooperation and

Development, 2012), success of a program was measured by the ability to fill teaching vacancies. Unfortunately, developing countries reported success as the ability to hire an individual, certified or not, to fill vacancies in these schools.

Shen (1998) found ACP programs could fill positions with certified science and mathematics teachers. Schools characterized as hard to staff had a large proportion of these teachers. Bowe et al. (2011) reaffirmed this research, showing that participants of science-specific ACPs had a higher tendency to work in districts or schools classified as hard to staff. ACP coursework had a stronger equity focus for candidates to address the knowledge and skills for teaching in these types of schools (Amichai & Ron, 2018; Chudgar et al., 2014; Dandalo Partners, 2017; Singh, 2017; Yin et al., 2019). Further research is needed to determine whether an equity focus positively affected teachers in hard-to-staff schools.

Teacher Retention

When teacher retention was the defining factor of successful ACPs, studies showed mixed results. Attrition rates were the highest immediately following the first year, regardless of the specific program (Ingersoll & Perda, 2010). Researchers who focused on retention as a measure of effectiveness found that lower teacher retention occurred mainly in the first 5 years of teachers' careers (Dupriez et al., 2016; Vancaeneghem, 2018). Multiple studies found that science and mathematics teachers were more likely to leave the field than were teachers in other subject areas (Ingersoll, 2001; Murnane et al., 1991; Smith & Ingersoll, 2004). In Israel, a 5-year longitudinal research study showed similar retention rates of 60% for science teachers who studied in both ACPs and TCPs (Weinberger & Donitsa-Schmidt, 2016). When comparing younger and older recruits to ACPs, Donaldson (2012) argued that, because older teachers made an informed decision to pursue education after previous careers, they were more likely to stay in teaching than were individuals who entered teaching immediately following college graduation. He found that 61.3% of older teachers remained after 3 years, compared to 40.1% of younger teachers.

Teacher Retention and ACP Preparation

Ingersoll et al. (2014) conducted the most extensive research comparing teacher preparation methods and their effects on retention rates. This study analyzed three US education databases to build a comprehensive picture of the impact of pedagogical studies on teacher retention. They created definitions of pedagogical training that ranged from "little to no pedagogy" to "comprehensive pedagogy" (p. 26). "Little to no pedagogy" was defined as having received either zero or one teaching methods course and having no previous teaching experience. "Comprehensive pedagogy" was described as having a semester of student teaching in addition to five to nine courses addressing teaching strategies and methods (p. 26). Science, as well as mathematics, teachers who were new to teaching were more likely to have "little to no pedagogy" (p. 24). Teachers with this lowest level of pedagogy were three times more likely to leave teaching than were those who had a comprehensive pedagogical preparation.

According to the Ingersoll et al. (2014) study, the more pedagogy and teaching practice candidates had, the higher their retention level. They also examined how classroom observations by the teaching candidates and their student teaching related to retention. Teachers were 65% less likely to leave teaching when these observations were included in their certification program. This result is consistent with the research of Corbell et al. (2010), which showed that the lack of onsite training of alternatively licensed science and mathematics teachers was a significant indicator of attrition. Many ACPs did not include student teaching internships or classroom observations (see Table 11.1), which suggests that teachers from ACPs were more likely to leave the profession.

Teacher Retention and Perceptions of Preparation

Researchers looked at how the teachers' perceptions of their preparedness affected retention rather than their actual coursework. Bowe et al. (2011) found no significant difference in retention when comparing ACP and TCP science teachers. Mentzer et al. (2019) found a 3-year lag in self-efficacy for ACP teachers behind TCP teachers using the Science Teacher Efficacy Beliefs Instrument (Riggs & Enochs, 1990) and Ohio State Teacher Sense of Efficacy Scale (Tschannen-Moran & Hoy, 2001). An Israeli study showed that leadership skills developed in the program positively contributed to their self-efficacy and performance. Enhancing teamwork skills was another factor helping graduates integrate successfully into the school community (Dori et al., 2019). This study also investigated professional satisfaction, commitment, and interaction with the school community, which were additional factors in other research studies explored further on.

Teacher Retention and Professional Commitment

A study conducted by Ramot and Donitsa-Schmidt (2021) on an alternative Israeli program during COVID-19 found that more than 90% of students began teaching immediately after completing the 3-month program. Of those, 60% declared that they intended to stay in teaching for more than 5 years, with 45% planning to stay more than 11 years. Corbell et al. (2010) examined science teacher commitment and satisfaction for TCP and ACP teachers in the United States, applying Rosenholtz's (1989) definition of teacher commitment – "the extent of their work investment, performance quality, satisfaction, attendance, and a desire to remain in the profession" (p. 422) – to the Perceptions of Success Inventory for Beginning Teachers. They found that out of the three factors from the inventory that contributed to retention, commitment – not satisfaction or retention intentions – was the most significant predictor of retention for all teachers. Interestingly, satisfaction was a significant predictor of retention for TCP teachers but not for the ACP teachers. When used to predict retention, the researchers could not account for the variance in ACP teacher data for satisfaction and commitment indicators.

Several researchers compared the reasons that ACP and TCP teachers entered teaching to determine differences in commitment and retention rates between ACP and TCP teachers. Morettini (2014) found that individuals interested in ACPs expressed a long-term desire to teach and described it as a passion or calling, much like TCP teachers. Other ACP teachers stated content-driven reasons for pursuing education as a second career, such as sharing their passion for science with children. Yin et al. (2019) found that science professionals moved into teaching motivated by idealistic educational ideas.

Schwartz and Dori (2020) demonstrated that an ACP for second-career chemistry teachers led to a positive transition into teaching, as measured using questionnaires, metacognitive teaching assignments, and interviews. They concluded that this finding resulted from teachers' desire to contribute to society, which was the most frequently ranked identity resource on their questionnaire. The research in this area went further to determine if these findings of idealism and passion for teaching led to higher retention. When coupled with a strong understanding of what teaching as a career entails through exposure to classroom observations and student teaching, some researchers have found a higher retention rate in career switchers than TCP teachers (Morettini, 2014; Thomas et al., 2005). Other factors that affect commitment were included in Corbell et al. (2010). They found that student success was a significant predictor of teacher long-term commitment for TCP teachers, but not for ACP teachers.

Student Achievement and ACP-Prepared Teachers

Researchers found conflicting evidence on the impact of students' standardized test performance when prepared by ACP teachers as compared to TCP teachers. Thomas et al. (2005) found that

ACP science teachers had a more robust content knowledge and encouraged students in higher-level thinking skills when compared to teachers from TCPs. In 2000, Goldhaber and Brewer found no evidence that students of ACP teachers with content degrees had lower test scores than students of TCP teachers. This finding was duplicated by Whitford et al. (2018), who found limited impact on achievement due to program design.

Other researchers have found, however, that TCP science teachers have higher retention and overall student achievement than ACP teachers (Bryant, 2014; Ingersoll et al., 2014; Marder et al., 2020). Boyd et al. (2009) found that the differences in student achievement when taught by ACP or TCP teachers varied by years of teaching. First-year teachers from TCPs with a focus on classroom management had students who performed better than ACPs, but teachers from ACPs in the second year of teaching, who were presumably now better at classroom management, were able to apply their content knowledge in a way that resulted in higher mathematics scores. Boyd et al. found that scores for 1st-year teachers were also higher when teachers had more on-the-job training or observation time of the actual job of teaching.

Confounding variables led to conflicting evidence when measuring the success of ACPs. For example, Thomas et al. (2005) argued that "any hope for the retention of alternatively certified teachers in high-needs urban settings, and perhaps any school setting, would be very closely linked to their success in guiding the development of students academically and personally" (p. 24). This statement conflates teacher placement and student achievement with retention. In the first semesters of teaching, the expectations of student academic performance, student motivation, and student behavior were three areas that Israeli middle school science ACP teachers identified as more challenging than did their TCP peers (Dori et al., 2019; Jordan et al., 2017).

Critiques of the Research

A strength of this research is acknowledging that there were weak correlations because of confounding factors such as controlling for "teacher characteristics" as they entered alternative programs (Boyd et al., 2009, p. 433). Researchers concurred that many variables, such as teacher confidence and preparation for "high-needs classrooms," affected teacher retention, but these variables could not be controlled (Mentzer et al., 2019, p. 37). Confounding variables such as the thoroughness of the preparation method, places of employment, student achievement, and teacher commitment and satisfaction may have affected the outcomes.

Because of this mixing of variables, it was challenging to compare ACPs against TCPs. Comparing research studies with so many varied factors was also difficult. Each researcher sought to create a unique study, but consequently, clean comparisons of the outcomes could not be made. Even the definitions of successful programs were different. Many different types of schools hired teachers (e.g., rural, urban, high and low socioeconomic status). Whether ACPs should expand or even continue was a difficult question to answer because of the confounding variables.

Conclusion

This chapter sought to review the science education literature on ACPs across the globe. The vast majority of the literature on ACPs found did not focus on science. The previous section described the difficulties in comparing studies and drawing conclusions. Many studies highlight the issue of findings conflicting with previous studies.

ACPs arose for a variety of reasons, including shortages of teachers and a desire to diversify the teaching profession. Ingersoll and Perda (2010) pointed out that we are not facing a shortage in the US overall, but we are facing shortages in some school districts or schools that are hard to fill. These shortages exist for many reasons, with two critical reasons being location of the schools (rural and urban) and socioeconomic factors. Africa and India face shortages due to population mobility and efforts to provide secondary education to more students (Chudgar et al., 2014; UNESCO, 2016).

ACPs are diverse in many ways. Requirements to teach vary greatly within and between countries. Filling classrooms with teachers results in program designs that provide concurrent preparation while teaching, short periods of preparation before teaching, or more extended preparation before teaching (Abell et al., 2006; Ingersoll et al., 2014). These diverse models are found across the globe. Multiple alternative pathways to science teaching ensures classrooms have teachers. Perhaps more studies, such as that from Ramot and Donitsa-Schmidt (2021), on tailored pathways might help address the specific needs of schools in a particular district, state, or country.

Measures of ACP success vary from placement of individuals in classrooms to retention of individuals in the teaching profession to student academic success. Again, there is no clear path for programs to follow. In many studies, ACPs and TCPs had similar impacts on their participants or reported conflicting outcomes. Boyd et al. (2009) argued that examining traditional vs. alternative routes to teaching was ineffective because each design had too many differing factors. In some cases, the many paths to licensure or certification overlapped in design features, while some were so unique as to be incomparable to other programs.

Many high-quality teachers come from alternative programs, and eliminating these pathways would be detrimental to filling science positions. Alternative routes provided essential opportunities for some who may not have considered teaching while they were undergraduates. Acknowledged as key is that the alternative routes prepare the teachers and their students for success.

To understand how these programs address the needs of different jurisdictions needs further analyses. The findings of this chapter highlight the need for additional research on the recruitment of ACP teachers, program design and critical support structures for these teachers, and program impact on student achievement. The difficulty of the many confounding variables and measures of teacher effectiveness remains, however.

Areas that warrant further research at this time include the following:

1. An investigation of the unifying pedagogical aspects of programs viewed as effective and successful.
2. A comparison of programs between different countries focusing on program length, teacher preparation, recruitment strategies, practicum requirements, retention strategies, and the impact on student achievement and retention.
3. An equivalence analysis of the program designs of ACPs and TCPs, including the amount and depth of coursework.
4. A long-term comparison on the science career paths of the students of ACP teachers compared with those of TCPs.
5. A study of which supportive processes lead to the highest retention of ACP teachers in science classrooms.
6. Further research into how both traditional and alternative pathways can attract and retain high-quality teacher candidates.
7. An examination of whether a place exists for more tailored pathways than those described in this chapter.

To ensure that the varying curricula and approaches to teacher preparation do not compromise the profession, there is a need for additional research. At the core of all programs, whether traditional or alternative, is the importance of upholding the standards of education through fully accredited programs. Studies of the impact of teacher residencies, induction, and mentoring that extend beyond 3 years and programs for in-depth teacher professional learning may help researchers understand how to reduce the attrition of qualified science teachers. Ultimately, alternative programs, like TCPs, aim to produce high-quality, motivated, and engaged science teachers who can make a sustained and positive contribution to the lives of young people.

References

Abell, S., Boone, W., Arbaugh, F., Lannin, J., Beilfuss, M., Volkmann, M., & White, S. (2006). Recruiting future science and mathematics teachers into alternative certification programs: Strategies tried and lessons learned. *Journal of Science Teacher Education, 17*(3), 165–183. https://doi.org 10.1007/s10972-005-9001-4

Akiri, E., &, Dori, Y. J. (2019). *Assessing novice STEM teachers' and their mentors' professional growth* [Paper presentation]. European Science Education Research Association (ESERA) Conference, Bologna, Italy.

Alternative Routes to Licensure (8VAC20–23–90), Statutory Authority of the Code of Virginia §§ 22.1–16 and 22.1–298 (2018/2021). https://law.lis.virginia.gov/admincode/title8/agency20/chapter23/section90/

Amichai, S., & Ron, S. (2018). Making educational excellence in mathematics accessible to disadvantaged children: The case of Teach First Israel. *K-12 Mathematics Education in Israel: Issues and Innovations, 13*, 285–292. https://doi.org/10.1142/9789813231191_0031

Avargil, S., Kohen, Z., & Dori, Y. J. (2020). Trends and perceptions of choosing chemistry as a major and a career. *Chemistry Education Research and Practice, 21*(2), 668–684. https://doi.org/10.1039/C9RP00158A

Beleidsdomein Onderwijs en Vorming (2019). Beleidsprioriteiten onderwijs en vorming. [Policy priorities education and training]. *Bijdrage van het beleidsdomein Onderwijs en Vorming aan het regeerakkoord.*

Boone, W. J., Abell, S. K., Volkmann, M. J., Arbaugh, F., & Lannin, J. K. (2011). Evaluating selected perceptions of science and mathematics teachers in an alternative certification program. *International Journal of Science and Mathematics Education, 9*, 551–569.

Bowe, A., Braam, M., Lawrenz, F., & Kirchhoff, A. (2011). Comparison of alternative and traditional teacher certification programs in terms of effectiveness in encouraging STEM pre-service teachers to teach in high need schools. *Journal of the National Association for Alternative Certification, 6*(1), 26–45.

Boyd, D. J., Goldhaber, D. D., Lankford, H., & Wyckoff, J. H. (2007). The effect of certification and preparation on teacher quality. *The Future of Children, 17*(1), 45–68. https://doi.org/10.1353/foc.2007.0000

Boyd, D. J., Grossman, P. L., Lankford, H., Loeb, S., & Wyckoff, J. (2009). Teacher preparation and student achievement. *Educational Evaluation and Policy Analysis, 31*(4), 416–440. https://doi.org/10.3102/0162373709353129

Bryant, M. R. (2014). *Provisionally licensed teachers impact on student achievement* (UMI Number: 3681286) (Doctoral dissertation). Regent University. *ProQuest Dissertations Publishing.*

Burbank, M., Bates, A., & Schrum, L. (2009). Expanding teacher preparation pathways for paraprofessionals: A recruiting seminar series. *Teacher Education Quarterly, 36*(2), 199–216.

Carver-Thomas, D. (2018). *Diversifying the teaching profession: How to recruit and retain teachers of color.* Learning Policy Institute. https://learningpolicyinstitute.org/product/diversifying-teaching-profession-report

Charette, R. (2013). IEEE Spectrum commentary: "The STEM crisis is a myth" (2013). *Physics Today, 50*, 44–49. https://doi.org/10.1063/PT.5.8008

Chudgar, A., Chandra, M., & Razzaque, A. (2014). Alternative forms of teacher hiring in developing countries and its implications: A review of literature. *Teaching and Teacher Education, 37*, 150–161. https://doi.org/10.1016/j.tate.2013.10.009

Corbell, K., Booth, S., & Reiman, A. J. (2010). The commitment and retention intentions of traditionally and alternatively licensed math and science beginning teachers. *Journal of Curriculum and Instruction, 4*(1), 50–69. https://doi.org/10.3776/joci.2010.v4n1p50-69

Cowan, J., Goldhaber, D., Hayes, K., & Theobald, R. (2016). Missing elements in the discussion of teacher shortages. *Educational Researcher, 45*(8), 460–462. https://doi.org/10.3102/0013189X16679145

Dadvand, B., & Dawborn-Gundlach, M. (2020). *The challenge to retain second-career teachers.* University of Melbourne. Department of Teacher Education and Training. https://pursuit.unimelb.edu.au/articles/the-challenge-to-retain-second-career-teachers

Dandolo Partners. (2017). *Teach for Australia program evaluation report.* https://docs.education.gov.au/documents/teach-australia-program-evaluation-report

Darling-Hammond, L., Hyler, M. E., & Gardner, M. (2017). *Effective teacher professional development.* Learning Policy Institute. https://learningpolicyinstitute.org/product/effective-teacher-professional-development-report/

Darling-Hammond, L., & Youngs, P. (2002). "Defining 'highly qualified teachers:' What does 'scientifically-based research' actually tell us?" *Educational Researcher, 31*(9), 13–25. www.aera.net/publications/?id=439

Diekman, A. B., & Benson-Greenwald, T. M. (2018). Fixing STEM workforce and teacher shortages: How goal congruity can inform individuals and institutions. *Policy Insights from the Behavioral and Brain Sciences, 5*(1), 11–18. https://journals.sagepub.com/doi/10.1177/2372732217747889

Donaldson, M. L. (2012). The promise of older novices: Teach for America teachers' age of entry and subsequent retention in teaching and schools. *Teachers College Record, 14*(10), 1–37. www.tcrecord.org/Content. asp?ContentId=16677

Donitsa-Schmidt, S., & Weinberger, Y. (2014). Do alternative teacher education programs manage to attract different candidates and students? *Teacher Development, 18*(4), 530–545. https://doi.org/10.1080/13664530 .2014.963660

Dori, Y. J., Tal, T., Goldman, D., Sarid, A., Lavie-Alon, N., & Shwartz, G. (2019). *Alternative certification teachers' education programs: Characteristics of graduate's integration into the school system.* Chief Scientist, Ministry of Education, Israel (In Hebrew). https://edu.gov.il/sites/ChiefScientist/ongoingresearches/ongoingresearches/ Pages/preservice.aspx

Dupriez, V., Delvaux, B., & Lothaire, S. (2016). Teacher shortage and attrition: Why do they leave? *British Educational Research Journal, 42*(1), 21–39. https://doi.org/10.1002/berj.3193

Feistritzer, C. E. (1998). *Alternative teacher certification-An overview [Online].* www.ncei.com/Alt-TeacherCert. htm

Feistritzer, C. E. (2011). *Profile of teachers in the U.S. 2011.* National Center for Education Information. https:// nces.ed.gov/fastfacts/display.asp?id=28

Flemish Government. (2019). *Politiske prioriteter uddannelse og uddannelse. Bidrag fra Politikområde for uddannelse og erhvervsuddannelse til koalitionsaftalen, 2019–2024.* [Review of Policy priorities education and training. Contribution of the Education and Training policy area to the coalition agreement, 2019–2024]. Department of Education and Training. www.vlaanderen.be/publicaties/beleidsprioriteiten-onderwijs-en-vorming-bijdrage-van-het-beleidsdomein-onderwijs-en-vorming-aan-het-regeerakkoord-2019-2024

Friedrich, D., Walter, M., & Colmenares, E. (2015). Making all children count: Teach For All and the universalizing appeal of data. *Education Policy Analysis Archives, 23*(48). http://dx.doi.org/10.14507/epaa.v23.1797

García, E., & Weiss, E. (2019). U.S. schools struggle to hire and retain teachers. *Economic Policy Institute.* www. epi.org/publication/u-s-schools-struggle-to-hire-and-retain-teachers-the-second-report-in-the-perfect-storm-in-the-teacher-labor-market-series/

Goldhaber, D. D., & Brewer, D. J. (2000). Does teacher certification matter? High school teacher certification status and student achievement. *Educational Evaluation and Policy Analysis, 22*(2), 129–145. https://doi. org/10.3102/01623737022002129

Goldring, R., Taie, S., & Riddles, M. (2014). *Teacher attrition and mobility: Results from the 2012–2013 teacher follow-up survey* (NCES 2014–077). US Department of Education. National Center for Education Statistics.

Goss, P., Sonnemann, J., & Nolan, J. (2019). *Attracting high achievers to teaching.* Grattan Institute. https://grattan. edu.au/wp-content/uploads/2019/08/921-Attracting-high-achievers-to-teaching.pdf

Hargreaves, L., & Flutter, J. (2019). The status of teachers. In G. W. Noblit (Ed.), *Oxford research encyclopedia of education.* https://doi.org/10.1093/acrefore/9780190264093.013.288

Ingersoll, R. M. (2001). Teacher turnover and teacher shortages: An organizational analysis. *American Educational Research Journal, 38*(3), 499–534. https://doi.org/10.3102/00028312038003499

Ingersoll, R. M., Merrill, L., & May, H. (2014). What are the effects of teacher education preparation on beginning teacher attrition? *Consortium for Policy Research in Education.* https://doi.org/10.3102/0002831207306743

Ingersoll, R. M., & Perda, D. (2010). Is the supply of mathematics and science teachers sufficient? *American Educational Research Journal, 47*(3), 563–594. http://dx.doi.org.proxy.library.vcu.edu/10.3102/0002831210370711

Jordan, R., DiCicco, M., & Sabella, L. (2017). "They sit selfishly." Beginning STEM educators' expectations of young adolescent students. *RMLE Online, 40*(6), 1–14. https://doi.org/10.1080/19404476.2017.1320065

Koballa, T. R., Upson Bradbury, L., Mechew, D. C., & Glynn, S. M. (2006). *Conceptions of mentoring and mentoring practice in alternative secondary science teacher education.* Paper presented at the meeting of the Science, Technology Engineering and Mathematics Education Institute, Arlington, VA.

Kyriakides, A. O., & Houssart, J. (2016). Paraprofessionals in Cyprus and England: Perceptions of their role in supporting primary school mathematics. *Research in Mathematics Education, 18*(3), 249–266. https://doi.org /10.1080/14794802.2016.1189352

Ludlow, B. L., Conner, D., & Schechter, J. (2005). Low incidence disabilities and personnel preparation for rural areas: Current status and future trends. *Rural Special Education Quarterly, 24*(3), 15–24. https://doi. org/10.1177/875687050502400303

Marder, M., David, B., & Hamrock, C. (2020). Math and science outcomes for students of teachers from standard and alternative pathways in Texas. *Education Policy Analysis Archives, 28*(27). https://doi.org/10.14507/ epaa.28.4863

Mayer, D. (2019). Knowledge, policy and practice in learning teaching in Australia. In I. Mentor & M. T. Tatto (Eds.), *Knowledge, policy, and practice in teacher education: A cross-national study* (pp. 21–38). England: Bloomsbury Academic.

McConney, A., Woods-McConney, A., & Price, A. (2012). *Fast track teacher education: A review of the research literature on Teach For All schemes*. Murdoch University. Centre for Learning, Change, and Development. http://researchrepository.murdoch.edu.au/id/eprint/10228

Mentzer, G. A., Czerniak, C. M., & Duckett, T. R. (2019). Comparison of two alternative approaches to quality STEM Teacher prep: Fast track and embedded residency programs. *School of Science and Mathematics, 119*, 35–48. https://doi.org/10.1111/ssm.12314

Miller, J. W., McKenna, M. C., & McKenna, B. A. (1998). A comparison of alternatively and traditionally prepared teachers. *Journal of Teacher Education, 49*(3), 165–176. https://doi.org/10.1177/0022487198049003002

Morettini, B. W. (2014). Going back to school: Why STEM professionals decide to teach through alternative certification programs. *Journal of the National Association for Alternative Certification, 9*(2), 3–23. https://eric.ed.gov/?id=EJ1053330

Morrison, J., & Lightner, L. (2017). Putting paraeducators on the path to teacher certification. *Phi Delta Kappan, 98*(8), 43–47. https://doi.org/10.1177%2F0031721717708294

Murnane, R. J., Singer, J. D., Willett, J. B., Kemple, J. J., & Olsen, R. J. (1991). *Who will teach? Policies that matter*. Cambridge: Harvard University Press.

Ng, J. C., & Lizette, P. (2010). Should I stay or should I go? Examining the career choices of alternatively licensed teachers in urban schools. *The Urban Review, 42*(2), 123–142. https://doi.org/10.1007/s11256-009-0120-7

Nixon, R. S., Luft, J. A., & Ross, R. J. (2017). Prevalence and predictors of out-of-field teaching in the first five years. *Journal of Research in Science Teaching, 54*(9), 1197–1218. https://doi.org/10.1002/tea.21402

Organization for Economic Cooperation and Development. (2012). *Equity and quality in education: Supporting disadvantaged students and schools*. OECD Publishing. http://dx.doi.org/10.1787/9789264130852-en

Pennington, A., & Stanford, J. (2019). *Future work of Australian graduates: The changing landscape of university employment transitions in Australia*. The Centre for Future Work at the Australia Institute. http://hdl.voced.edu.au/10707/523863

Proweller, A., & Mitchener, C. P. (2004). Building teacher identity with urban youth: Voices of beginning middle school science teachers in an alternative certification program. *Journal of Research in Science Teaching, 41*(10), 1044–1062. https://doi.org/10.1002/tea.20036

Pugatch, T. (2017, April). Is teacher certification an effective tool for developing countries? *IZA World of Labor, Institute of Labor Economics*, 349–349.

Ramot, R., & Donitsa-Schmidt, S. (2021). COVID-19: Education policy, autonomy, and alternative teacher education in Israel. *Perspectives in Education, 39*(1), 372–389. https://doi.org/10.18820/2519593X/pie.v39.i1.23

Richmond, G., Bartell, T. G., Floden, R. E., & Jones, N. D. (2020). How research sheds light on the pivotal role of mentors in teacher preparation. *Journal of Teacher Education, 71*(1), 6–8. https://doi.org/10.1177/0022487119887752

Riggs, I. M., & Enochs, L. G. (1990). Toward the development of an elementary teacher's science teaching efficacy belief instrument. *Science Education, 74*, 625–637.

Rosenholtz, S. (1989). Workplace conditions that affect teacher quality and commitment: Implications for teacher induction programs. *The Elementary School Journal, 89*(4), 421–439. https://doi.org/10.1086/461584

Shwartz, G., & Dori, Y. J. (2020). Transition into teaching: Second career teachers' professional identity. *Eurasia Journal of Mathematics, Science and Technology Education, 16*(11), 1–19. https://doi.org/10.29333/ejmste/8502

Shen, J. (1998). Alternative certification, minority teachers, and urban education. *Education and Urban Society, 31*(1), 30–41. https://doi.org/10.1177/0013124598031001003

Singh, A. (2017, December 18). Teacher's crisis in India: 11 Lakh untrained teachers in workforce. *NDTV Education*. www.ndtv.com/education/teachers-crisis-in-india-11-lakh-untrained-teachers-in-workforce-1783246.

Smith, T., & Ingersoll, R. (2004). What are the effects of induction and mentoring on beginning teacher turnover? *American Educational Research Journal, 41*(3), 681–714. https://doi.org/10.3102/00028312041003681

Thomas, K. R., Friedman-Nimz, R., Mahlios, M. C., & O'Brien, B. (2005). Where are they coming from? Beyond the demographics of individuals seeking an alternative route to mathematics and science teacher licensure. *Action in Teacher Education, 27*(1), 15–25. https://doi.org/10.1080/01626620.2005.10463370

Tigchelaar, A., Brouwerb, N., & Vermunta, J. D. (2010). Tailor-made: Towards a pedagogy for educating second-career teachers. *Educational Research Review 5*(2), 164–183. http://dx.doi.org/10.1016/j.edurev.2009.11.002

Tozer, S., O'Connell, C., & Burstein, P. (2006). Four perspectives on alternate routes to teacher certification. *Success in High-Need Schools, 1*(2). www.northcentralcollege.edu/sites/default/files/documents/2016-11/Success

Tschannen-Moran, M., & Hoy, A. (2001). Teacher efficacy: Capturing an elusive construct. *Teaching and Teacher Education, 17*, 783–805.

UNESCO. (2016, October). *The World needs almost 69 million new teachers to reach the 2030 education goals.* UIS FACT SHEET, *29*, 1–16. http://uis.unesco.org/en/document/world-needs-almost-69-million-new-teachers-reach-2030-education-goals

Unruh, L., & Holt, J. (2010). First-year teaching experiences: Are they different for traditionally versus alternatively certified teachers? *Action in Teacher Education, 32*(3), 3–14. https://doi.org/10.1080/01626620.20 10.10463555

Vancaeneghem, J. (2018, September 5). Nearly half of secondary school teachers quit within five years. *HLN News.* www.hln.be/onderwijs/bijna-helft-leerkrachten-secundair-onderwijs-stopt-binnen-de-vijf-jaar~a4bcdad0/

Weinberger, Y., & Donitsa-Schmidt, S. (2016). A longitudinal comparative study of alternative and traditional teacher education programs in Israel: Initial training, induction period, school placement, and retention rates. *Educational Studies, 2*(6), 552–572. https://doi.org/10.1080/00131946.2016.1231679

Whitford, D. K., Zhang, D., & Katsiyannis, A. (2018). Traditional vs. alternative teacher preparation programs: A meta-analysis. *Journal of Child and Family Studies, 27*(671–685). https://doi.org/10.1007/s10826-017-0932-0

Whitford, D. K., Zhang, D., & Katsiyannis, A. (2019). Academic achievement of students taught by teachers from differing preparation programs. In C. A. Lubienski & T. J. Brewer (Eds.), *Learning to teach in an era of privatization: Global trends in teacher preparation* (pp. 213–227). New York: Teachers College Press.

Woods, J. R. (2016). *Mitigating teacher shortages: Alternative teacher education* [Policy Brief]. Education Commission of the States. www.ecs.org/mitigating-teacher-shortages-alternative-teacher-certification/

Wright, D. S., Balgopal, M. M., McMeeking, L. B., & Weinberg, A. E. (2019). Developing resilient K-12 STEM teachers. *Advances in Developing Human Resources, 21*(10), 16–34. https://doi.org/10.1177/1523422318814483

Yin, Y. M., Dooley, K., & Mu, G. M. (2019). Why do graduates from prestigious universities choose to teach in disadvantaged schools? Lessons from an alternative teacher preparation program in China. *Teaching and Teacher Education, 77*, 378–387. https://doi.org/10.1016/j.tate.2018.10.011

SECTION 3

Initial Teacher Preparation – Situated Aspects

Section Editor: David F. Jackson

The professional approach of many preservice science teacher educators who began their careers in the 1990s was heavily influenced by an extremely widely distributed edited volume (Schafer, 1994) in which many more experienced authors shared various aspects of their theoretical expertise, and quite a few intuitive/anecdotal insights as well. One major difference between that book and this one is that it made very little reference to empirical research studies. But another is that the earlier work implicitly but strongly presumed that essentially, all initial teacher preparation occurred, as reflected in its title, "behind the methods class door," and that, as a practical matter, the individual science teacher educator was largely unconstrained by external standards or regulations or potentially empowered by resources outside of the university setting. The chapters collected in this section are an attempt to remedy both of those deficiencies by reviewing and summarizing research on the many aspects of initial science teacher preparation today that are situated very much outside the door of the traditional teacher education classroom, and which can also very much influence the crucially important work that still occurs in that traditional setting.

Cofré, Vergara, Santibáñez, and Pavez, all from Chile, first describe their vision of the overall landscape of trends, challenges, and future directions in preservice science teacher education. Their analysis identifies four categories of issues as most important: the variety of routes to becoming a teacher and the bureaucratic structure of training systems in a variety of nations; important explicit differences in the curriculum of teacher preparation programs; characteristics of student practicum experiences in particular; and the relevance of research to the practice of science teacher educators, especially in relation to the development of pedagogical content knowledge (PCK) in science as a central focus. They conclude that, in many ways, there is a clear pattern of differences between European countries on the one hand and Asian and American countries on the other, in terms of both the level of education at which formal teacher preparation typically resides (graduate versus undergraduate or professional school), and general orientation (more academic/theoretical versus more practical, pragmatic, and field-based).

Liu, Yang, and Liu, all based in Beijing, survey research on the effects of formal policy, as enacted by various levels of government and/or professional organizations, on efforts to improve the quality of beginning science teachers. Specific aspects that they address include: the nature of formal qualifications required for entering the teaching profession; the importance of how quality teaching and teacher preparation are depicted and described in widely influential standards documents; how the design of training programs is influenced by the various institutions and stakeholders involved; and the recruitment and admission of students into programs. Their chapter also introduces a thread that all of the subsequent ones will pick up prominently, the overarching concern for equity.

Gilbert and Hobbs, in an antipodal collaboration between the United States and Australia, examine the diversity of partnerships that university-based teacher educators have formed with individual schools and school districts, larger networks of schools, and other professional and community organizations. They pay special attention to operationally defining the terminology used to communicate various kinds of practices within such partnerships, and they consider not only the best-known and most formalized type, known as Professional Development Schools in the US and the Alliance Model in Australia, but also those involving businesses, scientific researchers, and community organizations, especially in urban areas. A consistent finding across many of these types of interactions between prospective teachers, adults other than their university instructors, and children is that positive growth in their science teaching self-efficacy can hardly be presumed as a result – these authors emphasize the need for careful collaboration, communication, and coordination across an extended period of time in order for all concerned to overcome the inevitable challenges.

Childers and Hite, both from the United States, highlight the rapidly changing nature of the actual and potential role of emerging electronic information and communication technologies in initial teacher education. They focus heavily on considerations of equity, balancing their account by highlighting the frequent tradeoff between consideration of the inherent affordances of a technology and the often limited degree of access to it, both on the part of prospective teachers and their future students. They find that this is somewhat of a "moving target," and that both the actual or potential advantages and the often very challenging problems on which teacher educators and novice teachers focus the most vary greatly between nations and settings.

Another Chilean group, Izquierdo, Marzábal, Merino, Cabello, Moreira, Cuellar, Delgado, Manrique, and Soto, focus on research on the important but difficult issue of educating teacher candidates about one of the most frequent subjects of research in science education in the past decade, the role of discursive practices in teaching and learning. Their findings, organized and presented according to three theoretical-practical analytical dimensions (disciplinary/epistemological, linguistic, and pedagogical), often highlight a similar central issue in EACH dimension, which is that it is exceedingly difficult for preservice and novice teachers to teach in a way in which they themselves have not learned. For this reason, their central recommendation for action is that a coherent and consistent focus on the role of science discourse, across all courses and experiences in a teacher preparation program, is essential if this family of teaching approaches is to have any probability of success. They furthermore emphasize that that focus must be made explicit by the faculty and therefore hopefully prominent in the consciousness of the students, both at the elementary, secondary, and university levels.

Finally, Cooke-Nieves, Wallace, Gupta, and Howes, all of the American Museum of Natural History in the United States, describe the unique value that engagement with informal science learning environments (ISLEs) can have for developing science teachers, particularly in regard to addressing issues of educational equity. Key theoretical perspectives that are emphasized as naturally related to ISLEs include Place-Based Education and Science Identity. These authors' central argument, and perhaps for some a surprising one, is that experiences in learning and teaching about science in museums, zoos, parks, wildlife sanctuaries, gardens, aquaria, science centers, community-based organizations, and other designed settings can play an important and positive role even in the education of teachers who plan to work in more conventional classroom settings. This is presented as especially true when a goal is to broaden novice teachers' conceptions of what students from underrepresented groups are interested in, or are capable of, doing. But it is noted that there is a relative paucity of research explicitly examining the effect of ISLE experiences on diverse groups of students and of prospective teachers. Another prominent problem is that scaling up the "magic" of informal settings, both in terms of numbers of people and frequency of their interaction, is a significant challenge.

Reference

Schafer, L. E. (Ed.) (1994). *Behind the methods class door: Educating elementary and middle school science teachers.* Association for the Education of Teachers in Science (AETS) Yearbook. https://eric.ed.gov/?id=ED372923

12

PRESERVICE SCIENCE TEACHERS EDUCATION AROUND THE GLOBE

Trends, Challenges, and Future Directions

Hernán Cofré, Claudia Vergara, David Santibáñez, and José Manuel Pavez

Introduction

In recent years, there have been multiple efforts made to summarize, describe, and analyze initial teacher training in general (e.g., Conway et al., 2009; Valenčič & Vogrinc, 2011; Bauer & Prenzel, 2012; Flores, 2017 [and eight other articles in the special issue of *European Journal of Teacher Education*, Volume 40, Issue 3]), and preservice science teacher education (PSTE) in particular (e.g., Abell, 2000; Lederman & Lederman, 2015 [and six other articles in the special issue of *Journal of Science Teacher Education*, Volume 26, Issue 1]; Pedersen et al., 2017), around the globe. Although these analyses and comparisons have led to proposals of different qualities that science teacher training programs and their graduates should have, such as a strong understanding of the content and the nature of science (NOS), a developed pedagogical content knowledge (PCK), or a research-based pedagogy to face current student diversity (e.g., Darling-Hammond et al., 2005; Olson et al., 2015), it is impossible to identify the single best way to educate future science teachers (Lederman & Lederman, 2015).

On the other hand, in the context of new curriculum standards for science education, namely, the Next Generation Science Standards (NGSS) in the USA, Windschitl and Stroupe (2017) have indicated that teacher educators should consider modifying the practical experiences of preservice science teachers to be based on the principles of research in science education and focused on the achievement of learning by school students. However, several different national and international reports and comparative research studies have shown that significant transformations in initial teacher education in various countries are always connected to changing approaches to teacher professionalism in accordance with new government policies, which usually go beyond the traditional boundaries of the subject matter or science education research and are usually more related to the economic, cultural, or political context (Menter et al., 2017; Pedersen et al., 2017). This finding may explain the gap that still exists between the relevance that science education research assigns to the development of PCK in teacher training (e.g., Loughran et al., 2008) and the coverage that this type of knowledge has in science teacher training programs (e.g., Pedersen et al., 2017; McComas et al., 2018). This mismatch between research and policy in science teacher education could also explain one of the longstanding worldwide deficits in teacher training, i.e., the effective implementation of a curriculum that links theory and practice (e.g., Cofré et al., 2015; Flores, 2016).

DOI: 10.4324/9781003098478-15

Finally, there are many aspects of science teacher education that are still under discussion, such as whether consecutive teacher education is a better model than that of concurrent training (e.g., Zuzovsky & Donitsa-Schmidt, 2017), what the best indicators of effective science teaching are (McComas et al., 2018), and how to implement research-based education in science teacher programs (e.g., Flores, 2016; McComas et al., 2018).

In this context, this chapter describes and analyzes four of the most relevant aspects of PSTE around the world, namely, routes and training systems, the curricula or knowledge included in programs, the characteristics of practice or practicum experience, and the relevance given to educational research during initial education training. Specifically, it attempts to answer the following questions: What is the diversity of training frameworks in preservice science teacher education (degree requirements, training routes, etc.)? What kind of knowledge is considered critical to becoming a science teacher in different countries? What are the specific traits of practicum experience around the globe? What are the specific research experience requirements to become a science teacher in different countries?

To answer these questions, we examine not only the existing research on science teacher education and teacher education in general but also official reports from governments and international organizations that are focused on preservice teacher education (e.g., ministries of education and teacher education standards).

Structure of PSTE Around the Globe

The current history of teacher training policies demonstrates that a growing number of countries have opted for a standards-based curriculum structure (Table 12.1; see also Bauer & Prenzel, 2012). In most cases, there is a list of disciplinary and pedagogical knowledge that graduates must achieve by the end of the program, which can vary considerably in the level of detail of its description. Standards can be national (e.g., England, Russia, Taiwan) or vary by state or province (e.g., Canada, USA). In cases where these types of performance descriptions do not exist, there are other forms of close regulation by the government (e.g., China, South Korea, Argentina). In very large countries, centralized teacher training guidelines are generated but maintain local flexibility; in some cases, this flexibility depends on the geographical, economic, and cultural contexts of each region of the territory (e.g., China), while in others the administrative units of each region may define their own criteria, which may include idiomatic and religious conditions (e.g., Canada).

One area in which there is considerable international uniformity is that of the conditions for entering the teaching career. In all continents and in most cases, the requirement is at least a bachelor's degree (Table 12.1). Some countries have alternative requirements (e.g., Japan, Australia), and after the Bologna Process guidelines were implemented in most European countries, science teacher education moved towards a two-stage model, which includes a 3-year undergraduate program based on the subject matter that leads to a bachelor's degree and a 3-year (e.g., Portugal) or, more commonly, 2-year (e.g., Germany, Finland, France) professional master's degree in the teaching of the subject. Some countries have alternative routes, such as the case of the USA, where different states allow applications from previous science-related careers, or in South Korea, where it is possible to apply for pedagogy certification programs at the end of the second year of study towards a career unrelated to education. Most European countries have defined that the required master's degree must meet the 300 European Credit Transfer and Accumulation System (ECTS) requirement. In some cases, the defined requirements can be met during secondary education, as in the case of Macau, which has a 4-year integrated science program, the approval of which allows direct application to the teacher training program.

Two common models of initial teacher education are prevalent in many countries: the concurrent model, in which disciplinary studies and pedagogical studies are integrated and taught at the same

Table 12.1 Data about the structure of initial science teacher education in 25 countries

Country	National (NS)/State Standards (SS), Centralized Regulation (CR) or Own Programs (OP)	Typical Route: Bachelor's (B) or Master's (M) Requirement, Selective Test (ST), Others (O)	Number of Years	Admission Requirements: Grade Scores (GS), General Admission Exam (GAE), Special Test (ST), Interview (I), Other (O)	Exit Requirements: Graduation (G), Examination (E), Application for Working (AW), License (L), Bachelor (BEd), Master (MEd)	Model: Concurrent (C); Sequential (S)
Europe						
Czech Republic[2]	NS	B or M	4–5	GAE + I	G	S (mostly)
England[1]	NS	B	3–4	GS + ST	G	S
Finland[1,7]	NS	B + M	5	ST + O	G	C
France[1,7]	NS	B + M	5	ST	G	C or S
Germany[1]	NS	B + M	5	ST	MEd + E	C
Netherlands[2,3]	NS + OP	M	4	GAE + ST	G	S
Poland[2,5]	NS	B or M	4–5	GAE + ST	AW	C (mostly)
Portugal[1]	NS	M	5–6	No requirements	G	S
Russia[2,5,6]	NS	B or M	5	ST	E	C (mostly)
Slovenia[2,4]	CR	B, M or O	4–5	GAE	E	C or S
Middle East						
Israel[1]	NS	B	4–5	No requirements	L	C or S
Turkey[1,5]	CR	B	5	GAE	L + E	S
Americas						
Argentina[1,11]	CR	B	4	It depends on the university	G	C
Canada[1,8,9]	SS	B or M	4–5	It depends on the university	BEd	C or S
Chile[11]	NS	B	4.5–5	GS + GAE	G	C (mostly)
Colombia[11]	CR	B	4–5	ST	BEd	C
USA[1,9,10]	SS	B or O	5	States GAE	E + L	C or S
Asia						
China[1,12,17]	CR + NS	O	4	ST	G + L	C
Japan[1,3,19]	NS	B or M	4	GAE	L + MEd	C
Macau[12]	CR	B or O	4	No requirements	G	S
South Korea[1,3,18]	CR	O	4	GS + ST + I	MEd	C
Taiwán[13]	NS	ST	4	ST	E	C
Oceania						
Australia[1,3,15]	NS	B or M	4	GS + ST	G	S
Indonesia[14]	CR	B	4	GS + GAE	G	S
Africa						
South Africa[16]	CR	B	4	GS + ST + I	E	C or S

1 = Pedersen et al. (2017); 2 = Valenčič and Vogrinc (2011); 3 = OECD (2019); 4 = Štemberger (2020); 5 = Aykac and Sahin (2018); 6 = Valeeva and Gafurov (2017); 7 = Evagorou et al. (2015); 8 = Tippett and Milford (2017); 9 = Olson et al. (2015); 10 = Allan (2017); 11 = Cofré et al. (2015); 12 = Liu and Liu (2017); 13 = Tuan and Lu (2019); 14 = Faisal and Martin (2019); 15 = Treagust et al. (2015); 16 = Taylor et al. (2019); 17 = Zhang and Wan (2017); 18 = Im et al. (2016); 19 = Ramírez and Mekochi (2015).

time, and the sequential model, which focuses mostly on pedagogy following the disciplinary studies already completed by university graduates who are interested in going into teaching. Canada, Israel, South Africa, and many other countries currently offer both models (Table 12.1). In South Africa, for example, one model is a 3-year general bachelor of science (BSc) degree followed by a Postgraduate Certificate in Education (PGCE), and the second model is a 4-year bachelor of education (BEd) (McComas et al., 2018). In the United States, students with science degrees are increasingly being encouraged to skip traditional teacher preparation and instead take just a few summer seminars and move directly into the classroom (Olson et al., 2015; McComas et al., 2018). In other countries, such as France, Germany, or Japan, there is concurrent training, which is also seen in most Latin American countries (Cofré et al., 2015; Pedersen et al., 2017). Although it is difficult to determine which of these models is the most effective, a recent study using an important sample (11,978 student teachers from Israel) claimed that graduates of the sequential model outperformed graduates of the concurrent model in most of the measurements taken in the study (Zuzovsky & Donitsa-Schmidt, 2017). The authors proposed that although it is commonly perceived that the concurrent model allows for the better integration of curricular components, it might have, in fact, a negative effect on student outcomes because condensing all of the curricular components together might result in the shallow treatment of each component. Regarding the duration of the programs, the vast majority vary between 4 and 5 years (Table 12.1), and there is no evident relationship between duration and concurrent or sequential organization.

The admission criteria for science teacher education programs offer a variety of formats that are difficult to attribute to geographic or sociopolitical trends. Most of the countries reviewed select pre-service teachers based on standardized assessments. Such tests can either be focused on basic knowledge and intended for university selection in general (e.g., Slovenia, Turkey, Japan) or be specially designed for science teacher programs (e.g., Russia, Colombia, China). In some cases, both types of tests are applied (e.g., Netherlands, Poland). These tests are usually national in nature, although some countries have specific tests for different states or provinces (e.g., USA, Canada). The selection of applicants is usually carried out based on the achievement of either a minimum criterion-based score or a minimum percentile rank. The consideration of grades earned in secondary education is not common, although when such consideration exists, it occurs in combination with national or special test scores (e.g., England, Chile, Indonesia, Australia). In only some cases, the selection system incorporates personal interviews with the applicant, such as in Finland, the Czech Republic, and South Africa. In contrast, there are countries that prefer to rely on the quality of the training program itself, without special entry requirements (e.g., Israel, Portugal, Macau), while in other cases, selection is a condition defined by each university (e.g., Canada, Argentina). There is a clear relationship between incentives to choose a teaching career and the rigor of entry requirements. Due to the prestige of the profession and the economic stability it entails, several barriers must be overcome to enter the science teacher program in Finland, including previous pedagogical experience, multiple interviews, and selection tests. In the case of Taiwan, there is a selection test that measures Chinese, English, and mathematics, in addition to physics, chemistry or biology, which is passed by only 30% of applicants (Tuan & Lu, 2019).

In most cases, the requirement for graduation from the program is the approval of the courses or credits of the study plan, including professional practices and, eventually, a thesis (Table 12.1). In such cases, graduation is accompanied by a bachelor's degree in education. Countries such as Slovenia, Russia, the USA, and Taiwan require passing an exam. In the case of Taiwan, after completing one semester of internship, a first-level certificate is obtained. For the second level (qualification), written exams are taken in the department of education of the county in which one wants to work, and one must demonstrate his or her pedagogical skills in science by presenting a class in front of a committee of expert teachers (Tuan & Lu, 2019). In Japan, once the teacher's license is obtained, it must be updated periodically as a means of keeping up to date on new teaching strategies (Ramírez & Mekochi, 2015).

More data and comparative research are required to verify all these global trends. In the next section, we will review the great diversity that also exists in PSTE in relation to curricula.

Curricular Aspects of PSTE Around the Globe

Another question we are trying to answer in this chapter is: What kind of knowledge is considered critical to becoming a science teacher in different countries? To answer this question, we use pedagogical content knowledge (PCK) as a guiding framework since it has been recognized as an essential and unifying topic for the science teacher education field (Loughran et al., 2008; van Driel et al., 2014). There is a global trend in the preparation of science and mathematics teachers aimed at generating opportunities to develop student teachers' PCK (e.g., Aydin et al., 2015; Pedersen et al., 2017). PCK has also been recognized as an organizing framework for science methods courses (e.g., Olson et al., 2015; Sickel & Witzig, 2017). Considering the multiple dimensions recognized in PCK models, it is easy to notice variations of emphasis in science teacher education programs around the globe and even within the same country. In terms of coursework, programs typically cover three main areas with different emphases, namely, general pedagogy, science content, and science pedagogy (Pedersen et al., 2017; Figure 12.1). In most of the reviewed countries, science content courses represent the most significant proportion of the science teacher programs' curricula. For instance, in England, science content courses can represent up to 75% of the coursework. This is because students need to complete the requirements for a bachelor's degree in science first, and after this, they then complete 1 year of coursework focused on science education to obtain their certification for teaching. In countries such as the Czech Republic and Slovenia, this proportion can reach nearly 80% (Figure 12.1). This high proportion of science content courses in the curriculum contrasts with the findings of studies showing that subject matter knowledge (SMK) alone is not enough for effective teaching and that it is necessary to develop PCK and general pedagogical knowledge (GPK) (Zeidler, 2002; Förtsch et al., 2016; Mahler et al., 2017). For example, Mahler et al. (2017) studied the relationship between different types of teachers' knowledge, including SMK and PCK, and the performance achieved by their students. After analyzing the knowledge of 48 biology teachers and their respective students' achievements ($N = 1036$), these authors found a positive and significant relationship between teachers' PCK and students' performance, but not between teachers' SMK and their students' learning. On the other hand, in countries such as Japan, Turkey, and France, science content courses represent only slightly over 35% of the teacher preparation curricula (Figure 12.1).

General pedagogy courses consistently represent a smaller proportion of teacher preparation than science content courses. General pedagogy can represent as little as 5% in places such as England. Similarly, Slovenia, Portugal, and Turkey are some of the countries where general pedagogy courses represent 10% or less of the curriculum of programs (Figure 12.1). In contrast, in countries such as Japan and Macau, general pedagogy courses represent approximately 50% of the coursework, while most of the reviewed countries range between 20% and 30% (Figure 12.1). The different PCK models recognize the relevance of general pedagogy as essential knowledge to be developed in science teachers and as a foundation for teachers' PCK. Carlson and Daehler (2019) argue that this generic pedagogical knowledge is mostly developed in science teacher preparation programs, which can later be strengthened through teaching experiences. Therefore, it is crucial to provide teachers with a solid base regarding general pedagogy during their initial teacher preparation.

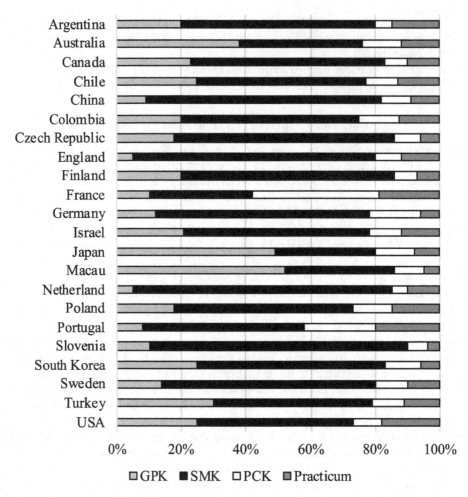

Figure 12.1 Proportions of the different curricular areas covered in science teacher preparation programs around the globe

Of the three main areas covered in science teacher education programs, PCK or science pedagogy represents the smallest proportion of the coursework. In most of the reviewed countries, it represents less than 15%, except for France and Turkey, where these courses represent, on average, 35% of the curricula of their teacher preparation programs (Figure 12.1). It is worth mentioning that in these two countries, the proportion of general pedagogy courses is low (≤ 10%), which helps to explain the higher ratio of science pedagogy courses, which are also known elsewhere as science methods courses (e.g., the USA) or courses in science didactics (e.g., Germany, Portugal). In contrast, there are countries where science methods courses represent as low as 5% of the curriculum, such as Argentina and Slovenia. Science methods courses play a crucial role in science teacher preparation, since they have the potential to promote integration between the subject matter and pedagogical perspectives, theoretical and practical dimensions, coursework, and student teaching experiences (Anderson, 1997). Research has suggested that the nature and quality of these courses are positively associated with effective teaching (Druva & Anderson, 1983; Smith, 1999), and they have the potential to impact the practice of new teachers (Abell & Bryan, 1997). However, there is strong evidence from science teacher preparation around the world that part of the curriculum focused on developing PCK is still small (Cofré et al., 2015; Pedersen et al., 2017).

In terms of practice or practicum experience, which is defined as a school-based initiation to professional practice that is supervised by school teachers and university supervisors, there is a great variation in the extent and models of different science teacher preparation programs around the globe (see also the next section). Such practicum experiences represent between 5% and 20% of the science teacher preparation programs' curricula in most of the reviewed countries (Figure 12.1). However, they account for as little as 5% or less of the curriculum in countries such as Slovenia and Macau. The case of South Africa is special as practicum experiences can represent up to 27% of the curriculum. The typical length of the science teacher preparation programs is 4 years, and the practicum ranges between 10 and 35 weeks total, with a final teaching internship lasting from 10 to 12 weeks. We elaborate more on the practicum experiences in the next section.

Practicum in the PSTE Around the Globe

Although practice or practicum experience is recognized as a core element in the PSTE curriculum, there is no consensus about the related goals, strategies or required competences (Flores, 2016). There is a great diversity of formulas to prepare, in the practical aspect, future science teachers, either in terms of duration, chronology or type of practicum (Table 12.2). For example, in Finland, science teachers have only two instances of professional practicum: one positioned at the end of their bachelor's degree training that involves working in a classroom for 5 weeks, and another classroom experience positioned at the end of their master's degree in education that has a duration of 8 weeks (Jyrhämä, 2007; Evagorou et al., 2015). This format contrasts with other nations in which practicum experience is included in a higher proportion of the curricular activities (Figure 12.1). Despite the differences, one of the first conclusions that can be obtained from the analysis of Table 12.2 is that, in most countries, the time devoted to practical training is close to 15 weeks in total throughout the curriculum. In most countries, there is an early and progressive approach to practicums in the real context of teaching (e.g., Poland, Czech Republic, Chile, and Canada), where the initial practices correspond to observation activities and can begin as early as the first year (Table 12.2). On the other hand, the final practicum, internship, or clinical experience usually has an average duration of 10 weeks, ranging from 6 weeks in China (Lui & Lui, 2017) to 24 weeks in England (Evagorou et al., 2015). Usually, this practice includes activities dedicated to working in the school context, where the preservice science teacher assumes all the responsibilities of an in-service teacher (e.g., plans and conducts lessons) and often conducts action research or writes reports on case studies about this experience.

As important as the structural aspects is the quality of the triad, which has been described as being crucial to the success of practical experience. The functioning of both the institutional relationship between the university and the school and the personal relationship between preservice science teachers, university supervisors, and school mentors is crucial, especially in facilitating the critical and constructive reflection that should be promoted in preservice teachers (Fayne, 2007; Lawson et al., 2015). For example, Busher et al. (2015), in a study that included more than 400 interns from England and Turkey (approximately 30% science teachers), showed that preservice teachers highly valued being able to know the needs of school students and to be able to work with more experienced teachers who taught them how to improve group management. However, the preservice teachers also criticized the practice when their school mentor teachers did not let them innovate or restricted them in their proposals for generating learning opportunities. In this same study, trainee teachers in both countries emphasized the need to have the opportunity to reflect on their practices to learn from their experiences and how the role of the supervising professor at the university is crucial in this task. Despite all the literature detailing the importance of mentoring and supervision,

Table 12.2 Examples of different models of practicums, internships, or school placements by country

Country	Task in the Practicum	Weeks and Temporality	Support by University and School
Europe			
Czech Republic[2]	All aim to link practical activities to references disciplines, especially subject didactics.	Four weeks at the second cycle (master's).	Mentors are experienced teachers who have accepted this activity as a professional duty.
England[1]	The role for preservice science teachers in their first year is to act as an observer-apprentice and watch experienced classroom teachers in action. They may support small groups of learners and begin to plan and coteach lessons. In the second year, they teach on their own.	In 2 years at two different schools. 24 weeks total. The majority of PGCE courses are based around two equal placements of 60 days (12 weeks) each year.	One tutor from the university and two mentors at the school (not necessarily a science teacher). Preservice science teachers are judged by six observed lessons.
Germany[1]	There is a first observation practice, and then two practices where the student oversees the course every four weeks.	Usually, two practicums, i.e., the first at the bachelor's degree program (10 ECTS), and the second a school internship at the master's degree level (10 ECTS). Between 5 and 15 weeks in total.	Teacher trainers from the school and from the university.
Netherlands[2,3]	Preservice teachers start with observation and small amounts of teaching and finish with a "leraar in opleiding" in which students work at a school with almost full responsibilities (in some cases, the schools pay a salary to the students).	Teaching practices start the first week of the 1-year program. The second semester is fully at school (15 weeks).	Teacher trainers from the school (mentor) and from the university (science educator). Training of mentors is offered.
Portugal[1,20]	The practicum involves an initial period of lesson observation and context analysis for the design of an individual project that integrates teaching and research. The teaching practice must be strongly supported by educational research.	48 ECTS (1 year). A total of 4–6 weeks of supervised teaching practice.	The practicum is school-based, but it also includes university-based supervision seminars.

Country	Task in the Practicum	Weeks and Temporality	Support by University and School
Russia[2,5,6]	From the first year onwards, preservice teachers start practicum teaching and visit schools 1 day a week in the first semester and each week in the second semester. Internships are available during summer months at training and other camps.	Four to 20 weeks. In the 4th year, the students teach in schools for a period of 10 weeks.	Teacher trainers are from the school and from the university.
Sweden[2,17]	Observation, guided lessons and assessed lessons. Every practicum period is included in a university course.	One-week introduction at the beginning of the program. After that, each program decides when the practicum takes place, but all programs have at least a half a year of placement (30 ECTS).	The university pays the municipality or directly to private schools for the placement. Training of mentors is offered.
Americas			
Brazil[19]	There are two or three observation practices at the beginning and then a practice where the student is fully teaching.	There are 400 hours of practice at schools beginning in the third year of the program (12.5% of the curriculum).	Teacher trainers from the university and mentors from the schools.
Canada[1,8,9]	Includes practicum placements and may include alternative educational formats ranging from observation to independent teaching as students progress through their program.	One day per week for 16 consecutive weeks. From 50 to 120 days. Students have 3 weeks of practicum interspersed within their first year. In their second and final years, students spend 7 months in a single field placement from the end of August until the end of March.	Students meet weekly on the university campus with their faculty advisor to participate in seminars on topics related to teaching and learning theory and to share their field experiences with their peers.
Chile[11]	Three formats, i.e., observation and context, teaching and responsibility. Usually includes a research report in the last practicum.	Since 2019, it is mandatory that the practicum correspond to 15% of the curriculum. Starting at the middle of the program and in the last year, students spend between 10 and 20 weeks at school, but not in a full-time model.	Teacher trainers from the university and mentors from the schools. University-based supervision seminars are included. Preservice teachers are judged by 2–3 observed lessons and a report about their whole practicum.

(Continued)

Table 12.2 (Continued)

Country	Task in the Practicum	Weeks and Temporality	Support by University and School
Asia			
China[1,12]	There are two practicums. First, the students observe teaching and management and then make report. Second, the students must teach.	For the first practicum, 1–3 weeks. For the last practicum, 12–15 weeks, usually in the last year of the program.	Guided by a university faculty member.
Japan[1,3,19]	Lesson study and daily journal writing for reflection.	2–4 weeks.	Pre- and post-meetings with a university professor.
Oceania			
Australia[1,3,15]	At the internship, student teachers must take over the full teaching for 20 hours each week.	The field experience is divided into two separate phases. For the first years, the experience occurs around 3 weeks each year/semester, with the expectation of an increasing practicing teaching load. The final internship lasts for 10 weeks.	Mentor teachers maintain the duty of care of the preservice teachers and provide feedback on lesson plans. University-based supervisors liaise with the mentor teachers and observe each teacher candidate's teaching at least once per placement.

★References are the same as those used in Table 12.1, except for the inclusion of 20 = Marcondes et al. (2017).

countries have many different models of practicum structure (Table 12.2). For example, in England, there are two kinds of mentor teachers at the school: one is a science teacher who focuses on classroom and students' issues, and the other is a nonscience teacher who focuses on school-context issues. However, in most countries, preservice teachers are supervised by a university teacher and a school teacher or mentor (e.g., Chile, Netherlands, Russia, Germany).

Much research has shown that supervising teachers' more reflective accompaniment improves the results of practicum experience (Fayne, 2007; Lawson et al., 2015). On the other hand, much evidence shows that the mentor teacher inherently plays a central role in the quality of the student's practical experience purely through the example that they model by their own performance, as well as the type of accompaniment they use and the type of explicit feedback they give to the student about the actions that they take (Cameron & Baker, 2004; Simpson et al., 2007). Despite all of this research, the profile for mentor teachers is quite different around the globe (Table 12.2). In some countries, these mentors must be school teachers with much experience in teaching practice. For example, in Portugal, a minimum of 5 years of experience is required, while in the Czech Republic, mentors are experienced teachers who accepted this activity as a professional duty that is considered to officially enhance their status. On the other hand, in other countries, there are no real requirements to fulfill this task, nor is it recognized as part of the professional career (Cofré et al., 2015; Flores et al., 2016).

Finally, instances of practice have been proposed as ideal contexts by which to generate real and effective opportunities for science teachers in training to develop their PCK on specific topics (e.g.,

Loughran et al., 2008) and to develop research skills. The issue of the inclusion of research experience in ITE will be discussed in the next section.

Research Experience in PSTE Around the Globe

Both research on initial teacher education and multiple international reports on improving the quality of teachers have proposed that the development of research competencies prepares teachers to better cope with a rapidly changing reality in schools (e.g., Darling-Hammond et al., 2005; Lavonen et al., 2007; Bauer & Prenzel, 2012; Flores, 2017; Valeeva & Gafurov, 2017; OECD, 2019).

Nevertheless, it can be said that the concept of research competencies or research-based education is a polysemic construct that is understood in different ways and in multiple contexts (e.g., Darling-Hammond et al., 2005; Alvunger & Wahlström, 2018). This diversity of conceptions about how a science teacher behaves like a researcher favors multiple paths to reach the end of an inquiry-based initial education. Thus, for example, research-based training can be understood as experiences such as attending a research-based science methods or education course; carrying out small investigations in general pedagogy or science methods courses; participation in theoretical courses in the field of educational research; the completion of a bachelor's or master's thesis in general pedagogy, science education, or even in a scientific content area; and reflections, autobiographies, or action research produced during practicum (e.g., Darling-Hammond et al., 2005; Lavonen et al., 2007; Olson et al., 2015; Marcondes et al., 2017). For instance, Alvunger and Wahlström (2018), in a study that included the analysis of a large number of course documents and a survey administered to student teachers and educators in four teacher education programs in Sweden, concluded that secondary school preservice teachers have a pedagogical identity that is mainly based on scientific (content) research. Therefore, the authors proposed that it is not sufficient to understand teacher education as research-based only from the fact that the student teachers write a bachelor's or master's thesis. In the same vein, there are also two points of view about what is the best context in which to learn a research-based pedagogy. Some scholars believe that developing the skills to implement research-based science teaching practices requires extended science-specific teaching method experiences (e.g., Lavonen et al., 2007; Olson et al., 2015), while others propose that research experience has to be linked with reflective practice, critical thinking, and collaborative educational processes, for example, in practicum action research at schools (e.g., Darling-Hammond et al., 2005; Flores et al., 2016; Marcondes et al., 2017).

Despite all of this literature that concludes that the integration of theory, practice, and research is a desirable trait for the improvement of initial teacher education, the need to promote inquiry in programs' curricula is still an unresolved issue (Conway et al., 2009; Pedersen et al., 2017). For example, in some countries, such as Turkey, Israel, or Argentina, there is no explicit development of educational research skills in science teacher programs (Cofré et al., 2015; Pedersen et al., 2017). Meanwhile, in most African countries, the research component is lacking in the curriculum (Ogunniyi & Rollnick, 2015; Taylor et al., 2019). For example, Taylor et al. (2019) found that after analyzing detailed information about secondary teacher programs in more than 14 countries, the inclusion of a research component was mentioned in only a few instances (e.g., Mauritius, Nigeria, and Zambia), and all cases studied in depth (Rwanda, South Africa, Uganda, and Senegal) did not reach a level of sophistication that integrates a research component with practicum, SMK, and PCK.

In Southeast or East Asian countries such as China, South Korea, Singapore, and Japan, an important research component is focused on the analysis of preservice science teachers' own practices and science instruction (Liu & Liu, 2017; Pedersen et al., 2017). In China, for instance, most normal universities include education research or science education research courses (Pedersen et al., 2017). These courses and a final thesis are the research experience required of most preservice science teachers, and this experience accounts for 10 to 15 credits in total (Liu & Liu, 2017). Although

Japan and South Korea do not usually have educational research courses, training programs in both countries offer opportunities to conduct practice research at the end of their training (Pedersen et al., 2017). Especially well known is the "lesson study" format in Japan, which can be defined as a traditional art of investigating teaching and learning and engaging with colleagues.

In Eastern European countries, research is included in teacher training programs but is not strongly emphasized. For example, in Slovenia, the Czech Republic, and Poland, research represents approximately 5% of the curriculum, which includes a final thesis (e.g., Valenčič-Zuljan et al., 2011; Vasutova & Spilkova, 2011; Zdybel et al., 2011; Aykac & Sahin, 2018). A country with somewhat more development in recent times is Russia (Menter et al., 2017; Valeeva &. Gafurov, 2017). The main forms of student research work in Russian teacher education institutions consist of classroom-based work organized as parts of seminars, school-based research activities that can be carried out over the teacher's own pedagogical practice, writing reports and presenting the results of the teacher's own pedagogical practice, designing didactic materials and electronic educational resources, and writing a term thesis or final qualification thesis (Menter et al., 2017; Aykac & Sahin, 2018).

In many American countries (e.g., Colombia, Chile, Canada), there is an explicit component of training in educational research (Cofré et al., 2015). In Brazil, for example, research is recognized as a desirable skill for teachers in official documents of the Ministry of Education. Although not yet implemented in all universities, research-focused training is currently included in many new programs that are trying to innovate in teacher training (Marcondes et al., 2017). In the case of Chile, biology teachers' education includes at least one research course in education or science education at all universities. These research courses are not merely theoretical but are applied in many cases to a final thesis, for which data are often gathered in connection to practicum experiences.

Finally, in most Western European countries, the programs develop student teachers' educational research skills both in courses and during practicums (e.g., France, Portugal, Germany, Finland). One of the best-known models is the one applied in Finland. In this country, preservice science teachers take courses on research methods that deal with the pedagogy of the student's main subject, and their master's thesis can be researched either in science or in science education (Evagorou et al., 2015). Finnish teachers, even at the elementary and early childhood education level, receive an academic education that includes courses in research methodology. Most notably, science teachers are required to write a master's thesis in education. The subject teacher program, in which students major in other disciplines, includes a seminar entitled "The Teacher as a Researcher." In this seminar, students carry out their own research on their chosen educational research theme (e.g., Lavonen et al., 2007).

Conclusions

In this chapter, we wanted to synthesize the enormous diversity that exists in PSTE around the world in the most efficient way possible. We have not tried to relate the characteristics of the programs to student performance on standardized tests because we believe that there are many other variables that influence these results. However, we have tried to relate the information from the programs to the research that exists on each topic within the science education literature and to suggest some guidelines towards future research in science teacher training. Despite evidence of the advantages of organizing sequential programs, most countries develop concurrent or mixed programs. Considering that a growing number of countries are training science teachers as graduate students and recruiting professionals from other areas, it seems relevant to assess the validity of attending SMK and GPK training first and PCK training later. Possibly a handful of countries may propose demanding admission requirements for teacher training, especially considering the modest incentives and social status that the teaching profession has in many countries. Understanding the routes carried out by countries where teachers are widely recognized socially and where the teaching profession is attractive to many applicants is key information necessary to help make the selection of the best applicants an international practice.

The different proportions of SMK, GPK, PCK, and practicum experience in different curricula make it difficult to establish the perfect recipe. We know that PCK is critical knowledge for teacher training, but countries with significantly higher student achievement seem to prioritize both PCK and GPK. For this reason, it seems relevant to study the content and methodologies of such courses to understand what learning experiences they offer to preservice science teachers and to ask ourselves to what extent the transformation of GPK into PCK is a process that must or can occur in initial training. Similarly, it would be worth understanding under what conditions the practicums and educational research experiences of future science teachers are connected to the development of PCK. We believe that research on these topics could stimulate a more convergent view of the changes that our training programs require at a global level.

Acknowledgments

This work was supported by the National Fund for Scientific and Technological Development (Fondo Nacional de Desarrollo Científico y Tecnológico de Chile, FONDECYT), project #1161812 awarded to Dr. Claudia Vergara and project #1181801 awarded to Dr. Hernán Cofré.

References

Abell, S. K. (Ed.). (2000). *Science teacher education. An international perspective.* Boston: Kluwer Academic Publishers.

Abell, S. K., & Bryan, L. A. (1997). Reconceptualizing the elementary science methods course using a reflection orientation. *Journal of Science Teacher Education, 8*(3), 153–166.

Allan, E. (2017). National requirements for secondary science preparation. In J. Pedersen, T. Isozaki, & T. Hirano (Eds.), *Model science teacher preparation programs: An international comparison of what works* (pp. 185–203). Charlotte: IAP.

Alvunger, D., & Wahlström, N. (2018). Research-based teacher education? Exploring the meaning potentials of Swedish teacher education, *Teachers and Teaching, 24*(4), 332–349.

Anderson, R. D. (1997). The science methods course in the context of the total teacher education experience. *Journal of Science Teacher Education, 8*(4), 269–282.

Aydin, S., Demirdogen, B., Nur Akin, F., Uzuntiryaki-Kondakci, E., & Tarkin, A. (2015). The nature and development of interaction among components of pedagogical content knowledge in practicum. *Teaching and Teacher Education, 46,* 37–50.

Aykac, N., & Sahin, H. (2018). Comparative analysis of teacher education systems in Bulgaria, Poland, Russia, and Turkey. *Educational Process: International Journal, 7*(4), 265–277.

Bauer, J., & Prenzel, M. (2012). European teacher training reforms. *Science, 336*(6089), 1642–1643.

Busher, H., Gündüz, M., Cakmak, M., & Lawson, T. (2015). Student teachers' views of practicums (teacher training placements) in Turkish and English contexts: A comparative study, *Compare: A Journal of Comparative and International Education, 45*(3), 445–466.

Cameron, M., & Baker, R. (2004). *Research on initial teacher education in New Zealand: 1993–2004 literature review and annotated bibliography.* Wellington: New Zealand Council for Educational Research.

Carlson, J., & Daehler, K. R. (2019). The refined consensus model of pedagogical content knowledge in science education. In A. Hume, R. Cooper, & A. Borowski (Eds.), *Repositioning pedagogical content knowledge in teachers' knowledge for teaching science* (pp. 77–92). Singapore: Springer.

Cofré, H., González-Weil, C., Vergara, C., Santibáñez, D., Ahumada, G., Furman, M., . . . R. Pérez (2015). Science Teacher Education in South America: The case of Argentina, Colombia, and Chile. *Journal of Science Teacher Education, 26,* 45–63.

Conway, P., Murphy, R., Rath, A., & Hall, K. (2009). *Learning to teach and its implications for the continuum of teacher education: A nine-country cross-national study.* Report Commissioned by the Teaching Council, University College, Cork, Ireland.

Darling-Hammond, L., Hammerness, K., Grossman, P., Rust, F., & Shulman, L. (2005). The design of teacher education programs. In L. Darling-Hammond & J. Bransford (Eds.), *Preparing teachers for a changing world.* Jossey-Bass, An Imprint of Wiley.

Druva, C. A., & Anderson, R. D. (1983). Science teacher characteristics by teacher behavior and by student outcome: A meta-analysis of research. *Journal of Research in Science Teaching, 20*(5), 467–479.

Evagorou, M., Dillon, J., Viiri, J., & Able, V. (2015). Pre-service science teacher preparation in Europe: Comparing pre-service teacher preparation programs in England, France, Finland and Cyprus. *Journal of Science Teacher Education, 26*, 99–115.

Faisal, F., & Martin, S. N. (2019). Science education in Indonesia: Past, present, and future. *Asia- Pacific Science Education, 5*(1), 1–29

Fayne, H. R. (2007). Supervision from the student teacher's perspective: An institutional case study. *Studying Teacher Education, 3*, 53–66.

Flores, M. A. (2016). Teacher education curriculum. In J. Loughran & M. L. Hamilton (Eds.), *International handbook of teacher education*. Dordrecht: Springer Press.

Flores, M. A. (2017). Practice, theory, and research in initial teacher education: International perspectives. *European Journal of Teacher Education, 40*(3), 287–290.

Flores, M. A., Vieira, F., Silva, J. L., & Almeida, J. (2016). Integrating research into the practicum: Inquiring into inquiry based professional development in post-Bologna initial teacher education in Portugal. In M. A. Flores & T. Al-Barwani (Eds.), *Redefining teacher education for the post-2015 era: Global challenges and best practice*. New. York: Nova Science Publisher.

Förtsch, C., Werner, S., von Kotzebue, L., & Neuhaus, B. J. (2016). Effects of biology teachers' professional knowledge and cognitive activation on students' achievement. *International Journal of Science Education, 38*(17), 2642–2666.

Im, S., Yoon, H. G., & Cha, J. (2016). Pre-service science teacher education system in South Korea: Prospects and challenges. *EURASIA Journal of Mathematics, Science and Technology Education, 12*(7), 1863–1880.

Jyrhämä, R. (2007). The function of practical Studies in teacher education. In J. Sihvonen & H. Niemi (Eds.), *Research – based teacher education in Finland: Reflections by Finnish teacher educators*. Turku: Finish Educational Research Association.

Lavonen, J., Krzywacki-Vainio, H., Akela, M., Krokfors, L., Oikkonen, J., & Saarikko, H. (2007). Pre-service teacher education in chemistry, mathematics, and physics. In E. Pehkonen, M. Ahtee, & J. Lavonen (Eds.), *How Finns learn mathematics and science* (pp. 49–67). Finland: Sense Publishers.

Lawson, T., Çakmak, M., Gündüz, M., & Busher, H. (2015). Research on teaching practicum – a systematic review. *European Journal of Teacher Education, 38*(3), 392–407.

Lederman, N. G., & Lederman, J. S. (2015). The status of preservice science teacher education: A global perspective. *Journal of Science Teacher Education, 26*, 1–6.

Liu, C., & Liu, E. (2017). An overview of professional preparation for preservice and in-service Science teachers. In L. L. Liang et al. (Eds.), *Chinese science education in the 21st century: Policy, practice, and research, contemporary trends, and issues in science education*, 45. https://doi.org/10.1007/978-94-017-9864-8_17.

Loughran, J., Mulhall, P., & Berry, A. (2008). Exploring pedagogical content knowledge in science teacher education. *International Journal of Science Education, 30*(10), 1301–1320.

Mahler, D., Großschedl, J., & Harms, U. (2017). Using doubly latent multilevel analysis to elucidate relationships between science teachers' professional knowledge and students' performance. *International Journal of Science Education, 39*(2), 213–237.

Marcondes, M., Finholdt, V., Leite, A., & Ramos, R. (2017). Theory, practice, and research in initial teacher education in Brazil: Challenges and alternatives. *European Journal of Teacher Education, 40*(3), 326–341. https://doi.org/10.1080/02619768.2017.1320389.

McComas, W. F., Reiss, M. J., Dempster, E., Lee, Y. C., Olander, C., Pierre Clément, Jan Boerwinkel, D., & Waarlo, A. J. (2018). Considering grand challenges in biology education: Rationales and proposals for future investigations to guide instruction and enhance student understanding in the Life Sciences. *The American Biology Teacher, 80*(7), 483–492.

Menter, I., Valeeva, R., & Kalimullin, A. (2017). A tale of two countries – forty years on: Politics and teacher education in Russia and England. *European Journal of Teacher Education, 40*(5), 616–629.

OECD (2019). Mapping initial teacher preparation system on the OECD Teacher Education Pathway. In *A flying start: Improving initial teacher preparation systems*. Paris: OECD Publishing. https://doi.org/10.1787/00c3dac0-en.

Ogunniyi, M. B., & Rollnick, M. (2015). Pre-service science teacher education in Africa: Prospects and challenges. *Journal of Science Teacher Education, 26*, 65–79

Olson, J. K., Tippett, C. D., Milford, T. M., Ohana, C., & Clough, M. P. (2015). Science teacher preparation in a North American context. *Journal of Science Teacher Education, 26*(1), 7–28.

Pedersen, J., Isozaki, T., & Hirano, T. (Eds.). (2017). *Model science teacher preparation programs an international comparison of what works*. Charlotte, NC: Information Age Publishing, INC.

Ramírez, E., & Mekochi, Y. (2015). Initial teacher education in Japan and Spain. A comparative study. *Revista Española de Educación Comparada*, 101–127.

Sickel, A. J., & Witzig, S. B. (2017). Science methods courses across contexts. In A. J. Sickel & S. B. Witzig (Eds.), *Designing and teaching the secondary science methods course* (pp. 223–250). Rotterdam: Brill Sense.

Simpson, T., Hastings, W., & Hill, B. (2007). I knew that she was watching me': The professional benefits of mentoring. *Teachers and Teaching: Theory and Practice, 13*, 481–498.

Smith, D. C. (1999). Changing our teaching: The role of pedagogical content knowledge in elementary science. In *Examining pedagogical content knowledge* (pp. 163–197). Dordrecht: Springer.

Štemberger, T. (2020). Educational research within the curricula of initial teacher education: The case of Slovenia. *Center for Educational Policy Studies Journal, 10*(3), 31–51.

Taylor, N., Deacon, R., & Robinson, N. (2019). *Secondary level teacher education in Sub-Saharan Africa. Teacher Preparation and Support, overview report.* Paper prepared for the Mastercard Foundation Report: Secondary Education in Africa: Preparing Youth for the Future of Work.

Tippett, C. D., & Milford, T. M. (2017). Canada – An overview of secondary science teacher education programs. In J. Pedersen, T. Isozaki, & T. Hirano (Eds.), *Model science teacher preparation programs: An international comparison of what works* (pp. 163–184). Charlotte: IAP.

Treagust, D., Won, M., Petersen, J., & Wynne, G. (2015). Science teacher education in Australia: Initiatives and challenges to improve the Quality of Teaching. *Journal of Science Teacher Education, 26*(1), 8–98.

Tuan, H.-L., & Lu, Y.-L. (2019). Science teacher education in Taiwan: Past, present, and future. *Asia-Pacific Science Education, 5*(1), 1–22.

Valeeva, R. A., & Gafurov, I. R. (2017). Initial teacher education in Russia: Connecting theory, practice and research. *European Journal of Teacher Education, 40*(3), 342–360.

Valenčič Zuljian, M., & Vogrinc, J. (2011). *European dimensions of teacher education – similarities and differences.* Univerza v Ljubljani, Pedagoška fakulteta, The National School of Leadership and Education.

van Driel, J. H., Berry, A., & Meirink, J. (2014). Research on science teacher knowledge. In *Handbook of research on science education* (pp. 848–870). New York: Routledge.

Vasutova, J., & Spilkova, V. (2011). *Teacher education in Czech Republic.* Valenčič & Vogrinc European Dimensions of Teacher Education – Similarities and Differences. Univerza v Ljubljani, Pedagoška fakulteta, The National School of Leadership and Education.

Windschitl, M., & Stroupe, D. (2017). The three-story challenge: Implications of the next generation science standards for teacher preparation. *Journal of Teacher Education, 68*(3), 251–261.

Zdybel, D., Bogucki, J., & Glodzick, B. (2011). *Teacher education system in Poland. A state of permanent reform.* Valenčič, & Vogrinc European Dimensions of Teacher Education – Similarities and Differences. Univerza v Ljubljani, Pedagoška fakulteta, The National School of Leadership and Education.

Zeidler, D. L. (2002). Dancing with maggots and saints: Visions for subject matter knowledge, pedagogical knowledge, and pedagogical content knowledge in science teacher education reform. *Journal of Science Teacher Education, 13*, 27–42.

Zhang, H., & Wan, D. (2017). Status of Chinese science education reforms: Policies and development framework. In *Chinese science education in the 21st century: Policy, practice, and research* (pp. 5–30). Dordrecht: Springer.

Zuzovsky, R., & Donitsa-Schmidt, S. (2017). Comparing the effectiveness of two models of initial teacher education programmes in Israel: Concurrent vs. consecutive. *European Journal of Teacher Education, 40*(3), 413–431.

13
PARTNERSHIPS IN K–12 PRESERVICE SCIENCE TEACHER EDUCATION

Andrew Gilbert and Linda Hobbs

Introduction: Calls for School Partnership Arrangements

Over the last 10 years, there have been increasing policy efforts to construct and maintain partnerships between schools and universities in order to develop teaching practice. The Australian Institute for Teaching and School Leadership (AITSL, 2011) argued that university schools of education should actively build partnerships with schools that involve "shared responsibilities and obligations" (p. 4). In the USA, the National Council for the Accreditation of Teacher Education (NCATE, 2010) posited that teacher preparation efforts should be housed within some form of school-university partnership. This was further supported by the Council for the Accreditation of Educator Preparation (CAEP, 2015) calling for teacher preparation in the USA to immerse themselves in clinical partnerships between university and schools. The American Association of Colleges of Teacher Education (AACTE, 2018) articulated that the difficult pedagogical work of becoming a teacher should be "closely integrated with educator preparation coursework and supported by a formal school-university partnership" (p. 11). The primacy of connecting teacher education with school professional teaching contexts is also garnering importance and influence in the United Kingdom (National Co-ordinating Centre for Public Engagement, 2014), South Africa (Departments of Basic Education and Higher Education and Training Secretariat, 2011), as well as Europe and Asia (de Mora & Wood, 2014). These policies call for work to address key issues related to bridging theory and practice in school contexts and represent a driving force in the construction of science teacher education research.

The goal of this systemic review is to articulate the overarching terrain regarding research addressing initial science teacher education partnerships that span university and school-based contexts. More specifically, how is partnership research enacted across initial K–12 science teacher education, and what are the associated impacts of those partnership activities on future science teachers?

Considering the Need for Science-Focused Partnerships

There are numerous issues that impact teacher preparedness and implementation of high-quality practice across K–12 science contexts. These issues include: a lack of confidence in science content (Banilower et al., 2018); a decrease in time spent on science in the primary classroom (del Prado Hill et al., 2017; Rosenshine, 2015); an overall lack of preparedness for integrated STEM (science, technology, engineering, and mathematics) teaching (Sikma & Minshew, 2018); declining

DOI: 10.4324/9781003098478-16

enrollments in mathematics and science in secondary schools (Kennedy et al., 2014); stagnating science achievement (Ndlovu, 2011); and continued use of traditional approaches to teaching science that do not represent the 21st-century science approaches to learning commensurate with modern society (Puslednik & Brennan, 2020). These issues are the driving force undergirding research efforts in science partnership arrangements around the globe.

Operationalizing Terms Associated with Partnerships

One of the challenging areas when considering the nature of partnerships is the varying lexicon used across global contexts (AATCE, 2018). We utilize the term preservice teacher (PST) to describe students working toward licensure and/or certification in a teacher education program. These experiences can include the accumulation of teaching experience hours across years of a teacher education program such as professional classroom experiences and short-term practicums and/or methods courses that are embedded within school sites. In addition, some programs require a capstone teaching experience, which can range from a semester to a year depending on the program, with structured support from university and school-based mentors. This is commonly called "student teaching" and/or "internship." Internship is most commonly used to describe this culminating teaching experience within professional development schools (PDS) in the United States (Parker et al., 2019).

We utilized Rossner and Commins's (2012) definition of partnerships, where "the concept of a genuine university-school partnership connotes a collaboration of professional conversations, collegial learning and aligned processes" (p. 2). These relationships can range, depending on the timing and context, for instance, to engage teacher candidates throughout their teacher education program (Jones et al., 2016), often embedded as part of a professional development school (PDS) context (Zembal-Saul et al., 2020), where engagement can include a wide range of goals impacting both the university and participating schools.

Search Parameters and Criteria for Inclusion

This systematic review was intentionally narrow, focusing solely on research investigating partnerships that directly involved preservice K–12 science teachers within some partnership arrangement. We bounded our artifacts to journal articles, books/chapters, as well as government and/or association reports published between 2005 and 2020. This intentional focus meant that the search terms "science education," "preservice," and "partnerships" were combined and searched across numerous databases including Education Research Complete, ERIC via EBSCO Host, SpringerLink, and Google Scholar. We followed the general guidelines from Margot and Kettler (2019) in terms of selection of databases and followed up that approach with a search of Google Scholar. As suggested by Alexander (2020), we also manually checked pertinent journals (back to 2015) and investigated reference lists from select articles, as well as cross-referencing the publication records of key researchers.

The parameters of inclusion were that all of the partnerships must be within initial preservice teacher education where research was conducted between schools and communities in conjunction with university-based programs per the definition earlier in this chapter. The search was open to all geographic regions but limited in scope to developing future science teachers. We did allow research related to STEM as long as the focus on science was a major aspect of the approach. We chose not to include dissertations, conference proceedings, etc., since that literature could represent a wide range of quality and would have added an additional layer of complexity to judging the overall quality. Regarding books and volumes, we focused the search on peer-reviewed publications with publishers that received either an A or B rating from the SENSE rating system. The following sections highlight the results and are presented through themes that emerged from the analysis.

Partnerships Connecting Methods Courses to School Contexts

The research highlighted within this section depicts PSTs enrolled in university science methods courses that worked directly with school partners to provide opportunities for teaching science in school contexts. This research represents PSTs' opportunities to engage with science teaching through informal school-based teaching experiences or through formal practicum where science teacher development is the focus. Jones (2008) proposed a model of partnership between preservice teacher and practicing classroom teachers arguing for the mutual benefit of offering a constructivist framework for the development of PST practice. These course-long relationships were conceptualized to directly address the concerns related to many of the artificial approaches to science teacher preparation where university course expectations are "directly related to the real classroom experiences rather than examples contrived by the lecturer, or through artificial lessons pre-service students conduct for each other" (p. 73). The goal was to improve the scaffolding of PSTs' growth in terms of science practice and build content-related confidence in future science contexts while simultaneously sustaining relationships between schools and universities.

The possibilities for connecting schools and university programs were also evident through an exploratory approach designed to construct triadic partnerships across PSTs, in-service teachers, and a university teacher educator in Tasmania, Australia (Kenny, 2009). This study utilized a reflective framework where teacher candidates engaged with a journaling process as they enacted inquiry-based science approaches in a school context. The journals served as a mechanism of communication between the partners as a means to develop science practice for PSTs. Kenny concluded that reflective triadic partnerships had the "potential to enhance the normal practical teaching experiences by providing authentic learning experiences that link the theory and practice in an area such as science which the pre-service teachers may otherwise not have the opportunity to experience" (p. 19). The importance here is that this approach increased PST confidence and instructional time teaching science and provided insights into how science could be enacted in the primary school setting. Kenny (2010, 2012) expanded this triadic approach by looking more deliberately into the dynamic across those relationships (PST, in-service teacher and university teacher educator). He claimed that the processes involved in the reflective teaching process (collaborative planning, peer support, mentoring from in-service teacher, and enacting inquiry science within a school setting) increased PSTs' perception of their own pedagogical content knowledge (PCK).

Flores (2015) examined self-efficacy of PSTs during a field methods course that incorporated a 5-week placement in a primary context. Using the Science Teaching Efficacy Belief Instrument B (STEBI-B), they found significant increases in self-efficacy as a direct result of engaging with the primary science classroom context. Science teacher efficacy is an important notion for future science teachers principally because teachers are more likely to teach science if they enjoy a high level of science teaching efficacy. The experiences of planning, teaching, and evaluating science lessons in real classroom contexts provides PSTs with successes that will carry them into future science teaching. The power of providing opportunities to witness and enact high-leverage science practice "must be the core work of teacher educators, knowing that preservice teachers' science teaching efficacy is malleable and that changing teacher attitudes is at the heart of educational reform" (Peterson & Treagust, 2014, p. 158).

The Science Teacher Education Partnership with Schools (STEPS) project (Jones et al., 2016) examined school-based approaches to science teacher preparation of primary teachers at five Australian universities. These partnerships were introduced to science methods units in response to observations that PSTs often completed their teaching degree without teaching science during their formal practicum. The project developed an interpretive framework as "a holistic, structural outline to guide universities and school in establishing and sustaining partnership work" (Jones & Chittleborough, 2018, p. 101), including the phases involved in partnership work, types of partnership, partnership practice, and guiding pedagogical principles (Chittleborough & Jones, 2018; Jones et al., 2016). Three main types of partnership arrangements included: (1) connective, referring to short-term opportunistic arrangements to benefit one or both partners; (2) generative, referring to long-term arrangements that are co-planned and offer opportunities for reflection and growth; and (3) transformative, referring to activities embedded in the ongoing practice of each institution where partners take joint responsibility for mutually agreed practice and engage explicitly in reflective inquiry as a means to direct professional growth. The notion of partnership therefore assumes that there are mutual benefits for all partners. Hobbs and Kenny (2018) argued that partnerships facilitate the nexus between the university and the profession, where "practice is no longer situated solely in schools, nor theory situated only at university" (p. 283). Clarity and careful articulation of the nature and quality of the learning experiences is needed to ensure mutual opportunities for learning. Growth (Hobbs & Campbell, 2018) through these types of partnerships can be measured as growth in identity, confidence, praxis and relations, and changes in attitudes, beliefs, and expertise.

Herbert and Hobbs (2018) warn that PST confidence gained during this type of partnership does not necessarily translate into quality teaching in schools, mainly because of the many pressures that teachers face once in the classroom. However, they argue that, "opportunity for reflection on successes and failures that might arise thus responding to the complex nature of teaching science allowing, and indeed perhaps encouraging, PSTs to take risks in their own learning" (Herbert & Hobbs, 2018, p. 802). A different type of partnership was reported by Cooper et al. (2018) in New Zealand, where the traditional formal practicum was restructured from a short-term teaching program to one that was embedded in primary schools 1 day per week over the academic year and culminated in a 3-week block. This change required reconceptualization of how the university and partner schools worked together in program delivery and assessment. This program required partnership negotiation at all levels of the schools and universities so that there was shared understanding and capacity. Critical was the appointment of associate lecturers who acted as the bridge between the university and schools, working closely with university faculty and staff at the school to support the PSTs. The example of Cooper et al. (2018) illustrates efforts in a number of countries to rethink the formal practicum to embed real opportunities for partnership that lead to quality outcomes for teachers of science.

All of these studies worked to create coherence between preservice programs and school-based practice and were carried out in primary/elementary contexts. In one study in secondary contexts in the United States, Campbell et al. (2019) investigated the possibilities for partnerships through the design and implementation of research-practice partnership. This qualitative, design-based research study investigated the associated impacts on ten in-service teachers over 17 months through the engagement of developing innovative approaches and implementing curriculum in classrooms. One of the goals was to investigate the impact of PST placement on in-service teacher practice. This proved difficult based on a number of structural factors related to the institution, where only a limited number of PSTs were able to be placed with teachers taking part in the study. These difficulties included placements being made by a central office at the university and various state-level expectations related to content preparation and licensure that dictated placement decisions.

Partnership Experiences Through School Networks

The context of school-university partnerships provides fertile opportunities to design experiences for student teaching internships. In Australia, there exist similar types of partnerships termed Alliances or Academies through the Teaching Academies Partnerships Program (Toe et al., 2020). While not specifically focused on the final part of the teacher education program, they are embedded partnerships involving networks of schools. The following section focuses on implications for interns and how their burgeoning teaching experiences can be influenced through a variety of partnerships between schools and universities.

The relationships created through PDS programs are typically framed to garner content and teaching goals across stakeholders, including students, mentor teachers, and PSTs, based on the long-term commitment and stability within the internship, and to build pathways for high-quality induction into teaching (Murray & Zembal-Saul, 2008). For instance, Barreto-Espino et al. (2014) tap into the continuity that exists across PDS programs from initial program courses through internship to build a framework for *science as argument*. A coherent and consistent framework for PSTs over the duration of their teacher education program is essential. Davis et al. (2020) found that placing PSTs in partner schools with mutual understandings developed through years of collegial interaction between university and partner school led to a safe and supportive environment for PSTs to develop their science teaching practice. The PDS model supports this continuity and consistent messaging about quality teaching:

> A number of interns observed their mentors teaching science in ways that were consistent with what they were learning in their methods courses. Those interns whose mentors did not teach in this way were at least supported in attempting to enact inquiry-based science lessons in their field placement classrooms
>
> (Zembal-Saul, 2009, p. 712).

The "context of school-university partnerships" provided the conditions for growth in interns' science practice (Avraamidou & Zembal-Saul, 2010) by building school cultures that engaged deeply with science content and practice by working shoulder to shoulder with experienced practitioners.

In another small-scale study (Swars & Dooley, 2010), 21 PSTs were placed within local PDS sites for 2 days per week over a three-semester period. This long-term engagement across several courses embedded within a school site is often a feature of PDS relationships. The PSTs engaged in their science methods classes at the school site and then directly entered classrooms to make connections between coursework. They found that meaningfully integrating science coursework and a practicum led to significant increases in science teaching self-efficacy, where "preservice teachers' beliefs in their skills and abilities to teach science effectively became significantly stronger during the PDS-based science methods courses" (p. 197).

In a survey study involving 224 PSTs in Turkish schools, as part of a model that links preservice teachers with secondary teacher classrooms, Bekiroglu et al. (2010) argued that PSTs were pleased to get opportunities to teach in school contexts with mentor support. However, PSTs indicated that mentor teachers were not committed to many important issues, and often PSTs wished they had more opportunities for teaching in those contexts. This idea was echoed by Suriel et al. (2018) as they contended that in middle school classrooms many interns have limited opportunities to engage in science teaching. The authors engaged interns and mentor teachers involved in a PDS program in a program where middle school children in the USA connected with secondary students and teachers in China on environmental issues such as water and air pollution. The findings suggested that the PDS site allowed support, development, and engagement with science such that it had a positive impact on interns as they reported gains in both understanding of content and teaching confidence.

The additional support of the PDS model is echoed in the Alliance Model in Australia, where a site director works with school teacher mentors and PSTs to build a nuanced understanding of the Graduate Australian Professional Teaching Standards (Toe et al., 2020). In addition to the additional support from the site director, PSTs participated in assessment circles where they present and discuss evidence of their progress towards these standards with school mentors, the site director, and academic staff. PSTs participating in Alliance placement have been shown to feel more classroom ready and more supported, and to understand the standards of teaching better than PSTs involved in traditional placements (Toe et al., 2020). Common to these examples is that the sites serve as a dynamic "living laboratory" (Zembal-Saul et al., 2020, p. 215) or "change laboratories" (Toe et al., 2020), which continue to provide powerful and supportive contexts for interns to trial contemporary research-informed teaching. In traditional practicum arrangements, trialing practice that might be different from those of their mentor teacher or outside the bounds of traditional school pedagogy can often be challenging for most interns who carry very little cachet in terms of pedagogical influence. However, the continuity of messages about science content and pedagogy across the academy and schools evident in these alternative models potentially better launches new teachers into their induction years.

Partnerships Linking Preservice Teachers with Organizations Beyond the Classroom

Partnerships with organizations that reside outside of the typical school university partnership can contain varying degrees of engagement with teacher educators, PSTs, interns, classroom teachers, scientists, and/or STEM related professionals. Pfeiffer and Tabone (2020) further argued that "Partnerships between industry, the education sector and the community are crucial in the development of healthy, robust and engaged communities" (p. 63). The following studies highlight processes and promises of partnerships specifically designed to impact future science teachers.

In a case study that connected secondary preservice teachers engaging with a community organization addressing environmental racism in a Chicago community (Varelas et al., 2018), the researchers described a long and supportive relationship with local schools. However, the study was carried out by partnering with a community organization and the university as a means to impact PST thinking regarding practice. The community organization took PSTs on a "toxic tour" of the community to see issues related to environmental racism firsthand and then provided support and materials for PSTs to consider for future pedagogical possibilities. The result had profound impact on PST understanding for the communities in which they teach and that had direct implications for how they saw socially just opportunities for science teaching.

School enrichment programs such as *Family Science Night* and other wide-ranging extracurricular service learning can also provide opportunities for PSTs to interact with students (Carpenter, 2015). These learning activities have been shown to be powerful as they provide "meaningful opportunities for preservice teachers to interact with K–12 students outside typical classroom situations" (p. 117). In Carpenter's study, these partnership activities led to increases in PSTs' joy toward science content and understanding of potential innovative pedagogy. In a similar approach, Zack et al. (2017) described that working with inquiry-based science pedagogy within a structured, after-school environment was a driver for increasing PST confidence in science teaching.

Studies also indicated that these types of authentic teaching experiences can be challenging for PSTs, as they are confronted by their limitations in knowledge and practice. In a mixed methods study from the USA, Dever and Clement (2011) investigated the effect of carrying out an authentic science experience within the context of a partnership between a teacher education program and local informal science institution. They found impacts on PSTs' self-efficacy for science teaching (using the STEBI-B) in the form or a statistically significant *negative* difference in how PSTs viewed their science teaching self-efficacy. They argued the activity demonstrated the degree to which PSTs felt they needed to improve their own content understanding. This had direct implications for how they viewed their future ability for teaching science on their own. This was corroborated in a similar study where PSTs' initial conceptions of self-efficacy were problematic as they began to better understand their own gaps in content knowledge (Hechter, 2011). These findings emphasize the need for careful collaboration, communication, and coordination (Hobbs & Campbell, 2018) to ensure PSTs do not flounder, and that there is time for PSTs to work through these challenges.

Other partnership efforts worked to directly connect PSTs with professional research scientists in order to demystify scientists' practices of data collection and research. A semester-long, small-scale study of PSTs engaged in an apprenticeship on a science research project led to increased confidence levels in enacting inquiry in their future classrooms (Brown & Melear; 2007). Similar findings arose from Kidman and Marangio (2018), who argued that "deliberate planning for networking between pre-service science teachers and scientists may well assist in the development of professionalism and teaching philosophies of pre-service science teachers" (p. 191). The essential point here is that the connections to the scientists were directly related to planning for instruction and provided a direct link to the translation of science content into learning opportunities in schools.

The Advancing Science by Enhancing Learning in the Laboratory (which was part of the larger Reconceptualising Maths and Science Teacher Education Programs project) involved teachers, secondary science PSTs, and leading scientists in the process of developing curriculum for schools in Australian contexts. This was designed to bridge the distance between the STEM professional and the classroom, while also including the PST. This model was comprised of four steps: (1) PST and scientist reflect on the nature of science and scientific practice; (2) PST and scientist translate research into curriculum concepts and practice, which are translated into website exemplars; (3) senior scientist, experienced PST, and teacher educator produce a resource that is trialed by teachers and teacher educators; and (4) the resource is packaged for school and teacher education. The final output included teacher education modules focused on contemporary science in the curriculum (White et al., 2018, p. 129). These synergistic activities provided a model that has continued to generate high-quality learning activities for a variety of secondary science students (Lim et al., 2019). The key was the continued engagement of the PST and the research scientist with the goal of building quality science teaching resources for the classroom.

Discussion and Conclusions

The goal of this chapter was to investigate the enactment of partnership research across initial K–12 science teacher education and to describe research findings regarding associated impacts of those approaches. The context of school-university partnerships, as Zembal-Saul et al. (2020) argued, provide the needed continuity and structure to incorporate research-based approaches in a supportive environment. This new space is a place for PSTs to take on the challenge of practice, which also can provide a lens for in-service teachers to reconsider their own pedagogy and how they engage with children in their future classrooms (Alemán et al., 2017; Gilbert et al., 2018). Partnerships can also assist the construction of more consistent school-wide culture, where all stakeholders buy into the process through co-designing learning intentions and activities, and maintaining an openness to continued dialog regarding partnership goals (Borda, 2018; Gilbert et al., 2020; Lemon et al., 2018; Zembal-Saul et al., 2020). This can lead to powerful engagement with pedagogical experiences that might be impossible without the support of the partnership.

One key feature of this review is that there exists much more research in primary (elementary) contexts than across secondary contexts. This may stem from the challenges highlighted by Campbell et al. (2019), where matching teacher content areas to PST content needs, placements made by centralized university offices, and state certification requirements can impact the ability for long-term connections between partners. These continued relationships are essential in sustaining successful partnerships. As such, Kruger et al. (2009) argued that all successful partnerships operate under the conditions of trust, mutuality, and reciprocity where *trust* relates to shared understandings for the goals, *mutuality* articulates how each partner understands that working together leads to a higher degree of success, and *reciprocity* recognizes the value that each partner holds toward the other. These conditions can only be built over time, and this balance between partners is the cornerstone of success and frames the ongoing maintenance of these relationships. This provides challenges for the field to consider how best to apply the tenets of successful partner relationships fostered in many primary settings (consistent numbers of PSTs, mentor teachers with long associations with university faculty, ongoing engagement in school sites and partners, teaching and working across institutional boundaries, etc.) and translate those into secondary contexts. These could mean removing placements from central offices and placing under the guidance of teacher education programs and tracking content area specializations for possible future partnerships with a cadre of school-based teachers. Successful secondary programs described in this chapter were often partnered with organizations outside of school-based contexts, which offered viable pathways to sidestep many of the structural issues faced while meeting the needs of partners, PSTs, and teacher education programs. An interesting aspect of working with outside organizations highlighted how partners provided additional resources, understanding, and guidance that may not be available within the university setting. This was highlighted by Varelas and colleagues' (2018) work with environmental racism and served as a powerful example for bringing issues of social justice into PSTs' consciousness and helping them understand pathways toward anti-racist pedagogy. This remains an elusive, yet essential, goal in science education, and by connecting PSTs with the communities, our schools serve to decrease the distance between all participants.

In totality, most of the studies incorporated into this chapter depict small-scale qualitative approaches with a few exceptions involving surveys and/or larger-scale qualitative work. This is emblematic of studies carried out within small cohorts in primary contexts. This leaves possibilities for larger-scale studies across entire programs or even studies combining multiple programs. In these small-scale studies many have found increased confidence and self-efficacy toward science teaching often coupled with increased desire to learn science content and conceptualize how that can translate into practice. The question becomes, what impacts might this have on future teacher careers? Do teachers who were immersed in partnership work in initial teacher education stay in the field longer? What is the nature of their pedagogical practice throughout their induction years? What large-scale and/or longitudinal work might be possible if a range of programs that are immersed in partnership work looked at the impacts of those graduates on the field at large? A fruitful avenue for science education researchers will be to expand the scope of partnership work to large-scale system approaches to partnerships across teacher education, such as through PDS and Alliance models, and then to study the impacts longitudinally. The infrastructure and longitudinal nature of partnership arrangements would provide the needed context and access to take on these larger-scale studies.

A complicating factor for considering the global context of partnerships is to be mindful of cultural issues that must be considered as we think about the parameters needed for engaging in meaningful partnership efforts. As an example, Faikhamta et al. (2018) argued that in Thailand, the conditions for designing and carrying out partnerships can be difficult because, "cooperating teachers and university mentors have not routinely participated in collaborative coaching and mentoring of their trainees. It is rare to see open communication between the three stakeholders – pre-service teachers, cooperating teachers and university mentors" (p. 14). We must stay ever-mindful that in a global world, relationships and building the trust needed for beneficial partnerships to form is not a simple task. The success of the partnerships was contingent on collaboration based on mutuality and reciprocity, careful coordination of timing, roles, and learning expectations and risk management, and communication for feedback on learning and relationship building.

The context of partnership sites has proven to be a driver for the development of future science teachers as they take on their initial development within the context of a supportive ecosystem steeped in inquiry-based innovative practice. This addresses an ongoing issue in science education where beginning teachers rarely experience reform-based teaching practice in authentic school settings. Partnerships also provided a powerful catalyst to link surrounding communities to engage with future teachers as a means to educate PSTs on the resources and strengths of the communities from which their students live. Lastly, partnerships beyond school contexts provided PSTs with opportunities to better understand the role of science research and scientists themselves. The totality of these wide-ranging approaches provides the science education community with an understanding for the breadth, depth, and possibilities that exist across the continuum of partnerships in science teacher education.

References

Alemán, E., Freire, J. A., & McKinney, A. (2017). School – university – community pathways to higher education: Teacher perceptions, school culture and partnership building. *The Urban Review, 49*, 852–873.

Alexander, P. (2020). Methodological guidance paper: The art and science of quality systematic reviews. *Review of Educational Research, 90*(1), 6–23.

American Association for Colleges of Teacher Education. (2018). *A pivot toward clinical practice: Its lexicon, and the renewal of educator preparation.* https://aacte.org/resources/research-reports-and-briefs/clinical-practice-commission-report/

Australian Institute for Teaching and School Leadership (2011). *Accreditation of initial teacher education programs in Australia: Standards and procedures.* Melbourne, VIC: Education Services Australia.

Avraamidou, L., & Zembal-Saul, C. (2010). In search of well-started beginning science teachers: Insights from two first-year elementary teachers. *Journal of Research in Science Teaching, 47*(6), 661–686.

Banilower, E., Smith, P., Malzahn, K., Plumley, C., Gordon, E., & Hayes, M. (2018). *Report of the 2018 NSSME+.* Chapel Hill, NC: Horizon Research, Inc.

Barreto-Espino, R., Zembal-Saul, C., & Avraamidou, L. (2014). Prospective elementary teachers' knowledge of teaching science as argument: A case study. *School Science and Mathematics. 114*(2), 53–64.

Bekiroglu, F., Kahveci, A., Irez, S., Seker, H., & Cakir, M. (2010). Evaluation of the faculty-school cooperation model: Secondary education views of pre-service science teachers. *Journal of Turkish Science Education, 7*(4), 148–171.

Borda, E., Warren, S., Coskie, T., Larson, B., Hanley, D., & Cohen, J. (2018). Cross-disciplinary, whole school education reform in secondary schools: Three critical components. *School University Partnerships, 11*(1), 46–56

Brown, S., & Melear, C. (2007). Preservice teachers research experiences in scientists laboratories. *Journal of Science Teacher Education, 18*, 573–597. https://doi.org/10.1007/s10972-007-9044-9

Campbell, T., McKenna, T., Fazio, x., Hetherington-Coy, A., & Pierce, P. (2019). Negotiating coherent science teacher professional learning experiences across a university and partner school settings. *Journal of Science Teacher Education, 30*(2), 179–199, https://doi.org/10.1080/1046560X.2018.1547033

Carpenter, S. (2015). Undergraduates' perceived gains and ideas about teaching and learning science from participating in science education outreach programs. *Journal of Higher Education Outreach and Engagement, 19*(3), 113–146.

Chittleborough, G., & Jones, M. (2018). Linking theory and practice through partnerships. In L. Hobbs, C. Campbell, & M. Jones (Eds.), *School-based partnerships in teacher education: A research informed model for universities, schools and beyond* (pp. 61–82). Dordrecht: Springer.

Cooper, B., Cowie, B., & Campbell, C. (2018). A New Zealand collaborative university-school partnership: Applying the STEPS framework. In L. Hobbs, C. Campbell, & M. Jones (Eds.), *School-based partnerships in teacher education: A research informed model for universities, schools and beyond* (pp. 212–221). Dordrecht: Springer.

Council for the Accreditation of Education Programs. (2015). *CAEP accreditation standards.* Washington, DC: Author.

Davis, E., Palincsar, A., & Kademian, S. (2020). Designing a practice-based elementary teacher education program and supporting professional learning in science teaching. In E. Davis, C. Zembal-Saul, & S. Kademian (Eds.), *Sensemaking in elementary science: Supporting teacher learning* (pp. 204–217). Routledge.

del Prado Hill, P., McMillen, S., & Friedland, E. (2017). The power of questions to bring balance to the curriculum in the age of new standards. *School-University Partnerships, 10*(2), 46–50.

de Mora, J. C., & Wood, K. (2014). *Practical knowledge in teacher education: Approaches to teacher internship programmes.* London: Routledge.

Departments of Basic Education and Higher Education and Training Secretariat. (2011). *Integrated strategic planning framework for teacher education and development in South Africa, 2011–2025* (Technical Report). Pretoria: The Departments of Basic Education and Higher Education and Training.

Dever, R., & Clement, S. (2011). Middle school pre-service teachers' sense of self-efficacy in relation to authentic learning experiences. *Electronic Journal of Science Education, 20*(5). http://ejse.southwestern.edu

Faikhamta, C., Ketsing, J., Akarat, T., & Suthida, C. (2018). Science teacher education in Thailand: A challenging journey. *Asia-Pacific Science Education, 4*(1).1–18. https://doi.org/10.1186/s41029-018-0021-8

Flores, I. M. (2015). Developing pre-service teachers' self-efficacy through field-based science teaching practice with elementary students. *Research in Higher Education Journal, 27*, 1–15.

Gilbert, A., Hobbs, L., Kenny, J., Jones, M., Campbell, C., Chittleborough, G., . . . Redman, C. (2018). Principal perceptions regarding the impact of school-university partnerships in Australian primary science contexts. *School-University Partnerships, 11*(2), 73–83.

Gilbert, A., Hobbs, L., Kenny, J., Jones, M., Campbell, C., Chittleborough, G., . . . Redman, C. (2020). "I realized that science isn't scary": In-service teacher insights regarding science-focused partnerships. *School-University Partnerships, 13*(1), 22–31.

Hechter, R. (2011). Changes in preservice elementary teachers' personal science teaching efficacy and science teaching outcome expectancies: The influence of context. *Journal of Science Teacher Education, 22*(2), 187–202. https://doi.org/10.1007/s10972-010-9199

Herbert, S., & Hobbs, L. (2018). Pre-service teachers' views of school-based approaches to pre-service primary science teacher education. *Research in Science Education, 48*, 777–809.

Hobbs, L., & Campbell, C. (2018). Growing through partnerships. In L. Hobbs, C. Campbell, & M. Jones (Eds.), *School-based partnerships in teacher education: A research informed model for universities, schools and beyond* (pp. 139–168). Dordrecht: Springer.

Hobbs, L., & Kenny, J. (2018). Visionary practice. In L. Hobbs, C. Campbell, & M. Jones (Eds.), *School-based partnerships in teacher education: A research informed model for universities, schools and beyond* (pp. 271–285). Dordrecht: Springer.

Jones, M. (2008). Collaborative partnerships: A model for science teacher education and professional development. *Australian Journal of Teacher Education, 33*(3). http://dx.doi.org/10.14221/ajte.2008v33n3.5

Jones, M., & Chittleborough, G. (2018). Growing university-school partnerships. In L. Hobbs, C. Campbell, & M. Jones (Eds.), *School-based partnerships in teacher education: A research informed model for universities, schools and beyond* (pp. 99–122). Dordrecht: Springer.

Jones, M., Hobbs, L., Kenny, J., Campbell, C., Chittleborough, G., Gilbert, A., Herbert, S. Redman, C. (2016). Successful university school partnerships: An interpretive framework. *Teaching and Teacher Education, 60*, 108–120.

Kennedy, J., Lyons, T., & Quinn, F. (2014). The continuing decline of science and mathematics enrolments in Australian high schools. *Teaching Science, 60*(2), 34–46.

Kenny, J. (2009). A partnership-based approach to professional learning: Pre-service and in-service teachers working together to teach primary science. *Australian Journal of Teacher Education, 34*(6). http://dx.doi.org/10.14221/ajte.2009v34n6.1

Kenny, J. (2010). Preparing primary teachers to teach primary science: A partnership-based approach, *International Journal of Science Education, 32*(10), 1267–1288.

Kenny, J. (2012). University-school partnerships: Pre-service and in-service teachers working together to teach primary science, *Australian Journal of Teacher Education, 37*(3), 57–82.

Kidman, G., & Marangio, K. (2018). "Meet the scientist": How pre-service teachers constructed knowledge and identities. In D. Corrigan et al. (Eds.), *Navigating the changing landscape of formal and informal science learning opportunities* (pp. 183–191). Springer. https://doi.org/10.1007/978-3-319-89761-5_11

Kruger, T., Davies, A., Eckersley, B., Newell, F., & Cherednichenko, B. (2009). *Effective and sustainable university-school partnerships: Beyond determined efforts by inspired individuals.* http://www.aitsl.edu.au/docs/default-source/default-document-library/effective_and_sustainable_university-school_partnerships.pdf

Lemon, N., Wilson, A., Oxworth, C., Zavros-Orr, A., & Wood, B. (2018). Lines of school-university partnership: Perception, sensation and meshwork reshaping of pre-service teachers' experiences. *Australian Journal of Teacher Education, 43*(10), 81–97. http://dx.doi.org/10.14221/ajte.2018v43.n10.5

Lim, K., Long, J. White, P., & Bentley, I. (2019). Designing hands-on inquiry-based activities: Incorporating contemporary science. *Teaching Science, 65*(2), 48–54.

Margot, K. C., & Kettler, T. (2019). Teachers' perception of STEM integration and education: A systematic literature review. *International Journal of STEM Education, 6*(2). https://doi.org/10.1186/s40594-018-0151-2.

Murray, O., & Zembal-Saul, C. (2008). Educate at Penn State: Preparing beginning teachers with powerful digital tools. *Journal of Computing in Higher Education, 20*(2), 48–58. https://doi.org/10.1007/s12528-008-9000-5

National Co-ordinating Centre for Public Engagement (NCCPE) (2014). *School-university partnerships: Fulfilling the potential.* Research Councils United Kingdom. www.publicengagement.ac.uk/sites/default/files/publication/supi_project_report_final.pdf

National Council for Accreditation of Teacher Education (NCATE). (2010). *Transforming teacher education through clinical practice: A national strategy to prepare effective teachers.* Washington, DC: Author.

Ndlovu, M. (2011). University-school partnerships for social justice in mathematics and science education: The case of the SMILES project at IMSTUS. *South African Journal of Education, 31*, 419–433.

Parker, A. K., Zenkov, K., & Dennis, D. (2019). Exploring the lexicon or lack thereof in clinical teacher preparation. *Action in Teacher Education, 4*(3), 249–264.

Peterson, J. E., & Treagust, D. F. (2014). School and university partnerships: The role of teacher education institutions and primary schools in the development of preservice teachers' science teaching efficacy. *Australian Journal of Teacher Education, 39*(9). http://dx.doi.org/10.14221/ajte.2014v39n9.2

Pfeiffer, L., & Tabone, K. (2020). A case study of a university industry STEM partnership in regional Queensland. In A. Fitzgerald, C. Haeusler, & L. Pfeiffer (Eds.), *STEM education in primary classrooms* (pp. 61–78). London: Routledge.

Puslednik, L., & Brennan, P. (2020). An Australian-based authentic science research programme transforms the 21st century learning of rural high school students. *Australian Journal of Education, 64*(2), 98–112. https://doi.org/10.1177/0004944120919890

Rosenshine, B. (2015). How time is spent in elementary classrooms. *Journal of Classroom Interaction, 50*(1), 41–53.

Rossner, P., & Commins, D. (2012). *Defining 'enduring partnerships:' Can a well-worn path be an effective, sustainable and mutually beneficial relationship?* Queensland College of Teachers. www.qct.edu.au/PDF/DefiningEnduringPartnerships.pdf.

Sikma, L., & Minshew, V. (2018). School-university partnership as professional development: The evolution of a leader in elementary science education. *School-University Partnerships, 11*(4), 37–47.

Suriel, R., Spires, R., Radcliffe, B., Martin, E., & Paine, D. (2018). Middle school to professional development: Interdisciplinary STEM for multiple stakeholders. *School-University Partnerships, 11*(1), 57–59.

Swars, S., & Dooley, C. (2010). Changes in teaching efficacy during a professional development school-based science methods course. *School Science & Mathematics, 110*(4), 193–202. https://doi.org/10.1111/j.1949-8594.2010.00022.x

Toe, D., Ure, C., & Blake, D. (2020). Final year teachers' views of professional experience in partnership schools. *Australian Journal of Teacher Education, 45*(2), 104–127.

Varelas, M., Morales-Doyle, D., Raza, S., Segura, D., Canales, K., & Mitchener, C. (2018). Community organizations' programming and the development of community science teachers. *Science Education, 102*(1), 60–84. https://doi.org/10.1002/sce.21321

White, P., Tytler, R., & Palmer, S. (2018). Exploring models of interaction between scientists and pre-service teachers. In S. Dinham, R. Tytler, D. Corrigan, & D. Hoxley (Eds.), *Reconceptualising maths and science teacher education* (pp. 92–110). Camberwell, VIC: ACER Press.

Zack, R., Vacha, E., & Staub, L. (2017). Science in action! Outreach program promotes confidence in teaching science. *The American Biology Teacher, 79*(9), 711–719.

Zembal-Saul, C. (2009). Learning to teach elementary school science as argument. *Science Education, 93*(4), 687–719.

Zembal-Saul, C., Badiali, B., McDyre, A., & Mueller, B. (2020). Learning to teach science in an elementary professional development school partnership. In E. Davis, C. Zembal-Saul, & S. Kademian (Eds.), *Sensemaking in elementary science: Supporting teacher learning* (pp. 204–217). New York, NY: Routledge.

14

THE MAGIC OF INFORMAL SETTINGS

A Literature Review of Partnerships and Collaborations that Support Preservice Science Teacher Education Across the Globe

Natasha Cooke-Nieves, Jamie Wallace, Preeti Gupta,
and Elaine Howes

Introduction

Learning science outside of school for a child can be viewed as almost magical – producing awe, inspiration, and curiosity (Rennie, 2014). But how do teachers learn how to plan, teach, and engage students for the real world? Traditionally, this is the responsibility of higher education institutions: to prepare science teachers to teach beyond even the most highly decorated classroom walls and connect content to real-life phenomena – people, places, and things in our local and global communities. This chapter provides a comprehensive review of peer-reviewed articles that focus on how preservice teachers learn to teach science in informal environments.

Research in this chapter is categorized under the umbrella term "informal science learning environments" (ISLEs), using Rennie's (2014) description of informal science education "as a catch-all term for science-related activities that are not part of a formal, assessable curriculum" (p. 120). In this review, ISLEs include: zoos, parks, wildlife sanctuaries, gardens, aquaria, museums, science centers, community-based organizations, and other designed settings (Rennie, 2014; NRC, 2009). Preference is given to research that advances the field by addressing gaps, challenges, and new methods, and offers suggestions for institutional advancement of teacher preparation.

Methods

To conduct this review, parameters were set to include research published since 2010, internationally focused on ISLEs and preservice science education. Using a reference management software, numerous searches were conducted on university digital libraries and repositories, Google Scholar, the Center for the Advancement of Informal Science Education, international journals, and research portals such as ResearchGate and Academia for key terms including preservice science teachers (PSTs), informal science, types of ISLEs (e.g., museum, science center), preservice science teacher identity, field trip, and place-based. Additionally, country names were added to the search for a broader and more inclusive global reach. In total, more than 115 papers representing more than 25 countries across five continents were reviewed (not all are cited due to limitations). Papers were

DOI: 10.4324/9781003098478-17

categorized for analysis based on what emerged in the research and previous literature reviews, which became the chapter's subsections: teacher identity, place-based education, gaps in the literature, and advancing the field.

Science Teacher Identity and Learning to Teach Science in ISLEs

Experiences at ISLEs in preservice preparation play an integral role in informing teacher identity development. Science teacher identity is multidimensional, relational, and grounded in place and time (Avraamidou, 2019). In this section, findings from recent studies are examined, investigating outcomes of ISLE experiences on PSTs by category, emphasizing the expansive ways in which informal environments play a role in shaping teacher identity.

Reform-based efforts and student-centered approaches. With an increase in educational reforms internationally, recent studies focus on a reform-minded science teacher identity (Avraamidou, 2014; Gupta et al., 2016; Luehmann, 2016). Reforms in science teacher education over the last decade center on the Framework for K–12 Teacher Education (NRC, 2012) and the Next Generation Science Standards (NGSS) (NGSS Lead States, 2013) in the United States, and Science Education for Responsible Citizenship (European Commission, 2015) in Europe. Similarly, there is evidence of reform and calls for action in New Zealand (Gilbert & Bull, 2013) and Finland (Vahtivuori-Hanninen et al., 2014), particularly with shifts toward competency-based education with 21st Century Learning (Barak, 2017), integrated STEM, context-based, interdisciplinary, and equity-based education. With new reforms that promote shifts in visions of science teaching and learning, educators are tasked with integrating new standards and practices into teacher preparation. ISLEs are particularly well suited to engage new teachers in these reforms, providing opportunities to practice reform-based instruction and draw on the rich resources ISLEs can provide.

Numerous studies explore how PSTs with experiences in ISLEs focus on creating student-centered approaches for learning (Adams & Gupta, 2017; Aquino et al., 2010). In reform-oriented teaching, instructional focus pivots away from a teacher-led model to one in which students are centered via increased opportunities for discussion and sensemaking. With this shift in the positioning of the teacher in instruction, studies investigate the role of identity in PSTs' teaching, how PSTs position themselves in their practice, how they think about teaching, and how they see themselves in varied contexts (Avraamidou, 2016; Kier & Lee, 2017). For instance, as part of a university methods course in Taiwan, preservice biology and physics teachers design and integrate museum resources into lessons (Chin, 2004). Throughout the experience, PSTs' roles changed in connection with the ISLE, shifting from visitors, to observers, to producers as they selected and integrated museum resources into their science lessons and learned how to represent these concepts in their teaching (Chin, 2004). Experiences teaching in ISLEs provide PSTs with learning how to teach science in flexible and adaptable ways for diverse learners, with ample resources provided in context (Chin, 2004). The notion of becoming a teacher who develops agency and can draw on and use accessible science, contextual, and cultural resources is intertwined with reform-minded science teacher identity development (Luehmann, 2016). Collaborations between educator preparation providers (EPPs) and ISLEs with intentionally developed experiences for PSTs also expand awareness of, exposure to, and access to rich science resources (Kisiel, 2013; Lemon & Weller, 2015).

In Australia, elementary PSTs engaged in a partnership with a wildlife sanctuary in which they experienced a tutorial of educational content from the ISLE, examined and critiqued online educator resources, and provided feedback for the ISLE (Lemon & Weller, 2015). In this science methods course, PSTs designed scaffolding for activities provided by the sanctuary, with overarching ideas for science in Australia similar to NGSS's cross-cutting concepts in the USA. Sharing activities with the ISLE was viewed, in this case, as a form of "enterprise education," an educational approach common in several European countries focused on developing specific skills and knowledge for the future such as innovative problem solving, and may include collaborative partnerships prospectively leading toward longer-term entrepreneurship (Elo & Kurtén, 2020; Lemon & Weller, 2015). Thus, the EPP-ISLE partnership helped PSTs develop "holistic capacity as educators," promoting possibilities for envisioning their futures as teachers through designing, implementing, and evaluating meaningful lessons in connection with sanctuary learning experiences (Lemon & Weller, 2015).

In a summer teaching residency component of an EPP at the American Museum of Natural History (AMNH) where PSTs learn to teach visitors using objects and artifacts on touch carts, researchers observed that "[i]dentity development becomes intertwined with the act of doing" (Gupta et al., 2016, p. 182). Encountering a diverse population of visitors in the residency, PSTs learned to alternate resources and strategies when teaching depending on their audience. Each visitor interaction helped PSTs determine which object to use and how. PSTs were able to build on this experience with objects for subsequent interactions applying alternating strategies, with learners adopting a learner-centered approach (Gupta et al., 2016).

A substantive affordance of ISLEs in learning to teach science is the opportunity to practice and enact teaching, bridging theory and practice. As PSTs in EPPs learn about the cycle of studying, practicing, and rehearsing teaching, ISLEs offer numerous chances to observe, try an approach, reflect and modify, and try something else (Adams & Gupta, 2017). A common argument in teacher education is that PSTs lack opportunities to test out the practices they will be responsible for enacting in the classroom – called a "disconnection between vision and actual teaching practice" (Hammerness et al., 2020) and a "problem of enactment" (Kennedy, 1999, p. 70). Finding opportunities to practice teaching is a challenge, and teachers often report feeling unprepared to teach science (Dorph, 2011). Similarly, teachers frequently cite a lack of resources for teaching science in rigorous and ambitious ways (Banilower, 2019). Examining PSTs' experiences learning to teach in a museum, Adams and Gupta (2017) explored how working with intergenerational visitors provides access, exposure, and awareness to diverse learners who bring with them a myriad of lived experiences, prior knowledge, and interests. PSTs' experiences engaging with visitors develops their teacher identity and contributes to building confidence in their skills and agency to enact equitable teaching practices (Adams & Gupta, 2017). In another study, PSTs conducted clinical experiences in a museum school as part of a teacher education course integrating community-based settings. Hamilton and Margot (2019) found community-based teaching allowed for practice-based teaching and broadened exposure to teaching in various settings outside of a traditional model.

Researchers advocate for the integration of informal science learning with EPPs for a multitude of reasons, including opportunities to practice teaching in a low-stakes environment, learning to teach through inquiry-based activities using diverse science resources and tools, developing content knowledge, enhancing familiarity with work that scientists' do, and increasing teacher confidence and self-efficacy (Adams & Gupta, 2017; Anderson, 2016; Avraamidou, 2014; Gupta et al., 2016). ISLEs have the potential to help new teachers apply an approach to teaching that might help meet the challenges that beginning teachers face (Avraamidou, 2014). Presently, science education literature provides few extensive, in-depth examples of EPPs that are integrated with informal science learning, particularly for beginning teachers (Avraamidou, 2014).

Shifts in teacher perceptions of ISLEs. Various studies demonstrate how planning and conducting field trips to ISLEs can be integrated into university courses. As some studies highlight, in-service teachers frequently feel unprepared and lack confidence in designing and leading field trips, and experience logistical difficulties. These findings are not surprising, as teachers are generally not taught how to do this. Thus, some teacher educators have made efforts to build confidence by weaving field trips, along with logistical planning, into preservice programs (Ateşkan & Lane, 2016; Macdonald et al., 2018; Bozdoğan, 2012). Studies find that integrating visits or projects connected to ISLEs into EPPs has potential to shift PSTs' perceptions of informal learning environments (Bozdoğan, 2016; Morentin & Guisasola, 2014). Notably, Kisiel (2013) found a change in

PSTs' conceptualizations of ISLEs from "places where students can learn" to "places that can also help support teachers." When examining PSTs' perceptions of ISLEs' usefulness for new teachers, 91% of responses changed to more positive ideas after a methods course integrating informal science experiences, particularly regarding awareness, pedagogical and content knowledge, motivation, and value for students (Kisiel, 2013, p. 82). This same study suggests that "even this limited exposure" to ISLEs can help reconceptualize their role in supporting teachers for their future classrooms (p. 85).

Several studies connect PSTs' experiences in ISLEs and what they envision for their future classrooms or "imaginaries" and the types of learning environments they want to create for their students (Adams & Gupta, 2017; Smetana et al., 2017). As Adams and Gupta found, the "pedagogical imaginaries" envisioned by PSTs were "student-centered, minds-on, hands-on learning environments" that promoted equitable practices and were responsive to diverse learners (2017, p. 14). An Australian study highlights how partnerships between ISLEs and EPPs can support teacher-capacity building in PSTs, establishing and leveraging relationships with cultural organizations in the community and contributing to expertise in content knowledge, curriculum development, and pedagogical enactment (Lemon & Weller, 2015). Lemon and Weller (2015) examined how opportunities to develop, implement, and assess curricula with students at a wildlife sanctuary enhance PSTs' ability to see themselves as teachers across learning settings, integrating access to resources and ability to cultivate similar partnerships in the future. Likewise, PSTs with experiences in ISLEs often highlight increased interest or curiosity in the subject (Tasdemir et al., 2014). In field experiences in ISLEs, PSTs engage as learners and develop science practices such as observation and developing hypotheses (Tasdemir et al., 2014). Thus, learning experiences at ISLEs can also play a role in PSTs' conceptions of "doing science" (Smetana et al., 2017). PSTs considered opportunities to participate and learn by "doing" (Lemon & Weller, 2015; Smetana et al., 2017; Tasdemir et al., 2014) in science investigations beneficial for their future students.

Contributing to teacher confidence, self-efficacy, and deeper content knowledge. In-service teacher graduates of a training program in Turkey credited their confidence in conducting field trips with their students to their preservice experiences (Ateşkan & Lane, 2016). Results from a similar multi-sited study indicate that PSTs' self-efficacy levels increased after organizing educational trips, suggesting the importance of this training received in EPPs (Hamurcu et al., 2019). In Durmaz and colleagues (2017), PSTs reported an increase in their self-confidence after teaching in science fairs as part of a university education course on community service, and they made connections to future science teaching. Additional studies highlight how ISLEs often allow for PSTs to assume greater autonomy, agency, and flexibility in their teaching, trying out new strategies and approaches as they are freed of some of the constraints of teaching in formal settings (Adams & Gupta, 2017; Wallace & Brooks, 2015).

A Swedish study investigated PSTs' science learning opportunities through small-group discussion in a course developed between two university-based EPPs and a local science center (Williams & Svensson, 2020). The study focused on group meetings where PSTs planned lessons to bring students to the science center. Findings indicate that PSTs demonstrated deeper content knowledge during group discussions. When conversations had greater variation, PSTs were more likely to reach a common understanding of a particular concept (Williams & Svensson, 2020). Similarly, studies indicate that deepening of PSTs' content knowledge following teaching and learning experiences at ISLEs is connected to an increased sense of efficacy (Haines & McClure, 2020; Saribaş et al., 2016; Stokes et al., 2017).

Several studies examined how PSTs' learning and teaching together in ISLEs provided opportunities for developing a community of practice where they developed shared experiences and collaborated as science learners and teachers (Adams & Gupta, 2017; Aquino et al., 2010). Through extended time in the ISLE interacting with resources, exhibits, objects, scientists, educators, and visitors, PSTs develop familiarity and confidence with the space, content, and strategies, often forming strong connections to the institution that shapes their ISLE-science teacher identity.

Place-Based Education

Literature on informal settings is often grounded in place-based education, in which place provides a central lens for meaningful context, environment, and connections critical to learning and teaching science. Place-based education (PBE) is rooted in the local environment and provides a foundation in which to make connections to phenomena and everyday life. Also referred to as "sense of place," "pedagogy of place," or "place conscious," PBE connotes a deep meaning associated with place, often including sociopolitical implications and local knowledge of the land (Ontong & Le Grange, 2015; van Eijck, 2010). For the present purposes, PBE is defined as

> the process of using the local community and environment as a starting point to teach concepts . . . across the curriculum. Emphasizing hands-on, real-world learning experiences, this approach to education increases academic achievement, helps students develop stronger ties to their community, enhances students' appreciation for the natural world, and creates a heightened commitment to serving as active, contributing citizens.
>
> (Sobel, 2004, p. 7)

Studies on PBE are growing internationally in science education, often incorporating aspects of ecological or indigenous knowledge systems and cultures. While research on PBE has existed for decades, the term is more recent (van Eijck, 2010), is frequently attributed to US scholars (Preston, 2015), and has often been embedded in cultural studies and natural history (Ontong & Le Grange, 2015; Preston, 2015) and environmental education (Adams et al., 2014; van Eijck, 2010). Preston (2015) explored how PBE has surfaced in Australia in environmental and outdoor education studies since 2000 and has emerged more recently in Australian curriculum in geography. In South Africa, scholars have advocated for a need for PBE in schools, especially given the social and political landscape deeply entwined in the construct of place, which could serve as a transformative tool used in schools and universities (Ontong & Le Grange, 2015). In some respects, a place-based educational approach complements a focus in teacher education on context-specific preparation, where programs aim to help PSTs learn deeply about and make meaning of their setting or place (Matsko & Hammerness, 2014).

In the US, PBE integrates an experiential, hands-on, inquiry focus – a critical strategy used by and associated with ISLEs (Subramaniam, 2020) as well as central to science education (Avraamidou, 2014). One US university EPP utilizes a place-based approach grounding science teacher learning into the use of the city and the abundance of resources including ISLEs like museums, conceiving an approach called "City-as-Lab" (Adams et al., 2016). Incorporating place as both a physical and social setting for learning to teach, and leverage in terms of teacher identity development, the program emphasizes the integration of informal science learning to provide more expansive opportunities for student learning and equitable science teaching (Adams et al., 2016). The program highlights how teachers develop a practice and identity connected to place, and learn to leverage and use it to make connections with students. In another EPP, PSTs and in-service teachers enroll in a seminar partnered with a museum to explore the city as a resource in "Science and the City" (Maulucci & Brotman, 2010). Grounded in equity science pedagogy, the seminar supports teachers to help students integrate science resources, drawing on students' funds of knowledge as assets.

Scholars have started to investigate the notion of place identity (Adams et al., 2016; Gross & Hochberg, 2016), highlighting self-efficacy and identity development for PSTs. An amalgam of both concepts, place identity is how an individual views themself in connection to meanings associated with a particular location and community (Gross & Hochberg, 2016). Investigating perceptions of place identity and connections to teaching identity with PSTs in Israel, researchers found that fostering place identity positively affects developing other identity aspects. In a course, PSTs design a field trip studying the place and people in the locality, as well as memories to that place paving "a pedagogical path to the integration of out-of-class learning into the development of place identity" (Gross & Hochberg, 2016, p. 1267). More research is needed on place-based out-of-class pedagogy to learn further about novice teachers' thinking as it relates to developing place identity (Gross & Hochberg, 2016).

Lived experiences are inextricably linked to place and are integral to developing teacher identity, informing how novice teachers engage in making sense of the world (Adams et al., 2016). Thus, the physical setting and environment are interwoven in how teachers perceive themselves, suggesting teacher identity is situational and context-specific. In rare instances, ISLEs have provided identification cards to PSTs during field experiences (Aquino et al., 2010). This ongoing connection offers greater access but also a component of trust and affiliation, fostering deeper connections to the place and associations to the institution, and suggests the development of ISLE-science teacher identities.

Existing Gaps in the Research

This section illustrates understudied areas of research on ISLEs and preservice science education. Through this review, it is evident that many studies on ISLEs and preservice teaching are positioned "in the moment" and lack longitudinal tracking of PSTs once they enter the profession or how ISLE experiences manifest in teaching; do not show impact on the funds of knowledge of PSTs of color (McLaughlin & Calabrese Barton, 2013); do not identify equity affordances in ISLEs when PSTs interact with visitors from different racial and ethnic backgrounds; and do not pose ISLEs as partners in teacher preparation to address reform recommendations (Avraamidou, 2014). In addition, a broader representation of ISLEs including aquariums, zoos, botanical gardens, and parks in the literature is needed.

Another area of significant study is the ways in which the cultural milieus of ISLE and university education are unique and overlap. Each of these sectors have existing practices, schema, and structures that form the culture of that space, and the people who work in those places have particular experiences, assets, and knowledge they bring to enact and transform the culture. When informal and university staff come together for a partnership, most often time is not taken to understand each other's cultures, assets and affordances, limitations, constraints, and the standpoints and experiences of all of the stakeholders involved (Gupta et al., 2010). Therefore, when partnerships are formed, assumptions are made, and sometimes those assumptions become barriers to sustaining those partnerships.

One typical limitation, as noted in Tran et al. (2019), is the diverse backgrounds that ISLE educators bring to the table, in terms of experience on what good teaching and learning look like in a classroom. Authors argue that other museums, as they did, should implement a professional learning program to bring everyone to common expectations. This limitation is also seen when partnerships are led/co-led by ISLE educators and university faculty in the limited school-based expertise ISLE educators tend to have in order to prepare a PST for their future classroom. Tran and King (2007) stated that there is limited recognition and understanding of ISLE educators in research and practice, and their pedagogical actions do not share a common understanding of best practice, which may be due to the absence of professional preparation grounded in a recognized knowledge base. As noted in Patterson (2021), ISLE educators who acted as mentors for preservice teachers enrolled in a university course placed less focus on attaining grades and knew few recent pedagogies. They focused instead on the inner workings of the cultural institutions they represented, how exhibitions were made, and how to find primary resources; and they made links to their future teaching, but more from a student lens rather than a teacher lens. The pedagogical connection was mainly left to the university, and for the PST mentee to process it rather than the ISLE educator to teach it. Thus, pedagogical content knowledge integrating teaching content knowledge in an informal setting is a learning process for the ISLE educator, as more and more partnerships form.

There is a need for systematic research efforts internationally to include ISLEs in the teaching and learning of science teachers. ISLEs extend PSTs' field experiences beyond what is customary with student teaching in schools. ISLE experiences shape a novice teacher's developmental trajectory and commitment to learning in and through practice, and have the potential to bring attention to and provide access to learning in informal settings. However, ISLE experiences are often unique and may be contextualized within the research as one-off elective courses, field trips, or with preference to elementary PSTs (Kisiel, 2014).

Another gap identified is a lack of longitudinal studies investigating the impact of ISLE experiences in learning to teach with in-service teachers in the classroom (Avraamidou, 2014, 2015; Bevan et al., 2010; Kisiel, 2013). While research in ISLEs often focuses on examining beliefs, knowledge, and attitudes, few studies have employed a sociocultural framing which can be helpful in considering both the social and cultural nature of ISLEs (Avraamidou, 2014). Additionally, most studies employ similar research methods such as mixed methods approaches incorporating surveys and interviews, descriptive ethnographies, or qualitative case studies. In each study, the methods used come with their own set of biases and interpretations, and the affordances and limitations associated with studying impact. Adopting a biographical approach, for instance, could shed light on the impact of ISLEs on PST learning throughout their lives, as opposed to concentrating on short-term experiences in a course through teachers' lived experiences (Avraamidou, 2014). This could also encourage ways to connect with PSTs' cultural backgrounds and identities. Leveraging the recommendation of teacher biographies or life histories, what might we learn from other types of methods, such as teacher action research with PSTs in ISLEs or collaborative culturally responsive research efforts? What are the opportunities for advancing the field and pushing methodological approaches in researching teaching and learning in ISLEs? What new ways might researchers consider for gathering data and studying long-term impacts? What practices and approaches might researchers design and implement for developing deeper understanding of teaching and learning in ISLEs connected to equity, inclusion, and access?

A critique of studies on ISLEs is that they are often undertheorized (Brody et al., 2007; Dawson, 2014b), requiring more defined and explicit theoretical constructs and framing that can be used to ground systematic research and inform selection of methodologies and assessments. This is particularly evident in regard to research centering on issues of equity, access, and inclusion at ISLEs (Dawson, 2014b; Rahm, 2014). As more studies in teacher education apply a critical race theory lens to ground research, adopting a critical pedagogy perspective can help disrupt inequities and promote inclusive and expansive practices. There is also potential for developing new theory relevant across places and settings that draws upon research on learning in ISLEs (Bell et al., 2012; NRC, 2009). Considering theoretical underpinnings that draw on social, cultural, and historical dimensions can allow for emergent ways of thinking about teaching and learning science to advance the kinds of research methodologies, assessments, and questions currently in the field.

Examining Issues of Equity

There is a gap in ISLEs reaching and providing services to PSTs (Kisiel, 2013). Researchers cite "limited documentation of implementation" for how traditional university EPPs support novice teachers with this exposure (Kisiel, 2013, p. 71). Little is known about more in-depth ISLE experiences and their impact on PSTs. Therefore, it can be inferred that PSTs who do not encounter these types of experiences may be at a disadvantage both as learners and as teachers.

Conceptions of ISLEs. Scholars argue that teachers' implicit conceptions of ISLEs such as museums may include concerns of maintaining control of student behavior and potential lack of awareness of the values that these institutions can bring to teaching and learning (Kisiel, 2013). Notably, Hsu (2016) suggested that science PSTs were able to improvise in the moment when they taught a mini lesson in a local museum on special science field trip days for public school students. This ability to spontaneously adapt and transition within a short period of time may provide PSTs with the advantage of learning to deal with technology issues, students with diverse needs, and classroom management early on.

Situating and contextualizing practices for diverse learners. In a museum-EPP partnership in which a graduate-level course at the ISLE is required for graduation, Aquino and colleagues (2010) empha-sized how interactive learning opportunities such as those afforded at the museum are not accessible to all students. The authors identified ways in which PSTs learned firsthand how museum exhibits culturally resonated with some students, as they were able to draw on lived experiences and prior knowledge, thus allowing for a reciprocity of learning and opportunities to develop trusting relation-ships between teachers and students in this specific environment (Aquino et al., 2010). ISLEs provide extensive opportunities for students and teachers to learn together (European Commission, 2015). Experiences with resources, exhibits, objects, tools, people, and collections for which museums and other ISLEs are known have the capacity to increase connections to science and make it accessible to a broader audience, including increased access to traditionally underserved areas and communi-ties with higher poverty (Aquino et al., 2010; Bevan et al., 2010). However, access to ISLEs can pose inequitable challenges, particularly for communities in rural, isolated, or disadvantaged areas (European Commission, 2015). ISLEs can provide a diverse array of experiences for learning outside of formal classroom environments beneficial for all students for whom there are great disparities amongst schools (Bevan & Dillon, 2010). ISLEs such as aquariums, museums, and science centers particularly offer experiences for learners to engage in sensemaking with phenomena, a key ingredi-ent in science educational reforms like the NGSS.

Museums have historically not been inclusive environments (Dawson, 2014a; Feinstein & Meshoulan, 2014). A recent British study exploring access to ISLE experiences through interviews with students and families finds that while variations existed, students from privileged backgrounds tended to engage in ISLE experiences more frequently (DeWitt & Archer, 2017). In addition, many felt that places like museums and science centers were not welcoming and posed financial and geographic barriers (DeWitt & Archer, 2017). Various ISLEs are striving to combat this challenge and are working to enhance equitable and inclusive practices (Hammerness & Adams, 2020; Hood, 2004; Persson, 2000) as well as research pertinent issues related to equity (Bevan et al., 2013; Daw-son, 2014b; DeWitt & Archer, 2017; Shein et al., 2019).

Reinforcing culturally responsive and sustaining teaching and learning. Opportunities to teach and learn with diverse audiences are critical to learning how to teach, providing engagement with individuals with different languages, ethnicities, and cultural backgrounds. The affordance of diverse audiences in ISLEs can enhance PSTs' awareness, sensitivity, flexibility, and understanding of oneself and work-ing with others – concepts and dispositions integral to teaching in culturally responsive, sensitive, and sustaining ways. Providing opportunities to learn to teach in such settings helps new educators learn about themselves as both teachers and learners, thus influencing and helping to shape the development of a science teacher identity (Gupta et al., 2016). Another affordance of ISLEs is the focus on real-world phenomena, where multiple entry points allow learners to make meaningful connections to their lives and to society. Drawing on students' cultural backgrounds, interests, and lived experiences and incorporating them as assets in the classroom is a central component of cultur-ally responsive education. In science, recognizing and valuing students' science capital in which par-ticipation in out-of-school science learning contexts like ISLEs is a key dimension that can enhance student engagement (Godec et al., 2017).

Advancing the Field: Scalability and Sustainability

ISLEs have potential to transform science teacher preparation in ways that can contribute to the pedagogical knowledge, identity, and resource allocation of a novice science teacher (Hsu, 2016). Partnerships between EPPs and ISLEs can provide access to enriched learning environments. PSTs learn to teach in more authentic ways, designing and practicing the art of teaching with many different audiences. Several studies demonstrate that PSTs grow in their understanding of the content and also their pedagogical content knowledge. The benefits can extend as the PST moves into their first years of teaching with a stronger set of resources and a broader network of educators and colleagues to tap and reflect with over time.

Collaboration between ISLEs and EPPs exist at different scales. In one local case (Hsu, 2016), PSTs worked with the ISLE to prepare activities in a 1-day event repeated twice a year. In that instance, the effort is on development of short, engaging activities and trying them out repeatedly with hundreds of families. Another case is when PSTs work with museum educators to develop a workshop for students during a field trip. Both examples allow PSTs to plan, enact, and revise lessons in an informal unstructured environment.

At a much larger scale, the Cultural Institutions for Teacher Education (CITE) partnership was designed as a collaboration with multiple cultural and science institutions in the informal field (see Figure 14.1) (Smetana et al., 2017). The goal is that after the PST completes the program, they should have not only content, theory, and methods courses in their educator toolkit but also a strong sense of agency ready to use their pedagogical expertise to teach science within a classroom and outside in any informal setting.

The AMNH Master of Arts in Teaching (MAT) residency program certifies earth science teachers and has developed sustainable partnerships with high-needs schools. The first residency in the 15-month program occurs during the summer at AMNH teaching with objects on touch carts in the cultural and scientific halls and exhibition spaces as well as assistant teaching in a youth science research program. The second set of residencies, which are clinical school experiences, occur in the fall and spring in local high-needs public schools with science, second language, and special education mentor teachers. During the last summer, the science PSTs conduct scientific research studies in the field and labs in astrophysics, paleontology, or geology with AMNH-based curators and postdoctoral scientists. The first AMNH-based residency sets the stage for a highly effective science teacher who gains agency, identity, knowledge of objects and exhibits; feels part of a community of professionals; and begins to develop a constructivist pedagogical mindset (Adams & Gupta, 2017; Gupta et al., 2016; Macdonald et al., 2018; MacPherson, Howes, et al., 2020; Wallace et al., 2020; Zirakparvar, 2015).

In each example, the goal is the same: finding effective ways for PSTs to learn to teach within a learning environment rich with resources, diverse visitors, and colleagues who bring a variety of expertise.

New Directions and Reflections

Opportunities to teach and learn from interactions with diverse audiences in ISLEs are essential to novice teachers, providing chances to engage with individuals with different languages, ages, localities, ethnicities, genders, and cultural backgrounds. Several examples described in this chapter offer approaches for scaling and modeling. Practitioners and researchers are encouraged to think creatively about the best ways to capture data that contribute to longitudinal studies.

Remote learning may serve as a potential solution to breaking down some walls of inequities, but it comes with its own enormous challenges, especially related to access. Some ISLEs have remote learning opportunities for teaching and learning that can serve PSTs well during their teacher

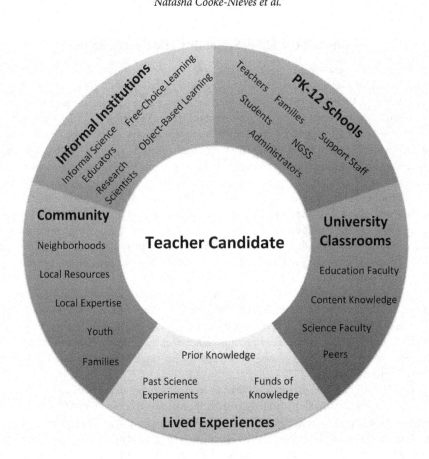

Figure 14.1   Science Teacher Learning Ecosystem © ASTE

Note: Smetana, L., Birmingham, D., Rouleau, H., Carlson, J., & Phillips, S. (2017). Cultural institutions as partners in initial elementary science teacher preparation. *Innovations in Science Teacher Education, 2*(2), p. 4. Retrieved from: https://innovations.theaste.org/cultural-institutions-as-partners-in-initial-elementary-science-teacher-preparation/

development. With a technology-enhanced approach, science PSTs can access digital resources produced by ISLEs, such as visualizing content (e.g., real-life phenomena, models, expert scientists), support conceptual understanding (e.g., access objects, exhibits, and halls through virtual field trips, using models to run simulations with different variables, virtual labs); and stop/start video to promote a student-driven discussion. In this reform-minded era, PSTs indicate that technology plays a clear role in engaging students as well as assisting them with formally assessing students and curriculum relevancy (Lux et al., 2017).

ISLEs recognize and value students' science capital in which participation in out-of-school science learning contexts is a key dimension that enhances student engagement (Godec et al., 2017). Implications for EPPs support their reorganization to include early and authentic field experiences in ISLEs. Simply put, practice and theory occur simultaneously (Arristia et al., 2014; Lux et al., 2017).

The authors suggest that ISLEs are essentially magical learning environments: designed spaces that instill a sense of wonder, awe, curiosity, inquiry, excitement, and inspiration to all visitors and learners. PSTs can envision future classrooms that glimmer with content-related objects to touch, historical connections and stories, live animals, flowering plants, and even imaginary visits to other countries via virtual field trips. ISLEs provide opportunities and experiences for novice teachers to try out lessons, learn about resources, and draw upon students' cultural backgrounds, interests, and lived experiences by enabling the aspiring science teacher to engage and take their learner on a journey outside of formal education. Hence, when assembling the EPP toolkit for a developing science teacher, ISLEs should be intentionally and seamlessly woven into the fabric of the toolkit itself.

References

Adams, A. E., Miller, B. G., Saul, M., & Pegg, J. (2014). Supporting elementary pre-service teachers to teach STEM through place-based teaching and learning experiences. *The Electronic Journal for Research in Science & Mathematics Education, 18*(5).

Adams, J., & Gupta, P. (2017). Informal science institutions and learning to teach: An examination of identity, agency and affordances. *Journal of Research in Science Teaching, 54*(1), 121–138.

Adams, J., Miele, E., & Powell, W. (2016). City-as-lab approach for urban STEM teacher learning and teaching. In L. Avraamidou & W. M. Roth (Eds.), *Intersections of Formal and Informal Science*. New York: Routledge.

Anderson, D. (2016). Museums as sites for learning the art of education. In L. Avraamidou & W. M. Roth (Eds.), *Intersections of formal and informal science* (pp. 166–177). New York: Routledge.

Aquino, A. E., Kelly, A. M., & Bayne, G. U. (2010). Sharing our teachers: The required graduate class at the American Museum of Natural History for Lehman College (CUNY). *New Educator, 6*(3–4), 225–246. https://doi.org/10.1080/1547688X.2010.10399603

Arristia, M. C., Rawls, E. S., Hammond Brinkerhoff, E., & Roehrig, A. D. (2014). The nature of elementary preservice teachers' reflection during an early field experience. *Reflective Practice, 15*(4), 427–444. https://doi.org/10.1080/14623943.2014.900018

Ateşkan, A., & Lane, J. F. (2016). Promoting field trip confidence: Teachers providing insights for pre-service education. *European Journal of Teacher Education, 39*(2), 190–201. https://doi.org/10.1080/02619768.2015.1113252

Avraamidou, L. (2014). Developing a reform-minded science teaching identity: The role of informal science environments. *Journal of Science Teacher Education, 25*(7), 823–843. https://doi.org/10.1007/s10972-014-9395-y

Avraamidou, L. (2015). Reconceptualizing elementary teacher preparation: A case for informal science education. *International Journal of Science Education, 37*(2), 108–135. http://dx.doi.org/10.1080/09500693.2014.969358

Avraamidou, L. (2016). Intersections of life histories and science identities: The stories of three preservice elementary teachers. *International Journal of Science Education, 38*(5), 861–884. https://doi.org/10.1080/09500693.2016.1169564

Avraamidou, L. (2019). Stories we live, identities we build: How are elementary teachers' science identities shaped by their lived experiences? *Cultural Studies of Science Education, 14*, 33–59.

Banilower, E. R. (2019). Understanding the big picture for science teacher education: The 2018 NSSME+. *Journal of Science Teacher Education, 30*(3), 201–208. https://doi.org/10.1080/1046560X.2019.1591920

Barak, M. (2017). Science teacher education in the twenty-first century: A pedagogical framework for technology-integrated social constructivism. *Research in Science Education, 47*, 283–303. https://doi.org/10.1007/s11165-015-9501-y.

Bell, P., Tzou, C., Bricker, L., & Baines, A. D. (2012). Learning in diversities of structures of social practice: Accounting for how, why and where people learn science. *Human Development, 55*, 269–284.

Bevan, B., Bell, P., Stevens, R., & Razfar, A. (Eds.). (2013). *LOST Opportunities: Learning in out-of-school time.* Dordrecht: Springer.

Bevan, B., & Dillon, J. (2010). Broadening views of learning: Developing educators for the 21st century through an international research partnership at the Exploratorium and King's College London. *The New Educator, 6*, 167–180.

Bevan, B. with Dillon, J., Hein, G. E., Macdonald, M., Michalchik, V., Miller, D., Root, D., . . . Yoon, S. (2010). *Making science matter: Collaborations between informal science education organizations and schools. A CAISE inquiry group report.* Washington, DC: Center for Advancement of Informal Science Education (CAISE).

Bozdoğan, A. E. (2012). The practice of prospective science teachers regarding the planning of education based trips: Evaluation of six different field trips. *Educational Sciences: Theory & Practice, 12*(2), 1062–1069. https://files.eric.ed.gov/fulltext/EJ981830.pdf

Bozdoğan, A. E. (2016). The effect of planetarium trip on pre-service science teachers' metaphorical perceptions about planetariums. *Malaysian Online Journal of Educational Sciences, 4*(4), 70–84.

Brody, M., Bangert, A., & Dillon, J. (2007). *Assessing learning in informal science contexts.* Commissioned paper by the National Research Council for Science Learning in Informal Environments Committee.

Chin, C.-C. (2004). Museum experience – A resource for science teacher education. *International Journal of Science and Mathematics Education, 51*(1), 31–39.

Dawson, E. (2014a). 'Not designed for us': How science museums and science centers socially exclude low-income, minority ethnic groups. *Science Education, 98*(6), 981–1008.

Dawson, E. (2014b). Equity in informal science education: Developing an access and equity framework for science museums and science centres. *Studies in Science Education, 50*(1), 209–247.

Dewitt, J., & Archer, L. (2017). Participation in informal science learning experiences: The rich get richer? *International Journal of Science Education, 7*(4), 356–373.

Dorph, R., Shields, P., Tiffany-Morales, J., Hartry, A., & McCaffrey, T. (2011). *High hopes – few opportunities: The status of elementary science education in California.* Sacramento, CA: The Center for the Future of Teaching and Learning at WestEd.

Durmaz, H., Dinçer, E. O., & Osmanoğlu, A. (2017). Conducting science fair activities: Reflections of the prospective science teachers on their expectations, opinions, and suggestions regarding science fairs. *Asia-Pacific Forum on Science Learning and Teaching, 18*(1), 1–25.

Elo, J., & Kurtén, B. (2020). Exploring points of contact between enterprise education and open-ended investigations in science education. *Education Inquiry, 11*(2), 18–35. https://doi.org/10.1080/20004508.2019.1633903.

European Commission. (2015). *Science education for responsible citizenship.* Brussels: Directorate-General for Research and Innovation, Science with and for Society. http://ec.europa.eu/research/swafs/pdf/pub_science_education/KI-NA-26-893-EN-N.pdf

Feinstein, N. W., & Meshoulan, D. (2014). Science for what public? Addressing equity in American science museums and science centers. *Journal for Research in Science Teaching, 51*(3), 368–394.

Gilbert, J., & Bull, A. (2013). *Building a future-oriented science education system in New Zealand: How are we doing?* Report prepared for New Zealand Council for Educational Research. www.nzcer.org.nz/system/files/Future-oriented%20science.pdf

Godec, S., King, H., & Archer, L. (2017). *The science capital teaching approach: Engaging students with science, and promoting social justice.* London: University College London.

Gross, M., & Hochberg, N. (2016). Characteristics of place identity as part of professional identity development among pre-service teachers. *Cultural Studies of Science Education, 11*, 1243–1268.

Gupta, P., Adams, J., Kisiel, J., & Dewitt, J. (2010). Examining the complexities of school-museum partnerships. *Cultural Studies of Science Education, 5*(3), 685–699.

Gupta, P., MacDonald, M., & Trowbridge, C. (2016). Breaking dichotomies: Learning to be a teacher of science in formal and informal settings. In L. Avraamidou & W. M. Roth (Eds.), *Intersections of formal and informal science* (pp. 178–188). New York: Routledge.

Haines, S., & McClure, C. (2020). Preparing preservice teachers using a civic engagement model: The effect of field experience on preservice teacher knowledge, skills, and attitude. *Science Education and Civic Engagement, 12*(2). http://new.seceij.net/wp-content/uploads/2020/09/Haines.pdf

Hamilton, E. R., & Margot, K. C. (2019, October). Preservice teachers' community-based field experiences. *Frontiers in Education, 4.* https://doi.org/10.3389/feduc.2019.00115

Hammerness, K., & Adams, J. (2020). *Informal science institutions and equity: Future-oriented historiography of research and practice.* Presentation at annual meeting of American Educational Research Association.

Hammerness, K., McDonald, S., Matsko, K. K., & Stroupe, D. (2020). How do teachers learn to teach science in ambitious and equitable ways? In D. Stroupe, K. Hammerness, & S. McDonald (Eds.), *Preparing science teachers through practice-based teacher education.* Cambridge, MA: Harvard Education Press.

Hamurcu, H., Karcı, G., Göbeklioğlu, G., Aymak, Ö., Atalay, S., & Topaloğlu, S. (2019). Self-efficacy beliefs of preservice primary school teachers about organization of educational school trips. *Journal of Research in Informal Environments, 4*(2), 102–116.

Hood, M. G. (2004). Staying away: Why people choose not to visit museums. In G. Anderson (Eds.), *Reinventing the museum: Historical and contemporary perspectives on the paradigm shift* (pp. 150–157). Oxford, UK: Rowman & Littlefield Publishers.

Hsu, P.-L. (2016). Science teaching experiences in informal settings: One way to enrich the preparation program for preservice science teachers. *Universal Journal of Educational Research, 4*(5), 1214–1222. https://doi.org/10.13189/ujer.2016.040535

Kennedy, M. M. (1999). The role of preservice teacher education. In L. Darling-Hammond & G. Sykes (Eds.), *Teaching as the learning profession: Handbook of teaching and policy* (pp. 54–86). San Francisco: Jossey Bass.

Kier, M. W., & Lee, T. D. (2017). Exploring the role of identity in elementary preservice teachers who plan to specialize in science teaching. *Teaching and Teacher Education, 61*, 199–210. https://doi.org/10.1016/j.tate.2016.10.016

Kisiel, J. F. (2013). Introducing future teachers to science beyond the classroom. *Journal of Science Teacher Education, 24*(1), 67–91. https://doi.org/10.1007/s10972-012-9288-x

Kisiel, J. F. (2014). Clarifying the complexities of school-museum interactions: Perspectives from two communities. *Journal of Research in Science Teaching, 51*(3), 342–367. https://doi.org/10.1002/tea.21129

Lemon, N., & Weller, J. (2015). Partnerships with cultural organisations: A case for partnerships developed by teacher educators for teacher education. *Australian Journal of Teacher Education, 40*(12), 40–58. https://doi.org/10.14221/ajte.2015v40n12.4

Luehmann, A. (2016). Practice-linked identity development in a science teacher education: GET REAL! science as a figured world. In L. Avraamidou (Ed.), *Studying science teacher identity: Theoretical, methodological and empirical explorations.* Rotterdam, The Netherlands: Sense Publishers.

Lux, N. A. J. B. I. A. (2017). Reflecting on the challenges of informal contexts: Early field experiences with technology in teacher education. *Contemporary Issues in Technology and Teacher Education (CITE Journal), 17*(2), 250–267.

Macdonald, M., Silvernail, D., Cooke-Nieves, N., Locke, S., Fabris, A., Biene, N. Van, & Passow, M. J. (2018). How museums, teacher educators, and schools, innovate and collaborate to learn and teach geosciences to everyone. *Terrae Didatica, 14*(3), 271–276. https://doi.org/10.20396/td.v14i3.8653525

MacPherson, A., Howes, E., Abowd, N., Gupta, P., Hammerness, K., & Kinzler, R. (2020). Preparing teachers to teach science in a non-university setting. In D. Stroupe, K. Hammerness, & S. McDonald (Eds.), *Preparing science teachers through practice-based teacher education.* Cambridge, MA: Harvard Education press.

Maulucci, M. S. R., & Brotman, J. S. (2010). Teaching science in the city: Exploring linkages between teacher learning and student learning across formal and informal contexts. *New Educator, 6*(3–4), 196–211. https://doi.org/10.1080/1547688X.2010.10399601

Matsko, K. K., & Hammerness, K. (2014). Unpacking the "urban" in urban teacher education: Making a case for context-specific preparation. *Journal of Teacher Education, 65*(2), 128–144.

McLaughlin, D. S., & Calabrese Barton, A. (2013). Preservice teachers' uptake and understanding of funds of knowledge in elementary science. *Journal of Science Teacher Education, 24,* 13–36.

Morentin, M., & Guisasola, J. (2015). The role of science museum field trips in the primary teacher preparation. *International Journal of Science and Mathematics Education, 13*(5), 965–990.

National Research Council. (2009). *Learning science in informal environments: People, places, and pursuits.* Committee on Learning Science in Informal Environments. Philip Bell, Bruce Lewenstein, Andrew W. Shouse, and Michael a. Feder, Eds. Board on Science Education, Center for Education. Division of Behavioral and Social Sciences and Education. Washington, DC: The National Academies Press

National Research Council. (2012). *A framework for K-12 science education: Practices, crosscutting concepts, and core ideas.* Committee on a Conceptual Framework for New K-12 Science Education Standards. Board on Science Education, Division of Behavioral and Social Sciences and Education. Washington, DC: The National Academies Press.

NGSS Lead States. (2013). *Next generation science standards: For states, by states.* Washington, DC: The National Academies Press. https://doi.org/10.17226/18290.

Ontong, K., & Le Grange, L. (2015). The need for place-based education in South African schools: The case of Greenfields Primary. *Perspectives in Education, 33*(3), 42–57.

Patterson, T. (2021). Historians, archivists, and museum educators as teacher educators: Mentoring preservice history teachers at cultural institutes. *Journal of Teacher Education, 72*(1), 113–125.

Persson, P. E. (2000). Community impact of science centers: Is there any? *Curator: The Museum Journal, 43*(1), 9–17.

Preston, L. (2015). The place of place-based education in the Australian primary geography curriculum. *Geographical Education, 28,* 41–49.

Rahm, J. (2014). Reframing research on informal teaching and learning in science: Comments and commentary at the heart of a new vision for the field. *Journal of Research in Science Teaching, 51*(3), 395–406.

Rennie, L. (2014). Learning science outside of school. In N. Lederman & S. Abell (Eds.), *Handbook of research on science education* (Vol. II, pp. 120–144). New York: Routledge.

Saribaş, D., Küçük, Z. D., & Ertepinar, H. (2016). Evaluating effects of an exhibition visit on pre-service elementary teachers' understandings of climate change. *Journal of Turkish Science Education, 13*(1), 19–30. https://doi.org/10.12973/tused.10154a

Shein, P. P., Dwinkels, D., & Chen, C-C. (2019). Equitable access to informal science education institutions. *The Asia-Pacific Education Researcher, 28*(2), 159–170.

Smetana, L., Birmingham, D., Rouleau, H., Carlson, J., & Phillips, S. (2017). Cultural institutions as partners in initial elementary science teacher preparation. *Innovations in Science Teacher Education, 2*(2), 1–10.

Sobel, D. (2004). *Place-based education: Connecting classroom and community.* Great Barrington: The Orion Society.

Stokes, D., Evans, P., & Craig, C. (2017). *Developing STEM teachers through both informal and formal learning experiences*. 18th Conference of ISATT, Salamanca, Spain.

Subramaniam, K. (2020). A place-based education analysis of prospective teachers' prior knowledge of science instruction in informal settings. *International Journal of Educational Research, 99.* https://doi.org/10.1016/j.ijer.2019.101497

Tasdemir, A., Kartal, T., & Ozdemir, A. M. (2014). Using science centers and museums for teacher training in Turkey. *Asia-Pacific Education Researcher, 23*(1), 61–72. https://doi.org/10.1007/s40299-013-0085-x

Tran, L. U., Gupta, P., & Bader, D. (2019). Redefining professional learning for museum education. *Journal of Museum Education, 44*(2), 135–146. https://doi.org/10.1080/10598650.2019.1586192

Tran, L. U., & King, H. (2007). The professionalization of museum educators: The case in science museums. *Museum Management and Curatorship, 22*(2), 131–149.

Vahtivuori-Hänninen, S., Halinen, I., Niemi, H., Lavonen, J., & Lipponen, L. (2014). A new Finnish national core curriculum for basic education (2014) and technology as an integrated tool for learning. In *Finnish innovations and technologies in schools* (pp. 21–32). Brill Sense. https://doi.org/10.1007/978-94-6209-749-0_2.

Van Eijck, M. W. (2010). Place-based (science) education: Something is happening here. In D. J. Tippins, M. P. Mueller, M. van Eijck, & J. D. Adams (Eds.), *Cultural studies and environmentalism: The confluence of ecojustice, place-based (science education), and indigenous knowledge systems.* Dordrecht: Springer.

Wallace, C. S., & Brooks, L. (2015). Learning to teach elementary science in an experiential, informal context: Culture, learning, and identity. *Science Education, 99*(1), 174–198. https://doi.org/10.1002/sce.21138

Wallace, J., Hammerness, K., Doykos, B., Fallona, C., Howes, E., Kinzler, R., . . . Weinstein, M. (2020, April). *Exploring outcomes of a museum-based teacher residency program through an equity in science education lens.* American Educational Research Association (AERA) Annual Meeting. San Francisco, CA.

Williams, A. T., & Svensson, M. (2020). Student teachers' collaborative learning of science in small-group discussions. *Scandinavian Journal of Educational Research,* 1–14.

Zirakparvar, N. A. (2015). A balancing act in the third space: Graduate-level earth science in an urban teacher-residency program. *Journal of Geoscience Education, 63*(3), 167–175. https://doi.org/10.5408/14-058.1

15
DISCURSIVE PRACTICES IN INITIAL SCIENCE TEACHER EDUCATION

*Mercè Izquierdo, Ainoa Marzábal, Cristian Merino, Valeria Cabello,
Patricia Moreira, Luigi Cuellar, Virginia Delgado,
Franklin Manrique, and Macarena Soto*

Introduction

In recent years, science education has increasingly focused on sustainability and socioscientific issues, aiming at preparing citizens for informed and responsible decision-making (Vesterinen et al., 2015). This in turn has involved the transformation of school science curricula and of teaching, learning, and assessment practices in classrooms. As these transformations have taken place, the relevance of discursive practices has become increasingly evident, since the classroom is understood as a discursive community where expressing and questioning ideas for collective meaning construction is expected (Mortimer & Scott, 2003).

Constructing shared meanings enables students to build better understandings of the natural world and get closer to current scientific knowledge (Couso, 2020; Schwarz et al., 2009). Thus, a more significant presence of dialogic interactions in the classroom is one of the relevant challenges in teaching planning and implementing (De Longhi et al., 2012); hence, it should become a significant part of teacher education.

School scientific language developed in the classroom through dialogic interactions is not new in science education research. Evidence of this is in the variety of names given to science dialogue at the school classroom (Kovalainen & Kumpulainen, 2005; Mortimer & Scott, 2020; Nichols & Tobin, 2000; Tobin et al., 1997). In this review, it seems the term *discursive practices* gathers the essential components that account for how the interactions are produced and managed during science teaching and learning.

Therefore, in this chapter, *science education discursive practices* (hereafter SEDP) are defined as the communicative actions that mediate the science teaching and learning processes and that, carried out by the teacher, seek to promote a collective construction of meanings in the classroom. SEDP are the argumentation, description, formulation of questions, explanations, or conclusions that, expressed by science teachers in a multimodal and dialogic way (Márquez et al., 2006), become learning opportunities for students.

SEDP are intended to involve all students in evaluating, reshaping, and expressing their understanding of world phenomena. Putting them into action requires robust teacher professional knowledge focused on planning and implementing discourse in the classroom to scaffold science learning. Promoting all students' participation in the science classroom enhances this aim by forming an inclusive discursive community (Lee & Luykx, 2007).

DOI: 10.4324/9781003098478-18

Despite the relevance of discursive practices for teaching and learning, several authors have documented how little importance teachers assign to this practice and their resistance to incorporate it as a central goal of science education (Kavanagh & Rainey, 2017; Kilinc et al., 2017; Rainey et al., 2020; Scott et al., 2018). According to those authors, this resistance can be explained by (1) scarce opportunities during initial teacher education to consider language as a central aspect of science teaching, (2) the existing gap between teacher education and pedagogical practice, (3) lack of support in the educational context, (4) traditional formative experiences during the practicum, (5) naïve epistemological visions, (6) limitations regarding pedagogical content knowledge and teacher pedagogical skills, and (7) low acknowledgment by many curricula or standardized evaluations of this educational objective.

This problem highlights the need to incorporate teacher education opportunities focused on opening and managing discursive practices for the future school context (Michaels & O'Connor, 2015). Preservice science teachers (hereafter PSTs) must recognize their responsibility in developing students' scientific communication skills. This requires acknowledging that scientific discourse is complex in nature, since it involves the ontological, epistemological, linguistic, and pedagogical considerations of linguistic and scientific communication (Yore & Treagust, 2006). Also, that scientific discourse is a socially valuable discourse, whose appropriation is one of schooling's purposes (Gee, 2008a, 2008b) and contributes to promoting equity and educational justice (Lee & Luykx, 2007).

To bring attention to discursive practices in initial science teacher education, the aim of this literature review is to identify the knowledge and experiences that enable PSTs to perform discursive practices to scaffold science learning in school classrooms.

Methodology

The bibliographic review was carried out through a documentary analysis consisting of three stages: literature search, selection, and categorization (Chang et al., 2010). In the literature search stage, theoretical and empirical proposals focused on discursive practices in initial science teacher education were collected. The selection of the terms for the bibliographic search included a set of keywords regarding discursive practices (discursive practices, communication resources, scientific discourse, dialogic science discourse and narratives) and also references to PST (preservice teacher, pre-service teacher, teacher education, training teacher, future teacher and science educator). Using these search words, several searches were carried out using three databases (Web of Science, ERIC, and SCOPUS) to ensure that all the selected studies came from peer-reviewed journals.

All the studies found were then subjected to a selection process by reviewing the titles and abstracts according to the following inclusion criteria: (a) studies published between 2000 and 2020; (b) empirical articles and literature reviews; (c) open access; (d) studies published in English, Spanish, and French, according to the authors' language expertise; and (e) studies developed with preservice science teachers.

After reading the selected studies, a categorization was carried out using three analytical dimensions suggested by Yore and Treagust (2006) and Scott et al. (2018) to organize the various aspects of discursive practices. According to the authors, the disciplinary and epistemological category included studies referring the aspects that configure disciplinary-adequate SEDP to the content to be taught. The linguistic category included studies referring to all those aspects that configure SEDP to support the specific linguistic features of scientific language. Finally, the pedagogical category included the studies that referred to the dynamic and practice of teaching oriented towards developing addressee-oriented discursive practices to foster science learning at the school level. Thus, all the studies included in the review were classified into these three dimensions – disciplinary and epistemological, linguistic, and pedagogical – where some of them could be included in more than one category.

Results

Through this literature review, we gathered evidence about PST disciplinary knowledge, communication, and pedagogical strategies that favor productive discursive teaching practices (De Longhi et al., 2012) to provide a synthesis of the state of knowledge in this field. After the bibliographic search and selection of research papers, based on the criteria presented in the methodology, 67 scientific articles were reviewed. The results are organized around the three proposed analytical categories as shown in Figure 15.1, where the main research contributions in each of them are highlighted as a summary of the results obtained.

The Disciplinary and Epistemological Dimensions of Science Education Discursive Practices

Regarding the disciplinary and epistemological dimensions of SEDP, 15 articles in this literature review refer to the aspects that configure disciplinary-adequate discursive practices, and to strategies that promote their strengthening during initial teacher education. Of the 15 articles, 13 consist of empirical research works that address different disciplinary and epistemological aspects of PST discursive practices, 10 of them through a qualitative approach, and 3 through a mixed approach. Qualitative studies focus on samples of highly variable size (between 1 and 86) of primary and secondary PSTs. The explanations or arguments in their narratives (e.g., Cassiano et al., 2016), interventions in real or simulated pedagogical contexts (e.g., Rainey et al., 2020), or interviews (e.g., Sagiannis & Dimopoulos, 2018), are analyzed using content analysis in most cases, but also through lesson studies (e.g., Feez & Quinn, 2017). On the other hand, mixed studies focus on samples of 24 to 48 PSTs and combine factor analysis of their outcomes in tests and surveys with content analysis of interviews (e.g., McNeill et al., 2016), pedagogical portfolios (e.g., Barnhart & van Es, 2015) or problem solving (e.g., Sadler & Donnelly, 2006).

According to the literature revised, having sophisticated disciplinary knowledge is a requirement for disciplinary-adequate SEDP production. When exploring the alignment between accepted scientific knowledge and the arguments constructed, Zembal-Saul et al. (2002) found that limitations and contradictions in PSTs' disciplinary topic understanding hindered their argumentative practices. Similarly, Marzábal et al. (2019), when exploring PST explanations, found that their performance was strongly influenced by their disciplinary knowledge, presenting different performances depending on the topic in which the explanation was framed.

Although the rest of the studies agree on the need for disciplinary knowledge, they point to other aspects that should also be considered. Sadler and Donnelly (2006) found that PSTs' disciplinary knowledge is often inert, requiring a more explicit approach to application contexts, such as socioscientific issues, to improve the quality of their arguments. In addition, Kulgemeyer and Riese (2018) identified the pedagogical content knowledge as a necessary mediator so that PSTs can reconstruct the disciplinary knowledge to produce disciplinary-adequate explanations, accessible to students.

Discourse production is also mediated by PSTs' visions of science and its forms of production and communication. Cabello and Topping (2018) found that PST construction of explanations is strongly linked to their beliefs about how scientific knowledge is constructed. Their findings are consistent with those of Justi and Mendonça (2016), who found that PSTs who presented naïve views of the nature of science could benefit from argumentative situations located in historical controversies to identify aspects of the nature of science and reflect on them.

These findings corroborate that there is a strong interrelation between the construction and the communication of knowledge (Yore, 2000), inherently associated with the purposes, norms, and practices of discursive communities (Gee, 2008a) and the participants' knowledge and experiences. Therefore, it is necessary that, in addition to promoting disciplinary knowledge (Sadler & Donnelly,

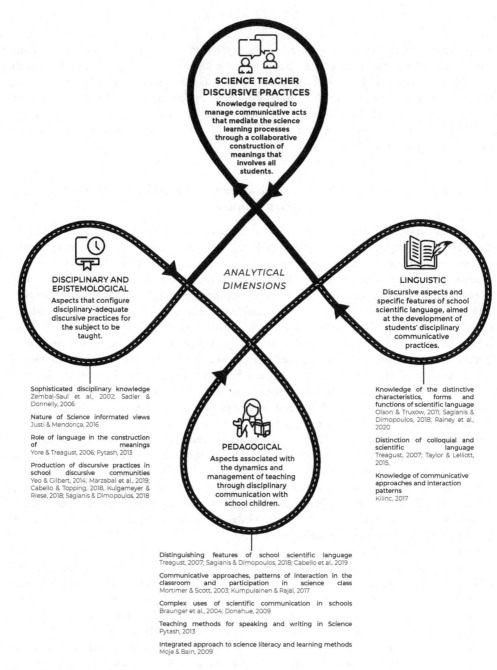

Figure 15.1 Analytical dimensions of science teacher discursive practices

2006), initial teacher education addresses disciplinary logic, reasoning modes, and knowledge production processes in scientific communities (Sagianis & Dimopoulos, 2018; Yore & Treagust, 2006). This knowledge should enable PSTs to recognize discursive practices as active processes of meaning-making (Pytash, 2013), adjusted in school discursive communities of practice, so the communicated ideas are accessible to all students.

According to the authors, the formative stage at the university should progressively approach the orchestration of those discursive practices in teaching contexts, considering the development of debates, discussions, and the formulation of explanations and arguments, teaching among peers, role-playing, design, and simulation of teaching practices, while in the context of the practicum experience, and the analysis of teaching rehearsals.

a. *Debates, discussions, explanations, and arguments.* The development of debates, discussions, and the formulation of explanations and arguments, in the context of initial teacher education, serves a double formative purpose. On the one hand, involvement in these discursive practices favors a more sophisticated level of disciplinary knowledge, as PSTs evaluate the adjustment between their ideas and the evidence gathered through observation and experimentation. In this sense, the use of arguments based on evidence to establish theories, models, explanations, and arguments about the natural world is recognized as an opportunity to overcome the existing weaknesses in understanding science and its ways of producing knowledge that is evident in initial teacher education (Zembal-Saul et al., 2002). Those strategies allow strengthening content knowledge and pedagogical content knowledge (Bartels & Kulgemeyer, 2019; Marzábal et al., 2019) and moving towards informed visions of the nature of science (Adúriz-Bravo et al., 2005; Justi & Mendonça, 2016). On the other hand, these scenarios become modeling opportunities in which PSTs experience the instructional strategies they are expected to implement in their future professional practice firsthand and to reflect on them (Windschitl et al., 2019).

b. *Role-playing and teaching practices simulations.* Teaching among peers, role-playing, and designing and simulating teaching practices challenge PSTs to manage discursive practices with teaching fictitious audiences. From a disciplinary standpoint, both an understanding of the scientific knowledge involved and the forms of production, use, and communication of this knowledge are required (Justi & Mendonça, 2016). The emphasis of teacher education in these situations should not be limited to disciplinary accuracy but also highlight the underlying epistemological aspects. This focus would allow advancing towards disciplinary-adequate and dialogic discursive practices less centered on teacher interventions, and where statements made by students and the teacher can be questioned and re-elaborated for collaborative construction of meaning.

c. *Teaching rehearsals.* Finally, the analysis of teaching rehearsals of PSTs in the context of their practicum with real audiences becomes an opportunity to monitor, provide feedback, and progressively adjust their performances. The evaluation of PSTs' discursive practices has shown potential for self-regulation, as long as they are structured and include peer evaluation and reflection in addition to assessment by teacher educators (Cabello & Topping, 2018; Marzábal et al., 2019). The instruments found in the literature, applied to the evaluation of the disciplinary and epistemological dimensions of PSTs' discursive practices, can contribute to structuring these evaluations by indicating function, form, and level as relevant criteria to be considered (Cabello & Topping, 2018; Kulgemeyer & Riese, 2018; Marzábal et al., 2019; Robertshaw & Campbell, 2013).

The empirical research papers reviewed provide strong evidence on the effectiveness of those strategies for developing PST knowledge that would result in disciplinary-adequate SEDP. However, even PSTs exposed to these types of strategy show resistance to noticing the crucial role of discursive practices in meaning-making (Rainey et al., 2020). Paying greater attention to PSTs' beliefs is necessary, for instance, to overcome the obstacles to embedding SEDP as a central aspect of science education.

The Linguistic Dimension of Science Education Discursive Practices

Regarding the linguistic dimension of SEDP, 21 articles in this literature review refer to the specific linguistic features of scientific language, and the interactions that enable the articulation of colloquial and scientific language. Of the 21 articles, 16 are empirical research papers that address different linguistic aspects of PST discursive practices, 14 of them through a qualitative approach and 2 through a mixed approach. Qualitative studies focus on the study of samples of highly variable size (between 1 and 60) of primary and secondary PSTs. The explanations or arguments in their narratives (e.g., Taylor & Lelliott, 2015), real or simulated interventions (e.g., Boyer, 2016), interactions between trainee and expert science teachers (e.g., Donahue, 2009), problem solving (e.g., Jamaludin & Hung, 2017), and interviews (e.g., Sadler & Zeidler, 2004), are analyzed using content analysis (e.g., Shanahan et al., 2011). On the other hand, mixed studies focus on samples from 36 to 66 PSTs, where discursive interactions between them are mainly analyzed in role-playing contexts or scientific discursive rehearsals aimed at developing and reflecting on argumentative practices (e.g., Scharfenberg & Bogner, 2019).

According to the literature reviewed, having knowledge about the different characteristics, forms, and functions of scientific language is an essential requirement for PSTs to promote productive interactions among students that contribute to the construction of scientific knowledge in schools. Sagiannis and Dimopoulos (2018) explored the extent to which primary school teachers recognize the special linguistic features of school science and are aware of its functionality. According to the results of this study, the scant attention paid to this aspect of initial teacher education and the traditional structure of science curricula make it difficult for PSTs to recognize the specific features of scientific language and its functionality.

Being able to relate the key scientific ideas of school science with the experiences and intuitive knowledge of students requires the ability to move between scientific and colloquial language. Taylor and Lelliott (2015) addressed this aspect in their research, highlighting the lack of flexibility of science teachers to adjust their SEDP during dialogic interactions in the science class. Kilinc et al. (2017) also addressed this issue, focusing on PST resistance to engage in dialogic discussions. Similar findings were obtained in both studies: disciplinary-focused science class design, detached from everyday life and socioscientific issues, lead to teacher-centered authoritative discursive approaches where students and teacher discourses remain disconnected, hindering students' learning.

Thus, the findings of these studies justify the need for strengthening PSTs' scientific communicative skills during initial science teacher education so that they can communicate through a broad repertoire of scientific discursive genres (Donahue, 2009) and multiple and symbolic forms of representation (Shanahan et al., 2011). Metalinguistic knowledge is also necessary for PST to acknowledge the characteristics, structures, and functions that are distinctive of scientific language (Sagiannis & Dimopoulos, 2018; Treagust, 2007), distinguishing it from the colloquial or familiar language to establish connections between both discourses (Olson & Truxaw, 2009).

The literature reviewed also highlights essential experiences to promote and develop the linguistic dimension of SEDP. Instructional strategies focus on analyzing the phenomena of learning to speak and write science as a central aspect of science education (Espinet et al., 2012), identifying possibilities, limitations, and conditioning factors of scientific communication (Sagiannis & Dimopoulos, 2018). The different experiences found in the literature focus on role-playing and discussion among PST, and also engaging in dialogical discussions with students in the practicum.

(a) *Role-playing and peer discussions.* To improve the learning of SEDP and especially the interactions between PSTs and their educators, it is suggested to practice role-playing, which impacts the development of pedagogical content knowledge, thinking carefully about the questions to pose during the experience to provide greater authenticity (Scharfenberg & Bogner, 2019), encourage peer discussion to promote the development of skills in problem resolution through simulated virtual environments (Jamaludin & Hung, 2017), and foster PSTs' former experiences in argumentation, by supporting and evaluating evidence in the rebuttal of the opponents' arguments to build more coherent and precise arguments and rebuttals (Iordanou & Constantinou, 2014).

(b) *Dialogic discussions with students.* Concerning practicum processes to improve the teaching of SEDP, the literature suggests promoting productive participation in the discourse and centering the analysis and reflections of PST on discursive patterns. These analysis and reflections should focus on identifying students' reasoning (Boyer, 2016), enhancing student participation through interactive dialogue to apprehend the school scientific discourse, and flexibly planning the interplay between the structural script of the conversation, the textbooks, and the learning activities (Taylor & Lelliott, 2015).

Regarding the evaluation of the linguistic aspects of discursive practices, several studies relate the development of these practices with monitoring and feedback among peers during initial education (Liang et al., 2010). It is evident that the structured, interactive, and constructive assessment situations, which require evaluating peer discursive practices, and responding to the criticism of others, promote the engagement in critical argumentation of one's discursive practices and the consideration of alternative ideas. In this sense, evaluation instances not only become an opportunity to reflect upon the linguistic features of discursive practices, but they also provide the space to acknowledge forms of production and communication of scientific knowledge (Erduran & Jiménez-Alexandre, 2007).

These instances require time (Fullan, 2007) and explicit scaffolding by teacher educators that consider PSTs' personal experiences and commitment (Moon et al., 2017; Sadler & Zeidler, 2004). To structure this scaffolding, Cabello and Topping (2018) suggest considering structural linguistic components of discursive practices. Among these are coherence, sequence, the connection between the parts of the explanation and clarity of the language used, its relationship with everyday language, and other pedagogical elements for discussions such as analogies and demonstrations.

Despite the relevance of the SEDP in the development of disciplinary communicative practices in the school context, studies have shown that PSTs do not have sufficient opportunities to develop a robust knowledge of scientific language during their initial education (Feez & Quinn, 2017). This hinders the dialogic discourse management in the classroom (Kilinc et al., 2017) and the support that PSTs can provide to students while examining aspects and functions of language, linguistic choices, characteristics of discourse genres, and diverse representation forms (Rainey et al., 2020).

The Pedagogical Dimension of Science Education Discursive Practices

In the pedagogical dimension of SEDP, 31 articles of this review refer to the dynamics and practice of teaching, both in the classroom and in teacher education. From this body of knowledge, 25 articles were empirically guided works, and 6 were theoretical. The selected empirical articles followed primary qualitative techniques for data collection and analysis, leading the methodological trend. Indeed, 16 articles can be categorized as qualitative ones, 6 used a mixed methods approach, and 3 had a quantitative predominance. On the one hand, the qualitative works examined an ample range of experiences, i.e., single case studies, and larger samples. On the other hand, the participants varied from 1 to 86 PSTs and primary students. The more frequent data gathering techniques were open questionnaires (e.g., Pytash, 2013), participants' reflections (e.g., Benedict-Chambers & Aram, 2017), video recordings (e.g., Drumond et al., 2015), interviews, and dialogs (e.g., Rainey et al., 2020), analyzed mainly by emergent or defined categories and content analysis. Similarly, the studies guided by a mixed approach were conducted with primary and secondary PSTs and secondary students, in samples from 22 to 221 participants. Within this group, there was not a technique predominance; the authors used tests, interviews, problem-solving exercises, analysis of teaching plans and games for learning to teach, and focus groups, among others. On the other hand, the few studies with a quantitative approach varied their sample between 39 and 109 PSTs, used simulations of discursive practices and microteaching (e.g., Cabello & Topping, 2018), and analyzed their data gathered using predefined or emergent categories.

The works in this dimension include discursive strategies and resources used by teachers to communicate disciplinary ideas with students in the classroom and dynamics or experiences to support PST understanding of educational approaches and practices that promote school disciplinary communicative skills.

Addressing disciplinary communicative skills intentionally and explicitly in the classroom is needed for the pedagogical awareness of PSTs about the unique features of school scientific language, necessary to produce a school scientific discourse that is more accessible and understandable for students (Cabello et al., 2019; Pytash, 2013; Sagiannis & Dimopoulos, 2018). It is essential to specify the similarities and differences between the discourse of expert science and school science (Treagust, 2007) and to reconfigure the classroom scientific discourse, keeping some of their main features (Sagiannis & Dimopoulos, 2018). The strategic use of learning opportunities is crucial so that students can not only access the ideas constructed in the classroom but engage them in its production (McNeill et al., 2016; Treagust, 2007) as participants of a school discursive community (Sagiannis & Dimopoulos, 2018).

Diverse studies have oriented research at the school level about the analysis of scientific discourse, identifying interaction patterns, communication approaches, and teacher intentions and specifying that alternating between the dialogic and authoritarian discourse is a norm and not an exception in the classroom (López-Neira et al., 2020; Mortimer & Scott, 2003). The asymmetries generated by the authoritarian dialogue – with little expression, contrast, and reformulation of ideas by the students – accentuate the gap in learning opportunities, possibly causing resistance in students to apprehend the scientific discourse (Brown et al., 2005), or low participation in the dialogues constructed in the classroom (Lewthwaite & Wiebe, 2014). This participation is related to the classroom discursive community's norms and codes, significantly impacting how students develop their identities as science learners (Kumpulainen & Rajal, 2017). However, classroom dialogue can also reduce the participation frequency gap by increasing the quality of student interventions, contributing to equity and educational justice, especially in groups that speak a non-native language different from the one in which science is taught (Lewthwaite & Wiebe, 2014).

The literature suggests that teachers need to include opportunities to explore various scientific genres to plan instruction that encourages students to learn how to think, read, and write as scientists (Braunger et al., 2004; Donahue, 2009). Moreover, they should embed disciplinary practices supported by reading, writing, and reasoning instead of separately approaching communicative practices and science methods (Moje & Bain, 2009).

The studies that point towards discursive practices in the science classroom highlight the importance of the dialogic function of scenarios for teaching and pedagogical resources.

(a) *Scenarios for teaching.* Within the scenarios, the inclusion of socioscientific issues favors argumentation and explanation practices (i.e., Evagorou et al., 2014; Garrido & Couso, 2015), although teachers may see themselves limited in their implementation since they are usually interdisciplinary subjects (Sezen-Barrie et al., 2015).

(b) *Pedagogical resources.* Regarding resources, propositional, pictorial, manipulative, and computational modes have been explored to construct classroom narratives. In this sense, multimodality has been shown to be a path to draw attention to reasoning, clearly scaffold discursive actions, and model scientific discourse production (Kaartinen, 2009; Mottart et al., 2009). The elaborated use of scientific text has also shown potential for the understanding and later production of various discursive genres, also providing experiences that allow PSTs to anticipate possible difficulties of their students when faced with scientific texts (Donahue, 2009; Ortiz & Fernández, 2016; Sadler & Donnelly, 2006). Finally, some interactive communication resources have been explored as support for promoting discursive practices in the classroom, such as the practice of argumentation based on evidence. It has been observed that, although ICTs can promote specific skills in students, they can also limit their interactions, in contrast to other types of activities such as experimental ones, where the exchange of ideas among peers is enriched (Baggott La Velle et al., 2003).

Teachers must reflect on the role of student ideas in constructing classroom knowledge and consider them when mediating learning processes – for instance, posing questions that encourage the development and expression of their thinking (Kademian & Davis, 2018), or inviting them to engage in discursive disciplinary practices. Several authors have highlighted the need for producing and refining SEDP collaboratively, with the permanent support of a community of PSTs and teacher educators. This support has to promote addressee-oriented SEDP that acknowledge the need for an inclusive approach (Pytash, 2013; Rainey et al., 2020; Windschitl et al., 2012).

Studies oriented towards the development of the pedagogical component of discursive practices during initial teacher education (ITE) focus mainly on their accompaniment and assessment through simulation and modeling (Benedict-Chambers & Aram, 2017; Cabello et al., 2019; Cabello & Topping, 2017, 2018; Drumond et al., 2015; Kulgemeyer & Riese, 2018).

a. *Simulations.* Simulations or student–teacher role-playing among peers favor a detailed description of PSTs' discursive movements that influence classroom discourse to promote school learning (Drumond et al., 2015). While there is agreement about simulations having advantages in preparing to respond to some challenges of future practice, the difficulty of simulating authentic student interactions and interventions is also acknowledged (Findeisen et al., 2020). We can help overcome this limitation of simulated strategies through inventories of students' most common ideas in various subjects so that PSTs can know them beforehand and adjust their classroom discourse to consider them (Benedict-Chambers & Aram, 2017).

b. *Modeling.* Modeling of the production of scientific discourses oriented toward diverse audiences has shown potential in the development of pedagogical skills and scientific content knowledge in PSTs, to the extent to which the considered criteria and the processes involved in the reconfiguration of the discursive practices are made explicit (Lee & Glass, 2017).

PSTs' decision-making to adjust discursive practices to student ideas in various scenarios has been the focus of a recent assessment instrument (Kulgemeyer & Riese, 2018). This instrument not only makes it possible to identify the extent to which PSTs are capable of adapting their discursive practices, but it also allows to guide their instruction. Most studies in this area also emphasize the critical role of reflection on discursive practices during its development (Benedict-Chambers & Aram, 2017; Cabello et al., 2019; Cabello & Topping, 2017; Lee & Glass, 2017). Communicative processes among PSTs that are based on reflection can guide the construction of knowledge in future classes and help them adopt a more dialogic position regarding students, which favors their participation and empowerment (López-Neira et al., 2020).

Finally, for the development of students' disciplinary communicative practices, PSTs require that initial teacher education contributes to seeing themselves as teachers with expert knowledge on how to communicate in science. The awareness that the production of discursive practices must be taught and not only "assigned" is necessary for PSTs to recognize the need for learning methods to teach students how to speak and write in Science (Pytash, 2013).

Towards an Initial Education that Embeds Science Education Discursive Practices as a Central Aspect of Science Education

An exhaustive literature review on science teachers' discursive practices has been carried out, identifying fundamental knowledge and experiences required to develop those discursive practices during initial teacher education. In this final section we discuss the results found in two strategic areas: the potential contributions of the accumulated knowledge to decision-making in science teacher education programs, and projections for future research and development in the field arising from the identification of tensions and knowledge gaps in the area.

Implications for Initial Science Teacher Education Programs

Regarding science teacher education, the findings of the reviewed research suggest that discursive practices remain as one of the challenges of science teachers' initial education. However, the studies carried out so far make it possible to identify some specific actions that teacher educators can take into consideration.

The development of the disciplinary and epistemological dimensions within initial science teacher education enables PSTs to recognize discursive practices as meaning-making processes and to produce disciplinary-adequate discursive practices. This requires not only disciplinary knowledge, but also about scientific practices and reasoning modes, and knowledge production processes in scientific communities. The research papers provide evidence of the effectiveness of a progressive approach to PSTs' discursive practices production, offering multiple opportunities for planning, testing, and reflecting on these practices, with teacher educators' scaffolding.

On the other hand, the development of the linguistic aspects of initial science teacher education is expected to enable PSTs to communicate through a broad repertoire of scientific discursive genres and multiple forms of representation. Studies developed on the linguistic dimension highlight the importance of providing PSTs with sufficient opportunities to acquire linguistic and metalinguistic knowledge regarding communication in science, recognizing the distinctive features of scientific language to promote the development of students' scientific communication practices, and allowing them to participate in the school discursive community.

Finally, concerning the pedagogical dimension, it is crucial that PSTs can strategically use learning opportunities to engage students in producing science discursive practices collaboratively. This requires having a broad repertoire of communication approaches, alternating dialogic and authoritarian discourses in the science classroom to construct knowledge in an accessible and understandable manner. According to the literature reviewed, producing and refining SEDP, with the permanent support of a community, enables PSTs to recognize communication management strategies to support students' learning.

The identified pieces of knowledge and the broad repertoire of proposed instructional and evaluative strategies allow ensuring that PSTs have enough opportunities to question traditional teaching practices, move forward towards informed visions of nature of science, and develop the disciplinary, linguistic, and pedagogical knowledge required to situate language as a central element in teaching and learning. Although these three dimensions have been useful in organizing the research contributions regarding discursive practices of PSTs, they should be articulated in teaching practices, and in initial science teacher education as well. Evidence suggests that PSTs in education programs with reductionist approaches, that address those different dimensions in an atomized way, fail to connect these components with each other. On the other hand, initial teacher education programs where instructional opportunities are articulated for PSTs to produce, in a collaborative and scaffolded manner, a wide variety of scientific discourses, enabling them to design, manage, and critically evaluate the scenarios, knowledge, and resources they require for teaching.

Although these guidelines may be useful for transforming the instructional processes of science teacher education, they are still indications of a general nature, which do not make distinctions for the various discursive communities of current educational systems. Since the collective construction of meanings is produced through discursive practices, moving forward towards a science education for all students requires science teachers who are capable of managing dialogic communication approaches that include all students as participants of a particular and diverse school discursive community. Therefore, if we expect all school students, regardless of their linguistic, cultural, ethnic, and geographic diversity (among others), to engage in school science discursive practices, initial science teacher education should provide – in addition to everything previously mentioned – greater knowledge of diversity in the school system and foster positive attitudes towards inclusion. Moving towards an initial science teacher education that provides PSTs with enough opportunities to support students' learning and promote the development of disciplinary communication skills for all citizens, can critically contribute to equity and educational justice.

Trends and Directions for Future Research and Development in the Field

It is evident that there are still knowledge gaps in which research in initial education for science teachers can and must continue to contribute. As long as not enough research is performed to produce evidence that supports science initial teacher education in key learning practices, we take the risk of basing decisions on ideologies or unverified assumptions that limit the construction of a transforming formative experience for PSTs (Windschitl et al., 2012).

Regarding the disciplinary and epistemological dimension, there seems to be evidence that effective strategies for developing PST knowledge that will result in disciplinary-adequate SEDP. However, even PSTs exposed to these types of strategies show resistance to incorporating discursive practices into their teaching (Rainey et al., 2020). Paying greater attention to PST beliefs is necessary, for instance, through practitioner research, to overcome the obstacles of embedding SEDP as a central aspect of science education. The present literature review has found few contributions focused on characterizing how these formative opportunities help transform epistemological views and beliefs regarding the importance of disciplinary communicative practices in PSTs. Thus, more studies in this regard would be significant contributions.

From this review, there are still knowledge gaps regarding the linguistic component of discursive practices as well. For instance, conceptions and knowledge of PSTs have not been explored in depth regarding the role of literacy in teaching and learning their disciplines (Shanahan et al., 2011). Also, the absence of studies that address the science teachers' literacy level is noticeable, typically implicitly assuming that they can recognize specific linguistic features of scientific language (Sagiannis & Dimopoulos, 2018).

Despite the convergences identified in the pedagogical dimension, knowledge gaps still persist regarding the teaching practice in school contexts that are specifically considered diverse – for instance, exploring the extent to which discursive practices impact identity building in students as science learners (Kumpulainen & Rajal, 2017). Likewise, it would be fruitful to inquire under what conditions the development of SEDP during initial teacher education can be transferred to classroom practice (Marzábal et al., 2019) in order to advance towards PSTs' self-regulation of performance and strengthen their professionalism in real teaching contexts.

It is also necessary to develop more research about relations between the disciplinary, linguistic, and pedagogical dimensions of the SEDP, with the purpose of exploring in greater detail how these components are developed and intertwined during initial teacher education. This would allow us to gather evidence to organize science teacher initial education, considering in which way they integrate, and allowing PSTs to have a broad repertoire of discursive practices for teaching. This repertoire is what will finally make it possible for science teachers to flexibly adapt to diverse teaching contexts, forming school discursive communities that embrace diversity of current science classes. This could significantly contribute to making science education responsive to diversity and more meaningful for all students (Kumpulainen & Rajal, 2017).

We hope that this chapter inspires researchers that are interested in this field to share their knowledge and experiences and contribute, from diverse epistemological, theoretical, and methodological frameworks, to move towards an initial teacher education that places SEDP as a central – rather than peripheral – aspect of teaching and learning processes of school science.

References

Adúriz-Bravo, A., Bonan, L., Galli, L. G., Revel Chion, A. R., & Meinardi, E. (2005). Scientific argumentation in pre-service biology teacher education. *Eurasia Journal of Mathematics, Science and Technology Education, 1*(1), 76–83.

Baggott La Velle, L. B., McFarlane, A., & Brawn, R. (2003). Knowledge transformation through ICT in science education: A case study in teacher-driven curriculum development-case study 1. *British Journal of Educational Technology, 34*(2), 183–200.

Barnhart, T., & van Es, E. (2015). Studying teacher noticing: Examining the relationship among pre-service science teachers' ability to attend, analyze and respond to student thinking. *Teaching and Teacher Education, 45*, 83–93.

Bartels, H., & Kulgemeyer, C. (2019). Explaining physics: An online test for self-assessment and instructor training. *European Journal of Physics, 40*(1), 015701.

Benedict-Chambers, A., & Aram, R. (2017). Tools for teacher noticing: Helping preservice teachers notice and analyze student thinking and scientific practice use. *Journal of Science Teacher Education, 28*(3), 294–318.

Boyer, E. (2016). Preservice elementary teachers' instructional practices and the teaching science as argument framework. *Science & Education, 25*(9–10), 1011–1047.

Braunger, J., Donahue, D., Evans, K., & Galguera, T. (2004). *Rethinking preparation for content area teaching.* San Francisco: Jossey-Bass.

Brown, B. A., Reveles, J. M., & Kelly, G. J. (2005). Scientific literacy and discursive identity: A theoretical framework for understanding science learning. *Science Education, 89*(5), 779–802.

Cabello, V. M., Real, C., & Impedovo, M. (2019). Explanations in STEM areas: An analysis of representations through language in teacher education. *Research in Science Education, 49*(4), 1087–1106.

Cabello, V. M., & Topping, K. J. (2017). Role-playing for learning to explain scientific concepts in teacher education. *Journal of Science Education, 18*(2), 67–70.

Cabello, V. M., & Topping, K. J. (2018). Making scientific concepts explicit through explanations: Simulations of a high-leverage practice in teacher education. *International Journal of Cognitive Research in Science, Engineering and Education, 6*(3), 35–47.

Cassiano, K. F. D., Mesquita, N. A., & Ribeiro, P. G. (2016). Conhecimento pedagógico e conhecimento químico na formação de professores: A construção da identidade docente. *Química Nova, 39*(2), 250–259.

Chang, Y., Chang, C., & Tseng, Y. (2010). Trends of science education research: An automatic content analysis. *Journal of Science and Educational Technology, 19*, 315–331.

Couso, D. (2020). Aprender ciencia escolar implica construir modelos cada vez más sofisticados de los fenómenos del mundo [Learning school science involves building increasingly sophisticated models of world phenomena]. In D. Couso, M. R. Jiménez-Liso, C. Refojo, & J. A. Sacristán (Eds.), *Enseñando Ciencia con Ciencia* (pp. 63–74). Madrid: Penguin Random House.

De Longhi, A. L., Ferreyra, A., Peme, C., Bermudez, G. M., Quse, L., Martinez, S., . . . Campaner, G. (2012). La interacción comunicativa en clases de ciencias naturales [Communicative interaction in natural sciences lessons]. *Revista Eureka sobre Enseñanza y Divulgación de las Ciencias, 9*(2), 178–195.

Donahue, D. (2009). Reading across the great divide: English and math teachers apprentice one another as readers and disciplinary insiders. *Journal of Adolescent & Adult Literacy, 47*(1), 24–37.

Drumond, R., da Rocha, J. R., Evagorou, M., & Florentino, V. (2015). Argumentation in Science Teacher Education: The simulated jury as a resource for teaching and learning. *International Journal of Science Education, 37*(7), 1113–1139.

Erduran, S., & Jiménez-Alexandre, M. P. (2007). *Argumentation in science education perspectives from classroom-based research.* Dordrecht: Springer.

Espinet, M., Izquierdo, M., Bonil, J., & Ramos, L. (2012). The role of language in modeling the natural world: Perspectives in science education. In Fraser et al. (Eds.) *Second international handbook of science education* (pp. 1385–1403). Springer International.

Evagorou, M., Guven, D., & Mugaloglu, E. (2014). Preparing elementary and secondary pre-service teachers for everyday science. *Science Education International, 25*(1), 68–78.

Feez, S., & Quinn, F. (2017). Teaching the distinctive language of science: An integrated and scaffolded approach for pre-service teachers. *Teaching and Teacher Education, 65*, 192–204.

Findeisen, S., Deutscher, V. K., & Seifried, J. (2020). Fostering prospective teachers' explaining skills during university education – Evaluation of a training module. *Higher Education*, 1–17.

Fullan, M. (2007). *The new meaning of educational change*. New York: Teachers College Press

Garrido, A., & Couso, D. (2015). Socio-scientific issues (SSI) in initial training of primary school teachers: Pre-service teachers' conceptualization of SSI and appreciation of the value of teaching SSI. *Procedia-Social and Behavioral Sciences, 196*, 80–88.

Gee, J. P. (2008a). "Basic information structure" and "academic language": An approach to discourse analysis. In K. Cooper & R. White (Eds.), *Critical literacies in action: Social perspectives and teaching practices* (pp. 143–158). Leiden: Brill Sense.

Gee, J. P. (2008b). Learning in semiotic domains. *Literacies, Global and Local, 2*, 137–149.

Iordanou, K., & Constantinou, C. P. (2014). Developing pre-service teachers' evidence-based argumentation skills on socio-scientific issues. *Learning and Instruction, 34*, 42–57.

Jamaludin, A., & Hung, D. (2017). Problem-solving for STEM learning: Navigating games as narrativized problem spaces for 21st century competencies. *Research and Practice in Technology Enhanced Learning, 12*(1), 1–14.

Justi, R., & Mendonça, P. C. C. (2016). Discussion of the controversy concerning a historical event among pre-service teachers. *Science & Education, 25*(7–8), 795–822.

Kaartinen, S. (2009). Meaningfulness via participation: Sociocultural practices for teacher learning and development. *Teachers and Teaching: Theory and Practice, 15*(5), 601–616.

Kademian, S. M., & Davis, E. A. (2018). Supporting beginning teacher planning of investigation-based science discussions. *Journal of Science Teacher Education, 29*(8), 712–740.

Kavanagh, S. S., & Rainey, E. C. (2017). Learning to support adolescent literacy: Teacher educator pedagogy and novice teacher take up in secondary English language arts teacher preparation. *American Educational Research Journal, 54*(5), 904–937.

Kilinc, A., Demiral, U., & Kartal, T. (2017). Resistance to dialogic discourse in SSI teaching: The effects of an argumentation-based workshop, teaching practicum, and induction on a preservice science teacher. *Journal of Research in Science Teaching, 54*(6), 764–789.

Kovalainen, M., & Kumpulainen, K. (2005). The discursive practice of participation in an elementary classroom community. *Instructional Science, 33*, 213–250

Kulgemeyer, C., & Riese, J. (2018). From professional knowledge to professional performance: The impact of CK and PCK on teaching quality in explaining situations. *Journal of Research in Science Teaching, 55*(10), 1393–1418.

Kumpulainen, K., & Rajal, A. (2017). Dialogic teaching and students' discursive identity negotiation in the learning of science. *Learning and Instruction, 48*, 23–31.

Lee, O., & Luykx, A. (2007). Science education and student diversity: Race/ethnicity, language, culture, and socioeconomic status. *Handbook of Research on Science Education, 1*, 171–197.

Lee, T. D., & Glass, B. (2017). talking science: It's not elementary! improving elementary pre-service teacher discourse skills through a scaffolded "science talks" assignment. *Journal of Interdisciplinary Teacher Leadership, 1*(2), 13–18.

Lewthwaite, B., & Wiebe, R. (2014). Responding to students' learning preferences in chemistry. *Journal of Science Teacher Education, 25*(3), 263–287.

Liang, L. L., Ebenezer, J., & Yost, D. S. (2010). Characteristics of pre-service teachers' online discourse: The study of local streams. *Journal of Science Education and Technology, 19*(1), 69–79.

López-Neira, L., Labbé, C., & Villalta, M. (2020). Digital game for the development of classroom verbal interaction strategies: Enhanced pre-service teacher training model with technology. *Culture and Education, 32*(3), 441–469.

Márquez, C., Izquierdo, M., & Espinet, M. (2006). Multimodal science teachers' discourse in modeling the water cycle. *Science Education, 90*(2), 202–226.

Marzábal, A., Merino, C., Moreira, P., & Delgado, V. (2019). Assessing science teaching explanations in initial teacher education: How is this teaching practice transferred across different chemistry topics? *Research in Science Education, 49*(4), 1107–1123.

McNeill, K. L., Katsh-Singer, R., González-Howard, M., & Loper, S. (2016). Factors impacting teachers' argumentation instruction in their science classrooms. International *Journal of Science Education*, *38*(12), 2026–2046.

Michaels, S., & O'Connor, C. (2015). *Conceptualizing talk moves as tools: Professional development approaches for academically productive discussion*. Socializing Intelligence Through Talk and Dialogue, 347–362.

Moje, E. B., & Bain, R. (2009). *Teacher education for disciplinary literacy learning*. Michigan: University of Michigan.

Moon, A., Stanford, C., Cole, R., & Towns, M. (2017). Analysis of inquiry materials to explain complexity of chemical reasoning in physical chemistry students' argumentation. *Journal of Research in Science Teaching*, *54*(10), 1322–1346.

Mortimer, E. F., & Scott, P. H. (2003). *Meaning making in secondary science classrooms*. Maidenhead: Open University Press.

Mortimer, E. F., & Scott, P. H. (2020). Turning points in communicative approaches to science classroom discourse. In N. C. El-Hani, M. Pietrocola, F. E. Mortimer, & M. Rita Otero (Eds.), *Science education research in Latin America* (pp. 254–276). Leiden: Brill Sense.

Mottart, A., Vanhooren, S., Rutten, K., & Soetaert, R. (2009). Fictional narratives as didactical tools: Using Frank McCourt's Teacher Man in pre-service teacher education. *Educational Studies*, *35*(5), 493–502.

Nichols, S., & Tobin, K. (2000). Discursive practice among teachers co-learning during field-based elementary science teacher preparation. *Action in Teacher Education*, *22*(2), 45–54.

Olson, M. R., & Truxaw, M. P. (2009). Preservice science and mathematics teachers and discursive metaknowledge of text. *Journal of Adolescent & Adult Literacy*, *52*(5), 422–431.

Ortiz, F., & Fernández, P. (2016). Diseño instruccional para argumentación científica en línea [Instructional design for online scientific argumentation]. *Interdisciplinaria*, *33*(2), 231–249.

Pytash, K. E. (2013). Secondary preservice teachers' development of teaching scientific writing. *Journal of Science Teacher Education*, *24*(5), 793–810.

Rainey, E. C., Maher, B. L., & Moje, E. (2020). Learning disciplinary literacy teaching: An examination of preservice teachers' literacy teaching in secondary subject area classrooms. *Teaching and Teacher Education*, *94*, 1–12.

Robertshaw, B., & Campbell, T. (2013). Constructing arguments: Investigating pre-service science teachers' argumentation skills in a socio-scientific context. *Science Education International*, *24*(2), 195–211.

Sadler, T. D., & Donnelly, L. A. (2006). Socioscientific argumentation: The effects of content knowledge and morality. *International Journal of Science Education*, *28*(12), 1463–1488.

Sadler, T. D., & Zeidler, D. L. (2004). The morality of socioscientific issues: Construal and resolution of genetic engineering dilemmas. *Science Education*, *88*, 4–27.

Sagiannis, S., & Dimopoulos, K. (2018). Greek primary school teachers' awareness of the special features of scientific language: Implications for science curricula and teachers' professional development. *The Curriculum Journal*, *29*(3), 387–405.

Scharfenberg, F. J., & Bogner, F. X. (2019). A role-play-based tutor training in preservice teacher education for developing procedural pedagogical content knowledge by optimizing tutor – student interactions in the context of an outreach lab. *Journal of Science Teacher Education*, *30*(5), 461–482.

Schwarz, C. V., Reiser, B. J., Davis, E. A., Kenyon, L., Achér, A., Fortus, D., . . . Krajcik, J. (2009). Developing a learning progression for scientific modeling: Making scientific modeling accessible and meaningful for learners. *Journal Research in Science Teacher*, *46*, 632–654.

Scott, C. E., McTigue, E. M., Miller, D. M., & Washburn, E. K. (2018). The what, when, and how of preservice teachers and literacy across the disciplines: A systematic literature review of nearly 50 years of research. *Teaching and Teacher Education*, *73*, 1–13.

Sezen-Barrie, A., Moore, J., & Roig, C. E. (2015). Discovering plate boundaries in data-integrated environments: Preservice teachers conceptualization and implementation of scientific practices. *International Journal of Science Education*, *37*(12), 2013–2037.

Shanahan, C., Shanahan, T., & Misischia, C. (2011). Analysis of expert readers in three disciplines: History, mathematics, and chemistry. *Journal of Literacy Research*, *43*(4), 393–429.

Taylor, D. L., & Lelliott, A. D. (2015). Dialogic talk in diverse Physical Science classrooms. *African Journal of Research in Mathematics, Science and Technology Education*, *19*(3), 255–266.

Tobin, K., McRobbie, C., & Anderson, D. (1997). Dialectical constraints to the discursive practices of a high school physics community. *Journal of Research in Science Teaching: The Official Journal of the National Association for Research in Science Teaching*, *34*(5), 491–507.

Treagust, D. F. (2007). General instructional methods and strategies. In S. Abell & N. Lederman (Eds.), *Handbook of research on science education* (pp. 373–391). New Jersey: Lawrence Erlbaum Associates, Inc.

Vesterinen, V. M., Tolppanen, S., & Aksela, M. (2016). Toward citizenship science education: What students do to make the world a better place? *International Journal of Science Education, 38*(1), 30–50.

Windschitl, M., Thompson, J., Braaten, M., & Stroupe, D. (2012). Proposing a core set of instructional practices and tools for teachers of science. *Science Education, 96*(5), 878–903.

Windschitl, M., Thompson, J., Braaten, M., & Stroupe, D. (2019). Sharing a Vision, Sharing Practices: How Communities of Educators Improve Teaching. *Remedial and Special Education, 40*(6), 380–390.

Yeo, J., & Gilbert, J. K. (2014). Constructing a scientific explanation – A narrative account. *International Journal of Science Education, 36*(11), 1902–1935.

Yore, L. D. (2000). Enhancing science literacy for all students with embedded reading instructive and writing-to-learn activities. *Journal of Deaf Studies and Deaf Education, 5*, 105–122.

Yore, L. D., & Treagust, D. F. (2006). Current realities and future possibilities: Language and science literacy – empowering research and informing instruction. *International Journal of Science Education, 28*(2–3), 291–314.

Zembal-Saul, C., Munford, D., Crawford, B., Friedrichsen, P., & Land, S. (2002). Scaffolding preservice science teachers' evidence-based arguments during an investigation of natural selection. *Research in Science Education, 32*, 437–463.

16

THE ROLE OF EMERGING TECHNOLOGIES IN SCIENCE TEACHER PREPARATION

Gina Childers and Rebecca Hite

Introduction

There is a global movement to foster the utilization of emerging technologies to enable innovative methods of K–12 science teaching and learning experiences. National and international professional organizations have espoused the importance of technology use for teaching and learning, innovation, and solving problems, calling for explicit integration into preservice science teacher preparation (Association for Science Teacher Education, 2021; International Society for Technology in Education, 2021; National Science Teaching Association, 2017; National Science & Technology Council, 2018). Among these calls, countries have developed actionable proposals and policies, such as the United States' National Education Association, Continental Education Strategy for Africa, the Conference on the Digital Transformation of Education Systems throughout Association of Southeast Asian Nations, and the European Commission's Digital Education Action Plan, to incorporate user-friendly technologies in learning environments and to build confidence and competency in facilitating learning with technology through professional learning opportunities (African Union, 2021; Association of Southeast Asian Nations, 2020; National Education Association, 2019; European Commission, 2021). The common objective among these entities is to empower educators to integrate emerging technologies to assist in and enhance teaching and learning.

In response, universities around the world are now integrating emerging technologies, such as interactive virtual reality classrooms (Lamb & Etopio, 2020) and gaming (Anderson & Barnett, 2011), in teacher preparation programs to support preservice science teachers (PSTs). Specifically, emerging technologies can be used in a multitude of ways including: (1) to enrich PSTs' science knowledge; (2) to support teaching PSTs how to effectively incorporate technology into lesson design; and (3) to develop PSTs' ability to practice, communicate, and reflect upon teaching demonstrations and facilitation of lessons (Anderson & Barnett, 2011; Bautstia & Boone, 2015; Frisch et al., 2017; Office of Educational Technology, 2021; Ritz & Fan, 2015). However, a meta-analysis conducted by Kay (2006) regarding preservice teachers' uses of traditional (non-emergent) technologies concluded there were concerns if teacher preparation programs are effectively preparing future teachers to use technology in the classroom, while also identifying a lack of quality research on technology in preservice teacher preparation. Therefore, for these initiatives and policies to be successful, conducting research and aiding PSTs to effectively design lessons that incorporate technology is paramount for the ever-changing landscape of education, technology, and the workforce.

DOI: 10.4324/9781003098478-19

Because emerging technologies are not a monolith, there are a variety of emerging technologies which may be modified and tailored as tools for instruction in science education learning spaces. Although there are varied definitions of emerging technologies, this chapter approached the term *emergent* using guidance from Oliveira et al. (2019), who described these tools as being novel in: (1) structure or design; (2) approach to support learning through development of knowledge and coordination of lesson activities; and (3) the facilitation of social interactions and communications (the latter of which was based on Gershon's (2017) article on the *newness* of new media construction and use). In this chapter, emerging technologies fitting this definition were examined in their ability to support PSTs in their learning of science (content) and/or facilitating learning activities in classrooms with emerging technology (pedagogy). Examples of emerging technologies explored in sampled literature included the following: virtual simulations and computational animations; game simulations or gaming; mobile and smartphone applications; digital storytelling, movie making, and podcasting tools; robotics; computer coding or programing tools; remote laboratories; virtual and augmented reality; Web 2.0 tools; 3D printing; and social media and blogging tools.

The purpose of this review was to examine research pertaining to the affordances as well as accessibility, equity, and global considerations of emerging technologies in preservice science teacher preparation experiences. As a concept, *affordances* were first described to investigate human perception through an ecological approach (Gibson, 1979), and later examinations by other researchers continued to revise the idea of affordances by differentiating between an object's utility and the usability of an object (McGrenere & Ho, 2000). Notably, perceived utility and usability are the two constructs of the *Technological Acceptance Model*, or TAM (Davis, 1989), a long-standing theory in technology research to model acceptance (use) of various technologies (Marangunić & Granić, 2015). Regarding how teachers utilize technology, the Technological Pedagogical Content Knowledge (TPACK) model provides a framework for how technology is incorporated into teachers' content knowledge and pedagogical knowledge for successful integration of technology into teachers' curriculum and instruction (see Chapter 23 in this volume for a review of TPACK). At present, there is a dearth of understanding how teachers, especially preservice teachers, are accessing emerging technologies in their teacher preparation and receiving benefits of those experiences. Thus, this review provides insight into the exciting and evolving world of emerging technologies, including a comprehensive assessment of the affordances of emerging technologies for PSTs in preparation programs. Further, this review provides an understanding of the extent to which, if any, notions of accessibility, equity, and global thinking are grounded within science teacher preparation efforts. The guiding questions that frame the purpose of this review are as follows:

1. Which emerging technologies are being researched for the purpose of preservice science teacher preparation?
2. Of these existing emerging technologies, what are the unique affordances of these tools for preservice science teachers?
3. How do the existing emerging technologies address accessibility, equity, and global perspectives?

Review Methodology

The systematic review method provides a means to sample refereed research as well as to clarify and summarize findings of the research therein to highlight current trends in education, identify gaps or needs for future research, inform current or future education policy development and implementation, and support professional development needs of practitioners (Gough & Thomas, 2016). In this review, the foci of the systematic review included, first, the types of emerging technologies being researched and, second, their affordances in preparing service science teachers. Third, the review explored how issues of accessibility, equity, and global perspectives in emerging technology utilization in preservice science teacher education were described in the sampled research studies. As the methodologies of the identified articles in this systematic review were varied (qualitative, quantitative, and mixed methods), a qualitative research synthesis (Suri & Clarke, 2009) was applied to establish a detailed and integrated picture of research articles concerning emerging technologies in preservice science teacher preparation programs. This method was ideal for this chapter, as "the purpose of research synthesis is to produce new knowledge by making explicit connections and tensions between individual study reports that were not visible before. . . [using] purposeful selection, review, analysis and synthesis of primary research reports on a similar topic" (Suri, 2011, p. 63). Since this chapter focused on emerging technologies, the review included research published within a 11-year period (2010–2021).

Article Selection

Articles included in this review were selected through a three-stage evaluation process conducted in February 2021. The first stage identified specific keyword combinations to address the review's research questions. These keyword combinations included the specific group of interest (preservice primary and secondary science teachers) and emerging technologies as defined by this review. The keyword combinations selected for this review are as follows: "preservice teachers" or "student teachers" and "emerging technology(ies)"; "technology(ies)"; "virtual"; "simulation"; "digital"; "mobile"; "gaming (or) games"; "augmented"; "remote"; or "haptics." The second stage of the process was to choose the specific databases and journals to search for refereed articles that were related to the review's focus. Initially, specific education journals with a focus on science or technology education were targeted based on the context, focus, and scope of the journal and their respective rankings (listed in the top 250 education journals via Scimago). The chosen journals – *Journal of Science Education and Technology, Computers & Education, Journal of Research on Technology in Education, Journal of Science Teacher Education, International Journal of Science Education, Science Education, Studies in Science Education, British Journal of Educational Technology, Australasian Journal of Educational Technology,* and *Research in Science Education* – yielded an initial count of 403 articles. Additionally, the search engines of ERIC, EBSCO, JSTOR, Sage Journals, and Google Scholar were used to identify peer-reviewed articles in their databases that related to this review's purpose. The database search yielded an additional 817 articles using the keyword combinations. A total of 1,220 articles were identified through the three-part evaluation process.

Article selection followed the evaluation process. This stage consisted of an in-depth inspection of the research articles to determine if the articles pulled from the journals and search engines aligned to the purview of this review. This stage required careful examination of the articles' research designs. Inclusion criteria focused on PSTs and the use of an emerging technology tool(s) either with the preservice teachers operating the technology to learn or reinforce science content knowledge, preservice teachers learning how to apply the emerging technologies in a classroom setting, or preservice teachers engaged with emerging technologies to build their pedagogical abilities in the teaching of science to K–12 students. Next, for the inclusion selection round, articles had to clearly define and describe the research question(s), research design, results, and the connection of the discussion to the field of preservice teacher education, with a major or sole focus on science teachers or science teaching. The inclusion criteria review round resulted in 137 articles. The final round related to exclusion criteria, removing articles that focused on preservice teacher perceptions of TPACK, how preservice teachers defined technology, and articles that did not have a defined research question(s), method, and discussion of implications of results. This final round of review based on exclusion criteria resulted in the sample of 54 articles for the review.

Article Analysis

The processes of article selection and article analysis were conducted by two science education researchers who have research and practitioner experiences in supporting the learning of science with the use of emerging technologies. The 54 articles were individually re-read for analysis and coding based on location of research, type and description of technology highlighted in the article, K–12 preservice level (primary, secondary, or K–12/unspecified), science domain (e.g., chemistry, life science), affordances of the technology to support PSTs either in learning science or using the tools to support the learning of science for students, and for issues discussed in regard to global perspectives, equity, and access to emerging technologies. Additionally, themes resulting from the exploration of the areas of technological affordances, accessibility, equity, and global issues were identified, documented, and analyzed for each research article. Once the sampled articles were coded based on the themes, descriptive statistics (frequency counts and percentages) were calculated for each coded category, and pertinent quotations were selected that emphasized the thematic category documented in data tables. Once the research articles were fully evaluated, an analytic table was created replete with the descriptive statistics to represent the salient information collected from research articles (i.e., type of emerging technology, location of research, and the level of preservice science teacher). The authors met thrice to discuss the analysis and coding process during the article analysis.

Framing

Themes were parsed by affordance for preservice science teacher preparation as well as accessibility, equity, and global issues relating to the described emerging technologies. The central theme, quantifying and qualifying the unique and novel affordances of the emerging technologies, provides insight into best practices and recommendations for preservice science teacher programs using these tools. Research suggests that many primary and elementary preservice teachers lack content knowledge, self-efficacy, and confidence to teach science effectively (Appleton & Kindt, 1999; Danielsson & Warwick, 2014); however, the integration of technology tools to learn science in the classroom promotes healthier views on teaching science (Rehmat & Bailey, 2014). For secondary PSTs, research suggests that they may have concerns in teaching controversial topics in science or facilitating instructional activities in the classroom to promote students' critical thinking and problem-solving skills (Borgerding & Dagistan, 2018; Davis et al., 2006). To address unease, application of technology usage to support preservice secondary teachers' abilities in facilitating instruction may be beneficial for learning (Baran, 2014; Maeng et al., 2013). Exploring emerging technologies through the frame of technological affordances, accessibility, equity, and global perspectives may not only identify areas of need in research and practice, but also address policy development and strengthen teacher preparation programs.

Findings of the Systematic Review

Descriptive Statistics

In this review, 54 articles met selection criteria to be examined for specific information relating to the type of emerging technology employed, the geographic location where the research took place, and the level (primary, secondary, or unspecified) of PSTs who participated in the study. There were 12 categories of emerging technologies identified and described in the research articles. Virtual simulations and computational animations represented almost a quarter ($n = 13$, 24%) of the emerging technologies in the review, followed by: digital storytelling, moving making, and podcasting tools ($n = 8$, 15%); virtual and augmented reality ($n = 6$, 11%); mobile technologies and smartphone applications ($n = 5$, 9%); game simulations or gaming ($n = 4$, 7%); robotics ($n = 4$, 7%); social media and blogging ($n = 4$, 7%); research articles featuring multiple technologies ($n = 4$, 7%); Web 2.0 tools and online resources ($n = 3$, 6%); coding or programing ($n = 1$, 2%); remote laboratories ($n = 1$, 2%); and 3D printing ($n = 1$, 2%). Over half of the research was conducted in either the United States ($n = 20$, 37%) or Turkey ($n = 14$, 26%). Other countries identified in the articles conducting research in emerging technologies with PSTs included Australia, Canada, Israel, England, Finland, Ghana, Greece, Nigeria, Romania, Saudi Arabia, South Africa, and Zimbabwe. Most of the articles in this review focused on primary PSTs ($n = 28$, 52%), with 18 articles (33%) focused on secondary, three articles (6%) included both primary and secondary PSTs, and the remaining five articles (9%) did not specify the level of participating PSTs in their studies.

Affordances of Emerging Technologies

In this review, the focus was on perceptions of PSTs and their experiences with emerging technologies. All articles reviewed discussed affordances of the emerging technologies related to perceived benefits, usability, and connections to learning from the perspectives of PSTs. The affordances theme was differentiated into eight categories described as follows: (1) modeling for more robust understandings of science content knowledge, teaching practices, and technology skills; (2) using tools to integrate into future lesson designs and classrooms; (3) facilitating communication and interactions between learners; (4) applying tools to increase motivation, self-efficacy, and interest to learn science content or teaching and technology skills; (5) reflecting on learning and teaching practices; (6) supporting creativity; (7) participating in learning activities, including self-directed learning, at the learners' convenience without physical or set time boundaries; and (8) creating a safe environment for science learning and teaching practices (see Table 16.1).

The most cited affordance documented in the review of the research articles ($n = 24$, 44%) was the notion that the emerging technologies studied had provided environments and opportunities for PSTs to learn science content in a novel or unique approach. Ulukök and Sari (2016) suggested that computer simulations, such as PhET (https://phet.colorado.edu/), supported PSTs' learning of science concepts. The authors stated the affordances of these simulations as being able "to concretize information, [to be] life-like and enjoyable, and [to make] learning easy and [to strengthen] conceptual understanding" (p. 473). Communication tools usage, such as social media, blogging, and podcasts, supported preservice science teacher knowledge and skill development related to both science content and pedagogical practices (Alghamdi & Alanazi, 2019; Frisch et al., 2017; Wall & Anderson, 2015).

As such, the second most cited affordance of emerging technologies in preservice science teacher preparation involved integrating these tools into future lessons and classroom environments ($n = 14$, 26%). Not only did these emerging technologies support PSTs' science content or teaching practice knowledge and skills, but they also encouraged PSTs to integrate these tools in lessons such as robotics (Yuan et al., 2019), digital gaming (Uluay & Dogan, 2016), and digital storytelling (Seckin Kapucu & Yurtseven Avci, 2020).

An additional documented affordance theme of emerging technologies was related to increase motivation, self-efficacy, and interest to learn ($n = 11$, 20%). Kim et al. (2015) noted that robotics promoted attitudes towards science, and Celik et al. (2020) proposed that mobile augmented reality applications can increase PSTs' motivations and attitudes. Although Mutlu and Acar Şesen's (2020) study indicated that a *real laboratory* may best support PST's attitudes towards chemistry, virtual laboratories also contributed to improving their attitudes in science overall.

Facilitation of communication is one of the key components found in the review. Approximately a quarter of research articles ($n = 13$, 24%) indicated that an affordance of emerging technologies is

Table 16.1 Frequency counts of meaningful discussions of affordances of emerging technologies

Category	#/%	Example
Affordances		
Modeling for more robust understandings of science content knowledge, teaching practices, and technology skills	24, 44%	"[T]he simplicity of the construction technique and accessibility of the technology suggest that slowmation may provide opportunities for widespread use by a variety of learners as a new way of representing science knowledge" (Hoban et al., 2011, p. 1003).
Using tools to integrate into future lesson designs and classrooms	14, 26%	"Many of the candidates also realized how video editing could be a powerful tool for creativity and communication with their own future students in science with the potential" (Hechter & Guy, 2010, p. 425).
Facilitating communication and interactions between learners	13, 24%	"[H]aving ready access to these [professional learning network] spaces using their mobile devices facilitated valuable collaborative learning conversations" (Kearney & Maher, 2019, p. 145).
Using tools to increase motivation, self-efficacy, and interest to learn science content or teaching and technology skills	11, 20%	"[T]he use of robotics modules integrated into science methods courses may be a way to engage preservice teachers emotionally (motivating and sustaining interest) and enhance their science content knowledge, while alleviating some of the fear associated with learning content such as physics" (Jaipal-Jamani & Angeli, 2017, p. 186).
Facilitating reflection on learning and teaching practices	7, 13%	"We propose to give VR a more prominent place in teacher training, with active experience that includes technology rich environments, the VR environment in particular, and the accompanying process of reflective thinking" (Nissim & Weissblueth, 2017, p. 58).
Supporting creativity	4, 7%	"[B]y choosing the tools and materials, as well as graphic menu options, the students are allowed to design the experiment, which they describe as an opportunity to improve their creativity" (Ulukök & Sari, 2016, p. 473).
Participating in learning activities, including self-directed learning, at the learners' convenience without physical or set time boundaries	3, 6%	"[T]he online context allowed the prospective teachers to participate at their convenience within the bounds of assigned deadlines" (Swanson & Harlow, 2013, p. 235).
Creating a safe environment for science learning and teaching practices	3, 6%	"The [preservice teachers] stated throughout the semester that [the mixed-reality teaching environment] provided them with a safe environment to practice their teaching skills without worrying about having a negative impact on real children" (Bautstia & Boone, 2015, p. 256).

enabling interactions between learners, facilitators, and the learning environment. These tools were cited to facilitate discussions (Nielsen & Hoban, 2015), encourage students to critique peers' ideas and provide feedback (Hoban et al., 2011; Ng & Nicholas, 2015; Wilkerson et al., 2016), and assist in supporting collaboration between learners (Kearney & Maher, 2019; Reisoğlu & Çebi, 2020; Say & Serdar Yildirim, 2020). Not only was communication an integral construct to aid in PSTs' learning and experiences, but also reflective practices as ($n = 7$, 13%) mediated by emerging technologies. Further, emerging technologies for communication and reflection were interconnected during PSTs' learning experiences individually and with their peers (Wilkerson et al., 2016, p. 31; Ng & Nicholas, 2015).

Supporting PSTs to engage in learning opportunities to express creativity was a promising theme regarding emerging technology use in sampled studies. The novelty of these tools was attributed to their allowances for customization by the learners. Ulukök and Sari (2016) shared that some computer simulations allowed learners to access graphic menu options for customization of the virtual environment and to choose specific tools or materials to design and conduct experiments. Because of the ability to modify and adapt the virtual environment to the leaners' needs, PSTs had new opportunities to express their creative thinking vis-à-vis science experimentation. Furthermore, the construction of artifacts, such as a digital story to learn science, promoted creative thinking among PSTs (Kotluk & Kocakaya, 2016).

The final two categories of affordances, convenience of self-directed learning (n = 3, 6%) and creating a safe environment (n = 3, 6%), were the least cited in the sampled research articles. However, the importance of these ideas should be highlighted when considering current and future research on emerging technologies with PSTs. As defined in this chapter, emerging technologies can be described as novel in structure or design or approach to support learning. These structures and approaches may affect how learners interact with and perceive the utility of the tool for teaching and learning (e.g., TAM and TPACK). Regarding convenience, Swanson and Harlow (2013) suggested videos and forums allowed learners to guide their own educational experience as they were able to participate in online activities at their own convenience. Likewise, other tools, such as ePortfolios, "could contribute to independent learning, as students can reflect on and assess their own learning and the goals they have achieved" (de Jager, 2019, p. 13). Perceived safety within learning environments was mentioned as a crucial element for preservice science teacher preparation. Virtual classrooms with teaching simulations, such as TeachME, "provided [preservice teachers] with a safe environment to practice their teaching skills without worrying about having a negative impact on real children" (Bautstia & Boone, 2015, p. 256). Other emerging technologies like social media platforms were perceived as a safe place to share ideas and feedback and to negotiate solutions to issues in education (Kearney & Maher, 2019). Other tools such as scenario-based virtual worlds permitted preservice teachers to present complex problems to students in a safe, low-stakes virtual space (Kennedy-Clark, 2011).

Accessibility and Equity Issues Regarding Emerging Technologies

The last research question explored if and how sampled articles broached and discussed important issues of equity and access to emerging technologies as well as the global nature of equity and access in reference to the use of emerging technologies among preservice teachers and their future students. Emerging technologies, as previously defined and discussed, afford new avenues to access information, communicate, collaborate, and thus experience preservice science teacher preparation. Such affordances of emerging technologies benefit the preservice science teacher in their growth of content knowledge and/or pedagogical skills from emerging technologies use as well as nurture their understandings of and confidence in using emerging technologies in future classrooms. However, this review requires serious consideration of whether PSTs would have access to these emerging technologies to garner these generative experiences during their preparation programs. To that end, this review explored the 54-article data set to determine to what extent, if any, were aspects of equity, access, and global perspectives discussed within the sampled studies.

Twenty-two articles acknowledged concerns in access, equity, and global perspectives; articles were further examined to explore the issue areas (categories) within each. Table 16.2 displays the 28 statements, drawn from the 22 articles, among three categories: access (n = 17, 61%), equity (n = 8, 29%), and global perspectives (n = 3, 10%). Access was the most common issue, in which the initial

Table 16.2 Frequency counts of meaningful discussions of access, equity, or the importance of global perspectives

Category (N = 28)	#/%	Example
Access (n = 17)		
Lack of access to emerging technologies due to poor upkeep or infrastructure	7, 25%	"The most common concern exercising the student teachers was the need to plan ahead well for a lesson or lessons centering on animation creation, which relied on access to both digital cameras and laptops. They needed to find out what resources were available in school and to test their functionality" (Wishart, 2017, p. 98).
Barriers to access due first time purchases or ongoing costs	6, 21%	"Kodu for the PC is free to download. Due to Kodu's accessibility, easier to use and visual appeal, as mentioned previously, we choose this software, because teachers are in need of reaching resources quite easily" (Uluay & Dogan, 2020, p. 108).
Reduced access or complete lack of access for underresourced communities	4, 14%	"[C]autions against conflating use of and access to technology with acquisition of technological literacy . . . the utility of information without a context within which to interpret it is dubious" (Schmidt & Fulton, 2016, pp. 305, 312).
Equity (n = 8)		
Emerging technologies as a form of privilege; leading to varied experiences and perceptions as a result	4, 14%	"The third theme reflected participants' views that being able to use technology is a 'privilege' . . . One participant from the high group mentioned, 'Not every child has the same privilege'" (Menon et al., 2017, p. 273).
Social considerations of emerging technologies	2, 7%	"The results of this study indicate that there is potential for a disparity in the use of ICT in science education, which depends on both gender and technical literacy" (Kennedy-Clark, 2011, p. 2232).
Emerging technologies may exacerbate extant inequities and digital divides	1, 4%	"Could the use of VRFTs [Virtual Reality Field Trips] reproduce educational inequities that are already present in the system?" (Harron et al., 2019, p. 702).
Equity as a salient theme in emerging technologies – focused on science teacher preparation	1, 4%	"The [ET] course also introduced PSTs to . . . promoting equity in the science classroom" (McGinnis et al., 2020, p. 89).
Global Perspectives (n = 3)		
Importance of communication and/or collaboration around the world	3, 11%	"The potential of these games and virtual worlds to create learning experiences across multiple contexts . . . thereby creates new opportunities for interactive exchanges in a larger global classroom" (Anderson & Barnett, 2011, p. 348).

purchase (*n* = 6) or needed infrastructure and maintenance (*n* = 7) of emerging technologies was central. Interestingly, a few articles indicated that emerging technologies may further reduce access or excuse a lack of access for underresourced communities. Harron et al. (2019) studied perceptions of virtual reality field trips (VRFTs) to a local museum among preservice elementary teachers in a science methods course. These authors found that many students saw this as a viable alternative for in-person experiences (pre-COVID -19), especially for low-income students. From their findings, the authors wonder how "VRFTs [may] unintentionally justify the lack of access to in-person field trips, particularly with low-income populations" (p. 702). The combination of viable alternatives and the lack of access as an idea is compelling, given that virtual experiences could enhance learning experiences that are inaccessible in the real world, like modifying variables for seed growth on the moon or manipulating coacervates on primitive Earth. Yet in this case, the museum is not inaccessible to *all* students in the real world, and it is costly to attend for *some* students who happen to have fewer resources to participate in the actual experience.

Just as emerging technologies are intended to enhance and not supplant authentic science learning experiences, they should not widen opportunities gaps among higher-income and lower-income students. An extension of this idea was related to concerns of inequity related to the use of emerging technologies in education contexts. The largest subcategory in equity ($n = 8$, 29%) was conceptualizing emerging technologies as a form of privilege and acknowledging that from that privilege, individuals would have varied experiences and perceptions of emerging technologies as a result ($n = 4$). Quinlan (2019) shared that elementary preservice teachers often have very little prior experiences and knowledge in science, and they may have a similar dearth in emerging technologies and should be accommodated as such. Despite the growth in the initial development and use of emerging technologies in education, it is important to emphasize that opportunity gaps may exist, and addressing equity and access issues is paramount in ensuring teachers are prepared to support student learning in a complex and changing education landscape including virtual and technology-based environments (Kennedy-Clark, 2011; Harron et al., 2019).

Global perspectives ($n = 3$, 10%) were the least represented notion among the three categories. Anderson and Barnett (2011) shared that the importance of utilizing emerging technologies is to create a learning environment that is conducive to communication and collaboration with other learners around the world. Furthermore, Say and Serdar Yildirim (2020) suggested emerging technologies aid in supporting communication between learners globally because these tools have specific features allowing for flexibility and autonomy in how and when to engage in collaborative learning sessions. The theme of flexible communication with a global audience is considered a convenient affordance of emerging technologies as preservice teachers noted the benefits as the ability to share resources and to obtain immediate feedback (Kearney & Maher, 2019). Additionally, Kearney and Maher (2019, p. 143) found in their study of PSTs using mobile devices for professional learning that the "apps were [being] used by PSTs to access global networks, and [were used as] a resource to ask for advice and to share and learn from experiences." These authors elaborate on their finding by discussing how one rural preservice science teacher commiserated with another rural preservice science teacher within the country (of Australia) as well as other teachers connecting with other colleagues globally, finding common experiences despite the vast spatial and cultural divides that separated them. Emerging technologies may establish avenues for not only students but also their future teachers to connect, communicate, and collaborate. This suggests that emerging technologies may diminish geographic boundaries.

Recommendations

Following is a description of the recommendations identified based on the review of the articles in this chapter in an effort to guide implementation and evaluation efforts for teacher educator programs and future research.

There is a need to design additional support mechanisms for PSTs when integrating emerging technologies into lessons or teaching experiences. Batane and Ngwako (2017), based on their study of preservice teachers incorporating technology into their teaching practice, found mitigating factors that influenced the incorporation of the tools, such as having access to the appropriate resources (Internet connection, access to software applications and/or devices) in schools, communicating the importance of technology to preservice teachers, and connecting research-based pedagogies to practices in the field. Interestingly, while the focus of this review was on preservice science teacher preparation, Hite et al. (2019) compared PSTs and in-service science teachers' acceptance of emerging technologies and found that in-service science teachers "use their technological, content, and pedagogical knowledge to mediate their instructional practice when accepting novel technologies" whereas PSTs had "little to no context for integrating their knowledge for utilizing novel technologies in science teaching" (p. 18). The challenge is to provide strategic support to PSTs to incorporate emerging technologies effectively.

Another area for future research is the need to promote safety and convenience as features that need to be addressed as the continuous evolution and adaptation of technology leads to questions regarding efficacy, security, and protection. Although preservice teachers appreciated that they could use virtual environments to practice teaching without any negative impacts to children (Bautstia & Boone, 2015), there are concerns of privacy and ethical issues regarding *big data* (i.e., a large and complex data set that continuously expands) and access through the utilization of educational technologies (Reidenberg & Schaub, 2018); and emerging technologies incorporated into the learning environment are not immune to these challenges. However, a benefit of these technologies is that it affords learners convenience related to self-directed learning. Learners can choose when and where to engage in the learning environment if they have Internet access and a digital device. The ability for self-directed learning within emerging technology spaces needs to be explored to investigate the efficacy of these tools in sustaining learning environments.

Perhaps the most notable finding of our exploration of access, equity, or global perspectives is that 32 of the 54 articles sampled had no mention of these issues. As emerging technologies become more incorporated in science classrooms by virtue of hybrid and blended learning, the research community needs to study how we may better prepare PSTs to make decisions regarding how emerging technologies are used in science classrooms. Without explicit education and research on these ideas, we may paradoxically create or broaden opportunity gaps among marginalized students from historically or geographically underresourced communities in science learning.

The primary revelation from this review indicates that the use of emerging technologies to support PSTs is a rapidly growing, continuously evolving field creating future research opportunities to investigate the efficacy, affordances, and accessibility of these tools in teacher preparation programs.

References

*Indicates that the article was used in the review but not cited in the chapter.

African Union. (2021). *Education, science & technology*. https://au.int/en/education-science-technology

*Agyei, E., Jita, T., & Jita, L. (2019). Examining the effectiveness of simulation-based lessons in improving the teaching of high school physics: Ghanaian preservice teachers' experiences. *Journal of Baltic Science Education, 18*(6), 816–832.

Alghamdi, A., & Hamad Alanazi, F. (2019). Creating scientific dialogue through social media: Exploration of Saudi preservice science teachers. *Research in Science & Technological Education, 37*(4), 471–491.

*Andersen, L., & Matkins, J. (2014). Web 2.0 tools and the reflections of preservice secondary science teachers. *Journal of Digital Learning in Teacher Education, 28*(1), 27–38.

Anderson, J., & Barnett, M. (2011). Using video games to support preservice elementary teachers learning of basic physics principles. *Journal of Science Education and Technology, 20*, 347–362.

Appleton, K., & Kindt, I. (1999). Why teach primary science? Influences on beginning teachers' practices. *International Journal of Science Education, 21*(2), 155–168.

Association for Science Teacher Education. (2021). *ASTE position statement on technology in science teacher education*. https://theaste.org/aste-position-statement-on-technology-in-science-teacher-education/

Association of Southeast Asian Nations. (2020, October 15). *Conference on the digital transformation of education systems throughout ASEAN*. https://asean.org/storage/2020/10/20190716_24x5BackdropAMFDesignProject.pdf

Baran, E. (2014). A review of research on mobile learning in teacher education. *Educational Technology & Society, 17*(4), 17–32.

*Baran, E., Uygun, E., & Altan, T. (2016). Examining preservice teachers' criteria for evaluating educational mobile apps. *Journal of Educational Computing Research, 54*(8), 1117–1141.

Batane, T., & Ngwako, A. (2017). Technology use by preservice teachers during teaching practice: Are new teachers embracing technology right away in their first teaching experience? *Australasian Journal of Educational Technology, 33*(1), 48–61.

Bautstia, N., & Boone, W. (2015). Exploring the impact of TeachME™ lab virtual classroom teaching simulation on early childhood education majors' self-efficacy beliefs. *Journal of Science Teacher Education, 26*, 237–262.

*Bhukuvhani, C., Kusure, K., Munodawafa, V., Sana, A., & Gwizangwe, I. (2010). Preservice teachers' use of improvised and virtual laboratory experimentation in science teaching. *International Journal of Education and Development using Information and Communication Technology, 6*(4), 27–38.

Borgerding, L., & Dagistan, M. (2018). Preservice science teachers' concerns and approaches for teaching socio-scientific and controversial issues. *Journal of Science Teacher Education, 29*(4), 283–306.

*Burron, G., & Pegg, J. (2021). Elementary preservice teachers' search, evaluation, and selection of online science education resources. *Journal of Science Education and Technology*, https://doi.org/10.1007/s10956-020-09891-z

Celik, C., Guven, G., & Cakir, N. (2020). Integration of mobile augmented reality (MAR) applications into biology laboratory: Anatomic structure of the heart. *Research in Learning Technology, 28*, 1–11.

Danielsson, A., & Warwick, P. (2014). 'All we did was things like forces and motion. . .': Multiple discourses in the development of primary science teachers. *International Journal of Science Education, 36*(1), 103–128.

Davis, E., Petish, D., & Smithey, J. (2006). Challenges new science teachers face. *Review of Educational Research, 76*(4), 607–651.

Davis, F. D. (1989). Perceived Usefulness, Perceived Ease of Use and User Acceptance of Information Technology. *MIS Quarterly 13*(3), 319–339.

de Jager, T. (2019). Impact of ePortfolios on science student-teachers' reflective metacognitive learning and the development of higher-order thinking skills. *Journal of University Teaching & Learning Practice, 16*(3), 1–19.

*Efendioğlu, A., & Yelken, T. (2016). How do the cognitive load, self-efficacy and attitude of preservice teachers shift in the multimedia science learning process? *Educational Research and Reviews, 11*(8), 743–764.

European Commission. (2021). *Digital education action plan (2021–2017)*. https://ec.europa.eu/education/education-in-the-eu/digital-education-action-plan_en

*Falode, O. (2018). Preservice teachers' perceived ease of use, perceived usefulness, attitude and intentions towards virtual laboratory package utilization in teaching and learning of physics. *Malaysian Online Journal of Educational Technology, 6*(3), 63–72.

*French, D., & Burrow, A. (2018). Evidence of science and engineering practices in preservice secondary science teachers' instructional planning. *Journal of Science Education and Technology, 27*, 536–549.

Frisch, J., Cone, N., & Callahan, B. (2017). Using personal science story podcasts to reflect on language and connections to science. *Contemporary Issues in Technology and Teacher Education, 17*(2), 205–228.

Gershon, I. (2017). Language and the newness of media. *Annual Review of Anthropology, 46*, 15–31.

Gibson, J. J. (1979). *The ecological approach to visual perception*. Boston, MA: Houghton Mifflin

Gough, D., & Thomas, J. (2016). Context and implications document for: Systematic reviews of research in education: Aims, myths and multiple methods. *Review of Education, 4*(1), 103–105.

Harron, J. R., Petrosino, A. J., & Jenevein, S. (2019). Using virtual reality to augment museum-based field trips in a preservice elementary science methods course. *Contemporary Issues in Technology and Teacher Education, 9*(4), 687–707.

*Hechter, R. P., Guy, M. D. (2010). Promoting creative thinking and expression of science concepts among elementary teacher candidates through science content movie creation and showcasing. *Contemporary Issues in Technology and Teacher Education, 10*(4), 411–431.

Hite, R., Jones, M. G., Childers, G., Chesnutt, K., Corin, E., & Pereyra, M. (2019). Preservice and in-service science teachers' technological acceptance of 3D, haptic-enabled virtual reality instructional technology. *Electronic Journal of Science Education, 23*(1), 1–34.

Hoban, G., Loughran, J., & Nielsen, W. (2011). Slowmation: Preservice elementary teachers representing science knowledge through creating multimodal digital animations. *Journal of Research in Science Teaching, 48*(9), 985–1009.

*Hovardas, T. (2016). A learning progression should address regression: Insights from developing non-linear reasoning in Ecology. *Journal of Research in Science Teaching, 53*(10), 1447–1470.

International Society for Technology in Education (2021, March 10). *Be bold with us*. www.iste.org/about/about-iste

*Jaipal-Jamani, K., & Angeli, C. (2017). Effect of robotics on elementary preservice teachers' self-efficacy, science learning, and computational thinking. *Journal of Science Education and Technology, 26*, 175–192.

★Karakoyun, F., & Yapier, İ. (2016). Use of digital storytelling in biology teaching. *Universal Journal of Educational Research, 4*(4), 895–903.

Kay, R. H. (2006). Evaluating strategies used to incorporate technology into preservice education: A review of the literature. *Journal of Research on Technology in Education, 38*(4), 383–408.

Kearney, M., & Maher, M. (2019). Mobile learning in preservice teacher education: Examining the use of professional learning networks. *Australasian Journal of Educational Technology, 35*(1), 135–148.

Kennedy-Clark, S. (2011). Preservice teachers' perspectives on using scenario-based virtual worlds in science education. *Computers & Education, 57*(4), 2224–2235.

Kim, C., Kim, D., Yuan, J., Hill, R., Doshi, P., & Thai, C. (2015). Robotics to promote elementary education preservice teachers' STEM engagement, learning, and teaching. *Computers & Education, 19*, 14–31.

Kotluk, N., & Kocakaya, S. (2016). Researching and evaluating digital storytelling as a distance education tool in physics instruction: An application with preservice physics teachers. *Turkish Online Journal of Distance Education, 17*(1), 87–99.

Lamb, R., & Etopio, E. (2020). Virtual reality: A tool for preservice science teachers to put theory into practice. *Journal of Science Education and Technology, 29*, 573–585.

★Lazar, I., Panisoara, G., & Panisoara, I. (2020). Adoption of digital storytelling tool in natural sciences and technology education by preservice teachers using the technology acceptance model. *Journal of Baltic Science Education, 19*(3), 429–453.

★Lehtinen, A., & Viiri, J. (2017). Guidance provided by teacher and simulation for inquiry-based learning: A case study. *Journal of Science Education and Technology, 26*, 193–206.

Maeng, J., Mulvey, B., Smetana, L., & Bell, R. (2013). Preservice teachers' TPACK: Using technology to support inquiry instruction. *Journal of Science Education and Technology, 22*(6), 838–857.

Marangunić, N., & Granić, A. (2015). Technology acceptance model: A literature review from 1986 to 2013. *Universal access in the information society, 14*(1), 81–95.

★McGinnis, J. R., Hestness, E., Mills, K., Ketelhut, D. J., Cabrera, L., & Jeong, H. (2020). Preservice science teachers' beliefs about computational thinking following a curricular module within an elementary science methods course. *Contemporary Issues in Technology and Teacher Education, 20*(1), 85–107.

McGrenere, J., & Ho, W. (2000, May). Affordances: Clarifying and evolving a concept. In *Proceedings of graphic interface*, Montreal.

★Menon, D., Chandrasekhar, M., Kosztin, D., & Steinhoff, D. (2017). Examining preservice elementary teachers' technology self-efficacy: Impact of mobile technology-based physics curriculum. *Contemporary Issues in Technology and Teacher Education, 17*(3), 336–359.

Mutlu, A., & Acar Şeşen, B. (2020). Comparison of inquiry-based instruction in real and virtual laboratory environments: Prospective science teachers' attitudes. *International Journal of Curriculum and Instruction, 12*(2), 600–617.

National Education Association. (2019). *NEA positions on technology and education.* www.nea.org/home/58795.htm

National Science & Technology Council. (2018). *Charting a course for success: America's strategy for STEM education.* www.whitehouse.gov/wp-content/uploads/2018/12/STEM-Education-Strategic-Plan-2018.pdf

National Science Teaching Association. (2017). *NSTA Position Statement: Science Teacher Preparation.* www.nsta.org/nstas-official-positions/science-teacher-preparation

Ng, W., & Nicholas, H. (2015). iResilience of science preservice teachers through digital storytelling. *Australasian Journal of Educational Technology, 31*(6), 736–751.

Nielsen, W., & Hoban, G. (2015). Designing a digital teaching resource to explain phases of the moon: A case study of preservice elementary teachers making a Slowmation. *Journal of Research in Science Teaching, 52*(9), 1207–1233.

★Nissim, Y., & Weissblueth, E. (2017). Virtual reality (VR) as a source for self-efficacy in teacher training. *International Education Studies, 10*(8), 52–59.

★Novak, E., & Wisdom, S. (2018). Effects of 3D printing project-based learning on preservice elementary teachers' science attitudes, science content knowledge, and anxiety about teaching science. *Journal of Science Education and Technology, 27*, 412–432.

Office of Educational Technology. (2021, March 10). *Educational technology in teacher preparation challenge.* https://tech.ed.gov/edtechtprep/

Oliveira, A., Behnagh, R., Ni, L., Mohsinah, A., Burgess, K., & Guo, L. (2019). Emerging technologies as pedagogical tools for teaching and learning science: A literature review. *Human Behavior and Emerging Technologies, 1*(2), 149–160.

★Polly, D., & Binns, I. (2018). Elementary education candidates' integration of technology in science units. *Contemporary Issues in Technology and Teacher Education, 18*(4), 631–647.

Quinlan, C. L. (2019). Use of schema theory and multimedia technology to explore preservice students' cognitive resources during an earth science activity. *Contemporary Issues in Technology & Teacher Education, 19*(3), 413–438.

Rehmat, A., & Bailey, J. (2014). Technology integration in a science classroom: Preservice teachers' perceptions. *Journal of Science Education and Technology, 23*, 744–755.

Reidenberg, J., & Schaub, F. (2018). Achieving big data privacy in education. *Theory and Research in Education, 16*(3), 263–279.

Reisoğlu, İ., & Çebi, A. (2020). How can the digital competencies of preservice teachers be developed? Examining a case study through the lens of DigComp and DigCompEdu. *Computers & Education, 156*, 1–16.

Ritz, J., & Fan, S. (2015). STEM and technology education: International state-of-the-art. *International Journal of Technology and Design Education, 25*(4), 429–451.

★Salar, R., Arici, F., Caliklar, S., & Yilmaz, R. (2020). A model for augmented reality immersion experiences of university students studying in science education. *Journal of Science Education and Technology, 29*, 257–271.

Say, S., & Serdar Yildirim, F. (2020). Investigation of preservice teachers' web 2.0 rapid content development self-efficacy belief levels and their views on web 2.0 tools. *International Journal of Educational Methodology, 6*(2), 345–354.

★Schmidt, M., & Fulton, L. (2016). Transforming a traditional inquiry-based science unit into a STEM unit for elementary preservice teachers: A view from the trenches. *Journal of Science Education and Technology, 25*, 302–315.

Seckin Kapucu, M., & Yurtseven Avci, Z. (2020). The digital story of science: Experiences of preservice science teachers. *Journal of Education in Science, Environment and Health, 6*(2), 148–168.

★Shively, C., & Yerrick, R. (2014). A case for examining preservice teacher preparation for inquiry teaching science with technology. *Research in Learning Technology, 22*, 1–13.

Suri, H. (2011). Purposeful sampling in qualitative research synthesis. *Qualitative Research Journal, 11*(2), 63–75.

Suri, H., & Clarke, D. (2009). Advancements in research synthesis methods: From a methodologically inclusive perspective. *Review of Educational Research, 79*(1), 395–430.

Swanson, L., & Harlow, D. (2013). Video of children as anchors in an online forum for elementary school teachers: A tool for positioning oneself as knowledgeable about physics. *Contemporary Issues in Technology and Teacher Education, 13*(3), 219–241.

Uluay, G., & Dogan, A. (2016). Preservice teachers' practices towards digital game design for technology integration into science classrooms. *Universal Journal of Educational Research, 4*(10), 2483–2498.

★Uluay, G., & Dogan, A. (2020). Preservice science teachers' learning and teaching experiences with digital games: KODU game lab. *Journal of Education in Science, Environment and Health, 6*(2), 105–119.

Ulukök, Ş., & Sari, U. (2016). The effect of simulation-assisted laboratory applications on preservice teachers' attitudes towards science teaching. *Universal Journal of Educational Research, 4*(3), 465–474.

Wall, S. D., & Anderson, J. (2015). Peer communication through blogging. *Contemporary Issues in Technology and Teacher Education, 15*(4), 514–540.

Wilkerson, M., Andrews, C., Shaban, Y., Laina, V., & Gravel, B. (2016). What's the technology for? Teacher attention and pedagogical goals in a modeling-focused professional development workshop. *Journal of Science Teacher Education, 27*, 11–33.

★Wilson, R., Goodman, J., Bradbury, L., & Gross, L. (2013). Exploring the Use of iPads to Investigate Forces and Motion in an Elementary Science Methods Course. *Contemporary Issues in Technology and Teacher Education, 13*(2), 105–126.

★Wishart, J. (2017). Exploring how creating stop-motion animations supports student teachers in learning to teach science. *Journal of Research on Technology in Education, 49*(1–2), 88–101.

★Wu, T., & Albion, P. (2019). Investigating Remote Access Laboratories for Increasing Preservice Teachers' STEM Capabilities. *Educational Technology & Society, 22*(1), 82–93.

★Yilmaz, M., & Siğirtmaç, A. (2020). A material for education process and the teacher: The use of digital storytelling in preschool science education. *Research in Science & Technological Education*. https://doi.org/10.10 80/02635143.2020.1841148

Yuan, J., Kim, C., Hill, R., & Kim, D. (2019). Robotics integration for learning with technology. *Contemporary Issues in Technology and Teacher Education 19*(4), 708–735.

17

POLICY IN K–12 SCIENCE TEACHER PREPARATION

Uniformity and Diversity from International Perspectives

Cheng Liu, Wenyuan Yang, and Enshan Liu

The quality of teachers and their teaching is critical for students' learning and achievement (Burroughs et al., 2019; Darling-Hammond, 2000, 2016; Darling-Hammond et al., 2009; Hattie, 2009; NRC, 2001; Organisation for Economic Co-operation and Development [OECD], 2005; Ulferts, 2019). What students should learn about science and how they should be taught are always described in standards – for example, the National Science Education Standards (NSES; National Research Council [NRC], 1996). Johnson et al. (2007) conducted research to investigate the relationship between effective teaching and students' achievement, based on the concept that effective teaching was NSES standards-based science instruction. They used a classroom observation protocol to evaluate the effectiveness of teachers' science teaching. The results showed that students of effective teachers performed better than their peers with ineffective teachers in an assessment of scientific achievement. Findings from this study indicate that teachers who can provide effective teaching may be the key to eliminate achievement gaps in science. However, in most countries, teachers in disadvantaged schools whose average intake of students falls in the bottom quarter of the PISA index of economic, social, and cultural status (ESCS) within the relevant economy are not effective, and the lack of well-prepared teachers may be a major barrier to improving students' learning (OECD, 2018, 2019). Well-prepared teachers are essential for improving K–12 school science teaching. The ultimate goal of teacher preparation is to get teacher candidates ready and well-prepared to teach effectively. Thus, policy in K–12 science teacher preparation matters because it may make an important difference in the quality of teachers and their teaching.

The goal of this chapter is to review policies for preparing science teachers from international perspectives; in particular, the policies shown in academic articles, reports, and books published internationally are examined. Heffron (2018) provided a simple and concise definition of policy, as follows, in his foreword to *The Wiley Handbook of Educational Policy*:

> Put simply, policy can be defined as a preferred future and the things one does to bring it about, a rare alignment of thought and action around the pursuit of an ideal.
>
> (p. xxvi)

Based on this definition, educational policy in K–12 science teacher preparation could be interpreted as a rational plan, codified in text such as laws or regulations, to articulate clear expectations

DOI: 10.4324/9781003098478-20

for candidates to become qualified science teachers (Bascia et al., 2005) and the way prospective science teachers are recruited and trained to achieve these expectations.

In this chapter, policies in K–12 science teacher preparation and related research are summarized into six topics as follows: (1) teacher qualifications, (2) standards depicting qualified science teachers or effective science teacher preparation, (3) design of prospective science teacher training programs, (4) admission and attraction to preservice science teacher education programs, (5) institutions responsible for science teacher preparation programs, and (6) addressing equity issues in teacher preparation.

Teacher Qualification in K–12 Science Education

In many countries and areas, the government uses teaching licenses, certifications, registrations, or alternative requirements as official qualifications for prospective teachers to enter the profession as full-time, in-service science teachers in K–12 schools. In both the US and Canada, certification is required to get a teaching job, although a highly diverse array of licenses is issued by different provinces, territories, and states (Olson et al., 2015). In China, the central government sets the national criteria for teacher licenses, and all local governments must meet the same criteria (Liu et al., 2015). Therefore, the requirement for individuals to be officially issued teacher licenses is the same all over the country, although candidates' qualifications are evaluated and approved by the administrative departments of education under the local governments. Cofré and colleagues' (2015) examination of the science teacher education system in Argentina, Chile, and Colombia showed that some sort of certification – albeit not a rigorous one – or test is required for teaching candidates to enter the K–12 education system and teach science. In Australia, graduates from accredited initial teacher education programs must apply for a provisional teacher registration to obtain a teaching position and then move from provisional to full registration in the first few years of their teaching career (Treagust et al., 2015). In England, France, Finland, and Cyprus, candidates who graduate from initial teacher programs in universities or other institutions approved by the government are fully eligible to be hired as a science teacher in K–12 school (Evagorou et al., 2015). In South Africa, candidates who earn either a 4-year or a 3-year bachelor's degree in their teaching subject with the addition of a 1-year postgraduate certificate in education program may apply for a job as a science teacher (Ogunniyi & Rollnick, 2015).

The valid period of qualification approved by governments varies among provinces, states, areas, and countries. In Canada, certificates issued by most provinces are permanent (Olson et al., 2015). The valid period of teacher qualification in Finland is similar; after graduating from an initial university-based teacher program, preservice teachers are approved by the government as qualified teachers to apply for teaching positions in K–12 schools and do not need to recertify (Evagorou et al., 2015). However, in the US, teaching licenses in most states are temporary and must be renewed before their expiration date (Olson et al., 2015). These limited-term licenses might be helpful not only to guide teachers for continuously participating in professional development but also potentially for removing incompetent teachers from classrooms, although the actual cases of forcible cancellation of licenses for this reason are not common. However, these limited-term licenses might also put too much pressure on new teachers because they are more vulnerable to being fired from school (Olson et al., 2015).

There is a broad consensus that teacher quality is the most important school variable influencing students' achievement, but the consideration of certain teacher characteristics, such as qualifications, as the indicators or correlates of teacher quality is somewhat more contentious (OECD, 2005). The impact of teacher qualification on student achievement has been investigated in some studies, but the results have been mixed. Darling-Hammond (2000) found that teacher quality variables, such as holding full certification and a major or minor degree in the field they teach, had more influence on predicting individual achievement than students' demographics. This indicates a correlation between measures of teacher certification and students' achievement, and the policies regarding teacher licensing may have a positive impact on the latter. Goldhaber and Brewer (2000) also investigated the relationship between types of certification held by teachers and students' test scores in both the mathematics and science domains. However, they concluded that students who had teachers with emergency credentials performed no worse than peers whose teachers had a standard teaching certification. There was a debate between these two research groups by publishing papers to respond to each other (Darling-Hammond et al., 2001; Goldhaber & Brewer, 2001). In another study, Darling-Hammond et al. (2005) found that certified teachers produced stronger student achievement gains than did uncertified teachers. However, Buddin and Zamarro (2009) found similar results to Goldhaber and Brewer's. Their study showed that teacher licensure test scores were unrelated to their teaching quality, and students' achievement was not correlated with teachers' degrees. This study focused only on those teachers who had passed the licensure tests, which were designed to set the minimum requirement of teachers' qualifications. Applicants who did not pass the test might indeed have worse classroom outcomes than those who passed; however, as applicants who failed the licensure test were not allowed to teach, no data were available on their students' achievement. Based on a review of previous studies, NRC (2001) pointed out that many science, mathematics, and technology teachers did not have sufficient content knowledge or adequate background for teaching their subject, although they had teacher licensing or passed certification examinations. Blömeke et al. (2016) used TIMSS 2011 data to examine the relation between student achievement and the quality of their teachers and instruction. They described teacher quality from three dimensions, including teacher education background, participation in professional development activities, and teachers' sense of preparedness, and found that teacher quality was significantly related to instructional quality and student achievement, and participation in professional development activities and teachers' sense of preparedness were, on average, the strongest predictors of instructional quality across many countries.

Standards Depicting Qualified Science Teachers or Effective Science Teacher Preparation

To improve teachers' quality, an emerging strategy across countries and areas has been the articulation of standards for what teachers should learn and be able to do (OECD, 2011; Darling-Hammond, 2017). Such standards approved by a government, organization, or association depict what a qualified science teacher or effective science teacher preparation program is. They can provide training objectives and design blueprints for teacher preparation programs.

In the US, the NSES (NRC, 1996) includes the *Standards for Professional Development for Teachers of Science*, based on which qualified science teachers must have knowledge and understanding of science, science teaching, and lifelong learning. In the same standards, the characteristics of high-quality preservice and in-service programs are described. Teaching based on certain standards, such as the NSES, is one of the most prominent characteristics of qualified science teachers. The National Council for Accreditation of Teacher Education (NCATE, 2008) issued *Professional Standards for the Accreditation of Teacher Preparation Institutions*, providing a blueprint for designing effective preparation programs. Morrell et al. (2020) wrote an editorial to introduce the *2020 Standards for Science Teacher Preparation* (2020 SSTP) and described its changes from the previous *2012 Science Teacher Preparation Standards*. One of the most important changes was explicitly based on NRC's (2012) *A Framework for K-12 Science Education: Practices, Crosscutting Concepts, and Core Ideas*. The 2020 SSTP was approved by the Association for Science Teacher Education (ASTE) and the National Science Teachers Association (NSTA). Morrell et al. (2020) believed that the SSTP could provide science teacher educators with a well-informed research base for policy discussions regarding science teacher preparation and could be a useful document to assist in reviewing science teacher preparation programs.

Treagust et al. (2015) outlined a similar standard, the *Australian National Professional Standards for Teachers*, which described what a qualified teacher should know and be able to do in Australia. The major components of this standard include professional knowledge (content and pedagogical knowledge), professional practice (within school), and professional engagement (within professional and school communities). They also mentioned the *Accreditation of Initial Teacher Education Programs in Australia: Standards and Procedures* to state the requirements for teacher preparation programs.

Design of Prospective Science Teacher Training Programs

In many countries and areas, the government approves a set of initial science teacher training programs or other alternative programs designed to help participants meet the qualification requirements. In 2015, editors of the *Journal of Science Teacher Education* organized a special issue focused on the status of preservice science teacher education all over the world. Science teacher educators from five continents, including Asia, Australia, Europe, North America, and South America, provided an overview of science teacher education in their local continent. This issue provides an international perspective and examples of preparing teachers for K–12 science education. Different prospective teacher training programs worldwide show common components and various considerations.

Theory and practice are both included in almost all preparation programs from different continents. Participants enrolled in these programs are required not only to take courses about the theory of education and pedagogy of teaching but also to take teaching practicums in school (Cofré et al., 2015; Liu et al., 2015; Liu & Liu, 2017; Evagorou et al., 2015; Ogunniyi et al., 2015; Olson et al., 2015; Treagust et al., 2015). However, the balance between practice and theory varies. For example, in Finland, participants spend about 100 hours practicing teaching during preparation (Evagorou et al., 2015). In Canada, the time spent on practice teaching ranges from fewer than 50 days to more than 120 days (Olson et al., 2015). OECD (2011) reported that many countries had moved their preparation programs toward a model based less on academic preparation and more on professional training in school settings, with an appropriate balance between theory and practice.

Science and pedagogy are usually included in many K–12 science teacher preparation programs all over the world (Cofré et al., 2015; Liu et al., 2015; Liu & Liu, 2017; Evagorou et al., 2015; Ogunniyi et al., 2015; Olson et al., 2015; Treagust et al., 2015). However, the analysis of these programs and their graduates shows that courses on science content, the nature of science, and the pedagogy of teaching science are insufficient. Olson et al. (2015) summarized three types of preservice teacher programs from which most bachelor of education (BEd) degrees were awarded, provided five examples of these programs, and pointed out that both science content and science pedagogy courses were not enough within these preservice science teacher programs in Canada. They also analyzed the background data of existing teaching forces to understand the science content background of teachers in the US (Olson et al., 2015). The results indicated that in high schools, 42% of earth science teachers, 29% of physics teachers, and 11% of high school chemistry teachers had had no coursework beyond the introductory level in their teaching subject. This lack of advanced coursework beyond the introductory level in a discipline was also the case in middle school for 64% of earth science teachers, 42% of physical science teachers, and 22% of life science teachers. Only 45% of general science teachers in middle school had taken one course in each of the four disciplines of biology, chemistry, physics, and earth/space science. In sum, many in-service teachers had not taken sufficient science courses during their preservice training. Backhus and Thompson's (2006) study also indicates that a course on the nature of science is rarely included in preservice science teacher education in the US. In addition, Olson et al. (2015) found that some elementary preparation programs in the US diluted the exposure of preservice teachers to the strategies for teaching science by requiring two or more reading methods courses but only one science teaching course, and by combining science teaching with teaching for another content area. Cofré et al. (2015) reviewed science teacher preparation education in South America and concluded that in most of these education programs, specific pedagogy for teaching science was insufficient. In particular, participants enrolled in preparation programs spent considerable time on learning general pedagogy and did not focus on learning how to teach science specifically.

Research experience in either education or science is also usually included in many science teacher preparation programs. Finnish candidate teachers are encouraged to adopt a research-oriented approach to develop their teaching skills and methods (Evagorou et al., 2015). Participants in the initial teacher program in Finland were educated on how to conduct research on their own teaching practices. In the meantime, they also have the option to experience pure scientific research. For instance, a physics preservice teacher must write a thesis that purely deals with physics or with the pedagogy of physics to complete their training programs. Similarly, in China, preservice teacher training programs from universities provide research experience in either science or education (Liu et al., 2015; Liu & Liu, 2017). In Australia, reflective teaching/educational research is included in the initial teacher education programs (Treagust et al., 2015). Cofré et al. (2015) reported that science teacher education programs in both Chile and Colombia include research training as well. Windschitl (2003) examined how preservice teachers' authentic science inquiry experiences were associated with their classroom practice. The results imply that teachers are better able to implement scientific inquiry when they have scientific research experience from preservice training programs; thus, research experience in science is necessary for each initial science teacher. Windschitl's study (2003) also found that preservice teachers who eventually used guided and open inquiry during their student teaching were those who had experience with authentic science research rather than individuals who merely understood the methods of scientific inquiry. This may indicate that authentic science research experiences should be provided in preservice science teacher training programs.

There may be no consensus on a single best way to educate future science teachers (Boyd et al., 2009; Lederman, & Lederman, 2015). However, most agree that we lack research examining how effectively preservice programs prepare teachers (Boyd et al., 2009; Olson et al., 2015).

Admission and Attraction to Preservice Science Teacher Education Programs

Boyd et al. (2009) found that some initial teacher programs may appear more effective in preparing teachers not because of program design, but because they were able to attract better teacher candidates. Although the sample of this study did not comprise science teachers, it might be a clue that the policies about admission and attraction to preservice science teacher education programs also matter.

Academic performance is sometimes the key indicator to be enrolled in science teacher preparation; for example, in China, admission into science teacher preparation programs is determined by applicants' scores on entrance exams to tertiary education as well as their grades in secondary education (Liu & Liu, 2017). The entrance exams are paper-and-pencil tests and are required to assess applicants' content knowledge and skills declared in national curriculum standards. In Chile, teacher education is possible only at universities, and applicants must take the university selection test, which measures the knowledge required in the national curriculum (Cofré et al., 2015). In France and Argentina, being successful at the secondary education final exam or having a secondary education certification is required to be enrolled in initial teacher education programs for both the elementary and secondary levels (Cofré et al., 2015; Evagorou et al., 2015).

However, the admission requirements for some programs include not only academic performance but also nonacademic assessments. For example, in Canada, applicants are enrolled in teacher preparation based on their academic and nonacademic performance (Olson et al., 2015). The academic assessment includes the requirements for applicants' academic performance, such as grade averages and ranking of their achievement, and the completion of specific courses or degrees. For example, an applicant who wants to be accepted into the elementary education program must have a high school diploma with a minimum average of 70% and completion of some mathematics, science, and humanities courses. Nonacademic performance is usually evaluated by a statement of experience with children or adolescents or written essays that express the applicants' statements, such as the desire to be a teacher. In Finland, applicants in the primary teacher education program must graduate from upper secondary school first; then, they must pass a paper-and-pencil test that is standardized across all universities. Finally, they are usually interviewed and must complete personality questionnaires. This final assessment is conducted at university (Evagorou et al., 2015). In England, applicants are assessed and selected by individual or group interviews, written tasks, and presentations (Evagorou et al., 2015).

However, many researchers have found that some admission standards are low. Treagust et al. (2015) mentioned that the low entry standards for teacher education programs were usually criticized in discussions on the reform of preparation programs in Australia. Sometimes, applicants can be enrolled in programs without university entrance test scores or with comparatively low scores. In Australia, education majors consist of a minimal number of high achievers and have the largest proportion of low achievers. Likewise, Olson et al. (2015) pointed out that science admission requirements for prospective elementary teachers were not sufficient in many teacher preparation programs in Canada and the US.

Policies aimed at attracting high-quality candidates to preservice science teacher education programs are also critical to improving teacher quality. Success in changing teaching into a more attractive profession might be one of the most effective ways to make more talented individuals apply for initial teacher training programs. The OECD (2011) analyzed policies in three countries (Singapore, England, and Finland) and summarized four interesting approaches that may directly address the attractiveness of teaching compared to other graduate professions. These approaches are:

1. Promotional programs targeted at groups who are "non-traditional" entrants to teaching.
2. Broadening selection criteria for new teachers with the aim of identifying applicants with the greatest potential, including interviews, preparing lesson plans, and demonstrating teaching skills.
3. Changing the role of seniority in determining teacher assignments to avoid situations where new teachers are assigned to the more difficult and unpopular schools, further disadvantaging students there and potentially damaging teachers' career development.
4. For desirable teaching jobs, qualities that are harder to measure, such as enthusiasm, commitment, and sensitivity to students' needs, are sometimes given greater weight in applications, where these are seen as more directly related to the quality of teaching and learning than to the traditional emphasis on qualifications and years of experience. (p. 9)

Institutions Responsible for Science Teacher Preparation Programs

In some countries and areas, such as Chile, universities are the only institutions responsible for providing science teacher training programs approved by the government (Cofré et al., 2015). Because a bachelor's degree with requirements for licensure is almost always required to teach in Canada and the US (Olson et al., 2015), universities are the main institutions to design and run teacher preparation programs. However, more institutions, such as vocational colleges at the secondary level, share the responsibility of operating prospective teacher training programs with universities at the tertiary education level. Most preservice science teacher training programs in China are offered by universities and colleges at the tertiary education level, and a small part of preparation programs are provided by vocational schools, such as early childhood normal schools (i.e., infant normal school) and secondary normal schools (Liu et al., 2015; Liu & Liu, 2017). In most cases of teacher preparation in Africa, elementary teachers are trained in colleges of education that are not regarded as tertiary institutions (Ogunniyi et al., 2015). Before the 1970s, primary school teachers were educated in secondary teacher training colleges in Finland; currently, teacher education is available at universities (Evagorou et al., 2015).

Ye et al. (2019) used an inductive analytical approach to review major policies to reform teacher education in China. Although the policies analyzed in this study were related to training teachers for all subjects rather than only in the science domain, these policies changed the system of K–12 science teacher education. This study revealed a series of policies that directly address the structural changes of the institutions responsible for prospective teacher training programs in order to improve the quality of teacher preparation. In 1999, the policy to include more institutions other than normal universities in the system of teacher education was promulgated, aiming to diversify prospective teacher training providers to foster competition in a system. Parallel to the 1999 policy, the structure of teacher preparation institutions changed through upgrading, merging, and eliminating institutions and schools. The aim of this structural change was to elevate the basic qualifications of training primary teachers from the senior secondary to the tertiary sub-degree level. The numbers and structures of institutions were adjusted in accordance with this policy; however, there was some skepticism about the effectiveness of this policy in improving the quality of the teacher education system.

Addressing Equity Issue in Teacher Preparation

Equity, especially in some rural or urban schools and multicultural contexts, is one of the topics of most concern in recent years. This concern has been demonstrated in the aforementioned standards. Williams and Atwater (2014) reviewed science teacher education policy in conjunction with standards and analyzed the degree to which the equity issue was taken into consideration and embedded in these standards, such as the NSES, NCATE standards, Common Core State Standards, the Framework for K–12 Science Education: Practices, Crosscutting Concepts, and Core Ideas, the National Board of Professional Standards of Teaching. Their analysis shows that the NCATE does not include standards specifically related to teaching for social justice, but NCATE standards are based on the belief that a qualified teacher should care about and teach for every student. Thus, NCATE standards can be considered as indirect guidance for preparing teachers to educate diverse students. On the contrary, the National Board of Professional Standards of Teaching includes standards directly related to equity and social justice. It requires science teachers to ensure that all students, including those from underrepresented groups, are encouraged to enter the world of science. In addition, Olson and colleagues (2015) reported that there had already been certain requirements for applicants for a teaching license in some US states, such as Wisconsin, where teachers must be aware of the students from minority groups with diverse cultures and take them into consideration.

Access to qualified science teachers is also an important issue for equity. As the most significant and costly resource in schools, teachers are central to school improvement efforts (OECD, 2005). However, OECD's (2018) report reveals that, in most countries, teachers in disadvantaged schools with low ESCS are less qualified, and principals feel that the lack of qualified teachers is a major barrier to improving students' learning. It is critical to ensure that all students have access to high-quality teachers. One policy implemented in China was expected to address this issue. In 2007, a special initial teacher training program, the Government-Sponsored Normal Students Program, was instituted. Applicants from rural areas were enrolled in preservice teacher education programs in normal universities. The government provided financial support to cover all tuition and extra allowance during preservice training. Once students enrolled in this program graduate, they must return to their home rural area to teach in a K–12 school for a period of usually 10 years (Liu & Liu, 2017). However, there is no compelling evidence regarding the effectiveness of this program, and most students enrolled in this program planned to break their contract (Zhou, 2010, cited in Wang & Gao,

2013). Teachers produced by this program highlighted not only economic constraints but also career hindrances, which made them reluctant to work in rural schools (Wang & Gao, 2013). Danhui and Campbell (2014) investigated the impact of teacher quality and students' access to qualified teachers in China. In their studies, teacher quality was measured by teachers' characteristics related to skills and knowledge, such as teacher experience, teacher preparation program and degree, and teacher certification. The results show an existing disparity between high and low socioeconomic status schools with respect to access to quality science teachers.

Similar incentive programs exist in the US, such as the National Science Foundation Robert Noyce Teacher Scholarship Program (Noyce Program), which provide funding for highly qualified science and mathematics majors to teach in high-need schools. Liou and Lawrenz (2011) investigated the effectiveness of the Noyce Program. They found that three factors – the amount of funding, race of the prospective teachers, and preparation for high-need schools – had significant relationships with perceived motivation to teach in a high-need school. Hanover Research's report (2014) also reveals that financial support, such as compensation, is not the only consideration for teachers in making their decisions regarding where to work. The incentives perceived by teachers also include strong principals, skilled and supportive colleagues, adequate resources for teaching, smaller student loads, autonomy, and high-quality professional development. In sum, the policy of financial incentives would be more effective when implemented as part of a broader, holistic plan of turning the profession of science teacher into an attractive one, rather than as a standalone initiative.

Summary

Lederman and Lederman (2015) explained the significance of reviewing various teacher preparation approaches from international perspectives in their editorial for the *Journal of Science Teacher Education* special issue on the status of preservice science teacher education all over the world.

> It would be nice to conclude that there is a single best way to educate future science teachers. However, we all know this will appropriately and fortunately never be the case. The profession of teaching is simply too complex and it is continually impacted by numerous contextual and political issues. If one views the history of how we have collectively viewed effective teaching (and its close association with empirical research on teaching), it is easy to see why there is so much variety in how one educates future teachers.
>
> (p. 1)

The aforementioned review of the policies in teacher preparation from all over the world shows that variety does exist in how prospective science teachers are trained. This variety provides us with a deeper look at what we were doing and reconsiders the approach by which the quality of teacher preparation may be improved. It seems that short-term licenses might be a possible regulation to decrease the number of incompetent teachers, but we must also be aware that it might put more pressure on new teachers compared to permanent licenses. Almost all the governments from different continents use certain ways to select and recruit candidates into various preparation programs to become qualified teachers, but the research results of the correlation between teacher qualification and students' achievements are mixed. The analysis of various designs of preparation programs indicates that the imbalance between theory and practice, insufficient science and pedagogy, or lack of research experience in preparation programs may be the possible reasons for the mixed results of correlation between teacher qualifications and students' achievement.

There is still much to learn about effective preparation (Boyd et al., 2009). More research and evidence is needed to investigate the impact of various training programs on science teachers' quality and students' science learning, the key components for the structure of effective preservice education systems, the effectiveness of each policy, and so on. It is rarely possible to predict clear, identifiable links between education policies and outcomes, especially given the lag between the time at which the initial cost of reform is incurred and the time when results may be evaluated (Schleicher, 2016). Therefore, large-scale and longitudinal research on teacher preparation policies is difficult to conduct (NRC, 2010). Qualitative research may make important contributions to policy studies; for example, qualitative studies on teacher qualifications could interpret the variations in quantitative findings, understand disappointing findings, and provide plausible explanations (Kennedy, 2008).

Educational policy usually involves massive reallocation of educational resources and affects millions of teachers' professional development and students' learning (Schleicher, 2016). This makes it essential and necessary for policy makers to design policies based on empirical studies. For example, policy makers will pay attention to avoiding setting too low requirements for scientific content learning or authentic research experience in science, when they can understand the results of science teacher preparation research. In addition, a cooperative system is needed, so that policy makers can be aware of and willing to take the initiative to work with academic researchers and science teacher educators to ensure that the policies are informed by the existing research, especially regarding the preparation of highly qualified science teachers.

Acknowledgments

Thanks to David F. Jackson and Gail M. Jones for reviewing this chapter.

References

Backhus, D. A., & Thompson, K. W. (2006). Addressing the nature of science in preservice science teacher preparation programs: Science educator perceptions. *Journal of Science Teacher Education, 17,* 65–81. https://doi.org/10.1007/s10972-006-9012-9

Bascia, N., Cumming, A., Datnow, A., Lethwood, K., & Livingstone, D. (2005). Introduction. In N. Bascia, A. Cumming, A. Datnow, K. Lethwood, & D. Livingstone (Eds.), *International handbook of educational policy* (pp. xiii–xxxvi). Dordrecht, The Netherlands: Springer. https://doi.org/10.1007/1-4020-3201-3

Blömeke, S., Olsen, R. V., & Suhl, U. (2016). Relation of student achievement to the quality of their teachers and instructional quality. In T. Nilsen & J. E. Gustafsson (Eds.) *Teacher quality, instructional quality and student outcomes* (pp. 21–50). IEA Research for Education (A Series of In-depth Analyses Based on Data of the International Association for the Evaluation of Educational Achievement (IEA)), *Vol 2.* https://doi.org/10.1007/978-3-319-41252-8_2

Boyd, D. J., Grossman, P. L., Lankford, H., Loeb, S., & Wyckoff, J. (2009). Teacher preparation and student achievement. *Educational Evaluation and Policy Analysis, 31*(4), 416–440. https://doi.org/10.3102/0162373709353129

Buddin, R., & Zamarro, G. (2009). Teacher qualifications and student achievement in urban elementary schools. *Journal of Urban Economics, 66,* 103–115. http://dx.doi.org/10.1016/j.jue.2009.05.001

Burroughs, N., Gardner, J., Lee, Y., Guo, S., Touitou, I., Jansen, K., & Schmidt, W. (2019). *Teaching for excellence and equity: Analyzing teacher characteristics, behaviors and student outcomes with TIMSS.* Switzerland: Springer International Publishing. http://dx.doi.org/10.1007/978-3-030-16151-4.

Cofré, H., González-Weil, C., Vergara, C., Santibáñez, D., Ahumada, G., Furman, M., . . . Pérez, R. (2015). Science teacher education in South America: The case of Argentina, Colombia and Chile. *Journal of Science Teacher Education, 26*(1), 45–63. https://doi.org/10.1007/s10972-015-9420-9

Danhui, Z., & Campbell, T. (2014). An examination of the impact of teacher quality and "opportunity gap" on student science achievement in China. *International Journal of Science and Mathematics Education, 13,* 489–513. https://doi.org/10.1007/s10763-013-9491-z

Darling-Hammond, L. (2000). Teacher quality and student achievement: A review of state policy evidence. *Education Policy Analysis Archives, 8*(1), https://doi.org/10.14507/epaa.v8n1.2000

Darling-Hammond, L. (2016). Research on teaching and teacher education and its influences on policy and practice. *Educational Researcher, 45*(2), 83–91. https://doi.org/10.3102/0013189X16639597

Darling-Hammond, L. (2017). Teacher education around the world: What can we learn from international practice? *European Journal of Teacher Education, 40*(3), 291–309. https://doi.org/10.1080/02619768.2017.1315399

Darling-Hammond, L., Berry, B., & Thoreson, A. (2001). Does teacher certification matter? Evaluating the evidence. *Educational Evaluation and Policy Analysis, 23*(1), 57–77. https://doi.org/10.3102/01623737023001057

Darling-Hammond, L., Holtzman, D. J., Gatlin, S. J., & Heilig, J. V. (2005). Does teacher preparation matter? Evidence about teacher certification, teach for America, and teacher effectiveness. *Education Policy Analysis Archives, 13*(42). https://doi.org/10.14507/epaa.v13n42.2005

Darling-Hammond, L., Wei, R. C., & Johnson, C. M. (2009). Teacher preparation and teacher learning: A changing policy landscape. In G. Sykes, B. Schneider, & D. N. Plank (Eds.), *Handbook of education policy research* (pp. 613–636). New York: Routledge for the American Educational Research Association. https://doi.org/10.4324/9780203880968

Evagorou, M., Dillon, J., Viiri, J., & Albe, V. (2015). Pre-service science teacher preparation in Europe: Comparing pre-service teacher preparation programs in England, France, Finland and Cyprus. *Journal of Science Teacher Education, 26*(1), 99–115. https://doi.org/10.1007/s10972-015-9421-8

Goldhaber, D. D., & Brewer, D. J. (2000). Does teacher certification matter? High school teacher certification status and student achievement. *Educational Evaluation and Policy Analysis, 22*(2), 129–145. https://doi.org/10.3102/01623737022002129

Goldhaber, D. D., & Brewer, D. J. (2001). Evaluating the evidence on teacher certification: A rejoinder. *Educational Evaluation and Policy Analysis, 23*(1), 79–86. https://doi.org/10.3102/01623737023001079

Hanover Research. (2014). *Review of teacher incentive programs*. Washington, DC: Author.www.hanoverresearch.com/media/Review-of-Teacher-Incentive- Programs-2.pdf

Hattie, J. (2009). *Visible learning: A synthesis of over 800 meta-analyses relating to achievement*. London: Routledge. https://doi.org/10.4324/9780203887332

Heffron, J. M. (2018). Foreword. In R. Papa & S. W. J. Armfield (Eds.), *The Wiley handbook of educational policy* (pp. xxi–xxvii). https://doi.org/10.1002/9781119218456

Johnson, C. C., Kahle, J. B., & Fargo, J. (2007). Effective teaching results in increased science achievement for all students. *Science Education, 91*(3), 371–383. https://doi.org/10.1002/sce.20195

Kennedy, M. M. (2008). Contributions of qualitative research to research on teacher qualifications. *Educational Evaluation and Policy Analysis, 30*(4), 344–367. https://doi.org/10.3102/0162373708326031

Lederman, N. G., & Lederman, J. S. (2015). The status of preservice science teacher education: A global perspective. *Journal of Science Teacher Education, 26*(1), 1–6. https://doi.org/10.1007/s10972-015-9422-7

Liou, P.-Y., & Lawrenz, F. (2011). Optimizing teacher preparation loan forgiveness program: Variables related to perceived influence. *Science Education, 95*(1), 121–144. https://doi.org/10.1002/sce.20409

Liu, C., & Liu, E. (2017). An overview of professional preparation for pre-service and in-service science teachers. In L. L. Liang, X. Liu, & G. W. Fulmer (Eds.), *Science education in China: Policy, practice, and research* (pp. 379–400). https://doi.org/10.1007/978-94-017-9864-8

Liu, E., Liu., C., & Wang, J. (2015). Pre-service science teacher preparation in China: Challenges and promises. *Journal of Science Teacher Education, 26*(1), 29–44. https://doi.org/10.1007/s10972-014-9404-1

Morrell, P. D., Park Rogers, M. A., Pyle, E. J., Roehrig, G., & Veal, W. R. (2020). Preparing teachers of science for 2020 and beyond: Highlighting changes to the NSTA/ASTE standards for science teacher preparation. *Journal of Science Teacher Education, 31*(1), 1–7. https://doi.org/10.1080/1046560X.2019.1705536

National Council for Accreditation of Teacher Education (NCATE). (2008). *Professional standards for the accreditation of teacher preparation institutions*. Retrieved January 30, 2021, from www.ncate.org/~/media/Files/caep/accreditation-resources/ncate-standards-2008.pdf?la=en

National Research Council (NRC). (1996). *National science education standards*. Washington, DC: National Academies Press. https://doi.org/10.17226/4962

National Research Council (NRC). (2001). *Educating practices for the new millennium*. Washington, DC: National Academies Press. https://doi.org/10.17226/9832

National Research Council (NRC). (2010). *Preparing teachers: Building evidence for sound policy*. Washington, DC: National Academies Press. https://doi.org/10.17226/12882

National Research Council (NRC). (2012). *A framework for K-12 science education: Practices, crosscutting concepts, and core ideas*. Washington, DC: National Academies Press. https://doi.org/10.17226/13165

National Science Teaching Association (NSTA). (2020). *2020 NSTA/ASTE standards for science teacher preparation*. Retrieved January 30, 2021, from https://static.nsta.org/pdfs/2020NSTAStandards.pdf

Ogunniyi, M. B., & Rollnick, M. (2015). Pre-service science teacher education in Africa: Prospects and challenges. *Journal of Science Teacher Education, 26*(1), 65–79. https://doi.org/10.1007/s10972-014-9415-y

Olson, J. K., Tippett, C. D., Milford, T. M., Ohana, C., & Clough, M. P. (2015). Science teacher preparation in a North American context. *Journal of Science Teacher Education, 26*(1), 7–28. https://doi.org/10.1007/s10972-014-9417-9

Organisation for Economic Co-operation and Development (OECD). (2005). *Teachers matter: Attracting, developing and retaining effective teachers*. Paris: OECD Publishing. https://doi.org/10.1787/9789264018044-en

Organisation for Economic Co-operation and Development (OECD). (2011). *Building a high-quality teaching profession: Lessons from around the world*. Paris: OECD Publishing. https://doi.org/10.1787/9789264113046-en

Organisation for Economic Co-operation and Development (OECD). (2018). *Effective teacher policies: Insights from PISA*. Paris: OECD Publishing. https://doi.org/10.1787/9789264301603-en

Organisation for Economic Co-operation and Development (OECD). (2019). *PISA 2018 results (Volume II): Where all students can succeed*. Paris: OECD Publishing. https://doi.org/10.1787/b5fd1b8f-en

Schleicher, A. (2016). *Teaching excellence through professional learning and policy reform: Lessons from around the world*. International Summit on the Teaching Profession. Paris: OECD Publishing. http://dx.doi.org/10.1787/9789264252059-en

Treagust, D. F., Won, M., Petersen, J., & Wynne, G. (2015). Science teacher education in Australia: Initiatives and challenges to improve the quality of teaching. *Journal of Science Teacher Education*, *26*(1), 81–98. https://doi.org/10.1007/s10972-014-9410-3

Ulferts, H. (2019). The relevance of general pedagogical knowledge for successful teaching: Systematic review and meta-analysis of the international evidence from primary to tertiary education. *OECD Education Working Papers*, No. 212. Paris: OECD Publishing. https://doi.org/10.1787/ede8feb6-en

Wang, D., & Gao, M. (2013). Educational equality or social mobility: The value conflict between preservice teachers and the free teacher education program in China. *Teaching and Teacher Education*, *32*, 66–74. https://doi.org/10.1016/j.tate.2013.01.008

Williams, S. M., & Atwater, M. M. (2014). Policy issues in science education: The importance of science teacher education, equity, and social justice. In M. Atwater, M. Russell, & M. Butler (Eds.), *Multicultural science education* (pp. 273–283). Dordrecht: Springer. https://doi.org/10.1007/978-94-007-7651-7_16

Windschitl, M. (2003). Inquiry projects in science teacher education: What can investigative experiences reveal about teacher thinking and eventual classroom practice? *Science Education*, *87*, 112–143. https://doi.org/10.1002/sce.10044

Ye, J., Zhu, X., & Lo, L. N. K. (2019). Reform of teacher education in China: A survey of policies for systemic change. *Teachers and Teaching*, *25*(7), 757–781. https://doi.org/10.1080/13540602.2019.1639498

Zhou, H. (2010). Analysis and policy adjustment on the contradiction of free of charge in normal education in practice. *Educational Research*, (8), 58–61, (in Chinese).

SECTION 4

Science Teacher Continuing Professional Development

Section Editor: Lauren Madden

Professional learning is critical to the development and success of all teachers, but in science, a discipline characterized by discovery and innovation, it is essential. In this section, six chapters explore various elements of professional learning for science teachers. These chapters address professional learning needs based on years of teaching experience, specific pedagogies and methodologies for professional development (PD), and frameworks for examining effective professional development.

Two chapters considered science teachers' professional learning with regard to specific career phases. In Chapter 18, Navy, Luft, and Msimanga focus on learning opportunities for teachers early on in their careers: newly hired teachers of science (NHTS). Using an Opportunities to Learn (OTL) framework, this review of 48 articles demonstrates that OTL are multidimensional and that factors related to these opportunities and the individual NHTS must align to ensure productive learning. Later, in Chapter 22, Blonder and Vesico present an examination of professional learning for science teachers through professional learning communities (PLCs) throughout the course of their careers. These authors use a life cycle model for phases of teacher career development (based off of Huberman's 1993 work) that ranges from early career teachers through those near retirement at the disengagement stage. In both these chapters, the authors found that the various frameworks employed allowed them to understand the nuanced and context-specific needs of science teachers.

The other chapters in this section focused on the purpose of science teacher professional learning and specific strategies for engaging in professional learning: teacher leadership, inquiry-based science teaching, culturally relevant science teaching, and technology-centric science teaching. In each of these chapters, the authors centered their work on identifying features of science professional learning related to their area of focus and highlighted examples of where future attention was needed. For example, in Chapter 19, Whitworth, Wenner, and Turbin explore science teacher leadership to continually improve education, put forth NGSS-aligned instruction in the US, and advocate for science. This review of 28 articles first offers an overview on the ways science teacher leaders are described and then the types of influence science teacher leaders have – on curricular and instructional decisions in their own classrooms and at the school level to assist in reforms and influence culture and climate. Chapter 20, by Ramnarain, Capps, and Hsu, explores science teacher professional development for inquiry-based instruction. These authors included 32 studies in their chapter and used a 2012 framework developed by the second author to describe categories as features of effective inquiry science professional development. In Chapter 21, Brown, Pringle, and Kotluk explore culturally relevant pedagogy and culturally responsive teaching practices and science teacher professional development: culturally responsive science teaching (CRST). This review of 19 articles identified various features of CRST present in the studies. Finally, in Chapter 23, Tan, Tao, and Tsai explore professional learning of science teachers through and with technology using the lens of TPACK, or technological pedagogical content knowledge.

Across the six chapters, several salient features emerged with regard to science teacher professional learning. One example feature is context. In both Navy et al. and Blonder and Vesico's chapter, the need to consider the individual teachers' context, including specific needs and stage of career, both early on and with experienced teachers was critical to the success of the PD. Context also played a role in Whitworth et al.'s work on science teacher leadership; administrative support, curriculum, and community-based contexts all influenced the effect of professional learning. Similarly, Tan et al. discussed the importance of context-specific technology professional development that allows teachers to engage with meaningful development related to their classroom practice. Another key element found in many of these chapters is the importance of collaboration. Ramnarain et al. found that collaboration was featured in more than two-thirds of the articles on inquiry-based science professional development. Likewise, Brown et al. addressed the influence of collaboration with community members and scientists in their work related to culturally relevant science teaching.

There were commonalities across the six chapters for future research. One common suggestion is to shift the focus of future research downstream and beyond the professional learning interventions themselves: toward teacher practices and student learning. For example, Brown et al. advised further study on how various components of professional learning (e.g., duration) might influence student learning and changes in teacher practice. They noted a need for "well-designed research to investigate methods and learning experiences used in the various professional development programs to prepare science teachers as 'culturally responsive' practitioners." On a similar note, Ramnarain et al. pointed out a need to identify which factors of professional development complement one another and to better understand how teachers' own authentic inquiry experiences influence their practice. In another example, Tan et al. proposed that attention be paid toward how various professional development approaches might influence enactment of high-leverage classroom practices. Whitworth et al. suggested that more research is needed on how teacher leadership professional learning influences communities, peers, and students. Finally, Navy et al. proposed future research as to how teachers' opportunities to learn affect student outcomes.

Several of the chapters, namely Blonder and Vesico and Brown et al., suggested more purposeful planning of professional learning based on teachers' interests and needs, further emphasizing the importance of context when thinking about professional learning overall. Additionally, this review revealed the uneven presence of publications pertaining to science teacher professional learning at the international level. Many researchers engaged in professional learning research in science often include science teachers in the studies they publish, which makes it difficult to find specific studies in science teachers. Additionally, this review revealed the uneven presence of publications pertaining to science teacher professional learning at the international level. Many researchers engaged in professional learning research in science often include science teachers in the studies they publish, which makes it difficult to find specific studies in science teachers. After all, there is a rich history of professional development studies around the globe. Figuring out how to include these studies in future reviews may be beneficial in depicting the professional learning of science teachers.

In order to develop a scientifically literate populace prepared to address the challenges of the future with innovation and creativity, science teachers must have the support of ongoing professional learning to best prepare their students. In conclusion, the six chapters in this section represent a broad and multifaceted perspective on science teachers' professional learning, identify key features for science educators to consider such as context and collaboration, and outline fruitful areas for future research.

18

THE LEARNING OPPORTUNITIES OF NEWLY HIRED TEACHERS OF SCIENCE

Shannon L. Navy, Julie A. Luft, and Audrey Msimanga

Introduction

The first years of teaching are some of the most formative in a teacher's career (Luft et al., 2015). For newly hired teachers of science (NHTS), there are numerous opportunities to strengthen the cognitive and instructional attributes toward science instruction as envisioned by the science education community. Unfortunately, these opportunities to learn (OTL) are often overshadowed by studies that depict the turbulence of the early years of teaching (e.g., Saka et al., 2013; Ritchie et al., 2011). While focusing on the challenges of learning to teach may be important in highlighting ways to better prepare and support NHTS, this view can be limiting, as it overlooks the OTL that should be cultivated and curated to ensure a strong professional foundation for NHTS.

This review of research was specifically conducted to understand the OTL that NHTS encounter in their first years of teaching. It builds on prior reviews of research of newly hired science teachers (Bianchini, 2012; Davis et al., 2006; Luft et al., 2015) by focusing on how NHTS learn to teach. In this review, we identify the OTL of NHTS and suggest what this means to teacher educators, induction specialists, colleagues, and administrators. The questions guiding this review are:

1. Where do OTL originate and exist for NHTS?
2. How do OTL influence NHTS?

Opportunities to Learn (OTL)

In this review of research, an OTL conceptual framework is used to provide insights into supporting the development of NHTS. OTL focuses on studying the inputs in a system, such as time, curriculum, coursework, or school setting, which enable the learning of an individual (McDonnell, 1995). With an OTL framework, it is possible to identify important aspects that support learning to teach.

One of the variations of OTL involves a situated perspective. This perspective recognizes that learners are embedded in environments that utilize different tools or resources (e.g., Cobb & Bowers, 1999; Korthagen, 2010; Lave & Wenger, 1991). How individuals participate in the environment influences what they come to know and do. With teachers, OTL in a situated perspective can occur in a classroom with students, in a school, or with a formal or informal group of teachers (Bell et al., 2013; Korthagen, 2010).

DOI: 10.4324/9781003098478-22

In this review of research, the OTL framework has a situated perspective focused on the learning of NHTS. This framing assumes that NHTS are learning on the job. The way in which science instruction is supported can occur through the access teachers have to materials to teach science, opportunities to practice and reflect upon their instruction, or policies that guide teaching science (Davis et al., 2016; Lotter & Miller, 2017; Navy et al., 2018).

Article Review Process

The recommendations of Alexander (2020) were followed when conducting this review of research. The first step was to define the population of interest and the period of time from which to draw articles. The population of interest consisted of elementary and secondary teachers of science in their first 5 years of teaching. The review spanned 10 years, 2011 thru 2020, which accounted for the increased attention on newly hired teachers globally and ensured sufficient time for this area of research to mature (Alexander, 2020).

Only peer-reviewed scholarly articles were included in this review. The articles were found by searching the databases of ERIC, Education Research Complete, and APA PsycINFO within EBSCO. In searching the databases, two search terms were used within the abstract field. The first term was "science teacher," and the second term was "induction," "newly qualified," "newly hired," "new," "beginning," "first-year," "second-year," "third-year," or "novice." This initial search resulted in 186 articles.

Inclusion criteria for the articles focused on the population and the quality of the study (see Alexander, 2020). Identifying these articles involved a two-step process. In the first step, the articles were reviewed to determine if more than half of the teachers in the study were science teachers in their first 5 years and if the data focused on the work of teaching. Studies in this group could follow teachers from their initial preparation years through their first years of teaching. Studies not meeting these criteria were eliminated for review.

In the second step of the review process, the quality of research in each publication was determined using a scoring rubric. The scoring rubric drew upon guidelines from the American Educational Research Association (AERA, 2006) and Clarke et al. (2013) and was similar to the rubric used by Luft et al. (2015). It had five areas: Research Question and Literature Review, Design and Procedures, Data Analysis, Results and Findings, and Discussion and Conclusions. In each of these areas, the score could be 1.0, 0.5, or 0.0. A score of 1.0 indicated a high degree of attainment of the criteria, while a score of zero indicated little or no attainment of the criteria. Studies with a score of zero in the Research Question and Literature Review or Design and Procedures were eliminated, regardless of the scores in the other areas. Articles not excluded needed a total score of at least 2.5 to be included in this review. This process resulted in 48 articles for this review, of which the majority were situated in the United States ($n = 38$). The remaining 10 articles were from Australia ($n = 4$), Europe ($n = 2$), New Zealand ($n = 2$), China ($n = 1$), and South Africa ($n = 1$).

These articles were organized into categories based on the initial OTL emphasized in the publication. A successive review of the pool of articles by two of the authors revealed three different sources of OTL, which were categorized as dimensions (Question 1). Inductive reviews of the studies within each dimension were then conducted to determine how the OTL influenced the NHTS, which resulted in different facets to OTL (Question 2).

OTL Experienced by NHTS

Dimension 1: OTL from Preparation Programs

In this dimension, initial preparation programs provided OTL that prepared science teachers for their first years in the classroom. Some of these studies followed teachers over time in order to determine the level of contribution of the preparation program. Other studies focused on teachers in their early years of teaching and made connections back to their preparation programs.

Purposeful Work With Students Provides Essential OTL Beneficial to NHTS

The different studies emphasize the importance of working in authentic environments prior to the first years of teaching. In working with students and educators, prospective science teachers were able to establish emerging attributes or orientations toward teaching science (e.g., Herman et al., 2013; Katz et al., 2013; Marco-Bujosa et al., 2020; Thompson et al., 2013). For instance, the study by Katz et al. (2013) described how prospective elementary teachers benefited from working in a museum setting with children. This program provided prospective teachers with an opportunity to contemplate how the teachers learned science and would ultimately teach children science. As 1st-year teachers, they drew upon this experience. Other studies illustrated how having an opportunity to work with students was conducive to building an emerging instructional repertoire. For example, Kang and Windschitl (2018) had prospective secondary science teachers learn and practice specific instructional moves with students. The field experience, as well as the focus on specific instructional moves in the preparation program, contributed to the development of the 1st-year teachers' emerging repertoire. Herman et al. (2013) had prospective teachers learn how to use the nature of science in their instruction. While the early opportunity to focus on the teaching of the nature of science was important to prospective teachers, it did not fully translate into the practice of NHTS.

Along with interacting with students, guided practice and school-based collaborations were also OTL for prospective science teachers. In their study of NHTS, Thompson and Emmer (2019) examined the influence of collaborations on teachers' instruction. In their program, prospective teachers, university science educators, and newly hired teachers worked collectively in classrooms to support the learning of students. These OTL enhanced the confidence and knowledge of both prospective teachers and NHTS. Similarly, Mitchener and Jackson (2012) illustrated how continuous encouragement to reflect on one's practice was conducive to the development of a NHTS. In this case study, Wendy learned how to reflect upon her instruction during her preparation program. As a new teacher, she continued this process of reflection with colleagues and university educators. Ultimately, she became more aware of the learning needs of her students and grew in her understanding of how to be a successful professional educator.

Focused OTL During Preparation Programming Lay Important Groundwork for Ongoing Learning, Which Over Time Is Aided by Community and Consistency

The studies in this theme illustrate a variety of OTL. One OTL focused on creating equitable learning environments for students (Kang & Zinger, 2019). This involved prospective teachers' contemplation of the inequities that exist in schools. Other OTL focused on cultivating a teacher's responsive and ambitious instructional practice by emphasizing reflective practice (Mitchener & Jackson, 2012), rehearsing core practices involved in the teaching of science (Kang & Windschitl, 2018; Thompson et al., 2013), or analyzing student work (Windschitl et al., 2011). Another OTL focused on building professional attributes, which included building an identity to teach science (Avraamidou, 2014; Katz et al., 2013) or an activist orientation (Marco-Bujosa et al., 2020). Regardless of the specific OTL, there was significant emphasis during the preparation program on cultivating these different approaches or attributes.

Among specific OTL, NHTS were just learning how to enact the advocated practices. For instance, Kang and Zinger (2019) found NHTS altered their views about structural inequities in discipline areas, with their views not well-developed in terms of a conscious focus on racism and inequity. Thompson et al. (2013) found NHTS differed in their implementation of specific teaching practices in their first year. Likewise, Windschitl et al. (2011) reported that some NHTS developed expert-like teaching as they used planning tools that supported their ongoing and collegial analysis of student work.

Essential factors that supported NHTS in these focused OTL involved consistency. Fletcher and Luft's (2011) study of six secondary science teachers revealed the result of a consistent emphasis on reform-based instruction during the preparation program and their first year in a classroom. Those who had both field experiences and coursework grounded in reform-based approaches held corresponding beliefs in their first year of teaching. In a study that created consistency through community, Marco-Bujosa et al. (2020) illustrated how the comradery of teachers throughout their preservice programs and first years in the classroom was essential in supporting their quest to create socially just environments. Likewise, Avraamidou's (2014) case study of a NHTS revealed the important role of the preparation program in helping the NHTS overcome challenging contextual factors as the teacher developed an identity for teaching science.

Dimension 1 Summary

This dimension emphasizes the importance of purposeful preparation experiences for future science teachers. OTL involved experiences with students and specific instructional approaches focused on student learning. These OTL provided NHTS with important foundational orientations in their teaching of science. In order to continue the ongoing cultivation of these orientations, it is important that teachers experience some degree of consistency framed by location, time, and/or community.

Dimension 2: OTL from Professional Learning Programs

Articles categorized into this dimension described induction and/or professional development (PD) programs that provided OTL for NHTS. These articles emphasized components of formal programs that were successful, or not, toward the learning of NHTS. Formal programs provided OTL beyond the initial preparation years and included facets that could foster NHTS ongoing learning.

Collaboration and Networking are Important OTL in Professional Learning Programs for NHTS

Professional learning programs provide opportunities for NHTS to connect and collaborate as a community. In one study, Paige et al. (2016) discussed the impact of a professional learning program on NHTS. By working collaboratively with academics to investigate an aspect of their instruction, the NHTS built their confidence and ability to teach science. Likewise, Williams et al. (2012) described a workshop approach in which four NHTS, expert classroom teachers, content experts, and researchers partnered to co-articulate the teaching of a science topic. The partnership approach ultimately helped improve the NHTS' pedagogical content knowledge (PCK).

A content mentor may be part of the collaborative program. For instance, Bang and Luft (2014) examined how an online mentoring program assisted two NHTS. As the mentors and NHTS interacted with one another, the NHTS had opportunities to practice, reflect upon, and evaluate their teaching. Similarly, McNally (2016) described how a distance mentoring program supported the instruction of eight NHTS. By watching and analyzing classroom videos of NHTS, the mentor helped NHTS focus on concrete evidence, consider the impacts of teacher actions on student learning, and determine next steps for instruction.

Networking comprised another OTL in professional learning programs. In this setting, NHTS can connect with other science education professionals for various instructional resources. In one study of 68 NHTS, Navy et al. (2019) found that attending a state science teachers' conference provided opportunities to network and connect with other professionals in the field as they selected and attended relevant and personally interesting sessions. In another study, Heredia and Yu (2017) studied how an informal induction program provided supplementary support to 143 NHTS. Their findings revealed that NHTS appreciated and benefited from the informal learning environment that allowed them to connect to like-minded individuals outside of their school sites.

Professional Learning Programs Provide Tools for OTL That Can Engage NHTS in Reflection on Their Knowledge and Practices

Various tools for learning have been embedded in programs to facilitate OTL. Some tools are designed to focus on the knowledge development of NHTS (Dawson & Carson, 2020; Pitjeng-Mosabala & Rollnick, 2018; Williams et al., 2012). For example, Pitjeng-Mosabala and Rollnick (2018) used a planning tool to help 14 secondary NHTS think deeply about the particulate nature of matter. The results of their study indicated that by using the tool, NHTS thought about the content they were teaching, which contributed to their PCK. Similarly, Dawson and Carson (2020) described how one NHTS implemented climate change materials he received from a PD program. The materials resulted in the teacher improving his instruction, which resulted in students improving their argumentation skills.

Other studies use electronic tools to facilitate OTL, which can support NHTS reflection and instruction (Bang & Luft, 2014; McFadden et al., 2014; McNally, 2016). McFadden et al. (2014), for instance, described how an online teacher induction program used asynchronous video annotation software as a tool for 16 secondary NHTS to reflect on their teaching practices. The study findings indicated that NHTS focused mostly on themselves and demonstrated lower levels of reflective practices. To enhance the reflection of NHTS through this type of tool, McFadden et al. (2014) recommend its use during the early years of teaching.

Professional Learning Programs Offer Additional OTL About Science Teaching and Student Learning Which May or May Not Have Been Experienced in an Initial Teacher Preparation Program

Science-specific induction or PD programs can support NHTS in learning about best practices in science instruction (e.g., Dawson & Carson, 2020; Luft et al., 2011; Navy et al., 2019; Pitjeng-Mosabala & Rollnick, 2018). In a mixed methods study, Luft et al. (2011) considered the impact of different induction programs on 98 NHTS' knowledge and instruction. The findings revealed that after 2 years, the NHTS in science-specific induction programs enacted more investigations and laboratories than teachers in other induction programs. Unfortunately, 5 years after the program concluded, the teachers in the science-specific induction program used more skill-based and verification laboratories (Wong et al., 2013). In a subsequent study, Bang and Luft (2013) revealed a missed opportunity to help NHTS learn how to use instructional technology in their classrooms. Their study of 95 NHTS found limited usage of technology in the classroom during their first 5 years, with even less technology use among NHTS in non-science-specific induction programs.

Professional learning programs with reduced hours, but focused on specific topics, could also provide OTL for NHTS. For example, Rosebery et al. (2016) enacted a professional learning program focused on student sensemaking in plant science. By the end of the program, the 26 NHTS developed a deeper understanding of the importance of sensemaking and had a greater commitment to the practice. In another study, Killough and Stuessy (2019) investigated the change in the beliefs of experienced teachers and NHTS after completing a professional learning program related to a specific science program. The program resulted in significant change in reform-based teaching beliefs about teaching science within the entire sample.

Dimension 2 Summary

Professional learning programs provide important OTL for NHTS. The opportunities can include collaboration, networking, tools to facilitate learning, and additional science-specific instructional support. Some studies suggested that the OTL in the programs were important in supporting professional development of NHTS. Other studies revealed the importance of deliberate program planning to ensure the maximization of OTL. These studies collectively indicate the critical importance of sustained and ongoing support for NHTS learning.

Dimension 3: OTL in Context

Articles categorized in this dimension describe how local school and/or national educational contexts provide and shape OTL for NHTS. Contextual factors can support or hinder NHTS learning. However, they are essential for NHTS' growth and learning, which result in the development of professional and social resilience.

Rules, Policies, and Expectations Within Local and National Contexts Shape OTL Experienced by NHTS

One contextual area that can influence OTL experienced by NHTS pertains to policy. For example, Navy et al. (2018) examined the impact of a policy at the classroom, school, and state level in a study of 12 NHTS in the US and South Africa. The alignment of policies at different levels afforded OTL for NHTS, but often there was policy misalignment that hindered their learning. The impact of policy can also be seen in implementing curricula associated with standardized testing. For instance, Strom (2015) described contextual and student factors that influenced the OTL within different classes of the same NHTS. The teacher was able to do more reform-based teaching instruction in the class that did not have the pressure and rigid curriculum associated with standardized testing. Similarly, Johnson and Dabney (2018) reported the lack of OTL in science as four new elementary science teachers were asked to prioritize the instruction of content areas (e.g., mathematics) associated with standardized tests.

In schools, administrators have an important role in enacting supportive policies that provide OTL for NHTS (e.g., Dubois & Luft, 2014; Haigh & Anthony, 2012; Rodriguez, 2015). For instance, administrators determine NHTS instructional assignments which can support or constrain NHTS learning. Dubois and Luft (2014) found US NHTS without an assigned classroom space (i.e., floating science teachers) were limited in their OTL. They were not near colleagues teaching the same content, nor did they have easy access to instructional materials. Administrators can also determine teaching assignments and guide additional responsibility expectations for NHTS which can impact OTL (e.g., Doney, 2013; Napier et al., 2020; Navy et al., 2020; Ortega et al., 2013; Sickel & Friedrichsen, 2015). Ortega et al. (2013) revealed how new instructional assignments and added responsibilities each year resulted in significant shifts between teacher-centered and reform-based instruction. Similarly, Sickel and Friedrichsen (2015) and Napier et al. (2020) reported how NHTS' additional or unexpected responsibilities limited their OTL about reform-based approaches.

Resources From School and Community Contexts Can Bolster OTL for NHTS, Whereas a Lack of Quality Resources May Constrain Development

A variety of studies conceptualize OTL through the lens of resources in school and community contexts. There are studies of schools or communities with and without adequate resources. Limited access to resources can hinder OTL (Dubois & Luft, 2014; Haigh & Anthony, 2012; Johnson & Dabney, 2018; Rodriguez, 2015). Social resources, for instance, provide important OTL among a group of 20 NHTS as they developed their instructional abilities (Haigh & Anthony, 2012). Additionally, at times, the relevance of resources can impact OTL of NHTS. For example, Rodriguez (2015) found that resources provided to a NHTS were geared toward an Anglo-based class and not a multicultural class, and as a result the NHTS spent time creating instructional materials aligned with the student population.

Other studies move beyond resources in isolation and consider the network of resources available to NHTS in school and community contexts. Navy et al. (2020) examined the primary and secondary resources that 15 secondary NHTS accessed to support their instruction. They found that a network of resources provided more coherent OTL, yet different resources were accessed in various ways by the NHTS. Similarly, Stroupe (2016) investigated five NHTS to see how teachers used resources to shape and learn from their practice. NHTS who combined the core resource of students' ideas with high-leverage teaching practices enacted ambitious pedagogy, whereas NHTS who combined students' ideas with textbooks and curricula enacted more traditional instruction.

Socialized Contexts Are Essential OTL for NHTS to Gain a Sense of Belonging in the Profession

A sense of belonging to a community is important in the initial years of teaching. Colleagues are an important part of the socialization process. In an absence of this supportive community, NHTS lack important OTL from colleagues and can experience professional isolation. Nehmeh and Kelly's (2018) study of newly hired physics specialists without access to physics networks resulted in experiences of professional isolation. Over time, the isolation they experienced became an important factor in their decisions to leave their first school. Similarly, Watters and Diezman's (2015) study reported how a sense of isolation contributed to NHTS leaving the teaching profession in the first 2 years of practice. In the absence of collegial professional relationships or collaborative teams, NHTS did not have a sense of belonging, nor did they have access to resources that ensured job satisfaction.

Administrators are also part of supportive communities. In one study, Saka et al. (2013) contrasted the administration an NHTS experienced in two schools. In the first school, the administration was focused on accountability and was notably absent from the teacher's classroom experiences. In the second school, the administration made the teacher feel as though he belonged to the community and even offered him a leadership position in the school. In another study, Haigh and Anthony (2012) described how school leadership helped NHTS in school contexts alongside various induction activities.

NHTS Experienced Classroom-Based OTL Differently Depending on Underlying Attributes

In teaching science, NHTS draw upon underlying attributes that can direct their instruction. Labeled as beliefs, attitudes, emotions, identity, or knowledge, these attributes can influence OTL. These attributes are evident in the classroom teaching experiences of NHTS. For instance, the case study by Ritchie et al. (2011) revealed how an NHTS responded to students in emotional ways that altered her body and facial reactions. The negative and positive emotions she experienced resulted in successful or unsuccessful classroom interactions. Similarly, Nichols et al. (2017) revealed how classroom experiences involving students resulted in emotional events that influenced their instruction. NHTS who viewed the learning of their students as solely their responsibility could become emotionally compromised when students did not perform adequately.

A different attribute that can connect with OTL is knowledge. Considering subject matter knowledge (SMK), Nixon et al. (2019) found that new physical science teachers were more knowledgeable about core concepts associated with SMK but less knowledgeable about connections of the concepts. In terms of PCK, Sickel and Friedrichsen (2018) concluded NHTS expanded their knowledge and increased the number of connections from their first to their second year of teaching.

In addition, the beliefs and identity of teachers can filter OTL experienced by NHTS. Wong and Luft (2015), for instance, investigated the beliefs of NHTS. They found that alignment of beliefs among NHTS and their mentors may have supported OTL. Alternatively, mismatched beliefs between NHTS and mentors may have provided limited OTL, which resulted in NHTS leaving the profession. Ozel and Luft (2013) found there was no difference in NHTS' conceptions (beliefs) about and enactment of inquiry; thus, OTL were untapped. Similar to beliefs, identity can be a conduit for OTL. Wei et al. (2019) illustrated how the identity and beliefs of an NHTS came from prior experiences which were important in the teacher's agency demonstrated in class. Similarly, Avraamidou (2020) revealed how elementary teachers built their identities as science teachers over time and in different ways. Their identity in science influenced how they viewed themselves as teachers of science and how they maximized different OTL.

NHTS Can Develop Resilience and Agency in Response to OTL in the Sociocultural and Institutional Contexts in Which They Work

Cognitive factors also intersect with the contextual OTL NHTS experience. One of these factors is resilience. Doney (2013) provided an account of NHTS who encountered stressful experiences from extracurricular duties, inexperience, multiple preparations, and work-life balance. Doney (2013) revealed how each stressful experience provided OTL for NHTS to access their protective factors (e.g., support systems, problem solving) and build resilience to challenges. Likewise, Nehmeh and Kelly (2018) described how two physics NHTS who taught in isolation developed resilience to overcome challenges in their contexts. Ultimately, the teachers exercised their own agency in their careers and transitioned to new school contexts.

Rodriguez (2015) also articulated how an NHTS enacted agency in response to sociocultural and institutional challenges. The teacher experienced many challenges working in a culturally diverse school, from Anglo-based resources to school-level low expectations of students. The teacher responded to these challenges as OTL by engaging with his own learning and enacting agency to resist the low-level expectations culture, create culturally relevant lessons, involve parents in the learning process, and implement science clubs. Similarly, agency was evident in Haigh and Anthony's (2012) study of 20 NHTS, some of whom developed their own resources when existing ones proved lacking.

Dimension 3 Summary

The contexts in which NHTS are situated provide OTL influenced by policies, school systems, classrooms, colleagues, and personal attributes. These are certainly some of the most important settings for OTL. Through these studies it is evident that contexts are not removed from the person; instead, they are connected and always influencing one another in productive and constraining ways.

Conclusions, Implications, and Future Directions

This review was framed around OTL to understand the nature and sources of NHTS' learning in programs and contexts. It views NHTS as individuals who are building and evolving their professional practice. In line with the situated perspective of OTL, emerging findings from this review indicate the potential of tools or resources embedded in environments where NHTS learn to teach. The review identified three dimensions of OTL: preparation programs, professional learning programs, and contexts in which NHTS learn how to teach science to students. In examining the different ways OTL exist for NHTS, it is possible to identify overarching conclusions, implications, and research suggestions for science teacher educators and researchers.

To begin with, NHTS are influenced by OTL that are multidimensional and multifaceted. OTL are multidimensional in that they exist in preparation and professional learning programs and are connected to the context in which an NHTS works. All these dimensions have varying OTL embedded within, which contributes to their multifaceted nature. As multifaceted experiences, OTL exist in different intensities, durations, and locations and can be connected to facets in other dimensions. In this view, if a NHTS has limited OTL in one dimension, another dimension may provide the necessary OTL. However, if challenges exist in all dimensions, a NHTS could struggle in the profession. Indeed, OTL, especially those that are sustained and ongoing, can enrich the quality of NHTS' experiences.

With an OTL orientation, there appear to be cross-cutting OTL that focus on working in classrooms with students and within communities. These OTL occur in each dimension and reside within ongoing interactions between NHTS and students as well as NHTS and colleagues in their communities. Communities, for instance, can reinforce and build NHTS' orientation toward student-centered science instruction. By interacting with students, NHTS can determine how their evolving science education knowledge and practice supports student learning.

In thinking about OTL, it is necessary to acknowledge the individuality of NHTS. NHTS are products of their experiences, and that is what influences how they interact with different OTL. Even if OTL are cumulative (i.e., layered upon each other), coherent (i.e., align with goals of the community), and consistent (i.e., repetitive over time), they may not result in productive learning for the NHTS. Instead, they may cascade in ways that result in unrealized learning opportunities for NHTS. The individual and OTL need to align in ways that can be accessed by and beneficial to NHTS.

For science teacher educators, it is important to support NHTS in recognizing OTL that can impact their work as a teacher. Deliberate and proactive integration of this aspect in teacher education programs can be beneficial to NHTS. Most importantly, these productive OTL should enhance their work in order to improve student learning. In some instances, the NHTS may need assistance in utilizing an OTL. For instance, if a NHTS is working excessively in planning classroom lessons, then providing a pathway for collaboration with colleagues in the same instructional area would be useful. Or perhaps a NHTS may need support in capitalizing on OTL. A NHTS who is working in a challenging setting may need assistance drawing upon students' ideas to improve their instruction. This could be focused OTL over time.

For science teacher education researchers, this area is ripe for research. Future research questions could include the following: How do OTL translate into improved teacher and student learning? How do NHTS engage in certain OTL, and why do they not engage in others? How can OTL align with one another in order to better support NHTS? Do NHTS use OTL to overcome personal and/or contextual challenges? How does the changing environment of technology and diversity interact with OTL? How do OTL for NHTS compare across national and international contexts? These questions and others would help provide a nuanced understanding of OTL for NHTS.

Finally, NHTS are malleable and constantly experience OTL. These OTL are supports for new teachers, but they are not linear inputs that result in contained outputs. Rather, OTL are varied and provide NHTS with a network that consists of dimensions and facets. NHTS engage in this network that produces iterative and evolving changes which vary by teacher. An essential task for the science teacher education community is to support the professional development of each NHTS. The OTL orientation has the potential to be transformative in NHTS support and development, changing the view of what it means to teach and learn as a NHTS.

Dedication

This chapter is dedicated to Audrey Msimanga, who passed away just before the chapter was submitted for publication. Her passion and dedication to education is evident in this chapter, along with all of her other published work.

References

Alexander, P. A. (2020). Methodological guidance paper: The art and science of quality systematic reviews. *Review of Educational Research, 90*(1), 6–23.

American Educational Research Association. (2006). Standards for reporting on empirical social science research in AERA publications. *Educational Researcher, 35*(6), 33–40.

Avraamidou, L. (2014). Tracing a beginning elementary teacher's development of identity for science teaching. *Journal of Teacher Education, 65*(3), 223–240.

Avraamidou, L. (2020). Science identity as a landscape of becoming: Rethinking recognition and emotions through an intersectionality lens. *Cultural Studies of Science Education, 15*(2), 323–345.

Bang, E., & Luft, J. A. (2013). Secondary science teachers' use of technology in the classroom during their first 5 years. *Journal of Digital Learning in Teacher Education, 29*(4), 118–126.

Bang, E., & Luft, J. A. (2014). Exploring the written dialogues of two first-year secondary science teachers in an online mentoring program. *Journal of Science Teacher Education, 25*(1), 25–51.

Bell, R. L., Maeng, J. L., & Binns, I. C. (2013). Learning in context: Technology integration in a teacher preparation program informed by situated learning theory. *Journal of Research in Science Teaching, 50*(3), 348–379.

Bianchini, J. A. (2012). Teaching while still learning to teach: Beginning science teachers' views, experiences, and classroom practices. In B. J. Fraser (Ed.), *Second international handbook of science education* (pp. 389–399). New York: Springer.

Clarke, A., Triggs, V., & Nielsen, W. (2013). Cooperating teacher participation in teacher education. *Review of Educational Research, 84*(2), 163–202.

Cobb, P., & Bowers, J. (1999). Cognitive and situated learning perspectives in theory and practice. *Educational Researcher, 28*(2), 4–15.

Davis, E. A., Janssen, F. J., & Van Driel, J. H. (2016). Teachers and science curriculum materials: Where we are and where we need to go. *Studies in Science Education, 52*(2), 127–160.

Davis, E. A., Petish, D., & Smithey, J. (2006). Challenges new science teachers face. *Review of Educational Research, 76*(4), 607–651.

Dawson, V., & Carson, K. (2020). Introducing argumentation about climate change socioscientific issues in a disadvantaged school. *Research in Science Education, 50*(3), 863–883.

Doney, P. A. (2013). Fostering resilience: A necessary skill for teacher retention. *Journal of Science Teacher Education, 24*(4), 645–664.

Dubois, S. L., & Luft, J. A. (2014). Science teachers without classrooms of their own: A study of the phenomenon of floating. *Journal of Science Teacher Education, 25*(1), 5–23.

Fletcher, S. S., & Luft, J. A. (2011). Early career secondary science teachers: A longitudinal study of beliefs in relation to field experiences. *Science Education, 95*(6), 1124–1146.

Haigh, M. A., & Anthony, G. J. (2012). Induction and efficacy: A case study of New Zealand newly qualified secondary science teachers. *Journal of Science Teacher Education, 23*(6), 651–671.

Heredia, S. C., & Yu, J. H. (2017). A Matter of Choice: Opportunities for Informal Science Institutions to Support Science Teacher Induction. *Journal of Science Teacher Education, 28*(6), 549–565.

Herman, B. C., Clough, M. P., & Olson, J. K. (2013). Teachers' nature of science implementation practices 2–5 years after having completed an intensive science education program. *Science Education, 97*(2), 271–309.

Johnson, T. N., & Dabney, K. P. (2018). Voices from the field: Constraints encountered by early career elementary science teachers. *School Science and Mathematics, 118*(6), 244–256.

Kang, H., & Windschitl, M. (2018). How does practice-based teacher preparation influence novices' first-year instruction? *Teachers College Record, 120*(8).

Kang, H., & Zinger, D. (2019). What do core practices offer in preparing novice science teachers for equitable instruction?. *Science Education, 103*(4), 823–853.

Katz, P., McGinnis, J. R., Riedinger, K., Marbach-Ad, G., & Dai, A. (2013). The influence of informal science education experiences on the development of two beginning teachers' science classroom teaching identity. *Journal of Science Teacher Education, 24*(8), 1357–1379.

Killough, J. K., & Stuessy, C. L. (2019). Changing beliefs about reformed teaching in science: Experience matters. *School Science and Mathematics, 119*(5), 255–261.

Korthagen, F. A. (2010). Situated learning theory and the pedagogy of teacher education: Towards an integrative view of teacher behavior and teacher learning. *Teaching and Teacher Education, 26*(1), 98–106.

Lave, J., & Wenger, E. (1991). *Situated learning: Legitimate peripheral participation.* Cambridge: Cambridge University.

Lotter, C. R., & Miller, C. (2017). Improving inquiry teaching through reflection on practice. *Research in Science Education, 47*(4), 913–942.

Luft, J. A., Dubois, S., Nixon, R., & Campbell, B. (2015). Supporting newly hired teachers of science: Attaining professional teaching standards. *Studies in Science Education, 51*(1), 1–48.

Luft, J. A., Firestone, J. B., Wong, S. S., Ortega, I., Adams, K., & Bang, E. (2011). Beginning secondary science teacher induction: A two-year mixed methods study. *Journal of Research in Science Teaching, 48*(10), 1199–1224.

Marco-Bujosa, L. M., McNeill, K. L., & Friedman, A. A. (2020). Becoming an urban science teacher: How beginning teachers negotiate contradictory school contexts. *Journal of Research in Science Teaching, 57*(1), 3–32.

McDonnell, L. M. (1995). Opportunity to learn as a research concept and policy instrument. *Educational Evaluation and Policy Analysis, 17*(3), 305–322.

McFadden, J., Ellis, J., Anwar, T., & Roehrig, G. (2014). Beginning science teachers' use of a digital video annotation tool to promote reflective practices. *Journal of Science Education and Technology, 23*, 458–470.

McNally, J. C. (2016). Learning from one's own teaching: New science teachers analyzing their practice through classroom observation cycles. *Journal of Research in Science Teaching, 53*(3), 473–501.

Mitchener, C. P., & Jackson, W. M. (2012). Learning from action research about science teacher preparation. *Journal of Science Teacher Education, 23*(1), 45–64.

Napier, J., Luft, J. A, & Singh, H. (2020). The science instruction of newly hired out-of-field secondary science teachers during their first three years. *Journal of Science Teacher Education, 31*(7), 802–820.

Navy, S. L., Luft, J. A., Toerien, R., & Hewson, P. W. (2018). Practices influenced by policy? An exploration of newly hired science teachers at sites in South Africa and the United States. *International Journal of Science Education, 40*(8), 919–939.

Navy, S. L., Maeng, J. L., & Bell, R. L. (2019). Learning from a state professional development conference for science teachers: Beginning secondary science teachers' experiences. *Journal of Science Teacher Education, 30*(4), 409–428.

Navy, S. L., Nixon, R. S., Luft, J. A., & Jurkiewicz, M. A. (2020). Accessed or latent resources? Exploring new secondary science teachers' networks of resources. *Journal of Research in Science Teaching, 57*(2), 184–208.

Nehmeh, G., & Kelly, A. M. (2018). Urban science teachers in isolation: Challenges, resilience, and adaptive action. *Journal of Science Teacher Education, 29*(6), 527–549.

Nichols, S. L., Schutz, P. A., Rodgers, K., & Bilica, K. (2017). Early career teachers' emotion and emerging teacher identities. *Teachers and Teaching, 23*(4), 406–421.

Nixon, R. S., Toerien, R., & Luft, J. A. (2019). Knowing more than their students: Characterizing secondary science teachers' subject matter knowledge. *School Science and Mathematics, 119*(3), 150–160.

Ortega, I., Luft, J. A., & Wong, S. S. (2013). Learning to teach inquiry: A beginning science teacher of English language learners. *School Science and Mathematics, 113*(1), 29–40.

Ozel, M., & Luft, J. A. (2013). Beginning Secondary Science Teachers' Conceptualization and Enactment of Inquiry-Based Instruction. *School Science and Mathematics, 113*(6), 308–316.

Paige, K., Zeegers, Y., Lloyd, D., & Roetman, P. (2016). Researching the effectiveness of a science professional learning program using a proposed curriculum framework for schools: A case study. *International Journal of Science and Mathematics Education, 14*(1), 149–175.

Pitjeng-Mosabala, P., & Rollnick, M. (2018). Exploring the development of novice unqualified graduate teachers' topic-specific PCK in teaching the particulate nature of matter in South Africa's classrooms. *International Journal of Science Education, 40*(7), 742–770.

Ritchie, S. M., Tobin, K., Hudson, P., Roth, W. M., & Mergard, V. (2011). Reproducing successful rituals in bad times: Exploring emotional interactions of a new science teacher. *Science Education, 95*(4), 745–765.

Rodriguez, A. J. (2015). Managing institutional and sociocultural challenges through sociotransformative constructivism: A longitudinal case study of a high school science teacher. *Journal of Research in Science Teaching, 52*(4), 448–460.

Rosebery, A. S., Warren, B., & Tucker-Raymond, E. (2016). Developing interpretive power in science teaching. *Journal of Research in Science Teaching, 53*(10), 1571–1600.

Saka, Y., Southerland, S. A., Kittleson, J., & Hutner, T. (2013). Understanding the induction of a science teacher: The interaction of identity and context. *Research in Science Education, 43*(3), 1221–1244.

Sickel, A. J., & Friedrichsen, P. (2015). Beliefs, Practical Knowledge, and Context: A Longitudinal Study of a Beginning Biology Teacher's 5 E Unit. *School Science and Mathematics, 115*(2), 75–87.

Sickel, A. J., & Friedrichsen, P. (2018). Using multiple lenses to examine the development of beginning biology teachers' pedagogical content knowledge for teaching natural selection simulations. *Research in Science Education, 48*(1), 29–70.

Strom, K. J. (2015). Teaching as assemblage: Negotiating learning and practice in the first year of teaching. *Journal of Teacher Education, 66*(4), 321–333.

Stroupe, D. (2016). Beginning teachers' use of resources to enact and learn from ambitious instruction. *Cognition and Instruction, 34*(1), 51–77.

Thompson, J., Windschitl, M., & Braaten, M. (2013). Developing a theory of ambitious early-career teacher practice. *American Educational Research Journal, 50*(3), 574–615.

Thompson, S. L., & Emmer, E. (2019). Closing the Experience Gap: The Influence of an Immersed Methods Course in Science. *Journal of Science Teacher Education, 30*(3), 300–319.

Watters, J. J., & Diezmann, C. M. (2015). Challenges confronting career-changing beginning teachers: A qualitative study of professional scientists becoming science teachers. *Journal of Science Teacher Education, 26*(2), 163–192.

Wei, B., Avraamidou, L., & Chen, N. (2019). How a beginning science teacher deals with practical work: An explorative study through the lens of identity. *Research in Science Education.* https://doi.org/10.1007/s11165-019-9826-z.

Williams, J., Eames, C., Hume, A., & Lockley, J. (2012). Promoting pedagogical content knowledge development for early career secondary teachers in science and technology using content representations. *Research in Science & Technological Education, 30*(3), 327–343.

Windschitl, M., Thompson, J., & Braaten, M. (2011). Ambitious pedagogy by novice teachers: Who benefits from tool-supported collaborative inquiry into practice and why?. *Teachers College Record, 113*(7), 1311–1360.

Wong, S. S., Firestone, J. B., Luft, J. A., & Weeks, C. B. (2013). Laboratory practices of beginning secondary science teachers: A five-year study. *Science Educator, 22*(1), 1–9.

Wong, sS. S., & Luft, J. A. (2015). Secondary science teachers' beliefs and persistence: A longitudinal mixed-methods study. *Journal of Science Teacher Education, 26*(7), 619–645.

19

SCIENCE TEACHER LEADERSHIP

The Current Landscape and Paths Forward

Brooke A. Whitworth, Julianne A. Wenner, and Dorit Tubin

Teacher leadership has become an increasingly popular topic discussed as a means to improve education (e.g., Wenner & Campbell, 2017). Enhancing teacher professional learning opportunities by cultivating teacher leaders (TLs) is one strategy that can be adopted to improve education (Lumpkin et al., 2016). TLs contribute to instructional leadership, reform efforts, and the practices of their profession (Printy & Marks, 2006). In addition, TLs support improving teacher quality and sustainable school improvement efforts (Hunzicker, 2017).

The development of *science* teacher leadership is a critical aspect in improving science education. In addition to supporting schools more generally as just described, specific to science it has been argued that science teacher leadership could help close science achievement gaps, move NGSS-aligned instruction forward in the United States, and advocate for science (Cheung et al., 2018; Luft et al., 2016; Wenner, 2017). These science-specific issues, in addition to the notion that science could be considered distinct from other content areas due to particularities in teacher content, attitudes, materials, safety, and reforms, provides impetus for the development of a *science* teacher leader (STL) rather than a more general TL to effectively support high-quality science education.

We assert there are three aspects of science teacher leadership: the science-specific issues, as discussed previously; the teacher aspects of pedagogy and identity development as both a teacher and, more specifically, a science teacher; and the development as a leader. As leaders, these individuals are influencers of other teachers, schools, and students and are recognized by others as leaders. This leadership is enacted through the social, cultural, and symbolic capital they brought with them and developed in the science teacher and leader positions (Figure 19.1). To this end, and based on our review of the literature, we define an STL as:

> A teacher of science, who influences others while developing their leadership identity, and who uses their social, cultural, and symbolic capital to advocate for science and promote student learning.

Attention to science teacher leadership and its development has, indeed, increased over the last decade (e.g., Criswell et al., 2018a; Luft et al., 2016; Hanuscin et al., 2016). Nevertheless, much of the literature on science teacher leadership is presented as teacher leadership that *so happens to be* within the field of science; the specific focus on the nuances of science teacher leadership are often absent. For example, while Sinha and Hanuscin (2017) present important insights from the implementation of their Science Teachers as Leaders program, the conclusions and implications from this research

DOI: 10.4324/9781003098478-23

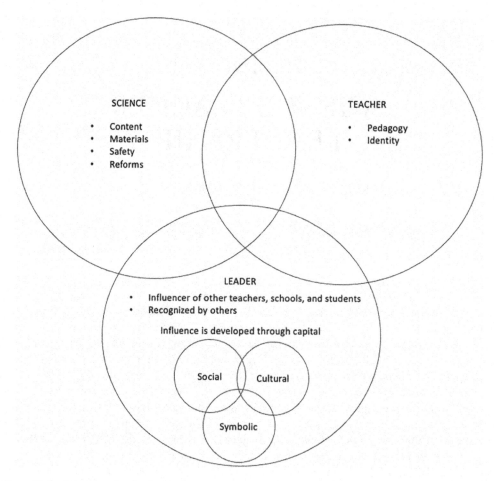

Figure 19.1   Science teacher leadership

for the support and development of TLs are rather general and could be applied to any content area. Consequently, there is still much to be learned about STLs that will move the field forward, and thus advance science education as a whole. Considering and more deeply understanding the intersections of science, teaching, and leadership will be a critical piece of this work.

To have a better sense of where the field could go, we review the current research on science teacher leadership and provide an overview of the field. Based on an inductive analysis of the current literature, this chapter attends to important practicalities, including who is an STL, how STLs are developed professionally, and the impact of STLs in schools and school systems. Based on these findings, we also suggest implications for science teacher professional development (in-service), policy makers, and those teachers who want to become STLs. Given that this is a chapter within a *Handbook for Science Teacher Education*, it is our hope that science teacher leadership may become more prevalent and nuanced throughout both preservice and in-service science teacher education.

Studies Examined in This Review

Numerous steps were taken in conducting this review of the research. First, parameters were set to identify potential studies. These initial parameters included identifying sources from 2000 to the present in which "teacher leadership," "teacher leader," "leadership," or "leader" were key terms or aspects of the research. Specific journals were then selected and identified as science, education, and/ or leadership specific. The journals selected were: *American Educational Research Journal, Innovations* (by ASTE), *International Journal of Leadership in Education, International Journal of Science Education, Journal of Research in Science Teaching, International Journal of Teacher Leadership, Journal of Science Education, Journal of Science Teacher Education, Phi Delta Kappan, Professional Development in Education, Research In Science Education, School Science & Mathematics, Science Education, Science Educator,* and *Teaching and Teacher Education*. The journals selected varied in impact factor scores, but all required peer review for articles to be included. Hand-searches were conducted in these journals, with additional electronic searches conducted to ensure no additional studies were missed. This initial search resulted in 315 studies.

In the second step of the review, studies with a focus on "teacher leaders" or "teacher leadership" were selected by reviewing abstracts and examining the paper for definitions of a teacher leader or teacher leadership to ensure the study had a teacher leader focus. For example, studies focused on principals or other types of leaders or that had a tangential leadership focus were eliminated at this step of the review. This narrowed our selection of studies to 77. From these studies, 35 studies that included a specific focus on in-service science teachers and were empirical research studies were selected. These criteria were selected due to the inclusion of this chapter in the professional learning of science teachers section of the *Handbook*. This step of the process eliminated studies that focused on preservice teachers, did not have a science focus, or were reviews or conceptual pieces.

Additional details were collected on these 35 studies. Overarching study details included the goal of the study, number of participants, data collection methods, and outcomes of the study. Details about the intervention type (e.g., homegrown versus outside source) and how STLs were prepared were also collected. We defined a "homegrown" source for the intervention as being developed by the school or district and an outside source as being a university course or coming from a university, commercial provider, or grant program. Specific participant details were also identified, including elementary versus secondary, United States versus outside the United States, and formal versus informal leadership role. Finally, details regarding the type of leadership were also identified: individual versus systemic/organizational view, focus on management of tasks versus people, view of leadership as innate or able to be taught, and how science teacher leadership was enacted as part of the study. In collecting these details, an additional seven studies were eliminated from inclusion as a result of either not having a specific science focus (e.g., included only one science teacher in a larger professional learning experience) or not having a specific teacher leader focus (e.g., focused on a teaching strategy rather than teacher leadership).

This extensive selection process led to 28 total studies being included for review. Of these 28 studies, 4 studies took place outside of the United States, and 24 were set in the United States. In addition, we found that 3 of the studies had an elementary focus, 18 had a secondary focus, and 7 had a K–12 focus. An inductive content analysis was conducted with these studies. Repetitive ideas were examined and are reported here as well as some ideas that emerged only once in the studies. Given the lack of literature in this area, the authors felt it important to include some ideas that emerged only once, as they may be of interest and a promising avenue for future research.

Findings

Science Teacher Leadership Defined

In general, the definitions of science teacher leadership are derived from the general literature on teacher leadership and reflect the same complex of goals and practices. The definitions in the reviewed papers were examined for either a formal or informal approach to defining teacher leadership, and it was found that those with a secondary focus tended to have a more formal approach to defining science teacher leadership, often as a science department head. When the studies were examined in terms of whether they were outside the United States (Netherlands, Australia, New Zealand) or based in the United States, there were no differences in the approach to definitions. In addition, there were no noticeable differences in the definitions based on how the studies approached the intervention (outside source or homegrown).

The unique qualities of science teacher leadership, however, were mentioned only in seven papers, and those dealt mainly with teacher leadership in the science departments. Only two papers emphasized advocating for science as a responsibility of STLs. While there is a consensus that teacher leadership consists of influencing others, the special needs of science as a subject matter (Spillane et al., 2001) are missing from the definitions. After analyzing the definitions' components from the reviewed papers, we will offer our definition for an STL. But, first we examine three aspects of the STL definitions: (1) Who are STLs? (2) Who and what are influenced by STLs? and (3) How do STLs practice their influence?

Who Are Science Teacher Leaders?

The definitions in the reviewed papers offer descriptions of TLs as:

- Any person who influences individuals and groups within an organization; those who lead within and beyond the classroom (Ritchie et al., 2006);
- "Go-to" people in the school in an area of leadership the principal identified as central to their school's success (Wenner & Campbell, 2017);
- Individuals who still have classroom teaching responsibilities as a main component of their professional responsibilities but also engage in work designed to improve school (Gul et al., 2019);
- Experienced science teachers who were appointed head of department (Rigano & Ritchie, 2003);
- People who wanted to continue learning (Collinson, 2012);
- Science teachers who are engaging in identity work of becoming "teacher leaders" (Jacobs et al., 2014);
- Those who not only engage in the practice of leadership, but who also identify themselves as teacher leaders (Sinha & Hanuscin, 2017); and
- Teachers who commit to contribute beyond their classroom (Luft et al., 2016).

As is apparent from the various definitions, STLs are experienced science teachers in formal (head of department) or informal positions in the school, who are engaged in influencing others, who are recognized as leaders by administrators and colleagues, and who work on their own (science) leadership identity. It seems that the most important aspects of the STL role are influencing others and developing a leadership identity, which are aspects involved in any leadership position (Tubin, 2017).

Who and What Are Influenced by Science Teacher Leaders?

In general, STLs most directly affect their colleagues and their school through a variety of methods.

Teachers

STLs develop teacher capacity in science content knowledge, pedagogical knowledge, and procedural knowledge specific to providing authentic investigative opportunities for students in line with the expectations of the national science curriculum (Lewthwaite, 2006). STLs help teachers in the establishment of goals and guide them toward achievement of those goals, thereby allowing them to be effective (Ritchie et al., 2006). They also influence other teachers towards improved educational practice (Rhoton & McLean, 2008) and mobilize commitment and energy into actions designed to improve learning (Rhoton & McLean, 2008).

Schools

Schoolwide, STLs help develop a vision for producing innovation in systems, which, within school systems, means improving the practice of teaching and learning (Criswell et al., 2018a) with the aim of increased student learning and achievement (Hanuscin et al., 2012). STLs take on increased responsibility for decision-making and activities outside of their classrooms and assist in reforms that impact the organizational processes within their school or district (Luft et al., 2016). In addition, STLs work with other school leaders to envision a better future, foster hope and honesty, tackle obstacles and impediments, and build community while improving the educational climate (Luft et al., 2016).

How Do STLs Influence Others?

In general, STLs influence others through their social, cultural, and symbolic capitals (Bourdieu, 1990). These three kinds of capital enable an agent to achieve a better social position in a given field. In the case of STLs, these types of capital help the science teacher to attain a leadership position among the power relations in the school. Before providing further detail, it is important to note that these types of capital overlap a great deal in reality, but for simplicity's sake, they are presented here separately.

Social capital refers to interpersonal relationships and the ability to use power, knowledge, and scarce resources to influence others. It is also about creating and maintaining networks of people and alliances to gain access to information and opportunities, to promote communication, and to distribute innovation (Eick et al., 2007). Holding the right social capital enables STLs to promote their leadership in two main ways. The first is to identify and fill structural holes, which is the brokerage between groups and networks that provide a vision of options otherwise unseen (Burt, 2004). For example, STLs engage in professional inquiry and participate in collaborative decision-making among different teachers (Hunzicker, 2012). They also design and facilitate PD in their schools/ districts by approaching collaborators for mentoring/coaching, presenting at conferences, and/or developing curricula, among other partnerships (e.g., Gul et al., 2019; Groothuijsen et al., 2019; M. Taylor et al., 2019). The second way to apply social capital is by motivating others toward certain goals, such as cultivating and encouraging colleagues to embrace new ideas, support the growth of others, and build consensus among diverse groups (Rhoton & McLean, 2008).

Symbolic capital refers to the ability to use "reputation for honor" (Bourdieu, 1990, p. 119) based on their education, credentials, awards, and/or title. STLs coordinate and manage preservice teachers (Wenner, 2017), analyze how supportive (or not) a school culture is for science (Sato et al., 2016), model effective science instruction (Cheung et al., 2018), advocate for science, build a collegial learning environment, and problem solve (Peacock, 2014). STLs are also tasked with ordering textbooks, purchasing laboratory supplies, arranging school science fairs, obtaining and translating standards documents for teachers (Spillane et al., 2001), or planning, designing, and providing many of the professional development (PD) opportunities (Khourey-Bowers et al., 2005). STLs' symbolic capital is what encourages others to learn from them, follow their lead, and recognize them as legitimate science education experts.

Cultural capital refers to the ability to evaluate and legitimately use knowledge in a specific context. Cultural capital exists in three different states: the *embodied* state that is an internalized scheme of appreciation and understanding (in the case of STLs, the importance and beauty of science); the *objectified* form, referring to objects such as books, works of art, and scientific instruments that require special cultural abilities to use; and the *institutional* form that is represented by a credential system (Swartz, 2012). STLs use cultural capital to position themselves in a leadership position by applying all three states. Through their embodied appreciation for science, they develop content knowledge, implement relevant and meaningful curriculum, and enact best practices in their classroom (Yow & Lotter, 2016). Having objectified cultural capital leads them to design teaching materials (Groothuijsen et al., 2019), create curriculum guides, recommend textbook/curriculum adoptions, and mentor teachers in their schools on inquiry practices (Eick et al., 2007). The STLs enact their *institutional* cultural capital by interacting with other STLs via their blogs, exchanging ideas and resources (Jacobs et al., 2014), and introducing new ideas for consideration and possible action within their schools or districts (Ritchie et al., 2006).

Consequently, for a person to operate as an STL, they must use their social, symbolic, and cultural capital to develop others' science teaching practices, advocate for science in school, and support an appropriate curriculum. Therefore, we arrived at our definition of an STL as:

> A teacher of science, who influences others while developing their leadership identity, and who uses their social, cultural, and symbolic capital to advocate for science and promote student learning.

How Are Teacher Leaders Developed and Prepared?

Science education needs STLs who fit our (literature-based) definition. Often it is assumed that if one is a successful science teacher, they may easily become a successful STL. However, given the complexity of their tasks, it is clear that teachers would benefit from additional training to become high-quality STLs. In this section, we report on the different models of STL development, describe characteristics of training programs, and note conditions that are supportive of STL development.

STL Development Models

In our review of the literature, 16 distinct STL training or PD models were presented. Of these, two programs could be characterized as homegrown (Cheung et al., 2018; Lewthwaite, 2006) in that the design of the program was crafted by schools or districts rather than an outside entity. Three models were partnerships between several schools or districts and universities, educational service agencies, and/or businesses (Eick et al., 2007; Khourey-Bowers et al., 2005; Klentschy, 2008). The remaining 11 STL development programs were designed and facilitated by university personnel. In particular, the program described in Hunzicker (2012, 2017) was a master's degree that encouraged leadership.

The duration and components of these programs were widely varied. However, each program went beyond a single workshop; a few programs lasted multiple years (e.g., Gul et al., 2019; Sinha & Hanuscin, 2017), with the vast majority of the programs lasting approximately one calendar year (typically including a "summer institute" and then other activities throughout the academic year). Within these programs, STLs took part in activities such as multi-hour PD sessions (e.g., Yow & Lotter, 2016), professional learning communities (PLCs; e.g., J. Taylor et al., 2019), receiving feedback from facilitators on their leadership activities (e.g., Sinha & Hanuscin, 2017), job-shadowing other STLs (e.g., Klentschy, 2008), serving as mentors for preservice teachers (e.g., Gul et al., 2019), and lesson study (e.g., Cheung et al., 2018). Overall, it appears that the designers of these STL development programs understood the importance of sustained contact, active learning, and collaboration over time as well as providing support in several different areas of STL responsibility.

It should be noted that two of these programs targeted science teacher leadership in addition to another content area or as part of a STEM teacher leadership umbrella. The program described by Yow and Lotter (2016) was for both mathematics and science middle school TLs, while the program described by Hunzicker (2012, 2017) was a master's degree in STEM education. In both of these programs, there were portions that were focused specifically on STLs and the particularities of science. The program described by Yow and Lotter (2016) had four main components, with one of these components being small-group content instruction. The science content groups focused on simple machines, ecology, or earth science. However, the other three components of the training (inquiry instruction, practice teaching, and reflection) did not appear to delineate between math or science teacher leadership, although one could argue that the practice teaching was necessarily content-specific. Similarly, the findings reported in Hunzicker (2012) describe the participants gaining content knowledge and content-specific research-based practices through their coursework in the master's in STEM education-based program, although this coursework is not described in depth. And, like the Yow and Lotter (2016) study, the program described by Hunzicker (2012, 2017) does not appear to delineate between the S-T-E-M content areas in terms of leadership skills and goals.

STL Development Components

As noted by Wenner and Campbell (2017), teacher leadership training typically includes components in three general categories: content, pedagogy, and leadership skills. This pattern held true for the programs reviewed here, although there were a few deviations in terms of the exclusion of one of these three components and/or inclusion of other salient components. All 16 STL training programs included some type of pedagogy or pedagogical content knowledge. For example, STLs in the program described by Eick et al. (2007) worked with science kits and discussed ways to present these kits to their colleagues in terms of instructional strategies. Five programs either did not provide that information or did not make clear from their description whether content knowledge was a part of the STL training. Four programs were content-specific and included a great deal of content knowledge instruction, such as the program described by Criswell and colleagues (Criswell et al., 2018a; Criswell et al., 2018b; Gul et al., 2019; Polizzi et al., 2019). Content knowledge was a large part of this program, as they sought to create master teacher fellows who could mentor physics and chemistry student teachers in addition to serving as a teacher leader within their schools and fields.

Twelve of the STL training programs referred to the inclusion of some type of leadership skills; however, these looked quite different across the programs. In the program described by Groothuijsen et al. (2019), leadership skills were framed in terms of coaching skills so that STLs could support others in a national reform in chemistry education. Luft et al.'s (2016) program focused on leadership skills in terms of "being a change agent" and emphasized ideas surrounding how to cultivate a shared vision and engage stakeholders in change. Other leadership skills presented in the programs reviewed here include the creation of a leadership plan (M. Taylor et al., 2019), creating a teacher leadership portfolio (Hunzicker, 2012, 2017), learning how to plan effective PD (Klentschy, 2008), and "disposition development" for leadership (Criswell et al., 2018a; Criswell et al., 2018b; Gul et al., 2019; Polizzi et al., 2019).

In addition to the three areas of training TLs typically receive, the studies reviewed here also brought forward two other areas of training to support STLs: opportunities for practice, and explicit attention to and reflection on TL definitions and/or frameworks. First, in terms of providing opportunities to practice, two programs described formalized components of their training in which STLs were able to practice a skill that would eventually be part of their responsibilities, and they received feedback on that practice. In the program described by Groothuijsen et al. (2019), STLs-in-training were given opportunities to lead regional PLCs while still receiving support on their coaching and leadership skills from the facilitators. Similarly, the program studied by Yow and Lotter (2016) provided opportunities within their summer institute for STLs to teach science and receive feedback from their school's coach during that time.

Next, explicit attention to and reflection on TL definitions and/or frameworks occurred in seven of the studies, as they asked STLs to reflect on the meaning of teacher leadership and compare their actions to those definitions, and/or to consider different frameworks for their learning and actions. One example of this comes from Cheung et al. (2018), who crafted a Science Teacher Leader Profile grounded in discussions with STLs. This profile was then used to inform the creation of PD for STLs and serve as a "common language with which to discuss and define the work of teacher leadership, as well as to identify priorities to pursue and skills to develop" (p. 43). Likewise, Sato et al. (2016) described a program in which "dimensions of a school science culture" became a framework around which STLs could have discussions and consider their future actions. Although it is difficult to compare outcomes for these different programs that contained additional training components, it appears that having time to practice as well as explicit attention to the philosophies and frameworks behind teacher leadership were useful to STLs-in-training.

Conditions Supportive of STL Development

The studies reviewed here noted that there are certainly conditions that support and facilitate STL development. Indeed, Wenner and Campbell (2017) as well as York-Barr and Duke (2004) noted that TLs must be supported not only in terms of training, but also through support from their principals, particular structures and school cultures that allow TLs to do their work, and clear expectations and recognition for meeting these expectations. The literature reviewed here is aligned with these previous reviews of teacher leadership in that STLs need supportive colleagues, administrators, and school culture in order to lead successfully.

All STL training programs reviewed here noted the importance of principal support at multiple levels, as principals can provide time and stipends as well as identify opportunities for informal and formal teacher leadership and provide recognition for this leadership (Farchi & Tubin, 2019). Three programs (Klentschy, 2008; Rhoton & McLean, 2008; Sato et al., 2016) formally included principals in their STL training programs. In the program described by Klentschy (2008), there were "awareness sessions" in which the training facilitators shared with the principals the importance of science instruction as well as how reform-oriented science instruction can support student learning in a variety of ways. The principals in the study described by Sato et al. (2016) attended the training along with teachers from their school so as to better understand and perhaps change their school's culture around science learning. Key to this principal participation, and to the calls for principal support in the other studies, is that the support is in terms of *understanding* the purposes of the training and science education more broadly, and to be partners in supporting science learning.

A second support to science teacher leadership in these training programs were the relationships formed amongst the participants and networks operated throughout the school year. Each of the STL training programs reviewed here had groups or cohorts of STLs going through the programs who continued to work together throughout the school year. Some of these interactions were formalized (such as monthly meetings in the study described by Khoury-Bowers et al., 2005), while other interactions were more on an as-needed basis when STLs required assistance from their colleagues. Additionally, STLs often pointed to the ongoing support of the training facilitators as being beneficial to their growth.

A final support for STLs that was mentioned frequently in the studies reviewed here was a school culture that supports science learning. Certainly, this may be the most important supportive aspect for *science* TLs in particular. As was noted in several elementary studies specifically, science is often pushed to the side in favor of reading and mathematics instruction. This culture of de-prioritizing science can make it difficult for an STL to gain traction with their work. Further, a school culture that does not support shared leadership or teacher leadership may stifle STLs. Both Lewthwaite (2006) and M. Taylor et al. (2019) took a more systemic view of school culture to explore its importance by making explicit the multiple components of a school culture that can impact teaching and learning.

What Are the Impacts of Science Teacher Leaders?

There is little research that effectively investigates how science teacher leadership impacts instructional practices or school change (Bintz et al., 2017; National Research Council, 2011). Many of the studies included in this review focus on developing a conceptual framework for science teacher leadership (e.g., Cheung et al., 2018; Criswell et al., 2018a; Hunzicker, 2017; Peacock, 2014) or on the evaluation of a professional learning program designed to develop STLs (e.g., Criswell et al., 2018a; Groothuijsen et al., 2019; M. Taylor et al., 2019). Within these studies, there are some impacts of STLs that can be inferred, but few impacts of STLs are explicitly stated in the included studies.

Impact on Science Teacher Leaders

The studies reviewed found a variety of evidence for how STLs themselves are impacted through their development. One overarching theme that emerged from the studies was that STL development is gradual and requires time and patience (e.g., Groothuijsen et al., 2019; Gul et al., 2019; Sinha & Hanuscin, 2017). In particular, one set of STLs suggested that 1 year of TL training was not sufficient to develop the knowledge, skills, and dispositions necessary to effect change and feel confident as an STL (Groothuijsen et al., 2019).

Confidence was identified as an outcome in the development of STLs (Sinha & Hanuscin, 2017; Yow & Lotter, 2016). As STLs develop and gain confidence in their knowledge and skills, they move from not leading, to leading, to becoming and being viewed as a leader (Sinha & Hanuscin, 2017). STLs' perceptions of themselves and their current leadership activities and abilities influence how and/or if they try to accomplish their leadership goals (Hanuscin et al., 2012; Hunzicker, 2012). Several studies found that as STLs gained confidence and self-efficacy, they also gained the content understanding, teaching practices, leadership skills, and dispositions needed to be successful STLs (e.g., Groothuijsen et al., 2019; Hunzicker, 2012; Rhoton & McLean, 2008; Yow & Lotter, 2016).

Additionally, STLs developed advocacy skills and were able to become agents of instructional change in their schools (Cheung et al., 2018) as well as in their districts and states (Howe et al., 2003). As STLs grow, they have the potential to take on roles in state organizations, present at conferences, write curriculum, and serve in government (Howe et al., 2003). Taking on these types of leadership activities can help to shape and develop an STL's professional vision and identity (Criswell et al., 2018a; Howe et al., 2003).

Impact on Peers and Colleagues

A few studies examined the impact of STLs on their peers and colleagues. In one study, site-based STLs positively influenced their peers to change their teaching practices (Klentschy, 2008). Other studies suggest that STLs provide resources to peers and advocate for them to teach science (Cheung et al., 2018; Rigano & Ritchie, 2003). However, impact was not explicitly measured. One study (Gul et al., 2019) suggested that STLs have the potential to impact student teacher practices as well, but this impact was not measured in the study. In terms of impact on peers, the articles typically discussed barriers to this. For example, Rigano and Ritchie (2003) examined the barriers one STL encountered in trying to change peers' teaching practices and found that the longer a teacher had been in the classroom, the harder it was to change their practices. In addition, the lack of school structure for STLs and collaboration opportunities for the teachers were identified as barriers that needed to be overcome to change peer practices.

Impact on Student Learning

Few studies have linked general TL learning opportunities with student learning outcomes (Jacob et al., 2015; Leithwood et al., 2004; Louis et al., 2010). Similarly, only three of the studies in the current review explicitly linked science teacher leadership to student learning and achievement. It is posited that as STLs seek to provide the best learning opportunities for their students and to impact the learning of their own students, student learning in their own classrooms is impacted first (Collinson, 2012). Rhoton and McLean (2008) found statistically significant gains in secondary student achievement on end-of-course tests following the implementation of an STL program designed to lead to systemic change in a rural district. In another study, positive significant gains in student achievement were found 6 years after the implementation of an STL professional learning (J. Taylor et al., 2019). It has been suggested that upon the completion of an STL intervention, there is an implementation dip, and that time is needed in order for the student achievement gains to be realized. This suggests that measuring student learning gains as a result of STL interventions may require longitudinal studies. Finally, Klentschy (2008) found that the use of scaffolded guided inquiry curriculum developed by STLs and implemented by teachers across a district led to significant gains in student achievement. Collectively, these results seem to indicate that the products and/or resources STLs develop may be able to impact student learning.

Impact on Educational Systems

None of the reviewed studies explicitly examined the impact of STLs on educational systems; however, some tentative impacts can be inferred from the studies. For example, STLs in one study were able to advocate for how much time was allocated to science teaching at the elementary school level (Cheung et al., 2018). In another study, STLs served as facilitators of change to solve school-based problems with a team of teachers and were able also to increase collegiality among teachers and department chair support (Khourey-Bowers et al., 2005). Another study suggested that science teacher leadership provides a career pathway for teachers that allows them to grow and build the skills they need to take on future roles within a school or district (Klentschy, 2008). The presence of a career pathway may support the retention of teachers in the field.

Discussion

The purpose of this chapter was to review the research on science teacher leadership and to provide a current overview of the field as well as implications for the future. Figure 19.2 provides a visual summary of the findings. As the findings indicated, PD and learning for STLs can be delivered by schools or districts, collaborative partnerships, or university personnel. It is characterized by sustained contact, collaboration, active learning, and coherence and is best supported by colleagues, principals, school culture, and clear expectations. In addition, PD and learning for STLs is focused on science content knowledge, pedagogical knowledge, and leadership skills and knowledge in the context of a TL framework with opportunities for practice. We posit that STLs need to develop all three types of knowledge to effectively develop as leaders as they learn to enact the social, cultural, and symbolic capital they hold. As STLs develop these knowledge and abilities, they can then impact themselves, peers and colleagues, student learning, and educational systems.

We defined an STL as: *A teacher of science, who influences others while developing their leadership identity, and who uses their social, cultural, and symbolic abilities to advocate for science and promote student learning.*

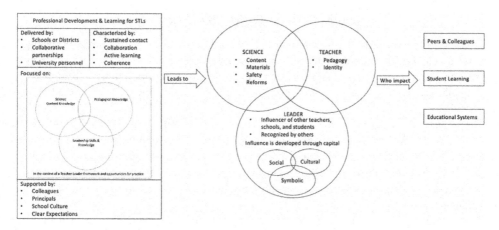

Figure 19.2 Visual summary of the findings

One may be tempted to think that this definition could apply to any subject area leadership (e.g., mathematics or history). However, we would argue that science teacher leadership differs from more generic teacher leadership in that to promote student learning effectively, STLs have an increased need to attend to materials and safety as well as to advocate for their subject area.

STLs must pay increased attention to resources, materials, and safety, unlike other subject areas. Consequently, to be a successful STL, one must: have the knowledge of the science phenomena and materials needed to support learning of that phenomena; learn how to acquire suitable materials (typically on a shoestring budget); and manage these materials, including chemicals, live and biological specimens, and various tools. Further, STLs must ensure that materials are not only stored safely but also utilized safely by teachers and students, and that the proper safety equipment and protocols are in place. These components that are required to teach science well – materials and safety – place additional responsibilities on science teachers and create the impetus for an STL who can support these pieces of science instruction.

In addition to managing materials and safety, STLs have a second, unique responsibility that other TLs may not have: advocacy for the teaching of their subject. Science is viewed as a prestigious subject in our societies; yet, in the United States, we often fail to view science as a priority for our students at the elementary level, which then has a "trickle-up" effect to students being less interested and/or less able to engage in more advanced science at the secondary and college levels. As such, STLs (particularly at the elementary level) often have to advocate simply for science to be taught. Additionally, STLs regularly advocate to secure funding, PD, and/or additional teachers for the subject, as literacy and mathematics often take center stage. We argue that the combined need for these advocacy skills as well as the management of materials and safety is unique to STLs.

Implications for Future Research

Based on our review of the literature, we propose implications and areas for future research. First, for professional learning facilitators and designers, we suggest how to develop and support strong STLs for all facets of their work. Second, for policy makers, we advocate for what might best support STLs in the field and how to incentivize, define, and acknowledge effective TLs. Third, for teachers who aspire to be STLs, we provide recommendations for a career trajectory in that direction. Finally, we provide an overview of areas of future research that are needed in science teacher leadership.

Implications for Professional Learning

Related to professional learning for STLs, it appears as though the triad of content, pedagogy, and leadership training (Wenner & Campbell, 2017) continues to be a useful framework. However, within the realm of these leadership skills, we contend that more attention must be paid to the cultural, symbolic, and social capital that support the work of STLs so they may be more effective and impactful.

Also, given the emergence of two additional components in this review – practice and attention to a TL framework – we might recommend that professional learning facilitators consider adding these into their training programs (note that this has been added into Figure 19.2 as a revision from Figure 19.1), as it may provide additional guidance, feedback, and confidence building for STLs-in-training. However, we would like to see more research in this area to confirm the value of these components.

The strong call for principal support for STLs and the successful inclusion of principals in three of the studies lead us to advocate for more principal involvement in professional learning programs. This could take the form of teacher-principal teams participating in STL programs, the inclusion of principals in particular sessions or activities, or a parallel (and perhaps less intense) program that walks principals through not only the science education topics, but also how to support STLs in their schools.

Finally, it may be important to formatively assess where STLs are in their thinking prior to designing an intervention (Hanuscin et al., 2012), as the results may indicate the need for individualized learning plans for STLs (Luft et al., 2016).

Implications for Policy

The potential for STLs to impact peers, student learning, and educational systems suggests they are critical stakeholders who should be included when an educational system is interested in effecting change. Policy makers should involve STLs as they consider changes and the adoption of new reform efforts. In addition, STLs can be important partners in the development of curriculum and working to prioritize science curriculum in schools, and even in the district. Further, policy makers must recognize the need to more equitably distribute resources across subject areas and provide more money, teaching hours, teachers, and laboratories for science teaching (Spillane et al., 2001).

Implications for Future STLs

In several of the training programs reviewed here, the facilitators encouraged STLs-in-training to consider a variety of ways as well as spaces in which they could lead. We wholeheartedly support this notion, with the reminder that science teacher leadership can look different depending on the context. As in Hanuscin et al. (2012), we might recommend that future STLs consider different dimensions of teacher leadership (e.g., Wenner & Campbell, 2017; York-Barr & Duke, 2004) as a starting point to acknowledge what one is already doing, and ways in which one might broaden their STL role.

We would also recommend that future STLs find like-minded individuals or other STLs with whom they can discuss ideas surrounding science teacher leadership. Given that having a network of teachers to work with was a strong component of the STL training programs described here, we see this as something that – in the absence of a more formal cohort or training group – could be formed by STLs themselves. STLs will inevitably run into roadblocks as they endeavor to support high-quality science for all students; having a group of like-minded individuals with whom one can share frustrations, ask questions, and craft solutions could prove invaluable.

Finally, we wish to remind future STLs that being a successful teacher does not always translate into being a successful STL. Being successful as an STL involves not only knowledge and skills, but also a disposition of caring and humility (Collinson, 2012) as well as leadership skills that must be cultivated. Therefore, we would urge future STLs to seek out training to learn the new skills, knowledge, and dispositions surrounding teacher leadership. Developing these provides a career trajectory and pathway to future roles in science education, whether as an experienced and effective STL (Howe et al., 2003) or as a pathway to becoming a district science coordinator or other potential career in science education (Luft et al., 2018; Whitworth et al., 2017).

Future Research on STLs

As evidenced from the review of the included studies in this chapter, there are several areas in which more research would be beneficial. To begin, the majority of studies were qualitative with a small sample size. In addition, many included case-study and/or self-report methodology. It may be that it is difficult to find large, representative samples to study because of the diversity of STLs and the ability of researchers to sufficiently define and identify who STLs are in different contexts. Another factor contributing to small sample sizes in research may be the issue of internal differentiation (chemistry, physics, biology, etc.) within the general category (science) at the secondary level of STLs. Being an STL implies one is *leading others*, and often, a chemistry or physics teacher may be the only teacher in that field for their school, or multiple schools. Therefore, we recommend that additional research on STLs should diversify the methodologies used to investigate STLs such that even small sample sizes can be more thoroughly investigated.

We suspect the fact that most studies in this review failed to explicitly address and/or investigate the impacts of interventions on STLs themselves, peers and colleagues, student learning, or educational systems is related to the issue of small/limited sample sizes. The issues surrounding defining an STL – particularly at the secondary level – make it difficult to explicitly link their work to impacts on teachers, students, and systems. Consequently, we would urge researchers to be thoughtful about how they could investigate STLs' impacts, perhaps thinking creatively about how to define or observe "impacts." Additionally, although it is no small task, we would encourage studies that are longitudinal and/or with larger sample sizes so that broader impacts may be investigated.

In terms of STL development, there are still many questions in need of investigation. Perhaps because so many academic researchers are affiliated with universities, the bulk of the STL development programs reviewed here were university-based rather than developed by school districts or other local entities. Given the findings related to the importance of capital, it would be important to investigate how homegrown STL development programs leverage local relationships and capital to support STLs, in addition to describing the differences between homegrown and university-based STL development programs. Further, the programs reviewed here were reported to be for *science* TLs, but much is still to be learned about the ways in which these leadership programs meet the unique needs of science educators and the field of science education, aside from science pedagogical content knowledge and content knowledge. Studies such as Luft et al. (2016) and Cheung et al. (2018) supported STLs in becoming advocates for science education, which speaks to teaching science-specific leadership skills. But there remains a need for research on the nuances of preparing one to lead within science education specifically.

There were few studies that examined science teacher leadership outside of the United States. The increased emphasis on science teacher leadership in the United States as compared to other countries might reflect cultural differences. As found by a study conducted by Hofstede et al. (2005), the United States is a society in which people on average hold the most individualistic values, when compared to 76 other counties and regions. As a leader is a combination of an individual seeking a power position and the recognition of others, it might be that Americans, relatively independent from group pressure, feel entitled to claim their leadership and easily become leaders. They can step into leading positions and lead projects, missions, or people, and claim their leadership recognition, without a group formally "crowning" them as a leader. Most other societies hold more collectivistic values and accordingly see "leaders" as holding a more formal and powerful position, which rarely fits the amorphic, changeable, and limited position of STLs. As such, more work may be needed to investigate how different countries conceptualize and define the role of STLs and/or how impacts of STLs compare in different cultures and countries.

Conclusion

In summary, science teacher leadership is a growing field, and initial evidence discussed here suggests STLs do, in fact, differ from other types of TLs. In general, this area is ripe for research, and there is much work yet to be done. Paths forward include examining the delivery, characteristics, focus, and supports embedded in STL PD that result in impact on STLs themselves, colleagues and peers, student learning, and school systems. This may require larger-scale or larger sample-size studies. In addition, a deeper understanding of the knowledge and skills of teacher leadership and how those play into the effectiveness of STLs is needed for the field. Finally, an examination of how STLs are conceptualized and differ outside of the United States would be an important addition to the field. As the field continues to explore science teacher leadership, there are many paths forward for future research that can build on and expand the current landscape of STL research.

References

Bintz, J., Mohan, L., Miller, B., Mohan, A., Galosy, J., & Stuhlastz, M. (2017). *Developing math/science teacher leadership: Symposium proceedings (Research Report No. 2017-04)*. Colorado Springs, CO: BSCS.

Bourdieu, P. (1990). *The logic of practice*. Stanford, CA: Stanford University Press.

Burt, R. S. (2004). Structural holes and good ideas. *American Journal of Sociology, 110*(2), 349–399.

Cheung, R., Reinhardt, T., Stone, E., & Little, J. W. (2018). Defining teacher leadership: A framework. *Phi Delta Kappan, 100*(3), 38–44. https://doi.org/10.1177/0031721718808263

Collinson, V. (2012). Leading by learning, learning by leading. *Professional Development in Education, 38*, 247–266. https://doi.org/10.1080/19415257.2012.657866

Criswell, B. A., Rushton, G. T., McDonald, S. P., & Gul, T. (2018a). A clearer vision: Creating and evolving a model to support the development of science teacher leaders. *Research in Science Education, 48*, 811–837. https://doi.org/10.1007/s11165-016-9588-9

Criswell, B. A., Rushton, G. T., Nachtigall, D., Staggs, S., Alemdar, M., Cappelli, C. J. (2018b). Strengthening the vision: Examining the understanding of a framework for teacher leadership development by experienced science teachers. *Science Education, 102*, 1265–1287. https://doi.org/10.1002/sce.21472

Eick, C. J., Ewald, M. L., Richardson, V. B., & Anderson, K. (2007). Building a leadership network supporting science education reform in rural east Alabama. *Science Educator, 16*(1), 8–12.

Farchi, T., & Tubin, D. (2019). Middle leaders in successful and less successful schools. *School Leadership & Management, 39*, 372–390

Groothuijsen, S. E. A., Prins, G. T., & Bulte, A. M. W. (2019). Towards an empirically substantiated professional development programme to train lead teachers to support curriculum innovation. *Professional Development in Education, 45*, 739–761. https://doi.org/10.1080/19415257.2018.1510427

Gul, T., Demir, K., & Criswell, B. (2019). Constructing teacher leadership through mentoring: Functionality of mentoring practices in evolving teacher leadership. *Journal of Science Teacher Education, 30*, 209–228. https://doi.org/10.1080/1046560x.2018.1558655

Hanuscin, D. L., Rebello, C. M., & Sinha, S. (2012). Supporting the development of science teacher leaders-Where do we begin? *Science Educator, 21*(1), 12–18.

Hanuscin, D. L., Sinha, S., & Hall, M. (2016). Supporting teachers in (re)constructing identities as leaders: The role of professional development. In *Studying science teacher identity* (pp. 197–218). Boston, MA: Brill Sense.

Hofstede, G. H., Hofstede, G. J., & Minkov, M. (2005). *Cultures and organizations: Software of the mind*. New York: McGraw-Hill.

Howe, A. C., & Stubbs, H. S. (2003). From science teacher to teacher leader: Leadership development as meaning making in a community of practice. *Science Education, 87,* 281–297. https://doi.org/10.1002/sce.10022

Hunzicker, J. (2012). Professional development and job-embedded collaboration: How teachers learn to exercise leadership. *Professional Development in Education, 38,* 267–289. https://doi.org/10.1080/19415257.2012.657870

Hunzicker, J. (2017). From teacher to teacher leader: A conceptual model. *International Journal of Teacher Leadership, 8*(2), 1–27.

Jacob, R., Goddard, R., Kim, M., Miller, R., & Goddard, Y. (2015). Exploring the causal impact of the McREL Balanced Leadership Program on leadership, principal efficacy, instructional climate, educator turnover, and student achievement. *Educational Evaluation and Policy Analysis.* https://doi.org/0162373714549620.

Jacobs, J., Beck, B., & Crowell, L. (2014). Teacher leaders as equity-centered change agents: Exploring the conditions that influence navigating change to promote educational equity. *Professional Development in Education, 40,* 576–596. https://doi.org/10.1080/19415257.2014.896272

Khourey-Bowers, C., Dinko, R. L., & Hart, R. G. (2005). Influence of a shared leadership model in creating a school culture of inquiry and collegiality. *Journal of Research in Science Teaching, 42,* 3–24. https://doi.org/10.1002/tea.20038

Klentschy, M. (2008). Developing teacher leaders in science: Attaining and sustaining science reform. *Science Educator, 17*(2), 57–64.

Leithwood, K., Louis, K. S., Anderson, S., & Wahlstrom, K. (2004). *Review of research: How leadership influences student learning.* Minneapolis, MN: University of Minnesota.

Lewthwaite, B. (2006). Constraints and contributors to becoming a science teacher-leader. *Science Education, 90,* 331–347. https://doi.org/10.1002/sce.20093

Louis, K. S., Leithwood, K., Wahlstrom, K. L., & Anderson, S. E. (2010). *Investigating the links to improved student learning: Final report of research findings.* Minneapolis, MN: University of Minnesota.

Luft, J. A., Dubois, S. L., Kaufmann, J., & Plank, L. (2016). Science teacher leadership: Learning from a three-year leadership program. *Science Educator, 25*(1), 1–9.

Luft, J. A., Whitworth, B. A., Berry, A., Kind, V., & Navy, S. L. (2018). Science education trajectories: Charting the course for teachers, educators, researchers, and policy makers. *Journal of Science Teacher Education, 30,* 63–79. https://doi.org/10.1080/1046560X.2018.1535226

Lumpkin, A., Claxton, H., & Wilson, A. (2016). Key characteristics of teacher leaders in schools. *Administrative Issues Journal, 4,* 59–67.

National Research Council. (2011). *Successful K-12 STEM education: Identifying effective approaches in science, technology, engineering, and mathematics.* Washington, DC: National Academies Press.

Peacock, J. (2014). Science instructional leadership: The role of the department chair. *Science Educator, 23*(1), 36–48.

Polizzi, S. J.; Ofem, B.; Coyle, W.; Lundquist, K.; Rushton, G. T. (2019). The use of visual network scales in teacher leader development. *Teaching and Teacher Education, 83,* 42–53. https://doi.org/10.1016/j.tate.2019.03.018

Printy, S. M., & Marks, H. M. (2006). Shared leadership for teacher and student learning. *Theory into Practice, 45,* 125–132.

Rhoton, J., & McLean, J. E. (2008). Developing teacher leaders in science: Catalysts for improved science teaching and student learning. *Science Educator, 17*(2), 45–56.

Rigano, D. L., & Ritchie, S. M. (2003). Implementing change within a school science department: Progressive and dissonant voices. *Research in Science Education, 33,* 299–317. https://doi.org/10.1023/a:1025483130881

Ritchie, S. M., Mackay, G., & Rigano, D. L. (2006). Individual and collective leadership in school science departments. *Research in Science Education, 36,* 141–161. https://doi.org/10.1007/s11165-005-9001-6

Sato, M., Bartiromo, M., & Elko, S. (2016). Investigating your school's science teaching and learning culture. *Phi Delta Kappan, 97*(6), 42–47. https://doi.org/10.1177/0031721716636872

Sinha, S., & Hanuscin, D. L. (2017). Development of teacher leadership identity: A multiple case study. *Teaching and Teacher Education, 63,* 356–371. https://doi.org/10.1016/j.tate.2017.01.004

Spillane, J. P., Diamond, J. B., Walker, L. J., Halverson, R., & Jita, L. (2001). Urban school leadership for elementary science instruction: Identifying and activating resources in an undervalued school subject. *Journal of Research in Science Teaching, 37,* 918–940.

Taylor, J. A., Stuhlsatz, M. A. M., & Bintz, J. (2019). The effect of a leadership development program for high school science reform on student achievement in science: A retrospective quasi-experiment. *Science Educator, 27*(1), 1–14.

Taylor, M., Klein, E. J., Munakata, M., Trabona, K., Rahman, Z., & Mcmanus, J. (2019). Professional development for teacher leaders: Using activity theory to understand the complexities of sustainable change.

International Journal of Leadership in Education, 22, 685–705. https://doi.org/10.1080/13603124.2018.1492023

Swartz, D. (2012). *Culture and power: The sociology of Pierre Bourdieu.* Chicago, IL: University of Chicago Press.

Tubin, D. (2017). Leadership identity construction practices: The case of successful Israeli school principals. *Educational Management, Administration and Leadership, 45,* 790–805.

Wenner, J. A. (2017). Urban Elementary science teacher leaders: Responsibilities, supports, and needs. *Science Educator, 25,* 117–125.

Wenner, J. A., & Campbell, T. (2017). The theoretical and empirical basis of teacher leadership: A review of the literature. *Review of Educational Research, 87,* 134–171.

Whitworth, B. A., Maeng, J. L., Wheeler, L. B., & Chiu, J. L. (2017). Investigating the role of a district science coordinator. *Journal of Research in Science Teaching, 54,* 914–936. https://doi.org/10.1002/tea.21391

York-Barr, J., & Duke, K. (2004). What do we know about teacher leadership? Findings from two decades of scholarship. *Review of Educational Research, 74,* 255–316.

Yow, J. A., & Lotter, C. (2016). Teacher learning in a mathematics and science inquiry professional development program: First steps in emergent teacher leadership. *Professional Development in Education, 42,* 325–351. https://doi.org/10.1080/19415257.2014.960593

20

PROFESSIONAL DEVELOPMENT OF SCIENCE TEACHERS FOR INQUIRY INSTRUCTION

Umesh Ramnarain, Daniel Capps, and Ying-Shao Hsu

Introduction

For nearly three decades, a cornerstone of science curriculum reform worldwide has been an emphasis on investigative approaches to science teaching wherein learners pursue evidence-based answers to scientific questions (Australian Curriculum Assessment and Reporting Authority [ACARA], 2012; Department for Education and Skills/Qualification and Curriculum Authority (2004); Israeli Ministry of Education, 2011; Ministry of Education of Singapore, 2007; NRC, 1996, 2012). Multiple terms have been used to describe such approaches to teaching science, including practical work (Abrahams & Millar, 2008; Dillon, 2008), scientific practice (NRC, 2012), project-based science (Blumenfeld & Krajcik, 2006; Marx et al., 1997), and even learning through investigating (Moeed, 2013; Reiser, 2004). However, perhaps the most durable term has been inquiry-based instruction (Dewey, 1910; NRC, 1996, 2012; Schwab & Brandwein, 1962). At the most general level, scientific inquiry refers to the "diverse ways in which scientists study the natural world and propose explanations based on the evidence derived from their work" (NRC, 1996, p. 23). Therefore, inquiry-based instruction should engage students in science learning in a way that reflects how practicing scientists learn (Crawford, 2014).

In spite of its long tenure, inquiry-based science teaching has remained an elusive ideal in many classrooms across the globe, as it is a sophisticated mode of instruction that demands much in the way of time and expertise to effectively enact (Crawford, 2000, 2007). Professional development (PD) is a well-recognized way of supporting teachers in both learning about and through inquiry (Loucks-Horsley et al., 2009). Over the last several decades, a host of inquiry PD initiatives have been designed to support practicing teachers in learning about inquiry and in enacting inquiry-based instruction in their classrooms. There are also many peer-reviewed journal articles on this topic. However, our knowledge of how to effectively support teachers in enacting inquiry is still a work in progress. A review of the literature on inquiry PD by Capps et al. (2012) investigated the degree to which accounts of inquiry-based science PD programs in published journal articles between 2000 and 2009 aligned themselves with characteristics of effective PD described in the literature (i.e., Darling-Hammond & McLaughlin, 1995; Garet et al., 2001; Loucks-Horsley et al., 2009; Penuel et al., 2007). Many of these characteristics are thought to be supportive in enhancing teacher understanding and practice of inquiry. The review found that although most PD programs did align with characteristics of effective PD – namely, total time, extended support, coherency with standards, modeling inquiry, reflection, and transference – there were a few notable exceptions: (1)

DOI: 10.4324/9781003098478-24

focusing on science content for teachers, (2) providing authentic inquiry experiences, and (3) supporting teachers in developing inquiry-based lesson plans. As the review is nearly a decade old, we were curious whether more recent research on inquiry PD has begun to address these deficiencies and how they have done this. Furthermore, we were interested in establishing whether there were any shifts in the extent to which the features of effective PD were reflected in inquiry PD programs from 2010 onwards.

In addition, due to recent literature and other developments in PD, we included two new features in our review. The first addition relates to the concept of transfer. In a review chapter on STEM PD, Luft et al. (2020) discussed how "working in communities is essential to promoting transfer" (p. 369). Collaborative work has been flagged as a key feature in other PD programs in impacting on student outcomes. In a detailed analysis of 25 programs, Blank et al. (2008) found that among programs that demonstrated positive impacts on student outcomes, ongoing teacher collaboration was featured. As collaboration was not explicitly included in Capps and colleagues' initial review, we included it here, referring to it as "collaborative community." The second new feature was blended learning. The most cited article on blended learning, by Garrison and Kanuka (2004), states that "blended learning is the thoughtful integration of classroom face-to-face learning experiences with online learning experiences" (p. 96). We adopted this definition in our analysis of PD programs. There is a strong rationale for blending face-to-face and online instruction. This is informed by a body of research about the design of effective teacher PD programs. Blended learning lends itself well to incorporating characteristics such as adequate time, collective participation, continuous support, and sustainability (Darling-Hammond & McLaughlin, 1995; Garet et al., 2001; Penuel et al., 2007). Blended learning also allows for the possibility of PD programs to be based in schools and to be facilitated by school-based PD teams (Owston et al., 2008). For example, teachers within the same school can collaborate in face-to-face sessions to develop hands-on activities, enact in the classroom, share their experiences online, and gain feedback from other school teachers and teacher educators. Through several design-enact-redesign cycles, new teachers learn from experienced teachers and teacher educators in the community. Such teacher-blended learning appears to promote teachers' understanding of, to change their beliefs about, and to develop their pedagogical content knowledge of inquiry teaching.

Review Methods

We reviewed articles in four major science education journals (*Journal of Research in Science Teaching, Science Education, International Journal of Science Education,* and *Journal of Science Teacher Education*) published between 2009 and 2020. We selected these journals because of their focus on science teacher education and their international prominence; thus, they would provide a fairly comprehensive picture of the current state of affairs for inquiry-based science PD internationally. Our selection criterion was that the article had to pertain to supporting teachers in learning about and/or enacting inquiry science teaching through a professional development intervention. Our inclusion criterion was broad in terms of what we considered PD and narrow in terms of inquiry. For PD, we included any study meant to support practicing science teachers in learning about inquiry through some type of professional learning opportunity. Thus, small-scale interventions with one or two teachers learning about inquiry during the school year were included in the review, but so were larger interventions, where many teachers learned about inquiry while engaging in scientific research over a summer research experience. For inquiry, we included only studies that purported to focus on teachers learning through scientific investigation; thus, we did not include PD interventions that focused on a single scientific practice (e.g., supporting teachers in learning about argumentation), if the practice was not situated in the broader context of an investigation. The selection process involved a manual search of all of the articles published in the four journals during the specified time period.

To accomplish this, we went to each journal's website and read the title and abstract of every article published between 2009 and 2020 to judge whether or not it met our inclusion criteria. A total of 32 articles fit our criteria (see Table 20.1 for a list of the studies).

Analyses of Studies

To begin the analysis process, we drew on procedures developed by Capps and colleagues (2012). Briefly, we developed a table to collect information on the following features: total time, extended support, and providing teachers with authentic experiences; as well as the core features of effective PD, including coherency with standards, development of lessons, modeling inquiry, reflection, transference, and content knowledge. In addition, we added the following features described in the introduction that were not included in the 2012 review: collaborative community and blended learning. Briefly, *total time* refers to the amount of time allotted for the PD. *Extended support* refers to programs that persisted over an extended period of time, which contrasts with a one-shot workshop. *Authentic experience* refers to PD programs where teachers conducted an inquiry study that was not predefined and was novel to the teacher. *Coherency* refers to PD programs that are aligned with local, state, or national standards. *Developed lessons* refers to programs where teachers learned about inquiry as a teaching strategy by designing inquiry lessons. *Modeled inquiry* refers to programs that modeled inquiry instruction for teachers during the PD. *Reflection* refers to programs where teachers were given the explicit opportunity to reflect on their experiences with inquiry. *Transference* refers to programs where there was explicit discussion about enacting inquiry in the classroom. *Content knowledge* indicates the PD program focused on science subject matter and content learning for teachers. *Collaborative community* refers to a community of practice in which teachers support each other in the PD program. *Blended learning* is blending face-to-face and online instruction. To determine alignment with the critical features of effective PD, the author team carefully read each article looking for evidence that the PD supported teachers with each of the targeted features identified in the literature. Programs were judged on the presence, absence, or quantity of each feature. We then looked for any evidence of longitudinal shifts in the representations of these features between the articles in the 2012 review and the more recent articles. As there were no major quantitative shifts, we conducted a qualitative comparison between how the features manifested in the 2012 review and in the current review. A final piece of the analysis was to identify features that complement each other in supporting the achievement of learning outcomes.

Results

Alignment With Previously Underrepresented Features

In general, the programs appear to draw on many features of effective PD defined in the literature (see Table 20.1). However, a focus on content knowledge, authentic inquiry experience, and developing inquiry lessons were still underrepresented compared to the other features. Clearly, science content knowledge is key to a teacher's ability to engage students in inquiry. This fact was underscored in a recent study by Diamond and colleagues (2014), which included a treatment group that participated in teacher workshops and a control group that did not. The researchers found that teacher content knowledge, and not the intervention, was the main driver of inquiry-based practice and student achievement. Thus, if teachers lack necessary knowledge of the discipline, it will be challenging for them to engage their students in inquiry, as it is hard to teach what one does not know. To enact inquiry, teachers will need to have deep subject matter knowledge for sure, but they will also need to know about the nature of science and the nature of inquiry. Supporting teachers in enhancing their subject matter knowledge and views on nature of science were featured in 24 of

Table 20.1 Inquiry professional development studies

Study	Goal	Level	Total Time	Extended Support	Coherence	Developed Lessons	Modeled Inquiry	Authentic Exp.	Reflect	Transfer	Content Know.	Collab. Comm.	Blended Learning
1) Oliveira (2010b) JRST	TK, Tpr	E	2 weeks+	y	y	n	y	n	y	y	n	y	n
2) Gerard et al. (2010) JRST	Tpr(~) SK	M	3 weeks	y	y	n	y	n	y	y	y	y	n
3) Fogleman et al. (2011) JRST	Tpr (~) SK	M	1 week+	y	y	n	y	n	y	y	n	y	n
4) Diamond et al. (2014)	TK, Tpr, SK	E	1 week	y	y	n	y	n	n	y	y	n	n
5) Seraphin et al. (2017) JRST	SK	E-HS	87 hours	y	y	n	y	n	y	y	y	y	y
6) Mupira & Ramnarain (2018) JRST	S goal orient	HS	~6 weeks	y	y	y	n	n	n	n	n	n	n
7) Granger et al. (2019) JRST	TK, TB, Tpr, SK	E	4.5 days	y	y	n	y	n	y	n	y	y	n
8) Yang et al. (2020) JRST	TK, Tpr, SK	E-HS	4 weeks +	y	y	n	y	y	y	n	y	y	n
9) Kanter et al. (2010) SE	TK, Sgoals	E-HS	3 weeks	n	y	n	y	n	y	n	y	n	n
10) Enderle et al. (2014) SE	TB, Tpr	E-HS	6 weeks	n	y	n/y	y	y/n	y	n	y	y	n
11) van der Valk & de Jong (2009) IJSE	Tpr	HS	50 hours	y	y	y	n	n	y	n	n	y	n
12) Santau et al. (2010) IJSE	TK, Tpr	E	7–10 days	y	y	n	y	n	n	n	y	n	n
13) Brand & Moore (2011) IJSE	Tpr, TB	E	two weeks+	y	y	y	y	n	y	y	y	y	n
14) Lewis et al. (2011) IJSE	TK	E	96 hours	y	y	n	y	n	n	n	y	y	n
15) Lumpe et al., 2012) IJSE	TB	E	80 hours+	y	y	n	y	n	y	n	y	y	n

Study	Focus	Level	Duration										
16) Lin et al. (2013) IJSE	TP	E	40 hours+	y	y	y	n	y	n	y	n	y	n
17) Capps et al. (2013) IJSE	TK	E-H	40+	y	y	n	y	y	y	y	y	y	y
18) Odegard et al. (2014) IJSE	TP	E	unclear	n	y	n	n	y	y	n	y	y	n
19) Lotter et al. (2016) IJSE	TP, TB	M	70 hours	y	y	n	n	y	y	y	y	y	n
20) Isik–Ercan (2020) IJSE	TP	E	unclear	y	y	y	n	n	y	y	y	y	n
21) Akerson et al. (2009) JSTE	TK	E	2 weeks	y	y	y	n	y	y	y	y	n	n
22) Oliveira (2010a) JSTE	TP	E	105 hours	y	y	n	n	y	n	n	y	y	n
23) Ebert et al. (2010) JSTE	TK (conceptual change)	S	Summ+ school year PD	y	y	n	n	y	y	y	y	y	n
24) Rushton et al. (2011) JSTE	TB, TP	HS	2 weeks	n	y	y	n	y	y	y	y	y	n
25) Singer et al. (2011) JSTE	TP	MS	3 weeks	y	y	n	n	y	y	n	y	y	n
26) Lotter et al. (2013) JSTE	TB, TP	HS	2 weeks	y	y	n	n	y	n	y	y	y	n
27) Haug (2014) JSTE	TP	E	monthly/year	n	y	n	n	y	y	n	y	y	n
28) Marshall et al. (2014) JSTE	SK	MS	2 weeks (multi-year)	y	y	y	n	y	n	y	y	y	n
29) Peters–Burton et al. (2015) JSTE	TB, TK	Secondary	1 week +	y	y	y	n	y	y	y	y	n	n
30) Cian et al. (2018) JSTE	TP, SK	Secondary	2 weeks+	y	y	y	n	y	n	n	y	n	n
31) Lederman et al. (2019) JSTE	TK, TP, SK	E-HS	10 days +	y	y	y	y	y	n	n	y	y	n
32) Lotter et al. (2020) JSTE	TK, TB, TP	M-HS	115 hours	y	y	y	n	y	n	n	y	n	n

Notes: Shows alignment with the critical features of professional development and the reported findings of each of the studies reviewed.
TB = Teacher Beliefs, Tpr = Teacher Practice, SA = Student Attitude, Tprep = Teacher Preparation, TK = Teacher Knowledge, Tat = Teacher Attitude, SK = Student Knowledge, E = Elementary, M = Middle, S = Secondary, Y = feature covered, N = feature not covered.

the studies we reviewed (Akerson et al., 2009; Capps et al., 2013; Diamond et al., 2014; Ebert et al., 2010; Enderle et al., 2014; Haug, 2014; Isik-Ercan et al., 2020; Kanter et al., 2010; Granger et al., 2019; Lederman & Lederman, 2019; Lewis et al., 2011; Lotter et al., 2013; Lotter et al., 2016; Lotter et al., 2020; Lumpe et al., 2012; Marshall et al., 2014; Odegaard et al., 2014; Oliveira, 2010a; Peters-Burton et al., 2015; Rushton et al., 2011; Santau et al., 2010; Seraphin et al., 2017; Singer et al., 2011; Yang et al., 2020). However, much less common was support in learning about the nature of inquiry, which was featured in only two of the studies (Akerson et al., 2009; Lederman & Lederman, 2019). Lederman, Abd-El-Khalick, and colleagues have long advocated for explicit and reflective instruction related to the nature of science (Akerson et al., 2000; Bell et al., 1998; Khishfe & Abd-El-Khalick, 2002), and more recently for the nature of inquiry (Lederman et al., 2014). We similarly maintain that a lack of understanding about inquiry would undoubtedly get in the way of effective inquiry teaching. Yet, given the limited scope of research in this area, there is a clear need for others to join the effort, as varied points of view would help shed light on the role PD can play in supporting teachers in developing more robust understandings about the nature of scientific inquiry and how this might impact their practice.

Another characteristic of effective PD that remains rare are authentic inquiry experiences for teachers. Only four studies reported providing teachers with opportunities to engage in inquiry that goes beyond the curriculum they are to enact with their students (Capps et al., 2013; Enderle et al., 2014; Lederman et al., 2019; Yang et al., 2020). One of the more typical forms of authentic inquiry experience is what is referred to as the research experience for teachers (RETs), where teachers are given the opportunity to join a scientist's lab for a period of time, often over a school break, to participate in the lab's research (e.g., Yang et al., 2020; Lederman et al., 2019; Enderle et al., 2014). Although teachers seldomly define their own research projects in these RETs, they do work at the elbows of a knowledgeable mentor, gaining important inquiry experience as a member of a research team. Such experiences are valuable to teachers, as few have had the opportunity to engage in authentic inquiry. On the other hand, RETs are costly, in terms of time, money, and human resources. Smaller-scale versions of RETs that focus on experiences that are authentic to the teacher have the potential to be more impactful in terms of supporting teachers' developing the understandings they need to enact inquiry in their classrooms (e.g., Capps & Crawford, 2013; see Blanchard et al., 2009). In these experiences, teachers engage in inquiry that may not be authentic to science per se but are authentic to them as learners. The experiences can provide many of the same features as a long-term lab or field-based experience in an expert's laboratory, but they put the teacher in the driver's seat.

In addition, and maybe more critically, such experiences can be tailored to the needs of the teacher, as they are not tied to external pressures, like a principal investigator's research program, or a graduate student's dissertation. This was supported in a recent study by Enderle and colleagues (2014) that compared a standard RET program to an alternative RET that focused on the proximal needs of teachers, namely providing them with inquiry experiences that were relevant to them as learners, and helping them translate these experiences into the classroom. Such programs can be designed to focus on issues that stand in the way of teachers engaging their students in inquiry. For example, some aspects of inquiry practice are less understood by teachers than others, and thus are more challenging to enact (Bismack et al., 2014; Capps et al., 2016). Recognizing this as an issue, one program supported teachers in developing the capacity to transform data within inquiry through intensive practice, as the researchers realized that few of the teachers had adequate knowledge in this area (Peters-Burton et al., 2015). Another program zeroed in on three challenging practices: argumentation, modeling, and questioning; and it provided teachers with instruction where they could practice these inquiry skills and then reflect on the instructional processes necessary to enact them (Lotter et al., 2016).

Providing teachers with opportunities to develop inquiry lessons is also underrepresented. Only 13 of the studies reported providing such opportunities for teachers (Akerson et al., 2009; Brand &

Moore, 2011; Cian et al., 2018; Enderle et al., 2014; Isik-Ercan, 2020; Lederman et al., 2019; Lin et al., 2013; Lotter et al., 2016; Lotter et al., 2020; Marshall et al., 2014; Mupira & Ramnarain, 2018; Peters-Burton et al., 2015; Rushton et al., 2011). Instead, most provided teachers with lessons designed by experts. Looking across the studies that did provide opportunities to develop lessons, we saw two general approaches. Most prominently, teachers were provided with an inquiry experience and then asked to use the experience as a model to develop a new lesson or unit (e.g., Akerson et al., 2009; Brand & Moore, 2011). Two studies used more of an apprenticeship model, having teachers work with experts to co-develop and co-teach an inquiry unit (Cian et al., 2018; Isik-Ercan, 2020). Common across both kinds of experiences were opportunities for peer and expert critique and personal reflection, particularly after the lesson was taught.

Alignment With Additional Features of Collaborative Community and Blended Learning

As aforementioned, due to recent literature and other developments in PD, we saw the need to include collaborative community and blended learning as additional features in the analysis.

Collaborative Community

Twenty-three of the 32 articles reviewed described programs where teachers worked in a collaborative community (see Table 20.1). These communities appeared to exist in two ways. In one way, during the PD, teachers were engaged in collaborative activities that gave rise to such communities. The communities created a space for teachers to share in their knowledge and experiences when participating in activities. These would, for example, entail sharing their ideas on teaching a unit through lesson planning (e.g., Lewis et al., 2011) or by making presentations to their peers, and then getting feedback (e.g., Akerson et al., 2009). Another function of these communities was for teachers to critically reflect upon their practices, such as in Oliveira (2010a) where elementary teachers watched and critiqued video recordings of their inquiry-based teaching practices in a discourse analysis for linguistic forms. While in some programs collaboration happened implicitly, in other programs, such as the Investigating and Questioning Our World Through Science and Technology (IQWST) approach to professional development (Fogleman et al., 2011), collaboration was more explicit in that "At the heart of these experiences are opportunities for discussion between teachers enacting the units" (p. 154).

In another way, some of these communities continued to exist after the PD, and they comprised of teachers at the same school or from neighboring schools collaborating with each other (e.g., Brand & Moore, 2011; Gerard et al., 2010; Yang et al., 2020). It was also evident that such communities play an important role in facilitating the transfer from PD to classroom practice. This was evident in Brand & Moore (2011), where the program based on a constructivist sociocultural model of PD supported teachers in examining their teaching practices in learner-centered collaborative group settings that encouraged them to critically analyze their instructional practices and to reconstruct their practices. Such communities also ensure that professional development is sustained over time, and this is regarded as important for the effectiveness of the program (e.g., Brand & Moore, 2011; Capps et al., 2013; Oliveira, 2010b).

Blended Learning

Although it is standard practice in PD to form active learning communities within schools either before or in between workshop experiences (Lin et al., 2013; Lumpe et al., 2012; Peters-Burton et al., 2015; van der Valk & de Jong, 2009; Yang et al., 2020), and to provide ongoing in-person PD

(Cian et al., 2018; Diamond et al., 2014; Fogleman et al., 2011; Granger et al., 2019; Haug, 2014; Lederman et al., 2019; Lotter et al., 2013; Lotter et al., 2016; Lotter et al., 2020; Marshall et al., 2014), only two of the 32 programs mentioned blending remote learning (e.g., using online technologies) with in-person learning to maintain connection with participants (Seraphin et al., 2017; Shea et al., 2016). Seraphin et al. (2017) guided teachers to understand and implement the "Teaching Science Inquiry" (TSI) model in the classroom for effective PD in inquiry teaching within a school year in an effective PD program. They applied blended learning to demonstrate how the PD programs influence students' inquiry learning experiences and interactions with teacher characteristics. The PD program provided face-to-face workshops, classroom implementation, a synchronous online follow-up, and an asynchronous online learning community built into a web-based platform. This effective PD program blended face-to-face and online communication to authentically demonstrate science knowledge, to explicitly model the TSI pedagogy, and to provide opportunities for implementation and reflection on inquiry teaching. Shea et al. (2016) also used online tools to promote learning but were less forehanded about the nature of their blending, only mentioning the use of "online interactions." We suspect that this is likely true of other PD programs, but they simply did not emphasize this feature in their publications.

Complementary Features That Impact on Learning Outcomes

A failure to connect a feature directly to teacher learning outcomes suggests that these features may capture surface characteristics and not the mechanisms that account for teacher learning (Scher and O'Reilly, 2009). It may be more useful to consider how features complement each other rather than studying the impact of individual features on learning outcomes. For example, in all programs reviewed, time is regarded as a significant feature for effective PD. The studies reviewed show that time for the programs varied quite drastically, and so it is difficult to define an optimal time for PD. Time appears to achieve its effectiveness for PD only if it is considered in tandem with other features. For example, in Lewis et al. (2011), the 96 hours of PD is a structural feature that resulted in effective PD when enabling other features evident in the program, such as explicit modeling, participation in inquiry-based science activities, and self-regulated learning reflection. Time is also a complementary feature with collaborative learning. This is evident in Lotter et al. (2020), where teachers were afforded the time for collaborative planning in order to create problem-based learning unit plans for specific content foci (e.g., cell biology, genetics, or anatomy); and in Lumpe et al. (2012), where peer coaching in the classroom as a form of collaborative learning was facilitated due to adequate time being provided.

Another pair of complementary features that is evident is reflection and collaborative community. In 23 of the programs reviewed, these two features existed in tandem (e.g., Gerard et al., 2010; Granger et al., 2019; Seraphin et al., 2017; van der Valk & de Jong, 2009) The aim of reflection in teacher education is to help teachers think critically about their own teaching in order to enhance their practice (Carter & Anders, 1996). The value of reflection for changing teacher beliefs of inquiry instruction during PD in instruction was evident in Rushton et al. (2011), which concluded that "The practice teaching and reflection on this teaching used during the PD seemed to play a critical role in changing teachers' beliefs about the effectiveness and feasibility of inquiry instruction" (p. 41). The relationship between reflection and collaborative community took place in two ways. First, the collaborative community created a forum for teachers to share their reflections. For example, in Lederman et al. (2019), the teachers were given a classroom reflection assignment each month. A classroom reflection protocol required them to describe and evaluate one of their lessons aimed at teaching the nature of scientific knowledge (NOSK) and/or scientific inquiry (SI), and then to share these reflections at meetings when the collaborative community convened. The relationship between collaborative community and reflection was also manifested in the manner in which teacher reflection was prompted by other members of a community. Such reflection often happened during whole-group discussions (e.g., Ebert et al., 2010; Enderle et al., 2014; Lin et al., 2013; Rushton et al., 2011). The interaction between these two features may in fact give rise to an amalgam feature of collaborative reflection, as described by Lin et al. (2013) in their study on the investigation of collaborative reflection on teachers' PD on inquiry-based science teaching. It is therefore apparent that participation in a collaborative community is a key stimulus to teachers' critical reflection of their teaching practices.

A Critique of Findings – Challenges for Science Teacher PD in Inquiry Teaching

The selected articles appear to draw on many features of effective PD programs. However, there were still underrepresented features and challenges for science teacher PD when enacting inquiry teaching in the classroom. It emerged that the previously underrepresented features of content knowledge, authentic inquiry experience, and developing inquiry lessons are still rare compared to the other features. The additional feature of blended learning was underrepresented in the review.

Engaging in Research Experience (Actual Inquiry) Is Still Rare

Given the rarity of research experiences for teachers in the literature, there is a clear need to: (1) build opportunities for teachers to have such experiences, (2) generate knowledge about how to best support them in learning from these experiences, and (3) generate knowledge about how to translate these experiences into their classrooms. Looking at the literature that does exist, we see some clear advantages of providing teachers with opportunities that are authentic to them rather than emphasizing cutting-edge research experiences in scientists' labs. The former can be more easily tailored to what the teachers need and are more scalable than the latter, and could thus impact many more teachers. Considering the support that teachers will likely need to learn from such experiences, it would seem crucial to identify the key inquiry skills that teachers tend to struggle with in their instructional practice (e.g., data reduction, engaging in argumentation, etc.). After identifying these skills, PD providers should develop opportunities where teachers could practice them. Through these experiences, there would be opportunities for researchers to investigate the kinds of support teachers will need to further develop these skills. Lastly, in considering how to translate such experiences into their teaching, we again surmise that in most instances, it would be valuable to model inquiry at levels of sophistication that are proximal to what those teachers would be expected to enact in their own classrooms, as many teachers, at least at first, may not be ready to directly transfer sophisticated forms of inquiry into their instructional repertoires. However, with continued experience, we would expect to see progress in teachers' translation, and documenting such progress could enhance our understanding of how to support this translation.

Providing Teachers With Opportunities to Develop Inquiry Lessons Is Still Rare

Moving forward, an open question is whether or not teachers should be in the business of developing inquiry lessons on their own, or whether it would be better to focus PD efforts on challenging aspects of inquiry teaching that may bear more fruit. For instance, several of the programs that did not have teachers develop inquiry-based lessons, instead focused on supporting teachers in developing questioning skills, with the aim of eliciting and extending student ideas within inquiry. One program built a reflective community around improving questioning practices in inquiry teaching, which included a book club, opportunities to engage in inquiry lessons, and journaling (Lin et al.,

2013). Another explicitly modeled questioning techniques and later had teachers examine and critique videos of themselves teaching in terms of these questioning techniques (Oliveira, 2010b). Relatedly, two other programs emphasized extending student thinking within inquiry. The first emphasized the importance of preparing teachers in how to respond to student ideas during the consolidation phases of inquiry in order to create opportunities to further student learning (Haug, 2014). The second had teachers create customizations to computer-assisted inquiry that would slow students down and help extend their thinking on a topic (Gerard et al., 2010). However, assuming there is a value to teachers developing inquiry lessons themselves, it would be useful to understand the efficacy and value of existing approaches to doing this (see results for common approaches) and develop alternative approaches that may be more effective. Quasi-experimental studies, like the one conducted by Enderle and colleagues (2014) to contrast different models of RET programs, could be used to test different models for supporting the development of inquiry lessons against one another, enhancing our understanding about their efficacy.

Content Knowledge, Particular Knowledge of Inquiry and NOS Is Still Underrepresented

Some possible avenues for future research would be to develop knowledge about how to support teachers in learning the more challenging aspects of the nature of inquiry and expanding the somewhat simplistic notion on the value of explicit instruction by contrasting different approaches in order to understand what about these approaches are most promising to support growth in teacher knowledge.

Blended Learning and Collaborative Community

Blended learning was underrepresented in the review, with only two programs explicitly featuring it. This was somewhat surprising in view of the strong rationale for blended learning based on the body of research about the design of effective teacher PD programs. However, we suspect this feature may actually be underreported, given the advancement of web-based technologies over the last decade. We think blended learning is probably now more commonplace. Although we did not find much evidence of it, going forward, we see great prospects for blended learning and collaborative inquiry being complementary features. A review by Keengwe and Kang (2013) shows that many PD programs outside of the purview of this review have blended face-to-face and online interactions for collaborative community for teachers' professional learning while implementing technology-enhanced inquiry instruction. The feature of collaborative inquiry is important in online interactions during blended learning in creating an effective community in designing, facilitating, and directing science teacher learning. Balancing socio-emotional interaction, building group cohesion, and facilitating and modeling respectful critical discourse are important for productive PD programs for inquiry teaching.

Conclusion

This chapter presented a critical review of research on the professional development (PD) of science teachers related to inquiry instruction. Using procedures developed in a review by Capps et al. (2012), we extended the original review to cover the last decade of empirical research on inquiry PD. In addition, due to recent literature and other trends in PD, we included two new features in our review, namely collaborative community and blended learning. We also identified and discussed features of professional development that complement each other in leading to learning outcomes.

From the review, it is evident that some core features of effective PD that have been widely documented (e.g., Garet et al., 2001; Penuel et al., 2007), such as coherency with standards, reflection, transference, and extended support, still remain well represented. We also learned that the status of previously underrepresented features of focusing on science content for teachers, providing authentic inquiry experiences, and supporting teachers in developing inquiry-based lesson plans remain the same. While rare, the instances of where these features did manifest in the reviewed programs offer some insight into their integration in future programs. Given the importance of these features for PD in inquiry instruction, we call for programs to incorporate these features more actively, and for research to be done on the effectiveness of these features for learning outcomes. Similarly, we note that blended learning that was incorporated as an additional feature was poorly represented among the articles included in this review. We found this to be an unexpected result, given that blended learning is not a new concept in education but in fact emerged as a popular pedagogical concept at the beginning of 2000 (Owston et al., 2008). Finally, we postulate that blended learning and collaborative community could potentially form a very viable complementary pair for effective PD inquiry instruction, and we invite research on this.

References

Abrahams, I., & Millar, R. (2008). Does practical work really work? A study of the effectiveness of practical work as a teaching and learning method in school science. *International Journal of Science Education, 30*(14), 1945–1969.

Akerson, V. L., Abd-El-Khalick, F., & Lederman, N. G. (2000). Influence of a reflective explicit activity-based approach on elementary teachers' conceptions of nature of science. *Journal of Research in Science Teaching, 37*, 295–317.

Akerson, V. L., Townsend, J. S., Donnelly, L. A., Hanson, D. L., Tira, P., & White, O. (2009). Scientific modeling for inquiring teachers network (SMIT'N): The influence on elementary teachers' views of nature of science, inquiry, and modeling. *Journal of Science Teacher Education, 20*(1), 21–40.

Australian Curriculum Assessment and Reporting Authority. (2012). *Shape of the Australian science curriculum.* Retrieved March 15, 2021, from https://docs.acara.edu.au/resources/Australian_Curriculum_-_Science.pdf.

Bell, R. L., Lederman, N. G., & Abd-El-Khalick, F. (1998). Implicit versus Explicit Nature of Science Instruction: An Explicit Response to Palmquist and Finley. *Journal of Research in Science Teaching, 35*(9), 1057–1061.

Bismack, A. S., Arias, A. M., Davis, E. A., & Palincsar, A. S. (2014). Connecting curriculum materials and teachers: Elementary science teachers' enactment of a reform-based curricular unit. *Journal of Science Teacher Education, 25*(4), 489–512.

Blanchard, M. R., Southerland, S. A., & Granger, E. M. (2009). No silver bullet for inquiry: Making sense of teacher change following an inquiry-based research experience for teachers. *Science Education, 93*, 322–360.

Blank, R. K., de las Alas, N., & Smith, C. (2008). *Does teacher professional development have effects on teaching and learning?* Analysis of evaluation findings from programs for mathematics and science teachers in 14 states. Washington, DC: Council of Chief State School Officers.

Blumenfeld, P., & Krajcik, J. (2006). Project-based learning. *The Cambridge handbook of the learning sciences*, 333–354.

Brand, B. R., & Moore, S. J. (2011). Enhancing teachers' application of inquiry-based strategies using a constructivist sociocultural professional development model. *International Journal of Science Education, 33*(7), 889–913.

Capps, D. K., & Crawford, B. A. (2013). Inquiry-based professional development: What does it take to support teachers in learning about inquiry and nature of science? *International Journal of Science Education, 35*(12), 1947–1978.

Capps, D. K., Crawford, B. A., & Constas, M. A. (2012). A review of empirical literature on inquiry professional development: Alignment with best practices and a critique of the findings. *Journal of Science Teacher Education, 23*(3), 291–318.

Capps, D. K., Shemwell, J. T., & Young, A. M. (2016). Over reported and misunderstood? A study of teachers' reported enactment and knowledge of inquiry-based science teaching. *International Journal of Science Education, 38*(6), 934–959.

Carter, K., & Anders, D. (1996). Program pedagogy. In Murray, F. B. (Ed.), *The teacher educator's handbook: Building a knowledge base for the preparation of teachers* (pp. 557–592). San Francisco, CA: Jossey-Bass.

Cian, H., Marshall, J., & Qian, M. (2018). Inquiry classroom patterns of student cognitive engagement: An analysis using growth curve modeling. *Journal of Science Teacher Education, 29*(4), 326–346.

Crawford, B. A. (2000). Embracing the essence of inquiry: New roles for science teachers. *Journal of Research in Science Teaching: The Official Journal of the National Association for Research in Science Teaching, 37*(9), 916–937.

Crawford, B. A. (2007). Learning to teach science as inquiry in the rough and tumble of practice. *Journal of Research in Science Teaching, 44*(4), 613–642.

Crawford, B. A. (2014). From inquiry to scientific practices in the science classroom. In *Handbook of research on science education, volume II* (pp. 529–556). New York, NY: Routledge.

Darling-Hammond, L., & McLaughlin, M. W. (1995). Policies that support professional development in an era of reform. *Phi Delta Kappan, 76*(8), 597–604.

Department for Education and Skills/Qualification and Curriculum Authority. (2004). *Science – The national curriculum for England*. London: HMSO.

Dewey, J. (1910). Science as subject-matter and as method. *Science, 31*(787), 121–127.

Diamond, B. S., Maerten-Rivera, J., Rohrer, R. E., & Lee, O. (2014). Effectiveness of a curricular and professional development intervention at improving elementary teachers' science content knowledge and student achievement outcomes: Year 1 results. *Journal of Research in Science Teaching, 51*(5), 635–658.

Dillon, J. (2008). A review of the research on practical work in school science. *King's College, London*, 1–9.

Ebert, E. K., & Crippen, K. J. (2010). Applying a cognitive-affective model of conceptual change to professional development. *Journal of Science Teacher Education, 21*(3), 371–388.

Enderle, P., Dentzau, M., Roseler, K., Southerland, S., Granger, E., Hughes, R., . . . Saka, Y. (2014). Examining the influence of RETs on science teacher beliefs and practice. *Science Education, 98*(6), 1077–1108.

Fogleman, J., McNeill, K. L., & Krajcik, J. S. (2011). Examining the effect of teachers' adaptations of a middle school science inquiry-oriented curriculum unit on student learning. *Journal of Research in Science Teaching, 48*(2), 149–169.

Garet, M. S., Porter, A. C., Desimone, L. M., Birman, B. F., & Yoon, K. S. (2001). What makes professional development effective? Results from a national sample of teachers. *American Educational Research Journal, 38*, 915–945. https://doi.org/10.3102/00028312038004915

Garrison, D. R., & Kanuka, H. (2004). Blended learning: Uncovering its transformative potential in higher education, *Internet and Higher Education, 7*, 95–105.

Gerard, L. F., Spitulnik, M., & Linn, M. C. (2010). Teacher use of evidence to customize inquiry science instruction. *Journal of Research in Science Teaching, 47*(9), 1037–1063.

Granger, E. M., Bevis, T. H., Southerland, S. A., Saka, Y., & Ke, F. (2019). Examining features of how professional development and enactment of educative curricula influences elementary science teacher learning. *Journal of Research in Science Teaching, 56*(3), 348–370.

Haug, B. S. (2014). Inquiry-based science: Turning teachable moments into learnable moments. *Journal of Science Teacher Education, 25*(1), 79–96.

Isik-Ercan, Z. (2020). 'You have 25 kids playing around!': Learning to implement inquiry-based science learning in an urban second-grade classroom. *International Journal of Science Education, 42*(3), 329–349.

Israeli Ministry of Education. (2011). *Syllabus of biological studies (10th – 12th Grade)*. Jerusalem, Israel: State of Israel Ministry of Education Curriculum Center.

Kanter, D. E., & Konstantopoulos, S. (2010). The impact of a project-based science curriculum on minority student achievement, attitudes, and careers: The effects of teacher content and pedagogical content knowledge and inquiry-based practices. *Science Education, 94*(5), 855–887.

Keengwe, J., & Kang, J. J. (2013). A review of empirical research on blended learning in teacher education programs. *Education and Information Technologies, 18*, 479–493.

Khishfe, R., & Abd-El-Khalick, F. (2002). Influence of explicit and reflective versus implicit inquiry-oriented instruction on sixth graders' views of nature of science. *Journal of Research in Science Teaching, 39*(7), 551–578.

Lederman, J. S., Lederman, N. G., Bartos, S. A., Bartels, S. L., Meyer, A. A., & Schwartz, R. S. (2014). Meaningful assessment of learners' understandings about scientific inquiry – The views about scientific inquiry (VASI) questionnaire. *Journal of Research in Science Teaching, 51*(1), 65–83.

Lederman, N. G., & Lederman, J. S. (2019). Teaching and Learning of Nature of Scientific knowledge and scientific inquiry: Building capacity through systematic research-based professional development. *Journal of Science Teacher Education, 30*(7), 737–762.

Lewis, E. B., van der Hoeven Kraft, K. J., Bueno Watts, N., Baker, D. R., Wilson, M. J., & Lang, M. (2011). Elementary teachers' comprehension of flooding through inquiry-based professional development and use of self-regulation strategies. *International Journal of Science Education, 33*(11), 1473–1512.

Lin, H. S., Hong, Z. R., Yang, K. K., & Lee, S. T. (2013). The impact of collaborative reflections on teachers' inquiry teaching. *International Journal of Science Education, 35*(18), 3095–3116.

Lotter, C., Carnes, N., Marshall, J. C., Hoppmann, R., Kiernan, D. A., Barth, S. G., & Smith, C. (2020). Teachers' content knowledge, beliefs, and practice after a project-based professional development program with ultrasound scanning. *Journal of Science Teacher Education, 31*(3), 311–334.

Lotter, C., Rushton, G. T., & Singer, J. (2013). Teacher enactment patterns: How can we help move all teachers to reform-based inquiry practice through professional development?. *Journal of Science Teacher Education, 24*(8), 1263–1291.

Lotter, C., Smiley, W., Thompson, S., & Dickenson, T. (2016). The impact of a professional development model on middle school science teachers' efficacy and implementation of inquiry. *International Journal of Science Education, 38*(18), 2712–2741.

Loucks-Horsley, S., Stiles, K. E., Mundry, S., Love, N., & Hewson, P. W. (2009). *Designing professional development for teachers of science and mathematics*. Thousand Oaks, CA: Corwin press.

Luft, J. A., Diamond, J. M., Zhang, C., & White, D. Y. (2020). Research on K-12 STEM professional development programs. In C. C. Johnson, M. J. Mohr-Schroeder, T. J. Moore, & L. D. English (Eds.), *Handbook of research on STEM education* (p. XX). New York: Routledge.

Lumpe, A., Czerniak, C., Haney, J., & Beltyukova, S. (2012). Beliefs about teaching science: The relationship between elementary teachers' participation in professional development and student achievement. *International Journal of Science Education, 34*(2), 153–166.

Marshall, J. C., & Alston, D. M. (2014). Effective, sustained inquiry-based instruction promotes higher science proficiency among all groups: A 5-year analysis. *Journal of Science Teacher Education, 25*(7), 807–821.

Marx, R. W., Blumenfeld, P. C., Krajcik, J. S., & Soloway, E. (1997). Enacting project-based science. *The Elementary School Journal, 97*(4), 341–358.

Ministry of Education of Singapore. (2007). *Primary science syllabus*. Singapore: Author.

Moeed, A. (2013). Science investigation that best supports student learning: Teachers' understanding of science investigation. *International Journal of Environmental and Science Education, 8*(4), 537–559.

Mupira, P., & Ramnarain, U. (2018). The effect of inquiry-based learning on the achievement goal-orientation of grade 10 physical sciences learners at township schools in South Africa. *Journal of Research in Science Teaching, 55*(6), 810–825.

National Research Council. (1996). *National science education standards*. Washington, DC: National Academy Press.

National Research Council. (2012). *A framework for K-12 science education: Practices, crosscutting concepts, and core ideas*. Washington, DC: National Academies Press.

Ødegaard, M., Haug, B., Mork, S. M., & Sørvik, G. O. (2014). Challenges and support when teaching science through an integrated inquiry and literacy approach. *International Journal of Science Education, 36*(18), 2997–3020.

Oliveira, A. W. (2010a). Developing elementary teachers' understandings of hedges and personal pronouns in inquiry-based science classroom discourse. *Journal of Science Teacher Education, 21*(1), 103–126

Oliveira, A. W. (2010b). Improving teacher questioning in science inquiry discussions through professional development. *Journal of Research in Science Teaching, 47*(4), 422–453.

Owston, R., Wideman, H., Murphy, J., & Lupshenyuk, D. (2008). Blended teacher professional development: A synthesis of three program evaluations. *The Internet and Higher Education, 11*(3–4), 201–210.

Penuel, W. R., Fishman, B. J., Yamaguchi, R., & Gallagher, L. P. (2007). What makes professional development effective? Strategies that foster curriculum implementation. *American Educational Research Journal, 44*(4), 921–958. https://doi.org/10.3102/0002831207308221

Peters-Burton, E. E., Merz, S. A., Ramirez, E. M., & Saroughi, M. (2015). The effect of cognitive apprenticeship-based professional development on teacher self-efficacy of science teaching, motivation, knowledge calibration, and perceptions of inquiry-based teaching. *Journal of Science Teacher Education, 26*(6), 525–548.

Reiser, B. J. (2004). Scaffolding complex learning: The mechanisms of structuring and problematizing student work. *The Journal of the Learning sciences, 13*(3), 273–304.

Rushton, G. T., Lotter, C., & Singer, J. (2011). Chemistry teachers' emerging expertise in inquiry teaching: The effect of a professional development model on beliefs and practice. *Journal of Science Teacher Education, 22*(1), 23–52.

Santau, A. O., Secada, W., Maerten-Rivera, J., Cone, N., & Lee, O. (2010). US urban elementary teachers' knowledge and practices in teaching science to English language learners: Results from the first year of a professional development intervention. *International Journal of Science Education, 32*(15), 2007–2032.

Scher, L., & O'Reilly, F. (2009). Professional development for K-12 math and science teachers: What do we really know? *Journal of Research on Educational Effectiveness, 2*(3), 209–249.

Schwab, J. (1962). *The teaching of science as enquiry.* In J. J. Schwab, & P. F. Brandwein, (Eds.), The teaching of science (pp. 1–103). New York: Simon and Schuster.

Seraphin, K. D., Harrison, G. M., Philippoff, J., Brandon, P. R., Nguyen, T. T. T., Lawton, B. E., & Vallin, L. M. (2017). Teaching aquatic science as inquiry through professional development: Teacher characteristics and student outcomes. *Journal of Research in Science Teaching, 54*(9), 1219–1245.

Shea, N. A., Mouza, C., & Drewes, A. (2016). Climate change professional development: Design, implementation, and initial outcomes on teacher learning, practice, and student beliefs. *Journal of Science Teacher Education, 27*, 235–258.

Singer, J., Lotter, C., Feller, R., & Gates, H. (2011). Exploring a model of situated professional development: Impact on classroom practice. *Journal of Science Teacher Education, 22*(3), 203–227

van der Valk, T., & de Jong, O. (2009). Scaffolding science teachers in open-inquiry teaching. *International Journal of Science Education, 31*(6), 829–850

Yang, Y., Liu, X., & Gardella Jr, J. A. (2020). Effects of a professional development program on science teacher knowledge and practice, and student understanding of interdisciplinary science concepts. *Journal of Research in Science Teaching, 57*(7), 1028–1057.

21

A LITERATURE REVIEW OF GLOBAL PERSPECTIVES ON THE PROFESSIONAL DEVELOPMENT OF CULTURALLY RESPONSIVE SCIENCE TEACHERS

Julie C. Brown, Rose M. Pringle, and Nihat Kotluk

Introduction

Professional development (PD) is a highly valued mechanism for continuing in-service science teacher education globally. Decades of research on PD have resulted in a collective understanding of program elements likely to lead to changes in teacher knowledge and instructional practices. Though PD programs vary widely in their delivery, they collectively seek to deepen subject matter and pedagogical knowledge; engage teachers as active learners within a collaborative context; enact coherent program activities aligned with school policies, practices, and expectations; feature substantive duration and sustainability, both in intensity and contact hours; and facilitate the systematic, critical reflection of teachers on their practices and beliefs (Luft & Hewson, 2014; Wilson, 2013).

At its core, the goal of PD for science teachers is to transform their practices in ways that increase opportunities for all learners (Rivera Maulucci et al., 2015). Science classrooms around the world have become more culturally diverse over the past few decades, in part due to globalization enabled by technological advancements and the expansion of capitalism (Benzce & Carter, 2011). The need for culturally relevant and responsive pedagogies has been fueled by this migration, which has led to increasing diversity in ethnicities and cultures and accompanying civil rights movements around the globe. Increasing diversity supports the need for additional PD, as the complex issues of the 21st century require scientific literacy globally and the circulation of diverse ideas presents opportunities for science teaching to be more relevant to learners. As classroom diversity rises, a pressing challenge is staying abreast of these changing demographics and the provision of equitable, responsive learning opportunities (NRC, 2012).

PD programs should also provide opportunities to develop teachers' understanding of how diverse students make sense of scientific ideas (Lewis et al., 2015). The increase in diversity has resulted in science teachers struggling to better serve students from cultures and ethnicities other than their own (Banilower et al., 2018). Teachers, therefore, need to be prepared as culturally relevant practitioners. The development of science teachers' cultural competence is rarely integrated into PD activities throughout the globe, however. The *Trends in International Mathematics and Science Study* (TIMSS) 2019 report, for instance, indicates that science teachers do not receive adequate PD, and meeting diverse student needs is the least common of all PD topics covered around the world (Mullis et al.,

DOI: 10.4324/9781003098478-25

2020). With the aim of increasing equitable science learning opportunities for all students, this chapter synthesizes the literature related to culturally responsive pedagogies in PD for science teachers globally. A research agenda to address emerging questions related to science teachers' development as culturally responsive practitioners is also proposed.

Culturally Relevant Pedagogy and Culturally Responsive Teaching

Reform efforts in science education have invested in evidence-based, discipline-specific pedagogy to ensure that all K–12 students have access to meaningful science learning. Despite these efforts, in the United States (US) for example, data on science achievement continue to reveal longstanding discrepancies among populations of learners, particularly in the area of science. In European and OECD countries a similar phenomenon exists. Unlike the US, while present, the call for culturally relevant education in these countries has only recently emerged (European Commission, 2017; OECD, 2018). Leading scholars in cultural diversity and education proposed two frameworks that both identified teachers' practices and cultural competencies within classrooms as sites for social change and social justice. These frameworks, *culturally relevant pedagogy* (Ladson-Billings, 1995) and *culturally responsive teaching* (Gay, 2010), with some differences in their orientation, have many similarities in their focus on academic success of students from diverse cultural and ethnic backgrounds.

Ladson-Billings in her pioneering work studying teachers of African American learners, identified academic success, cultural competence, and sociopolitical consciousness as domains of these successful teachers (Ladson-Billings, 1995, 2009). In her formulation of culturally relevant pedagogy, she prioritized teachers' ability to help students celebrate and appreciate their cultures of origin while gaining knowledge and skills to solve real-world problems (Ladson-Billings, 2014). In her framework, Gay (2010) defines culturally responsive teaching (CRT) as "using the cultural knowledge, prior experiences, frames of reference, and performance styles of ethnically diverse students to make learning encounters more relevant and effective for them" (p. 31). She posits that because CRT filters curriculum content and teaching strategies through the learners' lived experiences and cultural frames of reference, it has the potential to improve multiple kinds of achievement, thus positioning diverse students for success. Both frameworks give credence to teachers' cultural competence in their use of appropriate resources and cultural referents to better facilitate the learning of diverse students.

In this review, the term *culturally responsive science teaching* (CRST) is used to denote both culturally relevant pedagogy (CRP, Ladson-Billings, 1995) and culturally responsive teaching (CRT, Gay, 2010) in science contexts. In CRST, teachers possess meaningful understanding of the disciplinary science knowledge in ways that allow them to use metaphors and other representations to engage students' funds of knowledge (Gonzalez et al., 2005), and lived experiences. At the science classroom levels, teachers' pedagogical practices and cultural competencies provide a powerful avenue through which inclusive environments can be created and facilitated. Science teachers who are culturally responsive address the sociopolitical contexts in which students live and learn (Hayes & Juárez, 2012), while facilitating students' abilities to achieve high levels of academic success by nurturing their emotional, cultural, psychological, and physiological well-being (Ladson-Billings, 1995).

The need for teachers to be better prepared to effectively teach diverse students can hardly be understated (Hayes & Juárez, 2012), and, as embraced by Banks (1991), it is now a demographic imperative. Teachers are challenged to broaden their sociocultural consciousness (Villegas & Lucas, 2002) and to improve their repertoire of dynamic strategies consistent with the tenets of culturally relevant pedagogy. Developing a science teacher's ability to enact CRT is challenging (Mensah, 2013) and will require PD experiences grounded in systematic approaches to reform and enhance teachers' learning. While researchers have identified elements of effective PD in the general education sphere, this review looks to the body of research related to CRST in an effort to identify the mechanisms of teacher learning in this space.

Professional Learning for Culturally Responsive Science Teaching: A Global Perspective

Method

In this review, the following research questions are addressed:

1. What professional learning experiences are included in programs to develop CRST?
2. For what reasons are these experiences advocated?

To identify studies focusing on the PD for culturally responsive science teaching, the review is limited to recent peer-review research published in the last 10 years, from 2010 to 2020, excluding book chapters and published dissertations. For ensuring a comprehensive representation of the international research base, EBSCOhost's Academic Search Premier, APA PsychInfo, Education Source, ERIC, Professional Development Collection, Psychology and Behavioral Sciences Collection, Teacher Reference Center, and Google Scholar were used as electronic search engines. A set of search terms such as *professional development, professional learning, culturally relevant, culturally responsive, multicultural,* and *science* were used to search the databases, as well as using some operational definitions of terms like *cultural* relevan*, cultural* respon*, multicultural*,* and *science teach**.

The search process was completed in five steps. In each step, titles, keywords, and abstracts were reviewed to accept or reject articles for full-text review. Only articles that included PD for culturally relevant/responsive science teaching were considered. The search was limited to articles published in English, scholarly peer-reviewed journals, and full-text results. These delimitations and steps resulted in 20 articles. One article was excluded (Qureshi & Demir, 2019) at the last stage since it was a comparative study. A final total of 19 articles were included in this review. The inclusion and exclusion criteria and a brief of keywords used in the search process, as well as operational definitions of terms, are presented in Table 21.1.

Results

PD for culturally relevant science teaching is not a widely researched area. Such scholarship represents a fraction of the published studies on in-service science teacher PD globally, and the majority of this work comes out of the US. The availability of PD for culturally relevant science education is highly dependent on the politics of the nation and its embrace, or acceptance, of underrepresented populations. The European Commission (2017) has recently called for multicultural education initiatives, and consequently, scholarship on culturally responsive teaching has increased in European countries. This work is largely absent from a specific discipline and overwhelmingly confined to preservice contexts. (e.g., Acquah & Szelei, 2020; Civitillo et al., 2019; Kotluk & Kocakaya, 2018). In this section, key professional learning experiences that are common among programs aiming to develop culturally responsive science teachers is presented. The scope of scholarship in this space, in terms of countries represented, grade bands on which programs focused, and science content explored, is first described.

Nineteen studies containing professional learning experiences in support of in-service culturally responsive science teaching were identified for this review. Thirteen studies were based in the US and took place in all regions except the Northeast. Two additional studies contained multinational programs (US and South Korea; US and Trinidad and Tobago). The four remaining studies occurred in New Zealand, Trinidad and Tobago, and South Africa. The programs spanned early childhood to high school (or similarly named) science teaching contexts, were often labeled "K–12" in focus,

Table 21.1 Search steps, terms, options, and a summary of the inclusion/exclusion process

Steps	Search Terms	Search Options and Results	Articles Included (N = 19)
First Search	"cultural★ relevan★" AND "professional development" OR "professional learning" AND "science"	Find all search terms; apply related words; search within the full text of articles; limited to full-text results; scholarly (peer-reviewed) journals; from 2010 to 2020; document type article; language English. 27,091 results. Changed "select a field" to subject terms in all cases and yielded six results. Based on reading titles and abstracts, two were relevant and one was potential.	Nam et al. (2013); Sylva et al. (2010)
Second Search	"cultural★ respon★" AND "professional development" OR "professional learning" AND "science"	Two results, both viable based on title and abstract readings, one repeated (Sylva et al., 2010)	J. Brown and Crippen (2016a)
Third Search	"cultural★ respon★" AND "professional development" AND "science"	Expanded select field to "All text"; 35,937 results sorted based on relevance. Manually examined first 150 articles. Identified 9 fitting criteria.	Sigman et al. (2014); Vaughn and De Beer (2020); Alvaré (2015); George (2013); J. Brown et al. (2018); J. Brown and Crippen (2016b); Moseley et al. (2014); Tolbert (2015); Charity Hudley and Mallinson (2017); Grimberg and Gummer (2013); Chinn (2015)
Fourth Search	"cultural★" AND "professional development" AND "science"	Expanded select field to "All text"; 35,235 results sorted based on relevance. Manually examined first 150 results again. Identified 4 fitting criteria.	Kern et al. (2017); Chinn et al. (2014); B. Brown et al. (2019); Fakoyede and Otulaja (2020)
Fifth Search	"multicultural★" AND "professional development" AND "science teach★"	Expanded select field to "All text"; 30,650 entries sorted based on relevance. Manually examined first 150 results again. Identified 2 fitting criteria.	Qureshi and Demir (2019); Yoon and Martin (2019)

and centered on topics including climate change from indigenous and Western perspectives (Kern et al., 2017; Nam et al., 2013), agricultural and environmental science through Native Hawaiian and Western knowledge (Sylva et al., 2010), ecological mindfulness (Chinn, 2015), life science via cultural realia (Fakoyede & Otulaja, 2020), and large marine ecosystems (Sigman et al., 2014).

Professional Learning Experiences

Several common program experiences in which practitioners were engaged as they pursued cultur-ally responsive science teaching were noted. A synthesis of program experiences, along with scholars whose programs featured those experiences, is provided in Table 21.2 and explained subsequently. These program features are presented in no particular order.

Cultural Exposure

Cultural understanding and respect are at the core of culturally responsive science teaching. This review adopts Hall's (1995) definition of culture as "the systems of shared meanings which people who belong to the same community, group, or nation use to help them interpret and make sense of the world" (p. 176). Likewise, several programs exposed science teachers to specific cultural knowledge and practices in efforts to improve their awareness of nondominant ways of learning, perceiving, and interacting with natural phenomena. This exposure took on many forms, including cultural immersion field trips (Sylva et al., 2010), presentations by elders (Sigman et al., 2014), visits to museums (Vaughn & De Beer, 2020), and artifacts produced by members of different cultures (e.g., periodicals and oral histories) (J. Brown et al., 2018). During the summer component of their "culturally relevant agricultural and environmental professional development course," the K–12 US teachers with whom Sylva et al. (2010) worked spent 5 days in the Kohala Immersion experience

Table 21.2 Synthesized review of literature on professional development experiences for culturally responsive science teaching (CRST)

Author(s)	PD Feature				
	Cultural Exposure	Scientist, Community Expert Partnerships	Student Information-Gathering	Lesson or Unit Design	Critical Reflection
Alvaré (2015)		X		X	
B. Brown et al. (2019)		X		X	
Charity Hudley and Mallinson (2017)					X
Chinn et al. (2014)	X	X			
Chinn (2015)	X	X			
Fakoyede and Otulaja (2020)	X	X			X
George (2013)	X		X	X	X
Grimberg and Gummer (2013)	X		X	X	X
J. Brown and Crippen (2016a)			X	X	X
J. Brown and Crippen (2016b)			X	X	
J. Brown et al. (2018)	X		X	X	X
Kern et al. (2017)	X	X	X	X	X
Moseley et al. (2014)					X
Nam et al. (2013)		X			
Sigman et al. (2014)	X	X			
Sylva et al. (2010)	X			X	
Tolbert (2015)			X	X	X
Vaughn & De Beer (2020)	X	X			
Yoon and Martin (2019)	X			X	

where they learned traditional Hawaiian practices tied to school science concepts such as aquaculture and bioremediation (p. 11). Native Hawaiian teachers taught participants about "traditional Hawaiian pedagogical and communication strategies" and also traditional agricultural practices (p. 12).

In another example, Fakoyede and Otulaja (2020) reported on how Ms. Tumelo, a grade 10 life science teacher in the Black township of South Africa, used beads and beadwork as cultural realia to enhance her students' understanding of abstract organic compounds after participating in PD focused on creating culturally related instructional models. After exploring the importance of beads and beadwork to the Niger-Congo and Khoisan African indigenous communities, Ms. Tumelo designed instruction based on her students' community cultural wealth, a term created by Yosso (2005) that "reveals accumulated assets and resources in the histories and lives of Communities of Color" (p. 77). The use of beads as cognized and culturally situated tools aided students in producing meaning around organic macromolecules such as glucose, lipids, and proteins. Regardless of the method employed, all programs included cultural exposure as a way to expand teachers' awareness of and abilities to create culturally responsive science learning environments. A pitfall of cultural exposure may be that such experiences are limited in duration and predetermined in design; as such, interactions between teachers and members of a cultural community are controlled and potentially inauthentic. Thus, caution should be exercised so that cultural voyeurism is limited and "the persistence of stereotypic representations of 'others' in practice" does not result (Asher, 2007, p. 65). One way that scholars attempted to mitigate such experiences was through meaningful partnerships with community experts.

Partnerships With Scientists and Community Experts

Although inquiry-based and culturally responsive science instruction may be complementary, one clear distinction lies in the role of Western- and Indigenous Knowledge-based conceptual models (J. Brown, 2017). In scholarship on culturally responsive science teaching, traditional, native knowledge is often leveraged as a way to access and expand Western science knowledge (e.g., George, 2013). Of the PD programs reviewed, those that included partnerships with scientists and community experts did so to ensure that science content was concurrently presented through Western and native perspectives. The nature of these partnerships varied among programs, from climate scientists and tribal members presenting on the impact of climate change to local communities (Kern et al., 2017), to scientists and community experts engaging in the PD as both participant *and* presenter (Sigman et al., 2014).

In three, 1-week-long workshops on Alaska's large marine ecosystems (LMEs), for example, Sigman and colleagues (2014) aimed to help K–12 educators improve their Traditional Ecological Knowledge and Western science content, as well as their abilities to design place-based and culturally responsive lessons for Alaska Native cultures. Partnership with marine scientists and community elders enabled each workshop to contain 3–4 clear key ecosystem-scale ideas that could be explored through Western and Native perspectives. Furthermore, two of the workshops featured anthropologist or tribal environmental educator-guided museum tours to introduce participants to Alaska Native cultures that rely on the LMEs.

And, in American Indian reservations throughout Minnesota, Idaho, and Washington, Nam et al. (2013) engaged middle and high school science teachers in PD focused on incorporating place-based, culturally responsive strategies into climate science lessons. Their program incorporated expertise from university and reservation natural resource scientists to better understand local natural phenomena (e.g., wild rice production). The underlying argument for such partnerships emanated from cultural difference theory. That "the disconnect between the norms and priorities of the research community and the values, aspirations, and cultures of many historically underrepresented communities [act] as a key hurdle to broader [science] participation" (Sigman et al., 2014, p. 26).

Student Information-Gathering

Student information-gathering was employed in PD programs to achieve similar aims as cultural exposure: to learn more about students' lived experiences and cultural backgrounds. While such information resides at the microsystem level of Bronfenbrenner's (1994) ecological paradigm, it also endorses Ngo's (2013) argument that culture – while steeped in tradition – is also dynamic, "incomplete, continuously in the course of 'production'" at all levels (p. 962). Information-gathering experiences took many forms across the programs employing them, involving science teachers in completing fieldwork to construct a student cultural database (George, 2013), conducting student interviews (J. Brown et al., 2018), and developing questionnaires (Grimberg & Gummer, 2013).

In some instances, PD programs have used student information-gathering as a more familiar teacher practice and segue to understanding larger cultural norms and practices. In their work spanning the southeastern and midwestern US regions, J. Brown and colleagues found that secondary science teachers are more likely to enact rich, culturally responsive instruction after they have examined their own classroom- and student-level data (J. Brown & Crippen, 2016a) and reported using these data more frequently than cultural artifacts when making instructional design choices (J. Brown et al., 2018).

While instructing a 13-week course on science, education, and culture, George (2013) asked science teachers to interview students and create a database of their "traditional practices and beliefs" around a theme of the teacher's choosing that could be connected to conventional (i.e., Western) science (p. 2121). The value of this experience differed for teachers depending on the age of the children they taught. For example, primary school children were more likely to provide partially helpful information. This result prompted several science teachers to seek additional knowledge within the community. Some teachers met with parents and interacted with local experts and villagers. One teacher was even invited on a hike to observe bat caves by a student and her parent. These valuable student and cultural data were then leveraged as resources for thematically based Caribbean culture and conventional science unit design.

Grimberg and Gummer (2013) also involved two cohorts of K-8 science teachers "near or on American Indian reservations" in the US in student information-gathering (p. 16). During the 3-year PD on CRST through cultural points of intersection that each cohort engaged in, this information was kept in an ongoing portfolio and included reports on how students "make connections between science and topics relevant to [their lives] and their community" in addition to instructional approaches that prompt students to engage in science and engineering practices (p. 21). It is important to note, as with other programs aiming to support culturally responsive science teaching, student information-gathering was but one of many learning experiences provided by professional developers.

Lesson or Unit Design

According to Fakoyede and Otulaja (2020), "lesson planning is critical as it is the step-by-step, i.e., systematic, process of deciding what to teach and how students/learners should learn in the classroom" (p. 202). This is particularly important for culturally responsive science instructional design, as it is context-heavy and, as such, not easily adaptable to other settings (J. Brown & Livstrom, 2020). Resultantly, several PD programs in this review involved science teachers in lesson or unit design that they could later implement in their classrooms. The supports provided to science teachers involved in lesson or unit design varied by program, ranging from classification schemes to assist with cultural integration (George, 2013), modeling exemplary lessons (Yoon & Martin, 2019), and lesson planning templates (J. Brown et al., 2018) to mentoring (Tolbert, 2015) and collaboration (B. Brown et al., 2019; Sylva et al., 2010).

When providing PD focused on culturally relevant education and cognitive apprenticeship for nine K-5 STEM teachers in California, US, B. Brown and colleagues (2019) directly taught participants to organize their STEM lessons using a structure intended to advance equitable learning. This structure contained four components, including: "(a) establishing a problem, (b) modeling activities, (c) coaching, and (d) scaffolding activities" (pp. 784–785). Working in collaborative groups, the teachers applied these principles to the design of elementary-level, culturally relevant STEM lessons that contained real-life examples for students to relate, out-of-classroom experiences, and concretized abstract concepts.

In a second example, using a unit planning template and collaboration sessions, the five southeastern US high school life science teachers in J. Brown and Crippen's (2016a) study successfully designed science units that were responsive to students' lived experiences and cultural backgrounds. Additionally, modeled examples of CRST enabled teachers to include specific community knowledge and local issues in their biology, anatomy, and physiology units. In all instances of lesson or unit design, professional developers used multiple approaches to assist science and STEM teachers in successfully crafting instruction that was rich in disciplinary content and responsive to students and their communities.

Critical Reflection

Science teachers embodying CRST in their practice must be critically and sociopolitically conscious, understand the roles of culture in learning, and explicitly integrate students' backgrounds into science instruction (Mensah, 2013). Critical to their development as culturally relevant practitioners is transformation in the frames of reference guiding their instruction, student–teacher relationships, and critical awareness (Ladson-Billings, 1995, 2009). These frames are shaped by teachers' lived experiences and thus can be quite durable. Consequently, transformative learning of this nature can be facilitated by inducing disorienting dilemmas (i.e., experiences that challenge assumptions and beliefs shaping teachers' perspective) and critical self-reflection (Mezirow, 1990).

While teacher reflection was present in all PD programs, a select few explicitly mentioned engaging science teachers in the critical reflection of their beliefs and practices. Noting that "getting teachers to critically reflect on – and often fundamentally revise – their instructional approach in diverse classrooms is a perpetual challenge" (p. 1326), Tolbert (2015) analyzed culturally responsible mentoring conversations among Te Kotahitanga PD facilitators and four New Zealand Year 9 and Year 10 science teachers of indigenous Māori students. Tolbert found that culturally responsible mentoring of science teachers included facilitating conversations around themes including racism, instructional complexity, relationships, and relevance. Assisting their development as culturally responsive science educators, the mentors encouraged teachers to critically reflect on their own positionality, biases, and resources to support Māori students rather than blame their communities and families for challenges.

Through professional developer-led discussions in their "Language Variation in the Classroom" workshops, Charity Hudley and Mallinson (2017) supported US K–12 STEM educators in critically reflecting on "the dynamics of sociolinguistics, literacy, and culture . . . in the service of teaching predominantly African American student populations" (p. 638). The workshop focused on six, STEM teacher-selected topics, all of which had critical reflection as a central aspect: (1) conflict between school and student culture, (2) biases against non-standard dialects of English and students who speak them, (3) linguistic/cultural mismatches and student achievement, (4) confronting standard-English STEM texts, (5) structural linguistic issues, and (6) building linguistic and cultural competence (p. 644). During the workshops, the authors also guided teachers in critically assessing avenues for overcoming linguistic and cultural inequities within their classroom and schools.

In programs employing critical reflection as a key professional learning experience, all instances were facilitated either by the professional developers themselves (e.g., Charity Hudley & Mallinson, 2017; Tolbert, 2015), by resources such as structured reflective prompts (e.g., J. Brown & Crippen, 2016b), or by some combination of both (Moseley et al., 2014). In no instances did we note the use of teacher peers/colleagues in substantively facilitating this process.

Expanding the Research (Base) for Supporting the Professional Growth of Culturally Responsive Science Teachers

As discussed, the rapid and continued migration and the resulting increase in diverse populations have signaled a global attention to preparing culturally responsive science practitioners. As class-rooms become more diverse, it is imperative to prepare science teachers to meet the needs of students in contexts beyond the US. Of particular importance are the concerns that the increase in diversity of learners is linked to the larger social, economic, and political issues (Upadahyay et al., 2020). Thus, developing culturally responsive practitioners has a pivotal role in impacting the science trajectory of diverse learners in schools throughout the world. In this chapter, the content and goals of professional learning experiences for CRST were documented through the literature. Now, areas of future research will be identified to address critical questions that, when answered, contribute to global efforts to support the professional growth of culturally responsive science teachers and the advancement of CRT in schooling.

The review of literature on PD for CRST has provided insights into the nature of common program experiences that are enacted worldwide but to a greater extent in the US. Regardless of the diversity among the learners, educators seeking to facilitate the development of CRST have incorporated and focused on strengthening areas of disciplinary content and cultural knowledge, curriculum development, CRT skills, and other critical components of PD. While not the focus of this chapter, it is important to note that there exists a lack of research in areas related to science teachers' learning and the enactment of CRT practices. For example, of the teacher outcomes assessed across PD programs, classroom practices were infrequently examined. Furthermore, all instances were either qualitative via fieldnotes-assisted observations (e.g., Grimberg & Gummer, 2013; J. Brown & Crippen, 2016a) or based on self-reports through surveys and questionnaires (Kern et al., 2017). Instead, science teachers' disciplinary content knowledge (e.g., Sigman et al., 2014), cultural knowledge (Alvaré, 2015), self-efficacy or confidence for CRST (Nam et al., 2013), and awareness of instructional tools for CRST (Charity Hudley & Mallinson, 2017) were more often evaluated.

Moreover, the findings in general are varied and have laid bare the need for well-designed research to investigate methods and learning experiences used in the various professional development programs to prepare science teachers as 'culturally responsive' practitioners. In addition, consistent with Bottiani et al. (2018), there is not a strong knowledge base in the field to inform the work of PD providers, thus signaling the need for more rigorous CRST in-service intervention research.

Diversity in today's classroom demands that teachers be knowledgeable, responsive, and well prepared to work with a multicultural student population (Nieto & Bode, 2007; Sleeter & Bernal, 2004). The PD programs activities described in the literature were designed to address specific areas of science teaching that would enhance teachers' effectiveness as culturally responsive practitioners. This effectiveness included not only a depth of understanding of science content and science-specific pedagogies, but competence to enact culturally responsive science education. The effectiveness of PD, however, varies considerably. To date, the literature does not provide clear guidance as to the factors that contribute to attaining such effectiveness. As an example, there is a need for research that builds on Suriel and Atwater (2012), who found that the experience of being culturally "othered" positively influenced science teachers' levels of multicultural content integration into curriculum units while enrolled in a course on the topic. Future work in understanding how science teachers' experiences and identities shape their culturally responsive instruction is warranted. Moreover, although in-service teachers can benefit considerably from findings in general PD, attention needs to be paid to the definition of *positive impact* and how teachers translate learning of CRST into their practices.

Many teachers improved in their confidence and quality of curriculum materials, but the hesitancy to implement remains and stems around not feeling confident in their understanding of cultural ways of knowing and doing (B. Brown et al., 2019; George, 2013). Other studies show that even with support, teachers were least able to design instruction that was culturally based (J. Brown & Crippen, 2016a; Nam et al., 2013). Experts and teacher educators should therefore design PD programs not only for determining science teachers' beliefs or attitudes, but also to improve their curriculum skills. Teachers who attend these PD programs should be fully immersed in experiences from which they develop understanding of how to practice CRST in their classrooms. While beliefs and attitudes are indeed important, research seeking to understand science teachers' translation of those beliefs to practice is also essential.

A research design that seeks to evaluate the differential effects of PD programs over time and across multiple contexts is warranted. Increased and targeted experiences for developing culturally responsive and equitable teaching practices is sorely needed. To support this, what is warranted is an in-depth examination of the focus of the PD in relation to the contextual factors that are espoused in the literature. For instance, research focusing exclusively on how contextual factors influence ongoing PD programs and the impact of school culture on achieving the desired teacher outcomes. It is noted that, as scholar Geneva Gay stated, CRT is "never completely beyond context." Yet, this review of international literature suggests that many of the same practices being used to educate science teachers abroad are the same as those employed in the US. Advancing such research would provide a framework that would be applicable to PD programs with similar aims and would possibly inform ways to accelerate transformation in teachers' approach to teaching diverse students globally.

Many of the programs included theoretically informed structures and strategies to accelerate adult learners, such as developing teachers' abilities to exercise critical reflective judgment and become a discriminating skeptic of their own and others' underlying beliefs (Mezirow, 1990). Further understanding the impact of time on the structures is crucial for designing reforms and intervention that can improve the engagement of diverse students in science. For instance, how is duration of the experiences translated into teacher learning and classroom practices?

Internationally, researchers and teachers should focus on culturally responsive science education. As many scholars stated (European and US), there is a need for culturally responsive science teaching practices. This research base does not yet exist in European countries – where the need exists for CRST. Considering the research base on culturally responsive teaching in European countries, the researchers generally aim to determine the beliefs, attitudes, and perceptions of teachers about culturally responsive teaching. But, how these opinions and beliefs are reflected in the classroom setting, teaching activities, classroom management, and teacher-student relations can be also observed in the future research. It is advisable that more courses on culturally responsive pedagogy, in particular culturally relevant science education courses, should be added in teacher education programs in European countries, and studies can be conducted to determine how these courses influence teachers' ability to design, plan, implement, and evaluate teaching processes. This must occur at pre- and in-service levels, as the needs of these populations can be quite different. On the other hand, one of the biggest problems encountered in carrying out this research was the inadequacy of the research literature on culturally relevant science education in European countries. It would be beneficial for researchers to focus their efforts here. A clear limitation of this review is that only English-language papers were selected and synthesized. Resultantly, there are likely international studies of CRST not discussed. Multilingual scholars are encouraged to expand on this work in a way that more comprehensively represents the international landscape of culturally responsive science education research.

In conclusion, this review has shown that the field of CRST is in need of a strong theoretical and research-driven approach to preparing CRST. At this critical juncture, the growth of the field is being stymied by the lack of a substantial and well-established base of knowledge. Efforts should be made to broaden the research areas and the findings channeled into supporting the continued growth and responsiveness to the needs of diverse classrooms. While it is important to be intentional in developing CRST, within the PD space dialogue should be established with the larger teacher education community beginning in the preparation of preservice teachers around the globe.

References

Acquah, E. O., & Szelei, N. (2020). The potential of modelling culturally responsive teaching: Pre-service teachers' learning experiences. *Teaching in Higher Education, 25*(2), 157–173.

Alvaré, B. T. (2015). 'Do they think we live in huts?' – Cultural essentialism and the challenges of facilitating professional development in cross-cultural settings. *Ethnography and Education, 12*(1), 33–48.

Asher, N. (2007). Made in the (multicultural) USA: Unpacking tensions of race, culture, gender, and sexuality in education. *Educational Researcher, 36*(2), 65–73.

Banilower, E. R., Smith, P. S., Malzahn, K. A., Plumley, C. L., Gordon, E. M., & Hayes, M. L. (2018). *Report of the 2018 NSSME+*. Chapel Hill, NC: Horizon Research, Inc.

Banks, J. A. (1991). Teaching multicultural literacy to teachers. *Teaching Education, 4*(1), 133–142.

Bencze, L., & Carter, L. (2011). Globalizing students acting for the common good. *Journal of Research in Science Teaching, 48*(6), 648–669.

Bottiani, J. H., Larson, K. E., Debnam, K. J., Bischoff, C. M., & Bradshaw, C. P. (2018). Promoting educators' use of culturally responsive practices: A systematic review of inservice interventions. *Journal of Teacher Education, 69*(4), 367–385.

Bronfenbrenner, U. (1994). Ecological models of human development. In *International encyclopedia of education* (Vol. 3, 2nd ed.). Oxford: Elsevier. Reprinted in: Gauvain, M., & Cole, M. (Eds.). (1993). *Readings on the development of children* (2nd ed., pp. 37–43). New York: Freeman.

Brown, B. A., Boda, P., Lemmi, C., & Monroe, X. (2019). Moving culturally relevant pedagogy from theory to practice: Exploring teachers' application of culturally relevant education in science and mathematics. *Urban Education, 54*(6), 775–803.

Brown, J. C. (2017). A metasynthesis of the complementarity of culturally responsive and inquiry-based science education in K-12 settings: Implications for advancing equitable science teaching and learning. *Journal of Research in Science Teaching, 54*(9), 1143–1173.

Brown, J. C., & Crippen, K. J. (2016a). Designing for culturally responsive science education through professional development. *International Journal of Science Education, 38*(3), 470–492

Brown, J. C., & Crippen, K. J. (2016b). The growing awareness inventory: Building capacity for culturally responsive science and mathematics with a structured observation protocol. *School Science and Mathematics, 116*(3), 127–138.

Brown, J. C., & Livstrom, I. C. (2020). Secondary science teachers' pedagogical design capacities for multicultural curriculum design. *Journal of Science Teacher Education, 31*(8), 821–840. https://doi.org/10.1080/1046 560X.2020.1756588

Brown, J. C., Ring-Whalen, E. A., Roehrig, G. H., & Ellis, J. (2018). Advancing culturally responsive science education in secondary classrooms through an induction course. *International Journal of Designs for Learning, 9*(1), 14–33.

Charity Hudley, A. H., & Mallinson, C. (2017). "It's worth our time": A model of culturally and linguistically supportive professional development for K-12 STEM educators. *Cultural Studies of Science Education, 12*(3), 637–660.

Chinn, P. W. (2015). Place and culture-based professional development: Cross-hybrid learning and the construction of ecological mindfulness. *Cultural Studies of Science Education, 10*(1), 121–134.

Chinn, P. W., Businger, S., Lance, K., Ellinwood, J. K., Stone, J. K. I., Spencer, L., . . . Rowland, S. K. (2014). Kahua A 'o – A learning foundation: Using Hawaiian language newspaper articles for Earth Science professional development. *Journal of Geoscience Education, 62*(2), 217–226.

Civitillo, S., Juang, L. P., Badra, M., & Schachner, M. K. (2019). The interplay between culturally responsive teaching, cultural diversity beliefs, and self-reflection: A multiple case study. *Teaching and Teacher Education, 77*, 341–351.

European Union Commission (2017). *Preparing teachers for diversity: The role of initial teacher education*. Final report to Directorate General for Education, Youth, Sport, and Culture of the European Commission. Luxembourg: Publications Office of the European Union. https://op.europa.eu/s/orks

Fakoyede, S. J., & Otulaja, F. S. (2020). Beads and beadwork as cultural artifacts used in mediating leaners' agentic constructs in science classrooms: A case for place-based learning. *Cultural Studies of Science Education, 15*, 193–210.

Gay, G. (2010). *Culturally responsive teaching: Theory, research, and practice*. New York, NY; Teachers College Press.

George, J. M. (2013). 'Do you have to pack?' – Preparing for culturally relevant science teaching in the Caribbean. *International Journal of Science Education, 35*(12), 2114–2131.

Gonzalez, N., Moll, L. C., & Amanti, C. (Eds.) (2005). *Funds of knowledge: Theorizing practices in households, communities and classrooms*. New York, NY: Routledge.

Grimberg, B. I., & Gummer, E. (2013). Teaching science from cultural points of intersection. *Journal of Research in Science Teaching, 50*(1), 12–32.

Hall, S. (1995). New cultures for old. In D. Massey & P. Jess (Eds.), *A place in the world? Places, cultures and globalization* (pp. 175–213). Oxford, UK: Oxford University Press.

Hayes, C., & Juárez, B. (2012). There is no culturally responsive teaching spoken here: A critical race perspective. *Democracy and Education, 20*(1), 1.

Kern, A. L., Honwad, S., & McLain, E. (2017). A culturally relevant teacher professional development for teaching climate change to Native American students. *Journal of Education and Training Studies, 5*(10), 1–17.

Kotluk, N., & Kocakaya, S. (2018). Culturally Relevant/Responsive Education: What do teachers think in Turkey? *Journal of Ethnic and Cultural Studies, 5*(2), 98–117.

Ladson-Billings, G. (1995). Toward a theory of culturally relevant pedagogy. *American Educational Research Journal, 32*(3), 465–491.

Ladson-Billings, G. (2009). *The dreamkeepers: Successful teachers of African American children* (2nd ed.). San Francisco, CA: John Wiley & Sons.

Ladson-Billings, G. (2014). Culturally relevant pedagogy 2.0: Aka the remix. *Harvard Educational Review, 84*(1), 74–84.

Lewis, E. B., Baker, D. R., & Helding, B. A. (2015). Science teaching reform through professional development: Teachers' use of a scientific classroom discourse community model. *Science Education, 99*(5), 896–931.

Luft, J. A., & Hewson, P. W. (2014). Research on teacher professional development programs in science. In N. G. Lederman & S. K. Abell (Eds.), *Handbook of research on science education* (2nd ed., pp. 889–909). New York, NY: Routledge.

Mensah, F. M. (2013). Theoretically and practically speaking, what is needed in diversity and equity in science teaching and learning? *Theory Into Practice, 52*(1), 66–72.

Mezirow, J. (1990). How critical reflection triggers transformative learning. *Fostering critical Reflection in Adulthood, 1*(20), 1–6.

Moseley, C., Bilica, K., Wandless, A., & Gdovin, R. (2014). Exploring the relationship between teaching efficacy and cultural efficacy of novice science teachers in high-needs schools. *School Science and Mathematics, 114*(7), 315–325.

Mullis, I. V. S., Martin, M. O., Foy, P., Kelly, D. L., & Fishbein, B. (2020). *TIMSS 2019 international results in mathematics and science*. Retrieved from Boston College, TIMSS & PIRLS International Study Center website: https://timssandpirls.bc.edu/timss2019/international-results/

Nam, Y., Roehrig, G., Kern, A., & Reynolds, B. (2013). Perceptions and practices of culturally relevant science teaching in American Indian classrooms. *International Journal of Science and Mathematics Education, 11*(1), 143–167.

National Research Council. (2012). *A framework for K-12 science education: Practices, crosscutting concepts, and core ideas*. Washington, DC: The National Academies Press.

Ngo, B. (2013). Culture consciousness among Hmong immigrant leaders: Beyond the dichotomy of cultural essentialism and cultural hybridity. *American Educational Research Journal, 50*(5), 958–990.

Nieto, S., & Bode, P. (2007). School reform and student learning: A multicultural perspective. *Multicultural Education: Issues and Perspectives*, 425–443.

OECD (2018). *The lives of teachers in diverse classrooms*. OECD Education Working Paper No. 198. OECD Publishing, Paris. www.oecd.org/officialdocuments/publicdisplaydocumentpdf/?cote=EDU/WKP(2019)6&docLanguage=En

Qureshi, A. M., & Demir, K. (2019). A comparative review of the literature on Pakistani science teachers' professional development. *Science Education International, 30*(3).

Rivera Maulucci, M. S., Brotman, J. S., & Fain, S. S. (2015). Fostering structurally transformative teacher agency through science professional development. *Journal of Research in Science Teaching, 52*(4), 545–559.

Sigman, M., Dublin, R., Anderson, A., Deans, N., Warburton, J., Matsumoto, G. I., . . . Harcharek, J. (2014). Using large marine ecosystems and cultural responsiveness as the context for professional development of teachers and scientists in ocean sciences. *Journal of Geoscience Education, 62*(1), 25–40.

Sleeter, C., & Bernal, D. (2004). Handbook on research on Multicultural Education. *Critical Pedagogy, Critical Race Theory, and Antiracist Education: Implications for Multicultural Education,* 240–255.

Suriel, R. L., & Atwater, M. M. (2012). From the contribution to the action approach: White teachers' experiences influencing the development of multicultural science curricula. *Journal of Research in Science Teaching, 49*(10), 1271–1295.

Sylva, T., Chinn, P., & Kinoshita, C. (2010). A culturally relevant agricultural and environmental course for K – 12 teachers in Hawaii. *Journal of Natural Resources and Life Sciences Education, 39*(1), 10–14.

Tolbert, S. (2015). "Because they want to teach you about their culture": Analyzing effective mentoring conversations between culturally responsible mentors and secondary science teachers of indigenous students in mainstream schools. *Journal of Research in Science Teaching, 52*(10), 1325–1361.

Upadhyay, B., Atwood, E., & Tharu, B. (2020). Actions for sociopolitical consciousness in a high school science class: A case study of ninth grade class with predominantly indigenous students. *Journal of Research in Science Teaching, 57*(7), 1119–1147.

Vaughn, M. S., & De Beer, J. (2020). Contextualising science and mathematics teacher professional development in rural areas. *Perspectives in Education, 38*(2), 213–226.

Villegas, A. M., & Lucas, T. (2002). Preparing culturally responsive teachers: Rethinking the curriculum. *Journal of Teacher Education, 53*(1), 20–32.

Wilson, S. M. (2013). Professional development for science teachers. *Science, 340*(6130), 310–313.

Yoon, J., & Martin, L. A. (2019). Infusing culturally responsive science curriculum into early childhood teacher preparation. *Research in Science Education, 49*(3), 697–710.

Yosso, T. J. (2005). Whose culture has capital? A critical race theory discussion of community cultural wealth. *Race Ethnicity and Education, 8*(1), 69–91.

22

PROFESSIONAL LEARNING COMMUNITIES ACROSS SCIENCE TEACHERS' CAREERS

The Importance of Differentiating Learning

Ron Blonder and Vicki Vescio

Teacher Professional Learning Communities

Teacher professional development (PD) is a fundamental means for improving teachers' content knowledge as well as developing their pedagogical practices in order to help them teach to high standards (Creemers et al., 2013). For a period that has spanned more than 20 years now, professional learning communities (PLCs) have been touted as one of those effective forms of teacher professional development. One can look back to Dufour and Eaker's (1998) publication on PLCs for enhancing student achievement to see that, in an educational environment where reforms come and go at a fast pace, PLCs have had staying power. At a conceptual level, the characteristics of PLCs make them appealing as a model for professional development because they are grounded in teachers collaboratively working together on their problems of practice to improve teaching and learning. As schools across the globe have experienced accountability pressures, the move to use PLCs has proliferated because policy makers hope they will, indeed, improve teaching in a manner that leads to greater student achievement.

The literature identifies five features that make PLCs a desirable form of PD (Bolam et al., 2005; DuFour, 2004; Vescio et al., 2008). Although there are some variations of these elements as scholars like Bolam et al. (2005) identify additional attributes they posit as necessary for the effective functioning of PLCs, in this chapter we recognize the five features that are prevalent across a variety of the literature. The first feature of PLCs is that they operate under a shared set of norms and values that are developed by its participants to provide a foundation for the work to be done in a PLC. The second characteristic of PLCs is that its members have a collective responsibility for, and focus on, student learning. Key here is that the attention to student learning occurs in a manner that underscores the experiences of the learner as a result of how one teaches (Hadar & Brody, 2013). This is in contrast to using the work in PLCs as a way to simply try to improve students' scores on standardized tests (Cochran-Smith & Lytle, 2009). The third feature of PLCs is that its members engage in reflective dialogue about their teaching as well as student learning. The fourth characteristic is an underlying focus on collaboration. The final feature of PLCs is that the educators involved must be willing to examine and make public their own teaching practices (Vescio et al., 2008). Collectively, these five underlying features of PLCs work in tandem to create a theoretical foundation for successful teacher PD.

However, at a practical level, the enactment of PLCs has been more difficult. Based on the premise that PD is key to enhancing teachers' content knowledge and practices, many school districts

DOI: 10.4324/9781003098478-26

have mandated PLCs. This has led to a misunderstanding and misuse of PLCs relative to using the foundational features on which they are based. Specifically, there has been a trend to call all meetings of teachers PLCs regardless of the work that occurs (Vescio & Adams, 2015; Vescio et al., 2008; Watson, 2014). Even more troubling, school-level administrators have taken to mandating what happens in PLC meetings, and teachers simply comply, organizing their PLC meetings in a way that accomplishes handed-down tasks. The end result here is that educators look at PLCs as a part of accountability measures rather than as a viable path for professional development.

Fortunately, there are examples in the literature where groups of educators are engaging in PLCs in a manner that is faithful to its foundational characteristics (Fresko & Nasser-Abu Alhija, 2015; Lambson, 2010; Leite, 2006; Liu, 2013; Tammets et al., 2019). These examples provide us with a way to explore what is happening in PLCs as well as the impact they have on teacher learning. In examining the literature that compares both science and non-science teacher PLCs across the career span, we found similarities and differences that helped to provide us with a more complete view of the existing research. As a result, we decided to try to maintain a focus on science teachers' participation in PLCs, but when necessary, we broadened the scope of the literature and focused on the collective body of research related to PLCs across teachers' careers. The final question that we decided would undergird our work in the chapter is: How do PLCs address teacher needs during each stage of their careers?

As mentioned previously, what counts as a PLC has become ubiquitous in the everyday work of teaching (Vescio & Adams, 2015). This has led to a proliferation of teacher PD efforts that actually use the tenets of PLCs as a foundation but do not label what is being done as a PLC endeavor. Rather, such terms are used as teacher study groups (Lambson, 2010), communities of practice (Eshchar-Netz & Vedder-Weis, 2021), learning communities (Leite, 2006), teacher professional communities (Liu, 2013), and induction seminars or programs (Fresko & Nasser-Abu Alhija, 2015; Tammets et al., 2019). In our collaboration as we conceptualized this chapter, we began to question whether what something is called is as important as the work that is being done. With this in mind, we decided to focus on what was happening in the PD rather than what it was specifically called. We looked at the purpose of the research and the questions, the process that the teachers engaged in during their collaborative efforts, what the focus of results centered on, and the implications that the authors discussed.

As a result, the research articles we used to help us answer our overarching question focused on examining teacher collaboration and reflective dialogue that resulted in critical conversations about student learning and teachers' practices. We deemed that these essential elements connected well with the characteristic features of PLCs regardless of what a particular PD endeavor was called. We do not claim that this chapter engages in a systematic review of the literature, rather, it is focused on a sample of the research (Snyder, 2019) that helps us to address our interest of looking at PLCs across the careers of teachers. When conducting our search we looked for research published over the 15-year span from 2005 to 2020 to give us a stronger sense of trends in the literature. Additionally, we used search terms such as PLCs and teacher professional development, PLCs and science teacher professional development, PLCs and novice teachers, and PLCs and veteran teachers. We also substituted the term PLCs in each search with the terms collaborative teacher groups and communities of practice. The results of our search yielded a small group of studies that will be talked about in the context of attempting to answer our driving question for this chapter.

Phases of Teachers' Learning (PD) Needs Throughout Their Careers

Teachers' PLCs support their professional development among their peers. The PLC may include science teachers from the same school (e.g., Eylon et al., 2020; Jones et al., 2013) learning together in a PLC, or teachers who teach a specific subject (e.g., chemistry, physics) in a regional PLC

(Blonder & Waldman, 2021; Levy et al., 2020). In both contexts, the PLC usually includes teachers at different levels of seniority. Eshchar-Netz and Vedder-Weiss (2021) refer to the Community of Practice (CoP) model, where learning takes place through apprenticeship (Lave & Wenger, 1991). In the apprenticeship approach for PD, experienced members of the community enculturate newcomers, who gradually move from peripheral participation in the community's practice to a more central participation (Lave & Wenger, 1991). Eshchar-Netz and Vedder-Weiss (2021) identified three limitations of this approach to teachers' PD: (1) novice teachers can seldom act as legitimate peripheral participants, since they are obliged to do the same work that veterans do; (2) veterans' learning is neglected because they are expected to teach the novices; and (3) the power dynamics between veterans and novices may constrain the group's reflective inquiry and, consequently, its learning.

In order to provide suitable conditions within the PLC for the development of teachers in different career phases,[1] there is a need to understand the life cycle of a teacher's career and to study how the PLC can address the needs of teachers in each career phase, taking into account the PLC characteristics (Clarke & Hollingsworth, 2002). The study of teachers' PD is based on the life-long-learner notion (Baltes, 1987), whereby the teacher is perceived as a professional who continues to develop throughout their career. A model, developed by Huberman (1993), has become the touchstone for researchers in this field worldwide (Day, 2012; Fessler, 1995; Rolls & Plauborg, 2009; Sikes, 1985). This model suggests five career phases in a teacher's professional life cycle (Huberman, 1993). Understanding these phases as well as teachers' indecisions in each of them is essential in order to provide teachers with PD frameworks that address their needs (Clarke & Hollingsworth, 2002). The phases, described next, are based on empirical studies and are presented according to the teachers' years of experience (Figure 22.1).

First Phase: Career Entry (1–3 Years)

Teachers undergo a process of survival and discovery in their early career years, during which the gulf between their professional ideals and daily classroom life is exposed, and the self-doubts and initial enthusiasm are entwined. The survival motive is related to reality shock, e.g., difficulties in instructional management and dealing with disciplinary issues that occupy the teachers' time. The discovery motive is related to the teacher's initial enthusiasm about teaching and to being part of a new group of colleagues in school. The balance between these two motives (survival and discovery) influences the way teachers experience their first 3 years in the profession.

Second Phase: Stabilization (4–6 Years)

In this phase, teachers enter a period of stabilization, marked by a definitive commitment to the profession (or choosing to leave it). The teacher has already mastered the profession, has pedagogical stability, and can more easily navigate complex situations in class; she feels comfortable in class and experiences joy and stability. In addition, teachers in this phase feel that they belong to their colleagues' group. This phase is described as a junction in which teachers choose whether to leave their teaching career or to continue and develop their teaching identity (Day, 2012).

Third Phase: The Mid-Career Years (7–18 Years)

These years are marked by periods of experimentation and activism, or by a period of reassessment, during which teachers take stock of their careers and question their career choices. Huberman (1993) suggests that the reassessment phase is based on teachers feeling varying degrees of self-doubt, perceiving the routine of the teaching profession, and the lack of career opportunities. On the other hand, teachers can experience this career phase as an explorative phase. They already have control

Years of Teaching   **Themes/Phases**

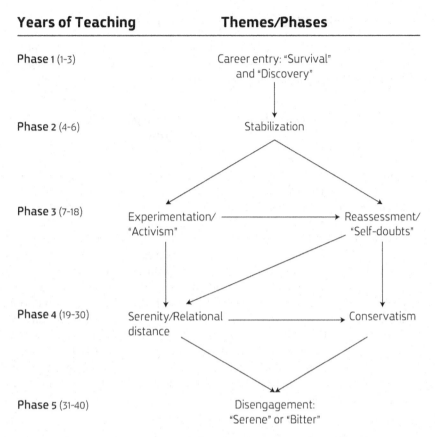

Phase 1 (1-3)   Career entry: "Survival"
                          and "Discovery"

Phase 2 (4-6)   Stabilization

Phase 3 (7-18)   Experimentation/ ⟶ Reassessment/
                      "Activism"   "Self-doubts"

Phase 4 (19-30)   Serenity/Relational ⟶ Conservatism
                      distance

Phase 5 (31-40)   Disengagement:
                          "Serene" or "Bitter"

Figure 22.1   Five career phases in a teacher's professional life cycle
Source: Modified from Huberman (1993).

of the basics of teaching, and they look for ways to vary their teaching in order to get better results. Additionally, teachers in this phase feel that routine teaching leads to burnout, and they look for new challenges to avoid this feeling. The challenges can be inside school or beyond, and this may lead to collaboration with other teachers.

Fourth Phase: Serenity (19–30 Years)

Teachers experience a period in which there is a gradual loss of energy and enthusiasm; however, this is compensated for by a greater sense of confidence and self-acceptance. This phase diverges into two possibilities: serenity and relational distance or conservatism. Teachers experience a shift, from teaching with fewer attempts to try new things with their students, to a phase involving more mechanical as well as more relaxed teaching. Serenity was found to be accompanied by a greater relational distance; these teachers felt that they had fulfilled their ambitions and maintained relations with only teachers who they appreciate; they do not volunteer to lead others. However, teachers in this phase, who will be at the age of 50–60, can also become more conservative, since there is a link between age and dogmatism. They tend to complain about their students, the new generation of teachers, and the school administrations (Huberman, 1993). These teachers are less inclined to be involved in leading changes or supporting their young colleagues and may even resist any proposed changes.

Fifth Phase: Disengagement (31–40 Years)

This is the last phase of a teacher's career. Teachers in their late-career stage move to a period of disengagement, manifested either by serenity or disappointment and bitterness. At this stage, they tend not to take on additional responsibilities beyond their teaching role (Huberman, 1993).

New Teacher Benefits From Participating in Learning Communities

As discussed previously, new teachers go through a process of survival and discovery that is characterized by learning to persist in the everyday context of delivering lessons and managing students (Rolls & Plauborg, 2009). At a theoretical level, this means that participation in professional development rooted in the tenets of PLCs should be helpful in supporting new teachers through this time of survival and discovery. In fact, a sample of the existing literature does indicate that new teachers get support through participating in professional learning communities with their colleagues. Specifically, research by Fresko and Nasser-Abu Alhija (2015) indicates that when novice teachers collectively engage in learning communities together, they benefit from being able to focus on needs that are specific to this stage of their careers. Additionally, a larger group of studies demonstrate that new teachers are supported in their professional growth through participating in learning communities comprised of teachers at varying levels of their careers (Jones et al., 2013; Lambson, 2010; Leite, 2006; Liu, 2013; Rinke, 2009; Tammets et al., 2019). In this section chapter, we provide an overview of this literature on new teacher benefits from participating in PLCs. It is important to note here that there was not a predominant body of literature on novice science teachers' participation in PLCs. As a result, in this section of our review, we examined literature from varying disciplines to provide greater depth to our review.

New Teacher-Only Professional Learning Communities

Literature that exclusively examined the learning of novice teachers, as a result of participating together in a type of PLC that met the criteria outlined for this review, was limited, and we found only one study that fit these conditions. Fresko and Nasser-Abu Alhija (2015) studied new teacher participation in an Israeli induction program that functioned as a PLC. Specifically, new teachers were required to attend a seminar that spanned over 56 hours of participation time. The seminar was based on the premise that new teachers have unique needs, and the goal was to have these novice educators engage in reflective, collaborative activities around issues that arose in their day-to-day teaching. Data analyzed from interviews and observations show that the focus of the seminar changed over time. Early in the academic year there was a need for the teachers to discuss difficulties they were having relative to classroom management, adjusting to the rules and norms of their schools, and in approaches to working with parents. As the year went on, however, the focus of the seminars shifted toward strategies for motivating students, assessing learning, and the emerging professional identities of the novice educators. The authors also found that across the span of the year the emotional and coping support provided by the PLC was an important part of the seminar for the novice teachers. Fresko and Nasser-Abu Alhija concluded that the induction PLC seminars were successful because all of the teachers were at the same level professionally, and that this gave them a safe space away from their schools where they typically felt they needed to do everything correctly. This was important, as they did not feel the pressure to be perfect and the seminar allowed them to "expose professional difficulties" (p. 45) in a space where they knew they could get support and assistance.

New Teacher Benefits From Mixed Experience-Level PLCs

A larger body of literature exists that explores the learning of novice teachers when they participate in PLC-type professional development in groups that contain teachers from varying stages of their careers. In some of these studies, the purpose of the collaborative efforts was to support new teachers' learning (Lambson, 2010; Leite, 2006; Tammets et al., 2019). In another small group of studies, PLCs met for varying reasons, and the results were, in part, discussed relative to aspects of novice teacher participation (Jones et al., 2013; Liu, 2013; Rinke, 2009). Collectively, these studies provide a picture of the benefits and potential barriers or drawbacks for using PLCs to support the growth of teachers who are at the beginning of their careers.

The first group of studies examined for this section of our review consisted of those that looked at novice teacher learning as a function of participating in learning communities that were comprised of teachers from various career stages (Lambson, 2010; Leite, 2006; Tammets et al., 2019). Despite the mixed levels of the teachers, these studies all focused on the experiences of novice teachers as a result of participating in some type of learning community. Each study called the teacher group that formed the basis of their research by varying names, including study groups (Lambson, 2010), extended professional communities (Tammets et al., 2019), and teaching practice groups (TPG) (Leite, 2006). Collectively, these studies demonstrate that participation in these collaborative efforts helps novice teachers, but that this assistance also comes with important considerations for educators to be aware of.

As would be expected, each of these studies talks of the benefits novice teachers experience from participating in professional development endeavors that involve teacher collaboration and reflective dialogue. For example, Tammets et al. (2019) studied learning and knowledge building (LKB) of novice teachers in Estonia as they participated in an extended professional community with mentors from their workplace and experts from a university. The authors defined an extended professional community as one that fosters interaction among people from different sub-communities of the same profession and indicated that it should "enable bidirectional transfer of knowledge" (p. 37) to foster both individual learning as well as knowledge-building practices across communities. Results from the study suggest that mentors in the extended professional communities were important in supporting the professional learning of novice educators. Additionally, Leite (2006) examined how a teaching practice group (TPG) contributed to the growth of new physical science teachers (chemistry and physics teachers) in Portugal. The TPG included members with a diversity of expertise, namely, teacher trainees (without teaching experience but with updated scientific and methodological knowledge), a mentor with some teaching experience in schools, and a university supervisor. The idea was that the mentors and supervisors would guide the teacher trainees to help them to learn from their own mistakes. The results indicate that to overcome the difficulties that these trainees anticipated they would encounter as novice teachers in their new schools, they intended to count on experienced teachers to help them. Finally, Lambson (2010) explored the experiences of three novice (1st-year) teachers who participated in an ongoing teachers study group as newcomers. The study group consisted of 4th-, 5th-, and 6th-grade teachers (students' age 8–10 years old) as well as the assistant principal and a facilitator who was a university teacher educator. Using the framework of legitimate peripheral participation espoused by Lave and Wenger (1991), the three novice teachers moved from peripheral to more central participation as their levels of talk and sharing increased across the school year.

Along with the positive impacts of professional learning community experiences for novice teachers, these studies demonstrate that there are also cautions that can be garnered. For example, Leite (2006) advises that, "the success of learning communities . . . will greatly depend on members' commitment, as well as on their capacity to adjust to the perceived needs of all members" (p. 21).

Lambson (2010) further suggests that how interactions are facilitated in PLCs, typically by experienced teachers, administrators, or university partners, is important for providing acceptance and access for new teachers to become full participating members who learn from as well as contribute to the learning of others. These cautions indicate a need for thoughtful consideration in terms of the expectations being placed on those who facilitate and participate in PLCs regardless of their career stage. The onus is on school administrators to move past assumptions that teachers know how to collaborate and that experienced teachers understand how to be leaders in learning communities. The key here is for administrators to articulate the goal of the PLC and to think through how different teachers at different career stages can contribute to that goal.

Another small group of studies we looked at for this review examined teacher learning across a wider spectrum of career stages, yet their results parsed out some key points about the learning and participation of novice teachers in learning community-type professional development endeavors. For example, Jones et al. (2013) examined the perceptions of and experiences with PLCs that all elementary science teachers in an urban district were required to attend. The model used for their PLC meetings included the teachers examining state and national standards for a particular science topic, considering their school's science test scores for that topic, and having discussions on ways to teach and assess the topic to ensure students would achieve the standards. Teachers were asked about the utility of participating in the science PLC that had members at different career stages. A majority of the participants believed that the PLC's experience was more useful for novice teachers (less than 3 years of experience) than for experienced ones (more than 3 years of experience). Additionally, doubts were raised regarding the ability of new teachers to share valuable knowledge with veteran teachers. In another study, Liu (2013) examined a learning community that engaged in joint lesson planning conferences in the context of language teacher reform in a university English education department in China. Liu conducted an analysis of the micro level of teacher-to-teacher interactions of a mixed experience group of educators and found that 59 of the 67 interactions reflected an expert-to-novice model of interaction. Liu concludes that the interplay between interactions and identities produced an asymmetrical power relationship that limited the participants' equal access to discourse resources, and hence constrained opportunities for learning of those with less power, typically more novice educators. In a final study that we examined for this section, Rinke (2009) claims that although research has shown the importance of teacher learning in communities, it has not explored generational perspectives within those communities. Her study followed two science teachers who represented the generation gap within a PLC. Rinke found that generational differences influenced the teacher's philosophy and perceptions of their role. She posits that this gap hinders possible collaborations of teachers from different generations within the PLC.

Despite the benefits that novice teachers can experience from participating in PLCs, this final group of studies that we reviewed collectively raise some important issues. Since the majority of PLCs seem to be conducted in cross-career level groupings, it is imperative to consider the impact experienced teachers can have on novice teachers. As Leite (2006) indicates, novice teachers expect to be able to depend on experienced teachers to support their learning in professional communities. Yet, if experienced teachers do not value the contributions of novice teachers, if they dominate the discursive interactions, and if generational gaps inhibit their collaboration, the potential of PLCs to foster the growth of novice teachers will not live up to its full potential.

PLC Characteristics That Enable Teachers From Different Stages to Benefit

As presented in Figure 22.1, after teachers go through their career entry and the stabilization stage, multiple trajectories bring those teachers to the last stage of disengagement from teaching.

Depending on their path, in their leaving stage, teachers can be either bitter or serene. Huberman (1989) explained that "The most harmonious trajectory would be:

Experimentation → Serenity → (serene) disengagement.
The most problematic trajectories would be these two:
Reassessment → (bitter) disengagement
Reassessment → Conservatism → (bitter) disengagement" (p. 38).

Being a PLC member can provide teachers with experiences, collaboration, and support that direct them toward a harmonious trajectory. Reassessment will be replaced by experimentation and activism if the PLC provides a supportive platform to discuss science learning in relation to teachers' own pedagogy and the possibility of examining new teaching practices for dealing with students' difficulties. This process might help teachers avoid sticking to routine teaching and conservatism and instead experience the midcareer stage as an explorative phase. Waldman (2020) studied the professional development of chemistry teachers who participated in regional PLCs in Israel. She used mixed methods (questionnaires and interviews) to learn how the teachers' participation in the PLCs influenced their professional development at different phases of their teaching career. She found that teachers in the midcareer and late stages (phases 3–5, Figure 22.1) reported that they greatly benefited from the implementation of new pedagogical ideas that they had experienced in their PLC. The new pedagogical resources that were introduced to the PLC were based on research in science teaching (such as diagnostic questionnaires and new chemistry lab experiments) provided by the PLC leaders, as well as resources for chemistry teaching proposed by the PLC members based on their experience. The PLC provided a venue to collaboratively discuss and examine these resources (Blonder & Waldman, 2021; Waldman & Blonder, 2020).

New teachers, on the other hand, reported that they hardly implemented any new resources. They reported that they benefited by interacting with more experienced PLC members, who they trust. The resulting model, which explained the PD of this group, included only trust (and not implementation of new practices). This result was also supported by interviews in which teachers in the first phase of their career stated that they were unable to implement new practices from the PLC in their class. The findings regarding these teachers are in agreement with the literature about their initial years of teaching. During this period, teachers face many professional challenges, since they lack the requisite knowledge and experience to deal with basic pedagogical issues of class management, and they focus mainly on surviving in the profession. Moreover, they do not tend to try new practices (Feiman-Namser et al., 1999; Huberman, 1989). By analyzing the interviews, the researchers found that the new teachers describe how colleagues in the PLC, who they trust, provide them with what they need for professional development, e.g., teaching materials, basic pedagogies for teaching the chemical content, and dealing with disciplinary issues. They felt confident in sharing in the PLC their difficulties, and in consulting with the more experienced teachers. In this PLC network, which serves as a regional model (as opposed to the school PLC), no hierarchical relationship exists among the PLC members. Therefore, the new teachers can reveal all their difficulties without being afraid of negative consequences that can affect their job.

For teachers in the second and the third groups, both variables (trust and adaptation of new practices) were found to contribute to their PD. Teachers in these phases have already established their basic teaching practice and are open to varying their teaching strategies. Their trust in their colleagues in the PLC was found to be the main predictor for teachers' PD. Namely, it is most important for teachers who are in the second and third phases of the career to build trust, and upon building this trust, they will be more willing to try out new teaching strategies that they experience in the PLC meetings. Teachers in the second phase usually experience professional stability and security, and the PLC can push them beyond focusing on their own teaching. In the third phase, the teacher has two possibilities (experimentation or reassessment). In this phase the PLC can lead teachers, who already have experienced the routine work of teaching, to choose the experimentation method of their choice. The PLC can provide a safe and supportive avenue for collaboration. However, that collaboration should be designed in a way that will not position the experienced teachers as mentors for the new teachers (Jones et al., 2013; Leite, 2006).

Collaborative examination of digital resources was implemented in PLCs for English teachers in Iran (Zonoubi et al., 2017). New and veteran teachers were engaged in discussions concerning resources; they were observed by supervisors three times and provided feedback on their teaching. In addition, the teachers observed their peers (at all experience levels), and they were encouraged to use digital resources and social networks (for example, LinkedIn, ResearchGate, and Telegram) as avenues to build their professional learning. They found that experienced teachers improved their "pedagogical self-efficacy" in terms of "learning more innovative teaching strategies" (p. 5). Novice teachers' pedagogical self-efficacy improved in terms of gaining confidence about their pedagogical decision-making, and they became more autonomous. Factors that led to this included collaborative reflection and learning through peer observations as well as feedback from a supervisor. Both teacher groups, novice and veterans, experienced growth in language proficiency. The authors suggest that critical thinking around teaching practices was how the PLC helped to change this self-efficacy.

Eshchar-Netz and Vedder-Weiss (2021) found that collaborative work on a new pedagogical aspect was an activity that could contribute to the PD of new and veteran science teachers in the PLC. They studied the regional community of practice (CoP) of 30 elementary science teachers (grades 3–9, 9–14 years old) and found that a collaborative planning discourse contributes to new teachers as well as to veterans. They stressed that in planning sessions, the teaching of the lesson has not yet taken place. "Hence, multiple points of view and suggestions . . . are legitimate and [can] be equally correct. . . . Planning is . . . a hypothetical debate in which uncertainty and doubt are considered legitimate and pose minimal risk to teachers' face." Therefore, the interactions in a planning session are less threatening. The authors found that the experienced teachers partially participated as mentors and deliberated on the content; they demonstrated how teachers examine different options and evaluate both the advantages and disadvantages. However, they also moderated their expert status by explicitly countering their own suggestion, positioning themselves as experts who can still learn from discussions with their colleagues in the group. The new teacher positioned herself as a mentee and therefore felt comfortable to "ask naïve questions and seek advice to advance her learning" (p. 14). The teachers in the co-planning session did not work to maintain their status, since the context of the planning did not force them to defend their teaching. Instead, the veteran teacher invited her less experienced colleagues to intervene and improve her suggestion for the lesson in order to plan the "best lesson plan," which will be later shared with the entire community of teachers.

In the chemistry PLC study (Waldman, 2020), trust did not contribute to the PD of teachers in the fourth and the fifth phases. These veteran teachers, who have many years of teaching experience, did not feel threatened by other teachers in the PLC. They have permanent jobs in their schools; therefore, they cannot be affected by the teachers in the PLC. These teachers implemented in their classes many practices that they had experienced in the PLC meeting, and this process contributed to their PD. This finding is interesting, since these teachers are very experienced and, according to Huberman, they should be at a relational distance, conservatism (phase 4), and even disengagement (phase 5). Often, at these stages the teachers are less enthusiastic (Huberman, 1993) and less willing to collaborate (Richter et al., 2011). However, Day and Gu (2007) characterized teachers in this phase as possessing a high sense of obligation and motivation. Their free-choice membership in the PLC can support the development of motivation by bringing new energy to teachers so that they will try new strategies in their class, along with the respect they receive from the other PLC members who appreciate their experience.

Discussion

Teachers' careers consist of different stages, each characterized by different needs, self-efficacy beliefs, and perceptions regarding the teaching profession and the teacher's identity (Day, 2012; Fessler, 1995; Huberman, 1989, 1993; Rolls & Plauborg, 2009; Sikes, 1985). Nevertheless, the main finding of the current review is that the literature about PLCs does not address the differentiated characteristics of teachers at different career stages. The few studies that referred to teachers at different career stages in the PLC distinguished only between the new teachers and the experienced ones (Ben Zion Raviv, 2019; Eshchar-Netz & Vedder-Weiss, 2021; Jones et al., 2013; Rinke, 2009) or examined only the new teachers (Fresko & Nasser-Abu Alhija, 2015). These studies did not refine their observations regarding the other stages discussed in the literature that divide teachers' career trajectories as a whole, from graduation to retirement, into various phases or stages. Research on new teachers' professional development through PLCs shows that teachers benefit from participating in PLCs. They learn from the more experienced members (Eshchar-Netz & Vedder-Weiss, 2021; Fresko & Nasser-Abu Alhija, 2015; Jones et al., 2013; Leite, 2006), who they perceive as mentors (Eshchar-Netz & Vedder-Weiss, 2021; Leite, 2006), and they communicate more with the more experienced teachers (Ben Zion Raviv, 2019). Thus, the experienced teachers assumed the status of mentors, which did not allow them to be wrong (Eshchar-Netz & Vedder-Weiss, 2021), and limited their opportunities to learn by communicating with others. Eshchar-Netz and Vedder-Weiss suggested that the process of collaborative planning (a new teacher with an experienced teacher) can reduce the need of experienced teachers to protect their status and that it provides them with opportunities to learn at the PLC meetings. Collaborative work on new digital resources was found to achieve the same positive effect of experienced teachers' PD.

However, Richter et al. (2011) found that teachers at later career stages prefer to personally develop their professional knowledge by reading the literature and are less willing to collaborate with peers. Namely, collaborative learning is not necessarily their preferred mode for professional learning. PLCs can address veteran teachers' preferences by providing connections to current research in science education. Academic perspective in science teaching can provide the veteran teachers with opportunities to be exposed to innovative ideas, materials, and pedagogies in science teaching, which are developed in science education research. PLC meetings should also include collaboration sessions to examine the innovative ideas. In these sessions, veterans will be able to share their experiences and demonstrate how they examine new ideas in a way that will benefit new teachers who can learn about pedagogical considerations (Eshchar-Netz & Vedder-Weiss, 2021). The veteran teachers will benefit from the co-examination of the innovative teaching, and they will be less threatened because they still do not have any experience with the discussed pedagogy; therefore, they will be able to learn from other perspectives, as well as be exposed to innovative ideas.

In the current literature review, we found only one study that examined the full range of teachers' career stages in the PLC (Waldman, 2020). This study found that trust, which is usually considered as an essential condition that enables teacher collaboration and their willingness to share their students' outcomes and difficulties (Hoy & Tschannen-Moran, 1999), plays a different role at different career stages. Additionally, it was found that teachers' implementation of new practices contributes differently to teachers at different stages. This study is significant, since it shows the different mechanisms by which PLCs influenced teachers at different stages. The results can guide PLC leaders when they plan their PLC meeting that includes, for example, the extent that attention is given to build trust, or at what stages it is effective to ask teachers to implement new pedagogies and to share their insights with other PLC members. More studies are needed to reveal other dimensions in which teachers' PD is developed differently in the PLC for teachers at different stages.

Recommendations

Using PLCs as an avenue for the professional development of science teachers across their career spans comes with careful considerations that have not routinely been addressed either in the existing literature or in the practice of conducting PLCs. As a result, our first recommendation is that scholars across all disciplines need to design research that more closely examines what might be lost or gained by expectations in PLC work that do not currently account for this differentiation. Having additional research to deepen the conversation around teachers' differing needs will allow for greater intentionality in the design of PLCs, and subsequent support for teacher learning at all career stages. Most significant, an expanded base of literature will bring forth an increased awareness that PLCs include teachers who have different needs, which can lead to fundamental changes in the intent and design of PLCs. This avenue of research has important implications for university faculty who work in partnership with local schools as well as for school administrators who use PLCs to support teacher learning.

Beyond working to increase the literature base on PLCs across the career span of teachers, our second recommendation is rooted in practical aspects of university faculty, school administrators, and teachers immediately enacting steps to consider this important phenomenon. In a significant number of school districts, the top-down directive to implement PLC comes with a lack of consideration for the needs of teachers. Whether PLCs are used in partnership with universities, are a mandated or voluntary part of professional development, or are used in individual schools, it is incumbent upon educators at all levels to consider key elements of the structure of the PLC. First, teachers should not be put into collaborative groups with the assumption that they all need the same thing and that they know how to collaborate to get there. Second, experienced teachers should not always be put in the role of mentor or leader, as this often disregards their own learning needs. It follows, then, that careful consideration of who will facilitate the work of teachers in a PLC needs to occur, and that those individuals will need to develop an understanding of how to differentiate the work of the PLC to maximize teacher learning. Finally, administrators (or university faculty) need to consider the composition of the members of a PLC. Specifically, should the PLC consist of new teachers alone, experienced teachers alone, or a mix of career-level teachers? And, if it is the latter, how will the work of the PLC be differentiated to meet various teachers' needs?

Our review of the literature on learning across the stages of teachers' careers as outlined by Huberman (1993) has produced some important considerations. Moving forward, we recommend that this line of research be extended to provide a greater depth of understanding. Additionally, we believe there are steps that can be taken immediately to address the issues relative to how PLCs are currently conceived and enacted. We believe that embracing the idea of differentiating PLCs can help to make them a more impactful endeavor for addressing the learning of all teachers.

Note

1. We will use both terms, *phase* and *stage* (Huberman, 1993).

References

Baltes, P. B. (1987). Theoretical propositions of life-span developmental psychology: On the dynamics between growth and decline. *Developmental Psychology*, *23*(5), 611–626. https://doi.org/10.1037/0012-1649.23.5.611

Ben Zion Raviv, G. (2019). *The characteristics of physics teachers attending a professional learning community in terms of their collegial interactions, perceptions about physics teaching, and their teaching practice* Bar-Ilan University]. Israel. file:///D:/my%20doc/papers/Book_PLC_Vescio/25.11.20/RavivGuyBenZion_physics%20teachers%20 in%20Israel.pdf

Blonder, R., & Waldman, R. (2021). The role of a WhatsApp group of a professional learning community of chemistry teachers in the development of their knowledge. In A. Information Resources Management (Ed.), *Research anthology on facilitating new educational practices through communities of learning* (pp. 820–843). IGI Global. https://doi.org/10.4018/978-1-7998-7294-8.ch041

Bolam, R., McMahon, A., Stoll, L., Thomas, S., & Wallace, M. (2005). *Creating and sustaining effective professional learning communities (No. RR637)* http://effect.tka.hu/documents/OtherLibraryElements/Creating-and-Sustaining-Effective-Professional-Learning-Communities-Extracto.pdf

Clarke, A., & Hollingsworth, H. (2002). Elaborating a model of teacher professional growth. *Teaching and Teacher Education, 18*, 947–967. https://doi.org/10.1016/S0742-051X(02)00053-7

Cochran-Smith, M., & Lytle, S. (2009). *Inquiry as stance: Practitioner research for the next generation.* New York, NY: Teacher's College Press.

Creemers, B., Kyriakides, L., & Antoniou, P. (2013). *Teacher professional development for improving quality of teaching.* Dordrecht: Springer Netherlands.

Day, C. (2012). New lives of teachers. *Teacher Education Quarterly, 39*(1), 7–26. www.jstor.org/stable/23479560

Day, C., & Gu, Q. (2007). Variations in the conditions for teachers' professional learning and development: Sustaining commitment and effectiveness over a career. *Oxford Review of Education, 33*(4), 423–443. https://doi.org/10.1080/03054980701450746

DuFour, R. (2004). What is a 'professional learning community'? *Educational Leadership, 61*(8), 6–11.

DuFour, R., & Eaker, R. (1998). *Professional learning communities at work: Best practices for enhancing student achievement.* Bloomington, IN: National Educational Service.

Eshchar-Netz, L., & Vedder-Weiss, D. (2021). Teacher learning in communities of practice: The affordances of co-planning for novice and veteran teachers' learning. *Journal of Research in Science Teaching, 58*(3), 366–391. https://doi.org/https://doi.org/10.1002/tea.21663

Eylon, B.-S., Scherz, Z., & Bagno, E. (2020). Professional learning communities of science teachers: Theoretical and practical perspectives. In Y. Ben-David Kolikant, D. Martinovic, & M. Milner-Bolotin (Eds.), *STEM teachers and teaching in the digital era: Professional expectations and advancement in the 21st century schools* (pp. 65–89). Springer International Publishing. https://doi.org/10.1007/978-3-030-29396-3_5

Feiman-Namser, S., Carver, C., Schwille, S., & Yusko, B. (1999). Beyond support: Taking new teachers seriously as learners. A better beginning: Supporting and mentoring new teachers. In M. Scherer (Ed.), *A better beginning: Supporting and mentoring new teachers.* Alexandria, VA: Association for Supervision and Curriculum.

Fessler, R. (1995). Dynamics of teacher career stages. In T. Guskey & M. Huberman (Eds.), *Professional development in education: New paradigms and practices* (pp. 171–192). New York, NY: Teachers College Press.

Fresko, B., & Nasser-Abu Alhija, F. (2015). Induction seminars as professional learning communities for beginning teachers. *Asia-Pacific Journal of Teacher Education, 43*(1), 36–48. https://doi.org/10.1080/13598 66X.2014.928267

Hadar, L. L., & Brody, D. L. (2013). The interaction between group processes and personal professional trajectories in a professional development community for teacher educators. *Journal of Teacher Education, 64*(2), 145–161. https://doi.org/10.1177/0022487112466898

Hoy, W. K., & Tschannen-Moran, M. (1999). Five faces of trust: An empirical confirmation in urban elementary schools. *Journal of School leadership, 9*(3), 184–208. https://doi.org/10.1177/105268469900900301

Huberman, M. (1989). The professional life cycle of teachers. *Teachers College Record, 91*(1), 31–57.

Huberman, M. (1993). *The lives of teachers.* London: Cassell.

Jones, M. G., Gardner, G. E., Robertson, L., & Robert, S. (2013). Science Professional Learning Communities: Beyond a singular view of teacher professional development. *International Journal of Science Education, 35*(10), 1756–1774. https://doi.org/10.1080/09500693.2013.791957

Lambson, D. (2010). Novice teachers learning through participation in a teacher study group. *Teaching and Teacher Education, 26*(8), 1660–1668. https://doi.org/10.1016/j.tate.2010.06.017

Lave, J., & Wenger, E. (1991). *Situated learning: Legitimate peripheral participation.* Cambridge Universty Press. www.amazon.com/gp/product/0521423740?ie=UTF8&tag=jrtvre-20&linkCode=as2&camp=1789&crea tive=9325&creativeASIN=0521423740

Leite, L. (2006). Prospective physical sciences teachers' willingness to engage in learning communities. *European Journal of Teacher Education, 29*(1), 3–22. https://doi.org/10.1080/02619760500478589

Levy, S., Bagno, E., Berger, H., & Eylon, B.-S. (2020). Motivators, contributors, and inhibitors to physics teacher-leaders' professional development in a program of professional learning communities. In

Y. Ben-David Kolikant, D. Martinovic, & M. Milner-Bolotin (Eds.), *STEM teachers and teaching in the digital era: Professional expectations and advancement in the 21st century schools* (pp. 159–184). Springer International Publishing. https://doi.org/10.1007/978-3-030-29396-3_9

Liu, Y. (2013). The social organisation of talk-in-interaction at work in a language teacher professional community. *Learning, Culture and Social Interaction, 2*(3), 195–207. https://doi.org/https://doi.org/10.1016/j.lcsi.2013.06.001

Richter, D., Kunter, M., Klusmann, U., Lüdtke, O., & Baumert, J. (2011). Professional development across the teaching career: Teachers' uptake of formal and informal learning opportunities. *Teaching and Teacher Education, 27*(1), 116–126. https://doi.org/https://doi.org/10.1016/j.tate.2010.07.008

Rinke, C. R. (2009). Exploring the generation gap in urban schools: Generational perspectives in professional learning communities. *Education and Urban Society, 42*(1), 3–24. https://doi.org/10.1177/0013124509342699

Rolls, S., & Plauborg, H. (2009). Teachers' career trajectories: An examination of research. In B. M., B. U., P. H., & R. S. (Eds.), *Teachers' career trajectories and work lives. Professional learning and development in schools and higher education* (Vol. 3). Springer. https://doi.org/10.1007/978-90-481-2358-2_2

Sikes, P. J. (1985). The life cycle of the teacher. In S. Ball & I. Goodson (Eds.), *Teachers' lives and careers* (pp. 27–60). Lewes: Falmer.

Snyder, H. (2019). Literature review as a research methodology: An overview and guidelines. *Journal of Business Research, 104*, 333–339. https://doi.org/https://doi.org/10.1016/j.jbusres.2019.07.039

Tammets, K., Pata, K., & Eisenschmidt, E. (2019). Novice teachers' learning and knowledge building during the induction programme. *European Journal of Teacher Education, 42*(1), 36–51. https://doi.org/10.1080/02619768.2018.1523389

Vescio, V., & Adams, A. (2015). Learning in a Professional Learning Community: The challenge evolves. In E. Hargreaves & D. Scott (Eds.), *The SAGE handbook of learning* (pp. 274–284). London: SAGE Publications.

Vescio, V., Ross, D., & Adams, A. (2008). A review of research on the impact of professional learning communities on teaching practice and student learning. *Teaching and Teacher Education, 24*(1), 80–91. https://doi.org/10.1016/j.tate.2007.01.004

Waldman, R. (2020). *Development aspects of the professional learning community of chemistry teachers* (Unpublished doctoral dissertation). Weizmann Institute of Science.

Waldman, R., & Blonder, R. (2020). A sense of community in a professional learning community of chemistry teachers: A study of an online platform for group communication. In Y. Ben-David Kolikant, D. Martinovic, & M. Milner-Bolotin (Eds.), *STEM teachers and teaching in the digital era: Professional expectations and advancement in the 21st Century schools* (pp. 111–139). Springer International Publishing. https://doi.org/10.1007/978-3-030-29396-3

Watson, C. (2014). Effective professional learning communities? The possibilities for teachers as agents of change in schools. *British Educational Research Journal, 40*(1), 18–29. https://doi.org/https://doi.org/10.1002/berj.3025

Zonoubi, R., Eslami Rasekh, A., & Tavakoli, M. (2017). EFL teacher self-efficacy development in professional learning communities. *System, 66*, 1–12. https://doi.org/https://doi.org/10.1016/j.system.2017.03.003

23

DIGITAL TECHNOLOGIES AND PROFESSIONAL LEARNING OF SCIENCE TEACHERS

A Technological Pedagogical Content Knowledge (TPACK) Perspective

Seng Chee Tan, Tang Wee Teo, and Chin-Chung Tsai

Introduction

In this Digital Age, there is widespread interest in using digital technologies such as information and communication technologies (ICT) in education. Specific to science education, various frameworks have been applied to make sense of how ICT contributes to science learning. For example, McFarlane and Sakellariou (2002) proposed two main approaches to using ICT for science learning. First, based on the inquiry approach of empirical science, ICT could support scientific investigation *with* ICT, such as the use of data loggers to acquire data for scientific experiments or the use of a spreadsheet to analyze and present data. Alternatively, an investigative approach could be carried out through ICT, such as exploring scientific phenomena using simulation software. Second, based on the model of scientific reasoning, learners could apply scientific reasoning skills to scientific reports and articles available on the Internet. Also, computer-mediated communication such as digital forums could support scientific discussion, argumentation, and communications among learners. Using a different lens, Aguilar and Pifarre Turmo (2019) proposed different roles of digital technologies: (a) technology as a *tutor*, such as an e-tutor to engage the student in creative activities; (b) technology as a *tool* to support creative thinking – for example, students using robotic tools to solve a challenge; and (c) technology as a *medium* for social, creative thinking. In essence, these are ways of framing and characterizing the diverse attributes of ICT and its relationship to science education.

Many applications of technologies in science education are related to the recognition of inquiry-based science as the approach for science learning (Higgins & Spitulnik, 2008). Inquiry science (Singer et al., 2000) engages students in scientific practices, such as identifying problems, proposing hypotheses, designing experiments, collecting data, analyzing data, and developing scientific arguments. These inquiry processes can be effectively supported by technologies. For example, the Web-based Inquiry Science Environment (WISE) (Linn et al., 2004) was developed to support inquiry-based science learning, and Knowledge Forum was used by students to ask inquiry questions and improve their science learning (Tan & Seah, 2011).

However, researchers cautioned that integrating digital technologies into education may not guarantee positive outcomes (Baker et al., 2018), due to several reasons. One reason is that teachers may not engage technology with transformative pedagogies that support student engagement.

DOI: 10.4324/9781003098478-27

Instead, they may simply use technology as a tool to deliver a traditionally teacher-centered lesson (So & Kim, 2009). Hew and Brush (2007), who reviewed 48 empirical studies, identified several barriers to the uptake of ICT by teachers. One major category of barrier is the lack of relevant knowledge and skills by teachers, including the skills and knowledge about using the technology, pedagogical knowledge in designing technology-mediated lessons, and handling related classroom management issues. Pertaining to science education, science teachers also encountered challenges in implementing digital technologies in their teaching (Nielsen et al., 2015), and research suggests that the ways that technologies have been applied in science classroom practices may not help to stimulate higher-level thinking and reasoning (Rodrigues, 2006). In many cases, the potential of technologies was harnessed not for higher-level learning but for simple academic tasks, such as retrieving information, or administrative functions, such as developing worksheets (Chang & Tsai, 2005).

In short, while there is an increasing interest in the use of technologies in education, research findings show that teachers' knowledge in integrating technology in education is lacking (e.g., Messina & Tabone, 2012). Consequently, professional development (PD) for teachers about integrating digital technologies into teaching and learning is critical. However, many PD programs are still using "inadequate strategies for bringing about change in teacher practices" (Fernandes et al., 2020, p. 674). In this regard, Harris and Hofer (2009) lamented that technology-centric approaches – including initiatives focusing on the use of software, demonstration of sample technology integration examples, large-scale reform efforts that are driven by technology, structured PD workshops or courses, and teacher education courses focusing on technology – were dominant but limiting features of past efforts to promote ICT in education. An alternative framing, one that is not dominated by technology, will help to chart a new research trajectory or focus on ICT-education studies.

In the context of seeking a non-technology-centric pedagogy, the technological pedagogical content knowledge or TPACK (Mishra & Koehler, 2006) became a prominent theme of research on the use of technologies for teacher education and motivated many studies in the new millennium. TPACK-based PD was highlighted as the main theoretical framework that helps teachers integrate digital technologies into science education (Fernandes et al., 2020). This chapter discusses research related to technologies and professional learning of science teachers, including the rationales for the use of TPACK to frame science teachers' professional learning, the theoretical underpinning of TPACK, the methodological foci, and the epistemological approaches of TPACK-based professional learning of science teachers and the key research outcomes.

A literature search was conducted in October 2020 using EBSCOhost Research databases that include Academic Search Complete, ERIC, and APA PsychArticles, among others. The search terms ("TPACK" or "TPCK" or "Technological Pedagogical Content Knowledge") and (science) and (in-service or practicing or professional development) were used, limiting to the years 2006 to 2020, which resulted in 143 articles. The abstract of each article was reviewed for relevance. Articles that focus on teacher professional development using TPACK-based approaches were short-listed, whereas articles that focus on preservice teachers only or measurement of TPACK only are excluded. The snowball method was used to trace other relevant articles that appeared in the reference lists. About 33 articles relevant to TPACK theory or TPACK-based PD approaches were eventually shortlisted. A constant comparison method was used to identify the key themes of the articles, which are presented in the subsequent sections of this chapter.

Theoretical Underpinning of TPACK

TPACK can be traced to Shulman's (1986) concept of pedagogical content knowledge (PCK), which refers to a teacher's professional knowledge that integrates pedagogy and content to facilitate effective learning of content by students. PCK amalgamates knowledge of content and pedagogy and relates to the expertise of a teacher in representing and teaching a subject, taking into consideration contexts of learning and learner characteristics, abilities and interests, as well as learners' difficulties in learning the specific topic. PCK is not a simple integration of component pedagogical and content knowledge, but unique teacher expertise that includes interpreting and transforming content knowledge to facilitate students' learning (Depaepe et al., 2013).

Recognizing the pervasive use of technologies in 21st-century classrooms, Mishra and Koehler (2006) incorporated technological knowledge into PCK and proposed technological pedagogical content knowledge (TPCK) as a teacher's professional knowledge and competency for 21st-century pedagogy. TPCK was conceptualized as development in three knowledge domains (pedagogy, content, and technology) as well as their intersections. The element of context was later added as a critical part, and the acronym evolved to TPACK (Koehler & Mishra, 2008; Voogt et al., 2013) and was subsequently adopted by practitioners and researchers widely. Since the emergence of the concept, TPACK has become a key theoretical framework that underpins both research studies on the use of technologies to support teacher PD, as well as the target outcomes for teachers' PD.

Unpacking TPACK

TPACK is unique as it is a complex amalgamation of multifaceted knowledge situated in the context of its applications in order to be useful. This form of knowledge embodies components of content knowledge, pedagogical knowledge, and technology knowledge. Content knowledge (CK) refers to knowledge of a subject or knowledge of a discipline. Pedagogical knowledge (PK) refers to knowledge about teaching and learning processes such as theories of learning and instructional design for effective learning. Technological knowledge (TK) is concerned with knowledge about technology, such as technical knowledge of operating software, understanding of the affordances of educational technology, and applications of technologies for learning. Pedagogical content knowledge (PCK), as proposed by Shulman (1986), refers to the expertise of interpreting and transforming content knowledge in the service of facilitating students' learning. Technological content knowledge (TCK) is about how appropriate technology can be employed for the teaching of a specific subject, such as the use of simulation to teach a physics concept. Technological pedagogical knowledge (TPK) refers to leveraging pedagogical affordances and constraints of technological tools for appropriate pedagogical designs and strategies, such as Web 2.0 tools for social constructivist learning. Technological pedagogical content knowledge (TPACK), the intersection of CK, PK, and TK, refers to integrative knowledge of how pedagogical knowledge, content knowledge, and technological knowledge are amalgamated holistically for achieving intended learning outcomes among students.

This view of TPACK is comprised of different component knowledge structures and is regarded as the integrative perspective (De Rossi & Angeli, 2018) because it assumes that TPACK is developed by the intersections of different component knowledge. An alternative to this perspective is a transformative view of TPACK (De Rossi & Angeli, 2018) that treats TPACK as a distinct body of knowledge amalgamated from content knowledge, pedagogical knowledge, knowledge of learners, knowledge of educational context, and ICT knowledge (Angeli & Valanides, 2009), which enables skillful design and implementation of technology-enabled learning. This view suggests that even teachers with extensive knowledge of computers may not perform better in designing technology-enabled lessons (Valanides & Angeli, 2008) if they do not possess TPACK to offer a meaningful learning experience for students. It also implies that TPACK must be explicitly taught in professional learning courses and not left to the teachers to synthesize the different knowledge types.

TPACK-Based Teacher PD Approaches and Outcomes

Prior to the emergence of TPACK, the prevalence of technology-centric approaches towards teacher PD was criticized by researchers (e.g., Harris et al., 2010) for neglecting the complex relationships among the technology, content, and pedagogy. Through using TPACK as the guiding epistemo-logical framing, various approaches are reported on teacher professional learning. Among these are instructional design approaches that engage teachers in designing lessons for formal courses under-pinned by TPACK development, tool-centric approaches that aim to develop teacher's TPACK using specific technology (e.g., IWB), and community-based approaches that engage teachers in professional learning communities, peer coaching, or partnership with industries (see Table 23.1).

Instructional Design and Planning

The approaches adopted by Niess et al. (2010), Jimoyiannis (2010), and Chen et al. (2015) (see Table 23.1, part A) have a common feature: two main components executed in sequence. First, teachers received PD on TPACK, and second, the teachers applied their TPACK knowledge and skills for instructional design and planning of lessons to be used in their classrooms.

The first component, PD on TPACK, aims to help teachers develop their understanding of TPACK and their competence in using TPACK for lesson design. There are some variations in terms of the curriculum of the PD and how the PD was conducted. Niess et al. (2010) focused on the use of spreadsheets to teach mathematics and science. Jimoyiannis (2010) implemented the TPASK curriculum for science teachers. By replacing "C" with "S," the curriculum focused on teachers' knowledge specific to science education (e.g., PSK, TSK, TPASK). Chen et al. (2015) followed Jang and Tsai's (2013) four-component approach: TK, CK, PCKCx, and TPCKCx (Cx means "in context"). During this PD phase, there were attempts to engage the teachers in discussion and reflection to deepen their knowledge of TPACK. Niess and colleagues' (2010) PD was comple-mented with online discussion, whereas Chen et al. (2015) used wikis for teachers to co-generate creative instructional strategies and to gain diverse perspectives.

The second main component of PD involved the application of TPACK to design lessons in schools. By doing so, teachers were engaged in the authentic task of designing lessons for specific contexts. This component relates TPACK with other practical considerations that science teachers have about harnessing technology in their science content teaching (Niess et al., 2010). It was con-cluded that relating TPACK with practical concerns could enrich teachers' learning experience and hence, TPACK development.

All three studies reported positive outcomes of their PD approaches. Niess et al. (2010) found all teachers showing a significant increase in TPACK self-efficacy beliefs; teachers in Jimoyian-nis's (2010) study indicated a meaningful understanding of TPASK in science education, developed increased TPACK knowledge, and shared challenges of integrating ICT in the science classroom; Chen et al. (2015) found that with wikis, teachers were able to co-develop creative strategies and design lively science content.

Instructional Design and Planning Through Onsite Workshop and Implementation

Similar to the instructional design and planning approach, the approaches adopted by Jaipal-Jamani and Figg (2015), and Kafyulilo et al. (2015) (see Table 23.1, part B) also engaged teachers in instruc-tional design and planning, but with a distinct feature that the PD was conducted onsite in the schools.

There are strengths of attending formal teacher PD organized for various schools, such as the benefit of interacting with teachers with different backgrounds and experiences, and therefore the higher probability of having access to new ideas. On the other hand, such a formal program may have a fixed curriculum or structure for accreditation purposes. Teachers in Jimoyiannis's (2010) study, for example, went through a 350-hour course. In this regard, the onsite PD arrangement

Table 23.1 TPACK-based PD approaches

Authors/ Country	Approach	Outcomes
A. Instructional design and planning approaches		
Niess et al. (2010) USA	• PCK based with technologies: (a) explore what it means to teach mathematics and science with spreadsheet, (b) strategies of teaching specific themes and units with spreadsheets, (c) assessment of students, and (d) electronic portfolio containing an instructional package of spreadsheet problems with worksheets and scoring rubric, the plan of integration. • Purely online course. Modeling and algebraic reasoning.	Qualitative: A case study of 12 K-8 teachers using spreadsheets. Observation of participants' teaching at the beginning of the course, portfolio of assignments, transcript of discussion, transcript of interview. All teachers showed a significant increase in TPACK self-efficacy beliefs; 8 at accepting level, 2 at adapting level, 2 at the exploring level.
Jimoyiannis (2010) Greece	• Technological Pedagogical Science Knowledge (TPASK) model. • Knowledge specific to science education (e.g., PSK, TSK, TPASK); 350-hour course over a semester, 180 hours for ICT in science, including designing artifacts applicable in schools. • Science teachers, including physics and chemistry teachers.	Qualitative: A case study of 6 science teachers. Semi-structured interview. Participants indicated a meaningful understanding of TPASK in science education, developed increased TPACK knowledge and shared challenges of integrating ICT in science classrooms.
Chen et al. (2015). Taiwan	• Wiki-based TPACK model. Wiki as a collaborative tool and curriculum based on Jang & Tsai's (2013) four-component approach: TK, CK, PCKCx, and TPCKCx (Cx means in context). • A semester-long course. • Science teachers, subjects not specified.	Qualitative: 16 in-service teachers in a graduate course. The data sources include reflective journal, online forum data, interview. Wiki provided an environment for co-designing of engaging content for their students; wiki discussion generated creative instructional strategies, and gained diverse perspectives; wiki and collaborative discussion generated ideas related to TPACK.
B. Instructional design and planning through onsite workshop and implementation		
Jaipal-Jamani and Figg (2015) Canada	• TPACK-based workshop. • Onsite PD, mentored by expert; teachers work collaboratively to develop content-based learning activities supported by technologies. • Teachers working on the topic of fluid mechanics.	Qualitative: A case study of 3 teachers using blogs for science. Teachers were able to translate theoretical ideas into practical applications; the onsite nature of PD facilitated collaborative planning and implementation; teachers develop new TPACK through just-in-time mentoring.
Kafyulilo et al. (2015) Tanzania	• TPACK-based workshop. • 1st cycle: Collaborative lesson design and implementation in schools; support by experts and online resource materials. • 2nd cycle: Repeat the first cycle. • Teachers teaching physics, biology, chemistry.	A mixed methods study was conducted with two secondary schools in Tanzania; 20 science teachers completed the professional development. Teachers showed a gain in technology integration knowledge and skills (TK, TPK, TCK, and TPCK). Teachers appreciated external support such as collaboration guidelines, expert guidance, exemplary lesson, and online materials.

(Continued)

Table 23.1 (Continued)

Authors/ Country	Approach	Outcomes
C. PD with specific technologies		
Trautmann & MaKinster (2010). USA	• PD using geospatial technologies such as GPS and GIS. • Eight-day workshop, followed by lesson design supported by weekly online discussion. • Teachers teaching general science, biology.	• Mixed methods. Survey of 11 teachers and a case study of 3 teachers. Pre-post questionnaires, teacher-created curriculum materials, teachers' reflections. • The survey shows an increase in teachers' interest and expertise in using geospatial technologies. Case studies show teachers' growth in three components of TPACK.
Jang (2010) Taiwan	• TPACK–COIR with interactive whiteboard (IWB) (TPACK Comprehension, Observation, Instruction, and Reflection) model focusing on the use of IWB. • Teachers teaching general science.	Qualitative: A case study with 4 science teachers: (a) IWBs as instructional tools to share their subject-matter knowledge and to express students' understanding; (b) IWB for representational repertoires and interactive strategies; (c) IWB with peer teacher coaching.
Jang and Tsai (2012) Taiwan	• TPACK-IWB questionnaire for teachers who used IWB and those who did not (assuming learning with experience of using IWB) • Teachers teaching general science.	Quantitative: 334 elementary school teachers who used IWB and 228 teachers. IWB teachers showed significantly better TPACK scores in CK, PCK in context, TK, and TPCK in context.
D. Community approach		
Ng and Fergusson (2019) Australia	• Schools-universities-industry partnership to develop science modules. • General science topics.	Mixed methods: Found school science teachers externalize their pedagogical knowledge and internalize content knowledge by interacting with scientists and technological knowledge by working with the technology partner.

allows teachers who have nuanced contextual knowledge of the schools and students to discuss design and strategies that could better address specific concerns or consider realistic constraints faced by the specific schools, so that targeted lesson design can be made to benefit the students in the schools.

The onsite approach also allows close guidance of teachers in their lesson design. The study by Jaipal-Jamani and Figg (2015) reported teachers developing a practice task collaboratively (e.g., how to use blogs to develop students' collaborative writing and communication skills for science-related topics), which was followed by a mentoring of implementation and a debriefing session. The teachers developed a new TPACK that could be translated immediately into practice through just-in-time mentoring. Similarly, Kafyulilo et al. (2015) reported how teachers engaged in collaborative design of technology-enhanced science lessons using the Interconnected Model of Professional Growth (IMPG, see Clarke & Hollingsworth, 2002). The IMPG model aims at developing teachers' knowledge and skills (personal domain), providing collaborative design and teaching experimentation opportunity (practice domain), providing support with resources and experts (external domain), and having teachers reflect on their technology integration knowledge and skills (consequences domain).

Professional Development with Specific Technology

Researchers have also attempted to develop teachers' TPACK with the use of specific technologies (Table 23.1 part C). This approach harnesses the unique values of technologies that facilitate pedagogical development or science learning in specific ways.

Jang (2010) integrated peer coaching with TPACK and proposed a TPACK–COIR (TPACK Comprehension, Observation, Instruction, and Reflection) model that focuses on PD using an interactive whiteboard (IWB). IWB was chosen for its resemblance to the traditional whiteboard and is suited for whole-class presentations, yet it caters to a variety of learning styles with easy-to-use interactive activities with students. IWB allows science teachers to integrate various resources such as Internet resources, animations, or e-books, and interactive activities with students. It allows teachers to use classroom management styles that they are already familiar with. In short, IWB provides a pedagogical bridge for teachers to transit from more traditional classroom teaching style to technology-enhanced lessons.

On the other hand, Trautmann and MaKinster (2010) helped science teachers to integrate geospatial technologies such as GPS and GIS into their lessons. Under a program called GIT Ahead, intensive 8-day workshops were conducted with teachers to introduce them to the technologies and how to help their students manipulate and synthesize complex data. This was followed by weekly discussions and reflections. In this case, the use of GPS and GIS offers the opportunity of working with authentic data.

The study by Niess et al. (2010) (part A) also focused on a specific type of software (Spreadsheet) that offered the affordance of data organization, data manipulation, and visualization that contributes to the development of scientific practices similar to what scientists do in their research work.

Community Approach

The community approach (Table 23.1, part D) has the unique feature of linking teachers with external communities beyond a school. Ng and Fergusson (2019) reported a schools-universities-industry partnership model in Australia – secondary school science teachers partner with scientists from universities and technology partners from industry to create e-modules under the Smart Science Initiative project. Later, in a full-day workshop, the teachers walked through one of these modules to plan how these modules can be implemented in their classes. These processes help strengthen the teachers' TPACK, which they can draw from when implementing the smart science modules with their students. Such a PD approach also offers teachers the rare opportunity to benefit from working with other professionals. The school science teachers contribute to the design of the modules by externalizing their pedagogical knowledge and understanding of students, and, in the process, internalize content knowledge by interacting with the scientists and technological knowledge by working with the technology partner.

Discussion

Strengths of TPACK for Science Teachers' PD

To iterate, research on TPACK is gaining traction because of growing concerns about technology-centric approaches (Harris et al., 2010) that may not work effectively. Prior to TPACK, the common approaches include the use of a technology-centric survey to investigate levels of application of technological tools in science classrooms (e.g., Keller et al., 2005). TPACK presents a more holistic framing by building on the foundation of PCK (Shulman, 1986; Depaepe et al., 2013) and attention to contextual situations and students' characteristics. The studies reviewed in this chapter showed the strengths of various programs and PD using TPACK-based design through quantitative survey results and qualitative case studies. These instruments and methods can also be used as a diagnostic to identify the gaps in teachers' development. For example, TPACK-based learning activities types (Harris & Hofer, 2009) were used to reveal weaknesses in teachers' TPACK, as demonstrated by Messina and Tabone (2012).

Methodological Approaches of TPACK-Based PD

Except for two studies (Jang & Tsai, 2012; Kafyulilo et al., 2015), all studies reviewed relied extensively on qualitative methods to evaluate the outcomes of TPACK, even though numerous self-report surveys on TPACK have been developed and adopted (e.g., Lin et al., 2013). Among the mixed methods or qualitative approaches, the use of various data sources has been attempted, including lesson plans, lesson observations, interviews, and questionnaires with embedded media. These are highly resource-intensive methods in terms of the time and effort needed to collect and analyze data. Nevertheless, they provide a means to probe contextualized TPACK knowledge or a more direct means to assess translation of TPACK into actions through lesson planning or implementation. There are at least two possible reasons for the preferred use of qualitative methods. First, except for Lin and colleagues (2013), the models generated from self-report survey data based on good fit indices did not successfully separate all seven components of TPACK. Researchers who take a transformative view of TPACK (e.g., Angeli & Valanides, 2009) argued that there might not be clear boundaries between some of these components, which are related to some extent. Second, survey methods are closely related to the integrative view of TPACK. From an epistemological perspective, a transformative view of TPACK that prizes contextualized development of TPACK rather than the use of self-report surveys is more useful for teacher development of TPACK (Pareto & Willermark, 2019). Thus, most studies had employed a qualitative or mixed methods design for evaluating the efficacy of teacher PD. That said, however, if a self-report survey is capable of differentiating various components of TPACK, it could be useful as a complementary tool in answering questions like the efficacy of sequential development of components of TPACK, or which aspects of TPACK are more difficult to be developed.

Theories in Action of TPACK-Based PD

To help teachers develop TPACK, a design-based approach "that is situated in action, context specific, and integrated in practical teaching" (Pareto & Willermark, 2019, p. 1186) is more viable. This is because the development of TPACK knowledge is grounded and situated in specific teaching and learning contexts (Koehler et al., 2014). The design-based situated approach is also backed up by empirical evidence in large-scale studies in a Nordic context (Pareto & Willermark, 2019). Researchers in PCK have been grappling with similar issues of integrative versus transformative views on teachers' development of PCK. There is empirical evidence that PCK developed not through the separate development of PK and CK, but only through targeted transformative/integrative PCK development (Evens et al., 2018). In this chapter, all the studies on TPACK-based PD highlight the practice of experiential elements. Implicit in these approaches is the fact that contextual applications and experience are critical to teacher development of TPACK, without necessarily attending formal workshops or courses. Consequently, there was no concern about the transfer of TPACK to authentic practices. This contextual application is critical to the success of PD, whether one adopts a transformative or integrative view of TPACK.

Another common element is collaborative lesson design, which engages teachers in solving a problem at hand through sustained inquiry and iterative improvement of ideas (Koehler et al., 2007).

In the context of designing technology-enhanced lessons, this "complex cognitive task takes skills and teachers combine what they know, believe and understand about teaching and learning, subject matter and technology" (Boschman et al., 2015, p. 252). Beyond the context of schools, Ng and Fergusson (2019) point to the potential of developing TPACK through interactions with other professional communities.

There are also attempts to develop teachers' TPACK through the use of a specific technology, for instance, the use of IWB. This approach, however, need not be a technology-centric approach that focuses on the technical skills of using a specific technology. For example, using IWB engages teachers in pedagogical reasonings of how IWB can be used to enhance students' learning. It is closer to the TPK to TPACK approach suggested by Koehler and colleagues (2014). IWB was chosen because of its resemblance with a traditional whiteboard and whole-class teaching, which means it is a mediation tool to help teachers transit from a familiar teaching approach to gradually expanding a new repertoire. In theory, other technologies could be chosen (e.g., virtual reality) while retaining similar approaches of PD. An example of this is PD on how to create seamless real and virtual learning science laboratory experiences for students (Zervas et al., 2015).

Suggestions for Future Research

As TPACK and TPACK-based PD are relatively new concepts, there are promising research ideas that have been reported but not extensively explored. First, there are different trajectories of TPACK-based PD approaches. Koehler and colleagues (2014) identified three broad types (PCK to TPACK, TPK to TPACK, and concurrent PCK and TPACK) and Harris (2016) proposed another 12 TPACK-related PD approaches (e.g., collaborative instructional design, PCK-focused, TPK focused). The comparative efficacy of these approaches remains to be verified. Consulting studies on PCK offers some clues. Evens et al. (2018) found that the development of PCK did not happen through separate development of PK and CK, but only through targeted PCK development.

Second, there is guiding teacher PD with the core set of TPACK instructional practices. Based on a model-based inquiry framework for science learning, Windschitl et al. (2012) derived a core set of high-leverage practices that could be used for preparing beginning teachers, as well as PD of practicing teachers. Similar studies have begun in the space of TPACK-based PD. In a similar vein, Harris and Hofer (2009) proposed learning activity types (LAT), which can be routinized as learning activities that help to develop science-related skills among students. Harris and Hofer (2009) have identified various activity types linked to compatible technologies (e.g., Wikipedia for research, concept mapping software for the knowledge web). LAT was reported as a critical way to help teachers concretize the TPACK concept and to operationalize it in their classrooms (Harris & Hofer, 2017). Empirical studies on the use of LAT with in-service teachers, however, are still lacking, possibly due to the numerous activities and complexity in identifying the acquisition of TPACK as a whole or in parts.

Third, research tends to report only positive outcomes. In reality, there could be challenges to most of these approaches. For example, Cheah et al. (2019) studied a science teacher who participated in an inter-school professional learning community (PLC) and analyzed the tensions this teacher faced when trying to implement what he had learned in the PLC at his own school. Using the Cultural Historical Activity Theory framework, it was found that the teacher experienced tensions and challenges that hindered his TPACK development, which includes the use of manipulation tools and thinking routines (tools), the changes in the school's routines (rules), and the lack of communication between the leader and the teacher (division of labor).

Finally, TPACK-based PD could also be informed by other approaches. One such approach is the Concerns-Based Adoption Model (CBAM) (e.g., Gabby et al., 2017) that examined the types of concerns as teachers progress through the adoption of technologies in classrooms, from concerns about self to tasks or activities, and finally to the impact on students. Fernandes et al. (2020) also identified other PD frameworks of integrating digital technologies into education, such as the use of activity theory to consider interrelated elements and teaching and learning approaches based on inquiry-science approaches.

Conclusion

This chapter reviewed the genesis of TPACK and discussed its evolution to become an empirically grounded construct that is well-studied in science education. Studies about TPACK in science education research have gained prominence as a result of its adoption in learning designs. Additionally, science education research in TPACK has strengthened in terms of methodological rigor (e.g., through better research instruments and analyses that examined the complex relationships between the various components of TPACK and variations of TPACK), resulting in the broadening and deepening of understanding about TPACK. Such understandings about TPACK have, in turn, been used to design and enact science teacher PD programs with a focus on the epistemologies of TPACK. Taking a transformative view of TPACK, most of the TPACK-based PD approaches reviewed in this chapter regard TPACK as a distinct body of knowledge amalgamated from content knowledge, pedagogical knowledge, knowledge of learners, knowledge of educational context, and ICT knowledge. They tried to avoid the bias of the technology-centric approach of PD. Instead, they preserve the pedagogical content knowledge of teaching science and emphasize the experience of translating theories into design and implementation. The maturation of new technology such as immersive virtual reality and augmented reality also brings potential opportunities for both science teachers and learners to explore science concepts, scientific inquiry, and the nature of science. The TPACK PD for science teachers should be evolving along with the innovation of technology to better address the diverse learning needs of science students. Moving forward, the science education research community can explore engaging TPACK to extend the PD of science teachers, critically examine the challenges and limitations of engaging TPACK in science classrooms, and integrate other effective teaching approaches with TPACK to enhance its impact on science teaching and learning outcomes.

References

Aguilar, D., & Pifarre Turmo, M. (2019). Promoting social creativity in science education with digital technology to overcome inequalities: A scoping review. *Frontiers in Psychology, 10*. www.frontiersin.org/articles/10.3389/fpsyg.2019.01474/full. https://doi.org/10.3389/fpsyg.2019.01474

Angeli, C., & Valanides, N. (2009). Epistemological and methodological issues for the conceptualization, development, and assessment of ICT-TPCK: Advances in technological pedagogical content knowledge (TPCK). *Computers & Education, 52*(1), 154–168. https://doi.org/10.1016/j.compedu.2008.07.006

Baker, J. P., Goodboy, A. K., Bowman, N. D., & Wright, A. A. (2018). Does teaching with PowerPoint increase students' learning? A meta-analysis, *Computers & Education, 126*, 376–387. https://doi.org/10.1016/j.compedu.2018.08.003.

Boschman, F., McKenney, S., & Voogt, J. (2015). Exploring teachers' use of TPACK in design talk: The collaborative design of technology-rich early literacy activities. *Computers & Education, 82*, 250–262. https://doi.org/10.1016/j.compedu.2014.11.010

Chang, C., & Tsai, C. (2005). The interplay between different forms of CAI and students' preferences of learning environment in the secondary science class. *Science Education, 89*(5), 707–724. https://doi.org/10.1002/sce.20072.

Cheah, Y. H., Chai, C. S., & Toh, Y. (2019). Traversing the context of professional learning communities: Development and implementation of Technological Pedagogical Content Knowledge of a primary science teacher. *Research in Science & Technological Education, 37*(2), 147–167. https://doi.org/10.1080/02635143.2018.1504765

Chen, Y-H., Jang, S-J., & Chen P-J. (2015). Using wikis and collaborative learning for science teachers' professional development. *Journal of Computer-Assisted Learning, 31*, 330–344. https://doi.org/10.1111/jcal.12095.

Clarke, D., & Hollingsworth, H. (2002). Elaborating a model of teacher professional growth. *Teaching and Teacher Education, 18*(8), 947–967. https://doi.org/10.1016/S0742-051X(02)00053-7

Depaepe, F., Verschaffel, L., & Kelchtermans, G. (2013). Pedagogical content knowledge: A systematic review of the way in which the concept has pervaded mathematics educational research. *Teaching and Teacher Education, 34*, 12–25. https://doi.org/10.1016/j.tate.2013.03.001

De Rossi, M., & Angeli, C. (2018). Editorial. Teacher education for effective technology integration. *Italian Journal of Educational Technology, 26*(1), 3–6. https://doi.org/10.17471/2499-4324/1055

Evens, M., Elen, J., Larmuseau, C., & Depaepe, F. (2018). Promoting the development of teacher professional knowledge: Integrating content and pedagogy in teacher education. *Teaching and Teacher Education, 75*, 244–258. https://doi.org/10.1016/j.tate.2018.07.001

Fernandes, G. W. R., Rodrigues, A. M., & Ferreira, C. A. (2020). Professional development and use of digital technologies by science teachers: A review of theoretical frameworks. *Research in Science Education, 50*(2), 673–708. https://doi.org/10.1007/s11165-018-9707-x

Gabby, S., Avargil, S., Herscovitz, O., & Dori, Y. J. (2017). The case of middle and high school chemistry teachers implementing technology: Using the concerns-based adoption model to assess change processes. *Chemistry Education Research and Practice, 18*(1), 214–232. https://doi.org/10.1039/C6RP00193A

Harris, J. (2016). In-service teachers' TPACK development: Trends, models, and trajectories. In M. C. Herring, M. J. Koehler, & P. Mishra (Eds.), *Handbook of technological pedagogical content knowledge (TPACK) for educators* (2nd ed., pp. 191–205). London, UK: Routledge.

Harris, J. B., & Hofer, M. J. (2009). Instructional planning activity types as vehicles for curriculum-based TPACK development. In C. D. Maddux (Ed.). *Research highlights in technology and teacher education 2009* (pp. 99–108). Chesapeake, VA: Society for Information Technology in Teacher Education (SITE).

Harris, J. B., & Hofer, M. J. (2017). "TPACK Stories": Schools and school districts repurposing a theoretical construct for technology-related professional development. *Journal of Research on Technology in Education, 49*(1–2), 1–15. https://doi.org/10.1080/15391523.2017.1295408

Harris, J. B., Hofer, M., Schmidt, D. A., Blanchard, M. R., Young, C. Y., Grandgenett, N. F., & Van Olphen, M. (2010). "Grounded" technology integration: Instructional planning using curriculum-based activity type taxonomies. *Journal of Technology and Teacher Education, 18*(4), 573–605. www.learntechlib.org/primary/p/30418/

Hew, K. F., & Brush, T. (2007). Integrating technology into K-12 teaching and learning: Current knowledge gaps and recommendations for future research. *Education Tech Research Dev 55*, 223–252. https://doi.org/10.1007/s11423-006-9022-5

Higgins, T. E., & Spitulnik, M. W. (2008). Supporting teachers' use of technology in science instruction through professional development: A literature review. *Journal of Science Education and Technology, 17*, 511–521. https://doi.org/10.1007/s10956-008-9118-2

Jaipal-Jamani, K., & Figg, C. (2015). A case study of a TPACK-based approach to teacher professional development: Teaching science with blogs. *Contemporary Issues in Technology and Teacher Education, 15*(2), 161–200. https://citejournal.org/volume-15/issue-2-15/science/a-case-study-of-a-tpack-based-approach-to-teacher-professional-developmentteaching-science-with-blogs/

Jang, S. J. (2010). Integrating the interactive whiteboard and peer coaching to develop the TPACK of secondary science teachers. *Computers & Education, 55*(4), 1744–1751. https://doi.org/10.1016/j.compedu.2010.07.020

Jang, S.-J., & Tsai, M.-F. (2012). Exploring the TPACK of Taiwanese elementary mathematics and science teachers with respect to use of interactive whiteboards. *Computers & Education, 59*(2), 327–338. https://doi.org/10.1016/j.compedu.2012.02.003

Jang, S.-J., & Tsai, M.-F. (2013). Exploring the TPACK of Taiwanese secondary school science teachers using a new contextualized TPACK model. *Australasian Journal of Educational Technology, 29*(4), 566–580. https://doi.org/10.14742/ajet.282

Jimoyiannis, A. (2010). Designing and implementing an integrated technological pedagogical science knowledge framework for science teachers professional development. *Computers & Education, 55*, 1259–1269. https://doi.org/10.1016/j.compedu.2010.05.02

Kafyulilo, A. C., Fisser, P., & Voogt, J. (2015). Supporting teachers learning through the collaborative design of technology-enhanced science lessons. *Journal of Science Teacher Education, 26*(8), 673–694. https://doi.org/10.1007/s10972-015-9444-1

Keller, J. B., Bonk, C. J., & Hew, K. (2005). The TICKIT to teacher learning: Designing professional development according to situative principles. *Journal of Educational Computing Research, 32*(4), 329–340. https://doi.org/10.2190/68XG-THRV-HT4D-ECA4

Koehler, M. J., & Mishra, P. (2008). Introducing TPCK. In The AACTE Committee on Innovation and Technology (Ed.), *Handbook of technological pedagogical content knowledge (TPCK) for educators* (pp. 3–29). New York, NY: Routledge.

Koehler, M. J., Mishra, P., Kereluik, K., Shin, T. S., & Graham, C. R. (2014). The technological pedagogical content knowledge framework. In J. M. Spector, M. D. Merill, J. Elen, & M. J. Bishop (Eds.), *Handbook of research on educational communications and technology* (4th Ed., pp. 101–111). New York, NY: Springer.

Koehler, M. J., Mishra, P., & Yahya, K. (2007). Tracing the development of teacher knowledge in a design seminar: Integrating content, pedagogy, & technology. *Computers and Education, 49*(3), 740–762. https://doi.org/10.1016/j.compedu.2005.11.012

Lin, T.-C., Tsai, C.-C., Chai, C. S., & Lee, M.-H. (2013). Identifying science teachers' perceptions of technological, pedagogical, and content knowledge (TPACK). *Journal of Science and Technology, 22*(3), 325–336. https://doi.org/10.1007/s10956-012-9396-6

Linn, M. C., Davis, E. A., & Bell, P. (2004). Inquiry and technology. In M. C. Linn, E. Davis, & P. Bell (Eds.), *Internet environments for science education* (pp. 3–28). Mahwah, NJ: Lawrence Erlbaum.

McFarlane, A., & Sakellariou, S. (2002). The role of ICT in science education. *Cambridge Journal of Education, 32*(2), 219–232. https://doi.org/10.1080/03057640220147568

Messina, L., & Tabone, S. (2012). Integrating technologies into instructional practices focusing on teacher knowledge. *Procedia- Social and Behavioral Sciences, 46*, 1015–1027. https://doi.org/10.1016/j.sbspro.2012.05.241

Mishra, P., & Koehler, M. J. (2006). Technological pedagogical content knowledge: A framework for teacher knowledge. *Teachers College Record, 108*(6), 1017–1054. https://doi.org/10.1111/j.1467-9620.2006.00684.x

Nielsen, W., Miller, K. A., & Hoban, G. (2015). Science teachers' response to the digital education revolution. *Journal of Science Education and Technology, 24*(4), 417–431. https://doi.org/10.1007/s10956-014-9527-3

Niess, M. L., van Zee, E. H., & Gillow-Wiles, H. (2010). Knowledge growth in teaching mathematics/science with spreadsheets. *Journal of Digital Learning in Teacher Education, 27*(2), 42–52. https://doi.org/10.1080/21532974.2010.10784657

Ng, W., & Fergusson, J. (2019). Technology-enhanced science partnership initiative: Impact on secondary science teachers. *Research in Science Education, 49*, 219–242. https://doi.org/10.1007/s11165-017-9619-1

Pareto, L., & Willermark, S. (2019). TPACK in situ: A design-based approach supporting professional development in practice. *Journal of Educational Computing Research, 57*(5), 1186–1226. https://doi.org/10.1177/0735633118783180

Rodrigues, S. (2006). Pedagogic practice integrating primary science and elearning: The need for relevance, recognition, resource, reflection, readiness and risk. *Technology, Pedagogy and Education, 15*(2), 175–189. https://doi.org/10.1080/14759390600769193

Shulman, L. S. (1986). Those who understand: Knowledge growth in teaching. *Educational Researcher, 15*(2), 4–14. https://doi.org/10.3102/0013189X015002004

Singer, J., Marx, R. W., Krajcik, J. S., Clay-Chambers, J. (2000). Constructing extended inquiry projects: Curriculum materials for science education reform. *Educational Psychologist, 35*(3), 165–178. https://doi.org/10.1207/S15326985EP3503_3

So, H.-J., & Kim, B. (2009). Learning about problem-based learning: Student teachers integrating technology, pedagogy and content knowledge. *Australasian Journal of Educational Technology, 25*(1), 101–116. https://doi.org/10.14742/ajet.1183

Tan, S. C., & Seah, L. H. (2011). Exploring relationship between students' questioning behaviours and inquiry task in an online forum through analysis of ideational function of questions. *Computers & Education, 57*(2), 1675–1685. https://doi.org/10.1016/j.compedu.2011.03.007

Trautmann, N. M., & MaKinster, J. G. (2010). Flexibly adaptive professional development in support of teaching science with geospatial technology. *Journal of Science Teacher Education, 21*, 351–370. https://doi.org/10.1007/s10972-009-9181-4

Valanides, N., & Angeli, C. (2008). Professional development for computer-enhanced learning: A case study with science teachers. *Research in Science and Technological Education, 26*(1), 3–12. https://doi.org/10.1080/02635140701847397

Voogt, J., Fisser, P., Pareja Roblin, N., Tondeur, J., & van Braak, J. (2013). Technological pedagogical content knowledge – A review of the literature. *Journal of Computer Assisted Learning, 29*(2), 109–121. https://doi.org/10.1111/j.1365-2729.2012.00487.x

Windschitl, M., Thompson, J., Braaten, M., & Stroupe, D. (2012). Proposing a core set of instructional practices and tools for teachers of science. *Science Education, 96*(5), 878–903. https://doi.org/10.1002/sce.21027

Zervas, P., Sergis, S., Sampson, D. G., & Fyskilis, S. (2015). Towards competence-based learning design driven remote and virtual labs recommendations for science teachers. *Technology, Knowledge and Learning, 20*(2), 185–199. https://doi.org/10.1007/s10758-015-9256-6

SECTION 5

Science Teacher Education – Central Tenets

Section Editor: Soonhye Park

Quality teaching is the most critical school-based factor contributing to student learning (Hattie, 2012). In this regard, science teacher educators have sought effective ways to support and develop preservice and in-service teachers who can enact quality teaching that promotes science learning for all students. This effort has been guided by an overarching question: "What should teachers know and be able to do in order to create inclusive and equitable opportunities to learn for all students from an array of personal, linguistic, social, and cultural backgrounds?" (Hollins, 2011). Chapters in this section address that question as an effort to identify central tenets for the deep thinking and practices that science teacher educators are encouraged to engage in to ensure inclusive and equitable access and opportunities for success for every student through quality science teacher education.

Chapter 24, "Science Teacher Professional Knowledge and Its Relationship to High-Quality Science Instruction," provides an analysis of the literature published between 2010 and 2020 that focus on the relationships between high-quality science instruction and teacher professional knowledge. The review reveals that the quality of teacher professional knowledge, particularly content knowledge and pedagogical content knowledge, is positively related to the quality of teaching practices and student learning outcomes across a wide range of science classrooms. With the finding, the chapter sheds light on the important role of science teacher education in developing strong content knowledge and pedagogical content knowledge as well as the connection between the two knowledge bases in both pre- and in-service science teachers. Additionally, the chapter proposes directions for future research on science teacher education regarding high-quality instruction that unpacks how highly effective teachers deliver high-quality science instruction, how teachers learn to deliver high-quality science instruction, and the influence of affective domains to the science teachers' learning to teach.

Chapter 25, "Indigenous Knowledge in Science Education: Implications for Teacher Education," first discusses how the integration of Indigenous knowledge into science curriculum can enhance culturally diverse learners' cognitive and affective learning outcomes in science classrooms based on embodied, situated, and distributed cognition theory. Next, the chapter reports a review of literature on science teacher education regarding teaching Indigenous knowledge. The review shows that Indigenous knowledge is often marginalized in the science classroom, and teachers' perceptions and understanding of Indigenous knowledge greatly influence their pedagogical orientations and pedagogical approaches to teaching Indigenous knowledge. With research findings indicating the positive impact of purposefully designed teacher education interventions on pre- and in-service science teachers' infusion of Indigenous knowledge, this chapter underscores the need of teacher education programs that help teachers develop nuanced understandings of Indigenous knowledge, undergo epistemological border crossings between Indigenous knowledge and Western science, and utilize Indigenous knowledge to create meaningful science learning opportunities for students.

Chapter 26, "Action Research: A Promising Strategy for Science Teacher Education," presents a narrative review of the literature on action research in science education, conducted by an international team of authors who sought to capture global perspectives in analyzing and synthesizing the literature. This chapter consists of two parts. The first part presents an analytical framework for categorizing and understanding how action research has been used in science teacher education that was developed based on the outcomes of the review. The second part examines cases of action research organized by four purposes of science teacher education: inquiring into students' cognition of science, improving science curriculum, developing science teachers, and promoting equity and social justice. Through a critical analysis of the cases, the authors demonstrate how action research can serve as a form of teacher education.

Chapter 27, "Including All Learners Through Science Teacher Education," synthesizes major research findings regarding science teacher education for teaching students with special needs. Using the social model of disability that conceptualizes disability as a socially constructed form of human diversity rather than as a deficit in need of remediation typically conceptualized in the medical model of disability, this chapter provides an overview of the literature on five focus areas of inclusive science teacher education: inclusive science content knowledge, inclusive science content pedagogy, inclusive and safe science learning environments, inclusive and equitable impact on student learning, and science teachers with disabilities. The review of relevant literature indicates that "inclusive teaching" in inclusive science teacher education often overlooks disability by placing great emphasis on culturally relevant pedagogy and other cultural frameworks. Given that, the authors urge researchers to pay more attention to the role of disability in educational equity and inclusiveness with the understanding of disability as one of socially constructed dimensions of human diversity.

Chapter 28, "The Role of Teacher Education in Teaching Science to Emergent Bilingual Learners," addresses the critical question: "What is the role of teacher education in teaching science to emergent bilinguals?" A systematic analysis of 38 empirical studies published since 2010 indicates that targeted science teacher education programs and interventions can support not only teachers' integration of emergent bilinguals' language/literacy development with science instruction through inquiry-based and contextualized science teaching approaches, but also teachers' shift toward a language-inclusion ideology where they value multiple forms of language as resources for science and language learning. Pointing out that most studies focused on whether or not a particular teacher education intervention impacts teachers' knowledge and/or practices, in order to advance the field, the authors call for future research on how, when, and why the intervention leads to desirable changes in teachers' ideologies, knowledge, or practices for improved conditions for emergent bilingual learning. Moreover, this chapter reveals the need for science teacher educators to help science teachers understand the role of linguistic hegemony in the education of emergent bilinguals through critical theory and counterhegemonic perspectives.

Finally, Chapter 29, "Educative Curriculum Materials and Their Role in the Learning of Science Teachers," examines how educative curriculum materials (ECM) contribute to science teachers' professional learning. By synthesizing research evidence that supports positive effects of ECM on pedagogical content knowledge, beliefs, and pedagogical design capacity in both pre- and in-service science teachers, this chapter highlights ECM as a promising vehicle for promoting science teachers' learning to teach. Additionally, this chapter reports ECM design features and conditions for ECM use that research has identified to enhance science teacher learning, which offers useful implications for teacher educators who seek to design research-supported teacher education programs and interventions that utilize ECM to advance science teachers' knowledge, beliefs, and practices. Showing a clear prevalence of smaller scale and case studies conducted mostly in US secondary schools, this chapter suggests more research with larger teacher populations in more diverse contexts in order to fully understand science teacher learning through ECM.

References

Hollins, E. R. (2011). Teacher preparation for quality teaching. Journal of Teacher Education, 62(4), 395–407.
Lidar, M., Lundqvist, E., Ryder, J., & Östman, L. (2020). The transformation of teaching habits in relation to the introduction of grading and national testing in science education in Sweden. *Research in Science Education, 50*(1), 151–173.

24

SCIENCE TEACHER PROFESSIONAL KNOWLEDGE AND ITS RELATIONSHIP TO HIGH-QUALITY SCIENCE INSTRUCTION

Vanessa Kind, Soonhye Park, and Kennedy Kam Ho Chan

Introduction

Research evidence illustrates consistently that teacher factors are responsible for student learning outcomes. Influential summaries of this position include Coe et al. (2014), who define "effective teaching" as "that which leads to improved student achievement using outcomes that matter to their future success" (p. 2) and the Organisation for Economic Co-operation and Development (OECD) (Guerriero, 2017), which explicitly connects raising student outcomes with improving the quality of the teaching workforce. Meanwhile, the United Nations' Sustainable Development Goal 4, agreed in 2015, promotes "inclusive and equitable quality education and promote lifelong learning opportunities for all" (United Nations Department of Economic and Social Affairs, 2015). This chapter attempts to answer the overarching question: In what ways can teacher education for pre- and in-service science teachers promote development of practices consistent with high-quality instruction? Achieving this relies on teachers possessing appropriate professional knowledge that contributes to high-quality instruction (Coe et al., 2014; Fischer et al., 2012). This chapter reviews empirical studies investigating the relationship between high-quality science instruction and teacher professional knowledge, and it explores the debates surrounding both (Chan & Hume, 2019; Kloser, 2014). The chapter then discusses implications for science teacher education and proposals for future research.

Context and Scope

Studies reviewed were obtained from literature searches of Web of Science and Scopus databases using the following keyword combinations: (1) "content knowledge" AND "science teacher"; (2) "subject matter knowledge" AND "science teacher"; (3) "pedagogical content knowledge" AND "science teacher"; (4) "knowledge of context" AND "science teacher"; (5) "contextual knowledge" AND "science teacher"; (6) "pedagogical knowledge" AND "science teacher." The keywords comprised four knowledge domains – namely, content/subject matter knowledge, pedagogical, pedagogical content, and contextual knowledge/knowledge of context) – common to many teacher professional knowledge models (discussed later in this chapter). These terms identified empirical studies that address relationships between science teacher knowledge and science instruction in

DOI: 10.4324/9781003098478-29

terms of teacher practices and student learning outcomes. Initial searches yielded approximately 950 papers from which selections were made. Of these, 400 articles were selected from 22 highly ranked, peer-reviewed journals publishing empirical research, including science education journals (such as *Journal of Research in Science Teaching, Journal of Science Teacher Education*), teacher education journals (for example *Teaching and Teacher Education, Journal of Teacher Education*), learning sciences journals (including the *Journal of the Learning Sciences*), and American Education Research Association (AERA) journals such as the *American Educational Research Journal*. Non-empirical articles and opinion statements ("op-eds") were excluded. Next, abstracts were screened to identify papers featuring relationships between teacher professional knowledge and teacher practices and student learning outcomes. Articles from any country reporting work undertaken with pre-/in-service teachers in early years and primary and secondary school settings (K–12) were included, while higher or tertiary education studies were excluded. No screening criteria related to methodology, theoretical stance, teacher professional knowledge model, or sample size. This resulted in about 70 articles, of which a representative selection was reviewed.

Defining "High-Quality Science Instruction" and "Teacher Professional Knowledge"

High-Quality Science Instruction

Achieving a working definition of "high-quality science instruction" is aided by a historical perspective. General, non-subject-specific connections between teachers' actions with what and how students learn were established from the 1960s onwards. Carroll (1963) defined "quality of instruction" as "a measure of the degree to which instruction is presented so that it will not require additional time for mastery beyond that required in view of aptitude" (p. 729). Rosenshine (1979) identified factors influencing high-quality instruction, including teachers' sequencing of tasks and using time efficiently, setting explicit goals, and organizing and structuring lesson content clearly and appropriately. Brophy and Good's (1986) review revealed that factors relating to quantity and pacing of instruction appear most consistently as significant to learning in a range of studies. They proposed "academic learning time" (ALT) and "active teaching," respectively, as descriptors for aspects of instruction: ALT includes pace and delivery of lessons, diagnosis of student needs, and provision of appropriate activities; active teaching includes providing feedback, practicing examples, and monitoring progress, not students working unaided; essentially, teachers directing and instructing students. In a meta-review, Wang et al. (1990) ranked variables that were teacher-oriented; related to out-of-school contexts; and "classroom instruction and climate" as impacting on learning first, second, and third, respectively. They reported that affective, school and contextual variables are also involved in generating good learning outcomes for students. Thus, "high-quality instruction" involves students establishing mastery of content, in a timescale allowing for contextual constraints, achieved by teachers applying appropriate content-specific and general classroom management techniques.

These qualities apply to science lessons: as an illustrative example, observations undertaken over time by school inspectors in England (Department of Education and Science, 1979; Ofsted, 2013) report that high-quality science instruction includes well-structured, challenging activities; good pacing of lessons; setting high expectations for learning; and clearly explaining concepts. In addition, effective, inquiry-led practical work; developing students' knowledge of scientific language/literacy; assessing students' scientific skills, attitudes, and knowledge; and evaluating impact of the science curriculum on learning are essential.

Researchers have explored many of these aspects in depth, including: misconceptions (Driver, 1983; Osborne & Freyberg, 1985); inquiry-based learning and practical work (Schwab, 1962; Osborne, 2014); the nature of science (American Association for the Advancement of Science

[AAAS], 1990, 1993); and scientific thinking (Klahr & Dunbar, 1988), among others. Adapting Coe et al.'s (2014) definition (quoted earlier) suggests that high-quality science instruction is "teaching that leads to student achievement *in science* using outcomes that matter to their future success." To achieve "mastery" in science means students must understand and apply scientific concepts using correct scientific language; solve problems by thinking scientifically; acquire factual knowledge about science and its applications in society; and undertake confirmatory and investigative practical work.

Translating to teacher professional knowledge means teachers require, at least, knowledge and expertise in inquiry-based learning; the ability to manage practical experiments, including demonstrations and "hands-on" and student-led investigations; understanding of misconceptions related to specific science concepts, and instructional strategies that address these; questioning skills that explore students' learning of science concepts; use of formative assessment techniques to give feedback; and instructional strategies that support students' learning of scientific reasoning, methods, and science knowledge.

Teacher Professional Knowledge

Teacher professional knowledge originates from Shulman's (1987) description of seven types of teacher knowledge, namely content (CK), pedagogical content (PCK), general pedagogical (GPK or PK); "educational ends, purposes and values" (curriculum knowledge, CuK); knowledge of students (KS); and educational contexts (CxK). Shulman proposed teachers' PCK "transforms" subject matter knowledge (SMK, a broader form of CK), and that PCK distinguishes teachers from subject specialists. These proposals inspired many PCK-focused models of science teacher professional knowledge, most showing or implying connections between knowledge types. Some models arise from researchers' assumptions or collaborations (Carlson et al., 2019; Gess-Newsome, 2015; Magnusson et al., 1999). Others originate from teacher education or research evidence (Mavhunga & Rollnick, 2013; Park & Oliver, 2008; Rollnick et al., 2008; Kind & Chan, 2019), or utilize evidence or underpinning ideas about learning as justifiers (Cochran et al., 1993). Researchers tend to agree that teacher professional knowledge includes combinations of SMK (or a variant), PCK (with varied sub-components), PK, knowledge of assessment (KA, sometimes subsumed into PCK), KS, and Knowledge of Context (CuK). Most models do not indicate if/how teacher knowledge develops over time, potentially in positive and negative ways, depending on context. As descriptions, models do not connect explicitly with high-quality instruction, but they provide frameworks for investigating development of instruction-related factors. Descriptions of knowledge types include factors required in high-quality instruction. Some descriptions categorize PCK: "enacted" (ePCK) is used by teachers when teaching; "personal" (pPCK) comprises activities and knowledge requirements prepared by an individual teacher; and "collective" or "collaborative" PCK (cPCK) is developed by two or more teachers via professional development, in-school working, or sourced online.

Connecting teacher professional knowledge with high-quality instruction to achieve student mastery of science assumes that teachers have a good understanding of CK/SMK relevant to lesson content; can select one or more instructional strategies appropriate for a student group; justify choices by explaining how these meet student learning needs; and track students' learning and adapt in-class activities accordingly.

Research Investigating Teacher Professional Knowledge and Student Learning

Projects within this strand are typically large-scale, quantitative studies investigating relationships between teacher knowledge (SMK/CK and/or PCK) and student learning, without accessing teachers' practices by classroom observation. In general, participants are experienced, in-service teachers from public, state-funded schools. Teachers' SMK/CK and students' knowledge are probed via one pencil-and-paper (or online equivalent) test issued to both groups, while pPCK is tested separately. Connections between teacher knowledge and learning are sought via statistical correlations between test results.

Sadler et al. (2013) probed teachers' SMK about properties of matter, motions and forces, and transfer of energy using a multiple-choice test with around 200 volunteer US teachers and about 10,000 students ages 10–13. Teachers' knowledge of students' misconceptions ("KOSM," a PCK component), for the same concepts, was tested separately. Students' reading and mathematics skills were also tested. Data show that students strong in reading and mathematics demonstrated significantly higher learning gains on items featuring misconceptions when taught by teachers with correct SMK and KOSM. Teachers with only correct SMK generated similar learning gains to those without SMK. If there was no misconception in an item, teachers' SMK alone generated high learning gains. Findings suggest that at the test-item level, teachers need specific SMK and awareness of misconceptions associated with this SMK to generate high-quality instruction. The authors note that "teachers . . . generally well versed in physical science still may have holes that affect student learning of a particular concept. . . [and] student performance . . . is associated with teacher knowledge of a particular concept" (p. 1041).

Gunckel et al.'s (2018) US-based study explored the impact of formative assessment and instructional strategies supporting a learning progression (Amin et al., 2014) about water moving through environmental systems following a 1-week professional development (PD) workshop. Teachers' and students' scores for CK were obtained via written accounts (CK). PCK was assessed by teachers' responses to three possible learning goals: vocabulary, transmitting information, and misconceptions (PCK). Analysis of pre- and post-data showed teachers who used the PD materials in school generated higher learning gains than those who had not, but they nevertheless relied on "school science" in their written accounts, not specialist CK presented in the workshop. Further, two sub-groups of five and six teachers whose effect sizes on student learning were above 0.75 and below 0.25, respectively, were compared.

Noting the sub-groups' small size, "knowledge of instruction" (an aspect of PCK) showed that possession of "more coherent" PCK (p. 1356) generated larger effect sizes. This project indicates that strong correlations between teachers' PCK and student learning are rare – perhaps reflecting the quality of teachers' PCK – and, as the authors note, occur due to local constraints.

A German study, Mahler et al. (2017), investigated the impact of PCK, CK, and CuK on 13- to 14-year-old students' science performance relating to their thinking about systems in biology. Teachers completed pencil-and-paper tests measuring CK, PCK, and CuK and planned teaching of lessons about an ecosystem. Students' learning was probed using a pencil-and-paper test pre- and post-teaching, and concept maps. Mahler et al. (2017) report significant positive relationships between student learning and teachers' PCK, but no connections with their CK or CuK. The authors claim CuK and CK impact student learning indirectly: CuK correlated positively with PCK, and CK is an "important pre-requisite for the development of PCK" (p. 230). Findings suggest CK relating to biological contexts may play a less explicit role in learning than physical science CK. Teacher professional knowledge components interact to impact student learning in complex ways, and outcomes are context dependent.

This strand indicates that quality of teacher professional knowledge (most often CK/SMK and/ or PCK) impacts students' learning outcomes positively. High-quality instruction relies on teachers possessing precise CK/SMK that matches curriculum requirements, and PCK that includes relevant knowledge of students' misconceptions. Achieving "mastery" in teaching requires adoption of PCK that meets students' learning needs, while embracing relevant CK/SMK. Developing new specialist CK/PCK in experienced teachers seems challenging, as practices are hard to change. Methodologically, variation in project outcomes occur because teachers and students interpret CK/SMK tests differently; and declarative or pPCK differs from actual teaching, bypassing real-time teaching practices (Chan & Hume, 2019).

Research Investigating Teacher Professional Knowledge, Teacher Practices, and Student Learning

Studies Targeting Teacher Improvement via Long-Term Professional Development Programs

These studies feature investigations targeting teacher improvement via long-term professional development (PD) interventions for in-service practitioners, typically delivered over one or two years. Most are large scale, featuring teacher and student test data and probing teacher practices using standard observation instruments and video recording.

Roth et al.'s (2011) quasi-experimental study evaluated a 100-hour "analysis of practice" PD program, delivered over 1 year to 32 US elementary school teachers. The PD was framed by ensuring inquiry-based teaching activities included development of students' understanding of science concepts. The program focused on food webs, electricity, the water cycle, and photosynthesis. Sixteen teachers who did not take the PD were controls. All teachers took CK tests pre-, mid-, and post-intervention; completed a video-based lesson analysis task comprising lesson clips; and were video-recorded teaching using materials from the PD program. Students' CK was also tested. Findings showed experimental teachers outperformed control group teachers on all measures in posttests. Students taught by experimental group teachers outperformed their peers in all topics. High student achievement correlated strongly with teachers' CK quality; their ability to analyze science teaching about how students thought about science concepts; and their ability to select appropriate content representations matching the learning goal of a lesson (p. 134). The authors note that "content knowledge and pedagogical content knowledge . . . will only impact student learning if teachers are able to apply that knowledge in their teaching" (p. 121).

A similar-scale project (Gess-Newsome et al., 2019) measured teacher knowledge, teacher practices, and student learning in a 2-year, 250-hour PD program for 50 US secondary biology teachers focusing on inquiry-oriented practices, enhancing their CK and developing pedagogy. Teachers were expected to implement the practices, video-record teaching, and collate student work in school. Mixed data collection methods including a biology knowledge test, the Reformed Teacher Observation Protocol (RTOP, Sawada, 2002) and video analysis were applied. The study identified CK-PCK and PK-PCK connections, suggesting these are sub-structures within PCK. The authors report unexpectedly that only teachers' ACK (the authors' version of SMK) substantially influenced student learning, while no correlation between teacher knowledge and student achievement was observed, although connections were apparent in qualitative data. The authors attribute this to the time required for teachers to apply professional learning (from the intervention) in classrooms, and impact students' learning. Teachers vary when implementing new practices, influenced by in-school challenges. Also, the PCK instrument may not measure ePCK accurately, as this assumed that PCK is embedded in planning for instruction; also, insufficient data may be available to fully assess students' learning outcomes.

Kanter and Konstantopoulos (2010) focused on a PD program about a 10- to 12-week project-based science (PBS) curriculum for 12- to 14-year-olds in the US, aiming to show connections to positive impact on science achievement, attitudes, and career plans of ethnic and racial groups underrepresented in science. Nine teachers received input on relevant CK and PCK, and explicit awareness of students' ideas. Students' achievement, attitudes, and engagement in and enjoyment of science were measured. Teachers' CK and PCK were measured pre- and post-participation; in addition, teachers analyzed video recordings of their teaching. Teachers' CK and PCK correlated with improvements in students' science achievement, but affective measures such as science attitudes and students' future career plans were unchanged. Further analysis revealed improvements in attitudes associated with increased frequency of inquiry-based activities, not teachers' overall CK and PCK.

Heller et al. (2012) report on three PD interventions, namely "Teaching Cases" (TC), "Looking at Student Work" (LaSW), and "Metacognitive Analysis" (MA). These delivered identical science content to US elementary teachers. TC included discussions of pre-structured written examples of classroom practice; LaSW involved teachers analyzing student work in conjunction with teaching; and MA engaged teachers in reflection on their learning experience. Adopting a randomized trial design, the study measured the impact of distinctive features of each PD on teachers' knowledge, with written justifications for test answers and students' knowledge. All three programs improved teachers' and students' CK scores. TC and LaSW courses improved the accuracy and completeness of students' written justifications of test answers. Yet, only TC showed sustained effects on teachers' written justifications. MA had no impact on teachers' practices. The authors note that TC was the only course to "engage teachers in critical analysis of tradeoffs among instructional options, with detailed consideration of science content embedded in decisions about classroom practice" (p. 355), which may have "deepened teacher conceptual understanding of the science" (p. 355).

These studies illustrate that intensive, well-supported, and well-attended PD programs alter teachers' professional knowledge and practices to deliver high-quality instruction. Again, the quality of teachers' CK seems a significant driver of PCK consistent with high-quality instruction, suggesting that CK-PCK connections are a sub-component (Gess-Newsome et al., 2019).

Studies Investigating Knowledge-Practice-Learning Connections in Classroom Environments

Studies in Germany investigated knowledge-practice-learning connections outside PD contexts. These large-scale, quantitative projects utilize a teacher professional knowledge model consistent with German teacher education, which develops PK, CK, and PCK. Data collection instruments included video-recordings of lessons and professional knowledge tests, and of students completing achievement and motivation/attitudes tests. Förtsch et al. (2016) examined the impact of German secondary biology school teachers' CK, PCK, and teacher practices on about 800 students' learning of cytology and neurobiology. Their PCK test focused on model use, use of experiments, and student errors, as these relate to knowledge of instructional strategies and awareness of student mistakes. Video analysis focused on how teachers prompted "cognitive activation" – that is, facets of instruction such as "dealing with students' conceptions" and "exploration of students' ways of thinking." This revealed that most teachers used few "cognitive activation" strategies but high frequency use correlated with students scoring better on achievement tests. Teachers' CK did not seem to impact the level of cognitive activation, or student achievement. In a similar, unrelated study, Keller et al. (2017) investigated cognitive activation for teaching electricity. Data were collected from around 80 experienced, in-service teachers and about 1600 students ages 15–16 in Germany and Switzerland. Findings show that teachers' PCK predicted students' achievement, and that PCK correlated with cognitive activation, which in turn predicted student achievement. This study also probed teachers' enthusiasm and students' motivation, reporting a statistically significant correlation. These papers suggest that teachers' instructional strategies, featuring techniques that actively target students' cognition enhance learning, but an enthusiastic learning environment is important.

Liepertz and Borowski (2019) studied 35 physics teachers and learning outcomes of about 900 students ages 14–15, focusing on forces. They collected teacher data using written tests and video recordings, and measured "student content knowledge" (SCK) via a multiple-choice test. The authors investigated interconnectedness between teacher knowledge types, finding that CK significantly influenced PCK. Student learning gains were low, neither CK nor PCK predicted student learning, and, surprisingly, PCK showed a slightly negative influence on learning. The authors concluded that the pencil-and-paper tests may not have measured knowledge sufficiently accurately, and that teachers' pedagogical reasoning should be investigated to establish rationales for choice of instructional strategies.

Small-scale studies in Asia used classroom observation to assess the impact of ePCK on students' learning experiences. These include Chan and Yung (2015), who investigated four Hong Kong biology teachers teaching grade 12 students the topic "polymerase chain reaction." They found that strong SMK is critical for supporting teachers' "in-the-moment" decisions and actions during content-related interactions with students. Strong SMK was consistent with noticing students' misconceptions, interpreting emergent responses, and inventing instructional strategies "on the spot" to support student learning. Tay and Yeo (2018) conducted an in-depth qualitative case study of one experienced high school physics teacher in Singapore. The teacher's CK, PK, KS, and knowledge of context (CxK) were transformed *in situ* to inform pedagogical micro-actions supporting students' development of scientific models and modeling skills. Another Singaporean study with an in-service elementary teacher (Seah & Chan, 2021) focused on science language. The teacher's knowledge of students' prior knowledge, language difficulties and abilities, and learning progress informed teaching practices that addressed science language demands. These studies yield insights that suggest possession of strong CK/SMK seems crucial in high-quality instruction, as this facilitates teachers in anticipating and handling students' conceptual learning.

Studies probing knowledge-practice-learning connections outside PD contexts reaffirm that teachers' knowledge and actions drive student achievement. Aspects of high-quality instruction emerging from these papers indicate that teacher motivation and attitude seem as crucial as CK and PCK to ensuring an environment that motivates students' learning of abstract concepts. Direct observation affords deeper insights into how "master" teachers act as exemplars. For larger-scale studies, a close fit between teacher knowledge, practices, and student learning seems vital to investigating the knowledge-practice-learning axis successfully.

Papers in this section illustrate consistently that CK/SMK is crucial in delivering high-quality instruction, whether developed via a PD program, or tested in a classroom observation study. Findings indicate that when and how to test teachers' CK/SMK is significant: using the same test for teachers and students implies a perfect match between what is planned and what is taught. Classroom observations afford in-depth insights into connections between teacher knowledge, practices, and learning; but studies are often small-scale, limiting generalizability. Papers reviewed here suggest that affective aspects of teaching, such as teachers' and students' motivation and attitudes also contribute to high-quality instruction.

Research Investigating Specific Instructional Strategies and/or Contexts

This strand briefly reviews research using specific instructional strategies or contexts. Typically, studies assess the impact of short-term interventions aiming to enhance one aspect of teachers' knowledge, with data collected via mixed methods. Student learning and teachers' practice data are not routinely collected.

Crippen (2012) reports that about 40 US secondary science teachers were trained in an argumentation technique ("argue-to-learn") in a 48-hour PD on human-induced climate change. The project aimed to build teachers' confidence in using argument-based strategies on the premise that passive science learning leads to teachers who "struggle with understanding and implementing . . . inquiry-based strategies" (p. 847). The PD included Toulmin's argumentation model, climate change lectures, and field-based data collection. Teachers completed a capstone argumentation project, working in groups. Data were collected via CK tests, teacher presentations, semi-structured interviews, and other artifacts. Findings revealed that the PD improved teachers' CK about climate change. However, for their capstone projects, teachers preferred unwarranted online information over arguments arising from information available from lectures and field data. Crippen reports teachers did not accept these as authentic sources; also, their argumentation skills focused on strings of "facts," then making a claim, rather than explaining how each fact supported a claim.

Museums offer informal science education (ISE) environments that enrich teachers' and students' science experiences and knowledge. Price and Chiu (2018) examined the impact of a science museum-based PD program on in-service teachers' CK, PCK, and attitudes towards science of teachers and students in a quasi-experimental study. Two cohorts of 100 teachers were split 2/3 and 1/3 into experimental and control groups. The experimental groups participated in 48-hour PD programs on ecology or physical science over one school year. Data were collected via pre- and posttests of CK, PCK ("science behaviors"), and attitudes. Students completed attitudes and CK tests. Teachers' and students' CK in experimental groups was enhanced compared to control groups, exhibiting medium effect sizes. Experimental group teachers reported more "hands-on," student-centered science than control group teachers. Of the attitudes measured, only anxiety and self-efficacy changed, consistent with treatment group teachers being less anxious and feeling more capable of teaching science post-PD.

Engaging teachers in inquiry-based science via participation in genuine scientific research aims to enhance their capabilities in leading investigative practical work in school. Cutucache et al. (2017) and Miranda and Damico (2013) report on the impact of two separate teacher-scientist partnership projects on teachers' knowledge, skills, and practice. Cutucache et al. (2017) collected mixed methods data from 28 US K–12 teachers with no prior research experience during and 4-month-post-participation in 4-week research projects. Findings revealed teachers' science CK, confidence, and perceptions of science processes were enhanced. Teachers realized scientific research "is a search for answers, and includes frustrations, collaboration, sharing and presenting results" (p. 734), and learned from working with high-grade technology and data analysis. Miranda and Damico (2013) report similar findings. They add teachers' comparisons of scientific research with students' classroom experiences: teachers report that school science "lacks authenticity" (p. 1254), in part due to curriculum and assessment demands and lack of time and resources; and that while teachers had to develop their own experimental designs, students were provided with procedures, behaving as "knowledge consumers" (p. 1254). Teachers planned to alter their practical activities to a stronger inquiry focus as a result.

These papers illustrate contrasts in outcomes for studies featuring specific instructional strategies. Introducing new classroom-based instructional strategies successfully requires that teachers understand the rationale for change and have the time and support needed to adopt the new strategy. The degree of familiarity and availability of classroom opportunities may impact implementation. Instructional strategies introducing new and/or outside school environments add breadth to science teaching and learning that teachers may not have previously considered or experienced. Hence, this type of study ensures teachers develop a range of instructional strategies that offer the potential of high-quality learning experiences that motivate all students.

Conclusions

These studies add to our understanding of high-quality instruction in science and teacher professional knowledge models. Firstly, evidence points to the CK-PCK connection as essential: teachers require high standard, misconception-free CK (or SMK, or other variant) as a prerequisite for devising or delivering instructional strategies that positively impact student learning abstract science concepts. Secondly, inquiry-based science is a key component of high-quality instruction when this is made meaningful for learning science and includes opportunities for student-led design. Thirdly, developing affective attributes in teachers and students creates a positive learning environment that facilitates cognitive activity. Fourthly, development of specific instructional strategies such as argumentation and via ISE enrich the science learning environment, enhancing students' learning by offering fresh perspectives on science-related issues or concepts.

For science teacher education, these studies illustrate that high-quality instruction improves significantly when teachers have time and appropriate support to master new knowledge and techniques. Preservice, this means providing practice- and knowledge-based opportunities that develop CK linked to precise PCK, with trial teaching in well-mentored environments. Specifically, CK-PCK evidence suggests preservice teacher education focuses on plugging CK/SMK knowledge gaps, ensures awareness of misconceptions, and develops instructional strategies that match students' capabilities. Productive techniques based on research evidence discussed earlier include use of video analysis of their own and "master" teachers' teaching, with opportunities to discuss how practice impacts learning outcomes; and discussion of specific classroom situations that feature students' learning challenges, such as misconceptions, techniques, and outcomes related to inquiry-based learning, and socioscientific issues.

From a research methods perspective, studies range from complex, large-scale quantitative investigations to small-scale, qualitative projects offering in-depth insights. Particularly in larger studies, care in instrument design is necessary to obtain a reasonable chance that the same attribute or knowledge is tested in teachers and students, or in one population via multiple sources. Alternative methods such as student–student oral discussions and collation of practical work and seatwork set by teachers based on their professional knowledge may provide student-based evidence that reflects learning realistically. Diverse or unexpected outcomes may arise due to variations in school type, context, and resources, information that is not routinely collected. This could be mediated by probing teachers' pedagogical reasoning to illuminate rationales behind classroom practices.

To progress research in this area, three avenues seem productive. Firstly, establishing in depth and detail how highly effective teachers – that is, teachers who are consistently regarded as delivering "high-quality instruction" – teach and achieve learning outcomes across the K–12 age range. This is no small undertaking, as the ranges of contexts and science content are extensive. Nonetheless, gaining a deeper understanding of "mastery" teaching points to expertise that is impactful and therefore desirable, setting (high) expectations for practice. Secondly, understanding how teachers learn to deliver high-quality instruction in science would be helpful. Longitudinal studies tracking teachers from pre- through to experience ("expert") in-service practitioners would provide insights into the influence of mentoring practices, teaching "practicums," types of teacher professional knowledge, and classroom environments and contexts on teacher development. Thirdly, affective aspects of education on high-quality instruction seem to be underestimated. Attitudes and motivation in relation to science are often studied and investigated separately from considerations of their potential impact on high-quality instruction and teacher professional knowledge. Studies jointly embedding these aspects in investigating high-quality instruction in science may yield new insights that could highly influence practice.

References

AAAS (1993). *Benchmarks for science literacy: A project 2061 report*. Oxford University Press.

American Association for the Advancement of Science [AAAS]. (1990). *Science for all Americans*. Oxford: Oxford University Press.

Amin, T. G., Smith, C. L., & Wiser, M. (2014). Student conceptions and conceptual change. In N. G. Lederman & S. K. Abell (Eds.), *Handbook of research on science education volume II* (pp. 57–81). New York and Abingdon, UK: Routledge.

Brophy, J. E., & Good, T. L. (1986). Teacher behaviour and student achievement. In M. C. Wittrock (Ed.), *Handbook of research on teaching* (pp. 328–375). New York and London: Macmillan.

Carlson, J., Daehler, K. R., Alonzo, A. C., Barendsen, E., Berry, A., Borowski, A., . . . Wilson, C. D. (2019). The refined consensus model of pedagogical content knowledge in science education. In A. Hume, R. Cooper, & A. Borowski (Eds.), *Repositioning pedagogical content knowledge in teachers' knowledge for teaching science* (pp. 77–94). New York: Springer. https://doi.org/10.1007/978-981-13-5898-2_2

Carroll, J. (1963). A model of school learning. *Teachers College Record, 64*, 723–733.

Chan, K. K. H., & Hume, A. (2019). Towards a consensus model: Literature review of how science teachers' pedagogical content knowledge is investigated in empirical studies. In A. Hume, R. Cooper, & A. Borowski (Eds.), *Repositioning pedagogical content knowledge in teachers' knowledge for teaching science* (pp. 3–76). New York: Springer. https://doi.org/10.1007/978-981-13-5898-2_1

Chan, K. K. H., & Yung, B. H. W. (2015). On-site pedagogical content knowledge development. *International Journal of Science Education, 37*(8), 1246–1278. https://doi.org/10.1080/09500693.2015.1033777

Cochran, K. F., DeRuiter, J. A., & King, R. A. (1993). Pedagogical content knowing: An integrative model for teacher preparation. *Journal of Teacher Education, 44*(4), 263–272. https://doi.org/10.1177/0022487193044004004

Coe, R., Aloisi, C., Higgin, S., & Major, L. E. (2014). *What makes great teaching? A review of the underpinning research.* Sutton Trust. www.suttontrust.com/wp-content/uploads/2014/10/What-Makes-Great-Teaching-REPORT.pdf

Crippen, K. J. (2012). Argument as professional development: Impacting teacher knowledge and beliefs about science. *Journal of Science Teacher Education, 23*(8), 847–866. https://doi.org/10.1007/s10972-012-9282-3

Cutucache, C. E., Leas, H. D., Grandgenett, N. F., Nelson, K. L., Rodie, S., Shuster, R., . . . Tapprich, W. E. (2017). Genuine faculty-mentored research experiences for in-service science teachers: Increases in science knowledge, perception, and confidence levels. *Journal of Science Teacher Education, 28*(8), 724–744. https://doi.org/10.1080/1046560X.2017.1415615

Department of Education and Science (1979). *Aspects of secondary education in England.* Department of Education and Science.

Driver, R. (1983). *The pupil as scientist.* Milton Keynes: Open University Press.

Fischer, H. E., Borowski, A., & Tepner, O. (2012). Professional knowledge of science teachers. In B. J. Fraser, K. Tobin, & C. J. McRobbie (Eds.), *Second international handbook of science education* (pp. 435–448). New York: Springer.

Förtsch, C., Werner, S., von Kotzebue, L., & Neuhaus, B. J. (2016). Effects of biology teachers' professional knowledge and cognitive activation on students' achievement. *International Journal of Science Education, 38*(17), 2642–2666. https://doi.org/10.1080/09500693.2016.1257170

Gess-Newsome, J. (2015). A model of teacher professional knowledge and skill including PCK: Results of the thinking from the PCK summit. In A. Berry, P. Friedrichsen, & J. Loughran (Eds.), *Re-examining pedagogical content knowledge in science education* (pp. 28–42). New York and Abingdon, UK: Routledge.

Gess-Newsome, J., Taylor, J. A., Carlson, J., Gardner, A. L., Wilson, C. D., & Stuhlsatz, M. A. M. (2019). Teacher pedagogical content knowledge, practice, and student achievement. *International Journal of Science Education, 41*(7), 944–963. https://doi.org/10.1080/09500693.2016.1265158

Guerriero, S. (2017). *Pedagogical knowledge and the changing nature of the teaching profession.* Paris: OECD Publishing. https://doi.org/10.1787/9789264270695-en

Gunckel, K. L., Covitt, B. A., & Salinas, I. (2018). Learning progressions as tools for supporting teacher content knowledge and pedagogical content knowledge about water in environmental systems. *Journal of Research in Science Teaching, 55*(9), 1339–1362. https://doi.org/10.1002/tea.21454

Heller, J. I., Daehler, K. R., Wong, N., Shinohara, M., & Miratrix, L. W. (2012). Differential effects of three professional development models on teacher knowledge and student achievement in elementary science. *Journal of Research in Science Teaching, 49*(3), 333–362. https://doi.org/10.1002/tea.21004

Kanter, D. E., & Konstantopoulos, S. (2010). The impact of a project-based science curriculum on minority student achievement, attitudes, and careers: The effects of teacher content and pedagogical content knowledge and inquiry-based practices. *Science Education, 94*(5), 855–887. https://doi.org/10.1002/sce.20391

Keller, M. M., Neumann, K., & Fischer, H. E. (2017). The impact of physics teachers' pedagogical content knowledge and motivation on students' achievement and interest. *Journal of Research in Science Teaching, 54*(5), 586–614. https://doi.org/10.1002/tea.21378

Kind, V., & Chan, K. K. H. (2019). Resolving the amalgam: Connecting pedagogical content knowledge, content knowledge and pedagogical knowledge. *International Journal of Science Education, 41*(7), 964–978. https://doi.org/10.1080/09500693.2019.1584931

Klahr, D., & Dunbar, K. (1988). Dual space search during scientific reasoning. *Cognitive Science, 12*(1), 1–48. https://doi.org/10.1016/0364-0213(88)90007-9

Kloser, M. (2014). Identifying a core set of science teaching practices: A Delphi expert panel approach. *Journal of Research in Science Teaching, 51*(9), 1185–1217. https://doi.org/10.1002/tea.21171

Liepertz, S., & Borowski, A. (2019). Testing the consensus model: Relationships among physics teachers' professional knowledge, interconnectedness of content structure and student achievement. *International Journal of Science Education, 41*(7), 890–910. https://doi.org/10.1080/09500693.2018.1478165

Magnusson, S., Krajcik, J., & Borko, H. (1999). Nature, sources, and development of pedagogical content knowledge for science teaching. In J. Gess-Newsome & N. G. Lederman (Eds.), *Examining pedagogical content knowledge: The construct and its implications for science education* (pp. 95–132). Kluwer Academic. https://doi.org/10.1007/0-306-47217-1_4

Mahler, D., Großschedl, J., & Harms, U. (2017). Using doubly latent multilevel analysis to elucidate relationships between science teachers' professional knowledge and students' performance. *International Journal of Science Education, 39*(2), 213–237. https://doi.org/10.1080/09500693.2016.1276641

Mavhunga, E., & Rollnick, M. (2013). Improving PCK of chemical equilibrium in pre-service teachers. *African Journal of Research in Mathematics, Science and Technology Education, 17*(1–2), 113–125. https://doi.org/10.1080/10288457.2013.828406

Miranda, R. J., & Damico, J. B. (2013). Science teachers' beliefs about the influence of their summer research experiences on their pedagogical practices. *Journal of Science Teacher Education, 24*(8), 1241–1261. https://doi.org/10.1007/s10972-012-9331-y

Ofsted, Office for Standards in Education (2013). *Maintaining curiosity*. Ofsted. https://assets.publishing.service.gov.uk/government/uploads/system/uploads/attachment_data/file/379164/Maintaining_20curiosity_20a_20survey_20into_20science_20education_20in_20schools.pdf

Osborne, J. (2014). Scientific practices and inquiry in the science classroom. In N. G. Lederman & S. K. Abell (Eds.), *Handbook of research on science education volume II* (pp. 579–599). London: Routledge.

Osborne, R., & Freyberg, P. (1985). *Learning in science: The implications of children's science*. New Zealand: Pearson Education.

Park, S., & Oliver, J. S. (2008). Revisiting the conceptualisation of pedagogical content knowledge (PCK): PCK as a conceptual tool to understand teachers as professionals. *Research in Science Education, 38*(3), 261–284. https://doi.org/10.1007/s11165-007-9049-6

Price, A. C., & Chiu, A. (2018). An experimental study of a museum-based, science PD programme's impact on teachers and their students. *International Journal of Science Education, 40*(9), 941–960. https://doi.org/10.1080/09500693.2018.1457816

Rollnick, M., Bennett, J., Rhemtula, M., Dharsey, N., & Ndlovu, T. (2008). The place of subject matter knowledge in pedagogical content knowledge: A case study of South African teachers teaching the amount of substance and chemical equilibrium. *International Journal of Science Education, 30*(10), 1365–1387. https://doi.org/10.1080/09500690802187025

Rosenshine, B. (1979). Content, time and direct instruction. In P. Peterson & H. Walberg (Eds.), *Research on teaching concepts, findings and implications* (pp. 28–56). San Pablo: McCutchan Publishing Corporation.

Roth, K. J., Garnier, H. E., Chen, C., Lemmens, M., Schwille, K., & Wickler, N. I. Z. (2011). Videobased lesson analysis: Effective science PD for teacher and student learning. *Journal of Research in Science Teaching, 48*(2), 117–148. https://doi.org/10.1002/tea.20408

Sadler, P. M., Sonnert, G., Coyle, H. P., Cook-Smith, N., & Miller, J. L. (2013). The influence of teachers' knowledge on student learning in middle school physical science classrooms. *American Educational Research Journal, 50*(5), 1020–1049. https://doi.org/10.3102/0002831213477680

Sawada, D., Piburn, M. D., Judson, E., Turley, J., Falconer, K., Benford, R., & Bloom, I. (2002). Measuring reform practices in science and mathematics classrooms: The Reformed Teaching Observation Protocol. *School Science and Mathematics, 102*(6), 245–253. https://doi.org/https://doi.org/10.1111/j.1949-8594.2002.tb17883.x

Schwab, J. J. (1962). *The teaching of science as enquiry*. Cambridge, MA: Harvard University Press.

Seah, L. H., & Chan, K. K. H. (2021). A case study of a science teacher's knowledge of students in relation to addressing the language demands of science. *International Journal of Science and Mathematics Education, 19*(2), 267–287. https://doi.org/10.1007/s10763-019-10049-6

Shulman, L. S. (1987). Knowledge and teaching: Foundations of the new reform. *Harvard Educational Review, 57*(1), 1–22. https://doi.org/10.17763/haer.57.1.j463w79r56455411

Tay, S. L., & Yeo, J. (2018). Analysis of a physics teacher's pedagogical 'micro-actions' that support 17-year-olds' learning of free body diagrams via a modelling approach. *International Journal of Science Education, 40*(2), 109–138. https://doi.org/10.1080/09500693.2017.1401752

United Nations Department of Economic and Social Affairs (2015). *Sustainable development goal 4*. United Nations Department of Economic and Social Affairs Sustainable Development. https://sdgs.un.org/goals/goal4

Wang, M. C., Haertel, G. D., & Walberg, H. J. (1990). What influences learning? A content analysis of review literature. *Journal of Educational Research, 84*(1), 30–43. https://doi.org/10.1080/00220671.1990.10885988

25

INDIGENOUS KNOWLEDGE IN SCIENCE EDUCATION

Implications for Teacher Education

Josef de Beer, Neal Petersen, and Meshach Ogunniyi

Introduction

The 21st century is characterized by a new sociopolitical context and new social realities (Adams et al., 2018) that are of utmost importance for both science and teacher education. Many countries battle with youth unemployment, changing population demographics (e.g., refugees and migrants, notably in Europe and the USA), and inequalities (Adams et al., 2018). With these social challenges, questions are raised about how science education can respond and how both pre- and in-service teacher education can sensitize teachers to these new realities.

In the classroom, science teachers are challenged. They have to facilitate learning in culturally diverse classrooms and show diverse learners how science is relevant to their lives and to modern society. Unfortunately, many school learners experience science lessons as neither interesting nor engaging, nor relevant (Anderhag et al., 2016; De Beer & Van Wyk, 2019; Zidny et al., 2020). Researchers report this low affective orientation as detrimental to student learning (De Beer et al., 2018). If students are not engaged in their learning, they are unlikely to become self-directed learners in a complex 21st century and the world of work (De Beer & Mentz, 2019).

Gilbert (2006) lists a number of problems facing science education and science curricula, namely: (a) curricula have become overloaded with knowledge; (b) isolated facts are taught, and students struggle to form connections; (c) lack of knowledge transfer to real-life situations; and (d) lack of relevance. Gilbert (2006) suggests that "context," as the basis for curriculum design and classroom teaching, could provide a solution to these problems. Context is defined as "a focal event embedded in its cultural setting" (Gilbert, 2006, p. 960; Davis & Ebbe, 1995).

Gilbert (2006) evaluates four different models of context, namely: (a) context as the direct application of concepts; (b) context as reciprocity between concepts and applications; (c) context as provided by personal mental activity; and (d) context as social circumstances. Indigenous knowledge (IK) can be a powerful vehicle in creating such context in the diverse science classroom, since IK offers a potential bridge between the social everyday life of the students and industrial life as reflected in the abstract concepts in science curricula (Gilbert, 2006). Consequently, the infusion of IK in the science curriculum holds affordances for contextualizing western science concepts, assisting learners to connect science to their everyday experiences.

DOI: 10.4324/9781003098478-30

What Is IK?

The different studies pertaining to IK reveal different definitions. For example, Ogunniyi (2004) states that IK consists of a variety of constructs or systems of thought governed by testable and non-testable generalizations. Battiste (2002, p. 2) defines IK as:

> A complex set of technologies developed and sustained by indigenous civilizations. Often oral and symbolic, IK is transmitted through the structure of indigenous languages and is passed on to the next generation through modelling, practice and animation, rather than through the written word.

Rankoana (2017, p. 63) offers the following description of IK:

> A systematic body of knowledge acquired by local people through the accumulation of experience, informal experiment, and understanding of their environment.

These definitions all highlight IK as a culture-based way of knowing derived from people's experiences with the world. This chapter adopts the view that IK is cultural knowledge developed over generations and embedded in problem-based thinking and experimentation to solve authentic problems. Further, this knowledge is holistic and underpinned by a worldview that sees humankind as living in harmony with the environment.

IK differs from western science since, while science is based on a mechanical worldview, IK is based on an anthropomorphic worldview (Ogunniyi, 2004, 2007). Ogunniyi et al. (2008) elaborates that IK systems are a "redemptive, holistic, and transcendental view of human experience with the cosmos" (p. 178). Sjöström (2007) concurs, noting that western science can be described by constructs such as positivism, objectivism, reductionism, rationalism, and modernism. In such a Cartesian perspective, human beings are seen as "separate from nature" (Zidny, 2020, p. 155). In contrast, IK systems are more holistic, and humans are seen to be in harmony with nature. This cosmo-anthropic view is well captured by Savelyeva (2017, p. 511), who states that:

> Everything in the universe, including humans, shares life and deserves the greatest respect . . . cosmos is a dynamic and ever-changing interpretive reality, which reflects human understanding, sense-making and interpretation of the universe.

Jones and Hunter (2003) and De Beer (2019a, p. 93) offer greater specificity regarding IK. In their discussions on IK, they indicate that: (a) it is based on experience; (b) it is tested over centuries of use; (c) it developed as a collective database of observable knowledge; (d) it is adapted to local culture and environment; (e) it is a living knowledge base that is dynamic and changing; (f) it is based on problem-solving; (g) it is orally transmitted, and sometimes encapsulated in metaphor; (h) it is often not possible to separate IK from ethics, spirituality, and metaphysics; (i) it is holistic, versus a reductionist (western science) approach; (j) it is an ecologically based approach; and (k) it comprises contextualized knowledge versus (often) decontextualized science knowledge.

These authors' views highlight the difficulties facing the science teacher when attempting to incorporate IK into the teaching of science themes. The holistic nature of IK, and focus on metaphysical aspects, seem to be in conflict with the empirical and objective nature of science. This apparent disjuncture will be discussed later in the chapter.

Science Knowledge and IK

Over the years, many authors have discussed the relationship between (western) science knowledge and IK. When referring to western science, we refer to science knowledge that meets the widely accepted tenets of science, i.e., it is empirical, objective, and inferential. IK, on the other hand, can be described as holistic and having metaphysical characteristics. There are two prevailing overarching views, with different perspectives on how IK connects to science, namely those of George (1999), and those of Taylor and Cameron (2016) and Zinyeka et al. (2016).

In their analysis, Taylor and Cameron (2016) pose three different perspectives on the relationship between western science and IK, while George (1999) describes four. Firstly, the "conventional" perspective, which requires conventional science explanations for observed events. Ramnarain (2021) illustrates this perspective with the example of the traditional use of lime juice to remove stains, and how this practice can be explained in terms of acid/oxide reactions. Secondly, the "on the horizon" perspective, which suggests that a current scientific explanation is not available, but it is likely to be developed. An example is the use of a decoction made from a plant from the verbena family, *Stachytarpheta spp.*, which is traditionally used for the treatment of worms in children. Although there is anecdotal evidence for its efficacy, the chemistry and pharmacology still need to be determined (Ramnarain, 2021). Thirdly, the "linked, but different principles" perspective illustrated by the traditional wisdom that eating too much sugar could cause diabetes, which is borne out by science. Finally, these knowledge systems may have "distinct" explanations. For example, some Venda people in South Africa hold the belief that people wearing red clothes stand a bigger chance of being struck by lightning, a belief with no scientific merit (Ramnarain, 2021).

Another prevailing view is evident in the discussions by Taylor and Cameron (2016) and Zinyeka et al. (2016), who propose three different perspectives on the relationship between science and IK (in contrast to four perspectives discussed earlier). They see one possible relationship as inclusive, which means that the larger construct of science includes IK and western science, and potentially other forms of knowledge. They see a second relationship as exclusive, with western science being distinct from IK. Both knowledge forms are distinct but equal, and they should be valued for their own worth. Finally, they consider western science and IK to be intersecting, which suggests there is a point of intersection among these two different knowledge bases. This intersection occurs at the point of procedural knowledge (know-how) and factual knowledge (know-what), but departs at explanatory knowledge (know-why). This point of departure is based on the use of spiritual aspects in IK explanation.

Within the IK community, there are different levels of acceptance of these views. Researchers such as De Beer (2012), De Beer and Petersen (2017), De Beer (2019a), and Petersen et al. (2019) are advocates for the "intersecting domain" view. These authors acknowledge that there are shared tenets between the two knowledge systems, and that by recognizing these tenets, students will have a better understanding of knowledge and culture, and the construction of knowledge. Within the "intersecting domain," the different knowledge systems provide an approach to understanding phenomena that have shared qualities. For example, many IK holders live in harmony with the environment and have solutions to the environmental degradation that we face in an era of industrialization and urbanization.

In contrast, Onwu and Mosimege (2004) suggest that western science and IK are two different systems, in need of different systems of verification. They are concerned that if the methods of western science are used to evaluate IK, then knowledge systems become subjected to a hierarchy of thought, and that can negatively impact IK. For Onwu and Mosimege (2004), IK systems have their own epistemological and ontological position, and these need to be regarded as part of the IK system.

The authors of this chapter suggest that science teachers should follow the "intersecting domain" perspective and emphasize the shared tenets of science and IK. This provides the opportunity to engage in inquiry activities, and it also serves as a means of contextualizing curriculum themes. However, the metaphysical aspects of IK should not be dismissed. Students should have an appreciation of the holistic nature of IK. De Beer (2020) shows that there are often plausible explanations for IK practices, which, at face value, seem to be irrational.

IK and Science Education

In terms of science education, science should be understood not only as a body of knowledge, but also as a way of thinking (Zidny et al., 2020). In order for students to experience both the knowledge of science (the so-called substantive nature of science) and engage in the processes of science (the syntactical nature of science), science teachers need to create learning opportunities for learners to experience, question, and study the phenomena around them. When these learning opportunities are provided to the students, they allow students to bring their IK to the learning experience (Sjöström, & Eilks, 2018). These learning opportunities should focus on who the students are and draw upon their ways of understanding, which are often based upon their experiences within their cultural and community settings. Zidny et al. (2020, p. 160) idealizes this view and states that:

> Indigenous ways of thinking can provide corresponding learners with a broader (more holistic) view of the world to understand science and nature beyond a non-western perspective.
>
> (p. 160)

By including the cultural component of science, through the introduction of IK, learners might experience science as more relevant to their daily lives.

Eilks and Hofstein (2015) claim that science education needs to adopt new pedagogies and approaches to improve the relevance of science education to students. One way to achieve this is by infusing IK. By capitalizing on the IK that learners bring to the classroom, science can be made more meaningful to culturally diverse learners, since IK "introduces different perspectives on nature and the human in nature" (Zidny et al., 2020, p. 145).

Eilks and Hofstein (2015) also suggest that science educators should carefully consider which tenets of science are communicated in the classroom. The focus on only the empirical and inferential might marginalize the tentative nature of science, and this might also lead to a dismissal of IK with its holistic nature. The images, experiences, or even discussions in the classroom need to be carefully considered. More importantly, science should be contextualized within local realities (Oluka, 2017).

When IK is put into place in the classroom, students benefit. Students can see the connection between science and the local and global community, along with its relationship to social responsibility, justice, and sustainability (Rankoana, 2017; Speight-Vaughn & De Beer, 2020). Referred to as glocalization, this orientation connects local and global contexts while maintaining the significant contributions of different communities and contexts (Patel & Lynch, 2013, p. 223).

De Beer (2019) illustrates such glocalization in science education (in the context of IK) with a practical example related to insecticides. IK holders (predominantly people from the Tsonga culture in Giyani in South Africa) have used the fever tree, *Lippia javanica*, as an insect repellant for decades (De Beer, 2019). Research has shown that the oils of this plant are very effective as an insecticide. The volatile oil of the plant contains myrcene, caryophyllene, linalool, and ipsdienone, and these substances compare well in terms of efficacy with Diethyltoluamide, a well-known mosquito repellant. As part of a community upliftment programme in South Africa, unemployed people in the Giyani district engaged in entrepreneurial activities making candles from *Lippia javanica*'s oils that are sold as insect repellants (De Beer, 2019b). Considering the dangers of insecticides to human and environmental health (Aktar et al., 2009), this example provides evidence of the environmental ethics of IK and could also provide students with examples of career and entrepreneurial opportunities related to IK (De Beer, 2019b). Additional examples range from food security to bioprospecting, antimicrobial and pharmacological studies, and applications in the cosmetic industry.

Framing the Infusion of IK Into Science Education

Embodied, situated, and distributed cognition (ESDC) provides an essential framing when talking about the infusion of IK into science education. The ESCD framework posits that cognition is not limited to the processing of internal information, but embedded physiologically in action, situated in the sociocultural world and distributed among agents and artifacts (Hardy-Vallee & Payette, 2008). As conceptualized by these authors, ESDC approaches provide multimodal experiences (different ways of sharing meaning) and can support students in their concept formation in science (Chahine, 2013; Ramnarain, 2021). In this view, different social, cultural, cognitive, physical, linguistic, and emotional experiences are connected to a student's learning of science. When engaging with IK, the student can use these modalities, as he/she engages with cultural artifacts, narratives, or practices, while constructing new knowledge.

For example, Jegede and Aikenhead (1999, p. 1) state that "the role of the social context is to scaffold the learner, and provide hints that help foster co-construction of knowledge while interacting with other members of the society." Gilbert (2006) agrees and states that when learners co-construct knowledge, they work in communities of practice to explore how scientific concepts are applied in everyday life. When science teaching is informed by learners' world views, smoother border crossings are facilitated as students explore how scientific principles/constructs are applied in everyday life (Jegede & Aikenhead, 1999).

Research shows that contextualization through IK can aid cognition (Petersen et al., 2019) by assisting students with meaning making as they enter into a "cognitive apprenticeship" (Gilbert, 2006) with the teacher. In social constructivist parlance, the teacher can more readily scaffold learning across the zone of proximal development (Vygotsky, 1978).

The infusion of IK, within an ESDC framing, can be illustrated by the following examples:

- When students engage with IK related to medicinal plant use, it is useful to follow the Kirby-Bauer technique to demonstrate the antimicrobial properties of culturally important medicinal plants. Students use their hands in performing the laboratory procedure (embodied cognition), and they engage with specific cultural narratives related to the plant use (situated cognition). Furthermore, students engage with such activities in groups (social constructivism), and they jointly construct meaning (distributed cognition).
- Mavuru and Ramnarain (2017) illustrate how a teacher can use IK to enhance student learning during a lesson on electrostatics. In their example, the teacher recognizes the rich cultural beliefs of learners on lightning. The teacher starts by recognizing that learners hold views that certain precautionary measures could be taken to avoid being struck by lightning (e.g., placing a car tire on the chimney of the house, or covering mirrors). Through guiding questions, the teacher facilitates a rich reflective discussion in the classroom.
- Another example of this type of instruction pertains to lessons about biological interactions. A teacher can focus on the plant *Adenia gummifera (impinda)*, which is found in rural communities of South Africa (De Beer & Van Wyk, 2019). This plant is often made into a decoction of the stems and sprinkled around the house to "keep evil spirits away" (De Beer & Van Wyk, 2019). Chemical analysis of the plant has shown that it has strong antimicrobial activity, and that it serves the same purpose as bleaches and antiseptic products in western households, to kill disease-causing pathogens. A reflective rich discussion can be followed.

A caveat, however, is that science teachers should not create the idea that IK can be validated only by using western science (De Beer, 2020).

IK and Science Teacher Education

Prior to the 1990s, relatively little research had been done on epistemological border-crossing between science and IK in both pre- and in-service teacher education. (Ogunniyi, 2004, 2007). However, since 1995, research on professional development for teaching IK has increased across the globe. Researchers, such as Aikenhead and Elliot (2010) worked in a Canadian context; Garroutte (1999) on American Indian science education; Sylva et al. (2010) on making the science curricula more relevant to students in Hawaii; and many others in the African context (Ogunniyi, 2004, 2007, 2011; Thomson, 2010; Cronje et al., 2015; Petersen et al., 2019; Le Grange, 2004, 2007; Zinyeka et al., 2016).

This section provides a brief overview of research literature on contextualizing science education through IK for teacher education. The review of literature was completed using Microsoft Academic Search. To identify potential papers, the keywords "IK" and "science teacher education" were used to locate literature from 2007 to 2021. Inclusion criteria identified articles that focused on curriculum and curriculum design, pedagogy, and teaching methodologies in the context of IK, specifically on IK in the context of pre- and in-service teacher education. Postcolonial literary studies were excluded in order to provide science teachers with insight into the pedagogical considerations of including IK in science curriculum themes. Initially, 65 sources were identified, all published in journals with relative high-impact indices, and the aforementioned criteria were used to narrow down the number of publications to the final 22 sources deemed relevant to this chapter.

Factors Militating Against the Use of IK in the Science Classroom

Research shows that several factors influenced the non-attainment of goals related to the infusion of IK in the science classroom. Shizha (2007) classifies these as attitudinal, institutional, and systemic. The latter author states that "in order to address both overt and hidden biases against IK in schools, teachers must first address their own personal attitudes" (p. 311). For example, De Beer (2019a) shows that some teachers view IK as pseudo-science.

Science Teacher IK and Pedagogical Skills

De Beer and Dudu (2021), Petersen et al. (2019), and Sebotsa (2020) found that science teachers generally show a lack of nuanced understanding of IK and its affordances in the science classroom. Authors such as Abd-El-Khalick et al. (1998) and Petersen et al. (2019) have shown that the views that teachers hold of science influence their selection of suitable pedagogies. If science teachers do not view IK as having an empirical basis, little inquiry learning is likely to take place in the classroom (Mothwa, 2011; De Beer, 2019). Specifically, they do not acknowledge that both the natural sciences and IK share tenets such as its empirical and inferential nature.

Both pre- and in-service teacher education should place emphasis on scaffolding nuanced understandings of both the tenets of science and IK (Mothwa, 2011; Petersen et al., 2019). Teachers should be assisted in their professional development on the use of effective approaches when teaching IK, which entail more than simply paying lip service to IK.

In order to address this lack of knowledge, preservice and in-service teacher education need to emphasize the nuanced understanding of the tenets of the natural sciences and the tenets of IK. This will foster epistemological border crossings (De Beer, 2019a). For example, when learners engage in a Kirby-Bauer technique in the laboratory, to test the antimicrobial properties of traditional medicinal plants, they not only validate IK, but they also engage in the processes of science (Petersen et al., 2019).

Science Teachers' Implementation of IK in the Classroom

The literature reflects on diverse ways or steps in which IK can be incorporated in the science classroom, namely fragmented, connected, sequenced, and integrated (Handayani et al., 2018). These steps align with the connections between the knowledge systems explained earlier. The most common approach to incorporating IK into the classroom is the fragmented approach, which involves science teachers providing a few examples. Unfortunately, this does not provide the opportunity to explore the true nature of IK. It pays lip service to IK and can be compared to the exclusive approach described earlier. A better approach, which is integrated, is proposed by De Beer and Mentz (2019), who advocate engaging students in authentic IK practices. One such example is engaging in ethnobotanical surveys, where students utilize the Matrix Method (De Beer & Van Wyk, 2019) to record the IK of local communities. (This is similar to the intersecting domain approach explained earlier.)

De Beer and Dudu (2021) have shown that many student teachers and practicing science teachers need effective pedagogies to teach IK in the classroom. Without these pedagogies, teachers only superficially address IK. These authors advocate for problem-based and cooperative learning approaches to help connect IK to the science in the classroom. In using IK, these approaches allow students to explore ill-structured problems and find solutions to authentic problems (De Beer, 2019).

IK Can Empower Learners

The science teacher has a responsibility to empower learners, and to promote transformation and social justice (Le Grange, 2019). Burke and Whitty (2018) argue that "our starting point is that equity is a crucial dimension for reconceptualizing teaching across different and diverse social contexts" (p. 272). De Beer and Mentz (2019) highlight that the holders of IK are, by definition, self-directed learners who had to solve authentic problems in their environments. The incorporation of IK in the classroom could provide authentic contexts to nurture problem-based learning and self-directed learning skills. Additionally, De Beer (2019b) argues that IK holds affordances for introducing students to possible careers and entrepreneurial opportunities.

Supporting Science Teacher Learning

Science teachers can be supported in different ways. Researchers at the North-West University in South Africa (De Beer, 2019; De Beer & Mentz, 2019; De Beer & Van Wyk, 2019; Petersen et al., 2019) have focused on short learning programs to better equip in-service science teachers to use inquiry-learning approaches while infusing IK into science curriculum themes. The Science and IK Project (SIKSP) of the University of the Western Cape, South Africa, focuses on preparing several cohorts of preservice and practicing teachers to implement an inclusive science-IK perspective in the classroom context (Ogunniyi, 2011). Studies on these programs have documented a significant growth of the use of IK among participants (e.g., Petersen et al., 2019), showing that teachers have developed more nuanced understandings of IK and appropriate pedagogies to use when teaching IK. Both preservice and in-service teachers found they could use IK to better connect with their students.

Indigenous Artifacts Are Important in IK Instruction

IK artifacts could be effective teaching and learning resources in the science classroom, such as indigenous games (Nxumalo & Mncube, 2019). Such artifacts make multimodal learning possible, and that could contribute to conceptual understanding (Hardy-Vallee & Payette, 2008).

By means of an illustration, science teachers in an effective teacher professional development program presented by the North-West University in South Africa learned to use the processes of science that included: hypothesizing, designing and conducting experiments, and interpreting data (De Beer, 2019; Petersen et al., 2019). In their professional development program, teachers were asked to share knowledge about different methods of destroying microorganisms, drawing on their IK. The teachers then generated questions and hypotheses and conducted their experiments that focused on understanding the antimicrobial activities of plants that are traditionally used for medicinal purposes. The teachers were given agar plates and extracts of medicinal plants (mainly alkaloids). They applied the extracts and then collected and analysed the data to see if the plant had the potential to inhibit microbial growth, or whether it could destroy microorganisms (De Beer & Whitlock, 2009; De Beer, 2019). With such an approach, teachers explore IK using integrated process skills (Sanders, 2010).

Examples of IK Instruction for Students

Supporting student understanding of IK is important. One approach involves using the processes of science to investigate IK practices, such as the inquiry into *karrikins* (De Beer, 2012). The Noongar people, native inhabitants of western Australia, use smoke treatments for their seeds before planting the crops. Through experimentation over decades, they came to realize that smoke treatment could lead to better seed germination. Flematti et al. (2007) realized that smoke contains butanolide derivatives known as *karrikins*, which are growth regulators. These researchers showed that the *karrikins* in smoke could lead to better seed germination, thus confirming the merit of this IK practice. De Beer (2012) shows how this IK could be interrogated in the school laboratory, where learners could: (a) do a literature review on this topic; (b) formulate hypotheses; (c) design and conduct experiments, keeping in mind which dependent and independent variables should be considered; (d) analyse and interpret the data, and draw conclusions; and (f) communicate their findings. Such an activity, embedded in problem-based and cooperative learning principles, also hold affordances for enhancing self-directed learning (De Beer, 2019b).

Helping students to become critical consumers of science can be facilitated with an investigation into the indigenous belief that music affects plant growth and germination (De Beer, 2019b). In the Maranao culture in the Philippines, for example, the planting of rice is accompanied by music, chanting, and dances (Dimaporo & Fernandez, 2007). Research by Bochu et al. (1998) and Chowdhury et al. (2014) indicate that sound waves influence plant morphology, biochemistry, and gene expression. Chowdhury and Gupta (2015) have shown that sound waves increase the concentration of metabolites in the cell. Wang et al. (2002) have showed an increase in intercellular Ca^{2+} when seeds are exposed to music. These researchers are, therefore, of the opinion that music could indeed stimulate seed germination. However, critics of this hypothesis question the quality of the journals in which these findings were published (De Beer, 2019c), and furthermore trace the belief that music could enhance plant growth or seed germination back to the 1973 publication, *The Secret Life of Plants*, that was shown to promote pseudoscience.

Conclusion

IK is often marginalized in the science classroom (Shizha, 2007; De Beer & Whitlock, 2009; De Beer, 2019a), which is unfortunate, as western science evolved from the indigenous sciences of the

Egyptians, Babylonians, Persians, Arabs, Indians, Mexicans, and Chinese (Ogunniyi, 2004, 2007, 2011). There are various attitudinal, institutional, and systemic reasons for this marginalization. The epistemological border-crossing between IK and western science in the school curriculum holds affordances to make science more relevant and interesting to culturally diverse learners. As mentioned, Gilbert (2006) suggests that contextualization could eradicate many of the problems faced by science education today, and IK could be an effective means to contextualize abstract concepts for students. However, this requires teachers to be well trained in the tenets of both knowledge systems. Research shows that the views that teachers hold of both science and IK, influence their pedagogical orientations (De Beer, 2019; Petersen, 2019). It is therefore important that science teachers understand the shared tenets between the two knowledge systems and utilize problem-based learning approaches when exploring IK in the classroom. Ogunniyi (2007), De Beer (2019), and De Beer and Dudu (2021) emphasize that IK should receive due attention in both pre- and in-service teacher education programs. IK can easily be incorporated into science education curricula, but teachers need suitable training. Especially in initial teacher education programs, it is of utmost importance to provide student teachers with nuanced understandings of IK, as well as conceptual frameworks underpinning such border crossings, e.g., how IK could aid conceptual development. Short learning programs for in-service teachers, as part of professional development programs, could effectively equip teachers to contextualize curriculum themes to diverse learners, and help them to connect their everyday worlds with the abstract world of science.

References

Abd-El-Khalick, F., Bell, R. L., & Lederman, N. G. (1998). The nature of science and instructional practice. *Science Education, 82*(4), 417–437.

Adams, J. D., Avraamidou, L., Bayram-Jacobs, D., Boujaoude, S. B., Bryan, L., Christodoulou, A., . . . Zembal-Saul, C. (2018). *The role of science education in a changing world.* NIAS Lorentz Center. www.lorentzcenter.nl/lc/web/2018/960/extra.php3?wsid=960&venue=Snellius

Aikenhead, G. S., & Elliot, D. (2010). An emerging decolonizing science education in Canada. *Canadian Journal of Science, Mathematics and Technology Education, 10*(4), 321–338.

Aktar, W., Sengupta, D., & Chowdhury, A. (2009). Impact of pesticides use in agriculture: Their benefits and hazards. *Interdisciplinary Toxicology, 2*(1), 1–12.

Anderhag, P., Wickman, P. O., Bergqvist, K., Jakobson, B., Hamza, K., & Saljö, R. (2016). Why do secondary school students lose their interest in science? Or does it never emerge? A possible and overlooked explanation. *Science Education, 100*(5), 791–813. https://doi.org/10.1002/sce.21231

Battiste, M. (2002). *IK and pedagogy in First Nations education: A literature review with recommendations.* Eskasoni: Apamuwek Institute.

Bochu, W., Yoshikoshi, A., & Sakanishi, A. (1998). Carrot cell growth response in a stimulated ultrasonic environment. *Colloids and Surfaces B: Biointerfaces, 12*(2), 89–95. https://doi.org/10.1016/S0927-7765(98)00061-7

Burke, P. J., & Whitty, G. (2018). Equity issues in teaching and teacher education. *Peabody Journal of Education, 93*(3), 272–284. https://doi.org/10.1080/0161956X.2018.1449800

Chahine, I. C. (2013). The impact of using multiple modalities on students' acquisition of fractional knowledge: An international study in embodied mathematics across semiotic cultures. *The Journal of Mathematical Behaviour, 32*(3), 434–449. https://doi.org/10.1016/j.jmathb.2013.04.004

Chowdhury, A. R., & Gupta, A. (2015). Effect of music on plants – an overview. *International Journal of Integrative Sciences, Innovation and Technology, 4*(6), 30–34.

Chowdhury, E. K., Lim, H., & Bae, H. (2014). Update on the effects of sound waves on plants. *Research in Plant Disease, 20*, 1–7.

Cronje, A., De Beer, J., & Ankiewicz, P. (2015). The development and use of an instrument to investigate science teachers' views on IK. *African Journal of Research in Mathematics, Science and Technology Education, 19*(3), 319–332.

Davis, S. H., & Ebbe, K. (Eds.). (1995). *Traditional knowledge and sustainable development.* Proceedings of the World Bank Conference on Traditional Knowledge and Sustainable Development, 27–28 September 1993, Washington, DC, United States.

De Beer, J. (2012). Investigating the influence of karrikins on seed germination. *The American Biology Teacher*, 74(5), 324–329. https://doi.org/10.1525/abt.2012.74.5.7

De Beer, J. (2019a). Glocalisation: The role of IK in the global village. In J. de Beer (Ed.), *The decolonization of the curriculum project: The affordances of IK for self-directed learning* (pp. 1–23). Cape Town: AOSIS.

De Beer, J. (2019b, October 21–25). *IK systems: Its affordances and restraints in school science.* Paper presentation. Proceedings of the UNISA ISTE Conference on Mathematics, Science and Technology Education, Mpumalanga, South Africa.

De Beer, J. (2019c). The sound of music and its effect on biological systems: Project-based learning tapping into adolescent's interests. *The American Biology Teacher*, 81(7), 507–512. https://doi.org/10.1525/abt.2019.81.7.507

De Beer, J. (2020). *An ethnobotanical and anthropological study of the medicinal and magic plants of Southern Bushmanland* (Unpublished doctoral thesis). University of Johannesburg.

De Beer, J., & Dudu, W. (2021). Border-crossings of IK in science teacher education. In S. Gravett & E. Henning (Eds.), *Glimpses into primary school teacher education in South Africa* (pp. 175–188). London: Routledge.

De Beer, J., & Mentz, E. (2019). The affordances of IK in decolonizing the curriculum, within a self-directed learning framework. In J. de Beer (Ed.), *The decolonization of the curriculum project: The affordances of IK for self-directed learning* (pp. 87–116). Cape Town: AOSIS.

De Beer, J., & Petersen, N. (2017). A laboratory investigation on the role of ethylene in seed germination from an IK perspective. *The American Biology Teacher*, 79(1), 55–61.

De Beer, J., Petersen, N., & Brits, S. (2018). The use of puppetry and drama in the biology classroom. *The American Biology Teacher*, 80(3), 175–181.

De Beer, J., & Van Wyk, B. E. (2011). An ethnobotanical survey of the Agter-Hantam, Northern Cape Province, South Africa. *South African Journal of Botany*, 77(2011), 741–754.

De Beer, J., & Van Wyk, B-E. (2019). Arguing for the inclusion of IK in the STEM curriculum: Possibilities and challenges. In J. de Beer (Ed.), *The decolonization of the curriculum project: The affordances of IK for self-directed learning* (pp. 117–142). Cape Town: AOSIS.

De Beer, J., & Whitlock, E. (2009). IK in the Life Sciences classroom: Put on your De Bono hats. *The American Biology Teacher*, 71(4), 209–216.

Dimaporo, I. B., & Fernandez, P. G. (2007). Indigenous seed, knowledge and rice production practices of the Maranaos in Mapantao, Lumba-Bayabao, Lanao Del Sur. *Philippine Journal of Crop Science*, 32(2), 77–92.

Eilks, I., & Hofstein, A. (2015). *Relevant chemistry education.* Rotterdam, The Netherlands: Sense.

Flematti, G. R., Goddard-Borger, E. D., Merritt, D. J., Ghisalberti, E. L., Dixon, K. W., & Trengrove, R. D. (2007). Preparation of 2H-furo [2,3-c] pyran-2-one derivatives and evaluation of their germination-promoting activity. *Journal of Agricultural and Food Chemistry*, 55(6), 2189–2194. https://doi.org/10.1021/jf0633241

Garroutte, E. M. (1999). American Indian science education: The second test. *American Indian Culture and Research Journal*, 23, 91–114.

George, J. M. (1999). *Conceptualised science teaching in developing countries: Possibilities and dilemmas.* Paper presentation. Proceedings of the 7th SAARDSE conference, Harare, Zimbabwe.

Gilbert, J. K. (2006). On the nature of 'context' in chemical education. *International Journal of Science Education*, 28(9), 957–976.

Handayani, R. D., Wilujeng, I., & Prasetyo, Z. (2018). Elaborating IK in the science curriculum for the cultural sustainability. *Journal of Teacher Education for Sustainability*, 20(2), 74–88.

Hardy-Vallee, B., & Payette, N. (2008). *Beyond the brain: Embodied, situated and distributed cognition.* Newcastle upon Tyne, UK: Cambridge Scholars Publishing.

Jegede, O. J., & Aikenhead, G. S. (1999). Transcending cultural borders: Implications for science teaching. *Journal for Science & Technology Education*, 17(1), 45–66.

Jones, M. E., & Hunter, J. (2003, July 11–14). *Enshrining IK in the natural sciences curriculum: Issues arising from the Maori case.* Paper presentation. RCSD Conference, Chang Mai, Thailand.

Le Grange, L. (2004). Multicultural science in South Africa's national curriculum statement. *African Educational Review*, 1(2), 204–219.

Le Grange, L. (2007). Integrating western and IK systems: The basis for effective science education in South Africa? *International Review of Education*, 53, 577–591.

Le Grange, L. (2019). Different voices on decolonizing the curriculum. In J. de Beer (Ed.), *The decolonization of the curriculum project: The affordances of IK for self-directed learning* (pp. 25–47). Cape Town: AOSIS.

Mavuru, L., & Ramnarain, U. (2017). Teachers' knowledge and views on the use of learners' socio-cultural background in teaching natural sciences in Grade 9 township classes. *African Journal of Research in Mathematics, Science and Technology Education*, 21(2), 176–186. https://doi.org/10.1080/18117295.2017.1327239

Mentz, E., & De Beer, J. (2019). The use of Cultural-Historical Activity Theory in researching the affordances of IK for self-directed learning. In J. de Beer (Ed.), *The decolonization of the curriculum project: The affordances of IK for self-directed learning* (pp. 49–86). Cape Town: AOSIS.

Mothwa, M. M. (2011). *Teachers' experiences of incorporating IK in the life sciences classroom* (Unpublished master's thesis). University of Johannesburg.

Nxumalo, S. A., & Mncube, D. W. (2019). Using indigenous games and knowledge to decolonise the school curriculum: Ubuntu perspectives. *Perspectives in Education, 36*(2), 103–118.

Ogunniyi, M. B. (2004). The challenge of preparing and equipping science teachers in higher education with knowledge and skills to integrate science and IK systems for learners. *South African Journal of Higher Education, 18*(3), 289–304.

Ogunniyi, M. B. (2007). Teachers' stances and practical arguments regarding a science-IK curriculum, paper 1. *International Journal of Science Education, 29*(8), 963–985.

Ogunniyi, M. B. (2011). The context of training teachers to implement socially relevant science education in Africa. *African Journal of Research in Mathematics, Science and Technology Education, 15*(3), 98–121.

Ogunniyi, M. B., & Ogawa, M. (2008). The prospects and challenges of training South African and Japanese educators to enact an indigenized science curriculum. *SAJHE, 22*(1), 175–190.

Oluka, S. (2017). African condition: Transforming STEM education. *Mosenodi Journal, 20*(1), 57–66.

Onwu, G., & Mosimege, M. (2004). IK systems and science and technology education: A dialogue. *African Journal for Research in Mathematics, Science and Technology Education, 8*(1), 1–12.

Patel, F., & Lynch, H. (2013). Glocalization as an alternative to internationalization in higher education: Embedding positive glocal learning perspectives. *International Journal of Teaching and Learning in Higher Education, 8*(1), 1–12.

Petersen, N., Golightly, A., & Dudu, W. T. (2019). Engaging pedagogies to facilitate the border-crossing between the natural sciences and IK: Implications for science teacher education. In J. de Beer (Ed.), *The decolonization of the curriculum project: The affordances of IK for self-directed learning* (pp. 143–180). Cape Town: AOSIS.

Ramnarain, U. (2021). Exploring embodied, situated, and distributed cognition. In I. C. Chahine & J. de Beer (Eds.), *Evidence-based inquiries in ethno-stem research: Investigations in knowledge systems across disciplines and transcultural settings* (pp. 309–321). Charlotte: Information Age Publishing.

Rankoana, S. A. (2017). *The use of IK in subsistence farming: Implications for sustainable agricultural production in Dikgale community in Limpopo province, South Africa.* Viewed on September 25, 2018, from http://creativecommons.org/licenses/by/4.O/.

Sanders, M. (2010). Teaching skills in the sciences. In H. van Rooyen & J. de Beer (Eds.), *Teaching science* (pp. 51–69). Johannesburg: Macmillan.

Savelyeva, T. (2017). Vernadsky meets Yulgok: A non-Western dialog on sustainability. *Educational Philosophy and Theory, 49*(5), 501–520. https://doi.org/10.1080/00131857.2016.1138851

Sebotsa, T. (2020). *Teachers' lived experiences of contextualised interventions, and its affordances for their professional development and self-directed learning in physical sciences* (Unpublished master's thesis). North-West University.

Shizha, E. (2007). Critical analysis of problems encountered in incorporating IK in science teaching by primary school teachers in Zimbabwe. *The Alberta Journal of Educational Research, 53*(3), 302–319.

Sjöström, J. (2007). The discourse of chemistry. *HYLE: International Journal for Philosophy of Chemistry, 13*(2), 83–97.

Sjöström, J., & Eilks, I. (2018). Reconsidering different visions of scientific literacy and science education based on the concept of *Bildung*. In Y. Dori, Z. Mevarech & D. Baker (Eds.), *Cognition, metacognition and culture in STEM education* (pp. 65–88). New York: Springer.

Speight-Vaughn, M., & De Beer, J. (2020). Contextualizing science and mathematics teacher professional development in rural areas. *Perspectives in Education, 38*(2), 213–226.

Sylva, T., Chinn, P., & Kinoshita, C. (2010). A culturally relevant agricultural and environmental course for K – 12 teachers in Hawaii. *Journal of Natural Resources and Life Sciences Education, 39*(1), 10–14. https://doi.org/10.4195/jnrlse.2008.0040k

Taylor, D., & Cameron, A. (2016). Valuing IKS in successive South African physical sciences curricula. *African Journal of Research in Mathematics, Science and Technology Education, 20*(1), 35–44. https://doi.org/10.1080/10288457.2016.1147800

Thomson, N. (2010). Science education researchers as orthographers: Documenting Keiyo (Kenya) knowledge, learning and narratives about snakes. *International Journal of Science Education, 25*(1), 89–115. https://doi.org/10.1080/09500690210126587

Vygotsky, L. (1978). *Mind in Society. The development of higher psychological processes.* Cambridge: Harvard University Press.

Wang, B., Zhao, H., Wang, X., Duan, C., Wang, D., & Sakanishi, A. (2002). Influence of sound stimulation on plasma membrane H+-ATPase activity. *Colloids and Surfaces B: Biointerfaces, 25*(3), 183–188. https://doi.org/10.1016/S0927-7765(01)00320-4

Zidny, R., Sjöström, J., & Eilks, I. (2020). A multi-perspective reflection on how IK and related ideas can improve science education for sustainability. *Science & Education, 29,* 145–185. https://doi.org/10.1007/s11191-019-00100-x

Zinyeka, G., Onwu, G. O. M., & Braun, M. (2016). A truth-based epistemological framework for supporting teachers in integrating IK into science teaching. *African Journal of Research in Mathematics, Science and Technology Education, 20*(3), 256–266. https://doi.org/10.1080/18117295.2016.1239963

26

ACTION RESEARCH

A Promising Strategy for Science Teacher Education

Allan Feldman, Nadja Belova, Ingo Eilks, Marika Kapanadze, Rachel Mamlok-Naaman, Franz Rauch, and Mehmet Fatih Taşar

Action research (AR) is an inquiry by teachers into their practice and their students' learning (Feldman & Minstrel, 2000). The main goal of this chapter is to describe how action research (AR) can be used as a strategy for science teacher education (STE) to address the question, "How does current research extend previous reviews of AR, most importantly, Laudonia et al. (2018)? Although much of what is presented here has ramifications for preservice STE, the focus is on practicing science teachers. The chapter begins with a brief overview of the nature of AR and then turns to the development of a framework for understanding AR in STE. That framework is then used to analyze exemplar cases of different modes of AR in STE.

Many definitions of AR can be found in the literature. This one by Feldman incorporates many of the criteria for AR used in this chapter:

> Action research happens when peopled are involved in researching their own practice in order to improve it and to come to a better understanding of their practice situations. It is action because they act within the systems that they are trying to improve and understand. It is research because it is systematic, critical inquiry made public.
>
> (Feldman, 2007, p. 242)

In AR, science teachers take on the aspects of a reflective practitioner (Schön, 1987), but go beyond reflection to the engagement in systematic inquiry, including the collection and analysis of evidence, and modification of their actions based on their new understanding. AR is usually described as occurring through a series of cycles in which practitioners engage in the following types of activities: uncovering of problems, dilemmas, or dissonances in practice; developing action steps, data collection about the actions, interpretation of the data, reconceptualization of the problem, and the development of new actions (e.g., Eilks, 2013; Feldman et al., 2018; Kemmis et al., 2014). Through AR science teachers can not only improve their practice, but their new understandings, when made public, can contribute to the field of science education (Feldman et al., 2018; Mamlok-Naaman & Eilks, 2012).

Review Process

This chapter presents a narrative review of the literature (Ferrari, 2015; Green et al., 2006) that builds upon past systematic reviews of action research specific to science education, as well as more

DOI: 10.4324/9781003098478-31

generic reviews (e.g., Cochran-Smith & Lytle, 1993; Feldman, 2017; Manfra, 2019; Noffke, 1997). A narrative review uses the techniques of a systematic review to select literature using collaborative processes such as consensus building and brainstorming. They use inductive, consultative, intuitive, comparative, and interpretive analysis methods. This was especially appropriate for the multiple voices of the chapter's international team of authors because it encouraged communication and deliberation.

The narrative process was used to bring the review up to date, and to include literature in other languages (e.g., Çaliskan & Serçe, 2018; del Pilar Díaz-Bazo, 2017; Dueñas & Pérez, 2020; Hairon, 2017).

The most recent systematic review of the literature on action research in science education was published in 2018 (Laudonia et al., 2018). For their review, authors searched in the Web of Science, ERIC, ResearchGate, and Google Scholar. They identified and analyzed 149 relevant journal articles and book chapters. It concluded by describing different modes and purposes of action research. This chapter builds upon the results from this review, as well as those cited earlier. This review began with the same search criteria as Laudonia et al. (2018) and extended the search to include the years 2017–2020. For example, the new search in the ERIC database for the timeframe of the last 5 years resulted in a total of 100 hits, which were individually analyzed. This led to a selection of 30 relevant journal articles. Because of the international nature of this handbook, the search was also done in other languages including German (Fachportal Pädagogik), Chinese (CKNI), Spanish and Portuguese (REDalyc), and Turkish. Google Scholar was also searched using the Spanish term for action research – *investigación acción*. In addition, the search included the two leading action research journals: *Action Research* and *Educational Action Research*. The results of the review was used to develop an analytical framework for categorizing and understanding how AR has been used in science teacher education. The framework served as the basis for the selection of the cases for this chapter. The framework, which is described in the next section, includes four modes and four purposes of AR for STE. Examples of science teacher action research for each purpose were selected using the narrative review process (Ferrari, 2015; Green et al., 2006) to illustrate how AR is a form of science teacher education.

A Framework for Action Research in Science Teacher Education

Several frameworks have been developed to categorize varieties of AR (e.g., Eilks, 2013; Feldman, 2017; Grundy, 1987; Laudonia et al., 2018; Noffke, 1997; Rearick & Feldman, 1999). The current review builds on Laudonia et al.'s framework of purposes and modes of science teacher AR, modified in relation to those of Grundy and Noffke.

Purposes

Laudonia et al. (2018) provide the following set of purposes for science teacher AR: inquiring into students' cognition of science, the improvement of science curriculum, and the professional development of science teachers. The first purpose is quite straightforward. For example, teachers, almost always as part of research programs initiated by URs, engage in teaching methods and help gather data to uncover and/or modify students' conceptions of science concepts. The second purpose is to develop, improve, and/or implement new curriculum materials or ways to teach the curriculum. Often these AR studies are tied to major reform efforts in science education. The third purpose is for teachers to improve their teaching and/or their way of being teachers. All three of these purposes were identified in the Laudonia et al. (2018) review. While there is not a clear way to map these onto Noffke's (1997) purposes, which include the professional, the personal, and the political, Laudonia et al. did not find clear examples to include AR for political purposes, and in particular equity and social justice. When science teachers engage in AR for this purpose, they challenge, expose, and try to decrease inequities and increase social justice.

Modes

The term "action research" has been used to describe a wide variety of activities in which science teachers and other practitioners are engaged in various sorts of inquiry. This ranges from the teachers being in the role of research assistant aiding outside researchers (e.g., URs) in the outsider's research project, to individual or groups of teachers identifying a problem, dilemma, or question about their practice that they seek to resolve. Laudonia et al. (2018) organized these as different modes of AR – technical, interactive, and teacher-centered. In technical AR[1] an external researcher sets the research focus based on a particular theoretical framework, while the teacher conducts the testing, assists in data gathering, and provides practical feedback. It is technical because the teachers are acting as technicians. Therefore, there are many in the field who would not consider this mode AR because the focus is not on the teachers' concerns but, rather, on those of the outside researcher (Feldman, 2017).

Interactive AR is often referred to as collaborative AR, where the collaboration is between the outside researcher and science teacher(s). It is collaborative in the sense that the outsider and insider(s) negotiate the focus of the research (the interest), develop the research methods and data collection process jointly, and decide on what actions ought to take place as a result of the study. In this mode, the outsider sometimes takes on the role of co-teacher as well as co-researcher.

The teacher-centered mode refers to science teachers who are the primary researchers in their classrooms (Mamlok-Naaman et al., 2005). They develop the focus of their research by identifying problems of practice, dilemmas, or dissonances; determine what methods are based for their investigations; and determine what types of actions to take. They may seek advice from external researchers or experts about, for example, research methods or relevant literature. Often groups of science teachers collaborate with one another on a common focus, acting as their critical friends. This is also sometimes referred to as collaborative AR, but rather than the collaboration being between an outside researcher and a teacher, it is among a group of teachers (Feldman et al., 2018). The teacher-centered mode differs from the interactive mode in that the teachers take the primary role in the project while outside researchers, if any, serve in a consultative role. Interactive and teacher-centered AR are often done with a practical orientation, which acknowledges that human activities are steeped in the moral and ethical, and that actions are based on deliberation, interaction, and group meaning-making about decisions about actions (Grundy, 1987).

Participatory action research (PAR) is another mode of AR, but was (in its original sense) not included in the Laudonia et al. (2018) review. PAR is typically associated with community-based AR done by people who are disenfranchised in some way. In this conception of PAR, ordinary, often marginalized, people, work together to investigate their social and political situations, either by themselves or in partnership with outsiders. Their investigations lead to new understandings of the forces that marginalize them and to actions that improve their lives (Rahman, 2008). As such, PAR has an emancipatory orientation and political purpose (Grundy, 1987).

Cases of Action Research in Science Teacher Education

This section of the chapter presents and examines cases of AR in science education. The cases are organized by four purposes for science teacher education, three proposed in Laudonia et al. (2018) and one added as a result of this review.

Inquiring into Students' Cognition of Science

Cognitive aspects and conceptual change are crucial aspects of the learning process for students. That said, there have been relatively few studies in which teachers investigated cognitive aspects of their students' learning, and those that were found typically do not address the effects of doing AR on the teachers. Laudonia et al. (2018) identified an early study (Whyte, 1986) and several more recent ones. This extension of that review found three recent studies. From its description, Essiam's study in Ghana appears to be a case of the technical mode of AR, in which the teachers had little role in the design, implementation, or analysis of the data. The same is the case for the Jordanian study of conceptual understanding of astronomy concepts by 4th-grade students (Abd Alrahman Hawamdeh, 2020).

In the Halim et al. (2014) study, which was done in Malaysia, a university supervisor and a student teacher engaged twenty-three 16-year-old students in activities to help overcome their misconceptions about forces in equilibrium. The supervisor and student teacher carried out the intervention, and used pre- and posttests to measure their effects. While the authors provide findings and recommendations for teaching, they do not address the effects of doing AR on the student teacher or the supervisor. This study is an example of the interactive mode in which an outsider researcher – in this case, the supervisor – and the student teacher collaborated in the study. All three studies have a technical orientation (Grundy, 1987), in which the problem to be solved is the uncovering and changing of students' misconceptions. In general both from this review and the earlier one by Laudonia et al. (2018), it appears that any resulting science teacher education that arises from AR for inquiry into students' cognition of science is typically a by-product of its purpose. A counterexample that stands out is the Project for Enhancing Effective Learning (PEEL) (Mitchell & Mitchell, 2008), which focused on cognitive issues in science education but also provided a collaborative setting that led to teacher growth and development.

Improving Science Curricula

This section includes several cases of how AR has been used with and by teachers for the improvement and implementation of science curricula. The first two used the interactive mode (Fazio & Melville, 2008; Lee & Yang, 2019), and the third was teacher-centered (Feldman, 1995).

Interactive AR

Lee and Yang (2019), two URs in Korea, worked with two 8th-grade science teachers who engaged in AR to improve their implementation of socioscientific issues (SSI)-based units. Each cycle of AR consisted of analysis, diagnosis, and the planning, taking, and evaluating of actions taken to implement the units. The collaboration was the focus of a study by Lee and Yang. They found the teachers faced several challenges in designing and implementing the SSI lessons. These included the need to change classroom cultures and dynamics; the need to learn new ways to teach so that the students would engage in discussion and argumentation; and the need to engage students in the moral thinking of SSI. They also found that the teachers worked hard to overcome these challenges, in which they were aided through the scaffolding provided by the AR as they reflected on their own experiences, developed understanding, and felt empowered to implement SSI in the classroom.

The second case was the use of AR to improve the implementation scientific inquiry (SI) and nature of science (NOS) in Canada (Fazio & Melville, 2008). Fazio and Melville (URs) worked with four science teachers over a time span of 8 months. The science teachers agreed on joint goals for the project – implementation of SI and NOS – but had their individual projects within the common group project. The teachers explored ideas and theories related to SI and NOS and critically examined their practices in light of this new knowledge. They developed new teaching practices and materials, and incorporated them into their practice.

The focus of Fazio and Melville's (2008) research was to describe and analyze each teacher's views, experiences, and teaching practices, and to uncover changes that could be attributable to their participation. They found the science teachers showed a deeper understanding of SI and NOS as well as a deeper knowledge about possible applications in their science classrooms, resulting in theory-based practice.

The hallmark of interactive AR is the collaboration between the outsiders (Lee and Yang, and Fazio and Melville) and insiders (the science teachers) in which they negotiate its focus, engage in the research methods and data collection process, and decide on what actions to take. In both of these cases, there was growth in the science teachers and improvement in the implementation of curricula.

Teacher-Centered AR

AR for the improvement of curriculum can also be done in the teacher-centered mode. An early example of this was the AR component of what was known as the "100 Schools Project," which took place in California in the early 1990s (Feldman, 1995). This was part of an attempt funded by the US National Science Foundation to transform secondary school science in the US from the traditional model of separate, yearlong courses in each science to a new model in which every science would be taught every year in grades 7–12 in a coordinated, developmental manner. The California site of this Scope, Sequence and Coordination (SS&C) project included an AR component in which 30 teachers, with facilitation from URs, investigated their own practice of transforming the curriculum in their schools (for examples of the teachers' AR, see Feldman et al. (1992). The science teachers identified their problems of practice and engaged in all aspects of AR, which are the characteristics of the teacher-centered mode. Although the overall focus of the AR was on the problem of developing and implementing SS&C curricula, it is a case of science teacher education through AR because they learned how to do AR, improved their abilities to construct and revise curriculum materials, and learned new forms of pedagogy.

Development of Science Teachers

AR done by science teachers can lead to their professional development. Although this was seen in the cases in the previous section, there is much AR done by science teachers that has its primary focus their growth as teachers (e.g., Borjas & De la Peña-Leyva, 2009; Küçük & Çepni, 2005; Mamlok-Naaman, 2018). These AR projects tend to be teacher-centered, although there are studies that are interactive. This section provides brief overviews of three cases.

Interactive AR

The first case is of an interactive project in Colombia, which was a collaboration between two URs and five secondary science teachers (Borjas & De la Peña-Leyva, 2009). The science teachers collaboratively evaluated and analyzed different models of the development of creative thinking and selected one of them to conceptualize new lessons. The URs studied the teachers' involvement in the AR through classroom observations, teacher focus groups, student interviews, and analysis of the project meetings. They found that the active participation of the science teachers in the design of the lessons and in the AR process was a transformative process, because it allowed the teachers to systematize their experiences and to improve their practice.

Teacher-Centered AR

The first case of teacher-centered AR for science teacher development was done in Tira, Israel (Mamlok-Naaman, 2018), where the language of instruction is Arabic. The Ministry of Education initiated a program of professional learning community (PLC) workshops for all chemistry teachers. The workshops operated on a cascade model, in which URs guided a group of teacher leaders, who facilitated PLCs in their local area. In Tira, the chemistry teachers conducted practitioner-oriented AR activities in their PLC. They identified concerns in their practice and raised questions about content as well as pedagogy, and engaged in cycles of AR processes. Mamlok-Naaman (2018) found that the AR activities led to the improvement of the teaching culture, including trust, ownership, and friendship; all of which enhanced the likelihood of creating a sustainable professional community of chemistry teachers.

Küçük and Çepni's (2005) study is a case of the professional development (PD) of in-service science teachers in Turkey to engage them in educational research to improve their practice. They decided to convene a science teacher AR group to involve science teachers to encourage them to plan and conduct research projects based on their own learning-teaching problems. The group consisted of eight experienced male middle school science teachers who took part in a 4-week PD course based on Feldman et al. (2018) in which they were taught research methods and were introduced to the AR process. Küçük and Çepni found by the end of the course that the teachers were engaging in reflective practice, had begun to use the research on science teaching and learning, and had become more aware of their own practical theories. Most importantly, the teachers recognized that they can be researchers, and their views about research changed dramatically.

Science teacher AR for the Promotion of Equity and Social Justice

The promotion of equity and social justice is a strong thread of scholarship and action within the field of science education, with an early focus on gender equity (e.g., Brickhouse et al., 2000; Smail, 1985; Solomon, 1997). A recent review of the literature by Bancroft and Nyirenda (2020) examined equity-focused science teacher professional development for the years 2001–17. The focus of the PD projects included English-language learners, low socioeconomic status (SES), students, and racial or ethnic minorities. Of the 35 studies reviewed, none were explicitly identified as AR or any other form of teacher inquiry. However, in a third, teachers co-constructed curriculum materials with the study authors. That said, there have been a number of studies in which science teachers have engaged in AR for equity and social justice (e.g., Bradley, 2019; Brenner et al., 2016; Buck et al., 2014; Capobianco, 2007; Capobianco & Ní Ríordáin, 2015; Furman et al., 2012; Laux, 2019; Nyström, 2007; Trauth-Nare & Buck, 2011). Three such cases are presented in this section, one interactive and two teacher-centered (Brenner et al., 2016; Furman et al., 2012; Nyström, 2007).

Interactive AR

The focus of the study by Nyström (2007) was to make science teaching more gender-inclusive in Swedish secondary schools. Nyström took on the role of group leader, critical friend, classroom observer, assistant teacher, and outside researcher as she worked with the four science teachers who did AR on their practice. The teachers focused on their own problem of practice related to gender issues, which resulted in their thinking in new ways about their teaching and their students, which led to changed classroom practices. An important outcome of the collaboration among the teachers and Nyström was the decision to engage the students in focus group discussions, which uncovered themes such as gendered power relations, the importance of family background (many of the families were recent immigrants to Sweden), and power relations between the teachers and the students.

Although the four science teachers each had their own AR focus, the project was originated and structured by Nyström. In fact, the focus groups, which were a major part of the AR, were initiated and analyzed by her, and after which the results were given to the teachers.

Teacher-Centered AR

The first case of teacher-centered AR for equity and social justice was a group of secondary science and mathematics teachers who engaged in AR as part of a 2 1/2-year PD effort focused on equity in Southern California (Brenner et al., 2016). The URs who coordinated the PD defined equity as "teachers acting as agents of change to meet the needs of their students in the multiple contexts of school, family, and community" (p. 822). The teachers conducted AR studies related to equity in their classrooms. Brenner, Bianchini, and Dwyer found that six of the seven teachers who completed the PD came to see themselves as more powerful change agents for their underserved students. The same six also changed their views of their students to being more willing to learn, and as being eager to assist with their teachers' AR. They were disappointed to find few changes in the teachers' views of the students' families and communities, of which more than 70% were Latinx.

The second teacher-centered case was done by Ben Muir, a preservice teacher in New York. He partnered with a practicing science teacher, Mr. Menotti (Furman et al., 2012). Their AR focused on the inequities that interfered with student learning of science content. When Ben first began at the school, Mr. Menotti was teaching a unit on farming and food distribution. Ben found the students were not engaged with the topic and wondered if it was due to living in an urban environment. Mr. Menotti agreed, and it became the theme of their collaborative AR. Together they designed three community-based experiences that included a visit to local markets and interviews of their produce managers, and debates about the environmental impact related to buying fruits and vegetables. Ben and Mr. Menotti interviewed the students in focus groups. The students talked about how the activities connected science to their everyday lives and influenced their family members' choices about where to shop and what to buy. Ben concluded that the activities had allowed the students to become experts of their own learning process, and that they taught him and Mr. Menotti about their science experiences in and outside the school.

Furman and Barton studied Ben's AR. They found, using a critical theory lens, how Ben became aware of and took advantage of the students' cultural capital, and took on a new, anti-deficit perspective of the students and their communities. In addition, Ben began to challenge the traditional role of teachers in the classroom as the source of knowledge and the students as recipients. This was of special importance because of the social class and cultural divide between Ben and his mostly high poverty, Latinx students.

All three of the preceding cases include a critical perspective in their analyses of the science teachers' AR. Based on Grundy's (1987) framework, we would expect these cases to also have an emancipatory orientation. However, this is not evident in the descriptions of the teachers' AR projects. In addition, we might expect AR for equity and social justice to have characteristics of PAR, but we did not see that in these cases.

Discussion

This chapter presented the results of a narrative review (Ferrari, 2015) of science teacher AR building upon previous reviews, including the most recent systematic review (Laudonia et al., 2018). First, it was found that AR can service science teacher education in a variety of ways. When the AR is used to inquire into students' cognition of science, it primarily serves URs who seek to uncover and modify students' misconceptions in science as evidenced in Essiam (2019) and Abd Alrahman Hawamdeh (2020). The science teachers who either assist the Urs or whose classrooms serve as the sites of the research gain some knowledge of cognitive aspects of science learning, and possibly some knowledge of academic research methods. Because it is the Urs' research on cognition that initiates and structures these studies, and the science teachers have a secondary role, they usually are the examples of the technical model of AR.

Second, AR has been used in science education for the purpose of developing or improving curriculum. As with AR studies into students' cognition, the primary purpose is not science teacher education. However, because science teachers take a more active role as part of either the interactive or teacher-centered mode, the AR results in science teacher learning, including how to engage in the practices of AR, how to construct and improve science curricula, and, in many situations, learning new forms of pedagogy (Fazio & Melville, 2008; Feldman, 1995; Lee & Yang, 2019).

AR for the development of science teachers has as its primary purpose science teacher education. These AR projects are often teacher-centered, which provides more opportunities for teacher growth than the other modes. In addition to the types of science teacher learning that can occur as a result of AR for the improvement of curriculum, AR for science teacher development often leads to teachers being changed in fundamental ways, including how they see themselves as professionals, the ways they envision student learning, and their commitment to the importance of the improvement of science teaching and learning (Borjas & De la Peña-Leyva, 2009; Küçük & Çepni, 2005; Mamlok-Naaman, 2018).

Finally, science teacher AR can serve to reduce inequities and promote social justice. This review found few examples of science teacher AR for this purpose. Although AR for equity and social justice focuses on serving the other – often students marginalized in science because of their race, ethnicity, first language, or immigrant status – it cannot be successful without science teachers learning new ways to reach the students, as well as changing their beliefs about who their students are as learners and human beings (Brenner et al., 2016; Furman et al., 2012; Nyström, 2007).

Overall, our chapter demonstrates that AR provides a distinctive approach to both research in science education and the development of science teachers and teaching. Since it is done *by* and *with* teachers, it offers numerous opportunities for teachers to learn by reflecting on their practice, based on collected evidence. Thus, it is a promising approach to science teacher education as a means of continued professional development. That said, if the primary reason for engaging science teachers in AR is to promote their learning, this review suggests that it be situated as teacher-centered and have purposes that are closely tied to teachers' work – e.g., their curriculum, their pedagogy, and/or their students – and in the ways they perceive themselves as teachers and/or their students as human beings. When this happens AR has the potential to strengthen teachers' self-image as professionals, as well as their self-efficacy. AR can encourage teamwork at school and collaboration between teachers and students, and it can enable teachers to have a voice and influence in the ever-ongoing process of updating and innovating educational practices. In addition, science teachers who engage in AR often take on a sense of ownership and can become leaders within their schools and LEAs.

This review found major gaps in the research on science teacher education. One is that AR is not very prominent in the traditional academic literature in science education. Reasons for this include that teachers are not expected to publish inquiries into their teaching and the culture of teaching does not support it. When teachers do share their new understandings with others, it is usually by talks with colleagues, professional development workshops, or contributions to teacher conferences and teacher journals. Also, AR is done in many countries in which English is not the first language, while the *lingua franca* of academic writing is English. Some ways to counter these reasons include encouraging science teachers to make their work public, and establishing and supporting networks of URs and teachers.

Another gap is the apparent lack of studies of critical AR, participatory AR, and AR for equity and social justice in the literature, especially as noted by Brenner et al. (2016) in secondary science education. It is not clear whether this is because the work isn't being done, or it isn't being published in traditional outlets, or those engaged in promoting social justice focus more on doing than writing about it. In any case, given the inequities amongst schools throughout the world, and the large numbers of students marginalized in science, this is an important area needing further research.

Note

1. Different frameworks use the same term differently. Grundy's use of technical refers to the theoretical orientation, while Laudonia et al. uses it to refer primarily to the relationship between the action researcher and outside researchers. For more information about problematic aspects of these relationships, see for example Elliot (1988).

References

Abd Alrahman Hawamdeh, A. (2020). How does the role-playing strategy affect the development of interpretive skill for astronomical phenomena among fourth-grade female students? *Action Research and Innovation in Science Education, 3*(2), 39–42. https://doi.org/10.12973/arise/295514

Bancroft, S. F., & Nyirenda, E. M. (2020). Equity-focused k-12 science teacher professional development: A review of the literature 2001–2017. *Journal of Science Teacher Education, 31*(2), 151–207. https://doi.org/10.1080/1046560X.2019.1685629

Borjas, M. P., & De la Peña-Leyva, F. (2009). Desarrollo de habilidades de pensamiento creativo en el área de ciencias naturales y educación ambiental. *Zona Próxima, 10*, 12–35.

Bradley, F. B. (2019). *Exploring new teacher beliefs: Identity, home-life, and culture in the classroom* (Publication Number 13904185) (Ph.D., University of South Florida). ProQuest Dissertations & Theses Global. Tampa, FL.

Brenner, M. E., Bianchini, J. A., & Dwyer, H. A. (2016). Science and mathematics teachers working toward equity through teacher research: Tracing changes across their research process and equity views. *Journal of Science Teacher Education, 27*(8), 819–845. https://doi.org/10.1007/s10972-016-9490-3

Brickhouse, N. W., Lowery, P., & Schultz, K. (2000). What kind of girl does science? The construction of school science identities. *Journal of Research in Science Teaching, 37*(5), 441–458.

Buck, G. A., Cook, K. L., Quigley, C. F., Prince, P., & Lucas, Y. (2014). Seeking TO improve African American girls' attitudes TOWARD science: A participatory action research project. *Elementary School Journal, 114*(3), 431–453. https://doi.org/10.1086/674419

Çaliskan, M., & Serçe, H. (2018). Action research articles on education in Turkey: A content analysis. *Ahi Evran University Journal of Kirsehir Education Faculty, 19*(1), 80–102.

Capobianco, B. M. (2007). Science teachers' attempts at integrating feminist pedagogy through collaborative action research. *Journal of Research in Science Teaching, 44*(1), 1–32. http://dx.doi.org/10.1002/tea.20120

Capobianco, B. M., & Ní Ríordáin, M. (2015). Navigating layers of teacher uncertainty among preservice science and mathematics teachers engaged in action research. *Educational Action Research, 23*(4), 581–598. http://dx.doi.org/10.1080/09650792.2015.1045537

Cochran-Smith, M., & Lytle, S. (1993). *Inside/outside: Teacher research and knowledge.* New York, NY: Teachers College Press.

del Pilar Díaz-Bazo, C. (2017). La investigación-acción en la educación básica en Iberoamérica. Una revisión de la literatura. *MAGIS. Revista Internacional de Investigacion en Educacion, 10*(20), 159–182.

Dueñas, O. R., & Pérez, L. F. M. (2020). Estado De La Formación Del Profesor Como Investigador Y Configuración De Colectivos Interesados En Tal Desarrollo A Partir Del Abordaje De Cuestiones Sociocientíficas. *Vivências, 17*(32), 9–30.

Eilks, I. (2013). Action research in science education: From general justifications to a specific model in practice. In T. Stern, A. Townsend, F. Rauch, & A. Schuster (Eds.), *Action research, innovation and change* (pp. 172–192). Oxford, UK: Routledge.

Elliot, J. (1988). Educational research and outsider-insider relations. *International journal of Qualitative Studies in Education, 1*(2), 155–166. https://doi.org/10.1080/0951839880010204.

Essiam, C. (2019). Effect of regular classroom tests on learning and understanding of concepts in chemistry. *ARISE – Action Research and Innovation in Science Education, 2*(2), 3–12. https://doi.org/10.12973/arise/111754

Fazio, X., & Melville, W. (2008). Science teacher development through collaborative action research. *Teacher Development, 12*(3), 193–209. https://doi.org/10.1080/13664530802259222

Feldman, A. (1995). The institutionalization of action research: The California'100 schools'. In S. E. Noffke & R. Stevenson (Eds.), *Educational action research: Becoming practically critical* (pp. 180–196). New York, NY: Teachers College Press.

Feldman, A. (2007). Teachers, responsibility and action research. *Educational action research, 15*(2), 239–252. https://doi.org/10.1080/09650790701314809

Feldman, A. (2017). An emergent history of educational action research in the English-speaking world. In L. L. Rowell, C. D. Bruce, J. M. Shosh, & M. M. Riel (Eds.), *The Palgrave international handbook of action research* (pp. 125–145). Springer Nature. https://doi.org/https://doi.org/10.1057/978-1-137-40523-4_8.

Feldman, A., Altrichter, H., Posch, P., & Somekh, B. (2018). *Teachers investigate their work. An introduction to action research across the professions* (3rd ed.). London and New York: Routledge.

Feldman, A., Mason, C., & Goldberg, F. (Eds.). (1992). *Action research: Reports from the field, 1991–92.* San Diego, CA: Center for Research in Mathematics and Science Education.

Feldman, A., & Minstrell, J. (2000). Action research as a research methodology for study of teaching and learning science. In A. E. Kelly & R. A. Lesh (Eds.), *Handbook of research design in mathematics and science education* (pp. 429–455). Mahwah: Lawrence Erlbaum.

Ferrari, R. (2015). Writing narrative style literature reviews. *Medical Writing, 24*(4), 230–235.

Furman, M., Calabrese Barton, A., & Muir, B. (2012). Learning to teach science in urban schools by becoming a researcher of one's own beginning practice. *Cultural Studies of Science Education, 7*(1), 153–174. https://doi.org/10.1007/s11422-011-9347-1

Green, B. N., Johnson, C. D., & Adams, A. (2006). Writing narrative literature reviews for peer-reviewed journals: Secrets of the trade. *Journal of Chiropractic Medicine, 5*(3), 101–117. https://doi.org/10.1016/S0899-3467(07)60142-6

Grundy, S. (1987). *Curriculum: Product or praxis.* New York: Falmer.

Hairon, S. (2017). Action research in Singapore: Where are we now? *Asia-Pacific Science Education, 3*(1), 5. https://doi.org/10.1186/s41029-017-0016-x

Halim, L., Yong, T. K., & Meerah, T. S. M. (2014). Overcoming students' misconceptions on forces in equilibrium: An action research study. *Creative Education, 2014.*

Kemmis, S., McTaggart, R., & Nixon, R. (2014). *The action research planner.* Singapore: Springer. https://doi.org/10.1007/978-981-4560-67-2.

Küçük, M., & Çepni, S. (2005). Implementation of an action research course program for science teachers: A case for Turkey. *The Qualitative Report, 10*(2), 190–207.

Laudonia, I., Mamlok-Naaman, R., Abels, S., & Eilks, I. (2018). Action research in science education – an analytical review of the literature. *Educational Action Research, 26*(3), 480–495. https://doi.org/10.1080/09650792.2017.1358198

Laux, K. (2019). *Changing High School Science Teacher Beliefs on Student Voice Through Action Research* (Publication Number 13903130) (Ph.D., University of South Florida). ProQuest Dissertations & Theses Global. Ann Arbor.

Lee, H., & Yang, J.-e. (2019). Science teachers taking their first steps toward teaching socioscientific issues through collaborative action research. *Research in Science Education, 49*(1), 51–71. https://doi.org/10.1007/s11165-017-9614-6

Mamlok-Naaman, R. (2018). Using the action research rationale to enhance the creation of teachers' professional learning communities (PLCs). *Action Research and Innovation in Science Education, 1*(1), 27–32.

Mamlok-Naaman, R., & Eilks, I. (2012). Action research to promote chemistry teachers' professional development: Cases and experiences from Israel and Germany. *International Journal of Mathematics and Science Education, 10*(3), 581–610. https://doi.org/10.1007/s10763-011-9306-z.

Mamlok-Naaman, R., Navon, O., Carmeli, M., & Hofstein, A. (2005). Chemistry teachers research their own work two case studies. In K. M. Boersma, O. De Jong & H. Eijkelhof (Eds.), *Research and the quality of science education* (pp. 141–156). Heidelberg: Springer. https://doi.org/10.1007/1-4020-3673-6_12.

Manfra, M. M. (2019). Action research and systematic, intentional change in teaching practice. *Review of Research in Education, 43*(1), 163–196. https://doi.org/http://dx.doi.org/10.3102/0091732X18821132

Mitchell, I., & Mitchell, J. (2008). The Project for Enhancing Effective Learning (PEEL): 22 Years of Praxis. In A. P. Samaras, A. R. Freese, C. Kosnik, & C. Beck (Eds.), *Learning communities in practice* (pp. 7–18). Springer Netherlands. https://doi.org/10.1007/978-1-4020-8788-2_1

Noffke, S. E. (1997). Professional, personal, and political dimensions of action research. *Review of Research in Education, 22*, 305–343. https://doi.org/https://doi.org/10.3102/0091732X022001305

Nyström, E. (2007). Exclusion in an inclusive action research project: drawing on student perspectives of school science to identify discourses of exclusion. *Educational Action Research, 15*(3), 417–440. https://doi.org/10.1080/09650790701549693

Rahman, M. A. (2008). Some trends in the praxis of Participatory Action Research. In P. Reason & H. Bradbury (Eds.), *The Sage handbook of action research* (2nd ed., pp. 49–63). Los Angeles, CA: Sage. https://doi.org/10.4135/9781848607934.n9.

Rearick, M., & Feldman, A. (1999). Orientations, product, reflections: A framework for understanding action research. *Teaching and Teacher Education, 15*(4), 333–350. https://doi.org/10.1016/S0742-051X(98)00053-5.

Schön, D. (1983). *The Reflective Practitioner: How professionals think in practice.* New York, NY: Basic Books.

Schön, D. A. (1987). *Educating the reflective practitioner.* San Francisco, CA: Jossey-Bass.

Smail, B. (1985). An attempt to move mountains: The 'Girls into Science and Technology'(GIST) project. *Journal of Curriculum Studies, 17*(3), 351–354. https://doi.org/10.1080/0022027850170308

Solomon, J. (1997). Girls' science education: Choice, solidarity and culture. *International Journal of Science Education, 19*(4), 407–417. https://doi.org/10.1080/0950069970190404

Trauth-Nare, A., & Buck, G. (2011). Using reflective practice to incorporate formative assessment in a middle school science classroom: A participatory action research study. *Educational Action Research, 19*(3), 379–398. https://doi.org/10.1080/09650792.2011.600639

Whyte, J. B. (1986). Starting early: Girls and engineering. *European Journal of Engineering Education, 11*(3), 271–279.

27

INCLUDING ALL LEARNERS THROUGH SCIENCE TEACHER EDUCATION

Michele Hollingsworth Koomen, Sami Kahn, and Teresa Shume

Background

Access to quality science education for all is a worldwide social justice issue, particularly for learners with special needs who have endured persistent discrimination and exclusion. Yet, while ongoing efforts to advance equity in science education have yielded important gains, people with disabilities remain underrepresented in STEM fields (NSF, 2017) where key tenets of the Salamanca Statement and Framework for Action on Special Needs Education (UNESCO, 1994) are unfulfilled. People with disabilities constitute a large segment of underrepresented groups across the globe remaining significantly underrepresented in scientific disciplines where they are denied accessible participation (Carabajal et al., 2017). While a social justice orientation in teacher education has benefited many underrepresented groups, disability is a "precarious guest" at the social justice table despite growing national and international emphasis on restructuring teacher education to reflect social justice orientations (Pugach et al., 2020). One reason for this absence is that disability is commonly viewed as an instructional challenge, "therefore it is decontextualized from the very structural and intersectional oppression that impact education" (Pugach et al., 2020, p. 9). Second, the weak treatment seems to indicate that disability does not hold parity with commonly referenced markers of social identity, including race, ethnicity, language, culture, gender, social class, and, more recently, religion, and sexual orientation (Pugach et al., 2020), something we hope to remedy through this chapter.

Students with special needs represent a substantial percentage of school populations (NCES, 2020). Yet, research literature continues to report that teachers feel underprepared to teach students with disabilities (Kahn & Lewis, 2014). Preservice and in-service science teacher education is vital to equip teachers to design instruction, assessment, and learning environments that meet the needs of *all* learners.

Historically, teacher education for both special and general education utilized a medical model of disability, an orientation that regards disability as a deficit in need of remediation (Ashby, 2012). Grounded in empiricist epistemology, traditional special education approaches to diagnosis and remediation of disabilities are typically congruent with learning environments where teacher-focused instruction and preparation for standardized testing are prevalent (Shume, 2020). Notably, in recent years, alternative orientations rooted in the social model of disability gained traction in teacher education (Ashby, 2012), including science teacher education (Koomen et al., 2018). Such perspectives embrace disability as a socially constructed form of human diversity, resonating broadly with inquiry-oriented learning environments (Connor et al., 2008).

DOI: 10.4324/9781003098478-32

To develop our organizing framework, we sought to incorporate global science teacher education standards through reviews of literature (e.g., Cofré et al., 2015; Ogunniyi & Rollnick, 2015) and outreach to colleagues and organizations including the East-Asian Association of Science Education (EASE), the European Science Education Research Association (ESERA), and the Southeast Asian Ministers of Education Organization (SEAMEO), among others. We identified numerous national standards for science teaching (e.g., Department of Basic Education, 2011) and/or for teacher education (e.g., Department for Education, 2011; SEAMEO, 2016), yet we observed the 2020 NSTA/ASTE Standards for Science Teacher Preparation (Morrell et al., 2018) to be rather unique in its focus on science teacher education. Given these standards resonated with international teacher education standards, we developed our organizing framework drawn from its key constructs in Table 27.1: content knowledge, content pedagogy, learning environments and safety environments, and impact on student learning.

We included as our fifth construct science teachers with disabilities as they are pertinent to the discussion of Inclusive Science Teacher Education (ISTE). This chapter will summarize research examining science teacher education in relationship to students with special needs, and, in keeping with a social model of disability, will highlight research related to specific disabilities within the five constructs, as appropriate.

Search Methodology

Given that this is the first *Handbook* chapter on ISTE, we executed search methodologies and parameters (Alexander, 2020) as follows: (1) foundational works while emphasizing and analyzing recent trends (± the 10 years between 2010 and 2020); (2) a subject focus on K–12 science teacher education; (3) recognizing limitations of the field with relatively little research when compared to other research areas; (4) establishing justifiable inclusion criteria for keywords based initially on *science teacher education AND students with disabilities OR inclusion*; (5) searching large databases (e.g., Teacher Reference Center) as well as alternative routes (conference proceedings such as ESERA or ASERA or non-US science teacher education journals such as *Asia-Pacific Journal of Teacher Education*, among others; (6) extending search results through recommended strategies from a reference librarian.

Table 27.1 Adaptation of NSTA/ASTE Standards for Science Teacher Education

Effective Teachers of Science . . .
Content Knowledge
Understand and articulate knowledge and practices of contemporary science and engineering.
Content Pedagogy
Plan learning units of study and equitable, culturally-responsive opportunities for all students based upon their understandings of how students learn and develop science knowledge, skills and habits of mind.
Learning Environments and Safety
Plan for engaging *all* students in science learning by identifying appropriate learning goals consistent with knowledge of how students learn science. Demonstrate biological, chemical, and physical safety protocols in their classrooms and workspace.
Impact on Student Learning
Analyze learning gains for students and use these to inform planning and teaching.

Source: Morrell, et al., 2018.

Note: Morrell, P., Pyle, E. J., Rodgers, M. P., Roehrig, G., & Veal, W. R. (2018). Standards for Preservice Teacher Preparation National Recognition: A joint project of the Association for Science Teacher Education and the National Science Teachers Association. Approved by ASTE Board of Directors (June 2018) and NSTA Board of Directors (July 2018). www.nsta.org/nsta-standards-science-teacher-preparation, retrieved 09/09/2021.

Our initial search led to many articles that were not relevant to ISTE. Thus, we refined our search based on keywords from our *a priori* categories and a recent edited book on ISTE (Koomen et al., 2018) such as: *ISTE AND students with disabilities/inclusive development of science content knowledge AND disciplinary core ideas OR conceptual change/science pedagogy AND universal design for learning/inclusive and safe learning environments AND students with disabilities/equitable assessments AND students with disabilities/science teacher with disabilities AND teacher education /*. We selected 60 articles that were published between 2010 and 2020 that focused on ISTE, excluding 18 articles that were not related to ISTE for students with disabilities (SWD). The remaining 42 articles were then sorted into *a priori* categories that best represented the content studied.

Inclusive Science Content Knowledge

In our review of the ISTE literature, disciplinary core ideas in science knowledge were embedded within a context, such as conceptual change (Wild et al., 2013) or fieldwork (Huffling et al., 2018), and not studied as a stand-alone element. Eight studies focused on two areas of ISTE content knowledge development in conceptual change and disciplinary literacy.

Conceptual Change

Conceptual change describes the pathways from students' pre-instructional notions about concepts or phenomena to the desired learning (Posner et al., 1982). Research on conceptual change related to SWD describes constructivist approaches to instruction that allow students to interact with materials and manipulatives in an inquiry-based manner in order to form their own meaningful connections to the environment (Kizilaslan, 2019). SWD may particularly benefit from specific accommodations to scaffold such progression. Wild (2013) and Wild et al. (2013) focused on students with visual impairments, with similar data collection methods of pre/post semi-structured teacher and student interviews. Across both studies, students benefited from the development of multisensory models and inquiry-based experiences (e.g., experiments with models, conducting surveys, interpreting data) to correct or refine misconceptions with concepts of seasonal change (Wild, 2013) and sound (Wild et al., 2013). Inquiry-based experiences had greater impact on students' conceptual understanding where, in the case of the teacher, students' conceptual understanding was more accurately assessed in the inquiry versus the traditional classroom due in part to the difficulties in accurately assessing conceptual change in students with visual disabilities using traditional written tests (Wild, 2013).

Disciplinary Literacy (DL)

Three studies focused on DL, specifically vocabulary acquisition, within science content knowledge. DL refers to "learning how to read, think about, write, communicate, and use information like each discipline's experts" (Zygouris-Coe, 2015, p. 36). Using outcomes of semi-structured interviews Koomen (2018) described Alejandro, a science teacher candidate with physical disabilities, who characterized himself as slow in reading when faced with decoding scientific vocabulary and advocated against the practice of "popcorn" reading where a student reads a selection and then "popcorns" another student to read the next passage, cold, putting SWD under pressure.

Promising results in vocabulary enhancement were reported in three studies using professional development (PD). The first two used strategic inclusive multimedia platforms in vocabulary instruction for in-service science teachers (Kennedy et al., 2017; Kennedy et al., 2018) using observations methods (video or on-site). Across both studies, teachers made gains in the amount of time they spent on vocabulary instruction and their implementation of these practices with fidelity. Lauterbach et al. (2020) used a combination of survey instrumentation and observation protocols to document the enhanced implementation of post-PD vocabulary strategies by science teachers ($n = 4$) with increased vocabulary of students with learning disabilities ($n = 55$).

In summary, these six studies allow us to understand the benefits to conceptual change for SWD when instructional teaching methods involve multi-sensory and inquiry-based learning experiences. Second, PD focused on vocabulary acquisition techniques illustrate that when teachers implement those strategies, the science vocabulary of their SWD increases. This review also points to gaps in the ISTE literature where additional areas of disability are studied, and in studies that focus on DL beyond vocabulary.

Inclusive Science Content Pedagogy

Fifteen studies in ISTE reported on inclusive science content pedagogies: co-teaching, differentiation, and Universal Design for Learning.

Models of Co-Teaching

Co-teaching is where educators specializing in science and special education may teach between and across university faculty, in-service teachers, and preservice teachers (Weinburg et al., 2020), and it is the subject of four studies in ISTE. Methods for data collection included surveys (King-Sears et al., 2014; Zimmer et al., 2018), narrative recounts (Kahn et al., 2018; Shume & DeSutter, 2018), and observations (King-Sears et al., 2014).

In co-taught science methods courses, faculty reported professional growth in their readiness to prepare teacher candidates to address learning needs of SWD (Zimmer et al., 2018), while special education faculty reported increased preparedness in science as a content area (Shume & DeSutter, 2018; Zimmer et al., 2018). Studies investigating methods courses co-taught between science or general education faculty and special education faculty revealed obstacles in ISTE, including time for planning (Shume & DeSutter, 2018), and the responsibility of collaborative parity (Shume & DeSutter, 2018) where the "one-teach-one-assist" model created roles that were perceived as dominant or subordinate (King-Sears et al., 2014). Kahn et al. (2018) paired teacher candidates from a university's student chapters of the national science and special education organizations to co-plan and co-teach inclusive science lessons at a local informal science center. Participants found the experience of collaborating with teacher candidate peers from other programs to be helpful for their professional learning and understanding of a range of equitable approaches.

Differentiation

Differentiation as a content pedagogy was at the heart of five ISTE studies. Differentiated instruction (DI) is an approach that eschews "teaching to the middle" and instead addresses learning diversity of students by attending to variations in readiness levels, student interest, and learner profiles (Tomlinson, 2017). Research methods used to study differentiation in ISTE included observations and field notes (Alghamdi & Azam, 2018; Eysink et al., 2017; Goodnough, 2010; Maeng & Bell, 2015; Tobin & Tippett, 2014), semi-structured interviews (Alghamdi & Azam, 2018; Goodnough, 2010; Maeng & Bell, 2015; Tobin & Tippett, 2014), pre/post questionnaires and responses to writing prompts (Tobin & Tippett, 2014), and measures of teacher self-efficacy and student domain knowledge (Eysink et al., 2017).

Alghamdi and Azam (2018) determined that 47 Saudi preservice teachers demonstrated increases in skills to plan and implement differentiated science lessons. However, the preservice teachers retained shallow perceptions of differentiation as a set of strategies rather than a philosophy of teaching after completing a specially designed science methods course focused on differentiation.

Conversely, Goodnough (2010) reported on 32 Canadian preservice teachers who learned about differentiated science instruction through project-based learning in a science methods course. The preservice science teachers first regarded differentiation as a set of strategies, but eventually developed more sophisticated perceptions of differentiation as an overarching framework of guiding principles.

Eysink et al. (2017) investigated in-service Dutch teachers' use of the STIP approach for differentiating primary science lessons. The STIP approach, named for an acronym of a Dutch term translating to "collaboration during differentiation in task, content, and process" (p. 108), employs a cooperative learning jigsaw procedure and takes students' cognitive needs into account. Even with limited teacher training (1 hour) use of the STIP approach resulted in increases in differentiation of tasks, content, and processes in science instruction compared to a control group.

Some research identified impediments to science teachers' abilities to use differentiation effectively to support SWD. Maeng and Bell (2015) found that teachers struggled to implement formative assessment, even though it is "a hallmark of differentiated instruction" (p. 2087). Similarly, pre-assessment was inadequately addressed in most of the preservice science teachers' projects on differentiation in Goodnough's study (2010). Finally, Tobin and Tippett (2014) report that Canadian elementary teachers expressed insecurities about trying differentiation as a new approach and identified constraints including lack of time and resources, as well as curricular and assessment demands.

Universal Design for Learning

Universal Design for Learning (UDL) is a framework comprised of three major principles (providing multiple means of engagement, multiple means of representation, and multiple means of action and expression) for guiding accessible instructional practices and proactively reducing barriers for all students, including SWD in science (CAST, 2018). Six studies using UDL were reviewed. ISTE researchers described how to support science teachers' use of UDL principles to develop inclusive NGSS Science and Engineering Practices (NGSS Lead States, 2013; Summy & Fetters, 2018), to design equitable inquiry experiences (Israel et al., 2018), and to mediate intensive science language demands (Newman Thomas et al., 2018). Co-teaching among faculty members, classroom teachers, and preservice teachers across science and special education figured prominently in professional learning centered on adopting and implementing UDL in inclusive science learning environments (Porter & Gee, 2018; Van Garderen et al., 2012).

Additionally, Kahn et al. (2017) analyzed early childhood teacher candidates' lesson plans during concurrent enrollment in science and special education methods courses. They found that teacher candidates used an equitable UDL framework more frequently during late-semester lesson planning, along with reduced use of separate materials, activities, or instruction.

Taken as a whole, the inclusive science content pedagogies described in this section hold promise in supporting both in-service and preservice teachers in developing inclusive science practices, and they provide viable options for science teachers to increase their preparation and confidence in teaching SWD (Kahn & Lewis, 2014). Importantly, when science and special education teacher candidates engaged in co-teaching or with people with disabilities, they grew in their understanding of how to develop greater accessibility and accommodations for SWD.

Like many areas of ISTE, additional research framed in these three areas might increase rigor in research methodologies and focus on long-term pedagogical and student learning outcomes of science teacher practices infused with inclusive pedagogies.

Inclusive and Safe Science Learning Environments

Eleven studies focused on lab and field experiences, social-emotional learning, and assistive technology.

Safe and Equitable Lab and Field Experiences

Laboratory and field experiences can present physical (e.g., inaccessible labeling of chemicals and equipment for students with visual impairments, uneven or rugged terrain that challenges students with mobility, sensory, or health challenges) and non-physical barriers (e.g., biases, negative assumptions about what students can or cannot do) to the full and safe participation of SWD (Carabajal et al., 2017). We identified five studies focused on inclusive and safe learning environments using methods of narrative inquiry (Koomen, 2018), surveys (Huffling et al., 2018; Koehler & Wild, 2019; Rule et al., 2011), descriptive recounts (Atchison & Carnahan, 2018), pre- and posttests (Huffling et al., 2018; Rule et al., 2011), exit interviews (Huffling et al., 2018), and reflective narratives (Rule et al., 2011).

In an online survey of 51 teachers of the visually impaired, Koehler and Wild (2019) found that students with visual impairments were included in laboratory activities related to physics (57%) and astronomy (59%) at relatively high levels compared to microscope activities (28%), dissections (34%), experiments involving pH (34%), and experiments involving chemical reactions (34%). Some of the specialized equipment that was cited as supporting students included braille and large-print measuring tools, talking scientific calculators, talking balances, and color identifiers. The authors stress the need for teacher preparation and PD programs to place greater emphasis on how to include students with physical and sensory disabilities in all science labs, while also teaching students *without* disabilities to work with students with physical disabilities to increase all students' participation in science labs. For a comprehensive narrative on making physics labs accessible to students with visual impairments, see Bülbül (2018).

Inclusive and exclusive lab experiences were the focus of two studies, one focused on teachers (Rule et al., 2011) and the other on a former student (Koomen, 2018). In their yearlong study, Rule et al. (2011) provided adaptive equipment and instructional support to 13 high school students with visual impairments and their 15 science and math teachers. The authors found that funding for adaptive equipment and training can improve teacher attitudes toward SWD in STEM and can help provide meaningful laboratory experiences for all students. The impact of exclusion in lab and field settings was highlighted in Koomen's (2018) collaboration with Alejandro, a young man with cerebral palsy who recalled experiences of exclusion from labs that left him feeling diminished. The findings of this study suggest that talking with students about their needs, becoming familiar with students' individualized education programs, and maintaining humor while recognizing that all students will make mistakes in labs can be beneficial in ensuring inclusive laboratory and field trip experiences.

Atchison and Carnahan (2018) had early and middle childhood and special education teacher candidates learn collaboratively with college students with mild-to-moderate cognitive and developmental disabilities who were in a 4-year non-degree program at the university. The authors found that community-building, explicit instruction followed by modeling, and reflection were key factors in supporting all of the students, and that the experiences of interacting with SWD in the methods course provided teacher candidates with invaluable experiences that positively impacted their attitudes and assumptions.

Even seemingly challenging field trips can be made accessible by teachers through support and collaboration. Huffling et al. (2018) describe a 2-year study using UDL to make herpetology field trips, including frog calls, accessible for students with hearing impairments. The authors found that the use of UDL improved experiences for all students, both with and without hearing impairments through creative problem solving (e.g., creating sonograms of the frog calls for all students to visualize; collaboratively developing ASL signs, such as "salamander = wet lizard" when they didn't exist) and recognizing students with hearing impairments as experts.

Social-Emotional Learning (SEL) for Inclusive Classrooms

Kahn and Lewis (2014) found that science teachers expressed concerns about the safety of students with disabilities, particularly those with emotional or behavioral challenges, in laboratory settings. SEL is an important aspect of ISTE where we identified two studies. SEL competencies include developing positive relationships, making responsible decisions, managing one's emotions, and negotiating conflict (Collaborative for Academic, Social, and Emotional Learning, 2020). Embedding SEL into a science curriculum can have significant impacts on students with and without disabilities. Counsell and Geiken (2019) developed a project called Ramps and Pathways to help teachers and young children with and without disabilities investigate physical science concepts. Data from the pilot and field testing suggest that participation in the program yielded socio-emotional developmental skills for students both with and without disabilities, according to teacher participants' observations.

González et al. (2019) documented the experiences of five biology teachers in Germany using a curriculum that integrated learning about the human body with SEL, where researchers conducted guided interviews subsequent to the intervention. Teachers reported improved cooperation, participation, and comfort in discussing emotions with teachers. However, there was no detectable increase in students' emotional self-regulation, possibly because the management and SEL strategies were embedded in the curriculum and it was not possible to tease out the impact of any individual strategy.

Assistive Technology (AT)

According to Taylor et al. (2020), AT consists of devices and services that improve curriculum access for SWD and can range from low-tech (e.g., pencil grips) to high-tech (e.g., smart devices). AT offers important avenues for science teachers to create accessible learning environments, yet most science teachers receive little to no training in their preservice education and feel inadequately prepared to incorporate assistive technology into their classroom practice (Kirch et al., 2007).

Carefully designed PD can help science teachers gain knowledge, skills, and dispositions to adopt assistive technology. Bargerhuff et al. (2010) conducted intensive workshops over three summers where science and special education teachers practiced using low-tech (e.g., tall ring stands) and high-tech (e.g., screen-reading software) AT. Teachers reported an increase in their preparedness to teach students with moderate to severe motor and/or sensory impairments (Bargerhuff et al., 2010) and also to be responsive to selection criteria relative to use in science lessons (Taylor et al., 2020).

Shortcomings experienced by in-service science teachers signal the importance of incorporating learning goals about AT into preservice science teacher education. Grande and Whalen's (2017) study showed that an assistive technology project in a science methods course can result in positive but limited learning gains for preservice teachers.

In summary, these 11 studies point to the value of training to positively impact teacher attitudes and confidence in support of SWD in K–12 science classrooms. The small number of studies identified and reviewed here focus only on a sliver of needed areas of study in developing and maintaining inclusive and safe learning environments.

Inclusive and Equitable Impact on Student Learning

Our search methodologies netted six studies focused on inclusive and equitable assessments in the areas of strengths-based instruction and standardized assessments and dilemmas.

Strengths-Based Instruction and Assessments

Science has historically focused on a narrow range of talents when, in fact, success in science is related to a wide range of strengths and skills (Sumida, 2010). Strength-based approaches to teaching and assessment encourage all students by normalizing the existence of strengths and challenges in every individual. Some researchers (Armstrong, 2012; Baum, 2009) advance the notion that students who are considered to have disabilities may also be gifted in part due to their neurodiversity.

Although the field of strength-based instruction and assessment for SWD is still emerging in science education, Kahn (2018) applied the key features to interviews with two individuals in their 20s with disabilities who reflected on their K–12 science experiences. The author interpreted the participants' experiences through a strengths-based lens to provide teachers and teacher educators with interventions, including formative assessment strategies, that could be utilized to capitalize their students' assets and interests while concurrently addressing areas of remediation.

Standardized Assessments and Dilemmas

Penfield and Lee (2010) and Maerten-Rivera et al. (2010) point out that despite the benefits of standardized assessments, especially in the US, they are biased toward white, middle to upper class and native English-speaking students. Underrepresented students, including students of color, low SES, learning English as a new language, and SWD, face many challenges with standardized assessments. Maerten-Rivera and team note that a high percentage of SWD underperform in standardized testing, especially in open-ended items where their responses may be unscorable or weak. Taylor and colleagues' (2018) literature review on science education for SWD focused on the need for alternatives and accommodations in standardized testing for SWD as a way to provide equal access to demonstrate knowledge.

Izci's work in Turkey (2018), using a questionnaire and semi-structured interview methodology, found that equipping science teacher candidates with fundamental knowledge of equitable practices is an uneven process, noting that the idea of fair assessment did not match candidates' practices with their students. Similarly, Siegel and Wissehr (2011) found that preservice teachers' knowledge of equitable assessment did not align with their practices in administering assessment tools.

These papers shed light on crucial needs in ISTE for greater development of assessment methods that identify students' strengths and interests, promote alternative assessments to accurately document learning for SWD, and practice applying equitable assessment tools within lessons and units taught by teacher candidates. Importantly, except in Kahn (2018), none of the research outlined outcomes related to formative assessment tools with SWD for in-service or preservice teachers.

Science Teachers With Disabilities

Broadening the STEM Education Workforce

Teacher shortages across levels and disciplines are a global phenomenon (UNESCO, 2016). Ensuring broad participation in STEM teaching that is representative of a given nation, and its classrooms, is essential for addressing teacher shortages and providing role models for all students to see themselves as future science teachers. Unfortunately, people with disabilities are underrepresented in the teaching workforce as a whole (Neca et al., 2020), including in STEM. Designing teacher preparation programs that encourage all students, including those with disabilities, to enter and stay in the science teaching profession while also preparing their teacher candidates to be well-prepared to teach

SWD, perhaps by leveraging the talents of their science and special education faculty, is of paramount importance. The following section describe two research studies on making science teacher education programs more inclusive and equitable.

Making Classroom Placements Accessible/Equitable

Koehler (2018) explored the experience of a preservice science teacher candidate with limited mobility due to muscular dystrophy as he completed science methods and student teaching in his last year toward a license in earth science. Aaron brought passion for the subject matter, deep content knowledge, attention to detail in his lessons, perseverance, and a lightheartedness and wit that put others at ease as he simultaneously dealt with challenges of teaching in a wheelchair. His teacher candidate peers grew in their own understanding of developing accessibility and accommodations for students with physical disabilities, while his university supervisor advocated for his placements with various stakeholders.

Alejandro (Koomen, 2018), a science teacher candidate with a physical disability, advocates for teachers who really like kids in order to get them excited about learning, put student questions at the center of instruction, deeply understand a student's individualized education program, are mindful of barriers in lab spaces or outdoor activities for students in wheelchairs, and work to develop varied methods of inclusion.

These two studies are remarkable in that they lift the actual experiences and voices of SWD as they make their way through teacher education programs. Their stories offer insight for teacher candidates and ISTE.

Conclusion: Themes and Areas for Future Study

Of 42 target articles, 13 were from edited books, 10 from journals focused on inclusion or special education (e.g., *Journal of Science for Students with Disabilities*) and 19 from science or teacher education research journals (e.g., *Journal of Science Teacher Education*). A preponderance of studies used qualitative research methodologies, featuring semi-structured interviews and/or classroom observations. Types of research methods included: semi-structured interviews (12); observational studies (7); reflective recounts (9); narrative overviews (11); pre/post questionnaires or tests (3). Notably, little research situates students and teachers with disabilities as partners rather than subjects. Research methods that involve talking with, rather than about, people with disabilities resonate with contemporary models of disability education, and can yield findings with high levels of validity and trustworthiness.

A persistent challenge encountered in all five sections of this review was that the overwhelming majority of science education research pertaining to SWD focuses on student learning, rather than on professional learning of educators. Moreover, within the research on educators' professional learning, studies on science teachers' attitudes and beliefs related to inclusive science education are notably more prevalent than research into science teachers' classroom applications of inclusive principles and practices, particularly within the domains of inclusive science content pedagogy, learning environments, and assessment. Consequently, a pressing need exists for studies, particularly longitudinal studies, that examine how science teachers translate professional learning into inclusive classroom practices.

Additionally, research centered on content pedagogy and equitable assessment shows that preservice teachers who demonstrate understanding of inclusive instructional and assessment practices often struggle to implement such practices in K–12 classrooms, reverting to familiar traditional practices and plans (e.g., Kahn et al., 2017). Given the fragility of pedagogical content for SWD

(Koomen, 2016), further research is needed to increase understanding of how to scaffold and retain preservice science teachers' professional learning in order to promote equitable STEM education for all.

Across studies, it appeared that providing teachers with adaptive materials and equipment (e.g., Rule et al., 2011) was more prevalent than training teachers to develop or access these items themselves. Given the effectiveness of low-cost, low-tech adaptations that are available to teachers (Taylor et al., 2020), science teacher educators may wish to place greater emphasis on these approaches in their courses.

Finally, during the review process it became apparent that "inclusive teaching" in ISTE tends to focus on culturally relevant pedagogy (Ladson-Billings, 1995) and other cultural frameworks where disability is often overlooked. If disability is to stand alongside other socially constructed dimensions of human diversity, science teacher education research must advance toward increased understanding of the role of disability in educational equity and inclusiveness.

References

Alexander, P. A. (2020). Methodological guidance paper: The art and science of quality systematic reviews. *Review of Educational Research, 90*(1), 6–23. https://doi.org/10.3102/0034654319854352

Alghamdi, A. H. K., & Azam, S. (2018). Differentiation in Saudi pre-service science teacher program. *Journal of Baltic Science Education, 17*(3), 428.

Armstrong, T. (2012). *Neurodiversity in the classroom: Strength-based strategies to help students with special needs succeed in school and life.* Alexandria, VA: ASCD.

Ashby, C. (2012). Disability studies and inclusive teacher preparation: A socially just path for teacher preparation. *Research and Practice for Persons with Severe Disabilities, 37*(2), 89–99. https://doi.org/10.1177/154079691203700204

Atchison, C. L., & Carnahan, C. R. (2018). Preparing tomorrow's teachers through first-hand perspectives of ability in an inclusively designed science methods course. In M. Koomen, S. Kahn, C. L. Atchison, & T. A. Wild (Eds.), *Towards Inclusion of All Learners through Science Teacher Education* (pp. 185–195). Brill Sense. https://doi.org/10.1163/9789004368422_020

Bargerhuff, M. E., Cowan, H., & Kirch, S. A. (2010). Working toward equitable opportunities for science students with disabilities: Using professional development and technology. *Disability and Rehabilitation: Assistive Technology, 5*(2), 125–135. https://doi.org/0.3109/17483100903387531

Baum, S. M. (2009). Talent centered model for twice exceptional learners. In J. S. Renzulli, E. J. Gubbins, et al. (Eds.), *Systems & Models for Developing Programs for the Gifted and Talented* (pp. 17–48). Creative Learning Press.

Bülbül, M. S. (2018). From academician's office to physics lab for students with special needs: A guide for transformation. In M. Koomen, S. Kahn, C. L. Atchison, & T. A. Wild (Eds.), *Towards Inclusion of All Learners through Science Teacher Education* (pp. 141–150). Brill Sense. https://doi.org/10.1163/9789004368422_016

Carabajal, I. G., Marshall, A. M., & Atchison, C. L. (2017). A synthesis of instructional strategies in geoscience education literature that address barriers to inclusion for students with disabilities. *Journal of Geoscience Education, 65*(4), 531–541. https://doi.org/10.5408/16-211.1

CAST (2018). *Universal design for learning guidelines version 2.2.* http://udlguidelines.cast.org

Cofré, H., González-Weil, C., Vergara, C., Santibáñez, D., Ahumada, G., Furman, M., & Pérez, R. (2015). Science teacher education in South America: The case of Argentina, Colombia and Chile. *Journal of Science Teacher Education, 26*(1), 45–63. https://doi.org/10.1007/s10972-015-9420-9

Collaborative for Academic, Social, and Emotional Learning (2020). *SEL framework.* https://casel.org/wp-content/uploads/2020/10/CASEL-SEL-Framework-10.2020-1.pdf

Connor, D. J., Gabel, S. L., Gallagher, D. J., & Morton, M. (2008). Disability studies and inclusive education-implications for theory, research and practice. *International Journal of Inclusive Education, 12*(5–6), 441–457.

Counsell, S. L., & Geiken, R. (2019). Improving STEM teaching practices with R&P: Increasing the full range of young children's STEM outcomes. *Journal of Early Childhood Teacher Education, 40*(4), 352–381. https://doi.org/10.1080/10901027.2019.1603173

Department for Education. (2011). *Teachers' standards: Guidance for school leaders, school staff and governing bodies.* Government of the United Kingdom. www.gov.uk/government/publications/teachers-standards

Department of Basic Education. (2011). *Curriculum and assessment policy statement (CAPS) natural sciences grades 7, 8, 9.* Republic of South Africa. www.thutong.doe.gov.za/supportformatrics/NonLanguageCAPSSenior Phase/tabid/5013/Default.aspx

Eysink, T. E., Hulsbeek, M., & Gijlers, H. (2017). Supporting primary school teachers in differentiating in the regular classroom. *Teaching and Teacher Education, 66,* 107–116. https://doi.org/10.1016/j.tate.2017.04.002

González, L. F., Hennemann, T., & Schlüter, K. (2019). Teachers' perception of an integrated approach to biology and emotional learning. *Journal of Science Education for Students with Disabilities, 22*(1), 1–25. https://doi.org10.14448/jsesd.11.0002

Goodnough, K. (2010). Investigating pre-service science teachers' developing professional knowledge through the lens of differentiated instruction. *Research in Science Education, 40*(2), 239–265. https://doi.org/10.1007/s11165-009-9120-6

Grande, M., & Whalen, J. (2017). Creating digital science texts: An opportunity for teacher candidates to understand and implement Universal Design for Learning. *Teacher Education and Practice, 30*(4), 616–630.

Huffling, L. Benavides, A., Matthews, C. E., Compton, M. V., Kurtts, S., & Carlone, H. B. (2018). Learning frog calls when you can't hear: Fieldwork with high school students who are deaf and hard-of-hearing. In M. Koomen, S. Kahn, C. L. Atchison, & T. A. Wild (Eds.), *Towards inclusion of all learners through science teacher education* (pp. 165–174). Brill Sense. https://doi.org/10.1163/9789004368422_018

Izci, K. (2018). Turkish science teacher candidates' understanding of equitable assessment and their plans about it. *Journal of Education in Science, Environment and Health, 4*(2), 193–205.

Israel, M., Shehad, S., & Wherfel, Q. M. (2018). Increasing science learning and engagement for academically diverse students through scaffolded scientific inquiry and universal design for learning. In M. Koomen, S. Kahn, C. L. Atchison, & T. A. Wild (Eds.), *Towards inclusion of all learners through science teacher education* (pp. 201–211). Leiden, the Netherlands: Brill Sense. https://doi.org/10.1163/9789004368422_022

Kahn, S. (2018). From access to assets: Strength-based visions for inclusive science education. In M. Koomen, S. Kahn, C. L. Atchison, & T. A. Wild (Eds.), *Towards inclusion of all learners through science teacher education* (pp. 105–114). Brill Sense. https://doi.org/10.1163/9789004368422_012

Kahn, S., Hartman, S. L., Oswald, K., & Samblanet, M. (2018). Promoting "science for all" through teacher candidate collaboration and community engagement. *Innovations in Science Teacher Education, 3*(2).

Kahn, S., & Lewis, A. R. (2014). Survey on teaching science to K-12 students with disabilities: Teacher preparedness and attitudes. *Journal of Science Teacher Education, 25*(8), 885–910. https://doi.org/10.1007/s10972-014-9406-z

Kahn, S., Pigman, R., & Ottley, J. (2017). A tale of two courses: Exploring teacher candidates' translation of science and special education methods instruction into inclusive science practices. *Journal of Science Education for Students with Disabilities, 20*(1), 50–68. https://doi.org/10.14448/jsesd.08.0004

Kennedy, M. J., Rodgers, W. J., Romig, J. E., Lloyd, J. W., & Brownell, M. T. (2017). Effects of a multimedia professional development package on inclusive science teachers' vocabulary instruction. *Journal of Teacher Education, 68*(2), 213–230. https://doi.org/10.1177/0022487116687554

Kennedy, M. J., Rodgers, W. J., Romig, J. E., Mathews, H. M., & Peeples, K. N. (2018). Introducing the content acquisition podcast professional development process: Supporting vocabulary instruction for inclusive middle school science teachers. *Teacher Education and Special Education, 41*(2), 140–157. http://dx.doi.org/10.1177/0888406417745655

King-Sears, M. E., Brawand, A. E., Jenkins, M. C., & Preston-Smith, S. (2014). Co-teaching perspectives from secondary science co-teachers and their students with disabilities. *Journal of Science Teacher Education, 25*(6), 651–680. https://doi.org/10.1007/s10972-014-9391-2

Kirch, S. A., Bargerhuff, M. E., Cowan, H., & Wheatly, M. (2007). Reflections of educators in pursuit of inclusive science classrooms. *Journal of Science Teacher Education, 18*(4), 663–692. https://doi.org/10.1007/s10972-007-9052-9

Kizilaslan, A. (2019). Linking theory to practice: Science for students with visual impairment. *Science Education International, 30*(1), 56–64.

Koehler, C. M. (2018). No student teacher left behind: Lessons learned from a science student teacher with a physical disability. In M. Koomen, S. Kahn, C. L. Atchison, & T. A. Wild (Eds.), *Towards Inclusion of All Learners through Science Teacher Education* (pp. 353–362). Brill Sense. https://doi.org/10.1163/9789004368422_038

Koehler, K. E., & Wild, T., A. (2019). Students with visual impairments' access and participation in the science curriculum: Views of teachers of students with visual impairments. *Journal of Science Education for Students with Disabilities, 22*(1), 1–17.

Koomen, M. H. (2016). Inclusive science education: Learning from Wizard. *Cultural Studies of Science Education, 11*(2), 293–325. https://doi.org/10.1007/s11422-015-9668-6

Koomen, M. H. (2018). A good teacher makes science lighthearted: Experiences in learning science from Alejandro. In M. Koomen, S. Kahn, C. L. Atchison, & T. A. Wild (Eds.), *Towards inclusion of all learners through science teacher education* (pp. 43–51). Leiden, the Netherlands: Brill Sense. https://doi.org/10.1163/9789004368422_005

Koomen, M. H., Kahn, S., Atchison, C., & Wild, T. (Eds.). (2018). *Towards inclusion of all learners through science teacher education*. Leiden, the Netherlands: Brill Sense.

Ladson-Billings, G. (1995). Toward a theory of culturally relevant pedagogy. *American Educational Research Journal, 32*(3), 465–491.

Lauterbach, A. A., Benedict, A. E., Yakut, A. D., & Garcias, A. A. (2020). Improving vocabulary outcomes in inclusive secondary science classrooms through professional development. *Journal of Science Teacher Education, 31*(1), 56–74. https://doi.org/10.1080/1046560X.2019.1661738

Maeng, J., & Bell, R. (2015). Differentiating science instruction: Secondary science teachers' practices. *International Journal of Science Education, 37*(13), 2065–2090. https://doi.org/10.1080/09500693.2015.1064553

Maerten-Rivera, J., Myers, N., Lee, O., & Penfield, R. (2010). Student and school predictors of high-stakes assessment in science. *Science Education, 94*(6), 937–962. https://doi.org/10.1002/sce.20408c

Morrell, P., Pyle, E. J., Rodgers, M. P., Roehrig, G., & Veal, W. R. (2018). Standards for preservice teacher preparation national recognition: A joint project of the Association for Science Teacher Education and the National Science Teachers Association. Approved by ASTE Board of Directors (June 2018) and NSTA Board of Directors (July 2018). www.nsta.org/nsta-standards-science-teacher-preparation, retrieved 09/09/2021.

National Center for Educational Statistics. (2020). *The conditions of education: Students with disabilities.* https://nces.ed.gov/programs/coe/indicator_cgg.asp

National Science Foundation. (2017). *Accountability for broadening participation in STEM biennial report to congress 2015–16.* www.nsf.gov/od/oia/activities/ceose/reports/CEOSE%202015-2016%20Biennial%20Report%20(Final).pdf

Neca, P., Borges, M. L., & Pinto, P. C. (2020). Teachers with disabilities: A literature review, *International Journal of Inclusive Education*, 1–19. https://doi.org/10.1080/13603116.2020.1776779

Newman Thomas, C., Van Garderen, D., Sadler, K., Decker, M., & Hanuscin, D. (2018). Applying a Universal Design for Learning framework to mediate the language demands of science. In M. Koomen, S. Kahn, C. L. Atchison, & T. A. Wild (Eds.), *Towards inclusion of all learners through science teacher education* (pp. 91–103). Brill Sense. https://doi.org/10.1163/9789004368422_011

NGSS Lead States. (2013). *Next generation science standards: For states, by states.* The National Academies Press. https://doi.org/10.17226/18290

Ogunniyi, M. B., & Rollnick, R. (2015). Pre-service science teacher education in Africa: Prospects and challenges. *Journal of Science Teacher Education, 26*(1), 65–79. https://doi.org/10.1007/s10972-014-9415-y

Penfield, R. D., & Lee, O. (2010). Test-based accountability: Potential benefits and pitfalls of science assessment with student diversity. *Journal of Research in Science Teaching, 47*(1), 6–24.

Porter, J., & Gee, K. (2018). A collaborative process for preparing pre-service general education and special education science teachers. In M. Koomen, S. Kahn, C. L. Atchison, & T. A. Wild (Eds.), *Towards inclusion of all learners through science teacher education* (pp. 339–352). Brill Sense. https://doi.org/10.1163/9789004368422_037

Posner, G. J., Strike, K. A., Hewson, P. W., & Gertzog, W. A. (1982). Accommodation of a scientific conception: Toward a theory of conceptual change. *Science Education, 66*(2), 211–227. https://doi.org/10.1002/sce.3730660207

Pugach, M. C., Matewos, A. M., & Gomez-Najarro, J. (2020). Disability and the meaning of social justice in teacher education research: A precarious guest at the table? *Journal of Teacher Education.* https://doi.org/10.1177/0022487120929623

Rule, A. C., Stefanich, G. P., Boody, R. M., & Peiffer, B. (2011). Impact of adaptive materials on teachers and their students with visual impairments in secondary science and mathematics classes. *International Journal of Science Education, 33*(6), 865–887. https://doi.org/10.1080/09500693.2010.506619

Shume, T. (2020). Conceptualising disability: A critical discourse analysis of a teacher education textbook. *International Journal of Inclusive Education.* https://doi.org/10.1080/13603116.2020.1839796

Shume, T., & DeSutter, K. (2018). Co-Teaching for Inclusiveness: How to teacher educators collaborated across disciplinary boundaries in an elementary science methods course. In M. Koomen, S. Kahn, C. L. Atchison, & T. A. Wild (Eds.), *Towards Inclusion of All Learners through Science Teacher Education* (pp. 317–328). Brill Sense. https://doi.org/10.1163/9789004368422_035

Siegel, M. A., & Wissehr, C. (2011). Preparing for the plunge: Pre-service teachers' assessment literacy. *Journal of Science Teacher Education, 22*(4), 371–391. https://doi.org/10.1007/s10972-011-9231-6

South-East Asian Ministers of Education Organization. (2016). *Southeast Asian guidelines for early childhood teacher development and management*. UNESCO Office Bangkok and Regional Bureau for Education in Asia and the Pacific. https://unesdoc.unesco.org/ark:/48223/pf0000244370

Sumida, M. (2010). Identifying twice-exceptional children and three gifted styles in the Japanese primary science classroom. *International Journal of Science Education*, *32*(15), 2097–2111. https://doi.org/10.1080/09500690903402018

Summy, S., & Fetters, M. (2018). Universal Design for Learning in Science: A framework that supports the needs of all. In M. Koomen, S. Kahn, C. L. Atchison, & T. A. Wild (Eds.), *Towards Inclusion of All Learners through Science Teacher Education* (pp. 125–135). Leiden, the Netherlands: Brill Sense. https://doi.org/10.1163/9789004368422_014

Taylor, J. C., Koehler, K., Rizzo, K., & Hwang, J. (2018). The rise of measurement: Assessing science and the implications for students with special needs for inclusive science education. In M. Koomen, S. Kahn, C. L. Atchison, & T. A. Wild (Eds.), *Towards Inclusion of All Learners through Science Teacher Education* (pp. 267–275). Leiden, the Netherlands: Brill Sense. https://doi.org/10.1163/9789004368422_029

Taylor, M., Lohmann, M., & Kappel, A. (2020). Using assistive technology to support science instruction in the inclusive elementary classroom. *Journal of Special Education Technology*. https://doi.org/10.1177/0162643420947826

Tobin, R., & Tippett, C. (2014). Possibilities and potential barriers: Learning to plan for differentiated instruction in elementary science. *International Journal of Science and Mathematics Education*, *12*, 423–443. https://doi.org/10.1007/s10763-013-9414-z

Tomlinson, C. A. (2017). *How to differentiate instruction in academically diverse classrooms* (3rd ed.). Alexandria, VA: ASCD.

United Nations Educational, Scientific and Cultural Organization Institute for Statistics. (1994). *Salamanca declaration and framework for action on special needs education*. https://unesdoc.unesco.org/ark:/48223/pf0000098427

United Nations Educational, Scientific and Cultural Organization Institute for Statistics. (2016). *The world needs almost 69 million new teachers to reach the 2030 education goals* (UIS Fact Sheet No. 39). http://uis.unesco.org/en/document/world-needs-almost-69-million-new-teachers-reach-2030-education-goals

Van Garderen, D., Hanuscin, D., & Lee, E. (2012). QUEST: A collaborative professional development model to meet the needs of diverse learning in K-6 science. *Psychology in the Schools*, *49*(5), 429–443. https://doi.org/10.1002/pits.21611

Weinburg, A. E., Sebald, A., Stevenson, C. A., & Wakefield, W. (2020). Toward conceptual clarity: A scoping review of co-teaching in teacher education. *The Teacher Educator*, *55*(2), 190–213. https://doi.org/10.1080/08878730.2019.1657214

Wild, T. A. (2013). Teacher perceptions regarding teaching and learning of seasonal change concepts of middle school students with visual impairments. *Journal of Science Education for Students with Disabilities*, *16*(1), 1–13. https://doi.org/10.14448/jsesd.05.0001

Wild, T. A., Hilson, M., & Hobson, S. (2013). Conceptual understanding of sound by children with visual impairments. *Journal Visual Impairment and Blindness*, *107*(2), 107–116. https://doi.org/10.1177/0145482X1310700204

Zimmer, K. E., McHatton, P. A., Driver, M. K., Datubo-Brown, C. A., & Steffen, S. (2018). Innovative communities: Embedding special education faculty in science methods courses. *Teacher Education Quarterly*, *45*(4). 73–92.

Zygouris-Coe, V. I. (2015). *Teaching discipline-specific literacies in grades 6–12: Preparing students for college, career, and workforce demands*. Routledge. https://doi.org/10.4324/9780203073162

28

THE ROLE OF TEACHER EDUCATION IN TEACHING SCIENCE TO EMERGENT BILINGUAL LEARNERS

Edward G. Lyon and Sara Tolbert

Introduction

Given upward trends in international migration, teaching emergent bilingual[1] or multilingual students is an issue of global significance. Around the world, teachers are increasingly likely to teach students whose cultural backgrounds and home languages differ significantly from their own (Nieto, 2005). Yet, for decades, teachers consistently report being underprepared to teach students from non-dominant backgrounds, and emergent bilinguals in particular (Banilower et al., 2018; Faltis & Valdes, 2016; Salloum et al., 2020). A complex interplay of factors could account for this reporting: perceptions about who emergent bilinguals are and their ability to learn complex science ideas, limited understanding of language acquisition and how students use language in academic settings, and lack of tools and supports to engage in responsive teaching (National Academies of Sciences, Engineering, and Medicine [NASEM], 2018). Teacher education can play a critical role in addressing these factors. Janzen (2008) noted the presence of multiple theoretical perspectives, but no clear consensus, to guide the teaching of content, including science, to emergent bilinguals. Since then, an increasing number of review articles, reports, and handbook chapters have demonstrated consensus that science teachers should be prepared to address the linguistic features of science and incorporate diverse students' cultural practices and funds of knowledge,[2] while engaging students in inquiry-based science (e.g., asking questions, analyzing data, developing models) (Buxton & Lee, 2014; Lee & Luykx, 2007; Villegas et al., 2018).

Given the promising research around science teaching for emergent bilinguals, yet the consistent challenges science teachers still face, this chapter addresses the critical question, "What is the role of *teacher education* in teaching science to emergent bilinguals?" Janzen's (2008) review identified only a few distinct studies that address teacher education (e.g., Lee et al., 2004; Stoddart et al., 2002). In an updated review, Buxton and Lee (2014) concluded that science teacher education research still lacks progress in helping teachers "balance supporting ELs' [English Learners] academic goals with supporting ELs in the sociocultural and sociolinguistic challenges they face in school science" (p. 219). What is the state of the field now? The EBSCO database was used to identify empirical research published in peer-reviewed academic journals from 2010 to 2021 that met the following criteria: (1) described and/or reported on teacher professional learning experiences or interventions (e.g., preservice teacher preparation, in-service professional development); (2) involved PreK–12 science teachers as participants (but could additionally involve other subject matter teachers, administrators,

DOI: 10.4324/9781003098478-33

teacher educators); and (3) addressed teaching (ideologies, knowledge, and/or practices) in classrooms with emergent bilinguals. Thirty-eight publications met these criteria and were reviewed. Both authors systematically analyzed these publications in relation to (1) the theoretical perspective and/or instructional framework, (2) the professional learning context and approach, and (3) findings or conclusions drawn. The review is organized around three parts: Foundations for teaching science to emergent bilinguals, professional learning approaches to support the teaching of science to emergent bilinguals, and facilitating shifts in teacher ideology, knowledge, and practice toward science teaching for emergent bilinguals.

Foundations for Teaching Science to Emergent Bilinguals: Converging on the Integration of Language, Literacy, and Science

In the last four decades, multiple theoretical perspectives have contributed to research on teaching content subjects such as science to emergent bilinguals. This knowledge base has, in turn, informed teacher education programs that serve to prepare and support science teachers to teach emergent bilinguals (Lee & Stephens, 2020). Language acquisition theorists Jim Cummins and Stephen Krashen's work, for example, have been foundational in the field of bilingual and multilingual education. Cummins (1980) introduced the view of language use in the classroom as either Basic Interpersonal Communications Skills (BICS) or Cognitive Academic Language Proficiency (CALP). He proposed that teachers should attend to differences in these two language domains and provide specialized support for ensuring that emergent bilinguals are supported to develop CALP in disciplinary-specific contexts. Krashen (1981) similarly illustrated that second-language acquisition does not occur through decontextualized instruction around grammar and form, but rather through meaningful and supportive communicative interactions in the target language. Krashen framed comprehensible input as language that can be understood without necessarily understanding every word uttered in a communication. The focus on comprehensible input is a key aspect of the commonly used Sheltered Instruction Observation Protocol (or SIOP) (Echevarria et al., 2000), which included content-independent strategies such as building on students' prior knowledge and experiences, front-loading vocabulary, visual representations, modifying texts, and translating text into students' native languages to make "academic language rich" content comprehensible for emergent bilinguals (Goldenberg, 2013). However, in light of new research and reforms, especially in science education, scholars have critiqued the SIOP model for its behaviorist underpinnings (Crawford & Reyes, 2015). Recent scholarship shows that is not sufficient to provide teachers with general strategies that promote access to disciplinary content. Research has departed from the BICS-CALPS dichotomy toward a more holistic view that emergent bilinguals can use multiple language forms and resources for scientific sensemaking in and outside of schools (Bunch, 2013). Teacher education research across the content areas has increasingly adopted sociolinguistic and disciplinary perspectives to articulate knowledge and practices for teaching (Bunch, 2013; Coyle, 2007; Lucas et al., 2008; Turkan et al., 2014). Yet, in teacher education practice, the teaching of language (or TESOL) methods separate from content methods is still a widespread model (Faltis & Valdés, 2016).

Recent national and international science teacher education research has drawn on sociolinguistic and disciplinary perspectives to articulate instructional frameworks, principles, or practices that converge around the integration of science, language, and literacy. For example, Llosa et al. (2016) investigated the impact of a teacher education intervention that developed and trained 123 elementary teachers in 66 schools through an inquiry-based curriculum with educative materials. The professional development, curriculum, and educative materials scaffolded emergent bilinguals' English-language development by connecting science ideas to students' prior knowledge or experiences in their home and community contexts, and by incorporating multiple modes of representation (e.g., textual and graphic formats) of scientific concepts. Other studies focused more explicitly on developing students' language and literacy, instead of just scaffolding science learning (Lara-Alecio et al., 2012; Shea et al., 2018; Weinburgh et al., 2014; Zwiep et al., 2011). For example, Shea et al. (2018) engaged 203 high school teachers from 17 schools in professional learning in which the key focus was enhancing language development and conceptual understandings through student talk. Talk, in other words, mediated science learning. Similarly, in working with 36 high school science teachers, Buxton and Caswell (2020) emphasized the *fluidity* of language and literacy development in learning science. In this latter approach, teachers were prepared to encourage students to fluidly use language through multiple texts and modes and for different communicative contexts (or registers), all while exploring and understanding scientific phenomena in contexts that are authentic to the science *and* to students. Although the studies mentioned here all focus on how language, literacy, and science are integrated (and not separate) domains, they emphasize and prioritize different aspects of this integration, such as inquiry-based science, oral language, student talk, and register.

Professional Learning Approaches to Support the Teaching of Science to Emergent Bilinguals

Science teachers require substantial support to learn new methods for working with emergent bilinguals. At the primary level, science is one of the least taught subjects due to teacher confidence and preparedness, as well as accountability measures that privilege mathematics and literacy (Banilower et al., 2018; NASEM, 2018). At the secondary level, science teachers have not generally identified as language teachers. Thus, integrating language, literacy, and science is a hurdle across grade levels. Lee and Buxton (2013) identified key understandings from research on in-service professional development for all grade levels that should inform professional development focused on integrating science and language pedagogies. In particular, professional development should be of sufficient duration and foster collaborative participation (e.g., amongst teachers). The professional development should also focus on both science and language content, engage teachers in model inquiry-based lessons, and demonstrate coherence between the professional development goals and intended outcomes (e.g., learn about and then use a curriculum that integrates language, literacy, and science).

In-Service Teacher Education

Recent in-service science teacher education research has typically included the core elements and structures laid out by Lee and Buxton (2013) and described earlier in this chapter, although the specific combination of activities (e.g., portfolio assessment, lesson studies, workshops) and timing/duration (summer institute, ongoing professional development during the school year) varied. Regarding collaboration, whereas some in-service professional learning approaches supported change for *individual* teachers (e.g., August et al., 2014; Lara-Alecio et al., 2012; Llosa et al., 2016), other approaches supported more systemic-level change for an entire teaching staff, including teachers working with administrators (Jackson et al., 2019; Shea et al., 2018; Zwiep et al., 2011). In the study by Buxton et al. (2017), professional learning involved collaborations among teachers, students, and families through a summer teacher institute, summer student science academies, and Saturday family workshops that were co-developed and co-facilitated with teachers. Buxton et al. found that teachers expressed increased empathy and more asset-oriented views of emergent bilingual students and their families through participating in these multifaceted aspects of professional learning, which the authors attributed to the collaboration with students and families.

The type of curricular resources that science teachers are likely to access in school settings without targeted support, such as science textbooks, provide limited teacher guidance for teaching science to emergent bilinguals (Smith et al., 2017). Teacher education provides a space for science teachers to use *educative* materials (e.g., through lesson plan templates, observation logs, portfolios, and assessments) that are designed to support teachers in both specific instructional decision-making and developing more general pedagogical knowledge that can be applied in new situations (Davis & Krajcik, 2005). The Promoting Science among English Language Learners (or P-SELL) Project translated their pedagogical approach into a full curriculum and set of educative teacher guides to help students meet state standards and to support elementary teachers in the integration of science, language, and literacy instruction (Lee et al., 2016; Llosa et al., 2016). While educative materials may play a role in mediating coherence between professional development goals and outcomes, more research is needed to know how exactly they support the teaching of emergent bilinguals (Buxton et al., 2013; Llosa et al., 2016; Smith et al., 2017).

Preservice Teacher Education

Research on preservice teacher preparation for emergent bilinguals has pointed to the critical role of mentoring, field experiences, and sustained immersive pedagogical experiences that bridge theory with practice. Rutt et al. (2021) found that the most common structural components of recent preservice science teacher education intervention studies for emergent bilinguals in the United States were consistent with the broader preservice teacher education research base. Rutt et al. also uncovered several common approaches in how these studies sought to prepare preservice teachers to teach science in classrooms with emergent bilinguals. These approaches include analyzing beliefs and forming new visions of science instruction and linguistic diversity, developing understanding of diverse learners, scientific knowledge and language demands, growing a beginning repertoire of practices and tools for science instruction and linguistic support, integrating content and language/literacy coursework, and collaboration across university faculty.

These approaches reinforce that teachers need multiple opportunities to understand and reflect on sociolinguistic and sociocultural perspectives on content learning through integrated coursework (Faltis & Valdés, 2016). Without this integration, science teachers may have difficulty integrating language and literacy development theories and methods into methods of science teaching (Stoddart et al., 2002). As an example, in the Secondary Science Teaching with English Language and Literacy Acquisition (SSTELLA) Project (see Lyon et al., 2018), secondary science method instructors co-developed a suite of *tools* (e.g., anchor learning segments, video clips, readings, rubrics) with project researchers that allowed the method instructors to translate the instructional framework (a *beginning repertoire* around integrating language, literacy, and science) into activities that resided within the method courses, but were also *integrated* into fieldwork (e.g., rehearsing a "science talk" using targeted supports for emergent bilinguals). In-service *mentor teachers* were also provided with training on how to mentor preservice teachers using the SSTELLA instructional framework. The SSTELLA project adopted a "tight but loose" collaboration model (Thompson & William, 2008). While the collaboration resulted in tools and activities that adhered to a common instructional framework, methods instructors adapted the tools and activities to their own regional teacher education, language education, and science education policies. While engaging faculty members across learning areas (i.e., mathematics, science, TESOL) to support preservice teachers in teaching emergent bilinguals, it is critical to develop consensus around and consistently use shared terminology and frameworks. Without this shared understanding, professional learning approaches lack coherence, and science teachers might experience confusion (Jimenez-Silva et al., 2016; Rillero et al., 2017). Science teachers also benefit from their collaboration with peers, researchers, professional development providers, and other experts. More sustained engagement in these collaborations is needed for science teachers to become fully proficient at integrating language/literacy and science in their teaching (Smit et al., 2018).

The overwhelming majority of the research on preservice and in-service teachers focused on whether or not interventions led to changes in teachers' knowledge of practices and/or student learning outcomes. However, little has been revealed about the complexities with regard to *how* the specific elements or structures lead to desired outcomes, or why outcomes might vary from one context or one teacher to another (Viesca et al., 2019).

Facilitating Shifts in Teacher Ideology, Knowledge, and Practice Toward Science Teaching for Emergent Bilinguals

Experimental and quasi-experimental in-service science teacher education intervention research has demonstrated that professional development can positively impact science teacher knowledge and instructional practices around teaching science with emergent bilinguals (Lara-Alecio et al., 2012; Lee et al., 2016; Shea et al., 2018). Studies have also demonstrated that emergent bilingual students (and monolingual English-speaking students) of teachers participating in the professional learning interventions outperform in language, literacy, and science measures students whose teachers did not participate in the intervention (August et al., 2014; Lara-Alecio et al., 2012; Llosa et al., 2016; Shea et al., 2018). At the preservice level, quasi-experimental research has illustrated that preservice teachers participating in integrated science-language teacher education programs demonstrate enhanced teaching of responsive science-language practices, such as facilitating productive student talk and contextualizing instruction, when compared to a baseline control group (Bravo, 2017; Lyon et al., 2018). Lyon et al. (2018) noted how some preservice teachers might have more opportunities to try out linguistically responsive scientific practices, such as facilitating productive science talk, in field placement than others. Thus, it appears that preservice teacher education must look more deeply at how preservice teachers learn and how they are being mentored and coached to carry out instructional practices in support of emergent bilinguals.

Smaller-scale and more qualitative studies have complemented experimental research to investigate what ideologies, knowledge, and practices shift when science teachers participate in teacher preparation or professional development intended to enhance opportunities for emergent bilingual students in science. While these studies, described next, suggest promising approach and activities, they also illuminate persistent challenges for teacher education.

Expanding Notions of Academic Language and Translanguaging

Recent research has widened definitions of academic language to include a range of linguistic resources such as lexical (vocabulary), syntactic (sentence structure), and discursive (message) language forms, used for different purposes and audiences – and these academic language forms include those that may be considered conversational, informal, or everyday (Bunch, 2014; Meier et al., 2020). Through preservice teacher coursework (Meier et al., 2020) or sustained professional learning for in-service teachers (Buxton & Caswell, 2020), science teacher education can expand science teachers' views of what counts as "academic language" and can help teachers better understand the role and purpose of different language registers (from more informal to more specialized) for different activities and different audiences (e.g., group discussion vs. formal presentation).

The study by Buxton and Caswell (2020) contributes to recent research internationally (see also Amin & Baddeddine, 2020; Licona & Kelly, 2020; Probyn, 2015) by highlighting the need for professional learning that helps science teachers encourage emergent bilingual (and multilingual) students to shift fluidly among their own linguistic resources to read, talk, and write in science classrooms (i.e., translanguaging; see García, 2009). Translanguaging pedagogy has the potential to disrupt false dichotomies between "academic" and "everyday" language and to affirm emergent bilinguals' sociocultural and linguistic identities (Kibler & Roman, 2013; Licona & Kelly, 2020; Probyn, 2015; Suárez, 2020). In a non-intervention study of translanguaging practices in South Africa, Probyn (2015) observed eight native IsiXhosa-speaking science teachers in classrooms with

IsiXhosa-speaking students and found that only one teacher enacted translanguaging pedagogy consistently and engaged the students' native language specifically for science learning (e.g., vs. for classroom management or building interpersonal relationships). Other studies have revealed that even teachers who share students' native languages may be challenged to overcome de facto language policies and colonial legacies that have privileged English over local languages/dialects (Amin & Badreddine, 2020; Lodge, 2020). The field of science teacher education should further investigate how to support teachers to enact translanguaging pedagogy and challenge exclusionary hegemonic language ideologies in science education (Amin & Badreddine, 2020; Kibler & Roman, 2013; Lodge, 2020; Probyn, 2015).

Considering Language While Assessing

Studies by both Lyon (2013a) and Siegel (2014) found that secondary science education coursework that addresses issues and practices around equitable assessing for emergent bilinguals can help preservice teachers become more knowledgeable about the role of language while assessing students. Part of what is required is helping preservice teachers move from understanding equitable assessment simply as "fairness" (eliminating bias) to a more sophisticated view that challenges students (with support) and uses assessment for science and language learning (Siegel, 2014). Yet, in practice, preservice science teachers grapple with whether or not language demands associated with science assessments (e.g., writing an evidence-based argument) should be (1) simplified/reduced or scaffolded, and (2) considered or not considered when interpreting and evaluating student work (Lyon, 2013b). Even if targeting support for emergent bilinguals, traditional forms of professional development around formative assessment may not be enough to move science teachers, preservice or inservice, beyond limited language supports or language development opportunities such as through multimodal teaching and use of graphic organizers/visual displays (Lyon, 2017). Although there is considerable research around the relationship of language, culture, and assessment in content areas, such as science, more work is needed to develop teacher preparation and professional learning models that demonstrate impact on science teachers' assessment practices.

Contextualizing Science Instruction

From a sociocultural perspective, science learning for emergent bilinguals is enhanced when instruction is meaningful and relevant, or contextualized (Buxton & Lee, 2014; Mavuru & Ramnarain, 2020; Rutt & Mumba, 2020; Tolbert, 2016). Contextualizing instruction can be understood as both planning lessons around relevant contexts as well as eliciting, adapting, and applying emergent bilingual students' lived experiences and funds of knowledge during instruction (Tolbert, 2016). Similar to the research trends in science teacher education related to academic language, translanguaging, and assessment, science teachers (at least, those participating in the intervention studies reviewed) appear to be ideologically in favor of contextualizing instruction (Stoddart & Mosqueda, 2015), yet struggle in planning and in practice to actually build science learning experiences from the cultural practices and funds of knowledge of their students (Buxton & Caswell, 2020; Lyon et al., 2018; Tolbert et al., 2019). Preservice teachers are more likely to draw on static and/or generic notions of culture (e.g., discussing scientific contributions from various cultures), or from contexts they themselves find relevant than from the authentic experiences of emergent bilingual students, even after participating in interventions designed to improve their abilities to contextualize instruction (Lyon et al., 2018; Rutt & Mumba, 2020; Tolbert & Knox, 2016; Tolbert et al., 2019). However, some research has demonstrated that teachers who are themselves bilingual and/or share students' cultural backgrounds demonstrate increased abilities to consider students' funds of knowledge when designing science activities than teachers who are not bilingual and/or do not share common cultural backgrounds (Mavuru & Ramnarain, 2020; Tolbert & Knox, 2016). For example, Mavuru and Ramnarain (2020) explored how, after targeted professional development on incorporating learners' funds of knowledge and diverse language practices in science, science teachers in South Africa, who were fluent in students' local languages and who share common cultural practices with their students, enacted more robust and contextualized science learning experiences with multilingual students.

Developing Empathy

Science teacher education has predominantly focused on changing teacher knowledge and practice around integrating science and language and enhancing the relevance of science instruction for emergent bilingual students. However, in the review of recent literature, two studies were identified that explicitly focused on enhancing English-dominant preservice teachers' capacity for empathy and care toward bilingual students in science. In one of these (Settlage et al., 2014), a guest instructor led predominantly white middle class preservice teachers in an unfamiliar 2-hour non-English-language (Spanish) physics activity (*Física en español*), while providing increased language scaffolds throughout the activity. As a result of this experience, mediated by reflective discussion and writing, preservice teachers were able to better empathize with what instruction might be like for an emergent bilingual student (Settlage et al., 2014). In another study by Arreguín-Anderson and Garza (2014), preservice bilingual teachers seeking bilingual certification in the US were paired with monolingual teachers not seeking bilingual certification during an 8-hour workshop with some components conducted in Spanish and others in English. The pairings were designed to support monolingual students' abilities to understand Spanish-language activities. The experience enhanced some participants' appreciation of emergent bilinguals' affective experiences during science learning and facilitated cross-cultural, multilingual collaborations between bilingual and monolingual preservice teachers (see also Evans et al., 2005). However, about half of the monolingual teachers resented the Spanish immersion components of the workshop. Both studies pointed to monolingual (or white English-dominant) preservice teachers' resistance to science instruction in a non-English language context. Linguistic hegemony and Whiteness remain as persistent challenges to supporting preservice teachers' abilities to teach in multilingual classrooms.

Emerging Roles and Future Directions of Science Teacher Education for Emergent Bilinguals

The critical question, "What is the role of *teacher education* in teaching science to emergent bilinguals?" guided this chapter. From a review of research published from 2010 to 2021, three critical points emerged. First, science teacher education has played a role by translating emerging sociolinguistic, disciplinary, and sociocultural perspectives into instructional frameworks that guide teacher education program goals and activities. The field has moved away from educating science teachers about general strategies for making science content accessible and comprehensible, and moved *toward* teaching that supports emergent bilinguals' language/literacy through inquiry-based and contextualized science instruction. Second, professional learning approaches to support the teaching of science to emergent bilinguals continues to draw on structures and approaches that reflect the broader teacher education research base. However, expanded collaborations across university faculty, teachers, and with families is an emerging area that warrants further exploration. Finally, teacher education can shift teachers' knowledge and practice around teaching science to emergent bilinguals by expanding their notions of academic language, language while assessing, and contextualized science instruction, and by fostering empathy for emergent bilinguals. Without targeted support through teacher education, science teachers could be at risk of falling into what Lemmi et al. (2019) call a *language-exclusion* ideology, where teachers value only technical science vocabulary, proper grammar, and other perceived "high status" forms of language, instead of a *language-inclusion* ideology where teachers value multiple forms of language (e.g., home language, dialects, colloquial discourse) as resources for science and language learning. While targeted teacher education programs and interventions can impact science teacher practice and science learning for emergent bilinguals, important tensions and questions remain and are outlined next.

Disrupting Hegemonic Language Ideologies

Science education has moved closer toward the perspective that students' own linguistic resources are important for science learning – i.e., a language-as-resource perspective. Yet, the perspective that students have a right to learn in their native languages and dialects (the language-as-right argument; cf. Ruiz, 1984) is less prevalent in science education and science teacher education research (Amin & Badreddine, 2020). The science teacher education studies reviewed lack attention to hegemonic assumptions, such as that "monolingualism" is the norm, emergent bilinguals are in "need of something," and that predominantly white native English (or dominant language/dialect) speaking content area teachers can simply adjust teaching through various strategies (Palmer & Martínez, 2013). Teachers' own hegemonic or counter-hegemonic language ideologies play a key role regarding if and how they engage students' home languages and dialects in the science classroom (Amin & Badreddine, 2020; Kibler & Roman, 2013; Lodge, 2020). More research is also needed to understand the role of teacher education in helping science teachers understand the role of linguistic hegemony and Whiteness in the education of emergent bilinguals (Settlage et al., 2014).

Bridging Communities of Practice

Collaboration across various communities, such as amongst teachers or university faculty, was a key approach in some, but not the vast majority of studies reviewed – especially for in-service teacher education. The field can work to develop and research science teacher education programs in which participants and stakeholders across disciplines (e.g., language development and science method instructors), partnerships (schools, researchers, teacher education programs), and communities (with students and their families) collaborate and co-construct activities for mutually beneficial learning (Buxton et al., 2017). To bridge these communities of practice, it will be important to expand upon the repertoire of educative materials and tools to use in science teacher education and research their roles.

Developing More Robust Theories of Change

Since 2010, there has been an expansion of science teacher education research, including experimental or quasi-experimental designs, to determine the impact of interventions or programs on science teaching for and science and literacy learning by emergent bilinguals. As the field conducts more large-scale studies that involve multiple programs, districts, and collaborations, the field needs to consider whether it behooves us, or not, as a field to bridge different projects into a clearer, theoretically and practically sound "theory of change" for both in-service and preservice teachers (Viesca et al., 2019). The key is not necessarily a magic combination of activities to optimize learning, but rather the identification of critical factors during teacher education that afford or constrain opportunities. Buxton et al. (2015) argue for considering teachers' multiplicities of enactment of their professional learning, rather than just strict fidelity of implementation. Rather than just asking if what we are doing is leading to teacher (or student) change, we need to better understand how and why certain structures and approaches shift or do not shift science teachers' ideologies, knowledge, and practice toward teaching emergent bilinguals. Teachers' multiplicities of enactment are constituted and informed by sociopolitical and cultural contexts across micro-, meso-, and macro-levels of schooling (Buxton et al., 2015). Ethnographic research can investigate these contexts and the tensions and nuances of how teaching practices, designed to support emergent bilinguals, are taken up or not during teacher preparation, induction, and professional learning (e.g., Heineke et al., 2019; Kibler & Roman, 2013; Settlage et al., 2014).

Closing Remarks

Teacher education can play a critical role in the teaching of science to emergent bilinguals and multilingual learners by developing theoretically and empirically grounded programs that strategically employ structures and approaches that can positively shift teachers' ideologies, knowledge, and practices. Research in this area is promising and has now spanned both preservice and in-service science teacher education. Yet, the field would now benefit by examining science teacher education through critical theoretical and counterhegemonic perspectives, exploring the impact of collaboration across communities, and connecting instructional frameworks and teacher education approaches to outcomes in the service of better understanding how and when science teacher education leads to changes in teachers' practices, knowledge or ideologies for improved conditions for emergent bilingual learning.

Notes

1. Academics and educators are increasingly using the term "emergent bilingual learners" or "emergent bilinguals" (García, 2009) to recognize students' ongoing acquisition of both English and native languages. Globally, the terms "multilingual learners" or "emergent multilingual learners" highlight the multiple linguistic and dialectical communities with which these students and their families identify (Zhao & Flewitt, 2020). For these reasons, this chapter uses the terms emergent bilingual or multilingual, even when referencing literature that uses terms such as "English Learner."
2. Historically situated and culturally developed knowledge and skills (e.g., work related, household management), originally of/for working-class Mexican American families (see Moll et al., 1992).

References

Amin, T., & Badreddine, D. (2020). Teaching science in Arabic: Diglossia and discourse patterns in the elementary classroom. *International Journal of Science Education, 42*(14), 2290–2330.

Arreguín-Anderson, M. G., & Garza, E. V. (2014). Bilingual pairs in teacher education: Exploring wild strategies in an environmental education workshop. *Action in Teacher Education, 36*(2), 171–184.

August, D., McCardle, P., & Shanahan, T. (2014). Developing literacy in English language learners: Findings from a review of the experimental research. *School Psychology Review, 43*(4), 490–498.

Banilower, E. R., Smith, P. S., Malzahn, K. A., Plumley, C. L., Gordon, E. M., & Hayes, M. L. (2018). *Report of the 2018 NSSME+*. Chapel Hill, NC: Horizon Research, Inc.

Bravo, M. A. (2017). Cultivating teacher knowledge of the role of language in science: A model of elementary grade pre-service teacher preparation. In *Science teacher preparation in content-based second language acquisition* (pp. 25–39). ASTE Series in Science Education. Switzerland: Springer International Publishing.

Bunch, G. C. (2013). Pedagogical language knowledge: Preparing mainstream teachers for English learners in the new standards era. *Review of Research in Education, 37*(1), 298–341.

Bunch, G. C. (2014). The language of ideas and the language of display: Reconceptualizing "academic language" in linguistically diverse classrooms. *International Multilingual Research Journal, 8*(1), 70–86.

Buxton, C. A., Allexsaht-Snider, M., Kayumova, S., Aghasaleh, R., Choi, Y. J., & Cohen, A. (2015). Teacher agency and professional learning: Rethinking fidelity of implementation as multiplicities of enactment. *Journal of Research in Science Teaching, 52*(4), 489–502.

Buxton, C. A., Allexsaht-Snider, M., Rodríguez, Y. H., Aghasaleh, R., Cardozo-Gaibisso, L., & Kirmaci, M. (2017). A Design-based model of teacher professional learning in the LISELL-B Project. In A. Oliveira & M. Weinburgh (Eds.), *Science teacher preparation in content-based second language acquisition* (pp. 215–234). ASTE Series in Science Education. Switzerland: Springer International Publishing.

Buxton, C. A., Allexsaht-Snider, M., Suriel, R., Kayumova, S., & Choi, Y. (2013). Using educative assessments to support science teaching for middle school English language learners. *Journal of Science Teacher Education*, *24*(2), 347–366.

Buxton, C. A., & Caswell, L. (2020). Next generation sheltered instruction to support multilingual learners in secondary science classrooms. *Science Education*, *104*(3), 555–580. Springer International.

Buxton, C. A., & Lee, O. (2014). English language learners in science education. In N. Lederman & S. Abell (Eds.), *Handbook of research in science education, volume II* (pp. 204–222). London: Taylor & Francis.

Coyle, D. (2007). Content and language integrated learning: Towards a connected research agenda for CLIL pedagogies. *International Journal of Bilingual Education and Bilingualism*, *10*(5), 543–562.

Crawford, J., & Reyes, S. A. (2015). *The trouble with SIOP®: How a behaviorist framework, flawed research, and clever marketing have come to define-and diminish-sheltered instruction for English language learners*. Portland, OR: Institute for Language & Education Policy.

Cummins, J. (1980). The cross-lingual dimensions of language proficiency: Implications for bilingual education and the optimal age issue. *TESOL Quarterly*, 175–187.

Davis, E. A., & Krajcik, J. S. (2005). Designing educative curriculum materials to promote teacher learning. *Educational Researcher*, *34*(3), 3–14.

Echevarria, J., Vogt, M., & Short, D. (2000). *Making content comprehensible for English learners: The SIOP model*. Boston: Allyn & Bacon.

Evans, C., Arnot-Hopffer, E., & Jurich, D. (2005). Making ends meet: Bringing bilingual education and mainstream students together in preservice teacher education. *Equity & Excellence in Education*, *38*(1), 75–88.

Faltis, C. J., & Valdés, G. (2016). Preparing teachers for teaching in and advocating for linguistically diverse classrooms: A vade mecum for teacher educators. In D. H. Gitomer & C. A. Bell (Eds.), *Handbook of research on teaching* (5th ed, pp. 549–592). Washington, DC: American Educational Research Association.

García, O (2009). Education, multilingualism and translanguaging in the 21st century. In A. Mohanty, M. Panda, R. Phillipson, & T. Skutnabb-Kangas (Eds.), *Multilingual education for social justice: Globalising the local* (pp. 128–145). New Delhi: Orient Blackswan.

Goldenberg, C. (2013). Unlocking the research on English learners: What we know – and don't yet know – about effective instruction. *American Educator*, *37*(2), 4–11.

Heineke, A. J., Smetana, L., & Sanei, J. C. (2019). A qualitative case study of field-based teacher education: One candidate's evolving expertise of science teaching for emergent bilinguals. *Journal of Science Teacher Education*, *30*(1), 80–100.

Jackson, J. K., Huerta, M., Garza, T., & Narvaez, R. (2019). Examining the effects of a professional development initiative on English learning and economically disadvantaged adolescents' scores on a high-stakes science test. *Journal of Science Teacher Education*, *30*(2), 122–143.

Janzen, J. (2008). Teaching English language learners in the content areas. *Review of Educational Research*, *78*(4), 1010–1038.

Jimenez-Silva, M., Rillero, P., Merritt, J., & Kelley, M. F. (2016). Working together to prepare teachers of science and language: Examining the value of collaboration among science and language faculty. *The Electronic Journal for Research in Science & Mathematics Education*, *20*(3), 73–91.

Kibler, A. K., & Roman, D. (2013). Insights into professional development for teachers of English language learners: A focus on using students' native languages in the classroom. *Bilingual Research Journal*, *36*(2), 187–207.

Krashen, S. D. (1981). *Second language acquisition and second language learning*. Oxford: Pergamon Press.

Lara-Alecio, R., Tong, F., Irby, B. J., Guerrero, C., Huerta, M., & Fan, Y. (2012). The effect of an instructional intervention on middle school English learners' science and English reading achievement. *Journal of Research in Science Teaching*, *49*(8), 987–1011.

Lee, O., & Buxton, C. A. (2013). Integrating science and English proficiency for English language learners. *Theory into Practice*, *52*(1), 36–42.

Lee, O., Hart, J. E., Cuevas, P., & Enders, C. (2004). Professional development in inquiry-based science for elementary teachers of diverse student groups. *Journal of Research in Science Teaching*, *41*(10), 1021–1043.

Lee, O., Llosa, L., Jiang, F., Haas, A., O'Connor, C., & Van Booven, C. D. (2016). Elementary teachers' science knowledge and instructional practices: Impact of an intervention focused on English language learners. *Journal of Research in Science Teaching*, *53*(4), 579–597.

Lee, O., & Luykx, A. (2007). Science education and student diversity: Race/ethnicity, language, culture, and socioeconomic status. In S. K. Abell & N. G. Lederman (Eds.) *Handbook of research on science education* (pp. 171–197). New York: Routledge.

Lee, O., & Stephens, A. (2020). English Learners in STEM Subjects: Contemporary views on STEM subjects and language With English learners. *Educational Researcher*, *49*(6), 426–432.

Lemmi, C., Brown, B. A., Wild, A., Zummo, L., & Sedlacek, Q. (2019). Language ideologies in science education. *Science Education, 103*(4), 854–874.

Licona, P., & Kelly, G. (2020). Translanguaging in a middle school science classroom: Constructing scientific arguments in English and Spanish. *Cultural Studies of Science Education, 15*, 485–510.

Llosa, L., Lee, O., Jiang, F., Haas, A., O'Connor, C., Van Booven, C. D., & Kieffer, M. J. (2016). Impact of a large-scale science intervention focused on English language learners. *American Educational Research Journal, 53*(2), 395–424.

Lodge, W. G. (2020). What's in a name? The power of the English language in secondary school science education. *Cultural Studies of Science Education, 15*, 287–301.

Lucas, T., Villegas, A. M., & Freedson-Gonzalez, M. (2008). Linguistically responsive teacher education preparing classroom teachers to teach English language learners. *Journal of Teacher Education, 59*(4), 361–373.

Lyon, E. G. (2013a). Learning to assess science in linguistically diverse classrooms: Tracking growth in secondary science preservice teachers' assessment expertise. *Science Education, 97*(3), 442–467.

Lyon, E. G. (2013b). What about language while equitably assessing science? Case studies of preservice teachers' evolving expertise. *Teaching and Teacher Education, 32*, 1–11.

Lyon, E. G. (2017). Exploring secondary science teachers' enactment of assessment practices to reflect responsive science teaching for English learners. *Journal of Science Teacher Education, 28*(8), 674–698.

Lyon, E. G., Stoddart, T., Bunch, G. C., Tolbert, S., Salinas, I., & Solis, J. (2018). Improving the preparation of novice secondary science teachers for English learners: A proof of concept study. *Science Education, 102*(6), 1288–1318.

Mavuru, L., & Ramnarain, U. (2020). Learners' socio-cultural backgrounds and science teaching and learning: A case study of township schools in South Africa. *Cultural Studies of Science Education, 15*, 1067–1095. https://doi.org/10.1007/s11422-020-09974-8

Meier, V., Aminger, W., McLean, M., Carpenter, S. L., Moon, S., Hough, S., & Bianchini, J. A. (2020). Preservice secondary science teachers' understanding of academic language: Moving beyond "just the vocabulary." *Science Education, 104*(2), 222–251.

Moll, L. C., Amanti, C., Neff, D., & Gonzalez, N. (1992). Funds of knowledge for teaching: Using a qualitative approach to connect homes and classrooms. *Theory into Practice, 31*(2), 132–141.

National Academies of Sciences, Engineering, and Medicine. (2018). *English learners in STEM Subjects: Transforming classrooms, schools, and lives.* Washington, DC: The National Academies Press. https://doi.org/10.17226/25182.

Nieto, S. (2005). Schools for a new majority: The role of teacher education in hard times. *The New Educator, 1*(1), 27–43.

Palmer, D., & Martínez, R. A. (2013). Teacher agency in bilingual spaces: A fresh look at preparing teachers to educate Latina/o bilingual children. *Review of Research in Education, 37*(1), 269–297.

Probyn, M. (2015). Pedagogical translanguaging: Bridging discourses in South African science classrooms. *Language and Education, 29*(3), 218–234.

Rillero, P., Koerner, M., Jimenez-Silva, M., Merritt, J., & Farr, W. J. (2017). Developing teacher competencies for problem-based learning pedagogy and for supporting learning in language-minority students. *Interdisciplinary Journal of Problem-Based Learning, 11*(2).

Ruiz, R. (1984). Orientations in language planning. *NABE journal, 8*(2), 15–34.

Rutt, A. A., & Mumba, F. M. (2020). Developing secondary pre-service science teachers' instructional planning abilities for language-and literacy-integrated science instruction in linguistically diverse classrooms. *Journal of Science Teacher Education, 31*(8), 841–868.

Rutt, A. A., Mumba, F., & Kibler, A. (2021). Preparing preservice teachers to teach science to English learners: A review. *Journal of Research in Science Teaching, 58*(5), 625–660.

Salloum, S., Siry, C., & Espinet, M. (2020). Examining the complexities of science education in multilingual contexts: Highlighting international perspectives, *International Journal of Science Education, 42*(14), 2285–2289. https://doi.org/10.1080/09500693.2020.1831644

Settlage, J., Gort, M., & Ceglie, R. J. (2014). Mediated language immersion and teacher ideologies: Investigating trauma pedagogy within a "Physics in Spanish" course activity. *Teacher Education Quarterly, 41*(3), 47–66.

Shea, L. M., Sandholtz, J. H., & Shanahan, T. B. (2018). We are all talking: A whole-school approach to professional development for teachers of English learners. *Professional Development in Education, 44*(2), 190–208.

Siegel, M. A. (2014). Developing preservice teachers' expertise in equitable assessment for English learners. *Journal of Science Teacher Education, 25*(3), 289–308.

Smit, J., Gijsel, M., Hotze, A., & Bakker, A. (2018). Scaffolding primary teachers in designing and enacting language-oriented science lessons: Is handing over to independence a fata morgana?. *Learning, Culture and Social Interaction, 18*, 72–85.

Smith, L. K., Hanks, J. H., & Erickson, L. B. (2017). Secondary biology textbooks and national standards for English learners. *Science Education, 101*(2), 302–332.

Stoddart, T., & Mosqueda, E. (2015). Teaching science to English language learners: A study of preservice teacher preparation. *Teacher Education and Practice, 28*(2–3), 269–286.

Stoddart, T., Pinal, A., Latzke, M., & Canaday, D. (2002). Integrating inquiry science and language development for English language learners. *Journal of Research in Science Teaching, 39*(8), 664–687.

Suárez, E. (2020). "Estoy Explorando Science": Emerging bilingual students problematizing electrical phenomena through translanguaging. *Science Education, 104*(5), 791–826.

Thompson, M., & Wiliam, D. (2008). Tight but loose: A conceptual framework for scaling up school reforms. In E. C. Wylie (Ed.), *Tight but loose: Scaling up teacher professional development in diverse contexts* (RR-08-29, pp. 1–44). Princeton, NJ: Educational Testing Service.

Tolbert, S. (2016). Contextualizing science activity. In E. Lyon, S. Tolbert, J. Solís, T. Stoddart, & G. Bunch (Eds.), *Secondary science teaching for English Learners: Developing supportive and responsive learning contexts for sense-making and language development.* Lanham, MD: Rowman & Littlefield Publishers.

Tolbert, S., & Knox, C. (2016). 'They might know a lot of things that I don't know': Investigating differences in preservice teachers' ideas about contextualizing science instruction in multilingual classrooms. *International Journal of Science Education, 38*(7), 1133–1149.

Tolbert, S., Knox, C., & Salinas, I. (2019). Framing, adapting, and applying: Learning to contextualize science activity in multilingual science classrooms. *Research in Science Education, 49*(4), 1069–1085.

Turkan, S., De Oliveira, L. C., Lee, O., & Phelps, G. (2014). Proposing a knowledge base for teaching academic content to English language learners: Disciplinary linguistic knowledge. *Teachers College Record, 116*(3), 1–30.

Viesca, K. M., Strom, K., Hammer, S., Masterson, J., Linzell, C. H., Mitchell-McCollough, J., & Flynn, N. (2019). Developing a complex portrait of content teaching for multilingual learners via nonlinear theoretical understandings. *Review of Research in Education, 43*(1), 304–335.

Villegas, A. M., SaizdeLaMora, K., Martin, A. D., & Mills, T. (2018). Preparing future mainstream teachers to teach English language learners: A review of the empirical literature. *The Educational Forum, 82,* 138–155.

Weinburgh, M., Silva, C., Smith, K. H., Groulx, J., & Nettles, J. (2014). The intersection of inquiry-based science and language: Preparing teachers for ELL classrooms. *Journal of Science Teacher Education, 25*(5), 519–541.

Zhao, S., & Flewitt, R. (2020). Young Chinese immigrant children's language and literacy practices on social media: A translanguaging perspective. *Language and Education, 34*(3), 267–285.

Zwiep, S. G., Straits, W. J., Stone, K. R., Beltran, D. D., & Furtado, L. (2011). The integration of English language development and science instruction in elementary classrooms. *Journal of Science Teacher Education, 22*(8), 769–785.

29

EDUCATIVE CURRICULUM MATERIALS AND THEIR ROLE IN THE LEARNING OF SCIENCE TEACHERS

Melina Furman, Mariana Luzuriaga, Margarita Gómez,
and Mauricio Duque

Introduction

In 1996 Ball and Cohen argued that regular curriculum materials (i.e., instructional materials based on the written curriculum) were usually limited in their design. Specifically, they suggested that these materials were designed without consideration for their enactment, particularly by not considering teachers' knowledge and beliefs. They posited a different approach that involved making curriculum "educative" by attending to teachers' learning as their central goal. Moving from materials as instructional guides toward mechanisms for teacher learning represented a new vision and opened questions about the role of curriculum materials within teacher education. Since this time, the notion of "educative curriculum materials" (ECM) has become a focal point for researchers.

ECM aim at guiding teachers in the organization, content, and pedagogy of given topics, scaffolding the enactment of effective teaching practices (Davis & Krajcik, 2005; Remillard, 2005). Their role is set within the framework of "pedagogical flow," that is, the transformation of the written or prescribed curriculum to the intended curriculum to the enacted curriculum (Remillard & Heck, 2014; Stein et al., 2007). Written curriculum refers to the definition of student learning goals and experiences, often set at national and local levels. These curricula are translated into sequenced, more specific content, strategies, and activities through instructional planning (i.e., the intended curriculum), and give way to what happens during their enactment in lessons (the enacted curriculum). Despite often being strongly aligned to the written curriculum, ECM are more closely related to day-to-day teaching, providing lesson plans, background knowledge, orientation for practice, and opportunities for teacher reflection (Krajcik & Delen, 2017). As such, they are conceived as mediators between the written and enacted curriculum (Schmidt et al., 1996).

ECM have gained importance in the educational field, becoming a widespread, regular source of consultation for teachers (Grossman & Thompson, 2008; Monney, 2014), as well as a key component of public policies worldwide (Mourshed et al., 2010). In science education, ECM have been widely used to support curriculum reform and professional development in many countries. Notable endeavors to support teachers in enacting student-centered science teaching, such as the Biological Sciences Curriculum Study or the Chemical Education Material Study, have consistently used ECM as an essential component.

DOI: 10.4324/9781003098478-34

ECM may include detailed lesson plans, benchmark lessons, activities and worksheets for students, textbooks, and even physical materials (e.g., lab materials and manipulatives) or software and web-based computer programs. They are typically distributed as printed or online booklets and can include complementary audio visual supports, such as model lesson video recordings, and digital platforms. They can be either commercially published, developed by nongovernmental organizations or universities, or distributed as part of national and state programs (Davis et al., 2016).

Along with the expansion of ECM is a thriving interest to explore the characteristics, uses, and effects of ECM in science education (Davis et al., 2016). Robust evidence shows that the use of science ECM has positive impacts on student learning (Albornoz et al., 2020; Arias et al., 2016; Davis et al., 2016; Granger et al., 2018; Harris et al., 2015). These positive effects often occur through the enactment of reform-oriented teaching practices, which combine direct instruction with inquiry, hands-on activities focused on integrating science content and skills such as argumentation, experimental design and data analysis, and project-based or context-based approaches (Arias et al., 2016; Dias et al., 2011; Furman et al., 2017; Schneider & Krajcik, 2002).

Yet, the original intent of ECM was to provide sustained, scalable, job-embedded, discipline-specific, learning opportunities for teachers (Davis et al., 2017). The literature includes less systematized findings on how ECM contribute to teacher learning (Davis et al., 2016; Granger et al., 2018; Mujawamariya, 2004; Taylor et al., 2015), with the role of ECM in teacher education and professional development being underresearched and undertheorized (Moore et al., 2021; Schneider, 2013).

Considering that substantial resources are being allocated to provide ECM as part of science teacher professional development efforts, understanding what is known of ECM's effects on teacher learning and identifying opportunities for future research are pressing needs. This chapter addresses these needs by presenting a systematic review of the literature to analyze the role of ECM on preservice and in-service science teacher education. Areas in which significant research exists are reported, along with other areas in need of further examination. This chapter also offers suggestions for science educators who work with teachers. The goal in conducting this review was to answer the following questions:

- How do ECM support teacher learning?
- Which ECM design features and conditions of use enhance science teacher learning?

Methodology

A systematic review of published research between 2001 and 2021 examining the effects of science educative curriculum materials on preservice and in-service teacher education was conducted. Given language fluency within the research team, documents in English, French, and Spanish were considered. First, sources such as Taylor and Francis, JSTOR, ERIH Plus, Elsevier, and Springer, as well as Google Scholar, were used to search for peer-reviewed studies, including different combinations of the following three categories of keywords and corresponding translations: (a) curriculum materials, instructional materials, educative curriculum materials and/or *manuels pédagogique* or *matériel didactique* (as usually referred to in French), and/or *materiales curriculares, guías didácticas*, or *recursos para la enseñanza* (as named in Spanish); (b) teacher learning, teacher education, preservice, and/or in-service teacher learning, professional development, and/or continuous professional development; and (c) science education, science teaching, and/or science instruction. A total of 110 peer-reviewed articles were found.

We screened this data set to exclude studies not specifically addressing teacher learning, the use of ECM, or science teaching. After applying these criteria, the sample was reduced to 36 articles.

Contributions of the effects and characteristics of ECM in other subject areas and nonempirical works were considered to define the theoretical and contextual framework of the review, but not the results. Table 29.1 summarizes the sample's characteristics.

General inductive qualitative data analysis was used to analyze and categorize studies. Each article was reviewed by at least two researchers, and unclear determinations were discussed conjunctly. Given that most studies focused on three dimensions of teacher learning, they were grouped according to the following categories: (a) teacher pedagogical content knowledge, (b) teacher beliefs, and (c) pedagogical design capacity. To address the second research question, we identified the design heuristics and conditions of use of the ECM described in each study and grouped them accordingly.

How Do ECM Support Teacher Learning?

In the review of literature, we found that ECM support pre- and in-service science teacher learning in three main dimensions: changes in teacher pedagogical content knowledge (PCK), changes in teachers' beliefs, and changes in teachers' pedagogical design capacity (PDC).

Changes in Teacher PCK

PCK refers to an amalgam of specialized knowledge that results from knowing students as learners, understanding content, anticipating student difficulties and misconceptions, developing effective teaching strategies for that content and that particular group of students, as well as being effective in assessing what and how much students have learned (Shulman, 1987). In science education, PCK implies teachers having a deep understanding of natural phenomena, as well as of the nature of scientific knowledge, and how they both can be approached and assessed in science lessons at school (Magnusson et al., 1999).

Developing teachers' PCK is identified as one of the most critical and challenging aspects in pre- and in-service science education (Gess-Newsome & Lederman, 1999). Interestingly, it is also one of the main teacher learning outcomes for which ECM have positive effects. The reviewed studies show that ECM supports the development of PCK in science teachers from different educational levels and contexts.

We found that, PCK being a complex construct, these studies refer to a range of PCK domains in more comprehensive or specific ways. For example, Flanagan et al. (2013) assessed multiple domains

Table 29.1 Sample characteristics

Teacher Education	
Preservice	5
In-service	28
Pre- and in-service	3
Educational Level	
Preschool	0
Primary/Elementary	11
Middle School/Secondary	24
Post-secondary	1
Studies' Methodology	
Case study (< 10 cases)	19
Multiple case study (≥ 10 cases)	8
Experimental or quasi-experimental	7
Review or meta-analysis	2

of PCK (content knowledge, knowledge of student thinking, and knowledge of strategies to move student thinking forward) for different item contexts and found that the use of ECM produced significant gains in 8th-grade science teachers across all PCK domains. On the other hand, most studies looked specifically at particular aspects of PCK, such as subject matter knowledge (SMK), teaching practices, and the understanding of the nature of science (NOS).

Various studies focused on teachers' SMK, showing that science ECM positively contributed to its development. This finding is relevant because research indicates that science teachers commonly identify their lack of SMK as a limiting factor in the implementation of reform-oriented science teaching practices (Luera et al., 2005). Moreover, considering that scientific knowledge is dynamic, deepening science teachers' SMK throughout their professional careers becomes important (Arzi & White, 2008).

In an experimental study evaluating the effects of a professional development (PD) program that included ECM addressing space science content knowledge, Granger et al. (2018) found that elementary teachers in the PD-plus-ECM group scored higher on the posttest than did the teachers receiving limited PD and traditional curriculum frameworks. Flanagan et al. (2013) also measured teachers' SMK and found that middle-school teachers gained knowledge on chemical reactions, the conservation of mass, and plant growth, three of the four topics covered in their in-service PD program. Gains further increased after using the provided ECM, but were milder in the topic of flow of matter. Similar findings were described in preservice teacher training: modeled instruction and use of ECM in field experiences had a positive significant impact in elementary student teachers' SMK about convection as a thermal energy process (Donna & Hick, 2017).

Changes in teachers' SMK were also perceived during the enactment of ECM. For example, Kademian et al. (2017) video-recorded and observed the implementation of a 4th-grade ecosystem unit. They found that teachers receiving ECM used scientific language and pertinent examples more frequently and accurately than did their peers during lessons. Along these lines, Roseman et al. (2017) showed robust evidence of teachers' gains in SMK related to plant and animal growth, particularly to identify and paraphrase scientific ideas, as well as to understand their coherence with lesson activities. Finally, changes in teacher SMK were also reported as the development of new understandings on molecular genetics, a grade 9–10 biology curricular content, within a curriculum reform process in Singapore (Tan & Nashon, 2013).

Another set of studies attended to changes in content-specific teaching practices as a learning outcome. Schneider and Krajcik (2002), for instance, found that, despite having previous experience with neither ECM nor reform-based teaching, science middle school teachers learned to contextualize lessons within real-life problems and driving questions and to guide their students in interpreting graphs. Teachers also learned how to assess students and consider their misconceptions (e.g., Coenders et al., 2010; Roseman et al., 2017; Schneider, 2013). Schneider also found that teachers could specifically align assessments to her proposed learning goals.

ECM also contributed to the incorporation of novel teaching strategies in science lessons, which enhanced teachers' PCK. Dajani (2017) found that ECM fostering content-based story writing in elementary level science lessons supported Palestine teachers in their PCK development. Middle school teachers have also been shown to enhance their use of scientific argumentation when using ECM. For example, Marco-Bujosa et al. (2016) found that most of their middle school teachers increased their use of argumentation as they used ECM. Moreover, some teachers were also able to extend their PCK of argumentation beyond specific lessons and apply it to science instruction, in general.

Finally, some studies focused on another key aspect of science PCK: its epistemological dimension, frequently referred to as the NOS. Research shows that both science teachers and students usually hold misconceptions about the NOS and that promoting a deeper understanding in this regard requires explicit teaching (Lederman, 1992). However, elementary school science teachers developed their NOS PCK when they used ECM, regardless of their previous knowledge (Lin et al., 2012). Similarly, Brunner and Abd-El-Khalick (2019) found that teachers addressed the NOS more often and in an informed manner during lessons when they had consulted and enacted ECM.

Changes in Teacher Beliefs

The second dimension of science teacher learning that ECM were found to support was changes in teacher beliefs. This finding is important because any sustainable science teacher education strategy requires opportunities for teachers to revise and enrich their beliefs. Teaching practices are strongly influenced by these beliefs, and they are difficult to modify (Pajares, 1992; Van Driel et al., 2007). In the literature, changes in teachers' beliefs were identified as focusing on the views of science and science teaching, teachers' self-efficacy, and beliefs on student learning.

One set of studies showed that teachers developed transformed views of science and science teaching. For example, Brunner and Abd-El-Khalick (2019) found that elementary teachers developed informed views on the NOS after using ECM explicitly targeting the empirical, inferential, and creative aspects of the NOS in trade books. Lin et al. (2012) also showed that teachers perceived changes in their beliefs on the NOS after using ECM aimed at fostering NOS teaching and guiding teachers' reflection in this regard. In another case, after using ECM focused on the use of data and media analysis for ecology and human impact lessons, 9th-grade biology teachers expressed belief in the importance of these teaching strategies to deepen student learning (Wyner, 2013). Moreover, as a result of these newly developed dispositions, teachers included the use of data and media analysis when planning for subsequent science lessons beyond those detailed in the ECM.

Likewise, a qualitative, longitudinal study based on teacher interviews and focus groups showed that ECM shaped middle school teachers' beliefs toward student-centered teaching (including the use of driving questions, modeling, and evidence-based argumentation) and, consequently, scaffolded the enactment of such practices (Pringle et al., 2017). Czajka and McConnell (2019) found that geoscience university teachers using ECM shifted their beliefs toward student-centered teaching practices as enhanced by the materials. They argued that this shift contributed to the adoption of teaching practices aligned with these newfound beliefs in a more sustained way, indicating that research-based ECM can be an effective PD tool. The findings of Tan and Nashon (2013) further supported these findings. Within the framework of a training program involving the use of research-based ECM, they found that middle school biology teachers in Singapore changed their beliefs on science teaching. In their own words, they moved away from their traditional, teacher-centered, content-focused way of thinking toward increasingly student-centered views on pedagogy.

Another group of studies found that ECM foster teachers' beliefs in their ability to enact specific teaching strategies and promote student learning, that is, teachers' self-efficacy (Bandura, 1977). Self-efficacy is key because it influences practice in all areas (Klassen & Tze, 2014). Li et al. (2021) developed an in-service secondary level PD program with ECM targeting teachers' self-efficacy on teaching climate change. While teachers typically considered this topic to be challenging, significant gains in self-efficacy were found in posttest scores, particularly regarding their understanding of content.

Granger et al. (2018) found that, besides SMK, teachers in the treatment group receiving PD with ECM experienced changes in their views of science inquiry, beliefs about reform-based teaching, and self-efficacy. This effect was greater on teachers with initial lower self-efficacy, and it increased as they perceived their own and their students' learning gains when implementing the ECM.

Similarly, McNeill et al. (2016) suggested that enacting ECM can support teachers in trying out specific teaching practices such as scientific argumentation instruction, enhancing their confidence to adopt them in their science lessons. Consistently, the same research team found that teachers' self-efficacy in scientific argumentation instruction increased as they enacted more lessons of the given multimedia ECM (Loper et al., 2019). However, some features, such as providing teachers with complementary videos that problematize their prior beliefs on argumentation, diminished the effects of ECM on self-efficacy, illustrating the need to design ECM carefully to consider teachers' starting points and to provide achievable challenges.

Finally, studies referring to teachers' beliefs about student learning were considered. Although the literature also usually addresses this aspect, it was rarely studied amongst the reviewed papers. In fact, only one study was found to inquire about teachers' beliefs on student learning when using ECM. Dias et al. (2011) conducted a self-study with one of the authors, who used inquiry-based ECM to teach 8th-grade physics and reflected on the experience. They found that he developed new, more culturally responsive ideas on how students learn from the suggested activities, as well as systematically observing and analyzing his own students' learning outcomes, perceived difficulties and misconceptions, and manifestations of students' motivation and commitment. Interestingly, the participating teacher was also a teacher educator involved in ECM-based PD interventions. In addition to changing his beliefs on student learning, findings indicate that he also changed his views on how other teachers can learn from the use of ECM during instruction.

Changes in Teacher PDC

The third dimension of teacher learning that studies referred to is PDC, that is, "teachers' ability to perceive and mobilize existing resources in order to craft instructional contexts" (Brown, 2009, p. 24). This concept is central, because it implies that teachers make grounded, goal-oriented pedagogical decisions regarding the use and adaptation of ECM according to their personal and professional characteristics, classroom contexts, and students' needs. Considering that many voices question teacher-proof conceptions of ECM, these studies are especially relevant, because they acknowledge teacher agency and highlight the importance of ECM being focused on sustained teacher learning.

The value of teachers learning to use ECM was reported by Penuel et al. (2007). In this study, teachers working with ECM developed an understanding of the proposed learning objectives and ways to better support student learning, two key elements in PDC. Teachers reported that being able to plan with and adapt ECM before they were used in the class was important to them. Ultimately, the opportunity to work with materials was a predictor of their effective use.

Researchers also found that designing and implementing ECM contributed to teachers' PDC. When teachers participated in professional learning opportunities focused on designing instructional materials with the goal of teacher and student learning, they demonstrated gains in their PCK and beliefs (Coenders et al., 2010; Mujawamariya & Lorette, 2004). Cycles of design and implementation of the ECM were important in these gains.

Finally, in subsequent studies, Beyer and Davis (2009a, 2009b, 2012) investigated how preservice elementary teachers used science ECM. They deployed two key design practices with teachers while they learned about ECM: criticizing and adapting the materials. They found that initiatives aimed at developing these practices had positive effects. Specifically, preservice teachers learned and applied specific, pertinent criteria to analyze and adapt ECM.

Which ECM Design Features and Conditions of Use Enhance Science Teacher Learning?

In addition to reporting results on teacher learning, most of the reviewed articles also made suggestions as to which ECM characteristics and conditions of use produced the observed effects. In terms of ECM characteristics, a variety of studies reported that teacher practice and knowledge were impacted (e.g., Granger et al., 2018; Kademian et al., 2017; Roblin et al., 2017; Schneider &

Krajcik, 2002). Davis and Krajcik's (2005) design heuristics were used as guidelines for the design of ECM by most researchers.

For instance, Roseman et al. (2017) included learning opportunities for teachers that targeted their PCK and SMK. They reported positive results among their groups of teachers when they included modeling activities for students to engage in phenomena inquiry, explanatory notes on the role of models, concrete orientations to guide student observations, and examples of sequenced questions to conduct classroom discussions, as well as possible expected answers. Similar educative features that address student misconceptions through concrete examples and notes about teaching the content have been found to be important in changing teacher practice and knowledge (Granger et al., 2018; Pringle et al., 2017; Schneider, 2013; Schneider & Krajcik, 2002). Furthermore, teachers using these features were shown to better understand underlying science ideas, because they often held misconceptions similar to those of their students.

On a different note, Beyer and Davis (2009b) evaluated the affordances and constraints of general supports (i.e., those describing principles of practice that relate to multiple lessons) and lesson-specific narrative supports (i.e., those providing particular, lesson-embedded examples of the principles). They found that preservice science teachers receiving the latter supports used them extensively when planning their assignments. However, teachers receiving general supports were able to better identify overarching teaching principles and apply them to upcoming lessons. Other studies also found that lesson-specific, embedded information was more effective and highly valued by teachers than were general descriptions about the overarching, underlying pedagogy of units (Beyer & Davis, 2009b; Janssen & Lazonder, 2015; Lin et al., 2012; Schneider & Krajcik, 2002), because teachers usually consult ECM when planning their lessons. Suggestions for teachers to do or try things beyond their classroom contexts (e.g., complementary reading suggestions to deepen and expand their content knowledge or trying out activities prior to lessons) were found to be unhelpful to the teachers (Schneider, 2013).

In terms of conditions of use, ECM were often present in other teacher learning programs, which most often included initial training sessions and ongoing workshops. In over 40% of the reviewed studies, ECM were included in these types of learning programs. Some of these studies found that solely providing ECM was insufficient and that complementary workshops can increase their effects (Lin et al., 2012; Pringle et al., 2017; Schneider & Krajcik, 2002). Reciprocally, other studies showed that the effects of workshops alone were limited and that ECM were needed to enhance teacher learning (Flanagan et al., 2013; Kademian et al., 2017).

Another PD feature that supplemented and contributed to ECM effects is instructional coaching (e.g., Coenders et al., 2010; Malanson et al., 2014; Schneider & Krajcik, 2002; Tan & Nashon, 2013). Typically, coaches provide teachers with individualized, context-specific and intensive support, as well as tailored one-on-one feedback on their performance (Knight, 2007). This feature contributes to the improvement of teaching in a sustained way (Kraft et al., 2018). For example, Kleickmann et al. (2016) tested the impact of coaching on elementary school science teachers while implementing ECM. Those who received extensive coaching outperformed the others in terms of their beliefs and motivation, instructional quality, and student performance. However, considering that coaching requires significant resource investments, particularly at a large scale (Kraft et al., 2018), further research is needed to evaluate to what degree and in which conditions instructional coaching will provide an added value on teacher learning with respect to the use of ECM.

A common element between workshops, coaching, and other initiatives, such as communities of practice (as seen, for example, in Coenders et al., 2008, 2010; Pringle et al., 2017; Tan et al., 2013), is that they provide further support to teachers during their ECM implementation. Moreover, sustaining the use of ECM over time and favoring teachers' reflection on their use is crucial to teacher learning (e.g., Dajani, 2017; Dias et al., 2011; Lin et al., 2012; Marco-Bujosa et al., 2016; Schneider,

2013; Tan et al., 2013). The study by Pringle et al. is illustrative in that it shows how teachers gained a deeper understanding about their areas of instruction when they systematically used ECM and reflected on their experiences throughout a 5-year professional learning program.

Conclusions

While ECM are important resources for teacher educators and teachers, interest has grown regarding their effects on teachers. This chapter presented a systematic review focusing on the effects of science ECM on pre- and in-service teacher learning.

Overall, ECM positively contributed to teacher learning in three main dimensions: PCK, beliefs, and PDC. This finding is encouraging, as it highlights the potential of using ECM for teacher education.

Evidence is limited, however, on the effects of ECM on general pedagogical knowledge, beyond content and lesson-specific teacher learning. While ECM are good for supporting teachers to enact specific types of lessons, whether any of these learning gains transfer to other disciplinary areas remains unclear. The very nature of ECM being lesson-based and anchored on specific contents may be responsible for this type of gain. Understanding if and how teacher knowledge and practices can be transferred to other settings is worth further research.

Studies also point to the importance of considering features that support learning and conditions of use when teachers work with ECM. Embedded, specific, concrete features addressing aspects closely related to the lessons' enactment (e.g., explanatory notes on content, suggested question guides, examples of frequent misconceptions, etc.) were found to be highly valued by teachers and to contribute to teacher learning.

The importance of further supporting teachers in the implementation of ECM by framing their use within other teacher PD strategies is also emphasized. Given that research has shown that teachers' uptake of ECM is dissimilar (Davis et al., 2016), special attention is placed on supporting their enactment. Additionally, fostering teachers' reflective practice was found to be key to promoting deeper, more perdurable teacher learning and, particularly, to developing PDC.

Without underestimating the advances in the field, a clear prevalence of case studies with few participating teachers, mostly set in the middle and high school levels in the US, was found. Further research on larger teacher populations in diverse contexts is needed to establish comprehensive understanding on the matter. Among these, delving into interventions in preservice teacher education must continue. On the other hand, studies focusing on evaluating the impact of different factors, such as particular conditions of use and teacher characteristics, on the effects of ECM could provide valuable insights.

This review is expected to contribute to educative designers, policy makers, and teacher educators to make informed decisions on the creation and use of ECM and to motivate renewed research initiatives, particularly on how to design large-scale PD programs that enable deep and sustainable change in science teaching practices as a result of fostering teachers' career-long professional learning.

References

Albornoz, F., Anauati, M. V., Furman, M., Luzuriaga, M., Podestá, M. E., & Taylor, I. (2020). Training to teach science: Experimental evidence from Argentina. *The World Bank Economic Review, 34*(2), 393–417. https://doi.org/10.1093/wber/lhy010

Arias, A. M., Davis, E. A., Marino, J.-C., Kademian, S. M., & Palincsar, A. S. (2016). Teachers' use of educative curriculum materials to engage students in science practices. *International Journal of Science Education, 38*(9), 1504–1526. https://doi.org/10.1080/09500693.2016.1198059

Arzi, H. J., & White, R. T. (2008). Change in teachers' knowledge of subject matter: A 17-year longitudinal study. *Science Education, 92*(2), 221–251. https://doi.org/10.1002/sce.20239

Ball, D. L., & Cohen, D. K. (1996). Reform by the book: What is – or might be – the role of curriculum materials in teacher learning and instructional reform? *Educational Researcher, 25*(9), 6–14. https://doi.org/10.3102/0013189X025009006

Bandura, A. (1977). Self-efficacy: Toward a unifying theory of behavioral change. *Psychological Review, 84*(2), 191–215. https://doi.org/10.1037/0033-295X.84.2.191

Beyer, C. T., & Davis, E. A. (2009a) Supporting preservice elementary teachers' critique and adaptation of science lesson plans using educative curriculum materials. *Journal of Science Teacher Education, 20*(6), 517–536. https://doi.org/10.1007/s10972-009-9148-5

Beyer, C. T., & Davis, E. A. (2009b) Using educative curriculum materials to support preservice elementary teachers' curricular planning: A Comparison between two different forms of support. *Curriculum Inquiry, 39*(5), 679–703. https://doi.org/10.1111/j.1467-873x.2009.00464.x

Beyer, C. T., & Davis, E. A. (2012). Learning to critique and adapt science curriculum materials: Examining the development of preservice elementary teachers' pedagogical content knowledge. *Science Teacher Education, 96*(1), 130–157. https://doi.org/10.1002/sce.20466

Brown, M. W. (2009). The teacher-tool relationship: Theorizing the design and use of curriculum materials. In J. T. Remillard, B. A. Herbel-Eisenmann, & G. M. Lloyd (Eds.), *Mathematics teachers at work: Connecting curriculum materials and classroom instruction.* New York: Routledge.

Brunner, J. L., & Abd-El-Khalick, F. (2019). Improving nature of science instruction in elementary classes with modified science trade books and educative curriculum materials. *Journal of Research in Science Teaching, 57*(2), 154–183. https://doi.org/10.1002/tea.21588

Coenders, F., Terlouw, C., & Dijkstra, S. (2008). Assessing teachers' beliefs to facilitate the transition to a new chemistry curriculum: What do the teachers want? *Journal of Science Teacher Education, 19*(4), 317–335. https://doi.org/10.1007/s10972-008-9096-5

Coenders, F., Terlouw, C., Dijkstra, S., & Pieters, J. (2010). The effects of the design and development of a chemistry curriculum reform on teachers' professional growth: A case study. *Journal of Science Teacher Education, 21*(5), 535–557. https://doi.org/10.1007/s10972-010-9194-z

Czajka, C. D., & McConnell, D. (2019). The adoption of student-centered teaching materials as a professional development experience for college faculty. *International Journal of Science Education, 41*(5), 693–711. https://doi.org/10.1080/09500693.2019.1578908

Dajani, M. M. Y. (2017). Introducing science stories in Palestinian elementary classrooms: Facilitating teacher learning. *Journal of Science Teacher Education, 28*(1), 73–91. https://doi.org/10.1080/1046560X.2017.1279509

Davis, E. A., Janssen, F. J. J. M., & Van Driel, J. H. (2016). Teachers and science curriculum materials: Where we are and where we need to go. *Studies in Science Education, 52*(2), 127–160. https://doi.org/10.1080/03057267.2016.1161701

Davis, E. A., & Krajcik, J. S. (2005). Designing educative curriculum materials to promote teacher learning. *Educational Researcher, 34*(3), 3–14. https://doi.org/10.3102/0013189X034003003

Davis, E. A., Palincsar, A. S., Smith, P. S., Arias, A. M., & Kademian, S. M. (2017). Educative curriculum materials: Uptake, impact, and implications for research and design. *Educational Researcher, 46*(6), 293–304. https://doi.org/10.3102/0013189X17727502

Dias, M., Eick, C. J., & Brantley-Dias, L. (2011). Practicing what we teach: A self-study in implementing an inquiry-based curriculum in a middle grades classroom. *Journal of Science Teacher Education, 22*(1), 53–78. https://doi.org/10.1007/s10972-010-9222-z

Donna, J. D., & Hick, S. R. (2017). Developing elementary preservice teacher subject matter knowledge through the use of educative science curriculum materials. *Journal of Science Teacher Education, 28*(1), 92–110. https://doi.org/10.1080/1046560X.2017.1279510

Flanagan, J. C., Herrmann-Abell, C. F., & Roseman, J. E. (2013, April). *Developing and evaluating an eighth grade curriculum unit that links foundational chemistry to biological growth: Using teacher measures to evaluate the promise of the intervention.* Paper presentation. NARST Annual International Conference, Rio Grande, Puerto Rico.

Furman, M., Luzuriaga, M., Taylor, I., Podestá, M. E., & Jarvis, D. (2017). From inception to implementation: An Argentine case study of teachers enacting early years inquiry-based science. *Early Years, 39*(4), 408–425. http://dx.doi.org/10.1080/09575146.2017.1389856

Gess-Newsome, J., & Lederman, N. G. (Eds.). (1999). *Examining pedagogical content knowledge: The construct and its implications for science education* (Vol. 6). Dordrecht: Springer Science & Business Media.

Granger, E. M., Bevis, T. H., Southerland, S. A., Saka, Y., & Ke, F. (2018). Examining features of how professional development and enactment of educative curricula influences elementary science teacher learning. *Journal of Research in Science Teaching, 56*(3), 348–370. https://doi.org/10.1002/tea.21480

Grossman, P., & Thompson, C. (2004). Learning from curriculum materials: Scaffolds for new teachers? *Teaching and Teacher Education, 24*(8), 2014–2026. https://doi.org/10.1016/j.tate.2008.05.002

Harris, C. J., Penuel, W. R., D'Angelo, C. M., DeBarger, A. H., Gallagher, L. P., Kennedy, C. A., & Krajcik, J. S. (2015). Impact of project-based curriculum materials on student learning in science: Results of a randomized controlled trial. *Journal of Research in Science Teaching, 52*(10), 1362–1385. https://doi.org/10.1002/tea.21263

Janssen, N., & Lazonder, A. W. (2015). Implementing innovative technologies through lesson plans: What kind of support do teachers prefer? *Journal of Science Education and Technology, 24*(6), 910–920. https://doi.org/10.1007/s10956-015-9573-5

Kademian, S. M., Arias, A. M., Davis, E. A., & Palincsar, A. S. (2017). Supporting the use of scientific language: Teachers' use of content-foregrounded educative features. *Journal of Science Teacher Education, 28*(2), 146–168. https://doi.org/10.1080/1046560X.2016.1277596

Klassen, R. M., & Tze, V. M. C. (2014). Teachers' self-efficacy, personality, and teaching effectiveness: A meta-analysis. *Educational Research Review, 12*, 59–76. https://doi.org/10.1016/j.edurev.2014.06.001

Kleickmann, T., Tröbst, S., Jonen, A., Vehmeyer, J., & Möller, K. (2016). The effects of expert scaffolding in elementary science professional development on teachers' beliefs and motivations, instructional practices, and student achievement. *Journal of Educational Psychology, 108*(1), 21–42. https://doi.org/10.1037/edu0000041

Knight, J. (2007). *Instructional coaching: A partnership approach to improving instruction.* Thousand Oaks: Corwin Press.

Kraft, M. A., Blazar, D., & Hogan, D. (2018). The effect of teacher coaching on instruction and achievement: A meta-analysis of the causal evidence. *Review of Educational Research, 88*(4), 547–588. https://doi.org/10.3102/0034654318759268

Krajcik, J., & Delen, I. (2017). The benefits and limitations of educative curriculum materials. *Journal of Science Teacher Education, 28*(1), 1–10. https://doi.org/10.1080/1046560X.2017.1279470

Lederman, N. G. (1992). Students' and teachers' conceptions of the nature of science: A review of the research. *Journal of Research in Science Teaching, 29*(4), 331–359. https://doi.org/10.1002/tea.3660290404

Li, C. J., Monroe, M. C., Oxarart, A., & Ritchie, T. (2021). Building teachers' self-efficacy in teaching about climate change through educative curriculum and professional development. *Applied Environmental Education and Communication, 20*(1), 34–48. https://doi.org/10.1080/1533015X.2019.1617806

Lin, S. F., Lieu, S. C., Chen, S., Huang, M. T., & Chang, W. H. (2012). Affording explicit-reflective science teaching by using an educative teachers' guide. *International Journal of Science Education, 34*(7), 999–1026. https://doi.org/10.1080/09500693.2012.661484

Loper, S., McNeill, K. L., González-Howard, M., Marco-Bujosa, L. M., & O'Dwyer, L. M. (2019). The impact of multimedia educative curriculum materials (MECMs) on teachers' beliefs about scientific argumentation, *Technology, Pedagogy and Education, 28*(2), 173–190. https://doi.org/10.1080/1475939X.2019.1583121

Luera, G. R., Moyer, R. H., & Everett, S. A. (2005). What type and level of science content knowledge of elementary education students affect their ability to construct an inquiry-based science lesson? *Journal of Elementary Science Education, 17*(1), 12–25. https://doi.org/10.1007/bf03174670

Magnusson, S., Krajcik, J., & Borko, H. (1999). Nature, sources, and development of pedagogical content knowledge for science teaching. In J. Gess-Newsome & N. G. Lederman (Eds.), *Examining pedagogical content knowledge* (Vol. 6, pp. 95–132). Dordrecht: Kluwer Academic Publishers.

Malanson, K., Jacque, B., Faux, R., & Meiri, K. F. (2014). Modeling for fidelity: Virtual mentorship by scientists fosters teacher self-efficacy and promotes implementation of novel high school biomedical curricula. *PLoS ONE, 9*(12), 1–24. https://doi.org/10.1371/journal.pone.0114929

Marco-Bujosa, L. M., McNeill, K. L., González-Howard, M., & Loper, S. (2016). An exploration of teacher learning from an educative reform-oriented science curriculum: Case studies of teacher curriculum use. *Journal of Research in Science Teaching, 54*(2), 141–168. https://doi.org/10.1002/tea.21340

McNeill, K. L., Katsh-Singer, R., González-Howard, M., & Loper, S. (2016). Factors impacting teachers' argumentation instruction in their science classrooms. *International Journal of Science Education, 38*(12), 2026–2046. https://doi.org/10.1080/09500693.2016.1221547

Monney, N. (2014). L'analyse interprétative de l'utilisation du matériel pédagogique par des enseignants du primaire en classe multiâge. *Canadian Journal for New Scholars in Education, 5*(1), 1–9.

Moore, N., Coldwell, M., & Perry, E. (2021). Exploring the role of curriculum materials in teacher professional development, *Professional Development in Education. 47*(2–3), 331–347. https://doi.org/10.1080/19415257.2021.1879230

Mourshed, M., Chijioke, C., & Barber, M. (2010). *How the world's most improved school systems keep getting better.* London: McKinsey & Company.

Mujawamariya, D., & Lorette, N. (2004). Du matériel didactique de sciences conçu pour des enseignants en milieu francophone minoritaire: mise à contribution du potentiel des étudiants maîtres. *Francophonies d'Amérique, 18*, 37–50. https://doi.org/10.7202/1005348ar

Pajares, M. F. (1992). Teachers' beliefs and educational research: Cleaning up a messy construct. *Review of Educational Research, 62*(3), 307–332. https://doi.org/10.3102/00346543062003307

Penuel, W. R., Fishman, B. J., Yamaguchi, R., & Gallagher, L. P. (2007). What makes professional development effective? Strategies that foster curriculum implementation. *American Educational Research Journal, 44*(4), 921–958. https://doi.org/10.3102/0002831207308221

Pringle, R. M., Mesa, J., & Hayes, L. (2017). Professional development for middle school science teachers: Does an educative curriculum make a difference? *Journal of Science Teacher Education, 28*(1), 57–72. https://doi.org/10.1080/1046560X.2016.1277599

Remillard, J. T. (2005). Examining key concepts in research on teachers' use of mathematics curricula. *Review of Educational Research, 75*(2), 211–246. https://doi.org/10.3102/00346543075002211

Remillard, J. T., & Heck, D. J. (2014). Conceptualizing the curriculum enactment process in mathematics education. *ZDM, 46*(5), 705–718. https://doi.org/10.1007/s11858-014-0600-4

Roblin, N. P., Schunn, C., & McKenney, S. (2017). What are critical features of science curriculum materials that impact student and teacher outcomes? *Science Education, 102*(2), 260–282. https://doi.org/10.1002/sce.21328

Roseman, J. E., Herrmann-Abell, C. F., & Koppal, M. (2017). Designing for the Next Generation Science Standards: Educative curriculum materials and measures of teacher knowledge. *Journal of Science Teacher Education, 28*(1), 111–141. https://doi.org/10.1080/1046560x.2016.1277598

Schmidt, W. H., Jorde, D., Cogan, L., Barrier, E., Ganzalo, I., Moser, U., . . . Wolfe, R. G. (1996). *Characterizing pedagogical flow: An investigation of mathematics and science teaching in six countries.* Dordrecht: Kluwer Academic Publishers.

Schneider, R. M. (2013). Opportunities for teacher learning during enactment of inquiry science curriculum materials: Exploring the potential for teacher educative materials. *Journal of Science Teacher Education, 24*(2), 323–346. https://doi.org/10.1007/s10972-012-9309-9

Schneider, R. M., & Krajcik, J. (2002). Supporting science teacher learning: The role of educative curriculum materials. *Journal of Science Teacher Education, 13*(3), 221–245. https://doi.org/10.1023/A:1016569117024

Shulman, L. S. (1987). Knowledge and teaching: Foundations of the new reform. *Harvard Educational Review, 57*(1), 1–22.

Stein, M. K., Remillard, J., & Smith, M. S. (2007). How curriculum influences student learning. In F. K. Lester (Ed.), *Second handbook of research on mathematics teaching and learning.* Greenwich: Information Age.

Tan, Y. S. M., & Nashon, S. M. (2013). Promoting teacher learning through learning study discourse: The case of science teachers in Singapore. *Journal of Science Teacher Education, 24*(5), 859–877. https://doi.org/10.1007/s10972-013-9340-5

Taylor, J. A., Getty, S. R., Kowalski, S. M., Wilson, C. D., Carlson, J., & Van Scotter, P. (2015). An efficacy trial of research-based curriculum materials with curriculum-based professional development. *American Educational Research Journal, 52*(5), 984–1017. https://doi.org/10.3102/0002831215585962

Van Driel, J. H., Bulte, A. M., & Verloop, N. (2007). The relationships between teachers' general beliefs about teaching and learning and their domain specific curricular beliefs. *Learning and Instruction, 17*(2), 156–171. https://doi.org/10.1016/j.learninstruc.2007.01.010

Wyner, Y. (2013). The impact of a novel curriculum on secondary biology teachers' dispositions toward using authentic data and media in their human impact and ecology lessons. *Journal of Science Teacher Education, 24*(5), 833–857. https://doi.org/10.1007/s10972-013-9335-2

SECTION 6

Science Teacher Education – Emerging Areas

Section Editor: Rachel Mamlok-Naaman

Science education is an ever-developing entity, aligned with particular pedagogies and instructional techniques. It is influenced by changes and reforms in the curricula around the world – students' cognitive and affective aspects, political, cultural, and socioeconomic factors, scientific and technological innovations, as well as theories and studies in learning and teaching (Mamlok-Naaman & Taitelbaum, 2019). However, any new pedagogical idea depends on its enactment by teachers, since they are key to developing sustainable reforms and innovations in educational practice (Mamlok-Naaman et al., 2018). Professional learning requires experience in acting in complex practical situations – developing knowledge, practice, and identity (Close et al., 2014), or trying (as much as possible) to connect the science curriculum to authentic and context-based situations (Mamlok-Naaman, 2016; Habig et al., 2018). In addition, the role of emotions in science teacher education should not be neglected (Woolfolk Hoy, 2013).

The notion of teacher knowledge first came to prominence in science education at the end of the 20th century; there has been an increasing body of literature on what teachers know and must do in order to carry out their work (Mulholland & Wallace, 2005). One of the goals of the science teaching community is to develop more effective and scientifically aligned strategies to teach high school students. Accomplished teaching of science can be defined in terms of the knowledge that teachers use in their teaching (Magnusson et al., 1999). This knowledge has been categorized as subject-matter knowledge and pedagogical content knowledge (PCK). PCK is concerned with the teaching and learning of a particular domain: knowing how students learn within that domain, knowing their common misconceptions, and the specific challenges of that domain, as well as being able to apply this knowledge to teaching and learning within that particular domain:

> The key to distinguishing the knowledge base of teaching lies at the intersection of content and pedagogy, in the capacity of a teacher to transform the content knowledge he or she possesses into forms that are pedagogically powerful and yet adaptive to the variations in ability and background presented by the students. (Shulman, 1987, p. 15)

Mamlok-Naaman and colleagues (2013) suggested that effective teacher education should be long term in nature, characterized by a variety of methodological settings, placing a subject-didactic focus on selected novice issues, e.g., controversial issues (Mamlok-Naaman & Mandler, 2020), and encouraging cooperation between teachers and researchers. However, there are many different models for continuous professional development for science teachers around the world, aiming at achieving these goals (Blonder & Mamlok-Naaman, 2019; Jones et al., 2016; Wong & Luft, 2015).

Chapters 30–35 elaborate on emerging areas in science education and elucidate the need for studying and developing these areas in science teacher education. The authors show how new methodologies, approaches, and pedagogies are embedded in science teachers' education and professional development. Three chapters emphasize teacher needs, while the other three chapters concentrate more on the curriculum component. Vedder-Weiss (Chapter 31) claims that a better understanding of the development of science teacher identity is the key to better understanding the obstacles science teachers face in implementing quality teaching. Such an understanding can offer a framework through which teacher education structures and processes can be effectively designed and evaluated. In Chapter 32, Bellocchi and Amat review studies that identify the role emotions play in teaching and learning science, and they identify key outcomes and fruitful directions for future research. Allen et al. (Chapter 34) review the literature on practitioners and researchers that collaborate to design, improve, and study science education. They examine how perspectives of science teacher education can be enriched by strands of research that are collaborative in nature – where educators, researchers, and other community members learn together.

Peters-Burton and Knight (Chapter 35) stress the use of STEM in promoting equity in the science classroom by modeling strategies such as cognitive apprentices, problem solving in authentic contexts, decision making, and STEM practices to both preservice and in-service teachers. Of the four content areas that comprise STEM (science, technology, engineering, and mathematics), science has played a prominent role in promoting integrated STEM in K-12 schools. The Next Generation Science Standards (NGSS Lead States, 2013) take an integrated approach, including engineering design, disciplinary content ideas, and engineering practices, in addition to mathematical and computational thinking. This multidisciplinary instructional view not only illustrates how one content area can inform another; it also infuses key components of doing STEM, including design thinking, inquiry, and analytic thinking,

Giamellaro et al. (Chapter 33) deal with contextualization, which serves as an interface between science, science teacher, and public education. According to them, teachers need to develop a clear understanding of science content specific to that context, and the pedagogical skills needed to effectively bring content and context together, since contextualization usually leads to student-centered learning. Learning this skill set will require long-term and intensive preparation; many reforms in science education over the last 20 years, such as project-based learning or socioscientific instruction, recommend connecting science content to contexts outside of the classroom. Decision making is also one of the topics in Chapter 30, in which Reiss discusses understanding "controversial" issues. In addition, Reiss examines different controversial issues that arise in science education, and how one can teach them in science education in elementary and secondary schools.

In summary, the uniqueness of these chapters is that they not only deal with science education, but they focus on science *teacher* education. The authors discuss the issue of how to educate science teachers by using concepts, frameworks, and approaches such as teacher identity, the role of emotions, equity, contextualization, inquiry, and collaboration. The ideas and research reviews are comprehensively covered; they elucidate the critical role of teachers in attaining the ultimate goal of quality education in the sciences in general, and becoming acquainted with the new emerging areas in science education in particular.

References

Blonder, R., & Mamlok-Naaman, R. (2019). Teaching chemistry through contemporary research versus using a historical approach. *Chemistry Teacher International (CTI)*, open-access, 20180011. https://doi.org/10.1515/cti-2018-0011

Close, W., Conn, J., & Hunter G. (2014). Becoming physics people: Development of integrated physics identity through the Learning Assistant experience. *Physical Review Physics Education Research*, *12*, 010109.

Habig, S., Blankenburg, J., van Vorst, H., Fechner, S., Parchmann, I., & Sumfleth, E. (2018). Context characteristics and their effects on students' situational interest in chemistry. *International Journal of Science Education*, *40*, 1154–1175.

Hazzan, O., Heyd-Metzuyanim, E., Even-Zahav, A., Tal, T., & Dori, Y. J. (2018). Research–practice partnerships in STEM education: An organizational perspective. In O. Hazzan, E. Heyd-Metzuyanim, A. Even-Zahav, T. Tal, & Y. J. Dori, *Application of management theories for STEM Education*. Springer Briefs in Education. Springer. https://doi.org/10.1007/978-3-319-68950-0_3

Jones, M. G., Corin, E., Andre, T., Childers, G., & Stevens, V. (2016). Factors contributing to lifelong science learning: Amateur astronomers and birders. *Journal of Research in Science Teaching*, *54*, 412–433.

Magnusson, S., Krajcik, J., & Borko, H. (1999). Nature, source, and development of pedagogical content knowledge. In J. Gess-Newsome & N. G. Lederman (Eds.), *Examining pedagogical content knowledge* (pp. 95–132). Dordrecht, the Netherlands: Kluwer.

Mamlok-Naaman, R. (2016). Curriculum implementation in science education. In K. S. Taber & B. Akpan (Eds.), *Science education, an international course companion* (pp. 199–210). Rotterdam, Boston, and Taipei: Sense Publishers.

Mamlok-Naaman, R., Eilks, I., Bodner, A., & Hofstein, A. (2018). *Professional development of chemistry teachers*. Cambridge: RSC Publications.

Mamlok-Naaman, R., Franz, R., Markic, S., & Fernandez, C. (2013). How to keep myself being a professional chemistry teacher? In I. Eilks & A. Hofstein (Eds.), *Teaching chemistry – A studybook: A practical guide and textbook for student teachers, teacher trainees and teachers* (pp. 269–298). Rotterdam, Boston, and Taipei: Sense Publishers.

Mamlok-Naaman, R., & Mandler, D. (2020). Education for sustainable development in high school through inquiry-type socio-scientific issues. In S. Obare, C. Middlecamp, & J. Peterman (Eds.), *Chemistry education for a sustainable society* (pp. 69–78). Washington, DC: American Chemical Society.

Mamlok-Naaman, R., & Taitelbaum, D. (2019). The influences of global trends in reaching and learning chemistry on the chemistry curriculum in Israel. *Israel Journal of Chemistry*, *59*, 1–11.

Mulholland, J., & Wallace, J. (2005). Growing the tree of teacher knowledge: Ten years of learning to teach elementary science. *Journal of Research in Science Teaching*, *42*, 767–790. https://doi.org/10.1002/tea.20073

Next Generation Science Standards: For states, by states (NGSS) (2013). *Lead states*. The National Academies Press.

Shulman, L. S. (1987). Knowledge and teaching: Foundations of the new reform. *Harvard Educational Review*, *57*, 1–22.

Wong, S. S., & Luft, J. A. (2015). Secondary science teachers' beliefs and persistence: A longitudinal mixed-methods study. *Journal of Science Teacher Education*, *26*, 619–645. https://doi.org/10.1007/s10972-015-9441-4

Woolfolk Hoy, A. (2013). A reflection on the place of emotion in teaching and teacher education. In M. Newberry, A. Gallant, & P. Riley (Eds.), *Emotion and school: Understanding how the hidden curriculum influences relationships, leadership, teaching, and learning* (Advances in Research on Teaching, Vol. 18, pp. 255–270). Bingley: Emerald Group Publishing Limited. https://doi.org/10.1108/S1479-3687(2013)0000018017

30

LEARNING TO TEACH CONTROVERSIAL TOPICS

Michael J. Reiss

The Value of Controversial Issues in the Teaching of Science

Several arguments can be advanced as to why controversial issues (or topics) should be taught in school science. For a start, some issues are controversial because the science is not yet clear (Wellington, 1986). Teaching them can therefore help students to appreciate that science is not always about certainties. A recent example was the question of whether wearing masks reduced the transmission of COVID-19. Because COVID-19 arose only towards the very end of 2019, this question was being asked (in the spring and summer of 2020) before careful empirical work had been undertaken to address the issue.

A second reason for teaching controversial issues in science is that this can be motivating for students (Yuliastini et al., 2018). Different students may be motivated by different approaches to teaching, but many students enjoy thinking about and discussing issues where the answer is not clear-cut and where there are genuine differences of opinion.

A third reason overlaps with the first two, and that is that many contemporary problems in society where science plays a part are "wicked" in the sense that they cannot be solved straightforwardly. The term "wicked problem" was introduced by Horst Rittel and its most well-known formulation was produced by Rittel and Webber (1973):

> The search for scientific bases for confronting problems of social policy is bound to fail, because of the nature of these problems. They are "wicked" problems, whereas science has developed to deal with "tame" problems. Policy problems cannot be definitively described. Moreover, in a pluralistic society there is nothing like the undisputable public good; there is no objective definition of equity; policies that respond to social problems cannot be meaningfully correct or false; and it makes no sense to talk about "optimal solutions" to social problems unless severe qualifications are imposed first. Even worse, there are no "solutions" in the sense of definitive and objective answers.
>
> (p. 155)

Examples of "wicked problems" that might be discussed in school science include many ecological issues (such as tackling the loss of biodiversity in an area), many health issues (such as the "causes" of obesity), and issues to do with energy generation (such as whether wind power is better than gas-fired power stations for electricity production).

DOI: 10.4324/9781003098478-36

What Is a Controversial Issue?

Much of the academic literature in education on controversial issues start with the work of Dearden, who proposed an *epistemic* criterion in which "a matter is controversial if contrary views can be held on it without those views being contrary to reason" (Dearden, 1981/1984, p. 86). Dearden pointed out that several possible kinds of controversial issues may be distinguished:

> cases where we simply have insufficient evidence to settle the matter, though in principle there is no reason why it should not be settled as more or better evidence becomes available . . . where consideration-making criteria are agreed but the weight to be given them is not . . . where there is no agreement even on the criteria as to what will count . . . where not just individual criteria but whole frameworks of understanding are different.
>
> (pp. 86–87)

A large literature in education on controversial issues has grown in the light of Dearden's argument (e.g., Bridges, 1986; McLaughlin, 2003; Hand, 2008). Michael Hand (2008), in particular, has defended and developed Dearden's epistemic account, arguing that "What distinguishes teaching-as-settled from teaching-as-controversial (or directive from nondirective teaching) is not a pedagogical method or style, but the willingness of the teacher to endorse one view on a matter as the right one" (Hand, 2008, p. 213). Hand is explicit that "The English word 'controversial' means simply 'disputed,' and the existence of dispute is an unpromising criterion for what should be taught nondirectively" (p. 214).

However, the epistemic identification of the controversial is not the only one (e.g., Wellington, 1986; Hess, 2009). The opening chapter of the book *The Challenge of Teaching Controversial Issues* states:

> In general terms a controversial issue is one in which
>
> - the subject/area is of topical interest
> - there are conflicting values and opinions
> - there are conflicting priorities and material interests
> - emotions may become strongly aroused
> - the subject/area is complex.
>
> (Claire & Holden, 2007, pp. 5–6)

This is a much broader definition that that provided by Dearden. It is also much more in line with how the phrase "controversial issue" is understood by most people, including school students.

Controversial Issues in Science Education

A detailed conceptual analysis of controversial issues in science education is provided by Levinson (2006). Levinson used McLaughlin's (2003) classification of controversial issues into nine categories of reasonable disagreement and extended these to school science:

1. Where insufficient evidence is as yet available to settle a matter, but where such evidence could in principle be forthcoming at some point.
2. Where evidence relevant to settling a matter is conflicting, complex, and difficult to assess.
3. Where the range of criteria relevant for judging a matter are agreed, but the relevant weight to be given to different criteria in a given decision is disputed.

4. Where a range of cherished goods cannot simultaneously be realized, and where there is a lack of a clear answer about the grounds on which priorities can be set and adjustments made.
5. Where the criteria relevant for judging a matter are broadly agreed, but there is dispute about the proper interpretation of a criterion or criteria, given the indeterminacy of many concepts.
6. Where there are different kinds of normative consideration of different force on both sides of an issue, and it is hard to make an overall judgement.
7. Where there is disagreement about the criteria relevant for judgement.
8. Where the differing "total experiences" of people in the course of their lives shape their judgements in divergent ways.
9. Where there is no agreement about whole frameworks of understanding relevant for judgement.

An example of category 1 would be whether a particular individual is likely to develop Huntington's disease, which, as Levinson points out, could be settled by an unambiguous genetic test. An example of category 9, at the other end of the spectrum, would be "Fundamentalist creationists work from different premises and use different truth criteria from evolutionists to establish their claims" (Levinson, 2006, p. 1212). An evolutionist bases their conclusions on scientific evidence (involving the dating of fossils, biogeography, molecular genetics, and so on) interpreted within an evolutionary paradigm (dating from the work of Darwin and Wallace, and informed by the subsequent contributions of Mendel and others), whereas the first line of authority for a fundamentalist creationist is the scriptures of their religion, typically backed up by a history within their community as to how those scriptures are interpreted.

As Zeidler and Sadler (2008) point out, socioscientific issues (SSI) may, by their nature, be controversial but (as Levinson pointed out earlier), the converse is not necessarily the case. Zeidler and Sadler go on to maintain that "SSI tend to have implicit and explicit ethical components and require some degree of moral reasoning" (p. 800). One reason why SSI are controversial is precisely because humanity simply does not have a single widely agreed moral framework within which ethical conclusions can be agreed.

In common with the majority of the literature, and in the light of what has been presented thus far, this chapter therefore adopts a broad understanding of "controversial" and examines the different sorts of controversies that arise in science education. Consider, for example, whether the theory of evolution, a well-established scientific theory, is a controversial issue. As Levinson's classification makes clear, the theory of evolution is not controversial in the sense that the genetic modification of organisms is – where the controversy is not over the basic science, but over whether we should or should not genetically modify organisms. In terms of science, rather than ethics, the consequences of anthropogenic climate change might be deemed controversial, at least in part on the grounds that there is much that we genuinely don't know about these consequences, but this is not what is meant by the theory of evolution being controversial. Although, as with any science, there is uncertainty at the edges of the science, the core ideas of evolution have been well-established within the science for many decades. Among the overwhelming majority of scientists, the theory of evolution is nowadays no more scientifically controversial than is the Periodic Table, quantum dynamics, or plate tectonics. So, evolution is not a controversial issue on the epistemic understanding of controversy. But we all know of the furor that regularly surrounds it in many countries (Deniz & Borgerding, 2018) in the courts, in the media, and in schools – it is controversial in the broader sense of the term.

How Might One Teach About Controversial Issues in Science Education?

Three approaches as to how controversial issues might be taught in school science were developed by Reiss (1993) from Bridges (1986). One is the approach of *advocacy*, where the teacher argues for the position they hold. For example, one teacher might assert, "There is no such thing as animal rights; only humans have rights." Another might assert, "If human rights exist, then they exist for other species too, so long as those species are capable of experiencing pains and pleasures." One problem for the position of advocacy is that in a school classroom, a teacher is almost always in a more powerful position than their students. There is therefore a risk that when a teacher adopts a model of advocacy in the teaching of a controversial issue, they may end up trampling on students' autonomy.

A second approach is one of *affirmative neutrality*, in which the teacher presents to their students as many sides of a controversy as possible, without indicating which they themselves support. This approach is more balanced than the approach of advocacy, though the teacher may find it difficult to avoid indicating their own views, especially if pushed by students. An additional problem is that the lesson may end up being somewhat dry and fail to engage the interest and involvement of many in a class.

A third approach is one of *procedural neutrality*, where the teacher acts as a facilitator. Information about the controversy and different points of view are elicited from students and source material. The teacher does not reveal their own position. This approach has a number of advantages, but the collation of suitable source material may require a considerable investment of time by the teacher unless the developers of a course provide curriculum materials for students. Without suitable source material, this approach runs the risk of failing to elicit a sufficient range of views from the students, in which case the lesson may become unbalanced or require the teacher to intervene in a manner more appropriate to the approach of affirmative neutrality or even advocacy.

Not all science educators have been convinced that these three approaches are appropriate. Oulton et al. (2004) argue that teachers have to make judgements about what information to present, and such judgements about controversial issues are necessarily subjective: "Even if the teacher thinks that they have presented matters as fairly as possible, others with different worldviews may still judge the presentation to be biased" (p. 416). They therefore argue that:

> An alternative, and to our knowledge as yet untested, approach, based on the reality of controversy, is to be open about the fact that balance can never be fully achieved but counter this by developing in pupils a critical awareness of bias and make this one of the central learning objectives of the work.
>
> (pp. 416–417)

The Importance of a Good Understanding of the Nature of Scientific Knowledge

There is a risk that some school students may think, when writing about or discussing a controversial issue, that any point of view is acceptable. This is not the case. Learners need to have a good grounding in the relevant science. Consider, for example, the issue of whether countries should invest in nuclear power. Here are some of the things one would want students (depending on their age) to know:

- Nuclear power relies on energy released from reactions that occur within the nuclei of atoms – unlike chemical reactions that occur between atoms and molecules.
- In principle, nuclear power can be obtained from nuclear fission, nuclear decay, or nuclear fusion. Nuclear fusion is still at the research stage. Nuclear decay, in which an unstable nucleus releases energy while releasing alpha particles, beta particles, or gamma radiation, produces only relatively small amounts of energy but has some niche uses (it is used in a type of nuclear battery that has no moving parts yet generates electricity). Conventional nuclear power plants use nuclear fission, in which a nucleus spits into two or more smaller nuclei.

- In 2019, nuclear power produced about 10% of global electricity generation (International Energy Agency, 2019). However, this percentage is falling, as aging plants are beginning to close more quickly than new ones are coming on stream. Rare but heavily publicized accidents – such as those at Chernobyl in the Ukraine in 1986 and at Fukushima in Japan in 2011 – have contributed to a political climate in which nuclear power is viewed with greater suspicion than was once the case.

Although the preceding list of bullet points is intended to be factual, some readers (and students in schools) might feel it is beginning to stray from science into more value-laded areas. Consider the sentence in the third bullet point: "Rare but heavily publicized accidents – such as those at Chernobyl in the Ukraine in 1986 and at Fukushima in Japan in 2011 – have contributed to a political climate in which nuclear power is viewed with greater suspicion than was once the case." Who decided what is "rare"? Does the phrase "heavily publicized" somehow imply that nuclear power generation is subject to greater adverse scrutiny than other forms of power generation? How robust is the evidence that "nuclear power is viewed with greater suspicion than was once the case," and is this a scientific statement? Of course, these are precisely the sorts of issues a teacher might want students to consider. Such teaching would not only help students to better understand the topic of nuclear power but might also give students a better understanding of some of the issues that fall within the nature of science (Kötter & Hammann, 2017).

Other pieces of knowledge could have been presented in the list that would have been even more contentious. Advocates of the benefits of nuclear power often point to the fact that, notwithstanding the rare Chernobyl or Three Mile Island (1979, USA) accidents, nuclear power generation is safer than other methods of generating electricity (e.g., Markandya & Wilkinson, 2007), makes far less of a contribution to global climate change, and allows electricity to be generated even when there is no wind and it is dark (unlike renewable power generation that relies on wind or solar power). Those who are less persuaded of the benefits of nuclear power point to the difficulties of dealing with nuclear waste, to the huge financial and human costs when there are occasional accidents, and to developments in battery technology which mean that we may be able before long to store the fruits of wind and solar power generation for subsequent use much more effectively when generation is not possible or demand increases (e.g., Ylönen et al., 2017).

Again, this points to the difficulty of establishing precisely what "the facts" are. It is good for students to appreciate that there can be an important scientific controversy that is not reducible to issues of values or ethics but has to do with scientific uncertainty. A final point is the value of students coming to realize that scientific knowledge varies in its robustness. It is possible that we will find other types of nuclear power in addition to nuclear fission, nuclear decay, or nuclear fusion, but this is very unlikely. Our existing knowledge is robust. However, despite ongoing advances in battery technology (e.g., Ma, 2021), our knowledge of their ability to store extremely large amounts of chemical energy efficiently is much less robust. This is science and technology being undertaken at the cutting edge.

The Value of Student Research and Argumentation

Controversial topics can be taught in a number of ways and can allow students to undertake research through reading relevant literature. There is a growing literature on the benefits of students undertaking independent practical research projects (Bennett et al., 2018; Rushton et al., 2021), and quite a lot is known about how school science textbooks and other materials can be made more readable (Sutton, 1992; Wellington & Osborne, 2001; Susetyadi et al., 2020). In addition, a number of studies have been undertaken on the possible benefits for school students of reading literature (whether in books, on the Internet, or elsewhere) so as to inform their scientific views.

Britt et al. (2014) define scientific literacy "as the ability of people to understand and critically evaluate scientific content in order to achieve their goals" (p. 105). Their definition goes beyond merely listing scientific concepts, principles, or vocabulary to be learned, being more in line with calls to focus on the skills and knowledge required to read and use scientific texts rather than simply understanding the main point of a text. Ritchie et al. (2010) showed that getting students to write could enhance student understanding of the issues relevant to their writing, and Ristanto et al. (2017) showed that guided inquiry instruction was more effective than conventional approaches at enhancing students' scientific literacy.

There is a large research base on the value of student argumentation for their learning of science. Erduran and Jiménez-Aleixandre (2007) begin by pointing out the growing realization of the importance of discourse in knowledge production. Allied to this is a sociocultural perspective "which points to the role of social interaction in learning and thinking processes, and purports that higher thinking processes originate from socially mediated activities, particularly through the mediation of language" (p. 4). Argumentation is particularly suited to controversial topics. Controversial topics are ones where different people hold different views, so there is benefit to students being able to articulate their own views and listen to those of others. In such articulation and listening, students can deepen their own views and improve the quality of their arguments by enhancing both their knowledge of the relevant science and the validity of their reasoning.

Another reason why argumentation is especially appropriate to leaning about controversial topics is that practical work often plays a smaller part in learning about such topics (Ping et al., 2020). Typically, what is a matter of contention cannot be resolved through practical activities that rely on the facilities and time scale available in a school classroom or laboratory. Rather, what is needed is the collation of relevant information, listening to others, and the use of discussion to develop a considered position.

This leads on to the value of including ethical thinking in school science. There are many controversial topics where ethics plays a role, particularly in biology (stem cells, genetically modified organisms, and cloning, for example), but also in other scientific disciplines (green chemistry and sustainable electricity production, for example). Too often in school science teaching, little consideration is given to the quality of ethical reasoning (Chen & So, 2017). One can be most confident about the validity and worth of an ethical conclusion if three criteria are met (Reiss, 2010). First, if the arguments that lead to the particular conclusion are convincingly supported by reason. Second, if the arguments are conducted within a well-established ethical framework. Third, if a reasonable degree of consensus exists about the validity of the conclusions, arising from a process of genuine debate.

Might Some Controversial Issues Be Better Thought of as Sensitive Issues?

Despite the adoption in this chapter of a broad understanding as to what is meant by a controversial topic, so that the epistemic criterion does not trump all other considerations, much writing and teaching in science education about controversy focuses on issues having to do with epistemology. There is much of value in this. After all, we want students to search for scientific truth and to appreciate when it can be found and when claims to have found it are premature.

Yet, too great an emphasis on epistemology can be unhelpful in the classroom and can even lead to shouting matches between students, and a refusal to hear the points of views of others – precisely the opposite of what is wanted. It has been suggested that some controversial issues – particularly ones where individuals are heavily personally invested in them – might better be thought of as sensitive issues, on the grounds that:

> as humans most of us are quite good at knowing how to behave when dealing with some-
> one for whom an issue is sensitive (think a bereaved friend or colleague, or someone

worried about their sexual identity or whether their country should go to war): we are careful with our language, more hesitant in our speech, more alert to the possibility that the other person may be upset by something we say or some feature of our non-verbal communication.

(Reiss, 2019, p. 357)

This approach shifts the emphasis from epistemology to pedagogy. One strength of this approach is that many teachers are good at dealing with sensitive issues, naturally respecting the feelings of students, even if they do not always agree with them (Lowe, 2015).

Examples of Teaching Controversial Issues in Science Education

In this part of the chapter, three particular topics are examined to consider how they might be taught in school science. The precise content and approach will vary depending on the age and other characteristics of the students concerned; nevertheless, there are some general considerations that apply.

Evolution

In a number of countries, evolution has long been seen as the exemplar instance of a controversial topic in school science, not in terms of controversy over the basic science but more in terms of the depth of feelings it arouses and the very different positions about it that people occupy (Hermann, 2008). Most biologists see evolution not only as central to their discipline, but as the core on which the rest of biological knowledge ultimately hangs. There are countries in which evolution is not included within the school curriculum for reasons of religion, and the topic is rarely included within elementary schools. Nevertheless, the importance of evolution for biology means that it is well represented in high school biology courses, even though it is cognitively demanding (Harms & Reiss, 2019).

The scientific understanding of biodiversity is far from complete, and very little is known with any great confidence about the early history of life on Earth (Maynard Smith & Szathmary, 2000). How did the earliest self-replicating molecules arise? What caused membranes to exist? How key were the earliest physical conditions – temperature, the presence of water, and so on? The scientific presumption is either that these questions will be answered by science, or that they will remain unknown.

Whereas there is only one mainstream scientific understanding of biodiversity, there are a considerable number of religious ones (Pew Research Center, 2014). Many religious believers are perfectly comfortable with the scientific understanding, whether or not God is presumed to have intervened or acted providentially at certain key points (e.g., the origin of life or the evolution of humans). But many other religious believers adopt a more creationist perspective or that of intelligent design, and it is this that makes evolution a controversial topic (Reiss, 2011).

Many teachers of school biology are unsure how, if at all, to respond to creationism and intelligent design in the classroom (Deniz & Borgerding, 2018; Branch et al., 2021). If questions about the validity of evolution or issues about creationism and intelligent design arise during science lessons, they can often be used to illustrate a number of aspects of the nature of science, such as how interpretation of data provides evidence to test ideas and develop theories, that there are some questions that science cannot currently answer, and some that science cannot address, and that scientific ideas change over time.

In a mixed methods study that used surveys and interviews to explore the views of Christian high school teachers in California and Hawaii, Mangahas (2017) found that teachers' beliefs regarding evolution and their Christian faith were varied and complex. While the surveys showed that the stronger the teachers' religious beliefs, the more negative they were about the theory of evolution, the interviews revealed a nuanced set of classroom practices, with a number of teachers saying that their beliefs "caused them to model respectful disagreement while also pointing out any problem areas in evolutionary arguments" (p. 34). Generally, the teachers "were supportive of the teaching of evolution in Christian schools as it engaged students in critical thinking and better prepared them for college" (p. 35).

In a study in Israel of junior high school and high school biology teachers and of those responsible for developing classroom materials and training teachers, Siani and Yarden (2020) found a range of positions about the teaching of evolution, with some teachers opposed and some in favor. One Jewish religious former chief supervisor at the Ministry of Education stated:

> Because, in all, this is a controversial subject . . . I think it's done with a lot of sensitivity. Not with power. Gradually, teacher-training courses were opened and teachers could register, no one forced teachers to register. It was not done in a forceful way, so I did not get any complaints. I felt as an instructor that I had to stand by the teachers and give them tools so that they could face students who asked.
>
> (p. 439)

Climate Change

Anthropogenic climate change (i.e., changes in the climate that result from human activities) can be considered a controversial topic, but for reasons that are somewhat different from those that make evolution a controversial topic. While the scientific evidence for anthropogenic climate change has strengthened greatly over the last couple of decades, there is still more genuine controversy about the basic science than there is about the basic science of evolution. Furthermore, while there are connections between religiosity (a composite measure that takes into account not only religious beliefs but also practices – such as regular worship – and experiences – such as believing that God speaks to one) and non-acceptance of anthropogenic climate change, the relationship is complex (Carr et al., 2012).

The topic of climate change can be a valuable one to teach in schools (Sharma, 2012). Among school students, the topic is rarely as personal as evolution is to some students, and the fact that the science is more contested gives students more opportunities to adopt a range of positions. It is a multidisciplinary topic, even within science drawing on biology, chemistry, earth science, and physics, and is conceptually perhaps less difficult for some students to understand. It can also be used to help students develop their digital technology skills (Bush et al., 2016). There is a literature developing on school students' understandings and alternative conceptions about climate change (Dawson, 2015).

A recent systematic review concluded that didactic, top-down approaches to climate change education have predominated and have generally been ineffectual in affecting students' attitudes and behavior (Rousell & Cutter-Mackenzie-Knowles, 2020). More positively, though, the review identified:

> participatory approaches which empower communities of learners to design their own climate change projects and modes of engagement with the issue . . . A small number of studies also focused specifically on affective approaches which provoke emotional and somatic responses to climate change issues and concerns through engagement with art, imagery and narrative . . . digital technology has also emerged as an approach which has multiple applications for producing innovative and empowering forms of climate change education . . . lastly, a very small contingent of the literature is orientated towards child-framed

approaches to climate change education, which draw on the unique perspectives and experiences of children and young people to inform new frameworks and methods for teaching and learning about climate change.

(p. 202)

This suggests that if students are empowered by being given the opportunity to manage their own learning to a certain extent, they engage with the issue to a greater extent and derive more benefit from their learning. It seems likely that this conclusion is not restricted to climate change education.

Vaccines

Most school and popular accounts of vaccination start with Jenner's work and an account of his classic 1796 experiment on 8-year-old Edward Phipps. Graphs are presented showing dramatic decreases, thanks to vaccination, in the incidence of smallpox, with its eventual eradication, to this day the only human disease eradicated by immunization. Yet, controversies over vaccination have existed since vaccines were first introduced over 200 years ago (Durbach, 2004). Despite this, vaccination is not normally thought of as a controversial topic in the way that evolution and anthropogenic climate change are. However, vaccination education may be improved by considering it thus.

Nineteenth-century objections included the arguments that vaccination did not work, or was unsafe, and that its compulsory introduction (e.g., the 1853 Compulsory Vaccination Act in the UK) violated personal liberties. Today's objections to vaccination overlap with these and include the following: vaccines don't always work; vaccines are not totally safe; requiring, or even just incentivizing, someone to be vaccinated or to have their child(ren) vaccinated violates personal liberties; vaccines are often made in ways that are morally unacceptable; the scientists or companies that make vaccines can't be trusted; governments that advocate vaccination uptake can't be trusted; vaccines are unnatural; vaccines are part of a conspiracy to poison us, take over our minds, or control us in some other way (Reiss, 2020). The role of science in addressing these objections is limited. For example, objectors who cite efficacy or safety concerns are not saying that a cost-benefit analysis on the grounds of efficacy or safety comes down against the use of vaccines – indeed, such cost-benefit analyses very strongly support vaccine efficacy and safety. Rather, objectors are saying that vaccines don't *always* work and aren't *totally* safe. One cannot argue against these objections on scientific grounds.

Consider the objection that vaccines are often made in ways that are morally unacceptable. Students would benefit from appreciating that what one means by "morally acceptable" is itself controversial. For example, a number of widely used vaccines use cells lines derived from fetuses that were electively aborted decades ago. While for many people elective abortions (i.e., terminations rather than miscarriages) are, at least in certain circumstances, permissible, for many other people they are not, often on religious grounds. These differences of opinion – deeply held convictions – cannot be reconciled by any method of science. They simply lie beyond science, being situated in the domain of moral philosophy or values more generally.

Examination of the reasons why people are hesitant about vaccines or reject them reveals a range of overarching considerations having to do with history and identity. Many groups whose members show low uptake of vaccines have had a history of poor treatment or even abuse by the medical and broader establishment. Careful interviewing has revealed deep suspicions about vaccines amongst many black populations who were historically discriminated against both directly and indirectly (Lockyer et al., 2020). More generally, people vary greatly in the extent to which they trust those in power. This way of conceptualizing vaccine hesitation or rejection has important implications for vaccine education. It entails treating learners, whatever their age, with respect, rather than dismissing their concerns.

These conclusions about vaccination education mesh with the conclusions about climate change education and evolution education. Together, they suggest how teaching about controversial science topics can lead to an education that is respectful of learners and effective in teaching about science.

References

Bennett, J., Dunlop, L., Knox, K. J., Reiss, M. J., & Torrance-Jenkins, R. (2018). Practical Independent Research Projects in science: A synthesis and evaluation of the evidence of impact on high school students. *International Journal of Science Education, 40*, 1755–1773. https://doi.org/10.1080/09500693.2018.1511936

Branch, G., Reid, A., & Plutzer, E. (2021). Teaching evolution in U.S. public middle schools: Results of the first national survey. *Evolution: Education and Outreach, 14*, 8. https://doi.org/10.1186/s12052-021-00145-z

Bridges, D. (1986). Dealing with controversy in the curriculum: A philosophical perspective. In J. J. Wellington (Ed.), *Controversial issues in the curriculum* (pp. 19–38). Oxford: Basil Blackwell.

Britt, M. A., Richter, T., & Rouet, J.-F. (2014). Scientific literacy: The role of goal-directed reading and evaluation in understanding scientific information. *Educational Psychologist, 49*(2), 104–122. https://doi.org/10.1080/00461520.2014.916217

Bush, D., Sieber, R., Seiler, G., & Chandler, M. (2016). The teaching of anthropogenic climate change and earth science via technology-enabled inquiry education. *Journal of Geoscience Education, 64*(3), 159–174. https://doi.org/10.5408/15-127

Carr, W. A., Patterson, M., Yung, L., & Spencer, D. (2012). The faithful skeptics: Evangelical religious beliefs and perceptions of climate change. *Journal for the Study of Religion, Nature and Culture, 6*(3), 276–299. https://doi.org/10.1558/jsrnc.v6i3.276

Chen, Y., & So, W. M. (2017). An investigation of mainland china high school biology teachers' attitudes toward and ethical reasoning of three controversial bioethics issues. *Asia-Pacific Science Education, 3*, 1. https://doi.org/10.1186/s41029-016-0012-6

Claire, H., & Holden, C. (Eds.). (2007). *The challenge of teaching controversial issues.* Stoke-on-Trent: Trentham.

Dawson, V. (2015). Western Australian high school students' understandings about the socioscientific issue of climate change. *International Journal of Science Education, 37*(7), 1024–1043. https://doi.org/10.1080/09500693.2015.1015181

Dearden, R. F. (1981/1984). *Theory and practice in education.* London: Routledge & Kegan Paul.

Deniz, H., & Borgerding, L. A. (Eds.) (2018). *Evolution education around the globe.* Springer. https://doi.org/10.1007/978-3-319-90939-4

Durbach, N. (2004). *Bodily matters: The anti-vaccination movement in England, 1853–1907.* Durham, NC: Duke University Press.

Erduran, S., & Jiménez-Aleixandre, M. P. (Eds.). (2007). *Argumentation in science education: Perspectives from classroom-based research.* Springer. https://doi.org/10.1007/978-1-4020-6670-2

Hand, M. (2008). What should we teach as controversial? A defense of the epistemic criterion. *Educational Theory, 58*, 213–228. https://doi.org/10.1111/j.1741-5446.2008.00285.x

Harms, U., & Reiss, M. J. (Eds.). (2019). *Evolution education re-considered: Understanding what works.* Springer. https://doi.org/10.1007/978-3-030-14698-6

Hermann, R. S. (2008). Evolution as a controversial issue: A review of instructional approaches. *Science & Education, 17*, 1011–1032. https://doi.org/10.1007/s10972-012-9328-6

Hess, D. E. (2009). *Controversy in the classroom: The democratic power of discussion.* New York, NY: Routledge.

International Energy Agency. (2019). *Nuclear power in a clean energy system.* International Energy Agency. www.iea.org/publications/nuclear

Kötter, M., & Hammann, M. (2017). Controversy as a blind spot in teaching Nature of Science. *Science & Education, 26*, 451–482. https://doi.org/10.1007/s11191-017-9913-3

Levinson, R. (2006). Towards a theoretical framework for teaching controversial socio-scientific issues. *International Journal of Science Education, 28*, 1201–1224. https://doi.org/10.1080/09500690600560753

Lockyer, B., Islam, S., Rahman, A., Dickerson, J., Pickett, K., Sheldon, T., . . . Sheard, L. (2020). Understanding Covid-19 misinformation and vaccine hesitancy in context: Findings from a qualitative study involving citizens in Bradford. *UKmedRxiv*, 2020.12.22.20248259. https://doi.org/10.1101/2020.12.22.20248259

Lowe, P. (2015). Lessening sensitivity: Student experiences of teaching and learning sensitive issues. *Teaching in Higher Education, 20*(1), 119–129. https://doi.org/10.1080/13562517.2014.957272

Ma, J. (Ed.). (2021). *Battery technologies: Materials and components.* Hoboken, NJ: Wiley.

Mangahas, A. M. E. (2017). Perceptions of high school biology teachers in Christian schools on relationships between religious beliefs and teaching evolution. *Journal of Research on Christian Education, 26*(1), 24–43. https://doi.org/10.1080/10656219.2017.1282902

Markandya, A., & Wilkinson, P. (2007). Electricity generation and health. *The Lancet, 370*(9591), 979–990. https://doi.org/10.1016/S0140-6736(07)61253-7

Maynard Smith, J., & Szathmary, E. (2000). *The origins of life: From the birth of life to the origin of language.* Oxford: Oxford University Press.

McLaughlin, T. (2003). Teaching controversial issues in citizenship education. In A. Lockyer, B. Crick, & J. Annette (Eds.), *Education for democratic citizenship: Issues of theory and practice* (pp. 149–160). London: Routledge.

Oulton, C., Dillon, J., & Grace, M. (2004). Reconceptualizing the teaching of controversial issues. *International Journal of Science Education, 26*(4), 411–423. https://doi.org/10.1080/0950069032000072746

Pew Research Center. (2014). *Religious groups' views on evolution.* Pew Research Center. www.pewforum.org/2009/02/04/religious-groups-views-on-evolution/

Ping, I. L. L., Halam, L., & Osman, K. (2020). Explicit teaching of scientific argumentation as an approach in developing argumentation skills, science process skills and biology understanding. *Journal of Baltic Science Education, 19*(2), 276–288. https://doi.org/10.33225/jbse/20.19.276

Reiss, M. J. (1993) *Science education for a pluralist society.* Milton Keynes: Open University Press.

Reiss, M. J. (2010). Ethical thinking. In A. Jones, A. McKim, & M. Reiss (Eds.), *Ethics in the science and technology classroom: A new approach to teaching and learning* (pp. 7–17). Rotterdam: Sense.

Reiss, M. J. (2011). How should creationism and intelligent design be dealt with in the classroom? *Journal of Philosophy of Education, 45*, 399–415. https://doi.org/10.1111/j.1467-9752.2011.00790.x

Reiss, M. J. (2019). Evolution education: Treating evolution as a sensitive rather than a controversial issue. *Ethics and Education, 14*(3), 351–366. https://doi.org/10.1080/17449642.2019.1617391

Reiss, M. J. (2020). Science education in the light of COVID-19: The contribution of History, Philosophy and Sociology of Science. *Science & Education, 29*(4), 1079–1092. https://doi.org/10.1007/s11191-020-00143-5.

Ristanto, R. H., Zubaidah, S., Amin, M., & Rohman, F. (2017). Scientific literacy of students learned through guided inquiry. *International Journal of Research & Review, 4*(5), 23–30.

Ritchie, S. M., Tomas, L., & Tones, M. (2011). Writing stories to enhance scientific literacy. *International Journal of Science Education, 33*(5), 685–707. https://doi.org/10.1080/09500691003728039

Rittel, H. W. J., & Webber, M. M. (1973). Dilemmas in a general theory of planning. *Policy Sciences, 4*, 155–169. https://doi.org/10.1007/BF01405730

Rousell, D., & Cutter-Mackenzie-Knowles, A. (2020). A systematic review of climate change education: Giving children and young people a 'voice' and a 'hand' in redressing climate change. *Children's Geographies, 18*(2), 191–208. https://doi.org/10.1080/14733285.2019.1614532

Rushton, E. A. C., Charters, L., & Reiss, M. J. (2021). The experiences of active participation in academic conferences for high school science students. *Research in Science & Technological Education, 39*(1), 90–108. https://doi.org/10.1080/02635143.2019.1657395

Sharma, A. (2012). Global climate change: What has science education got to do with it? *Science & Education, 21*, 33–53. https://doi.org/10.1007/s11191-011-9372-1

Siani, M., & Yarden, A. (2020). "Evolution? I don't believe in it." *Science & Education, 29*, 411–441. https://doi.org/10.1007/s11191-020-00109-7

Susetyadi, A. D., Permanasari, A., & Riandi, R. (2020). The feasibility and readability test of stem-based integrated science teaching book model themed "blood as transportation system on our body." *Journal of Physics: Conference Series, Science and STEM Education, 1521*, 042054. https://doi.org/10.1088/1742-6596/1521/4/042054

Sutton, C. (1992). *Words, science and learning.* Milton Keynes: Open University Press.

Wellington, J. (Ed.). (1986). *Controversial issues in the curriculum.* Oxford: Basil Blackwell.

Wellington, J., & Osborne, J. (2001). *Language and literacy in science education.* Buckingham: Open University Press.

Ylönen, M., Litmanen, T., Kojo, M., & Lindell, P. (2017). The (de)politicisation of nuclear power: The Finnish discussion after Fukushima. *Public Understanding of Science, 26*(3), 260–274. https://doi.org/10.1177/0963662515613678

Yuliastini, I. B., Rahayu, S., Fajaroh, F., & Mansour, N. (2018). Effectiveness of POGIL with SSI context on vocational high school students' chemistry learning motivation. *Jurnal Pendidikan IPA Indonesia, 7*(1), 85–95. https://doi.org/10.15294/jpii.v7i1.9928

Zeidler, D. L., & Sadler, T. D. (2008). Social and ethical issues in science education: A prelude to action. *Science & Education, 17*, 799–803. https://doi.org/10.1007/BF03173684

31

PROFESSIONAL IDENTITY AS A FRAMEWORK FOR SCIENCE TEACHER EDUCATION AND PROFESSIONAL DEVELOPMENT

Dana Vedder-Weiss

Over the years, vast efforts have been invested in improving science teaching and learning through reform policies, curricula, and teacher preparation and professional development (PD) programs. Yet, throughout the world, science teaching is still far from meeting the expectations set by these programs (Deneroff, 2016). Through a review of literature in the field of science teacher identity, this chapter asserts that a better understanding of the development of science teacher identity is key to understanding the obstacles science teachers face in implementing high-quality teaching (Avraamidou, 2014a; Rushton & Reiss, 2020). Such understanding can offer a framework through which teacher education structures and processes can be designed and evaluated.

This chapter is structured as follows: It opens with an argument for the importance of science teacher identity, in terms of the quality of their instruction, their well-being, and retention, followed by a discussion of how scholars conceptualize science teacher identity and the different dimensions they attribute to it. Then it elaborates on arenas that shape teacher identity, including individual variables and personal histories, preparation and PD programs, and school life. To evaluate the body of knowledge on science teacher identity, it briefly discusses the methods by which it had been constructed thus far. The chapter concludes with implications for practice and research. This chapter does not present an extensive literature review but rather highlights some emerging understandings that have the potential to inform the field of teacher education.

Why Is Science Teacher Identity Important?

Identity has been repeatedly shown to shape science teachers' instruction and, hence, to have critical implications for students' learning (Avraamidou, 2014a). Distinguishing between elementary and secondary school teachers is important in this discussion. The difficulties elementary teachers face in embracing reform science teaching (e.g., inquiry approaches) have been traditionally attributed primarily to deficits of disciplinary knowledge and confidence (e.g., Smith et al., 1989). Only recently have scholars begun to suggest considering these difficulties through the identity lens, arguing that teaching a subject teachers do not identify with (e.g., enjoy, value, and feel confident in) impedes their motivation and ability to improve their teaching (Danielsson & Warwick, 2014). In contrast, secondary school science teachers often easily identify as science people, as they usually have formal science education, strong disciplinary knowledge, and an understanding of the nature of science

DOI: 10.4324/9781003098478-37

(Chung-Parsons & Bailey, 2019). Since science was their initial career choice, secondary school teachers typically have strong interest and confidence in science (Beijaard et al., 2000). Yet they, too, face many challenges in implementing high-quality teaching, and many of them continue to teach in traditional ways even after participating in preparation and PD programs designed to promote reform-based practice (Deneroff, 2016).

Scholars increasingly argue that to understand difficulties in implementing reform-based teaching in elementary and secondary schools, considering teachers' knowledge, perceptions, and beliefs is insufficient. For example, studying the implementation of a new inquiry-based science curriculum, Enyedy et al. (2006) argued,

> The current ways of modeling teaching (based on a teacher's content knowledge, pedagogical knowledge, beliefs about the nature of science, beliefs about the nature of learning, and curricular goals and plans) miss an important aspect of what it means to be a teacher and how decisions are made on the fly during teaching. . . . What is missing is how these five factors are mediated by a teacher's multiple professional identities.
>
> (p. 69)

Understanding science teachers' professional identity and ways to support it is important not only to improve teaching but also to support teachers' well-being and retention. Reports around the world repeatedly indicate that a high proportion of science teachers leave the profession within their first 5 years (e.g., García & Weiss, 2019; Weldon, 2018). The development of professional identity has been shown to explain beginning teachers' emotional experience, their integration into the profession, and consequently, their retention (Luehmann, 2007; Saka et al., 2013; Schaefer, 2013). To better support these processes, understanding what constitutes and shapes teachers' professional identity is critical.

What Is a Science Teacher Identity?

How Do Scholars Conceptualize Science Teacher Identity?

For many decades, identity has been a focus of psychological research, which viewed it as a relatively stable internal characteristic of the individual. Psychological approaches place teacher knowledge, beliefs, and attitudes at the center of the teaching practice and argue that changing what teachers know and believe is key to the development of their instruction (Beijaard et al., 2004; Van Driel et al., 2001). A focus on such cognitive constructs, however, does not allow a comprehensive understanding of everything involved in becoming a teacher, in interpreting and reinterpreting experiences, and in creating and recreating an image of oneself as a teacher of science (Korthagen, 2017; Luehmann, 2007; Sutherland et al., 2010). Thus, recent conceptions of identity, namely sociocultural perspectives, have been shifting toward a more dynamic and situated view. According to this view, while identity involves a unique personal background, it is also highly contextualized and mediated through social interactions (Beauchamp & Thomas, 2009; Rushton & Reiss, 2020). Identity according to sociocultural perspectives, and as summarized by Avraamidou (2016), is (a) socially constructed and constituted; (b) dynamic and fluid, constantly formed and reformed; and (c) complex and multidimensional, consisting of various interrelated subidentities.

The sociocultural approaches view identity not only as the way teachers view themselves but also as the way they perform as certain kinds of teachers and the way they are recognized by others (Gee, 2000). Identity, according to these frameworks, involves the ways these teachers position themselves regarding teaching, learning, science, their students, and their colleagues, as well as through the way others position them. Identity is defined not just internally by teachers but also externally by inclusive or exclusive reactions of others to their performance (Holland et al., 1998).

According to sociocultural perspectives, identity development is an inherent part of learning. Learning is a transformation of identity; that is, it changes who the learner is. More specifically, learning to teach science is situated within a community of practice of science teaching, where identities are negotiated in and through practice (Lave & Wenger, 1991). As teachers (novices and veterans) participate in the practices of science teaching, changes take place – in the way they teach science, the meaning they make of it, the way they see themselves, and the ways their teaching community sees them. These changes constitute the formation and reformation of their professional identity. Through social interaction in the science teaching community, teachers learn to view and perform as members of the science teachers' community and as certain types of teachers – for example, as teachers for social justice or, more broadly, as reform-minded science teachers (Chen & Mensah, 2018; Luehmann, 2007).

A Multidimensional View of Identity

Scholars have defined science teacher identity through various subidentities and dimensions and have highlighted how tensions between these dimensions shape teachers' instruction and impact their well-being (e.g., Enyedy et al., 2006). A common distinction is between a *science* identity and a *teacher-of-science* identity, both of which are important for high-quality science teaching (e.g., Chung-Parsons & Bailey, 2019; Varelas et al., 2005). Many elementary science teachers do not identify as a "science person" (Kane & Varelas, 2016). They hold negative attitudes toward science and stereotypical images of school science and science teachers, which they do not relate to or desire to become (Marco-Bujosa et al., 2020a). In contrast, in secondary schools, science teachers often identify more as disciplinary experts than as pedagogical experts (Beijaard et al., 2000). Thus, while they have a strong science identity (strong disciplinary affinity), their pedagogical identity is not as developed (Chung-Parsons & Bailey, 2019).

In addition to the distinction between the pedagogical and the disciplinary identity, science teacher identity is often conceptualized with relation to a certain ideal type of teaching and, more specifically, to what scholars refer to as "reform-minded" science teaching (Luehmann, 2007). For example, the literature on social justice science teaching highlights social justice as an identity dimension that includes "believing that every child has the right to learn and have free access to science, providing quality science learning opportunities to all students, and identifying with others committed to teaching science in elementary classrooms" (Chen & Mensah, 2018, p. 422; see also Marco-Bujosa et al., 2020b). Similarly, literature on inquiry science teaching distinguishes between the Traditional Science Teaching subidentity and the Inquiry Teaching subidentity, showing how tensions between these competing subidentities explain the challenges science teachers face implementing inquiry instruction (Danielsson & Warwick, 2014; Enyedy et al., 2006; Segal et al., 2019).

A different approach to professional identity dimensions is offered by the Dynamic Systems Model of Role Identity (DSMRI; Garner & Kaplan, 2019), which suggests that teachers enact and negotiate multiple role identities, contingent on the context. For example, during a PD program, a teacher may enact a teacher role, a learner role, and a scientist role. According to the DSMRI, each role identity is comprised of four elements: (a) ontological and epistemological beliefs; (b) purposes and goals; (c) self-perceptions and self-definitions; and (d) perceived action and future possibilities. A DSMRI-based case study of a 1st-year elementary science teacher (Liel) in an Israeli democratic school illustrated possible tensions teachers experience between these components (Vedder-Weiss et al., 2018). Liel found himself employing authoritarian classroom management practices, which he experienced as standing in tension with his goals, self-perceptions, and values as a teacher in a democratic school: "I came here to be a respecting enabling person, who encourages dialog . . . It was hard for me to 'put on' the role of a strict disciplinarian" (p. 231).

In sum, identity development does not take place *in addition to* or *in relation to* learning; rather, learning *is* identity development. Understanding the development of science teachers' identity as an inherent aspect of their education and PD, therefore, is crucial to improving science teaching at both elementary and middle school levels. The following section discusses different arenas that shape the development of science teachers' identity.

What Shapes the Development of Science Teacher Identity?

Since identity is a dynamic, multidimensional, fluid construct, its development is a complex non-linear ongoing process (Avraamidou, 2016; Rushton & Reiss, 2020). The factors that shape science teacher identities may fall into three major arenas: (a) individual variables and personal histories; (b) preservice preparation and beginning teachers' induction; and (c) in-service socialization and PD programs.

Personal Histories and Individual Variables

Experiences as learners in a school system strongly influence teacher identity, especially early in their career (Danielsson & Warwick, 2014). Having spent more than 15,000 hours at school as students (Rutter et al., 1979), teachers bring with them images of what school is about and what teaching should look like. The cumulative effect of the culture of the schools they went to and the teachers they met shapes how they view themselves as teachers and the kind of teachers they wish to become or avoid becoming (Avraamidou, 2016).

More specifically, elementary science teachers commonly have negative experiences as science learners, making it hard for them to identify as science persons (Kane & Varelas, 2016). For example, in Avraamidou's (2016) case study, Nina represented many elementary teachers in Cyprus and elsewhere who had little interest in science as children ("I don't remember much science when I was young. . . . I was never really into science. . . . I was never really curious about how the world works" [p. 162]), and whose prior experiences with science learning at school were often discouraging ("I had many bad memories of science at school, experiments that I could not understand . . . boring lessons. I just couldn't get it" [p. 163]). Additionally, the science teachers Nina met during her schooling years "in both elementary and high school were very strict and kind of strange." She particularly remembered one teacher she described as "the stereotype scientist, bald, wearing glasses and usually in a suit" (p. 163). The teachers Nina remembered could not serve as resources upon which she could base her teacher-of-science identity.

Science learning experiences in higher education also shape teacher identity. Secondary school teachers with strong science backgrounds more easily identify as science persons, whereas elementary school teachers, who often did not major in science in their graduate education, have a low sense of mastery with science content and practice and low self-efficacy in science teaching (Danielsson & Warwick, 2014; Gunning & Mensah, 2011). Nevertheless, as demonstrated by Avraamidou (2014b), such teachers can shift their identity trajectory if given opportunities to "think and do science in contemporary ways" (p. 235).

The impact of personal schooling histories and science learning experiences and expertise on teacher identities is entangled with social markers (e.g., race, gender, and ethnicity). Moore (2008) illustrated how challenging experiences of science learning at school as a "little black girl" shaped Mrs. Martin's "sense of duty" (p. 699) as a science teacher who needed to support African American students' science learning so that they would enter science-related careers. In contrast, Mr. O'Neal, an African American male teacher at a predominantly White community college, believed "it was challenging for his students to accept a young-looking, African American male [college] science teacher." Moore argued that, collectively, the teachers in her study revealed "gender and racial oppression in their narratives . . . in learning science in high school and/or college and then in teaching science" (p. 697). However, their relative positioning and different life histories led them to construct different professional identities. She, thus, showed how teachers are not the construction of only social markers but have multiple positions that intersect throughout their life history, shaping their professional identity.

Preservice Preparation and Beginning Teacher Experiences

Throughout their preparation, teachers are exposed to different contexts, educators, and ideas that can reshape their initial professional identity and form a foundation on which their identity can continuously evolve (Adams & Gupta, 2017). A number of studies have underscored that the quality of preparation programs plays an important role in the development of science teacher identities (e.g., Avraamidou, 2014b; Danielsson & Warwick, 2014). More specifically, and in alignment with sociocultural identity approaches, field experiences emerge as having a greater impact on identity than theoretical coursework at the university (Richmond, 2016). In field experiences, student teachers can perform as teachers within the authentic context of the teaching community, translate their conceptions and ideas into practice, and examine them against the reality of the school in ways that can either strengthen or challenge their identities. These experiences offer opportunities for the student teachers to try on different identities, perform as teachers in different ways, position themselves in different roles, and receive various types of recognition by students, other teachers, their peers, and their mentors. Arguably, the initial development of a science teacher identity largely depends on how much and how freely student teachers can practice being science teachers in their teacher preparation field experiences (Chen & Mensah, 2018).

Field experiences can have a particular impact on certain identity dimensions. For example, they can provide opportunities for student teachers to practice reform-oriented teaching in ways that contribute to the development of a reform-minded identity (Luehmann, 2007, 2016). Field experiences can impact the development of a social justice teacher identity by offering opportunities to expand sociocultural awareness. Marco-Bujosa et al. (2020b), for example, showed how interacting with students in an urban high school allowed a student teacher to develop awareness of his privileged White man status: "It was just a moment for me of realizing my background and my history and what I'm bringing into the school, and what the students are bringing" (p. 17).

On the other hand, field experiences can also draw student teachers away from the reform-oriented identities that preparation programs aim to foster (Avraamidou, 2014b). In Chen and Mensah's (2018) study, for example, Eva's classroom context contradicted the university-promoted discourse of teaching and learning, leading to tensions in her developing professional identity. Once student teachers enter the school community and face its traditional discourse, it is often easier for them to neglect the reform discourse to receive recognition and become part of their new teaching community. Mentors play a crucial role in such processes of identity negotiation by the teaching experiences they afford, the modeling they provide, the ways they mediate school culture and classroom interaction, the support they provide for emotional tensions, and, perhaps most importantly, in the ways they scaffold the teachers' own reflections on their experiences (Luehmann, 2007; Marco-Bujosa et al., 2020b; Nichols et al., 2017).

Recently, teacher emotions have also been recognized as playing a central role in shaping beginning teacher identity (e.g., Melville & Bartley, 2013; Rivera Maulucci, 2013), especially regarding tensions between subidentities. Emotional episodes that result from a conflict between teacher beliefs and expectations and classroom reality offer opportunities for either identity transformation or confirmation. Nichols et al. (2017) illustrated how pleasant emotional experiences confirmed 1st-year teachers' identities, while unpleasant ones challenged their emergent identities and led to their transformation. For example, when a teacher experienced unpleasant emotional episodes, it "signaled deep conflict between his 'fantasy' teacher identity (I can teach them all and save them all) and his 'survival' teacher identity (I just have to find a way to cope)" (p. 415). Similarly, a teacher entering the classroom wanting to be "that teacher that inspires a child," aiming to "make all of these kids love science" (p. 416) but facing a reality in which this was "just not happening" experienced great emotional stress, leading her to revise the kind of teacher she wanted to become: "If I make a difference in one of their lives, then it doesn't matter if I've taught them chemistry or balancing equations. I'm not there just to teach science. I'm there to make a difference in somebody's life" (p. 416).

As school-based field experiences often create clashes between subidentities and undermine the reform-oriented identities nurtured by preparation programs, scholars have suggested incorporating experiences in informal learning environments. For example, Adams and Gupta (2017) described a museum-based experience where student teachers leveraged museum structures and resources to try on different teaching approaches with diverse visitors. They showed how the affordances of the museum supported the development of greater understandings of how people learn and how to apply various resources to engage diverse learners. Reflecting on these experiences, student teachers could think of the kind of teachers they wanted to become and to imagine themselves, their teaching, and the learning environments they will shape as more student-centered, responsive, and diverse. Similarly, Luehmann (2016) presented a case study of one teacher's field experiences leading an after-school science club. Luehmann argued that this out-of-school practice afforded social-justice identity development that can happen only outside the constraints of school high-stakes accountability culture.

A different form of field experience that has the potential to impact science teachers' identity is authentic research experience at a science site. Varelas et al. (2005) studied identity development of beginning science teachers during and after 10-week summer apprenticeships at a science lab. The researchers showed how the teachers came to appreciate certain science practices and dispositions (e.g., messiness and risk taking) and how these reshaped their *disciplinary* identity. However, these science practices and dispositions were not equally incorporated into their *science teacher* identity, instead triggering a sense of conflict between the practice of science and the practice of schooling.

School Socialization and In-Service PD

Notwithstanding the importance of identity work in preservice programs, ongoing negotiation of identities throughout teachers' careers arguably shape their instruction (Melville & Bartley, 2013). Throughout their different professional learning experiences, teachers continuously shape and reshape their identity (Beauchamp & Thomas, 2009). Research demonstrates how well-designed in-service PD programs can impact science teachers' identity. For example, Kane and Varelas (2016) explored the ways in which elementary school science teachers who participated in a yearlong PD course developed their teacher-of-science identities. These teachers tried on new teaching practices they learned in the course, and as they discussed the impact these practices had on their students' engagement, their identification as science people gradually grew, just as their students, most of whom were African American and Latinx, also began to identify as people of science. Similarly, Luehmann and Markowitz (2007) followed secondary science teachers through their half-day university laboratory experience with their students. The authors concluded that the program offered both students and teachers resources for identity work. As students were able to be recognized differently than in school by their peers and teachers (e.g., as scientists and as committed, enthusiastic, and capable students), the teachers also benefited from collaborating with the scientists, taking on new roles and receiving recognition as scientific, committed, and competent science teachers.

Professional identity evolves across formal PD processes and workplace informal learning opportunities, such as ongoing teaching experiences, interactions with students, and informal conversations with colleagues (Adams & Gupta, 2017). The culture of the schools in which teachers work is a powerful socializing force, often more powerful in shaping teacher identity than any PD program. The culture that still dominates many schools emphasizes "traditional practices of schooling, which perpetuate the teacher as authority, students as recipients of knowledge, and science as a body of knowledge" (Carlone et al., 2010, p. 943), undermining the reform-minded identity (Varelas et al., 2005). Given the situated nature of identity, identity work with colleagues at school is more likely to shape school instruction than identity work taking place outside the school in formal PD programs (Lefstein et al., 2020). Thus, the work-embedded day-to-day, difficult-to-trace, fleeting conversations between teachers are where the "on-the-job social construction of what it means to be a science teacher" is taking place (Deneroff, 2016, p. 214).

Spontaneous conversations between teachers about their work are difficult to study and support. However, teachers discuss their work and construct their identity also in department meetings and in the increasingly popular in-school professional learning community meetings (Lefstein et al., 2020; Melville & Bartley, 2013). Research on science teacher identity in these contexts is scarce. One study that investigated science department meetings is Melville et al. (2007), which examined audio recordings of an Australian secondary school's staff meetings. Although the study was not specifically framed through the identity lens, it shows how these meetings promoted teachers' identity as teachers of science. Similarly, Segal et al. (2019) analyzed audio recordings of one Israeli elementary science teacher team discussing out-of-classroom teaching. They showed how the teachers in this team constructed their professional identities in their on-the-job discourse and the tensions that arose between competing identities, for example between the reform-minded teacher identity, the homeroom teacher identity, and the policy enactor identity. Segal et al. further illustrated different means by which the teachers reconciled these tensions, allowing them to construct themselves as "good teachers" operating in a complicated, constraining system. Yet, such reconciliation limited the teachers' agency – the sense that they can cope with this system in ways that afford reform-oriented and out-of-classroom teaching.

When thinking about the ways school life shapes teacher identity, the impact of educational policies and reforms is also relevant. For example, Richmond (2016) suggested that in the US, three policies stand out as having a great impact on teacher identity: the reform advancing the Next Generation Science Standards frameworks (NGSS Lead States, 2013), high-stakes teacher evaluation instruments and policies, and private governing bodies taking over schools to increase student test scores. Such policies and reforms alter expectations and support, revise priorities and discourses, and, hence, change who counts as a good science teacher.

How Do Scholars Study Science Teacher Identity?

To evaluate the accumulating knowledge on science teacher identity, its implications, and limitations, the ways this body of knowledge has been developed should be considered. Most research on science teacher identity is qualitative, explorative, and based on interviews (e.g., Danielsson & Warwick, 2014), narratives (e.g., Moore, 2008), and reflective writing (e.g., Luehmann & Markowitz, 2007). Other data sources include teachers' drawings (Avraamidou, 2014b) and online forum posts (Adams & Gupta, 2017). Observations are increasingly used, mostly classroom observation or teacher preparation observations (e.g., Chung-Parsons & Bailey, 2019). In most cases, however, observations are used not as the primary data source, but rather as triangulation for other sources (e.g., Enyedy et al., 2006). In a few studies, observations are used for video-stimulated recall interviews, in which teachers are shown video excerpts from their teaching and asked to reflect on these excerpts, aiming to understand the connections between their narrated identity and teaching performance (Upadhyay, 2009).

A large part of the research on science teacher identity (if not most of it, although often not explicitly framed this way) is based on a case-study method, either a single case study of one science teacher (e.g., Rivera Maulucci, 2013) or multiple compared and contrasted case studies (e.g., Moore, 2008). A few cases are based on a self-study, in which the researcher is a teacher studying (alone or in collaboration with other researchers) her or his own identity development, analyzing self-recorded data, such as reflective journals, videotaped instruction, lesson plans, and student work (e.g., Akerson et al., 2014; Vedder-Weiss et al., 2018). Large-scale studies and quantitative methods are rare in research on science teacher identity. A few studies have measured specific dimensions of teacher identity, such as teaching self-efficacy (Settlage et al., 2009).

Many of the studies on teacher identity span the duration of a teacher education course or program, usually up to 1 or 2 years. Notable exceptions that demonstrate a more longitudinal approach are Avraamidou's (2014b) study, which followed a beginning elementary science teacher throughout 5 years, and Deneroff's (2016) study, which followed an exemplary high school science teacher for 3 years.

In sum, while research on science teacher identity has greatly advanced the field's understanding of the development of identity, its implications, and ways to support it, this research is generally qualitative, explorative, small scaled, short term, and largely based on teachers' own reflections.

Implications for Practice and Research

Science teachers' identity is gradually becoming a prominent lens through which professional learning may be designed and evaluated. Supporting the development of science teachers' identity is key to helping them face obstacles in implementing high-quality teaching and to their well-being and retention (Avraamidou, 2014a; Rushton & Reiss, 2020). The growing body of research offers many practical implications to consider. In what follows, four central directions of implications are highlighted for teacher education and PD, concluding with implications for research that can further advance the field's understanding of teacher identity development.

Identity Development as Inherent to Professional Learning Processes

According to sociocultural perspectives, identity development is an inherent aspect of teacher professional learning (Lave & Wenger, 1991). Thus, identity should be thought of not as an additive feature for teacher education, but rather as a constant inherent part of any teacher development process. Identity development is not an object for a special type of activity or course. It is a lens through which every course and activity could be designed and assessed. Moreover, facilitating identity development should not be thought of as a distinctive act or as an end that may be achieved while sitting in class theoretically discussing the kind of teacher one wishes to become. As identity develops through interaction within the different components of teacher education, and especially through authentic experiences within a community of the practice of science teaching, explicit discussions on identity should be anchored in practical field experiences.

Attending to Different Identity Dimensions and Tensions Between Them

Acknowledging the different dimensions of science teacher identity is critical to the understanding of teacher development processes. This acknowledgment includes aspiring to support the development of both teacher disciplinary identity (a science-person identity) and pedagogical identity (a teacher-of-science identity) and accounting for the differential challenges these identities pose for elementary and secondary school teachers. Thus, for example, an elementary science teacher preparation program should consider how to foster disciplinary identity, while a secondary program should highlight more the pedagogical dimension. Either way, these identities could not be achieved through simply focusing on knowledge and perceptions regarding science, learning, and schooling; they must also involve exploring the meaning that teachers make of them in relation to earlier schooling and science learning experiences. This meaning making requires: (a) supporting teachers in eliciting relevant previous educational experiences; (b) exploring how they shape their perceptions, beliefs, emotions, and behavior; (c) identifying the tensions and clashes they create with other identity dimensions, including those that the teacher preparation program is promoting (e.g., the reform-minded teaching identity); (d) reflecting on the impact these tensions have on teachers' emotions and instruction; (e) deliberating on ways to cope with these tensions; and (f) examining the suggested alternatives in practice.

Creating Multiple Diverse Opportunities for Authentic Field Experiences

While all teacher education interactions play a role in teacher identity development, practical field experiences have been shown to play a greater role than theoretical courses (Chen & Mensah, 2018; Richmond, 2016). Field experiences do not only offer opportunities for student teachers to practice the enactment of different teaching methods. It offers them opportunities to try on different teaching identities and perform roles as different kinds of teachers. Thus, the identity framework provides an additional rationale for allocating more resources to field experiences and highlights the benefits of diversifying the student population with which student teachers practice teaching and the learning environments in which they practice, including informal environments. Also needed are spaces for scaffolded reflection on how field experiences nurture or undermine different identity dimensions. While practice itself plays an important role in constructing identity, teacher educators play a critical role in affording and facilitating these processes. For example, they can support teachers in exploring their emotions after a stressful teaching experience, examining how these emotions signal identity tensions, how these tensions shape teachers' reactions in class, and how they can be further coped with.

Supporting Identity Development in In-Service PD Programs

Since professional identity continuously forms and reforms throughout teachers' careers (Avraamidou, 2016), identity development should be supported not only in preparation programs but also, and perhaps even more so, in in-service PD programs and workplace interactions. PD programs could be designed according to principles similar to the ones suggested earlier, including affording varied teaching experiences in school and out of school, as well as spaces for scaffolded reflection on identity tensions these experiences raise. PD programs should also create opportunities, especially for elementary school teachers, for authentic scientific research experiences, preferably with their students. These programs should not only aim to advance teacher knowledge and understanding of the nature of science, but also their disciplinary identity, including their sense of belonging to a science community. Alongside well-designed PD programs, identity development should also be supported in on-the-job interactions between colleagues, for example in in-school professional learning communities. Such communities can serve as spaces for practicing teachers to continuously explore and construct their identity in relation to their colleagues and to their own school culture (Lefstein et al., 2020).

Implications for Research on Science Teacher Identity

From a sociocultural perspective, identity is constantly and dynamically formed through social interaction at various times and contexts (Beauchamp & Thomas, 2009; Rushton & Reiss, 2020).

Accordingly, more longitudinal research on beginning but also veteran teachers is needed if the field is to understand not only the formation of identity in the first years of teaching, but also its reformation throughout teacher careers. Also needed is more ecological research that explores how science teachers' identity develops *across* the different contexts of their professional and personal lives. Highlighting the situated nature of identity and the important role of interaction and recognition, this research should give more room to observations as primary data sources, as well as for video-stimulated recall interviews. Additionally, while preservice teacher education and formal PD programs are extremely important, more attention should be directed to exploring identity construction in informal on-the-job interactions. Such research could employ a participatory-research approach, wherein teachers act as researchers, collecting self-recordings of their classroom, PD courses, and teamwork interactions, and analyzing them in collaboration with other researchers. Finally, the field should begin considering tools that allow for rigorous large-scale evaluation of identity development during teacher education and PD programs. The development of such tools should tackle the challenge of designing them based on a well-defined theoretical framework.

References

Adams, J. D., & Gupta, P. (2017). Informal science institutions and learning to teach: An examination of identity, agency, and affordances. *Journal of Research in Science Teaching, 54*(1), 121–138.

Akerson, V. L., Pongsanon, K., Weiland, I. S., & Nargund-Joshi, V. (2014). Developing a professional identity as an elementary teacher of nature of science: A self-study of becoming an elementary teacher. *International Journal of Science Education, 36*(12), 2055–2082.

Avraamidou, L. (2014a). Studying science teacher identity: Current insights and future research directions. *Studies in Science Education, 50*(2), 145–179.

Avraamidou, L. (2014b). Tracing a beginning elementary teacher's development of identity for science teaching. *Journal of Teacher Education, 65*(3), 223–240.

Avraamidou, L. (2016). Studying science teacher identity. In L. Avraamidou (Ed.), *Studying science teacher identity* (pp. 1–14). Rotterdam: Sense Publishers.

Beauchamp, C., & Thomas, L. (2009). Understanding teacher identity: An overview of issues in the literature and implications for teacher education. *Cambridge Journal of Education, 39*(2), 175–189.

Beijaard, D., Meijer, P. C., & Verloop, N. (2004). Reconsidering research on teachers' professional identity. *Teaching and Teacher Education, 20*(2), 107–128.

Beijaard, D., Verloop, N., & Vermunt, J. D. (2000). Teachers' perceptions of professional identity: An exploratory study from a personal knowledge perspective. *Teaching and Teacher Education, 16*(7), 749–764.

Carlone, H. B., Haun-Frank, J., & Kimmel, S. C. (2010). Tempered radicals: Elementary teachers' narratives of teaching science within and against prevailing meanings of schooling. *Cultural Studies of Science Education, 5*, 941–965.

Chen, J. L., & Mensah, F. M. (2018). Teaching contexts that influence elementary preservice teachers' teacher and science teacher identity development. *Journal of Science Teacher Education, 29*(5), 420–439.

Chung-Parsons, R., & Bailey, J. M. (2019). The hierarchical (not fluid) nature of preservice secondary science teachers' perceptions of their science teacher identity. *Teaching and Teacher Education, 78*, 39–48.

Danielsson, A. T., & Warwick, P. (2014). 'You have to give them some science facts': Primary student teachers' early negotiations of teacher identities in the intersections of discourses about science teaching and about primary teaching. *Research in Science Education, 44*(2), 289–305.

Deneroff, V. (2016). Professional development in person: Identity and the construction of teaching within a high school science department. *Cultural Studies of Science Education, 11*(2), 213–233.

Enyedy, N., Goldberg, J., & Welsh, K. M. (2006). Complex dilemmas of identity and practice. *Science Education, 90*(1), 68–93.

García, E., & Weiss, E. (2019). *The teacher shortage is real, large and growing, and worse than we thought. The first report in "The Perfect Storm in the Teacher Labor Market" series.* Economic Policy Institute. www.epi.org/publication/the-teacher-shortage-is-real-large-and-growing-and-worse-than-we-thought-the-first-report-in-the-perfect-storm-in-the-teacher-labor-market-series/

Garner, J. K., & Kaplan, A. (2019). A complex dynamic systems perspective on teacher learning and identity formation: An instrumental case. *Teachers and Teaching, 25*(1), 7–33.

Gee, J. P. (2000). Identity as an analytic lens for research in education. *Review of Research in Education*, 25(1), 99–125.

Gunning, A. M., & Mensah, F. M. (2011). Preservice elementary teachers' development of self-efficacy and confidence to teach science: A case study. *Journal of Science Teacher Education*, 22(2), 171–185.

Holland, D., Lachicotte, W., Skinner, D. D., & Cain, C. (1998). *Identity and agency in cultural worlds*. Cambridge, MA and London, England: Harvard University Press.

Kane, J. M., & Varelas, M. (2016). Elementary school teachers constructing teacher-of-science identities. In L. Avraamidou (Ed.), *Studying science teacher identity* (pp. 177–195). Rotterdam: Sense Publishers.

Korthagen, F. (2017). Inconvenient truths about teacher learning: Towards professional development 3.0. *Teachers and Teaching*, 23(4), 387–405.

Lave, J., & Wenger, E. (1991). *Situated learning: Legitimate peripheral participation*. New York, NY: Cambridge University Press.

Lefstein, A., Vedder-Weiss, D., & Segal, A. (2020). Relocating research on teacher learning: Toward pedagogically productive talk. *Educational Researcher*, 49(5), 360–368.

Luehmann, A. (2007). Identity development as a lens to science teacher preparation. *Science Education*, 91, 822–839.

Luehmann, A. (2016). Practice-linked identity development in science teacher education: GET REAL! Science as a Figured World. In L. Avraamidou (Ed.), *Studying science teacher identity* (pp. 15–47). Rotterdam: Sense Publishers.

Luehmann, A. L., & Markowitz, D. (2007). Science teachers' perceived benefits of an out-of-school enrichment programme: Identity needs and university affordances. *International Journal of Science Education*, 29(9), 1133–1161.

Marco-Bujosa, L. M., Levy, A. J., & McNeill, K. (2020a). A case study exploring the identity of an in-service elementary science teacher: A language teacher first. *Research in Science Education*, 50(1), 79–98.

Marco-Bujosa, L. M., McNeill, K. L., & Friedman, A. A. (2020b). Becoming an urban science teacher: How beginning teachers negotiate contradictory school contexts. *Journal of Research in Science Teaching*, 57(1), 3–32.

Melville, W., & Bartley, A. (2013). Constituting identities that challenge the contemporary discourse: Power, discourse, experience, and emotion. *Science Education*, 97(2), 171–190.

Melville, W., Wallace, J., & Bartley, A. (2007). Individuals and leadership in an Australian secondary science department: A qualitative study. *Journal of Science Education and Technology*, 16(6), 463–472.

Moore, F. M. (2008). Positional identity and science teacher professional development. *Journal of Research in Science Teaching*, 45(6), 684–710.

NGSS Lead States. (2013). *Next generation science standards: For states, by states*. Washington, DC: The National Academies Press.

Nichols, S. L., Schutz, P. A., Rodgers, K., & Bilica, K. (2017). Early career teachers' emotion and emerging teacher identities. *Teachers and Teaching*, 23(4), 406–421.

Richmond, G. (2016). Making sense of the interplay of identity, agency, and context in the development of beginning science teachers in high-poverty schools. In L. Avraamidou (Ed.), *Studying science teacher identity* (pp. 219–235). Rotterdam: Sense Publishers.

Rivera Maulucci, M. S. (2013). Emotions and positional identity in becoming a social justice science teacher: Nicole's story. *Journal of Research in Science Teaching*, 50(4), 453–478.

Rushton, E. A., & Reiss, M. J. (2020). Middle and high school science teacher identity considered through the lens of the social identity approach: A systematic review of the literature. *Studies in Science Education*. https://doi.org/10.1080/03057267.2020.1799621

Rutter, M., Maughan, B., Mortimore, P., & Ouston, J. (1979). *Fifteen thousand hours: Secondary schools and their effects on children*. Cambridge, MA: Harvard University Press.

Saka, Y., Southerland, S. A., Kittleson, J., & Hutner, T. (2013). Understanding the induction of a science teacher: The interaction of identity and context. *Research in Science Education*, 43(3), 1221–1244.

Schaefer, L. (2013). Beginning teacher attrition: A question of identity making and identity shifting. *Teachers and Teaching*, 19(3), 260–274.

Segal, A., Vedder-Weiss, D., & Trachtenberg-Maslaton, R. (2019, April 5–9). *Tensions in teacher professional identity and talk about teaching in informal learning environments*. Paper presentation. American Educational Research Association Annual Meeting, Toronto, Canada.

Settlage, J., Southerland, S. A., Smith, L. K., & Ceglie, R. (2009). Constructing a doubt-free teaching self: Self-efficacy, teacher identity, and science instruction within diverse settings. *Journal of Research in Science Teaching*, 46(1), 102–125.

Smith, D. C., & Neale, D. C. (1989). The construction of subject matter knowledge in primary science teaching. *Teaching and Teacher Education, 5*(1), 1–20.

Sutherland, L., Howard, S., & Markauskaite, L. (2010). Professional identity creation: Examining the development of beginning preservice teachers' understanding of their work as teachers. *Teaching and Teacher Education, 26*, 455–465.

Upadhyay, B. (2009). Negotiating identity and science teaching in a high-stakes testing environment: An elementary teacher's perceptions. *Cultural Studies of Science Education, 4*(3), 569–586.

Van Driel, J. H., Beijaard, D., & Verloop, N. (2001). Professional development and reform in science education: The role of teachers' practical knowledge. *Journal of Research in Science Teaching, 38*(2), 137–158.

Varelas, M., House, R., & Wenzel, S. (2005). Beginning teachers immersed into science: Scientist and science teacher identities. *Science Education, 89*(3), 492–516.

Vedder-Weiss, D., Biran, L., Kaplan, A., & Garner, J. K. (2018). Reflexive inquiry as a scaffold for teacher identity exploration during the first year of teaching. In E. Lyle (Ed.), *The negotiated self: Employing reflexive inquiry to explore teacher identity* (pp. 225–235). Leiden and Boston: Brill Sense.

Weldon, P. (2018). Early career teacher attrition in Australia: Evidence, definition, classification and measurement. *Australian Journal of Education, 6*(1), 61–78.

32

EMOTION AND SCIENCE TEACHER EDUCATION

Alberto Bellocchi and Arnau Amat

How Are Emotions Conceptualized in Science Teacher Education?

The short answer is, "in many ways": as many as there are researchers investigating the topic. It is not possible to provide a definition of emotion that can encompass the range of theoretical, and a-theoretical, representations found in studies of science teachers' emotions. In fields such as education, sociology, psychology, and philosophy, there is evidence of some convergence around *componential* theories or definitions (e.g., Scherer, 2005; Thoits, 1989; Turner, 2007; Zembylas, 2005). Such theories and definitions draw attention to linguistic (emotion) labels, physiological arousal, expressive body actions, action tendencies, and cultural dimensions as representing components of emotions or emotional experiences.

In contrast to these approaches, critical scholars attend to the ways in which members of marginalized demographics are subjugated through a perpetuation of an emotion-reason dichotomy and the ways in which the motivating force of emotion as an act of resistance can be quashed by cultural expectations (cf. Ahmed, 2004; Chapman, 2006; Moisander et al., 2016). Although emerging science education research is beginning to consider these critical perspectives, such conceptualizations of emotion remain rare in our field.

This chapter offers an overview of some key issues faced by science teachers with respect to emotions and discusses common topics of research interest from which implications for science teacher education can be derived. The goal is to illustrate the different ways in which empirical science education research has demonstrated the importance of emotions for science teacher education at the preservice and in-service levels, and how this can inform teacher educators. After a brief overview of the search strategy for selecting articles, four review sections based on an inductive development of themes evident in published studies are introduced. Then the first section of the review frames the role of emotions in science teachers' work and identity formation – a central topic in research on science teacher emotion, and a foundational phenomenon that impacts all aspects of a science teacher's work and learning. Following this broad topic, two specific areas of inquiry are presented where multiple studies have addressed the role of emotion in science teacher education. The two topics represent key reform and research foci within our field. The first area addresses science teacher emotions in relation to science inquiry. In the second area, the focus is on socioscientific issues. Each section is restricted to discussion of science teacher emotions, and it is acknowledged here that each article also presents a range of outcomes that are unrelated to emotions. The sections end with

DOI: 10.4324/9781003098478-38

discussion of implications for preservice and in-service science teacher educators based on emotional outcomes derived from the reviewed studies.

Considering recent and past reviews of research on emotion in science education, teacher education, and science teacher education, this chapter offers different foci and perspectives from previous efforts (cf. Bellocchi, 2019; Davis & Bellocchi, 2018; Sinatra et al., 2014; Zembylas, 2005). Whereas some of the theoretical, empirical, and practical implications for emotions on teacher education have been addressed elsewhere (see Bellocchi, 2019), this chapter is targeted exclusively at work produced *by* science educators *about* science teachers.

As is evident from early attempts to discuss research on emotion in our field, the scant literature available in the past presses authors to develop arguments for the need for research from general education studies on affect and teaching (e.g., Zembylas, 2005). Early science education research is also inclined to bundle science teacher issues with broader studies whose focus is on students' affect, leaving the direct focus on science teachers' *emotions* something to yearn for (e.g., Watts & Alsop, 1997). Nonetheless, thanks to Zembylas's pioneering review effort that differentiates *emotion* as a topic for science education research from the omnibus construct *affect*, he paves the way for subsequent syntheses that focus on science teachers' emotions, although some time will pass before this becomes an exclusive review topic.

Attention of review authors on the role of emotions in science learning predominantly attends to select studies focusing on student emotions, and science teacher's *topic* emotions – that is, emotions directed at specific matters such as teaching evolution and climate change (Sinatra et al., 2014). However, despite only attending to teacher emotions as a small section of their review, Sinatra et al. (2014) present studies whose exclusive attention is directed at science teachers. Subsequent to that review, Davis and Bellocchi (2018) discuss a select range of studies with interrelated theoretical and methodological approaches to emotions research in science education contexts spanning high school, elementary school, and preservice teacher education, thereby repeating the review pattern laid out by their forebearers. As we have seen, available reviews increasingly address science teachers' emotions, but, until now, no review addresses this topic exclusively.

With the growth in published works since the initial framing and impetus offered by Zembylas (2005), an exclusive focus on science education research on emotions is now possible that moves beyond topics covered in broader reviews of emotion in teacher education (i.e., Bellocchi, 2019) and student and teachers' affect in science (Watts & Alsop, 1997). The present chapter is unique amongst its kin in that it offers a review of empirical journal articles to canvas key outcomes that can inform science teacher education practice, providing a suitable complement and extension to past contributions.

Identifying and Selecting Articles About Science Teachers' Emotions

The guiding question for this review is: *What implications can be drawn for science teacher education from the study of science teachers' emotions?* The question is initially addressed by locating empirical journal articles through a multi-database literature search including ERIC + Education Source via EBSCO-Host, APAPsychInfo, APAPsych Articles, APAPsych Books, Academic Search Elite, eBook Collection via EBSCOHost, ProQuest (16 Databases), and Scopus. The search period ranges from all years up to and including September 2020. A systematic search for title, abstract, or keywords using the terms emoti★, affective, and feeling★ in combination with derivations of science teacher education is conducted (e.g., preservice science teach★, chemistry science teach★, in-service science teach★, science teacher training, professional learning/development, etc.). Reference management software is used to initially deduplicate the library, followed by a manual deduplication. This process yields 149 unique results. Title and abstract screening produces 60 articles, and after full text-screening to identify substantive research outcomes relating to science teacher emotions, 44 articles are retained. Full-text analysis is undertaken to develop three inductive themes for the literature review presented herein (cf. Grant & Booth, 2009). The themes include: (1) science teachers' work and identity, (2) science inquiry, and (3) socioscientific issues education. These themes provide novel topics relating to emotions and science teacher education that extend beyond studies represented in past reviews (i.e., Davis & Bellocchi, 2018; Sinatra et al., 2014; Zembylas, 2005). Included articles are chosen based on the presence of multiple empirical studies representing each theme, whether the studies show a clear focus on emotion (not affect or feelings alone), whether the studies present clear implications for science teacher education, and whether the publications are written in English. All included studies are published in peer-reviewed journals.

Emotions and Science Teachers' Work and Identity

The studies included in this section point to diverging issues faced by preservice teachers with different backgrounds and different prior experiences with science. On the one hand, elementary teachers face negative school experiences with science as foundational for avoidance of the subject and negative attitudes towards it. On the other, career-change scientists experience the emotions associated with shifts in identity.

A teacher's encounter with the early years of teaching is well recognized as a tumultuous ride. The immediacy of students' needs is self-evident, but in addition to this, there are staffroom environments to negotiate, school policies, and ceaseless state-mandated reforms that create multiple axes that compete for beginning science teachers', and all teachers', time and attention. Moreover, it is important to take into account that the construction of their teachers' identity is a lifelong process: it begins in their school years, as a science student; proceeds in college in a teacher education degree; and continues as a school teacher (cf. Abell & Bryan, 1997). For elementary teachers, science has been frequently identified as a subject with which teachers have limited experience or where they lack confidence with their disciplinary knowledge (Zembylas & Buhlman Barker, 2002). Awareness and recognition of these dimensions of the profession drives Zembylas and Buhlman Barker to acknowledge directly and cater for the emotional journey that their elementary teachers will experience. Focusing on two preservice teachers, one male and one female, they identify emotions that these educators bring to their studies of science education and those that emerge after instruction that is designed to shift preservice elementary teachers to form more positive attitudes towards science. Zembylas and Buhlman Barker conceptualize their science methods course as a site for preservice teachers to develop feelings of emotional comfort and freedom as they develop as learners and in relation to science and science teaching. The diverse range of activities in the course (assignments, reflections, discussions) become an avenue for exploring preservice teachers' prior conceptions, ideas, attitudes, emotions, expectations, desires, and imaginations. Collaborative conversations with peers provide a second avenue for preservice teachers to support one another emotionally and in relation to science pedagogy.

The two case study teachers differ in their predispositions towards science, with the female preservice teacher having entered the methods course with an overall positive attitude stemming from her positive school experiences with science, which she attributed as being formative aspects of her passion for the subject. Although successful and enthusiastic about elementary school science, the male teacher in the study developed a negative attitude after unpleasant emotions experienced in high school science classes.

The researchers claim that aspects of their methods course, such as an experience with octopi and individual and group reflections, transformed the female preservice teacher's initial positive attitude and emotions towards science into even more positive emotions. Although this claim is somewhat tenuous empirically, data analyses about the male teacher's classroom experiences did reveal that his enthusiasm for science had been reinvigorated. His initial frustration, anxiety, and uncertainty evaporated as he engaged in activities that bring different disciplines like science and art together. Reminiscent of his own elementary days, these activities renewed his lost enjoyment of science, and this becomes transformative as he recognized the negative impact his high school learning, which focused on highly abstract concepts and unengaging forms of instruction, had on his views of science. Freedom to explore science in an emotionally supportive environment are two aspects of Zembylas and Buhlman Barker's science education course that both teachers attributed to their positive attitudes and pleasant emotions related to science. Aside from the focus on emotions, Zembylas and Buhlman Barker's exploratory study indicates that elementary preservice teachers can have transformative emotional experiences when their university science teaching experiences are designed with the preservice teacher's emotions and predispositions in mind.

Career-changing or second-career scientists are preservice or in-service science teachers with university qualifications in science, who subsequently study teacher education (Ritchie et al., 2011). These educators are at times recent science graduates who switch to education and become teachers, or people who have held careers in science (e.g., industry, academia) for varying lengths of time before making the switch to teaching. It is common for these pre-/in-service teachers to have very deep knowledge of science, albeit often in one specific discipline, and to have experience with applications of science in research or applied endeavours that confer some advantages to their teaching. However, lack of familiarity with school science classrooms, limited experience with schools and young people in learning contexts, the short education courses they often complete in recognition of prior studies, and the rapid timeframes in which the transition to becoming teachers occurs can present situations that are highly emotional and may be experienced for the first time by these preservice teachers. Initial expectations that career-change scientists have for teaching soon collide with school and classroom realities during practicum and work.

The emergence of pleasant emotions in an Australian elementary teacher's class is the focus of Ritchie et al.'s (2011) study. Vicky, the teacher, is a former engineering graduate and a career-change scientist. In the study, Vicky reviewed lesson videos from her elementary classroom recorded by the researchers and coded lesson segments with different emotion labels. Analysis reveals that Vicky's pleasant emotions are associated with dialogic classroom interactions where students and the teacher contribute turns at talk. In the dialogic interactions, humor is present whereby the teacher and students engage in laughter as the teacher asks questions about one group's topic. In one lesson, Vicky is apprehensive initially about the student task she has set. When interactions unfold in a positive way, she experiences pleasant emotions. This pattern of interaction stands in contrast to a flatter emotional tone in a second lesson. Having enjoyed the pleasant interactions of the first lesson, Vicky's expectations are that the second lesson might unfold similarly. When she interacts with student groups, however, her questions fall flat, and Vicky becomes despondent and reports unpleasant emotions. Another swing towards pleasant emotions takes place in a third lesson. This time, Vicky approaches the lesson with positive expectations, and when these expectations are met during classroom interactions, she reports positive emotions. An important implication of the emotional outcomes that Ritchie et al. identify is that teachers can learn to abandon flat interactions that do not meet students' expectations for learning science, towards those that do meet student expectations. The emotional tone of interactions offers an avenue for teachers to discern the two types of interaction.

The nature of science teachers' work is central to identity formation; a phenomenon closely dependent on emotional experiences. Studies of science teachers' identity that report emotional outcomes address topics including nature of science instruction (Akerson et al., 2014), professional development (Mbowane et al., 2017), and the experiences of career-changing scientists in becoming science teachers (Ritchie et al., 2007). The focus on emotion in these studies is derived from conceptualization of identity as a dynamic phenomenon involving discourses, experiences, and emotions.

In-service secondary science teachers' participation in science fairs offers scope for professional development (Mbowane et al., 2017). Through these experiences, teachers' identities are shaped around their roles as judges, organizers, and mentors during fairs. Several factors form part of professional identity, including professional knowledge, attitudes, beliefs, norms and values, emotions, and agency. Mbowane et al. (2017) report that science teacher emotions center around enjoyment of working with students during the fairs. More specifically, the learners' growing conceptual skills, success, the acknowledgments and awards they received from the school, and sharing in the learners' achievements are the sources of teacher enjoyment and pleasant emotions. Teacher identities emerge, in part, from the emotional experiences that take place during science fairs.

Forming a professional identity as an elementary teacher of the nature of science (NOS) presents emotional challenges (Akerson et al., 2014). The first author, Akerson, took leave from her academic post to explore NOS instruction in a 3rd-grade class. Using self-study, Akerson et al. (2014) tracked changes in Akerson's efforts to form an identity as a teacher of NOS. To begin with, there is Akerson's mixed emotions about re-entry into teaching. Nervousness characterises her doubts about becoming a teacher again. Excitement about the start of school and delight on the first day are more dominant in Akerson's emotional reports. With the commencement of NOS instruction in the second week of teaching, excitement is a dominant emotion. Emotions of care for the students also become prominent especially as Akerson begins to consider the challenges of teaching a diverse group with needs that sometimes far outweigh those of her lessons and as her bonds with the students grow stronger. These emotional experiences remind Akerson that she is teaching people, not NOS, and this constitutes one factor shaping her identity as a teacher of NOS. Moreover, the experience focuses Akerson's attention on the needs of her preservice teachers who will also face the emotions associated with forming teacher identities.

Ritchie et al. (2007) focus on the changing identities of career-change scientists who encounter different contexts and professional cultures in a teacher education course. In the course, preservice secondary teachers share their science stories, and these become resources for developing teacher identities as they transition from their scientist identities. The article focuses on one preservice teacher, Tanya, who is also a co-author.

Tanya shares perspectives on scientific practice and becoming a science teacher that present a contradiction between private and public spheres. In the public version of science, for example, Tanya represents the "prettiest picture" of science as a truth-seeking endeavour and identifies this as a desirable representation to share with future students (Ritchie et al., 2007; p. 233). As Tanya and three other colleagues discuss this idea, the notion that science is a *pursuit* of truth evolves from the discussion. Although Tanya acknowledges the tentative nature of science and the efforts scientists go to represent a favourable view of their work, she maintains the desire to share a pretty picture with her students. This is the first contradiction Tanya encounters as she is forming a teacher identity. A second contradiction arises from the reactions of people who know Tanya as a scientist and question her choice to become a teacher. In contrast to the positive emotional tone that characterises her sharing of stories from her scientific work that she can use with students, Tanya is hurt and saddened by the reactions of others and questions her own choice to change careers. One's investment in an identity, such as scientist, is not an individual affair. Identities arise in the context of our social milieu, and as Tanya's story reveals, when a shift in identity is underway, the milieu responds. Ritchie et al. (2007) consider that there is a large emotional investment made by an individual in forming and maintaining a science identity. It may take more time than what is available during a teacher education course for a career-change scientist to experience a level of success with a science teacher identity comparable with their (past) science identity. At the heart of these transitions in identity is emotional commitment to one identity over another, creating tensions as preservice teachers experience the change.

The identification of two empirical journal articles in this review (i.e., Ritchie et al., 2007, 2013) suggests that we need to learn much more about career-changing scientists' emotional experiences to generate more robust suggestions that can inform the design and implementation of preservice and in-service science education.

Implications of Emotion for Science Teachers' Work and Identity

It is clear from this review that emotions are critical to teachers' work and formation of science teacher identity. Although elementary teachers may face challenges associated with lack of confidence with content knowledge, their career-change counterparts experience identity upheavals, in each case shaping how preservice teachers perceive themselves with respect to the subject. Whereas career-change scientists' emotions are associated with perceptions from friends and loved ones shaping their emerging teacher identities, elementary teachers' emotions are directed at perceptions derived from student actions. For elementary teachers, unpleasant emotions can drive them to use conservative teaching approaches that afford greater control to the teacher, thereby undermining science education reforms such as science inquiry and project-based learning (see also the next section). Elementary preservice teachers could benefit from considering their past school experiences during science education courses, as we saw with Zembylas and Buhlman Barker's study, to address the sources of past emotional experiences. Normalizing the kinds of interactions experienced during reform-based instruction could help preservice teachers to reinterpret their unpleasant emotions. For example, developing an understanding that uncertainty is part of science inquiry could help preservice elementary teachers to refocus their attention and their students' attention on addressing any encountered barriers. Developing understandings about the specific emotions, such as frustration, encountered during science inquiry or project-based work, is a normal part of the problem-solving nature of these instructional and learning approaches and could help school students understand that these are emotions they need to work with. Another approach could involve preservice elementary teachers making explicit their own emotions, and ideas or desires, regarding science teaching and learning by using emotional diaries or creating spaces of open and collaborative discussion with peers. The benefits are likely to be twofold: (1) externalizing emotions; and (2) working on emotions that operate against effective science instruction.

For career-change scientists, it is unlikely that university courses will be lengthened to provide more time to resolve any identity issues that may arise. What Ritchie et al. (2007) suggest is that there is a need to provide identity-focused instruction in teacher education courses for career-changing preservice teachers. Studies like those of Ritchie et al. (2007, 2013) could be used as reflective prompts for new cohorts of teacher education students, prompting reflection and discussion of strategies for managing the potential turmoil some candidates may encounter as they transition to becoming science teachers. Teacher educators could attend to the fact that these transitions can be emotional times for career-changing scientists. It is not possible to avoid (unpleasant) emotional experiences for some people, but by acknowledging this fact and openly discussing this with preservice teachers, it may prepare preservice teachers for the identity work so that it comes as less of a surprise.

Emotion and Science Inquiry

Interest in the role of emotions in the enactment or support of science inquiry instruction forms the focus of three included studies (i.e., Adler et al., 2019; Dreon & McDonald, 2012; Ritchie et al., 2013). Whereas Dreon and McDonald (2012) address beginning science teachers' emotional engagement with science inquiry through a phenomenological study of two teachers, Ritchie et al. (2013) attend to the emotions aroused in four beginning teachers who are implementing extended scientific investigations. In this way, these researchers have more exploratory orientations than Adler et al. (2019), whose study investigates the effects of interventions on teachers and preservice teachers' open inquiry practices. All three studies report the resulting benefits that arise when teachers engage science inquiry in preservice and in-service settings. In each study, emotional trajectories of science teachers include experiences of unpleasant emotions and pleasant emotions that align with various aspects of teacher learning about science inquiry.

Two key ideas tie together the central findings of the three studies with respect to the role of emotions in teaching and learning science inquiry:

1. Emotional trajectories across pleasant and unpleasant emotions impact pedagogical choices;
2. When unpleasant emotions are resolved, science teachers develop positive views of science inquiry.

In the initial stages when science teachers engage in science inquiry, either through professional development or with their school students, emotions such as anxiety, fear, concern, worry, and discomfort are reported (Adler et al., 2019; Dreon & McDonald, 2012; Ritchie et al., 2013). For example, two beginning chemistry teachers report discomfort and anxiety associated with enactment of science inquiry pedagogy relating to three key aspects of their lived experiences, including self-efficacy about science content, control beliefs pertaining to unpredictable outcomes during inquiry lessons, and teacher identity based on the ways in which school students view their teachers (Dreon and McDonald, 2012). This anxiety, stemming in part from feeling judged by their students, impacts pedagogical choices the teachers make, serving as a force of resistance to future use of science inquiry with their classes.

Teachers' apprehension about science inquiry does not result purely from experiences with classroom implementation. Ritchie et al. (2013) find that beginning science teachers report an atmosphere of fear in science staffrooms towards science investigations. This staffroom angst leads the beginning teachers in Ritchie and colleagues' study to prepare well for their own experiences with student investigations. As the beginning teachers undertake investigations with their classes, they come to see the benefits of open inquiry and find ways to address student needs by providing scaffolding in the forms of conducting preliminary activities, emphasizing the importance of writing skills to support scientific report writing, and monitoring students skills during the investigations. As they scaffold student inquiries, teachers' emotions range from mild forms of fear, frustration, and anger. Over time, as school students' confidence, skills, and independence improve, highly pleasant emotions are reported by teachers. Pleasant emotional experiences from positive student outcomes provide reassurance to these science teachers that open inquiry is worth pursuing in their classrooms.

In contrast to the classroom teaching experiences reported earlier, Adler and colleagues' (2019) focus is on the impact of metacognitive prompts in fostering science teachers' reflections on open inquiry during professional development. Metacognitive prompts encourage teachers to reflect on their learning and the open inquiry process. Relating to emotions, the metacognitive prompts draw out teachers' reports of happiness, worry, surprise, frustration, satisfaction, and despair. These emotions are associated with cognitive categories including planning, monitoring, debugging, and evaluation. For example, happiness is associated with reaching a conclusion in the planning stage of the inquiry. Worry and surprise relate to concerns about inquiry results, such as when hypotheses are not supported empirically. Performing the inquiry surfaces frustration at the inquiry process and satisfaction when issues are resolved.

Implications for Science Teacher Education on Science Inquiry

It is clear in the studies reviewed that unpleasant emotional experiences are part of doing science inquiry. Rather than trying to avoid these unpleasant emotions, it is their resolution that brings about pleasant emotions and encourages science teachers to continue with science inquiry instructions. When unpleasant emotional experiences associated with science inquiry are resolved, science teachers develop positive views of this pedagogical approach and are encouraged to pursue it with their classes. As the reviewed studies reveal, resolution of unpleasant emotions can arise through careful planning and preparation before enacting science inquiry with school students (cf. Ritchie et al., 2013). Professional development where science teachers experience the design and implementation of science inquiry, as in Adler and colleagues' study, can become a testing ground not only for pedagogy but also for dealing with the uncertainty some beginning teachers experience when implementing science inquiry with students for the first time (cf. Dreon & McDonald, 2012). Metacognitive prompts during professional learning experiences offer one way of scaffolding science teachers' reflections on science inquiry processes and associated emotions. It is also clear when we contrast Adler and colleagues' findings with those of Ritchie et al. that careful teacher preparation and prior exposure and experience with conducting scientific investigations (either through professional development or teacher education) are key approaches to changing science teachers' first encounters with student investigations.

Emotion and Socioscientific Issues in Science Teacher Education

Socioscientific issues (SSI) can be defined as issues which arise from the connection between science and society, which people probably face in their daily lives, and which frequently involve scientific and moral dilemmas (Sadler, 2004; Kolstø, 2001). Genetic engineering and climate change are examples of staple topics in the repertoire of socioscientific issues research and practice. Understanding the role of emotions in the decision-making processes in such contexts is the focus of the two studies of secondary preservice science teacher education included in this section (Lee et al., 2012; Topçu et al., 2011). Drawing on Sadler and Zeidler's (2005) model, three forms of reasoning – rationalistic, emotive, and intuitive – are adopted to interpret preservice science teachers' decision-making about SSIs. Discussion will focus on emotive informal reasoning that involves empathy and sympathy as key ways of making decisions. According to Sadler and Zeidler, emotive reasoning patterns refer to the ways in which college students display empathy, care, and concern for the well-being of others.

Topçu et al. (2011) report on the emotions associated with the informal reasoning practices of 39 Turkish preservice teachers discussing six genetic engineering scenarios and a global warming scenario in an interview. In all seven scenarios, the researchers' interpretations show how informal reasoning involves cognitive and affective processes that preservice teachers use to resolve and negotiate ill-structured issues. Informal reasoning processes also inform decisions to accept or reject positions or solutions related to specific SSIs. Topçu et al. paired combinations of the three forms of informal reasoning in the preservice teachers' responses, including rationalistic-emotive, rationalistic-intuitive, and emotive-intuitive. Empathy and sympathy are identified as emotions involved with emotive reasoning.

An example of such decision-making processes relates to cloning. Preservice teachers consider the future impact of reproductive cloning on a child and the child's parents. Empathy with the (cloned) child and its parents informs the preservice teachers' decision-making processes in this context. An interesting result is that although other genetics-based SSI are resolved through the rational informal reasoning approach, human cloning relies on emotive and intuitive categories of reasoning. In this respect, Topçu et al.'s outcomes show how the nature of different SSIs is associated with the informal reasoning patterns used by preservice teachers in forming decisions about the issues. The contrasting reasoning processes in the different SSI contexts are explained by the fact that the cloning example relates to humans, a proximal context, whereas gene therapy is situated in a context that is distal to human experience.

In the second study, Lee et al. (2012) used power generation, climate change, and embryonic stem cell research as SSI topics to design 2-week units for 18 Korean preservice teachers to investigate the extent to which preservice teachers' ecological worldviews, socioscientific accountability, and values of social and moral compassion are enacted. It is the latter element that has connections to the emotions, because social and moral compassion requires empathy and respect for others and other species. The results offered from discussion groups suggest that preservice teachers show some degree of compassion in relation to climate change and embryonic stem cells. When considering power generation and nuclear energy, however, most preservice teachers ignored ecological consciousness, showing egoistic and anthropocentric views.

As far as global warming is concerned, even though preservice teachers express compassion towards underdeveloped nations that suffer from climate change, they ignore the responsibility of developed nations in relation to global warming. Preservice teachers express beliefs that the trade in emissions rights can facilitate development in underdeveloped nations, thereby contributing to benefits worldwide. In contrast, when considering the issue of embryonic stem cell research, the impact of this issue on human beings generates a level of compassion among the participants in one group discussion, even though the preservice teachers' specific positions on the issue do not change because of expressing compassion. One preservice teacher recalls her personal experience when she saw an ultrasound image of her nephew, as a 4-week-old embryo. Although no human features could be seen in the picture, she recognized a potential human being in that mass of cells. Sharing this argument and her personal experience was persuasive enough to challenge the convictions of some of her groupmates. Some of them were able to comprehend her point but did not change their initial position. Lee et al. conclude that preservice teachers approach each of the SSI topics emotionally, but they rarely view themselves as moral agents who can participate in resolving the issues.

As reported in Topçu and colleagues' research, preservice teachers' compassion in Lee and colleagues' study seems context-dependent. Preservice teachers do not apply the same moral principles to the issues studied: being compassionate towards underdeveloped nations when it comes to negotiating climate change does not transfer to being compassionate about other issues, such as nuclear power. Finally, it is important to highlight that during group discussions, preservice teachers experienced moral conflicts when emotive reasoning was used. Although these conflicts do not necessarily lead to a change in initial positions, they oblige preservice teachers to put themselves in someone else's shoes and show sensitivity to different thoughts and feelings.

Implications for Science Teacher Education on Socioscientific Issues

In this section, implications from the reviewed studies are presented only as far as they relate to preservice teachers' emotions. A key reflection that is useful for framing the implications of preservice teachers emotions for socioscientific issues education is posed by Topçu et al. That is, if emotive, or empathetic and sympathetic, forms of reasoning that involve moral- and religious-based arguments are common when preservice teachers reason about socioscientific issues, then we must prepare these teachers for dealing with similar forms of reasoning in their future school classrooms. Science teacher educators are encouraged to explore this idea and identify ways in which preservice teachers might address such issues in their classrooms. One way of achieving this could be to support science teachers in private and open reflection on their emotional experiences associated with socioscientific issues and associated peer debates. Guided reflections on differences in the way that teachers defend different controversial topics could help them to self-identify what informs their arguments and those arguments which induce the most intense emotions. Hearing diverse arguments from peers and colleagues will also expand science teachers' engagement with diverse evidence or forms of argumentation in favor of or against a particular issue.

Considering the context-dependency of informal reasoning in SSIs reported in the reviewed studies, teacher education programs could provide a range of issues not only to expand the diversity of opportunities for informal reasoning, but also to provide opportunities for preservice teachers to reflect on the diverse ways of reasoning when confronting a wide range of socioscientific issues. Drawing explicit attention to differences in reasoning could be one way to help preservice teachers uncover any implicit incoherence in their arguments as a first step to informing how they deal with such issues, if they should choose to make such changes in their reasoning.

Evolving the typologies of reasoning, such as the one adopted in the reviewed studies based on Sadler and Zeidler's work, could assist teachers to understand the different factors shaping their reasoning. An important consideration could be to re-evaluate categories of informal reasoning which tend to pit emotion against reason through the identification of *rational* and *emotive* informal reasoning categories. A useful distinction to consider could be the difference between rational and irrational arguments, with the acknowledgment that a person is likely to be emotional in both instances (cf. Alsop, 2011; Bellocchi, 2017; Ritchie & Tobin, 2018; Zembylas, 2005). The intensity of emotion one feels towards a topic may, as the studies in this section reveal, result from other systems of belief (i.e., religious, moral code). Helping preservice teachers to understand their own and their students' belief systems would offer scope for then addressing any associated emotions. Strong emotive responses to an issue could be probed as a sign of conflict between a person's values and the controversial issue under investigation. When preservice teachers are led to explore their emotions and reasons for different choices, this may open the way for their future understanding of their school students' experiences with similar topics. Such approaches may encourage a sensitive and respectful pedagogy that does not dismiss presumed irrational reactions from students.

Concluding Remarks

It is no longer necessary for science education scholars to alert readers that emotions are important for being and becoming a science teacher. Sufficient past and ongoing scholarship attests to this fact (cf. Bellocchi, 2019; Davis & Bellocchi, 2018; Sinatra et al., 2014; Zembylas, 2005). However, there is still an insufficient number of studies addressing science teachers' emotions, or emotions in science education more broadly, when we compare that number with other topics in our field (see Fortus, 2014; Wickman, 2017). This chapter has provided an overview of those studies that frame issues faced by science teachers at preservice and in-service levels and showcased three topics of interest for science education reform and emotion research: teachers' work and identity; science inquiry; and socioscientific issues. Although they are not exhaustive, this selection of topics extends the focus of prior reviews of emotions in science education (i.e., Davis & Bellocchi, 2018; Sinatra et al., 2014; Zembylas, 2005). Moreover, the chapter is unique in offering implications the existing research has to offer science teacher educators who are eager to advance their practice by attending to the emotions of preservice and in-service teachers. Hopefully this chapter piques the interest of science teacher educators such that they may join the efforts to expand our field's understanding of the emotions for science teaching and learning to teach science by engaging in further research.

There is a clear need for science teacher educators and researchers to engage further with emotion theories. As outlined at the beginning of the chapter, not all studies reporting on science teacher emotions make connections to the plethora of theories available from various disciplinary traditions. As we have seen in the socioscientific issues topic, a-theoretical approaches, with respect to emotions, can lead to perpetuation of an emotion-reason dichotomy that has been abandoned by science educators and emotions scholars. Perpetuating emotion-reason dichotomies is not likely to move us forward as a field in our quest to improve instruction and conditions for science teachers. Of course, there is value to a-theoretical work with respect to the emotions when such work is couched in a relevant research design (e.g., phenomenology, ethnomethodology, poststructuralism).

Obvious benefits are identifiable for preservice teachers and in-service teachers when discussion and awareness of emotions forms part of teacher education (e.g., Zembylas & Buhlman Barker, 2002). For some, initial encounters with teaching science, transitioning to become a science teacher, having to teach a subject towards which one harbours strong unpleasant emotions, or dealing with controversial topics that trigger the teacher's and student's emotions, can all present surprise elements that catch a teacher off guard emotionally. It is clear from the reviewed studies that consideration and reflection on one's emotions during preservice and in-service learning offers one way to reduce the at-times surprise need to respond to one's own or their students' emotions. A teacher's awareness of his own emotions is also a precursor for an empathetic understanding of their students' emotions. This is important when managing discussions about triggering topics such as climate change and evolution.

A common issue in the studies reviewed is the acknowledgment of the *presence* of science teachers' emotions across different contexts. Studies that demonstrate engagement and open discussion *about* teachers' emotions in teacher education and professional learning are few. Zembylas and Buhlman Barker's study is an exception in this regard. It offers an example of how direct and open attention to emotions in teacher education can become a turning point for elementary teachers who display reluctance towards teaching science. Similarly, we might expect that teacher education designed for any purpose (e.g., reforms, identity formation, SSI, NOS) will also benefit from direct consideration of how emotions might play out in the classroom for the teacher and students. Creating a safe space in which science teachers' voices, with their personal and emotional experiences, could be shared and listened to could be an effective way of encouraging sympathy towards others' opinions and feelings. Although some of the expressed opinions could go against one's own opinions, or could even be painful for people who are listening, this safe space can be sustained by being aware of our own and other people's emotions, and acting accordingly (Alexakos et al., 2016).

A dispassionate science education is well known to be one of the reasons school students are being turned off by school science. Perhaps inclusion of emotions in science teacher education can be a vehicle for addressing students and teachers' needs more effectively than instruction that neglects this formative and central aspect of the human condition.

Acknowledgment

The Australian Research Council Discovery Early Career Grant (DE160101053) awarded to Alberto Bellocchi also supported this work. Any opinions, findings, and conclusions or recommendations expressed in this article are those of the author and do not necessarily reflect the views of the Australian Research Council.

References

★ Studies included in review

Abell, S. K., & Bryan, L. A. (1997). Reconceptualizing the Elementary Science Methods Course Using a Reflection Orientation. *Journal of Science Teacher Education, 8*(3), 153–166.

★Adler, I., Zion, M., & Rimerman-Shmueli, E. (2019). Fostering teachers' reflections on the dynamic characteristics of open inquiry through metacognitive prompts. *Journal of Science Teacher Education, 30*, 763–787. https://doi.org/10.1080/1046560X.2019.1627060

Ahmed, S. (2004). Affective economies. *Social Text, 22*, 117–139. https://doi.org/10.1215/01642472-22-2_79-117

★Akerson, V. L., Pongsanon, K., Weiland, I. S., & Nargund-Joshi, V. (2014). Developing a professional identity as an elementary teacher of nature of science: A self-study of becoming an elementary teacher. *International Journal of Science Education, 36*(12), 2055–2082. https://doi.org/10.1080/09500693.2014.890763

Alexakos, K., Pride, L. D., Amat, A., Tsetsakos, P., Lee, K. J., Paylor-Smith, C., . . . Smith, T. (2016). Mindfulness and discussing "thorny" issues in the classroom. *Cultural Studies of Science Education, 11*, 741–769.

Alsop, S. (2011). The body bites back. *Cultural Studies of Science Education, 6*, 611–623.

Bellocchi, A. (2017). Interaction ritual approaches to emotion and cognition in science learning experiences. In A. Bellocchi, C. Quigley, & K. Otrel-Cass (Eds.), *Exploring emotions, aesthetics and wellbeing in science education research* (pp. 85–106). Dordrecht, The Netherlands: Springer. https://doi.org/10.1007/978-3-319-43353-0_5

Bellocchi, A. (2019). Emotions and teacher education. In G. Noblit (Ed.), *The Oxford research encyclopaedia of education*. London, UK: Oxford University Press. https://doi.org/10.1093/acrefore/9780190264093.013.773.

Bellocchi, A., Quigley, C., & Otrel-Cass, K. (Eds.). (2017). *Exploring emotions, aesthetics, and wellbeing in science education research*. Dordrecht, The Netherlands: Springer. https://doi.org/10.1007/978-3-319-43353-0

Chapman, M. (2006). Postcolonialism: A literary turn. *English in Africa, 33*, 7–20.

Davis, J. P., & Bellocchi, A. (2018). Emotions in learning science. In S. M. Ritchie & K. G. Tobin (Eds.), *Eventful learning: Learner emotions*. Leiden, The Netherlands: Brill. https://doi.org/10.1163/9789004377912_002

★Dreon, O., & McDonald, S. (2012). Being in the hot spot: A phenomenological study of two beginning teachers' experiences enacting inquiry science pedagogy. *Teachers & Teaching, 18*, 297–313. https://doi.org/10.1080/13540602.2012.629837

Fortus, D. (2014, June). Attending to affect in science education. *Journal of Research in Science Teaching, Virtual Issue*. http://onlinelibrary.wiley.

Grant, M. J., & Booth, A. (2009). A typology of reviews: An analysis of 14 review types and associated methodologies. *Health Information Library Journal, 26*(2), 91–108. https://doi.org/10.1111/j.1471-1842.2009.00848.x.

Kolstø, S. D. (2001). Scientific literacy for citizenship: Tools for dealing with the science dimension of controversial SSI. *Science Education, 85*, 291–310.

★Lee, H., Chang, H., Choi, K., Kim, S.-W., & Zeidler, D. L. (2012). Developing character and values for global citizens: Analysis of pre-service science teachers' moral reasoning on socioscientific issues. *International Journal of Science Education, 34*(6), 925–953. https://doi.org/10.1080/09500693.2011.625505

★Mbowane, C. K., de Villiers, J. J. R., & Braun, M. W. H. (2017). Teacher participation in science fairs as professional development in South Africa. *South African Journal of Science, 113*, 1–7. https://doi.org/10.17159/sajs.2017/20160364

Moisander, J. K., Hirsto, H., & Fahy, K. M. (2016). Emotions in institutional work: A discursive perspective. *Organization Studies, 37*, 963–990. https://doi.org/10.1177/0170840615613377

★Ritchie, S. M., Kidman, G., & Vaughan, T. (2007). Professional learning opportunities from uncovering cover stories of science and science teaching for a scientist-in-transition. *Cultural Studies of Science Education, 2*, 225–242. https://doi.org/10.1007/s11422-006-9044-7

Ritchie, S. M., & Tobin, K. G. (Eds.). (2018). *Eventful learning: Learner emotions*. Leiden, The Netherlands: Brill. https://doi.org/10.1163/9789004377912

★Ritchie, S. M., Tobin, K. G., Hudson, P., Roth, W.-M., & Mergard, V. (2011). Reproducing successful rituals in bad times: Exploring emotional interactions of a new science teacher. *Science Education, 95*, 745–765. https://doi.org/10.1002/sce.20440

★Ritchie, S. M., Tobin, K. P., Sandhu, M., Sandhu, S., Henderson, S., & Roth, W.-M. (2013). Emotional arousal of beginning physics teachers during extended experimental investigations. *Journal of Research in Science Teaching, 50*, 137–161. https://doi.org/10.1002/tea.21060

Sadler, T. D. (2004). Informal reasoning regarding SSI: A critical review of research. *Journal of Research in Science Teaching, 41*, 513–536.

Sadler, T. D., & Zeidler, D. L. (2005). Patterns of informal reasoning in the context of socioscientific decision making. *Journal of Research in Science Teaching, 42*(1), 112–138.

Scherer, K. R. (2005). What are emotions? And how can they be measured? *Social Science Information, 44*(4), 695–729.

Sinatra, G., Broughton, S. H., & Lombardi, D. (2014). Emotions in science education. In R. Perkun & L. Linnenbrink-Garcia (Eds.), *International handbook of emotions in education* (pp. 415–436). London: Routledge.

Thoits, P. A. (1989). The sociology of emotions. *Annual Review of Sociology, 15*, 317–342.

★Topçu, M. S., Yilmaz-Tuzun, O., & Sadler, T. D. (2011). Turkish preservice science teachers' informal reasoning regarding socioscientific issues and the factors influencing their informal reasoning. *Journal of Science Teacher Education, 22*, 313–333. https://doi.org/10.1007/s10972-010-9221-0

Turner, J. H. (2007). *Human emotions: A sociological theory*. London, UK: Routledge.

Watts, M., & Alsop, S. (1997). A feeling for learning: Modelling affective learning in school science. *The Curriculum Journal, 8*, 351–365.

Wickman, P-O. (2017). Back to the drawing board: Examining the philosophical foundations of educational research on aesthetics and emotions. In A. Bellocchi, K. Otrel-Cass, & C. Quigley (Eds.), *Exploring emotions, aesthetics and wellbeing in science education research* (pp. 39–54). Dordrecht, Springer. https://doi.org/10.1007/978-3-319-43353-0_2

Zembylas, M. (2005). Emotions and science teaching: Present research and future agendas. In S. Alsop (Ed.), *Beyond Cartesian dualism: Encountering affect in the teaching and learning of science*. Dordrecht, The Netherlands: Springer.

*Zembylas, M., & Buhlman Barker, H. (2002). Preservice teacher attitudes and emotions: Individual spaces, community conversations and transformations. *Research in Science Education, 32*, 329–351. https://doi.org/10.1023/a:1020862000107

33

LEARNING TO TEACH SCIENCE FROM A CONTEXTUALIZED STANCE

*Michael Giamellaro, Kassandra L'Heureux, Cory Buxton,
Marie-Claude Beaudry, Jean-Philippe Ayotte-Beaudet,
and Talal Alajmi*

Many reforms in science education since 2001, including project-based learning, socioscientific instruction, ambitious science teaching, and culturally responsive pedagogy, ask teachers to connect science content to contexts outside of the classroom. While these approaches are different in important ways, they are similar in asking teachers to lead students through the process of connecting science content and context. Contextualizing instruction is universally difficult, but there are similarities across approaches that can be used to prepare science teachers to effectively use multiple approaches to contextualization.

Context is operationalized here as a set of complex, relatively stable conditions that can be experienced and communicated, and that have behavioral relevance for learning (Stark et al., 2017). It is a social reality (Engle et al., 2011) and becomes a mediating tool when it facilitates learning through authentic practice (Vygotsky, 1978). Context always impacts learning, even when it is not explicitly addressed or designed for, and it stimulates cognitive and affective processing for the learner (Giamellaro, 2014). Learners have variable and subjective access to a context through curriculum and instruction, as well as through their other lived experiences.

Contextualization is the mechanism that connects the material and temporal world to the world of ideas through experience (Giamellaro, 2017). It is the process of connecting science knowledge to context, and this can be done by the learner, by curriculum, or through instruction. However, contextualized curriculum or instruction does not automatically lead to contextualized knowledge for students (King & Ritchie, 2012). Contextualization through curriculum implies an intentionality in linking content and context.

The difficulties of contextualized science teaching are bound to the complexity of the real world in general. The lack of bounded variables, clear "answers," or well-defined problems can be challenging for teachers and students. Extensive teacher support is needed for the implementation of contextualized science approaches (Brown & Crippen, 2016) that often require introspection of personal identity as well as a wholesale change in approach to teaching. Teacher identity and belief systems are common barriers to implementing contextualized science as the approaches ask teachers to reframe their relationship to contexts in and outside of school (Lupión-Cobos et al., 2017). Preservice teacher (PST) preparation programs have limited instructional time and cannot dwell on curriculum or instructional approaches that teacher candidates may never see in professional practice. In-service teacher (IST) development programs also suffer from limited time, competing mandates, and a sense of innovation fatigue. The goal of this chapter is to examine commonalities

DOI: 10.4324/9781003098478-39

439

that could inform a method for preparing teachers to lead contextualized science learning as a broad foundation for the spectrum of contextualization approaches.

Methods

As part of a broader study, we conducted a systematic review of published research between 2001 and 2020 that examined contextualization in science learning, resulting in 3,986 documents. The Web of Science (WOS) database was searched for titles, keywords, and abstracts which include, but are not limited to, terms and topics in science learning and/or development, contextualization, context-based, place-based, real-world, authentic, culturally responsive, experiential, outdoor, and fieldwork. This approach biased the sample to include only published works but added the quality filter of peer review. For the review presented in this chapter, we screened this data set to include only articles that addressed supports for ISTs or PSTs to teach from a contextualized stance, resulting in 131 articles.

We used general inductive qualitative data analysis to screen abstracts, review articles, and condense the data into categories. At least two screeners reviewed each article, and unclear determinations were negotiated by the team. Articles were excluded if they did not focus on science education learning or development ($n = 28$), did not fit our definition of contextualization ($n = 38$), or were written in languages beyond our team's ability ($n = 8$), resulting in a sample of 57 articles.

Following screening we categorized the studies into five general approaches to contextualization: authentic science practices (ASP), culturally responsive science (CRS), out-of-class experiences (OOC), socioscientific inquiry (SSI), and context-based curriculum (CBC), defined in Table 33.1. Our labels are intended to highlight how the included studies approached contextualization rather than the broader goals of an individual study. Our team recognizes other approaches to contextualization (e.g., project-based learning, immersive technologies) that were not represented in the sample, perhaps because this literature fails to address both the role of contextualization *and* teacher development.

Results and Discussion

Operationalizing Contextualization

A key factor in determining the approaches to contextualization was how each paper described why, how, and to what ends the authors intentionally connected science knowledge or skills to contexts outside of the classroom. Our first consideration was the degree to which the approaches emphasized the importance of science knowledge versus the importance of the context itself – whether students were asked to use context to better understand science, or to use science to better understand the context. The authentic science practices (ASP), culturally responsive science (CRS), and context-based curriculum (CBC) groups highlight the science content knowledge and the role of the context in helping to build understanding, motivation, relevance, and engagement. In these approaches the context is highly valued, and students must come to understand the nuance and details of it, but the measured learning outcomes are focused on the science. Socioscientific inquiry (SSI) and out-of-classroom experiences (OOC) value science learning but tend to place a higher value on students learning about the context.

While few papers explicitly used the term *contextualization*, they all operationalized the process, even if implicitly. The ASP approach uses the context to teach science through the lived experiences of practicing scientists. In these papers, contextualization is operationalized as helping learners to see and experience how science knowledge and skills are used in authentic science research, often parallel to scientists who participate as partners. The skills and knowledge are situated in instances of

Table 33.1 Five approaches to contextualized science education

Approach	n	Definition (Provides Teacher Supports for Instruction On . . .)	Germane Context	How Contextualization Is Operationalized
Authentic science practices (ASP)	14	Student participation in practices that are parallel to the activity of practicing scientists. Includes teacher-scientist partnerships and research experiences for teachers.	Scientists' communities of practice	Context to understand, do, and see relevance of science.
Culturally responsive science (CRS)	13	Using students' sociocultural backgrounds to frame science content as relevant and accessible. Includes translanguaging and funds of knowledge.	Students' broad lived and historical experiences	Context to see relevance for science. Often considered from a *third space*. (communal spaces distinct from home and school/work spaces)
Out-of-class experiences (OOC)	12	Fostering experiences in a non-classroom setting, including informal and outdoor environments, to highlight or explore science content.	Accessible places in which science content is readily experienced	Understand context through science lens.
Socioscientific Inquiry (SSI)	11	Couching science content within societal issues often with a focus on decision-making and ethical or moral considerations.	Societal arenas impacted by science-based decisions	Science to understand and operate within context.
Context-based curriculum (CBC)	7	Using or developing curriculum that uses narrative devices to couch science content in real and relevant scenarios. Includes problem-based learning.	Spheres of life in which science is generally useful.	Context to understand and provide relevance for science.

data collection and analysis and are typically aligned to ongoing research outside of school. Examples include Research Experiences for Teachers, Teacher-Scientist Partnerships, and Citizen Science. In ASP, *science is relevant because it has real and important applications beyond school and it is engaging work when the task is to solve real problems.*

The CRS approach asks teachers to consider the contexts, including linguistic contexts, that students experience outside of class and to use those contexts to help students find relevance in the science content. This work often considers how various contexts mingle, converge, and conflict. Arguably, this is the most challenging operationalization of contextualization for teachers because the contexts are broad, varied, and difficult for the teacher to know in a meaningful way. In the CRS approach, *science is relevant because it is part of everyday lived experience.*

OOC approaches vary more than the other approaches on the degree to which they operationalize contextualization as focusing on the science content or the context itself. In all of these studies there is an intentionality about the place in which learning occurs, whether a museum, a schoolyard, or a natural environment, and there tend to be clear science learning goals. In OOC, *science is engaging because it can be seen and experienced in specific places that reveal otherwise inaccessible aspects of the science-context interactions.*

In the SSI approach, students are asked to see society as a context in which science adds value to the public decision-making process, a space where ethics and morality must also play a role. Many of these studies refer to an informed citizenry as a goal. Contextualization is operationalized as a sociocultural space where the processes and products of science must be used to solve difficult challenges. In SSI, *science is relevant because it is an important tool for society, and it is engaging because it helps us make sense of complicated topics.*

CBC approaches operationalize contextualization as showing how science is applied in practice but focus on problems that are assumed to be relevant to students' daily lives. Curricula focus on context-specific applications of science (e.g., safety of GMO foods), though unlike ASP, they may not be tightly bound to the practices or problems that scientists are currently investigating. Unlike CRS, the approach is not focused on the individual lived experiences of the students. In CBC, *science is important because it can have a direct impact on your own life.*

Teacher Skills, Understanding, and Contextualization

How each approach operationalizes contextualization is more than an academic observation. It has important consequences for how each approach is designed and enacted. Asking students to make sense of their own experiences is a very different task from asking students to make sense of an abstract context. Similarly, applying science knowledge to an immediate experience is quite different from applying it to a hypothetical aspect of one's own life, and still more dissimilar from applying it to an abstract, societal problem. While there are important differences in how each approach operationalizes contextualization, and while each has some discrete skills associated with it, there are skills and understandings that cross approaches. Table 33.2 lists key skills and knowledge that teachers must develop, beyond broader science teaching skills, in order to successfully enact the various contextualization approaches. These skills were identified across studies in each contextualization approach group.

Included in these skills, teachers must be able to see science content in a context, to identify how conceptual science knowledge is applied or revealed in context. They must understand big-picture science concepts while identifying them as phenomena in authentic contexts. Our analysis coalesced around the idea that contextualized instruction requires that teachers deeply understand the context and that this often involves knowledge that is outside of the traditional bounds of science. Understanding context in this way may include: a nuanced understanding of students' home cultures; the cultures that are bound to a specific place; specific details of physical places in authentic settings;

Table 33.2 Teacher skills and knowledge required for successful enactment of contextualized science approaches

Skills or Knowledge	Contextualization Approaches
Understand esoteric science content and skills	ASP, OOC, SSI, CBC
Understand where science phenomena occur locally	CRS, OOC, CBC
Understand cultural-historical views and values across cultures	CRS, SSI
Navigate intersections of science, culture, ethics, history	CRS, SSI
Develop locally relevant curriculum	OOC, CBC
Build relationships with scientists	ASP, OOC
Teach scientific argumentation	ASP, SSI
Understand student lives outside school	CRS, CBC
Manage logistics and student safety	ASP, OOC

the skills, practices, and cultures of specific science communities of practice; and moral, ethical, historic, or humanistic values associated with the science topic. Indeed, truly understanding context may involve all of these aspects. In addition to knowledge of content and knowledge of pedagogy, teachers must develop a knowledge of context that plays an equally important role in contextualized instruction.

Teachers' underlying preparation, skills, and assumptions bound to context may position them for more effective contextualization. For example, PSTs in bilingual programs were shown to have more nuanced, more asset-oriented, and less stereotypical understanding of cultural contexts (Tolbert & Knox, 2016). In other words, surface-level understanding of contexts may not be enough, and teachers may need direct and focused development work to more deeply understand the contexts germane to the curriculum. Deep understanding of cultural contexts, and how they can be intertwined with science instruction, requires long-term commitment and teacher immersion, as Chinn (2006) showed to be effective in developing native Hawaiian-referenced science curriculum and PD. Cultural contexts are not dichotomous, and brief introductions to context risk this misconception. Particularly in places with complicated "confluences of indigeneity and modernity," education can become a hybrid space where the multiple cultural contexts can come to be understood individually and convergently (Handa & Tippins, 2013). While teachers can empower students to bring their own experiences into the classroom, students may not be willing or able to bring in cultural knowledge that is robust enough to allow the teacher to make meaningful science connections (George, 2013). Teachers run the risk of students perceiving science knowledge as superior to or disconnected from indigenous knowledge, and therefore, teachers must use local resources to better understand local and indigenous knowledge (Waldrip et al., 2007).

Teacher Motivations and Confidence With Contextualization

Teacher confidence, motivations, and beliefs were common themes throughout the studies and across approaches, often positioned as a barrier, sometimes as a goal, and always as an interaction between personal and external ways of knowing. Contextualization always implies a personal connection to a context, whether the ethical issues of SSI, the local applications in CBC, biographical relationships in CRS, the enculturation into science of ASP, or a sense of place through OOC. Teachers' beliefs around advocacy, their backgrounds, and therefore their own identities as science learners and practitioners have an impact on their motivation to contextualize instruction. Because contextualization often reaches outside of the perceived objectivity of science, cultural differences in moral, religious, and ethical values create anxiety around teaching SSI issues for some teachers (Kapici & Ilhan, 2016). When teachers perceive tensions between student beliefs and their own, they can be unwilling to adopt a contextualized stance (Kara, 2012). The topics that might cause such tension were not consistent across the geographical regions reported in these papers, suggesting that contextualization must have a local component and teacher supports must start with the actual needs of the teachers involved.

Local knowledge is a rich source of contextualized science knowledge, but the way that teachers conceive of indigenous knowledge has an impact on its use in the classroom and teachers' ability to work this knowledge into instruction (Anderson et al., 2015; Singh-Pillay et al., 2017). Teachers who saw CRS as a two-way exchange were more effective in finding concrete science examples within traditional American Indian knowledge (Nam et al., 2013). Similarly, teachers are often asked to assimilate into a culture of science that may be distant from their own. Wallace and Brooks (2015) have shown that teachers experiencing this tension have a harder time considering the needs and identities of their students, but that when well-supported, teacher identities can change in ways that lead to more inclusive pedagogy. Several papers caution against seeing teachers' inner aspects as barriers and, rather, encourage supported introspection and understanding of teacher needs (e.g., Brown & Crippen, 2017; Singh-Pillay et al., 2017)

Overall, teachers see the value of contextualized instruction, and yet may waver in their motivation to enact it. Teachers have multiple motivations that are both inward, such as an interest in becoming more knowledgeable in the content, as well as outward, such as creating opportunities for students (Rebull et al., 2018). They are often unsure of how to enact contextualized approaches (Torquati et al., 2013). Without well-conceived PD, contextualization can be perceived as too time consuming, and the lack of curriculum resources as problematic (Kara, 2012). For example, external factors, including momentum of traditional curriculum, parental or student wariness of novel approaches, lack of peer support, and uncertainty about ability to achieve science competencies, can create hesitancy to adopt contextualized instruction (Lupión-Cobos et al., 2017). The reviewed studies suggest that brief PD experiences were not enough to overcome perceived barriers to implementing contextualized inquiry and that motivations must be addressed systemically.

Emergence of Student-Centeredness

Throughout what we consider to be science contextualization literature, there is an implicit assumption that through contextualization, individual students will be able to develop a sense of relevance or personal meaning for the science content. It is not surprising, then, that across the approaches student-centeredness was an outcome of supporting teachers to contextualize the curriculum. It is surprising, however, that this outcome was often described as unexpected. Tanzanian teachers, entrenched in a cultural norm of teacher-centered instruction, indicated that highly scaffolded PD helped them to see locally relevant science issues that would lead to bringing more of their students' lives into the classroom (Boger et al., 2013). Teachers in Kenya who were hesitant to implement CBC changed their perspectives when they saw how positively students responded to it, how students began leading the investigations and became "actively emancipated curious learners" (Anderson et al., 2015). In the Kenyan example and several others, it was the students' reactions that convinced the teachers to enact more contextualized, student-centered instruction. Intentionally shifting authority in the classroom can open the curriculum to students' cultural and ethnic resources and leave PSTs feeling more capable of working with a diversity of students (Titu et al., 2018).

PD helped ISTs change from a focus on indirect experiences to students' direct experiences that provided them with expertise/authority they could bring to the table (Brown & Crippen, 2017). In other cases, teachers' own experiences as the students in PD helped them to develop "insights into exploratory behavior" and the potential for students' observations, questions, and wonderings as material to work with (Hughes-McDonnell & Burgess, 2011), or to reconceptualize science research as something that all students could do effectively (Peters-Burton et al., 2015). It seems that starting with student-centeredness can lead to contextualization, or starting with contextualization can lead to student-centered learning. Of course, teachers must be open to these changes. One study found that a PD approach that focused on the concerns of individual teachers allowed all teachers to move toward more student-centered instruction (de Putter-Smits, 2020).

Supporting Teachers With Strategies for Enactment

At the center of this review is the question of how teachers can be supported to enact contextualized science instruction. The skills and knowledge listed in Table 33.2 provide an outline for what a PD series or methods course could address, particularly if focused on those skills that span multiple approaches. Figure 33.1 suggests specific strategies that can be used to help PSTs and ISTs develop contextualized instruction skills. In considering such PD, one must also consider the barriers to contextualization that teachers must overcome, including limited instructional time, ethical concerns,

1. Provide ongoing, intensive, crosscutting PD initiatives
2. Develop PD around a crosscutting contextualization framework that spans approaches
3. Problematize the complexity of context
4. Provide specific instruction on the context
5. Provide instruction on connecting specific contexts to specific science content
6. Make a clear distinction between understanding context and teaching through context
7. Provide contextualized immersion experiences for teachers
8. Model authentic practices as well as contextualized instruction
9. Understand and build from teachers' past experiences and belief systems
10. Provide teachers choice and agency with the contexts used in instruction
11. Build PD around contextualized curriculum development
12. Coaching or mentor ISTs in contextualized instruction
13. Prioritize authentic science experience in undergraduate coursework
14. Incentivize professional science training prior to teaching.

Figure 33.1   Strategies to support teachers in contextualized instruction

alignment to standards or testing, lack of training, limited curriculum materials, and the complexity that is bound to real contexts.

There is a clear recognition in this body of work that *there are two different steps to contextualizing instruction: understanding the context from the perspective of the content and* then *implementing relevant curriculum with students.* When contextualized instruction did not materialize within the reviewed studies, a disconnect between learning and enacting was often the culprit. Peters-Burton et al. (2015) showed that teachers changed their ability to apply scientific reasoning to data-driven, authentic problems following a cognitive apprenticeship with scientists but then did not readily apply these changes to their own teaching. Supplementing a teacher research experience with instruction on how to translate that to the classroom, however, can improve contextualization in lesson plans (Herrington et al., 2012). In one study, teachers developed a sense of how contextualized approaches build student interest when the teachers acted as students and specific instructional moves were modeled (Roehrig et al., 2011). Schumacher and Reiners (2013) helped PSTs consider implementation before they were ready to do so on their own by asking them to evaluate videos of "authentic" contextualized lessons to determine where students might need support. Across the OOC set, there was agreement that the more teachers are exposed to their own OOC learning, the better the development of their pedagogical and science knowledge.

Asking teachers to learn new pedagogies, new science content, as well as new contexts was repeatedly described as overwhelming for teachers, even with PD that would be considered extensive in other fields. However, several studies did see positive results when teachers received sufficient support in content, context, *and* were specifically supported to implement them in the classroom. Following a 1-year, intensive, research experience for teachers, and despite resistance to change, teachers showed a significant positive change in contextualized practices, a change they attributed to self-efficacy and confidence built from a combination of the research experience and matched pedagogical instruction (Amolins et al., 2015). It is clear that context, content, and pedagogy need to be scaffolded together, and this should happen in PST programs, through teacher research experiences, and through modeled experiences with local contexts (Windschitl, 2003).

One strategy, described heavily in the SSI studies, includes *teachers learning how to problematize the complexity itself* (e.g., Sadler et al., 2006), a task often associated with long-term, ongoing, and intensive PD. There was a common call for extensive and intensive PD approaches. There is a sense from these studies that contextualization skills are not picked up in a brief workshop. For example, a short PST experience of working with students in a school garden left the PSTs with the perception of learning opportunities, but the PSTs still relied on teacher-centered pedagogies that did not work well with a contextualized orientation (Rosenthal, 2018). Non-science early childhood educators improved CRS instruction and attitudes towards CRS only superficially after a year of intensive PD but made much more significant gains after 2 years of sustained and intensive PD (Roehrig et al., 2011). Similarly, a two-course graduate sequence helped but did not entirely overcome teachers' difficulties with implementing SSI (Glazewski et al., 2014). Extended support in the classroom, including coaching and mentoring, may be a more effective PD approach if trying to address the vast conceptual and practical knowledge involved with these contextualization approaches (Lehman et al., 2006).

Within the ASP, CRS, and OOC studies, findings explicitly state *that teacher PD should incorporate immersion into the authentic environments to make sense of the complexity.* This includes collaboration with experts, practice of science skills in authentic environments, and teacher immersion into their students' cultures. In Trinidad and Tobago, George and Lubben (2002) had teachers focus on local contexts and shift their focus from student deficits to the everyday contexts of their students' lives. Teachers expanded their information sources, looking more externally into the community than they were used to. Across the ASP studies, scientists as mentors were also shown to be widely effective in helping teachers to understand how science skills and knowledge could be contextualized in authentic practice.

Regardless of the PD teachers participate in, *teacher background may be a better predictor for enactment of contextualized curriculum.* Windschitl (2003) showed that teachers who were most likely to adopt contextualized science practices were not those who had the deepest theoretical views on the pedagogy, but those who had prior professional experience or undergraduate experience using the specific practices. Further, teachers are most likely to implement those science skills that relate to personal pre-teaching science experiences (Sezen-Barrie et al., 2015). Because teachers need to identify the science in a given context, a lack of content knowledge also can be problematic (Glazewski et al., 2014). When elementary teachers, who may have very little science education and experience, are asked to contextualize science, they are likely to focus on the context over content if not supported (Yerrick & Beatty-Adler, 2011). The importance of teacher experiences implies a need for a three-pronged approach that would include better recruitment of science professionals to teaching careers, a greater focus on authentic science experiences in undergraduate and PST experiences, and the provision of similar experiences during long-term IST PD efforts.

Given the importance of teacher background experience, *PD is most likely to succeed when teacher needs are understood and the intervention is responsive to those needs.* In one study, teaching experience level was a good predictor of teacher concerns with CBC, and all teachers were able to progress when their specific concerns were addressed (de Putter-Smits et al., 2020). Papers across the SSI and CBC approaches stressed the importance of teacher agency in choosing the topics of study in order to align with teachers' experiences and knowledge. Both Sadler et al. (2006) and Nam et al. (2013) stress that teachers who are focused on barriers to enactment have different PD needs from those of teachers who are trying to optimize contextualization for student learning. Formative assessment during the PD can help to identify the changing needs over time (Roehrig et al., 2011), and involving teachers in the planning can help to appropriately match the needs with the PD (Yerrick & Beatty-Adler, 2011).

Developing their own contextualized curriculum was empowering for teachers (George & Lubben, 2002) and they were more likely to implement CBC when they had a significant role in developing the curriculum (Elster, 2009). A lack of contextualized curriculum is often reported as a barrier to enactment, perhaps due to the localized nature of the context featured in many of these approaches, and so the curriculum development approach to PD also helps to break down this barrier. For example, the provision and adaptation of specific curriculum materials for conducting local citizen science projects led to a commitment of implementation for hesitant teachers in Tanzania (Boger et al., 2013). However, teachers can experience tension when trying to map local contexts back onto a macro-level curriculum because many cultural practices and beliefs are not clearly aligned to current science explanations (George & Lubben, 2002). This suggests that *support for contextualization of curriculum needs to be cyclical, as teachers consider micro-level contexts and macro-level standards.*

There is a call across studies in the SSI group, and supported by papers in the other groups, for the teaching of specific contextualization skills in PST programs, such as argumentation and ethical reasoning. When a contextualization framework is lacking, teachers often try to use contexts but fail to connect them to broader themes (Klosterman et al., 2012). *A crosscutting contextualization skills framework would be necessary for a systemic approach to PD.* Teachers must come to see contextualized approaches as in alignment with and supportive of standards, not an alternative (Sadler et al., 2006); and this, too, is a skill that must be learned. The cautionary tale across these studies is that learning to enact contextualized approaches requires a vast set of skills and knowledge that exceeds what can be reasonably acquired within an isolated PD intervention and may require a concerted effort that spans PST programs or systemic IST PD programs over multiple, intensive years.

An Agenda for Future Research

This collection of largely self-report studies provides a starting point for more objectively examining how teachers can be supported to effectively contextualize their instruction in ways that lead to improved learning outcomes. Only a few studies included observation or measurement of enactment, and this gap represents a much-needed opportunity for future research. Across these approaches, researchers need to move toward tracking these teacher interventions to determine their impact on students.

Developing and testing initial ideas that are presented through the specific instances of these papers into crosscutting pedagogies is an important next step in this work. It would be worthwhile to test interventions common to one approach across the other approaches. For example, it would be worthwhile to know if teacher beliefs have as great an impact on CBC or OOC approaches as they do within SSI. Similarly, it would be worth testing whether mentorship can improve contextualized instruction in SSI as it does in ASP approaches.

The strength of considering all of these approaches as instantiations of a common learning phenomenon is the ability to compare more readily across studies. To reliably do so would require the development of instruments to measure inputs and outcomes of contextualization (Giamellaro, 2017), and the studies presented here may provide a good starting point. A crosscutting contextualization skills framework would be necessary for developing and testing a systemic approach to PD. While the skills and PD strategies described here were variably successful for supporting individual approaches, it is not clear to what extent they would be successful across approaches. The gold standard in this field would be to create and test a PST program that introduced all of these approaches through the lens of contextualization and measured PSTs' ability to translate between approaches, eventually implementing them in practice.

Conclusion

In order to create PST methods courses or IST PD opportunities that treat contextualization as a common phenomenon, the field needs to better understand the implications for how we operationalize contextualization. The five approaches described in this review operationalize contextualization differently, and this results in different ways of thinking about science education. Is place-based science engaging because it can be seen and experienced, revealing otherwise inaccessible aspects of the science-context interactions, or is it engaging because the task is to solve real problems? Is science relevant because it is part of everyday lived experience, because it has real and important applications beyond school, or because it is an important tool for society? Is science actually perceived by students as important because it can have a direct impact on their own lives? Probably all of these considerations are true and important. Certainly, how one answers such questions will have an impact on how a teacher approaches contextualization as well as on the student outcomes. The first step in such an approach is to ask the question of why contextualization is to be used in a teaching-learning sequence. The second step is to pick the appropriate approach to meet those goals.

If these five approaches are based on different operationalizations of contextualization, and the skill sets needed for each are not all common, is it worthwhile to aggregate them for the purposes of teacher education? We argue that it is. Throughout the papers we reviewed, the authors describe similar barriers to implementation (e.g., standards, testing, time, lack of material and professional support). If teachers can learn to overcome these barriers broadly, they are better positioned to address them when adopting any of the other approaches, or a new approach that has not yet been developed. If teachers can learn to see these barriers as applying to contextualization broadly, they can develop transferable tools for overcoming the barriers. Also, in considering the full breadth of approaches, findings from each can advance the other more quickly when they are recognized as of a kind.

Perhaps the most important finding from this review is at once the most obvious and the most underdeveloped in science teacher education: *context matters*. It is not just the background; it is an essential mediating tool (Vygotsky, 1978). Teachers and their students cannot be expected to understand context and how it relates to science content without any support for doing so. This is a challenging problem to solve in teacher education because it is difficult, perhaps impossible, to address at scale.

Given the right support, teachers can become more adept at teaching from a contextualized stance, though there are no shortcuts to doing this work and teachers need to be directly involved. Measuring and self-reflecting on beliefs, confidence, and self-efficacy seems like a good starting place across these approaches. Providing teachers with a supported, perhaps ongoing, immersion experience into the context could be next (Rebull et al., 2018). Some building blocks of contextualized instruction, such as teaching authentic scientific practices (Miller & Kastens, 2018), or surface-level context, such as general patterns of research within a domain, can be learned episodically (Mishra et al., 2019). Teachers must then be involved in developing or adapting the curriculum, but they must be supported and collaborative in this process. They can also accelerate their contextualized science instruction by recognizing synergies such as those that exist between students' cultural backgrounds and local, authentic science contexts (Tolbert & Knox, 2016). Still, transfer to new contexts can be elusive (Mandrikas et al., 2018), and this is a skill that must be learned by both teachers and students. Finally, teachers need specific tools and methods for bringing together the context and content for their students.

The need for teachers to develop or adapt their own curriculum, to make sure it is localized and aligned to culturally bound morality and ethics, to make sure it is true to the practices and understanding of science, and to deliver it in such a way that students have agency and see relevancy is an unrealistic expectation if this work is not addressed in a long-term, intentional, and intensive way. Teacher confidence with contextualized methods results from competence in them. PD needs to be designed around actual teacher needs, it needs to support teachers over the long term as they develop competence, and teachers need to experience their students' engagement when these approaches are enacted well. These many requirements for success lead us to conclude that there would be benefit from ISTs and PSTs learning to teach from a contextualized stance first and then branching out to the specific approaches. If they learn how to become more knowledgeable about specific science content, local or germane contexts, and the pedagogy used to bring them together, they should be able to see what student-centered pedagogy looks like and how it is experienced by students. As contextualization emerges as a phenomenon that crosses reform approaches, science education will benefit from the efficiency of understanding and applying it broadly and regularly.

References

Amolins, M. W., Ezrailson, C. M., Pearce, D. A., Elliott, A. J., & Vitiello, P. F. (2015). Evaluating the effectiveness of a laboratory-based professional development program for science educators. *Advances in Physiology Education, 39*(4), 341–351. https://doi.org/10.1152/advan.00088.2015

Anderson, D., Nashon, S., Namazzi, E., Okemwa, P., Ombogo, P., Ooko, S., & Beru, F. (2015). Transformations in Kenyan science teachers' locus of control: The Influence of contextualized science and emancipated student learning. *Journal of Science Teacher Education, 26*(7), 599–617. https://doi.org/10.1007/s10972-015-9440-5

Boger, R., Yule, S., & Sparrow, E. (2013). Strategies for teaching to a changing world: Lessons from Arusha, Tanzania. *International Research in Geographical and Environmental Education, 22*(3), 209–225. https://doi.org/10.1080/10382046.2013.817655

Brown, J. C., & Crippen, K. J. (2016). The growing awareness inventory: Building capacity for culturally responsive science and mathematics with a structured observation protocol. *School Science and Mathematics, 116*(3), 127–138. https://doi.org/10.1111/ssm.12163

Brown, J. C., & Crippen, K. J. (2017). The knowledge and practices of high school science teachers in pursuit of cultural responsiveness. *Science Education, 101*(1), 99–133. https://doi.org/10.1002/sce.21250

Chinn, P. W. U. (2006). Preparing science teachers for culturally diverse students: Developing cultural literacy through cultural immersion, cultural translators and communities of practice. *Cultural Studies of Science Education, 1*(2), 367–402. https://doi.org/10.1007/s11422-006-9014-0

de Putter-Smits, L., G. A., Nieveen, N. M., Taconis, R., & Jochems, W. (2020). A one-year teacher professional development programme towards context-based science education using a concerns-based approach. *Professional Development in Education, Published Online*, 18. https://doi.org/10.1080/19415257.2020.1712616

Elster, D. (2009). Biology in context: Teachers' professional development in learning communities. *Journal of Biological Education, 43*(2), 53–61. https://doi.org/10.1080/00219266.2009.9656152

Engle, R. A., Nguyen, P. D., & Mendelson, A. (2011). The influence of framing on transfer: Initial evidence from a tutoring experiment. *Instructional Science, 39*(5), 603–628. https://doi.org/10.1007/s11251-010-9145-2

George, J. M. (2013). 'Do you have to pack?' – Preparing for culturally relevant science teaching in the Caribbean. *International Journal of Science Education, 35*(12), 2114–2131. https://doi.org/10.1080/09500693.2012.760138

George, J. M., & Lubben, F. (2002). Facilitating teachers' professional growth through their involvement in creating context-based materials in science. *International Journal of Educational Development, 22*(6), 659–672. https://doi.org/10.1016/S0738-0593(01)00033-5

Giamellaro, M. (2014). Primary contextualization of science learning through immersion in content-rich settings. *International Journal of Science Education, 36*(17), 2848–2871. https://doi.org/10.1080/09500693.2014.937787

Giamellaro, M. (2017). Dewey's yardstick: Contextualization as a measure of experience in learning and education. *SAGE Open, 7*(1), 1–11. https://doi.org/10.1177/2158244017700463

Glazewski, K., Shuster, M. I., Brush, T., & Ellis, A. (2014). Conexiones: Fostering socioscientific inquiry in graduate teacher preparation. *Interdisciplinary Journal of Problem-Based Learning, 8*(1). https://doi.org/10.7771/1541-5015.1419

Handa, V. C., & Tippins, D. J. (2013). Tensions in the third space: Locating relevancy in preservice science teacher preparation. *International Journal of Science and Mathematics Education, 11*(1), 237–265. https://doi.org/10.1007/s10763-012-9364-x

Herrington, D. G., Luxford, K., & Yezierski, E. J. (2012). Target inquiry: Helping teachers use a research experience to transform their teaching practices. *Journal of Chemical Education, 89*(4), 442–448. https://doi.org/10.1021/ed1006458

Hughes-McDonnell, F. J., & Burgess, D. R. (2011). Teacher explorations of science and science learning generate insights into inquiry and teaching. *LEARNing Landscapes, 4*(2), 195–213. https://doi.org/10.36510/learnland.v4i2.396

Kapici, H. O., & Ilhan, G. (2016). Pre-service teachers' attitudes toward socio-scientific issues and their views about nuclear power plants. *Journal of Baltic Science Education, 15*(5), 642–652.

Kara, Y. (2012). Pre-service biology teachers' perceptions on the instruction of socio-scientific issues in the curriculum. *European Journal of Teacher Education, 35*(1), 111–129. https://doi.org/10.1080/02619768.201 1.633999

King, D., & Ritchie, S. M. (2012). Learning science through real-world contexts. In B. J. Fraser, K. Tobin, & C. J. McRobbie (Eds.), *Second international handbook of science education* (Vol. 24, pp. 69–79). Springer Netherlands. http://link.springer.com/10.1007/978-1-4020-9041-7_6

Klosterman, M. L., Sadler, T. D., & Brown, J. (2012). Science teachers' use of mass media to address socio-scientific and sustainability issues. *Research in Science Education, 42*(1), 51–74. https://doi.org/10.1007/s11165-011-9256-z

Lehman, J. D., George, M., Buchanan, P., & Rush, M. (2006). Preparing teachers to use problem-centered, inquiry-based science: Lessons from a four-year professional development project. *Interdisciplinary Journal of Problem-Based Learning, 1*(1). https://doi.org/10.7771/1541-5015.1007

Lupión-Cobos, T., López-Castilla, R., & Blanco-López, Á. (2017). What do science teachers think about developing scientific competences through context-based teaching? A case study. *International Journal of Science Education, 39*(7), 937–963. https://doi.org/10.1080/09500693.2017.1310412

Mandrikas, A., Stavrou, D., Halkia, K., & Skordoulis, C. (2018). Preservice elementary teachers' study concerning wind on weather maps. *Journal of Science Teacher Education, 29*(1), 65–82. https://doi.org/10.1080/104 6560X.2017.1423458

Miller, A. R., & Kastens, K. A. (2018). Investigating the impacts of targeted professional development around models and modeling on teachers' instructional practice and student learning. *Journal of Research in Science Teaching, 55*(5), 641–663. https://doi.org/10.1002/tea.21434

Mishra, C., Ha, S. J., Parker, L. C., & Clase, K. L. (2019). Describing teacher conceptions of technology in authentic science inquiry using technological pedagogical content knowledge as a lens. *Biochemistry and Molecular Biology Education, 00*(00), 1–8.

Nam, Y., Roehrig, G., Kern, A., & Reynolds, B. (2013). Perception and practices of culturally relevant science teaching in American Indian classrooms. *International Journal of Science and Mathematics Education, 11*(1), 143–167. https://doi.org/10.1007/s10763-012-9372-x

Peters-Burton, E. E., Merz, S. A., Ramirez, E. M., & Saroughi, M. (2015). The effect of cognitive apprenticeship-based professional development on teacher self-efficacy of science teaching, motivation, knowledge, calibration, and perceptions of inquiry-based teaching. *Journal of Science Teacher Education, 26*(6), 525–548. https://doi.org/10.1007/s10972-015-9436-1

Rebull, L. M., Roberts, T., Laurence, W., Fitzgerald, M., French, D., Gorjian, V., & Squires, G. K. (2018). Motivations of educators for participating in NITARP, an authentic astronomy research experience professional development program. *Physical Review Physics Education Research, 14*(2), 020102. https://doi.org/10.1103/PhysRevPhysEducRes.14.020102

Roehrig, G. H., Dubosarsky, M., Mason, A., Carlson, S., & Murphy, B. (2011). We look more, listen more, notice more : Impact of sustained professional development on head start teachers' inquiry-based and culturally-relevant science teaching practices. *Journal of Science Education and Technology, 20*(5), 566–578.

Rosenthal, J. L. (2018). Teacher candidates in the garden. *Science Activities: Classroom Projects and Curriculum Ideas, 55*(1), 20–27. https://doi.org/10.1080/00368121.2017.1403875

Sadler, T. D., Amirshokoohi, A., Kazempour, M., & Allspaw, K. M. (2006). Socioscience and ethics in science classrooms: Teacher perspectives and strategies. *Journal of Research in Science Teaching, 43*(4), 353–376. https://doi.org/10.1002/tea.20142

Schumacher, A., & Reiners, C. S. (2013). Designing authentic Learning environments in chemistry lessons: Paving the way in pre-service teacher education. *Science & Education, 22*(9), 2173–2191. https://doi.org/10.1007/s11191-012-9552-7

Sezen-Barrie, A., Moore, J., & Roig, C. E. (2015). Discovering plate boundaries in data-integrated environments: Preservice teachers' conceptualization and implementation of scientific practices. *International Journal of Science Education, 37*(12), 2013–2037. https://doi.org/10.1080/09500693.2015.1061226

Singh-Pillay, A., Alant, B. P., & Nwokocha, G. (2017). Tapping into basic 7–9 science and technology teachers' conceptions of indigenous knowledge in Imo State, Nigeria. *African Journal of Research in Mathematics, Science and Technology Education, 21*(2), 125–135. https://doi.org/10.1080/18117295.2017.1327240

Stark, S. M., Reagh, Z. M., Yassa, M. A., & Stark, C. E. L. (2017). What's in a context? Cautions, limitations, and potential paths forward. *Neuroscience Letters, 680*, 77–87. https://doi.org/10.1016/j.neulet.2017.05.022

Titu, P., Ring-Whalen, E. A., Brown, J. C., & Roehrig, G. H. (2018). Exploring changes in science teachers' attitudes toward culturally diverse students during an equity-focused course. *Journal of Science Teacher Education, 29*(5), 378–396. https://doi.org/10.1080/1046560X.2018.1461006

Tolbert, S., & Knox, C. (2016). 'They might know a lot of things that I don't know': Investigating differences in preservice teachers' ideas about contextualizing science instruction in multilingual classrooms. *International Journal of Science Education*, *38*(7), 1133–1149. https://doi.org/10.1080/09500693.2016.1183266

Torquati, J., Cutler, K., Gilkerson, D., & Sarver, S. (2013). Early childhood educators' perceptions of nature, science, and environmental education. *Early Education & Development*, *24*(5), 721–743. https://doi.org/10.1080/10409289.2012.725383

Vygotsky, L. S. (1978). *Mind in society*. Cambridge, MA: Harvard University Press.

Waldrip, B. G., Timothy, J. T., & Wilikai, W. (2007). Pedagogic principles in negotiating cultural conflict: A Melanesian example. *International Journal of Science Education*, *29*(1), 101–122. https://doi.org/10.1080/09500690600718195

Wallace, C. S., & Brooks, L. (2015). Learning to teach elementary science in an experiential, informal context: Culture, learning, and identity. *Science Education*, *99*(1), 174–198. https://doi.org/10.1002/sce.21138

Windschitl, M. (2003). Inquiry projects in science teacher education: What can investigative experiences reveal about teacher thinking and eventual classroom practice? *Science Education*, *87*(1), 112–143. https://doi.org/10.1002/sce.10044

Yerrick, R., & Beatty-Adler, D. (2011). Addressing equity and diversity with teachers through informal science institutions and teacher professional development. *Journal of Science Teacher Education*, *22*(3), 229–253. https://doi.org/10.1007/s10972-011-9226-3

34

LEARNING IN AND THROUGH RESEARCHER-TEACHER COLLABORATION

Eve Manz, Sara C. Heredia, Carrie D. Allen, and William R. Penuel

Introduction

This chapter examines how science teacher education perspectives can be enriched by strands of research that are collaborative in nature – where educators, researchers, and other community members learn together. In the research reviewed, teachers are co-participants alongside researchers in terms of designing and testing new systems of activity, and each brings their own expertise coupled with their own uncertainty as to what will be the best way to organize science and engineering[1] learning for and with youth. These partnerships take up essential questions and challenges in science education – some that have proved intractable for decades – including how to support deep and meaningful science learning for children and youth; how to support teachers to shift practices in ways that are sustainable; and how to address equity, justice, and power in science classrooms and school systems.

As the chapter details, a collaborative perspective calls for a re-definition of science teacher learning to include the disruption, redesign, and development of infrastructures for science teaching and learning. This systems-focused view is a necessary complement to the emphasis on educators' understandings, practices, and identities that have typically informed design and analysis in science teacher education research (National Academies of Science and Engineering, 2016). A major focus has been teacher learning of content, gains in efficacy related to the specific curricula and/or science teaching practices, and increased pedagogical content knowledge for teaching in science. However, the challenges and foci currently facing the field require forms of development that are not yet known by researchers and that transcend what individuals can know and do, requiring attention to the systems within which teachers learn and act.

This chapter examines collaboration, and the learning collaboration affords, through the lens of *expansive learning*, in which "learners learn something that is not yet there, [where] the learners construct a new object and concept for their collective activity, and implement this new object and concept in practice" (Engeström & Sannino, 2010, p. 2). What is "not yet there" are well-articulated objects for what it takes to develop concepts from research and practice so that they produce infrastructures for creating and sustaining equitable change in science education. These infrastructures include more than the designs for professional learning that are a common focus of science teacher education research: they include supports for making sense of, challenging, and transforming educational systems. The chapter describes five mechanisms that support expansive learning in science education, drawing on a review of science education literature related to research on teacher-researcher collaboration since the 1990s.

DOI: 10.4324/9781003098478-40

Theoretical Framing

To analyze collaborative researcher-teacher learning, this chapter draws from Jean Lave's (1996) description of theories of learning as stipulating a *telos* (direction of learning), *subject-world relations*, and *learning mechanisms* (Table 34.1). Sociocultural theorists (e.g., Lave, 1996; Packer, 2010) conceptualize the world and person acting and learning in it as jointly constituted. This chapter draws

Table 34.1 Metaphors guiding research on science teacher education[2]

Theory	Telos	Subject-World Relation	Learning Mechanisms/Organizing for Learning
Learning as acquisition	Teachers acquire skills and understandings, e.g., understanding of nature of science or pedagogical content knowledge for teaching science	• Subject and independent world • Learning and knowledge relatively independent of context • Productive beliefs and understandings static and known • Researcher as subject is often invisible	• Accommodation, adaptation, and assimilation • Transfer and/or application • Structured engagement with and practice of knowledge (e.g., through cognitive conflict, worked examples, self-explanation, reflection)
Learning as participation	Teachers develop identities, perspectives, and teaching practices that support shifts in their science teaching, often toward more meaningful and practice-based learning for students.	• People and practices co-constitute each other and shift together • Context is often taken up as definable and as fixed or slow-changing; while the practices of individuals and local communities shift, the "practice" as a whole is taken as static or beyond the bounds of design • Contexts outside of the community of practice of focus may be rendered invisible (e.g., of researchers, the non-designed for contexts of teachers)	• Participation in collective activity • Apprenticeship • Practice within and across settings
Learning as Expansion	Transformation and creation of culture; horizontal movement and hybridization rather than vertical and linear development	• People, practices, and worlds co-constitute each other • Context inseparable from activity, therefore site of studying and supporting shifts to same extent as people and activity are • Centers multiple contexts, boundary crossings, subjectivity of all participants, including researcher	• Surfacing multiple values and points of view[3] • Engaging with organizational tensions • Co-designing artifacts to support educators' practice • Infrastructuring • Re-mediating relations

additionally from Packer (2010), who points out that the researcher, too, must be seen as constituting the world they seek to study, and Bang and Vossoughi (2016), who direct us to orient to the quality of subject–subject relations by treating the categories of "researcher" and "researched" as porous and as a focus for re-imagining.

Science teacher learning and science teacher education research has typically been informed by "learning as acquisition" and/or "learning as participation" metaphors (Engeström & Sannino, 2010; Sfard, 1998) (Table 34.1). Research has been predominantly focused on documenting ways that teachers acquire knowledge and skill needed for teaching, or how they apprentice into practice-focused science instruction. From the perspective of both of these approaches, researchers bring the theory or framework for evaluating teachers' practice, and the broader contexts of teaching, as taking place within dynamically changing school and district environments and are rarely considered as objects worthy of attention.

First, an assumption of science teacher education research based in acquisition and participation metaphors is that researchers are in the position to specify the targets of teacher education; that is, that we know what constitutes good teaching. In fact, partly due to our positions outside schools, but also because of the tentativity and insufficiency of the frames we bring to the study of equitable teaching and educational justice, we are in a poor position as researchers to offer such prescriptions. Further, researchers are engaged in debates and shifts in *our own* understanding of the goals of science education, how to develop learning environments that support students' agency and meaningful learning, and how to disrupt frameworks to develop just and equitable learning environments (Berland et al., 2019; Fortney et al., 2019; Parsons, 2019).

In addition, acquisition and participation metaphors do not provide the conceptual and design tools to engage fully teachers' context or to move beyond context as an explanatory variable. Limited and incoherent opportunities to learn (National Academies of Sciences Engineering and Medicine, 2016) and local norms and politics (Oakes & Lipton, 2002) make it difficult for teachers to adopt new teaching practices. Traditionally, science teacher education research has focused on the remediation of deficits in teachers' understandings and beliefs through professional learning programs, rather than looking to understand how the organizational context shapes and influences the ways in which science teachers make instructional decisions (Allen & Heredia, 2021) or for researchers to hold themselves to account for supporting the design of conditions for effective implementation (Penuel, 2019a). Ignoring organizational conditions that shape teacher learning is, in part, overlooking local histories, cultural dynamics of school and science, and issues of power that show up within school buildings and science teachers' classrooms.

This chapter reviews and calls for further development of *collaborative* teacher learning research in science education and argues that taking up the telos, relations, and learning mechanisms of expansive learning can provide useful strategies and implications for the field. The research reviewed here takes the perspective that researchers and teachers must work together, bringing different foci and expertise, to develop new understandings and practices. A second premise is that to accomplish equity-oriented change, systems of activity must become objects of redesign and levers for change (Allen & Heredia, 2021; Penuel, 2019a). Third, to support expansive learning, collaborative research demands strategies for changing traditional divisions of labor and attending to interactional dynamics as shaped by power, history, and intersectional identities of participants (Gutiérrez & Jurow, 2016).

Review of Collaborative Strands of Science Teacher Education Research

Collaborative learning has a long history in educational research, with groups of educators and researchers explicitly challenging and seeking to blur divisions of labor between researcher and educator established in the early 20th century that limited teacher agency and created alignments of education research with administration of education (Cuban, 1993). This work has been driven by a commitment to inquiry grounded in practice and to developing respectful and mutually trusting relationships between educators and researchers (Cochran-Smith & Lytle, 1993; Zeichner, 1995). This chapter reviews work from 1995 to 2020 within strands of science education research that have emphasized collaborative learning with educators (Table 34.2).

To conduct this review, the team used the criteria that papers needed to: (1) focus on science or engineering education; (2) describe how science teachers were involved in design, implementation, and/or analysis; and (3) consider learning by teachers, researchers, and/or the system. Further, the team recognized that research on collaborative learning has occurred within particular strands of research or families of methodological approaches (e.g., co-generative dialogue, design-based research) (Table 34.2). By reading multiple seminal papers on these approaches, the team developed search terms, conducted searches, and read abstracts and methods sections to determine whether studies met inclusion criteria. The authors supplemented searches by including pieces that were familiar, given the authors' expertise in the area of science teacher-researcher collaborations; mining the reference lists of papers; and conducting backward searches for literature citing seminal papers for newer approaches.

Table 34.2 Approaches that have used researcher-teacher collaboration

Approach	Description	Seminal Pieces and Example Science Education Studies
Joint Inquiry	Small groups of researchers and teachers engaging in collaborative learning that emphasize the teacher as inquirer and knower, the need to rethink and democratize what counts as knowledge about practice, and altering the accepted roles and content of research practice.	• Roth et al. (2002) • Herrenkohl et al. (2010) • Esteban-Guitart et al. (2018) • Hamza et al. (2018) • Areljung et al. (2021)
Collaborative Design and Co-Design	Collaborators, drawing on differing expertise and goals, design and iterate on curriculum, assessments, and routines to support sustained changes to classroom practice. Often connected to design-based research.	• Reiser et al. (2000) • Voogt et al. (2015) • Hundal et al. (2014) • Kidron and Kali (2017)
Design-Based Implementation Research	A form of design-based research focused on building capacity within systems for sustainable and equitable change, drawing from design-based research and policy implementation studies.	• Hall et al. (2021) • Penuel (2019a, 2019b)
Improvement Science/ Networked Improvement Communities	Groups and networks of collaborators use systems analysis tools and structured inquiry cycles to design and test incremental changes to educational practices.	• Bryk et al. (2015) • Thompson et al. (2019) • Campbell et al. (2019) • Riedy et al. (2018)
Social Design Studies	Participants seek to transform institutional structures and relationships through engaging participants in uncovering contradictions, constructing new practices and tools, and, often, promoting justice by envisioning and enacting radical new possibilities for activity and learning.	• Bang and Vossoughi (2016) • Gutiérrez and Jurow (2016) • Bang et al. (2010) • Kumpulainen et al. (2018)

Articles were reviewed to understand commonalities and differences across approaches to collaborative researcher-teacher learning. The team first developed a description of the theoretical underpinnings, strategies, and forms of learning occurring in each approach. These initial descriptions highlighted the ways that aspects of an expansive learning frame guided the strategies and forms of learning described across studies. Further, the team began to see some patterns across approaches, in terms of the kinds of mechanisms of learning they supported. The remainder of the paper is organized to describe these mechanisms, because they can help orient designers of science teacher education toward ways of organizing and examining learning in teacher-researcher collaborations.

Mechanisms for Learning and Ways of Organizing Collaboration

The remainder of the chapter describes mechanisms for learning in collaboration, guided by an expansive learning frame (see Table 34.1) and considers their implications for ways of organizing and attending to researchers' and science teachers' learning.

Surfacing Multiple Values and Points of View

The articles reviewed underlined the importance of surfacing, valuing, and designing for the perspectives of different participants, including, but not limited to, researchers and teachers. Design-focused lines of work invite stakeholders' viewpoints at multiple stages (Bang et al., 2016; DiSalvo et al., 2017). Efforts to rethink organizational systems of science teaching and learning report the importance of structured protocols for surfacing different perspectives (Riedy et al., 2018). Surfacing multiple points of view is necessary for expansive learning, because it allows participants to understand each other's activities, values, and constraints and to develop goals for shared activity (Reiser et al., 2000). Further, surfacing different perspectives helps participants understand contradictions in and across their systems of activity; for example, teachers' perceptions of their goals for professional learning as compared to the goals that districts and universities were designing professional learning to address (Yamagata-Lynch & Haudenschild, 2009). This work is essential to expand from individuals acting within constraints toward collective activity to shift systems (Engeström & Sannino, 2010).

Herrenkohl et al. (2010) describe two ways of organizing collaborations to support surfacing different perspectives. The context is their joint inquiry into implementing student roles that support scientific theory building and evaluation in upper elementary grades. They identify pivotal episodes in their collaboration where multiple points of view on a lesson allowed them to expand the space of activity. Several of these concerned the relative balance of "intellectual" and "procedural" direction for students in their roles in small-group investigations and report-outs; where teachers' concerns for, and understanding of, classroom organizational routines were integral to designing and orchestrating the science learning environment. Second, the authors highlight the importance of the researcher taking on a co-teaching role, allowing her to think with teachers and students in moments of orchestration and to experience the risks and responsibilities teachers face (see also Hamza et al., 2018; Roth et al., 2002).

Research focused on surfacing different points of view highlights that knowledge of science teaching is multi-perspectival and situated. Researchers' views of the constraints teachers face or the multiple goals and needs they juggle in teaching practice are often incomplete and can, when not challenged, lead to deficit views of teachers (Gray et al., 2021). A second theme is variation in when and how different perspectives are invited into collaborative research, how varying perspectives shape the collaboration, and how they are reported. These choices have remained an enduring source of tension (Areljung et al., 2021; Calabrese Barton & Johnson, 2002; Ormel et al., 2012). Researchers and practitioners report struggling to develop and orchestrate roles that balance the time, risk, responsibility, and ownership of collaborative work. One strategy that may be productive is to create space for participants to act as boundary crossers and brokers; for example, placing researchers in co-teaching roles, compensating teachers to engage in research, or involving participants (e.g., district coaches, graduate students) whose roles offer space and support for hybridity.

Co-Designing Artifacts to Support Educators' Practice

Collaborative efforts often center the development of a tangible product or process and engage participants throughout theory development, design, analysis, and refinement of products and understandings (Penuel et. al, 2007; Voogt et al., 2015). Teachers, researchers, and other participants might co-develop innovative student-centered science laboratory experiences (Aksela, 2019), after-school programs promoting argumentation through environmental health study (Hundal et al., 2014), or learning experiences incorporating researcher-designed technology (Tissenbaum et al., 2012; Matuk et al., 2015).

Co-designing artifacts emerges both from a concern for the usability of researcher-designed materials (Penuel et al., 2007) and from evidence on how design can support teachers' beliefs, understandings, and practice (Reiser et al., 2000; Voogt et al., 2015; Peel et al., 2020). More fundamentally, co-design orients to how to shift the work of science teaching and learning in a specific context or across multiple contexts as something that is not yet known. An expansive learning perspective recognizes that tools, norms, and materials are central to activity and highlights the potential of joint development of these system components – both for surfacing different perspectives and for shifting teaching and learning. Forms of learning include classroom materials that embody shared interests of science teachers and researchers (Reiser et al., 2000); theoretical refinement of design principles and principled practical knowledge (Bereiter, 2014; Kidron & Kali, 2017; Manz & Suárez, 2018) and increased agency and ownership on the part of teacher participants (Severance et al., 2016; Voogt et al., 2016).

Kali and colleagues (Kali et al., 2018; Kidron & Kali, 2017) describe co-design efforts with middle school teachers, representatives of an NGO, and school administrators to support interdisciplinary, technology-enhanced learning experiences extending science disciplinary ideas. They analyzed 22 dilemmas surfaced by practitioner teams enacting units, finding that 50% were new solutions to dilemmas surfaced in initial design work with researchers, 41% were new solutions to new dilemmas (not anticipated by researchers), and 9% (2 dilemmas) represented anticipated dilemmas where anticipated solutions were enacted (Kidron & Kali, 2017). They documented how productive deviations allowed researchers and teachers to develop new understandings of core principles of the theory. These included the role of sequencing and depth, as well as the utility of and support for students developing and revising artifacts.

This work supports critical reflection on the part of science education researchers about how products and processes embody joint learning and about how our design and implementation practices allow us to learn from teachers. The studies described report the time-intensiveness of the work of co-design and describe the need for articulated roles that honor different expertise and availability. They highlight the importance of opening up and supporting roles for educators that move beyond implementer and provider of "practical" feedback, showing the contributions teachers make toward conceptualizing the parameters of designs and their principled adaptations, guided by an understanding of and stake in the purpose of design choices. Finally, they report on challenges to sustainability. Even when products and processes have been developed with one set of educators, they may not last in these contexts after the initial expenditure of time and resources (Fishman et al., 2011; Sabelli & Dede, 2013). In addition, artifacts and processes developed by co-design teams will need to be re-contextualized in new settings.

Engaging with Organizational Tensions

One way that collaborations can work to improve sustainability is to intentionally attend to organizational tensions that emerge in change efforts (Allen & Heredia, 2021). Collaborative teams have used tools to help participants surface aspects of the organizational environment and infrastructure that influence educational reform efforts (Riedy et al., 2018). They also incorporate mechanisms to align different aspects of the system toward collective goals for improvement (Thompson et al., 2019). This work supports actors within the system to identify areas of confluence and congruence, as well as areas of tension and misalignment to the network's stated goals and visions for improvement. These tensions then become the object of joint activity between researchers, science teachers, and other relevant stakeholders.

An example of a project that developed tools to surface and address organizational tensions in science education is Thompson and colleagues' partnership with a district to implement ambitious science teaching with a focus on supporting English-language development (Thompson et al., 2019). The collaborative team of district science and English-language development directors, principals, and science education researchers surfaced a need to support all students in scientific explanation and argumentation. The team used a driver diagram, a tool used to develop a working theory linking specific actions to making progress on a common aim (Bryk et al., 2015), to coordinate implementation of ambitious science teaching practices across the district. Local actors within a school's professional learning community (PLC) could modify and adapt the driver diagram to support local implementation. The driver diagram coordinated the work between professional learning communities and supported science teachers at each of the schools to identify how their implementation of ambitious science teaching aligned with the overall improvement goals and vision for science teaching and learning of the district.

Teams can collect data to monitor and track improvement efforts within systems. Collaborative teams have highlighted the different ways that data is typically used in research as compared to in-school settings and have sought to develop data collection and analysis procedures that support multiple and varied uses across the team. Measures are designed to inform stakeholders on how the intervention is working, under what conditions, and for whom; thereby supporting iteration at a time scale that works for educational practitioners (Yeager et al., 2013). For example, Thompson and colleagues (2019) co-designed exit tickets that asked students to report their experience with the new tools and scaffolds co-designed within the PLCs. This provided evidence of the users' experience (in this case, the students) as teachers adopted and adapted new instructional practices to support modeling. Analysis of the practical measures by the teachers and coaches supported local actors to identify unanticipated sources of tension emerging at the intersection of youth's experiences, teachers' practices, and organizational goals.

Attending to and engaging with organizational tensions allows for various pathways to improvement, as local actors can modify and adapt innovations from other parts of the system (Thompson et al., 2019; Wingert et al., 2020). This work further underlines the importance for designing professional learning to surface organizational tensions, making space for teachers and collaborators to reason about these tensions, and treating teachers' sensemaking as a focus for analysis (Manz & Suárez, 2018; Allen & Heredia, 2021).

Infrastructuring

Engaging with organizational tensions often leads to a desire to *transform* the conditions that make it hard for teachers to enact new teaching practices. A recurring source of organizational tension experienced by teachers is incoherence in the "instructional guidance infrastructure" (Hopkins & Spillane, 2015) of schools and districts. This infrastructure is comprised, among other things, of standards, assessments, curriculum materials, as well as routines and practices for professional development. It also encompasses the rules and processes for allocating students and teachers to classes, and for certification and evaluation of teachers (Hopkins & Spillane, 2015; Woulfin, 2015). Many of these infrastructures are invisible to outside partners like researchers, at least until they become an obstacle to efforts to change educational systems. At that point, the continuous, layered, and political work of maintaining these infrastructures can become visible.

The work of *infrastructuring* involves purposeful efforts to change infrastructures to be more equitable and to promote a more just distribution of meaningful opportunities to learn (Bell, 2019; Penuel, 2019b). Infrastructuring is a distinct mechanism for expansive learning, because it entails the redesign of tools and processes to open up space for new activities at the classroom level to take place. Infrastructuring can involve the tearing down or redesign of problematic infrastructures, or it can involve the creation of new ones in the service of supporting a particular vision of learning.

An example comes from the work of the inquiryHub partnership between the University of Colorado and Denver Public Schools. The main focus of the work was on co-designing new curriculum materials to support students' engagement with meaningful phenomena and problems in science and engineering (Severance et al., 2016). But to support use of those materials in schools, the team discovered two problematic aspects of the existing instructional guidance infrastructure: the teacher evaluation system, and through-course assessments mandated by the district. The team continued to work on curriculum design but also began to support teachers in bridging gaps between the teacher evaluation system and the instructional model used in guiding curriculum design (Penuel, 2019b). In addition, the team began to support the district in redesigning assessments to align with the vision of teaching and learning, guiding the development of new curriculum materials (Penuel, 2019a).

In another project described by Hall and colleagues (Hall et al., 2021), researchers supported three different networks composed of mentor teachers, district specialists, and interim assessment specialists to support shifts in teaching across multiple schools. The schools did not share common curriculum materials, and so the challenge was to devise a means to support conversations and collaborations whereby educators could make shifts toward more phenomenon-based teaching in science. They decided to create both routines for collaboration and artifacts to represent a set of shared instructional principles, as well as a practice brief for assessment specialists.

Infrastructuring is not a typical focus of work in science teacher education, but it could be. Teachers found surfacing and addressing organizational tensions in the inquiryHub partnership to be a powerful learning experience that helped boost their commitment to the profession (Frumin, 2018). To engage in such work requires close alignment of the work of teacher-researcher teams with district calendars for such processes as curriculum adoption, assessment revision, and more (Penuel, 2019b). The kinds of infrastructures needed will likely depend on the particular equity projects that are focal in a partnership: an infrastructure for disrupting ableism in science education may look different from one that seeks to promote intergenerational learning spaces (Bell, 2019). Infrastructuring is *continuous* work, and it requires significant labor on the part of all involved; much of it may have a "patchwork" quality (Emilson et al., 2014) and feel as though it is not comprehensive, because it is undertaken by teams when they encounter difficulties implementing a focal design.

Re-mediating Relations

Re-mediating relations is a conscious and deliberate effort to attend to commonplace power dynamics and institutionalized inequities within and across multiple scales of practice (e.g., the classroom and community-based programs). This work draws on the notion of *re-mediation* from Kris Gutiérrez and colleagues (Gutiérrez et al., 2009) as a lens for reorganizing learning ecologies, rather than fixing deficits in individual learners (such as teachers). Re-mediating relations warrants a design team that includes a broad range of stakeholders reflective of the community (e.g., elders, guardians, youth) who are understood to bring valuable expertise and ingenuity necessary for bringing about desired social and educational changes (Gutiérrez & Jurow, 2016). Teaching and learning are thus seen as deeply embedded in and shaped by the local histories, politics, and values of the surrounding community, and part of the work of designing to support learning is to support greater expressions of actors' agency and opportunities for transformation of the learning environment and the people within it.

Re-mediating relations is integral for expansive learning, as it surfaces the contradictions within and across activity systems and supports the creation of "third spaces" (Gutiérrez, 2008) that open possibilities for new kinds of activity. Through re-mediation, actors expand the *materiality* of design and practices, offering greater potential for understanding and engaging with and in science. Rajala and Kumpulainen (2017) highlighted the ways that teachers' "agentic orientations" – such as their critical evaluations of an intervention or attempts to reconstruct their work conditions – became important and necessary material for understanding learning and supporting new technology and engineering-oriented learning opportunities within the Finnish school system (Rajala & Kumpu-lainen, 2017). Within Bang and colleagues' (2010, 2016) community-based design projects with Indigenous communities, the design team of university researchers, local educators, elders, and youth sought to support shifts in students' understanding of the practice of science "in relation to traditions of students' community-based practices, histories, and knowledge" (p. 577). The team determined the focus of the research–design efforts together, using *multiple points of view* of members, historical knowledge of pressing issues, and collective awareness of marginalizing social practices affecting teaching, learning, and access to participation in desired social practices (e.g., attaining college degrees in STEM) within the community. Through their design work, the team focused on designing curricula that supported a third space which expanded science learning arrangements that leveraged and honored both Western and Indigenous epistemologies and supported teachers in cre-ating learning environments that fostered youth in navigating these multiple epistemologies toward deeper conceptualizations of science and new possibilities for participation as scientific actors.

Re-mediating relations places particular attention on when, where, and how power is showing up in our work within science education. It encourages us to consider whose science knowledge, whose expertise, and whose histories are valued in science education; and to re-mediate the practices and structures that reproduce the inequities that lie at the intersections of such activity.

Conclusion

Examining collaborative science-researcher learning through the lens of expansive learning and understanding mechanisms for joint learning can help the field conceptualize the learning of sci-ence educators and researchers' role in supporting that learning in new ways. The descriptions of collaborative projects highlight that knowledge of teaching is multi-perspectival and situated; that joint learning is supported by, and embodied in, developing infrastructures for teaching and learning; and that these infrastructures extend beyond classrooms and schools. Further, collaborative research demonstrates how joint learning may require disruption: of traditional roles, of assumptions, of established power relations. These collective, embodied, extended, and nonlinear forms of learning are not ones that our field has typically attended to, particularly in our study of science teacher edu-cation. Within the mechanisms examined, the chapter uncovered specific strategies that can support joint work with educators, including developing hybrid roles and supporting boundary crossers; attending to organizational tensions and teachers' adaptations as a source for refining theories of sci-ence learning and teaching; rethinking the forms of data we collect with educators; engaging with and supporting shifts in assessment and accountability systems; and inviting youth and community members into supporting researcher-teacher collaborative learning by opening our perspectives to new concerns and strengths.

Readers may find themselves grappling with the question, "What about this description is specific to science education; could the information here could be true of any field?" Ultimately, the argument in this chapter is that how science teachers make decisions in their classrooms depends on how systems for science education are organized. That is, it is not only the disciplinary core ideas and practices that make up a focus on science education and science teacher learning, but also the specific history and organizational features of science education as it has been located in relation to youth, teachers, schools, and society. Similar to the need for the students to understand the personal, cultural, and historical context of science ideas and practices, science teacher education researchers need to understand, and engage with, how personal, cultural, and historical contexts shape the ways science education is resourced, organized, and assessed. For example, science education funding and the abundance of research funding for STEM education as tied to political and often militaristic aims supports educational outcomes that position students of color as technicians and commodities for the STEM workforce (Basile & Lopez, 2015). Our current social and political context (pandemics, climate change, and racial unrest) matters for how science education gets organized and will shape and be shaped by the next generations of learners. This requires thinking in a different way about the intersection of "science teacher education research" and the tools and approaches that must come from beyond it.

The work discussed in this chapter is both important and complex. It is supported not only by good intentions and knowledgeable teachers and researchers, but also by tangible tools, processes, and infrastructure. Questions that are important for the field to continue to consider and work on as we work with science educators include:

- What are the conditions under which teachers of science come to see themselves as designers and influencers of systems?
- What are divisions of labor that are productive and not exploitative in researchers' work with science educators?
- What are design processes for organizing ourselves to work together?
- What are routines, tools, and research infrastructures that can support new generations of researchers to learn to engage in this work and be able to do so in a way that is sustainable and recognized as valuable within their institutions?
- What new questions, aims, and possible relations emerge, when we transform science education infrastructures to be more equitable and just?

Notes

1. Consistent with the NRC Framework for Science and Engineering, this chapter takes a broad view of science education as supporting youth's learning about and with science, engineering, and technology. Throughout the paper, we use "science education" to refer to education that supports science and engineering practices and conceptual understandings.
2. Drawing from Engeström & Sannino (2010), Lave (1996), Sfard (1998), and Packer (2010).
3. The mechanisms for learning as expansion were developed through the review of the literature and are further explained in following sections.

References

Aksela, M. (2019). Towards student-centred solutions and pedagogical innovations in science education through co-design approach within design-based research. *LUMAT: International Journal on Math, Science and Technology Education, 7*(3), 113–139. https://doi.org/10.1080/02680513.2016.1265442

Allen, C. D., & Heredia, S. C. (2021). Reframing organizational contexts from barriers to levers for teacher learning in science education reform. *Journal of Science Teacher Education.* https://doi.org/10.1080/10465 60X.2020.1794292

Areljung, S., Leden, L., & Wiblom, J. (2021). Expanding the notion of 'ownership' in participatory research involving teachers and researchers. *International Journal of Research & Method in Education*, 1–11. https://doi.org/10.1080/1743727X.2021.1892060

Bang, M., Faber, L., Gurneau, J., Marin, A., & Soto, C. (2016). Community-Based design research: Learning across generations and strategic transformations of institutional relations toward axiological innovations. *Mind, Culture, and Activity*, *23*(1), 28–41. https://doi.org/10.1080/10749039.2015.1087572

Bang, M., Medin, D., Washinawatok, K., & Chapman, S. (2010). Innovations in culturally based science education through partnerships and community. In *New science of learning* (pp. 569–592). New York, NY: Springer.

Bang, M., & Vossoughi, S. (2016). Participatory design research and educational justice: Studying learning and relations within social change making. *Cognition and Instruction*, *34*(3), 173–193. https://doi.org/10.1080/07370008.2016.1181879

Basile, V., & Lopez, E. (2015). And still I see no changes: Enduring views of students of color in science and mathematics education policy reports. *Science Education*, *99*(3), 519–548.

Bell, P. (2019). Infrastructuring teacher learning about equitable science instruction. *Journal of Science Teacher Education*, *30*(7), 681–690. https://doi.org/10.1080/1046560X.2019.1668218

Bereiter, C. (2014). Principled practical knowledge: Not a bridge but a ladder. *Journal of the Learning Sciences*, *23*(1), 4–17.

Berland, L., Manz, E., Miller, E., & Stroupe, D. (2019). Working with and shifting the system: A response to Elby's commentary. *Journal of Research in Science Teaching*, *56*(4), 521–525. https://doi.org/10.1002/tea.21543

Bryk, A. S., Gomez, L. M., Grunow, A., & LeMahieu, P. G. (2015). *Learning to improve: How America's schools can get better at getting better*. Cambridge, MA: Harvard Education Press.

Calabrese Barton, A., & Johnson, V. (2002). Truncating agency: Peer review and participatory research. *Research in Science Education*, *32*(2), 191–214. https://doi.org/10.1023/A:1016078128502

Campbell, T., McKenna, T. J., Fazio, X., Hetherington-Coy, A., & Pierce, P. (2019). Negotiating coherent science teacher professional learning experiences across a university and partner school settings. *Journal of Science Teacher Education*, *30*(2), 179–199. https://doi.org/10.1080/1046560X.2018.1547033

Cochran-Smith, M., & Lytle, S. (1993). *Inside/outside: Teacher research and knowledge*. New York, NY: Teachers College Press.

Cuban, L. (1993). *How teachers taught: Constancy and change in American classrooms, 1880–1990* (2nd ed.). New York: Teachers College Press.

DiSalvo, B., Yip, J., Bonsignore, E., & DiSalvo, C. (Eds.). (2017). *Participatory design for learning: Perspectives from practice and research*. London: Taylor & Francis.

Emilson, A., Hillgren, P.-A., & Seravalli, A. (2014). Designing in the neighborhood: Beyond (and in the shadow of) creative communities. In P. Ehn, E. M. Nilsson, & R. Topgaard (Eds.), *Making futures: Marginal notes on innovation, design, and democracy* (pp. 35–62). Cambridge, MA: MIT Press.

Engeström, Y., & Sannino, A. (2010). Studies of expansive learning: Foundations, findings and future challenges. *Educational Research Review*, *5*, 1–24. https://doi.org/10.1016/j.edurev.2009.12.002

Esteban-Guitart, M., Serra, J. M., & Llopart, M. (2018). The role of the study group in the funds of knowledge approach. *Mind, Culture, and Activity*, *25*(3), 216–228. https://doi.org/10.1080/10749039.2018.1448871

Fishman, B. J., Penuel, W. R., Hegedus, S., & Roschelle, J. (2011). What happens when the research ends? Factors related to the sustainability of a technology-infused mathematics curriculum. *Journal of Computers in Mathematics and Science Teaching*, *30*(4), 329–353. www.editlib.org/p/36145

Fortney, B. S., Morrison, D., Rodriguez, A. J., & Upadhyay, B. (2019). Equity in science teacher education: Toward an expanded definition. *Cultural Studies of Science Education*, *14*(2), 259–263.

Frumin, K. (2018). *Researchers and practitioners in partnership: Co-design of a high school biology curriculum*. Cambridge, MA: Harvard Graduate School of Education.

Gray, R., McDonald, S., & Stroupe, D. (2021). What you find depends on how you see: Examining asset and deficit perspectives of preservice science teachers' knowledge and learning. *Studies in Science Education*, 1–32. https://doi.org/10.1080/03057267.2021.1897932

Gutiérrez, K. D. (2008). Developing a sociocritical literacy in the third space. *Reading Research Quarterly*, *43*(2), 148–164.

Gutiérrez, K. D., Morales, P. Z., & Martinez, D. C. (2009). Re-mediating literacy: Culture, difference, and learning for students from nondominant communities. *Review of Research in Education*, *33*(1), 212–245.

Gutiérrez, K. D., & Jurow, A. S. (2016). Social design experiments: Toward equity by design. *Journal of the Learning Sciences*, *25*(4), 565–598. http://dx.doi.org/10.1080/10508406.2016.1204548

Hall, J. L., Campbell, T., & Lundgren, L. (2021). Re-designing infrastructure as a strategy for crafting coherence across three networks focused on the implementation of the Next Generation Science Standards. *Journal of Research in Science Teaching*, 1–21. https://doi.org/10.1002/tea.21688

Hamza, K., Piqueras, J., Wickman, P. O., & Angelin, M. (2018). Who owns the content and who runs the risk? Dynamics of teacher change in teacher – researcher collaboration. *Research in Science Education*, *48*(5), 963–987. https://doi.org/10.1007/s11165-016-9594-y

Herrenkohl, L. R., DeWater, L. S., & Kawasaki, K. (2010). Teacher-researcher collaboration as a human science. In W. R. Penuel & K. O'Connor (Eds.), *Learning research as a human science. National Society for the Study of Education Yearbook*, *109*(1), 207–221.

Hopkins, M., & Spillane, J. P. (2015). Conceptualizing relations between instructional guidance infrastructure (IGI) and teachers' beliefs about mathematics instruction: Regulative, normative, and cultural-cognitive considerations. *Journal of Educational Change*, *16*(4), 431–450. https://doi.org/10.1007/s10833-015-9257-1

Hundal, S., Levin, D. M., & Keselman, A. (2014). Lessons of researcher – teacher co-design of an environmental health afterschool club curriculum. *International Journal of Science Education*, *36*(9), 1510–1530. http://dx.doi.org/10.1080/09500693.2013.844377

Kali, Y., Eylon, B. S., McKenney, S., & Kidron, A. (2018). Design-centric research-practice partnerships: Three key lenses for building productive bridges between theory and practice. *Learning, Design, and Technology*, 1–30.

Kidron, A., & Kali, Y. (2017). Extending the applicability of design-based research through research-practice partnerships. *EDeR. Educational Design Research*, *1*(2). https://doi.org/10.15460/eder.1.2.1157

Kumpulainen, K., Kajamaa, A., & Rajala, A. (2018). Understanding educational change: Agency-structure dynamics in a novel design and making environment. *Digital Education Review*, (33), 26–38.

Lave, J. (1996). Teaching, as learning, in practice. *Mind, Culture, and Activity*, *3*(3), 149–164. https://doi.org/10.1207/s15327884mca0303_2

Manz, E., & Suárez, E. (2018). Supporting teachers to negotiate uncertainty for science, students, and teaching. *Science Education*, *102*(4), 771–795. https://doi.org/10.1002/sce.21343

Matuk, C. F., Linn, M. C., & Eylon, B. S. (2015). Technology to support teachers using evidence from student work to customize technology-enhanced inquiry units. *Instructional Science*, *43*(2), 229–257. https://doi.org/10.1007/s11251-014-9338-1

National Academies of Sciences Engineering and Medicine. (2016). *Science teachers' learning: Enhancing opportunities, creating supportive contexts*. Washington, DC: National Academies of Sciences Engineering and Medicine.

Oakes, J., & Lipton, M. (2002). Struggling for educational equity in diverse communities: School reform as social movement. *Journal of Educational Change*, *3*(3–4), 383–406. https://doi.org/10.1023/A:1021225728762

Ormel, B. J., Roblin, N. N. P., McKenney, S. E., Voogt, J. M., & Pieters, J. M. (2012). Research – practice interactions as reported in recent design studies: Still promising, still hazy. *Educational Technology Research and Development*, *60*(6), 967–986. https://doi.org/10.1007/s11423-012-9261-6

Packer, M. (2010). Educational research as a reflexive science of constitution. *Learning Research as a Human Science*, *109*(1), 17–33.

Parsons, E. R. (2019). Why not an integrative and inclusive approach – hands on and "mindson?" A lesson for mentoring 21st century science education researchers. *Science Education*, *103*(5), 1284–1288. https://doi.org/10.1002/sce.21540

Peel, A., Dabholkar, S., Anton, G., Wu, S., Wilensky, U., & Horn, M. (2020). A case study of teacher professional growth through co-design and implementation of a computationally enriched biology unit. In M. Gresalfi, I. S. Horn, N. Enyedy, H.-J. So, V. Hand, K. Jackson, S. E. McKenney, A. Leftstein, & T. M. Philip (Eds.), *Proceedings of the international conference of the learning sciences*. International Society of the Learning Sciences.

Penuel, W. R. (2019a). Co-Design as infrastructuring with attention to power: Building collective capacity for equitable teaching and learning through Design-Based Implementation Research. In J. M. Pieters, J. M. Voogt, & N. N. P. Roblin (Eds.), *Collaborative curriculum design for sustainable innovation and teacher learning* (pp. 387–401). Cham, Switzerland: Springer.

Penuel, W. R. (2019b). Infrastructuring as a practice of design-based research for supporting and studying equitable implementation and sustainability of innovations. *Journal of the Learning Sciences*, *28*(4–5), 659–677. https://doi.org/10508406.2018.1552151

Penuel, W. R., Roschelle, J., & Shechtman, N. (2007). Designing formative assessment software with teachers: An analysis of the co-design process. *Research and Practice in Technology Enhanced Learning*, *2*(1), 51–74. https://doi.org/10.1142/S1793206807000300.

Rajala, A., & Kumpulainen, K. (2017). Researching teachers' agentic orientations to educational change in Finnish schools. In M. Goller & S. Paloniemi (Eds.), *Agency at Work* (pp. 311–329). Cham, Switzerland: Springer.

Reiser, B. J., Spillane, J. P., Steinmuler, F., Sorsa, D., Carney, K., & Kyza, E. (2000). Investigating the mutual adaptation process in teachers' design of technology-infused curricula. In DiSalvo, B., Yip, J., Bonsignore,

E., & DiSalvo, C. (Eds.) *Fourth international conference of the learning sciences* (pp. 342–349). International Society of the Learning Sciences.

Riedy, R., Van Horne, K., Bell, P., Penuel, W. R., Neill, T., & Shaw, S. (2018). Mapping networks to help education leaders gain insights into complex educational systems. In J. Kay & R. Luckin (Eds.), *13th international conference of the learning sciences* (Vol. 1, pp. 656–662). International Society of the Learning Sciences.

Roth, W. M., Tobin, K., Zimmermann, A., Bryant, N., & Davis, C. (2002). Lessons on and from the dihybrid cross: An activity – theoretical study of learning in coteaching. *Journal of Research in Science Teaching, 39*(3), 253–282. https://doi.org/10.1002/tea.10018

Sabelli, N., & Dede, C. (2013). Empowering design based implementation research: The need for infrastructure. *National Society for the Study of Education Yearbook, 112*(2), 464–480.

Sfard, A. (1998). On two metaphors for learning and the dangers of choosing just one. *Educational Researcher, 27*(2), 4–13.

Severance, S., Penuel, W. R., Sumner, T., & Leary, H. (2016). Organizing for teacher agency in curricular co-design. *Journal of the Learning Sciences, 25*(4), 531–564.

Thompson, J., Richards, J., Shim, S. Y., Lohwasser, K., Von Esch, K. S., Chew, C., . . . Morris, A. (2019). Launching networked PLCs: Footholds into creating and improving knowledge of ambitious and equitable teaching practices in an RPP. *AERA Open, 5*(3), 2332858419875718.

Tissenbaum, M., Lui, M., & Slotta, J. D. (2012). Co-designing collaborative smart classroom curriculum for secondary school science. *Journal of Universal Computer Science, 18*(3), 327–352.

Voogt, J., Laferriere, T., Breuleux, A., Itow, R. C., Hickey, D. T., & McKenney, S. (2015). Collaborative design as a form of professional development. *Instructional Science, 43*(2), 259–282. https://doi.org/10.1007/s11251-014-9340-7

Voogt, J. M., Pieters, J. M., & Handelzalts, A. (2016). Teacher collaboration in curriculum design teams: Effects, mechanisms, and conditions. *Educational Research and Evaluation, 22* (3–4), 121–140. https://doi.org/10.1080/13803611.2016.1247725

Wingert, K., Riedy, R., Campanella, M., & Penuel, W. R. (2020). Equity across state systems: Possibilities and tensions in understanding scale. In Gresalfi, M. & Horn, I. S. (Eds.), The Interdisciplinarity of the Learning Sciences, 14th International Conference of the Learning Sciences (ICLS) 2020 (Vol. 4, pp. 2453–2460). Nashville, TN: International Society of the Learning Sciences.

Woulfin, S. L. (2015). Highway to reform: The coupling of district reading policy and instructional practice. *Journal of Educational Change, 16*(4), 535–557. https://doi.org/10.1007/s10833-015-9261-5

Yamagata-Lynch, L. C., & Haudenschild, M. T. (2009). Using activity systems analysis to identify inner contradictions in teacher professional development. *Teaching and Teacher Education, 25*(3), 507–517. https://doi.org/10.1016/j.tate.2008.09.014

Yeager, D., Bryk, A., Muhich, J., Hausman, H., & Morales, L. (2013). *Practical measurement*. Palo Alto, CA: Carnegie Foundation for the Advancement of Teaching.

Zeichner, K. M. (1995). Beyond the divide of teacher research and academic research. *Teachers and Teaching, 1*(2), 153–172. https://doi.org/10.1080/13540

35

INTEGRATED STEM TEACHER EDUCATION

An Opportunity for Promoting Equity

Erin E. Peters-Burton and Kelly L. Knight

Of the four content areas that comprise STEM (science, technology, engineering, and mathematics), the discipline of science has played a prominent role in promoting integrated STEM within K–12 schools. The Next Generation Science Standards (NGSS Lead States, 2013) have an integrated approach, including both engineering design disciplinary content ideas and engineering practices, in addition to mathematical and computational thinking. This multidisciplinary instructional view not only illustrates how one content area can inform another but also infuses key components of doing STEM, including design thinking, inquiry, analytic thinking, and 21st-century skills as articulated by the Partnership for 21st Century Learning (Partnership for 21st Century Skills, 2009).

The goal of an integrated STEM approach is to enable the learner to build greater knowledge through the disciplinary connections and practices than possible through the teaching and learning of individual STEM subjects alone (Johnson, 2013; Moore et al., 2020). When learning from an integrated STEM curriculum as compared to single subjects, Becker and Park (2011) found from their meta-analysis that student cognitive performance improved, with the highest effect sizes seen on the primary level. Additionally, integration has the potential to give learners a broader range of access to learning, a more complex understanding of authentic phenomena, and perhaps enhanced learning outcomes given the same amount of time as studying each individual subject (Barrell, 2010; Breiner et al., 2012; Johnson et al., 2015; Roehrig et al., 2012).

To prepare educators for teaching integrated STEM curricula, teacher education programs which center the content knowledge and have an equity focus are critical. Margot and Kettler (2019) examined studies from the US, the UK, Saudi Arabia, South Korea, and Thailand that indicated teachers' content knowledge was correlated with teachers' comfort level for teaching STEM, and that teachers' comfort level and their perceptions of their students' readiness for STEM content integration influenced their willingness to engage in STEM integration. By supporting teachers' STEM integration content knowledge, they will be able to more effectively enact the various components of integrated STEM, which play a role in creating a more equitable educational environment.

Participation of Black, Indigenous, and people of color (BIPOC) in STEM fields is disproportionately low (Burris & Welner, 2005; Johnson & Sondergeld, 2020; Wiswall et al., 2014). The STEM workforce is comprised of only 11% African Americans, Native Americans, and Latinos collectively, even though these demographic groups make up 33% of the overall US population (Chubin et al., 2005). Integrated STEM education has the potential to increase the representation of these groups in the STEM pipeline (Burris & Welner, 2005; Johnson & Sondergeld, 2020; Sondergeld et al., 2020).

DOI: 10.4324/9781003098478-41

Teachers who are prepared to effectively teach integrated STEM have the ability to develop and implement more equitable and supportive learning environments including components such as cognitive apprenticeships, authentic contexts, real-world problem solving, and modeling of practices (Adeyemi, 2007; Johnson & Sondergeld, 2020; Wambugu & Changeiywo, 2008). Supportive educational environments have been positively linked to retention and persistence of BIPOC students in STEM fields (Cole & Espinoza, 2008; Fries-Britt et al., 2010; Hurtado et al., 2009). Cognitive apprenticeships, when coupled with culturally relevant teaching practices, can benefit diverse learners by centering them through meaningful interactions and contextualizing learning within their realities (Brown et al., 2018). Authentic STEM experiences, those that mimic the practices of STEM professionals in a real-world context, have also been effective in helping students gain insights into the disciplinary process and principles in STEM (Bauer & Bennett, 2003; Lynch et al., 2018). Demonstrating the relevance and usefulness of the STEM subjects being taught in class to students through the modeling of practices could improve STEM identity development and, therefore, participation of students who consider themselves "not STEM-minded," particularly BIPOC students. Meaningfully teaching with an integrated approach to STEM education offers all of these components, potentially providing a bridge for disenfranchised students to be included in instruction and offering a more equitable educational environment.

STEM education is an effort by educators to have students participate in problem solving and design in a "real-world" context using STEM habits of mind as a means to explore natural phenomena and/or design technologies in a manner that requires application of science, technology, engineering, and mathematics (Stehle & Peters-Burton, 2019). STEM can be characterized as the human endeavor of anticipating outcomes of the natural and designed world based on background knowledge, respect for evidence, making sense of what is observed, using logical reasoning, approaching unknowns systematically, and engaging in transparency for the purposes of replicability and evaluation (Peters-Burton, 2014).

The purpose of this chapter is to explain the state of teacher education related to integrated STEM education and to examine the ways that these professional development (PD) opportunities may or may not assist in broadening participation in STEM for BIPOC students. Because the literature on STEM PDs that have an explicit design for influencing teachers' consideration of equity or diversity in the classroom is sparse (Luft et al., 2020), we will critique the current literature for elements of integration that may provide an equitable classroom, such as the use of cognitive apprenticeships, authentic contexts, real-world problem solving, and modeling of practices. Future recommendations for research in the emerging field of integrated STEM teacher education will be made with an eye toward broadening participation.

Preservice STEM Teacher Education

Primary Level Preservice Teacher Programs Have a Variety of Approaches That Are Effective

To be effective in integrated STEM education delivery, teachers must master the STEM content knowledge. However, because primary teachers are responsible for teaching their students all core content areas, they are prepared as generalists (Li, 2008; Schwartz & Gess-Newsome, 2008). STEM subjects are typically not the focus of primary teacher education programs, and many preservice teachers (PSTs) express a lack of content knowledge, confidence, and interest in teaching STEM (Weiss et al., 2001). A variety of efforts have targeted helping preservice primary teachers to gain knowledge and build confidence to teach STEM to their students through methods classes in their required coursework.

Some teacher preparation programs approached STEM content knowledge and pedagogical content knowledge instruction to PSTs in a thematic way. Thirty-two PSTs participated in a methods course that used thematic engineering design modules to communicate interrelationships between the subjects of STEM. After the course, the PSTs were able to make more robust connections to engineering, technology, and mathematics, whereas prior to the course they only made connections to science (Cinar et al., 2016). In another study, 36 PSTs studied teaching methods for a semester using robotics. This course not only increased their science content knowledge, but it also improved interest and self-efficacy towards teaching in an interdisciplinary way (Jaipal-Jamani & Angeli, 2017). Other designs for elementary PST programs, such as a thematic oriented STEM certificate program that includes courses such as Chemistry of Life, Environmental Biology, and Engineering in Your World, have shown to improve confidence in and knowledge of STEM concepts for K-5 PSTs (Murphy & Mancini-Samuelson, 2012). Methods classes in teacher education programs that encourage interdisciplinary teaching have the potential to produce teachers who can support greater diversity in STEM. When students, particularly diverse and marginalized learners, learn how to think flexibly about disciplines, they can see how the different practices in the STEM disciplines can be used to apply their learning to real-world problem solving, a key component to raising sociopolitical consciousness in culturally relevant teaching practices (Ladson-Billings, 1995).

Maker activities provided another way to frame thematic integrated STEM instruction during methods classes, and preservice teachers expressed favorable attitudes in using maker activities in their future classrooms because such activities promoted problem-based learning and inquiry learning (Jones et al., 2017). Adams et al. (2014) used Place-Based Teaching in an elementary teacher methods class that resulted in improved teacher confidence as a STEM learner and teacher. Their study found that the connection of knowledge relevant to a particular place and the inquiry-oriented delivery of the methods class instruction helped the PSTs form a stronger science identity and increase the confidence in teaching STEM. Taking novel approaches to methods classes for preservice teachers using maker activities and Place-Based Teaching position elementary teachers so that they can provide inclusive classes that focus on problem solving and modeling of practices, rather than convergent information that requires only recall.

Other elementary STEM education programs approached teaching PSTs by partnering the PSTs with content area experts in all four STEM content areas and using software designed for physics simulations to help PSTs design and implement integrated STEM lessons. In a group comparison, the 31 PSTs who used the software had significantly higher problem-solving skills than the 31 PSTs who did not use the software in the methods course (Alan et al., 2019). The PSTs who used the software reported problems at the beginning of the course, but across time the PSTs realized there were various ways to solve problems and became more efficacious. In another project intended to improve elementary PSTs' skills in planning and teaching an integrated STEM lesson, researchers co-designed an integrated STEM unit with the PSTs to explicitly model skills in planning, teaching, and reflecting on integrated lessons (Bartels et al., 2019). Although PSTs were generally successful in planning and carrying out the STEM unit, PSTs carried a persistent belief that all four STEM areas needed to be present at all times for successful integration. These methods courses broke down the traditional barriers by creating authentic situations where PSTs had to persist in their problem solving. These habits of mind can serve as a model from which the PSTs can build classroom environments supportive of all students. However, providing a variety of models for integrating STEM could help PSTs at the elementary level be more flexible in the delivery of instruction.

Other approaches to enhance elementary PST knowledge of STEM included increasing coursework in those areas. In one STEM-focused elementary education program in the US, elementary PSTs were required to take two mathematics methods courses, two science methods courses, and one engineering methods course, consisting of more STEM coursework than is typically offered. This course sequence resulted in positive attitudes toward engineering for the PSTs (DiFrancesca et al., 2014). The additional exposure to the disciplinary methods courses did improve attitudes toward STEM for PSTs, but improved attitudes may not be enough for elementary teachers to conduct innovative instruction that is known to support students who are reticent to learning STEM, such as cognitive apprenticeships, creating authentic contexts for learning, and modeling disciplinary practices for students.

Secondary-Level STEM Preservice Teacher Programs Are Few, but Demonstrate Promise

Perhaps not surprisingly, there were few studies on teacher preparation programs for secondary teacher candidates. Perhaps due to the pervasive system of departmentalization at the secondary school level worldwide, there may be fewer opportunities for integrating STEM, and thus, fewer integrated teacher preparation programs offered at this time. Experiencing STEM coursework in separate, siloed departments (e.g., biology, chemistry, mathematics, engineering) while preparing to be a secondary teacher may contribute to a lack of preparation to teach integrated STEM (Nowikowski, 2017). It seems that the majority of efforts at the secondary level were placed in professional development for in-service teachers, which is explained later in the chapter.

However in one example, incorporating interdisciplinary teaching as an example in a methods course helped secondary preservice teachers broaden their conceptions of integrated STEM and improved their self-efficacy for teaching integrated STEM. Nowikowski (2017) suggested the following six tasks as design elements for a methods course used to build secondary preservice teacher STEM knowledge and efficacy: (a) establish a baseline of prior knowledge, (b) introduce authentic problem-based learning module that uses engineering design process as a reflection tool, (c) use a creative thinking task, (d) design an improved product, (e) have students identify problems in their own environmental context, and (f) revisit reflections. These design elements align well with what is known about features of instruction that support students who do not consider themselves "STEM-minded." Secondary-level PSTs taking a methods course designed with these tasks are themselves guided through a cognitive apprenticeship for an engineering design, setting the stage for these PSTs to help their students through cognitive apprenticeships.

In-Service Teachers Recommend Preservice Programs Include More Active STEM Integration

Some of the research related to integrated STEM preservice teacher preparation spans across all grade levels. Shernoff et al. (2017) interviewed mentor teachers currently integrating STEM in their classes (at elementary, middle, and high school levels) to find out what recommendations they had for preservice programs. The teachers proposed that more project-based and collaborative learning activities be taught in preservice programs to support integration of STEM subjects for more student-centered approaches. Teachers also identified resources such as model exemplar STEM lessons and mentoring by teachers experienced in integration approaches as being a key component for STEM-oriented preservice teacher preparation. Similarly, preservice teachers also indicated that maker activities could be employed to provide problem-based, student-centered learning, but access to resources could be problematic (Jones et al., 2017). The recommendations found from this study echo the features that are likely to help new teachers establish classrooms that promote equity in learning STEM.

In Turkey, some teacher education programs across K–12 grade levels have shifted to an integrated model in order to address their need for well-educated STEM teachers. Graduates of these integrated teacher preparation programs learn how to design and teach lessons using mathematically rigorous science education integrated into engineering and technology in the context of problem solving (Corlu et al., 2014). Ellerbrock and colleagues (2019) documented how one university and school district partnered to create a residency program for a middle school STEM teacher preparation. Graduates from this program had 100% job placement and 90% of the newly employed teachers receive the highest level of evaluation by administration (Ellerbrock et al., 2019). This model of integration expands the idea that all STEM disciplines need to be represented and provides another way for problem solving in an authentic context to be carried out in preservice teacher programs.

Partnerships Strengthen STEM Integration During Induction Years

Once a teacher candidate leaves the university to teach in their own classroom, there are challenges to sustaining support to teach integrated STEM for teachers in their induction years. Research on science teacher education has established that when doing an internship in a school setting, PSTs working with a mentor teacher who embraces student-centered learning will likely feel supported to teach with student-centered methods (Smolleck et al., 2006). Similarly, being paired with a mentor teacher who can successfully teach integrated STEM will support a PST's ability to teach integrated STEM, but teachers who are skilled in teaching integrated STEM are difficult to find (Boyle et al., 2013).

Schuster and colleagues (2012) studied the factors contributing to STEM teacher success in an aligned university-based teacher preparation program and teacher support during induction years and provide four recommendations. First, they recommend extending university-based resources beyond graduation so that university resources can support teachers in their induction years, particularly because teaching in the STEM areas may require ongoing specialized professional development. Second, the researchers noted that newly hired STEM teachers may be asked to teach a variety of classes requiring different preparation and to run STEM clubs. Using university-based personnel to mentor new STEM teachers and advocate on their behalf for reasonable working conditions can improve the transition from teacher candidate to successful teacher. Third, ongoing and inclusive professional development is recommended to keep the communication open among new teachers, mentors, and administrators. Finally, the researchers recommended that STEM inductee teachers be given structured opportunities to co-plan and co-teach classes with a veteran mentor teacher at the school (Schuster et al., 2012). Extending and combining resources from the university and districts can create a supportive environment that can help STEM teachers provide quality instruction for all students.

Partnerships With STEM Faculty and STEM Educators Broaden Teacher Conceptions of STEM

Moyer-Packenham and colleagues (2009) examined 7 years of results from a US federal program from the National Science Foundation that supported collaborations among STEM faculty, STEM education faculty, and K–12 teachers, called the Mathematics-Science Partnership (MSP). The MSP program funded both preservice and in-service teacher development programs across primary and secondary settings. It was found that the MSP program helped to bring together STEM faculty and K–12 teachers in a variety of different ways that go beyond the typical activities of STEM faculty (e.g., developing preservice preparation courses, preservice teacher recruitment activities). The review of program outputs showed that the program was successful in shifting teachers to be more successful in designing and implementing integrated STEM curriculum.

Programs partnering teachers with scientists, technologists, engineers, and mathematicians at different levels of their careers have had some positive results in broadening teacher conceptions and teaching practices about STEM. In a program promoting engineering innovation and design, teachers across one state in the US partnered with engineering students, engineering faculty, and industrial mentors to engage in two design projects. Participating collaboratively in one general and one more in-depth project was shown to help teachers learn more about innovation experiences and to better inform their students of potential career fields (Pinnell et al., 2013). Another statewide program in the US partnered with K–12 teachers, STEM and STEM education faculty, and business members. The outcomes included improved awareness and beliefs about STEM engagement, student preparation, and careers, particularly for the business members group (Sondergeld et al., 2016). Although these programs demonstrated positive outcomes in terms of content knowledge, innovative projects, and career awareness, they focused less on factors that could contribute to equity in STEM such as modeling of disciplinary practices and cognitive apprenticeships.

Challenges to Implementation of Integrated STEM Include Resources and Approach

The challenges of implementing integrated approaches to STEM education were examined closely by Shernoff et al. (2017), who interviewed 22 teachers at the elementary, middle and high school levels in the United States. Most of the teachers who participated in this study reported that they were already implementing integrated STEM education. Teachers identified their greatest challenges as a lack of physical and technology resources, dealing with changes to students' expectations and attitudes, and dealing with mixed abilities and gaps in students' understanding. Additionally, in another study, teachers felt that district mandated grade-level standards were too inflexible to combine even two subject areas (Margot & Kettler, 2019). Secondary teachers in particular felt that by integrating multiple content areas, some of the content would be added as an afterthought or left out completely (Asghar et al., 2012; Dare et al., 2019). Actions that would help overcome these challenges were reported by the teachers as increased physical and technology resources, support for collaboration and planning with colleagues, and more professional development, which poses opportunities for professional development that focuses not only on improved integration of STEM education, but also on issues of equity when teaching STEM education.

Resources were not the only challenge in implementing integrated STEM instruction, as reported by in-service teachers. Challenges were also faced by the approach to integration. Teachers who focused on their main discipline and then tried to integrate the other subject areas of STEM felt higher-level intrinsic challenges than teachers who understood the nature and pedagogy of integrated STEM education (Dong et al., 2020). In addition, teachers who had less content knowledge in the STEM areas faced higher-level intrinsic challenges than those teachers who have more content knowledge (Dong et al., 2020). As is the case with any topic of professional development, content knowledge mastery is essential in the context of the strategies that will be employed to deliver instruction (Desimone, 2009).

Teacher Perceptions Indicate Students Are Motivated by STEM Instruction

Teacher perceptions of student reaction to STEM instruction were also influential in implementing a shift in practice. Teachers in the United States across grades K–12 felt that the interdisciplinary nature of STEM was beneficial and a motivating factor for students, however, secondary teachers expressed potential systemic barriers to cross-disciplinary curriculum development due to the departmental nature of secondary schools (Margot & Kettler, 2019). A similar study in Turkish middle schools took place with 10 STEM teachers. These teachers felt that integrating STEM increased students' motivation in the course and improved student decision-making skills as well as providing multifaceted opportunities for students to engage in learning (Bakirci & Kutlu, 2018). Teachers seem to agree that a learning environment that integrates STEM so that students are solving problems in authentic contexts and learning disciplinary practices is motivating, but the departmental organization of secondary schools may prohibit meaningful integration of the STEM subjects. The lack of opportunity for integration at the secondary level due to systemic factors could diminish support for BIPOC students.

Factors for Successful Adoption of STEM Pedagogy and Curriculum Align With Factors That Promote an Equitable STEM Classroom

In a synthesis study, Margot and Kettler (2019) found that teachers viewed STEM curriculum as student-centered learning, which may be a drastic shift from teachers who are comfortable with a didactic instruction. They also found that teachers were concerned that STEM curriculum may not serve the needs of diverse learners and that it may hinder the direct instruction of science content. There is a delicate balance when it comes to developing curriculum integrating content areas. One thing that could potentially increase the viability of developing and implementing STEM curriculum was effective teacher collaboration (Asghar et al., 2012; Bruce-Davis et al., 2014; Stohlmann et al., 2012). A large-scale study of 600 K–12 teachers identified a general model of teacher behavior that is associated with an inclination to engage in and adopt innovative STEM instruction. Nadelson and Seifert (2016) gathered information from teachers prior to and after a six-day summer institute on teaching integrated STEM content. They found that four variables positively influenced adoption of integrated STEM instruction, listed here from most influential to least: (a) engaging in promoting STEM in the community, (b) engaging in STEM PD, (c) knowledge, perceptions, and engagement in core STEM practices, and (d) use of instructional technology (Nadelson & Seifert, 2016). The variables that lead to adoption of STEM integration align well with the factors that promote equity in the STEM classroom, such as authentic contexts, core practices, and real-world problem solving.

Model-Eliciting Activities Promote Elementary Teacher Readiness for STEM Instruction

Professional development programs focused specifically on the elementary level have had some success in supporting teachers to provide integrated STEM education. Baker and Galanti (2017) approached an integrated STEM professional development for K-6 teachers through the use of model-eliciting activities, which asks students to be explicit about their processes in developing a mathematical model for a phenomena or engineering design (Lesh et al., 2003). After a four-day summer institute, elementary teachers reported a readiness to teach integrated STEM using model-eliciting activities which were grounded in their current grade-level standards. The institute featured a tailored instructional design for the elementary teachers with purposeful grouping and differentiated instruction to encourage collaboration based on each teacher's individual context. The model-eliciting activities are built from authentic contexts and require divergent problem-solving processes, which has the potential to encourage all students to learn STEM subjects.

Successful Professional Development at the Secondary Level Includes Building Teacher 21st-Century Skills

Models of successful integration at the secondary level can give insights into replication of professional development opportunities for in-service teachers. In order to determine the lasting effects of a STEM PD on teaching practices, Avery and Reeve (2013) followed up with five secondary teachers 2 years after they had taken the PD. They offer six recommendations based on their qualitative study: (a) offer a supportive PD environment, (b) provide exemplar examples of the tasks in the PD, (c) provide training on managing group projects and student peer review, (d) align PD outcomes with standards-based pressures that teachers experience, (e) focus on giving teachers the skills to design lessons, and (f) focus on teaching teachers to integrate STEM concepts into lesson materials.

Wang et al. (2020) investigated the experiences of teachers at two schools and identified features, beliefs, practices, and challenges of the two models, a multi-classroom collaboration model and an extracurricular model. In the multi-classroom collaboration model, which occurs with three to five different teachers from different subject areas, has a real-world problem that centers the interdisciplinary instruction. Teachers started with content knowledge and learned both content and processes from each other to teach using a hands-on, student-centered approach. Challenges identified in this model include the need for a common meeting time for teachers and a common meeting time for students where they can work on a common project outside of classes. The extracurricular model also requires several different teachers with different backgrounds, who can help students make STEM connections while still addressing standards. These teachers create a large project that engages students across a school year, using problem-solving, hands-on instruction, and real-world contexts that require a collaborative effort for both the teachers and the students. The challenges with the extracurricular model include the need for a common meeting time for teachers, and the need for teachers to be flexible in terms of curricular choices and their views of integrated STEM.

Johnston and colleagues (2019) examined a middle school life science teacher's talk about engineering when teaching an engineering design-based unit to understand how the teacher integrated STEM in the lessons. They found the teacher's lessons had a flow that was parallel to an engineering design process, which made the process explicit and helped him treat his students as apprentice engineers. The ways he used engineering talk also helped students to expand and elaborate their design ideas, as well as focusing them in an authentic application by reminding them of their client's need when engaged in the life science inquiry. In a 3-week-long professional development designed to incorporate more STEM opportunities into secondary classrooms, 33 participating teachers were able to develop the complexity of their conceptions of the STEM discipline. Initially, the majority of teachers communicated their conceptions of STEM as the parts of the acronym or an engineering design process. Over the 3 weeks, the teachers moved to conceptions of STEM as integrated disciplines and STEM practices such as teamwork and communication (Ring et al., 2017). Another study examined disciplinary discourses in a 6th-grade class including ways of knowing, doing, talking, reading, and writing in the context of engineering and science. The teacher was able to skillfully merge technical discourses with everyday ones, allowing for a broader variety of student engagement in STEM practices. As a result, students were also able to merge science and engineering successfully (Aranda et al., 2020). These types of cognitive apprenticeships help to reveal to students the underpinnings of a discipline, thus creating a common understanding of the rationale for learning STEM content and practices.

Conclusion

Integrated STEM instruction has the potential to help students view STEM in a different light, thus harnessing the potential to achieve equitable STEM education. An examination of the research regarding the process for preservice and in-service teachers to learn to teach STEM in an integrated way reveals patterns that can be categorized in three hierarchical tiers. First, a mastery of content knowledge is the foundational step to growing STEM teachers who are adept at integrating STEM instruction. However, a strong foundation of knowledge itself is not enough. It is also necessary for educators to possess positive beliefs regarding integrated STEM instruction. The studies in this chapter reveal that teachers generally value STEM education and believe that students are more motivated by learning through an integrated STEM approach. Educators may be able to teach effectively to most students if they have required content knowledge and positive beliefs, but research also indicates there must also be an inclusive learning environment for students to have access and equitable opportunities to learn STEM. At the highest tier of teacher instruction regarding integrating STEM, teacher educators should model strategies such as being cognitive apprentices, using problem solving in authentic contexts, and demonstrating STEM practices in an explicit way to preservice teachers. Educators can use these models in their own instruction so that students not only gain the content knowledge of STEM but can also understand the practices and habits of mind. When teachers enable students to think like scientists, technologists, engineers, and mathematicians, students can leverage these skills across their educational and occupational trajectories.

Areas of Future Research

One pervasive finding in the research is the narrow view that educators hold, particularly at the primary level, of STEM integration. Many educators feel that they must integrate all content areas in an equal manner, which is not at all reflective of how STEM occurs in the real world or how it should be taught in K–12 schools. Based upon the limited research on secondary STEM preservice teacher preparation, there are many opportunities for additional research in this area. A first step is to determine what the characteristics are of existing preservice teacher programs in STEM. Next, determine what is working and what areas are in need of improvement to enable educators to be prepared to reach all students through integrated STEM instruction. A second step is to continue to investigate the variety of models of STEM integration in K–12 schools and learn from the success of programs to inform future integration of STEM. Third, examine the challenges that teachers experience when implementing integrated STEM and develop support systems within schools and districts to provide sustained models of teacher development and collaboration. Moreover, integrated STEM teacher education is an evolving area, and it is a fortuitous time to learn from research on enacted programs and continue to strive toward more inclusive models of STEM education.

References

Adams, A. E., Miller, B. G., Saul, M., & Pegg, J. (2014). Supporting elementary pre-service teachers to teach STEM through place-based teaching and learning experiences. *Electronic Journal of Science Education, 18*(5), 1–22.

Adeyemi, B. A. (2007). Learning social studies through mastery approach. *Educational Research and Review, 2*(4), 60–63.

Alan, B., Zengin, F. K., & Keçeci, G. (2019). Using STEM Applications for supporting integrated teaching knowledge of pre-service science teachers. *Journal of Baltic Science Education, 18*(2), 158–170. https://doi.org/10.33225/jbse/19.18.158

Aranda, M. L., Guzey, S. S., & Moore, T. J. (2020). Multidisciplinary discourses in an engineering design-based science curricular unit. *International Journal of Technology and Design Education, 30*(3), 507–529. https://doi.org/10.1007/s10798-019-09517-5

Asghar, A., Ellington, R., Rice, E., Johnson, F., & Prime, G. M. (2012). Supporting STEM education in secondary science contexts. *The Interdisciplinary Journal of Problem-based Learning, 6*, 85–125.

Avery, Z. K., & Reeve, E. M. (2013). Developing effective STEM professional development programs. *Journal of Technology Education, 25*(1), 55–69.

Baker, C. K., & Galanti, T. M. (2017). Integrating STEM in elementary classrooms using model eliciting activities: Responsive professional development for mathematics coaches and teachers. *International Journal of STEM Education, 4*(1), 10. https://doi.org/10.1186/s40594-017-0066-3

Bakirci, H., & Kutlu, E. (2018). Determination of science teachers' views on STEM approach. *Turkish Journal of Computer and Mathematics Education, 9*(2), 367–389.https://doi.org/10.16949/turkbilmat.417939

Barrell, J. (2010). Problem-based learning: The foundation for 21st century skills. In J. Bellanca & R. Brandt (Eds.), *21st century skills: Rethinking how students learn*. Bloomington, IN: Solution Tree Press.

Bartels, S. L., Rupe, K. M., & Lederman, J. S. (2019). Shaping preservice teachers' understandings of STEM: A collaborative math and science methods approach. *Journal of Science Teacher Education, 30*(6), 666–680. https://doi.org/10.1080/1046560X.2019.1602803

Bauer, K. W., & Bennett, J. S. (2003). Alumni perceptions used to assess undergraduate research experience. *The Journal of Higher Education, 74*(2), 210–230.

Becker, K., & Park, K. (2011). Effects of integrative approaches among science, technology, engineering, and mathematics (STEM) subjects on students' learning: A preliminary meta-analysis, *Journal of STEM Education, 12*, 23–37.

Boyle, J. D., Svihla, V., Tyson, K., Bowers, H., Buntjer, J. Garcia-Olp, M., . . Sample, S. (2013). Preparing teachers for new standards: From content in core disciplines to disciplinary practices. *Teacher Education and Practice, 26*(2), 199–220.

Breiner, J., Harkness, M., Johnson, C. C., & Koehler, C. (2012). What is STEM? A discussion about conceptions of STEM in education and partnerships. *School Science and Mathematics, 112*(1), 3–11.

Brown, B. A., Boda, P., Lemmi, C., & Monroe, X. (2018). Moving culturally relevant pedagogy from theory to practice: Exploring teachers' application of culturally relevant education in science and mathematics. *Urban Education, 54*(6), 775–803.

Bruce-Davis, M. N., Gubbins, E. J., Gilson, C. M., Villanueva, M., Foreman, J. L., & DaVia Rubenstein, L. (2014). STEM high school administrators', teachers' and students' perceptions of curricular and instructional strategies and practices. *Journal of Advanced Academics, 25*, 272–306.

Burris, C. C., & Welner, K. G. (2005). Closing the achievement gap by detracking. *Phi Delta Kappan, 86*, 594–598.

Chubin, D. E., May, G. S., & Babco, E. (2005). Diversifying the engineering workforce. *Journal of Engineering Education, 94*(1), 73–86.

Cinar, S., Pirasa, N., Uzun, N., & Erenler, S. (2016). The effect of STEM education on pre-service teachers' perception of interdisciplinary education. *Journal of Turkish Science Education, 13*, 118–142.

Cole, D., & Espinoza, A. (2008). Examining the academic success of Latino students in science technology engineering and mathematics (STEM) majors. *Journal of College Student Development, 49*(4), 285–300.

Corlu, M. S., Capraro, R. M., & Capraro, M. M. (2014). Introducing STEM education: Implications for educating our teachers for the age of innovation. *Education and Science, 39*(171), 74–85.

Dare, E. A., Ring-Whalen, E. A., & Roehrig, G. H. (2019). Creating a continuum of STEM models: Exploring how K – 12 science teachers conceptualize STEM education. *International Journal of Science Education, 41*, 1701–1720.

Desimone, L. M. (2009). Improving impact studies of teachers' professional development: Toward better conceptualizations and measures. *Educational Researcher, 38*(3), 181–199.

DiFrancesca, D., Lee, C., & McIntyre, E. (2014). Where is the "E" in STEM for young children? Engineering design education in an elementary teacher preparation program. *Issues in Teacher Education, 23*(1), 49–64.

Dong, Y., Wang, J., Yang, Y., & Kurup, P. M. (2020). Understanding intrinsic challenges to STEM instructional practices for Chinese teachers based on their beliefs and knowledge base. *International Journal of STEM Education, 7*(1), 47. https://doi.org/10.1186/s40594-020-00245-0

Ellerbrock, C. R., Vomvoridi-Ivanovic, E., Sarnoff, K., Jones, B., & Thomas, M. (2019). Collaborating to "grow our own": The helios STEM middle school residency program. *The Clearing House: A Journal of Educational Strategies, Issues and Ideas, 92*(4–5), 119–124. https://doi.org/10.1080/00098655.2019.1614516

Fries-Britt, S., Younger, T., & Hall, W. (2010). Underrepresented minorities in physics: How perceptions of race and campus climate affect student outcomes. In T. E. Dancy (Ed.), *Managing diversity: (Re)visioning equity on college campuses* (pp. 181–198). New York, NY: Peter Lang.

Hurtado, S., Cabrera, N. L., Lin, M. H., Arellano, L., & Espinosa, L. L. (2009). Diversifying science: Underrepresented student experiences in structured research programs. *Research in Higher Education, 50*(2), 189–214.

Jaipal-Jamani, K., & Angeli, C. (2017). Effect of robotics on elementary preservice teachers' self-efficacy, science learning, and computational thinking. *Journal of Science Education and Technology, 26*, 175–192.

Johnson, C. C. (2013). Conceptualizing integrated STEM education. *School Science and Mathematics, 113*, 367–368.

Johnson, C. C., Peters-Burton, E. E., & Moore, T. J. (Eds.). (2015). *STEM road map: A framework for integrated STEM education*. New York, NY: Routledge.

Johnson, C. C., & Sondergeld, T. A. (2020). Outcomes of an integrated STEM high school: Enabling access and achievement for all students. *Urban Education, 1–27,* https://doi.org/10.1177/0042085920914368

Johnston, A. C., Akarsu, M., Moore, T. J., & Guzey, S. S. (2019). Engineering as the integrator: A case study of one middle school science teacher's talk. *Journal of Engineering Education, 108*(3), 418–440. https://doi.org/10.1002/jee.20286

Jones, W. M., Smith, S., & Cohen, J. (2017). Preservice teachers' beliefs about using maker activities in formal K-12 educational settings: A multi-institutional study. *Journal of Research on Technology in Education, 49*(3–4), 134–148. https://doi.org/10.1080/15391523.2017.1318097

Ladson-Billings, G. (1995). Toward a theory of culturally relevant pedagogy. *American Educational Research Journal, 32*(3), 465–491. https://doi.org/10.3102/00028312032003465

Lesh, R., Lester, F., & Hjalmarson, M. (2003). A models and modelling perspective on metacognitive functioning in everyday situations where mathematical constructs need to be developed. In R. Lesh & H. M. Doerr (Eds.), *Beyond constructivism: A models & modelling perspective on mathematics problem solving, learning & teaching* (pp. 383–404). Hillsdale, NJ: Lawrence Erlbaum Associates, Inc.

Li, Y. (2008). Mathematical preparation of elementary school teachers: Generalists versus content specialists. *School Science and Mathematics, 108*(5), 169–172.

Luft, J. A., Diamond, J. M., Zhang, C., & White, D. Y. (2020). Research on K-12 STEM professional development programs. In C. C. Johnson, M. J. Mohr-Schroeder, T. J. Moore, & L. D. English (Eds.), *Handbook of research on STEM education* (pp. 361–374). Routledge. https://doi.org/10.4324/9780429021381

Lynch, S. J., Peters-Burton, E. E., Behrend, T., House, A., Ford, M., Spillane, N., . . . Means, B. (2018). Understanding inclusive STEM high schools as opportunity structures for underrepresented students: Critical components. *Journal of Research in Science Teaching, 55*(5), 712–748. https://doi.org/10.1002/tea.21437

Margot, K. C., & Kettler, T. (2019). Teachers' perception of STEM integration and education: A systematic literature review. *International Journal of STEM Education, 6*(1), 2–18.

Moore, T. J., Johnston, A. C., & Glancy, A. W. (2020). STEM integration: A synthesis of conceptual frameworks and definitions. In *Handbook of research on STEM education*. New York: Routledge.

Moyer-Packenham, P. S., Kitsantas, A., Bolyard, J. J., Huie, F., & Irby, N. (2009). Participation by STEM faculty in mathematics and science partnership activities for teachers. *Journal of STEM Education, 10*(3/4), 1–21.

Murphy, T., & Mancini-Samuelson, G. J. (2012). Graduating STEM competent and confident teachers: The creation of a STEM certificate for elementary education majors. *Journal of College Science Teaching, 42*(2), 18–23.

Nadelson, L. S., & Seifert, A. L. (2016). Putting the pieces together: A model K-12 teachers' educational innovation implementation behaviors. *Journal of Research in Innovative Teaching, 9*(1), 47–67.

NGSS Lead States. (2013). *Next generation science standards: For states, by states.* Washington, DC: The National Academies Press.

Nowikowski, S. H. (2017). Successful with STEM? A qualitative case study of pre-service teacher perceptions. *The Qualitative Report, 22*(9), 2312–2333.

Partnership for 21st Century Skills. (2009). *A framework for twenty-first century learning.* www.p21.org/

Peters-Burton, E. E. (2014). Is there a nature of STEM? *School Science and Mathematics, 114*, 99–101.

Pinnell, M., Rowly, J., Preiss, S., Franco, S., Blust, R., & Beach, R. (2013). Bridging the gap between engineering design and PK-12 curriculum development through the use the STEM education quality framework. *Journal of STEM Education, 14*(4), 9.

Ring, E. A., Dare, E. A., Crotty, E. A., & Roehrig, G. H. (2017). The evolution of teacher conceptions of STEM education throughout an intensive professional development experience. *Journal of Science Teacher Education, 28*(5), 444–467. https://doi.org/10.1080/1046560X.2017.1356671

Roehrig, G. H., Moore, T. J., Wang, H-H., & Park, M. S. (2012). Is adding the E enough? Investigating the impact of K-12 engineering standards on the implementation of STEM integration. *School Science and Mathematics, 119*, 31–44.

Schuster, D., Buckwalter, J., Marrs, K., Prittchet, S., Sebens, J., & Hiatt, B. (2012). Aligning university-based teacher preparation and new STEM teacher support. *Science Educator, 21*(2), 39–44.

Schwartz, R. S., & Gess-Newsome, J. (2008). Elementary science specialists: A pilot study of current models and a call for participation in the research. *Science Educator, 17*(2), 19–30.

Shernoff, D. J., Sinha, S., Bressler, D. M., & Ginsburg, L. (2017). Assessing teacher education and professional development needs for the implementation of integrated approaches to STEM education. *International Journal of STEM Education, 4*(1), 13. https://doi.org/10.1186/s40594-017-0068-1

Smolleck, L. D., Zembal-Saul, C., & Yoder, E. P. (2006). The development and validation of an instrument to measure preservice teachers' self-efficacy in regard to the teaching of science as inquiry. *Journal of Science Teacher Education, 17*(2), 137–163.

Sondergeld, T. A., Johnson, C. C., & Walton, J. B. (2016). Assessing the impact of a statewide STEM investment on K – 12, higher education, and business/community STEM awareness over time. *School Science and Mathematics, 116*(2), 104–110. https://doi.org/10.1111/ssm.12155

Sondergeld, T. A., Provinzano, K., & Johnson, C. C. (2020). Investigating the impact of an urban community school effort on middle school STEM-related student outcomes over time through propensity score matched methods. *School Science and Mathematics, 120*(2), 90–103. https://doi.org/10.1111/ssm.12387

Stehle, S. M., & Peters-Burton, E. E. (2019). Developing student 21st century skills in selected exemplary inclusive STEM high schools. *International Journal of STEM Education, 6*(39). https://doi.org/10.1186/s40594-019-0192-1

Stohlmann, M., Moore, T., & Roehrig, G. (2012). Considerations for Teaching Integrated STEM Education. *Journal of Pre-College Engineering Education Research (J-PEER)*, 2(1), 28–34. https://doi.org/10.5703/1288284314653

Wambugu, P. W., & Changeiywo, J. M. (2008). Effects of mastery learning approach on secondary students' physics achievement. *Eurasia Journal of Mathematics, Science, and Technology Education*, 4(3), 293–302.

Wang, H.-H., Charoenmuang, M., Knobloch, N. A., & Tormoehlen, R. L. (2020). Defining interdisciplinary collaboration based on high school teachers' beliefs and practices of STEM integration using a complex designed system. *International Journal of STEM Education*, 7(1), 3. https://doi.org/10.1186/s40594-019-0201-4

Weiss, I. R., Banilower, E. R., McMahon, K. C., & Smith, P. S. (2001). *2000 National survey of science and mathematics education*. Chapel Hill, NC: Horizon Research, Inc.

Wiswall, M., Stiefel, L., Schwartz, A. E., & Boccardo, J. (2014). Does attending a STEM high school improve student performance? *Evidence from New York City, Economics of Education Review, 40*, 93–105.

INDEX

Note: Page numbers in **bold** indicate a table, and page numbers in *italic* indicate a figure, on the corresponding page.

100 Schools Project, USA 356

abortion, as controversial topic 411
academic language, and emergent bilinguals 380, 382
academic learning time (ALT) 330
accountability: standards for teacher education 11; as type of research 8
ACP (alternative certification programs) *see* alternative pathways to science teaching
action research (AR) 352–362; article search process 352–353; background 352; collaborative AR 354; defined 352; improvement of science curricula 355–356; inquiring into students' cognition of science 355; interactive AR 354, 355, 356, 357; modes of 354; participatory (PAR) 354; PD of science teachers 356–357; promotion of equity and social justice 357–358; purposes of 353–354; as qualitative research 36–37; summary 358–360; teacher-centered AR 354, 356, 357, 358, 359; technical AR 354, 355
active teaching 330
adaptive equipment, for visually and hearing impaired 368, 372
administrators in schools: and opportunities to learn for new hires 250, 251; and PLCs 301, 306, 310; principal support for leadership development 264, 268
admission requirements for science teacher education **165**, 166, 235–236
Advancing Science by Enhancing Learning in the Laboratory, Australia 184
advocacy approach, teaching controversial topics 405–406
advocacy for science by teacher leaders 260, 266, 267

affirmative neutrality approach, teaching controversial topics 406
Africa: alternative pathways to teaching **148**, 154; Continental Education Strategy for Africa 218; PST education 173; teacher preparation policy 237; *see also specific countries*
after-school clubs, as PST field experiences 123
agency of teachers 252
Alaska Native culture, and culturally responsive science teaching 292
Alliance Model, Australia 182
allied political stuggle, in rightful presence 54, 56–57, 58
alternative pathways to science teaching 145–158; alternative certification programs (ACPs), defined 145; article search process 146; background 145–146; defined 145; diversification of teaching workforce 147; measures of effectiveness of ACPs 150–153; mentoring and program supports 150; program coursework comparisons 149–150; program designs 147, **148**, 149; reasons for 146–147; reasons that science professionals want to teach 148; recruitment of candidates into ACPs 149; shortages of science teachers 147, 151, 153–154; student achievement 152–153; summary 153–155; teacher job placement 150–151; teacher quality 150; teacher retention 151–152
ambitious science teaching (AST) 109, 110, 115, 116, 458
American Association of Colleges of Teacher Education (AACTE), USA 178
American Educational Research Association (AERA), USA 246

American Indian culture, and culturally responsive science teaching 292, 443

American Museum of Natural History (AMNH) 191; Master of Arts in Teaching residency program 197

antimicrobial properties of plants, as indigenous knowledge 344, 346, 347

apprenticeship approach for PD 302

approximations of practice: as pedagogy supportive of secondary PST learning 114; in science methods courses for elementary teachers 87–88

Argentina: PST education 164, **165**, 166, 168, *168*, 173; teacher preparation policy 232, 235

argumentation skills: on controversial topics 407–408; and educative curriculum materials 391; in high-quality science instruction 335–336

artifacts: co-designing, in collaborative researcher-teacher learning 457; cultural 291, 293; indigenous 344, 347

Asia: Conference on Digital Transformation of Education Systems throughout Association of Southeast Asian Nations 218

assessment: equitable, for science and language learning, in emergent bilinguals 381, 382; *see also* standardized tests

assistive technology (AT) 369

Association for Science Teacher Education (ASTE), USA 233; NSTA/ASTE Standards for Science Teacher Preparation 364, **364**

astronomy, in science methods course for elementary teachers 87

attitudes of teachers: as area of research 8–9; and classroom-based opportunities to learn 251–252; relationship between knowledge, attitudes, and beliefs 72–74; supporting, in science methods courses 85–86

audio recordings, in research on mentoring 140

Australia: alternative pathways to teaching **148**, 149–150; content courses for elementary teachers 85; digital technologies 319; effect of standardized texts on mentoring 138; emerging technologies research 222; emotion and science teacher education 429; informal science learning environments (ISLEs) 190–191, 193; partnerships in PST education 178, 180, 181, 182, 184; professional identity 420; PST education 164, **165**, 166, *168*, **172**; science methods course for elementary teachers 87; science teacher leadership 260; teacher preparation policy 232, 235, 236

Australian Institute for Teaching and School Leadership (AITSL) 178

Australian National Professional Standards for Teachers 234

authentic inquiry experiences, in PD for inquiry-based instruction 278, 281

authentic science practices (ASP), as approach to contextualization of science instruction 440–441, **441**, **442**, 443, 446

authoritarian dialogue 210

Basic Interpersonal Communications Skills (BICS) 377

beads, representing organic macromolecules 292

Belgium: alternative pathways to teaching 147, **148**, 150

beliefs of teachers: as area of research 8–9; and classroom-based opportunities to learn 251–252; in contextualizing instruction 443–444, 448; and educative curriculum materials 392–393; relationship between knowledge, attitudes, and beliefs 72–74; of secondary PSTs about teaching 102, 107; supporting, in science methods courses 85–86; teaching science to emergent bilinguals 380–382

BERA-RSA report 6

Bhutan: classroom emotional climate, in ethnography study 34

big data 227

Big Idea Tool 135

bilinguals *see* emergent bilinguals

biodiversity 409

Biological Sciences Curriculum Study 388

biology, secondary PST challenges and knowledge 110, 112

BIPOC (Black, Indigenous, and people of color) in STEM 465–466, 471

blended learning, in PD for inquiry-based instruction 275, 279–280, 282

body language of teachers 251–252

Brazil: PST education **171**, 174

Canada: action research 355; content courses for elementary teachers 84; emerging technologies research 222; inclusive science teacher education 367; indigenous knowledge in 345; PST education 164, **165**, 166, *168*, 169, **171**, 174; secondary PST research 108; teacher preparation policy 232, 234, 235–236

career-change scientists 429–431

career phases in teachers' professional life cycle 301–304, *303*, 309

case study, as qualitative research 32–33

certification of teachers 145–146, 232–233

chafing borderlands 75, 77

Challenge of Teaching Controversial Issues, The 404

Chemical Education Material Study 388

chemistry, secondary PST challenges and knowledge of 110–111, 112

Chile: PST education **165**, 166, *168*, 169, **171**, 172, 174; teacher preparation policy 232, 235, 236

China: alternative pathways to teaching 147, **148**; professional learning communities 305; PST education 164, **165**, 166, *168*, 169, **172**, 173;

secondary PST research 108; teacher preparation policy 232, 235, 236, 237–238; teacher training program for rural schools 147, 237–238
City-as-Lab, USA 193
CK *see* content knowledge (CK)
classroom observations for early childhood PSTs 74
climate change: as controversial topic, teaching 405, 410–411; emotion and science teacher education 433–434; and high-quality science instruction 335–336; partnerships with scientists and community experts 292
clinical experiences (student teaching) 119, 120
cloning, reproductive 433–434
coaching, instructional 394
co-designing artifacts, in collaborative researcher-teacher learning 457
Cognitive Academic Language Proficiency (CALP) 377
cognitive activation 334
cognitive apprenticeships 344, 466, 468, 472
cognitive learning perspectives, on PSTs in field experience research 123–124, 128
co-learning for preservice elementary and mentor teachers 88–89
collaboration: bridging communities of practice in teaching emergent bilinguals 383; as feature of PLCs 300, 301, 308, 309; onsite TPACK-based workshop **317**, 318; and opportunities to learn for new hires 248
collaborative community, in PD for inquiry-based instruction 275, 279, 280–281, 282
collaborative lesson design 320–321
collaborative PCK (cPCK) 331
collaborative researcher-teacher learning 452–464; article search process 455–456; background 452; co-designing artifacts 457; infrastructuring 458–459, 460; organizational tensions 458, 459; re-mediating relations 459–460; summary and recommendations 460–461; surfacing different perspectives 456–457, 459; theories of learning **453**, 453–454
colleagues: impact of science teacher leaders 265–266; importance in socialized contexts 251
College of Saint Teresa: PST program principles 121–122
Colombia: action research 356; PST education **165**, 166, *168*, 174; teacher preparation policy 232, 235
commitment and teacher retention 152
communication skills *see* discursive practices
community-based placements, as PST field experiences 123, 127
community ethnography 58–60, 62
Community of Practice (CoP) model 302, 308
community partnerships: of experts with culturally responsive science teachers 292; of organizations in PST education 183, 185; TPACK PD approach 319
comprehensible input 377

computer science education in national survey 21
computer simulations 222, 224
conceptual change, related to students with disabilities 365
Concerns-Based Adoption Model (CBAM) 321–322
concurrent model of teacher education 164, **165**, 166, 174
conditional knowledge 7
confidence, of science teacher leaders 265
Confucianism 32
connective partnership arrangement 181
consequential, and rigorous, elementary science teaching 83, 91
constructivist teaching practices 109
content courses for elementary teachers 84–85, **92**
content knowledge (CK) 315, 321; in high-quality science instruction 331, 332, 333, 334, 335, 336, 337
context: defined 439; models of, and indigenous knowledge 340
context-based curriculum (CBC) 440, **441**, 442, **442**, 443, 444, 446
contextualization of science instruction 439–451; article search process 440; background 439; defined 439; for emergent bilinguals 381–382, 443; operationalizing 440–442; recommendations 447; strategies for enactment 444–447, *445*; student-centeredness 444; summary 447–449; teacher motivations, confidence, and beliefs 443–444; teacher skills and understanding 442–443
contextualization of science instruction, approaches: authentic science practices (ASP) 440–441, **441**, **442**, 443, 446; context-based curriculum (CBC) 440, **441**, 442, **442**, 443, 444, 446; culturally responsive science (CRS) 440–441, **441**, **442**, 443, 446; out-of-class experiences (OOC) 440–442, **441**, **442**, 443, 445, 446; socioscientific inquiry (SSI) 440, **441**, 442, **442**, 443, 445–446, 447
controversial topics 403–413; approaches to teaching 405–406; background of value in teaching 403; defined 404; in science education 404–405; as sensitive issues 408–409; student research and argumentation 407–408; understanding the nature of science 406–407; as wicked problem 403
controversial topics, examples: climate change 405, 410–411, 433–434; evolution 405, 409–410; genetic engineering, cloning, and stem cell research 433–434; nuclear power 406–407, 434; vaccines 411–412
cooperating teachers: for PSTs in field experiences 127; for secondary PSTs 109–110; *see also* mentor teachers
CoP (Community of Practice) model 302, 308
CoRes tools to support PCK in mentoring 135
co-teaching: as alternative model for mentoring 136; in inclusive science teacher education 366

Council for Accreditation of Educator Preparation (CAEP), USA 178
COVID-19 403
creationism 405, 409
creative thinking, with emerging technologies **223**, 224
critical reflection, of culturally responsive science teachers 294–295
CRST *see* culturally responsive science teaching
cultural capital of science teacher leaders 261–262, 268
cultural diversity: in elementary teacher education programs 88, 90; increase in culturally diverse classrooms 287; in studies for early childhood PSTs 75
Cultural Historical Activity Theory framework 36, 321
Cultural Institutions for Teacher Education (CITE) 197
cultural issues: cultural exposure in CRST 291–292; expectations of mentors in different countries 138; and informal science learning environments (ISLEs) 194, 196; partnerships in PST education 185; science teacher leadership in individualistic *vs.* collectivistic societies 269–270; *see also* indigenous knowledge (IK)
culturally relevant pedagogy 288
culturally responsive science (CRS), as approach to contextualization of science instruction 440–441, **441, 442**, 443, 446
culturally responsive science teaching (CRST) 288, **291**, 291–292
culturally responsive teaching 10, 88, 123, 288; *see also* professional development (PD) of culturally responsive science teachers
cultural studies, and place-based education (PBE) 193
culture: defined 291; *see also* school culture
curricula: for science, improving with action research 355–356; written, intended, and enacted 388
curricular aspects of PST education internationally 167–169, **168**
curriculum knowledge (CuK), in high-quality science instruction 331, 332
curriculum materials: in field for elementary teachers 89; *see also* educative curriculum materials (ECM)
Cyprus: professional identity 417; teacher preparation policy 232
Czech Republic: PST education **165**, 166, 167, *168*, 169, **170**, 172, 174; secondary PST research 108

data *see* educational surveys
data analysis tools: commonly used software **23**; DataLab 20
data and media analysis 392
data collection and analysis, of PSTs in field experiences 124–125, **125, 126**
data loggers 313

debates, discussions, explanations, and arguments, as discursive practice 207
declarative knowledge 7
demonstration days 120
development, professional *see* professional development (PD)
development components for science teacher leaders 263–264
development models for science teacher leaders 262–263
dialectical approach, in mixed methods research 42, 45
dialogic discussions with students, as discursive practice 209
differentiated instruction 366–367
Digital Education Action Plan, European Commission 218
digital storytelling 222
digital technologies 313–324; data loggers 313; geospatial technologies (GPS and GIS) 319; information and communication technologies (ICT) 313–314; interactive whiteboard (IWB) **318**, 319, 321; roles as tutor, tool, medium 313; simulation software 313; spreadsheets 313, 319; TPACK *see* TPACK
digital technology skills 410
disabilities *see* inclusive education for students with disabilities
disciplinary literacy, within science content knowledge 365–366
discovery days 120
discursive practices, in science education (SEDP) 203–217; article search process 204; background 203–204; defined 203; disciplinary and epistemological dimensions 205–207, *206*, 212, 213; linguistic dimension *206*, 207–209, 212, 213; pedagogical dimension *206*, 209–211, 212, 213; summary and recommendations 212–214
discursive practices, specific, of science teachers *206*; debates, discussions, explanations, and arguments 207; dialogic discussions with students 209; modeling of scientific discourse 211; pedagogical resources 210–211; peer discussions 208; role-playing 207, 208, 211; scenarios for teaching 210; simulations 207, 211; teaching practices simulations, and teaching rehearsals 207
dispositions of teachers 8–9
disruption of guest/host relationalities, in rightful presence 54, 55, 57–58, 61
Distance Learning Dataset Training (DLDT) 26
diverse learners, supporting: with indigenous knowledge *see* indigenous knowledge (IK); museums and ISLEs 196, 197; as pedagogy supportive of secondary PST learning 115; *see also* culturally responsive teaching
diversity: of ACP-prepared teachers in workforce 147, 154; focus on, for PST preparation 74–75; *see also* cultural diversity

driver diagram 458
Du Bois, W. E. B. 42

early childhood, defined 70
early childhood education (ECE), inequities in science for 69
early childhood preservice teachers (EC-PSTs) 69–82; article search process 70–72, 78–79; background 69; complexities revealed by longitudinal studies 75; defined 70; diverse paths in becoming 71, *71*; diversity, equity, and inclusion 74–75; favorable features of EC profession 70, 77; field experiences and influences 74; professionals for preparation 77; recommendations 75–77; relationship between knowledge, beliefs, and attitudes 72–74; summary 77–78
earth sciences, secondary PST knowledge 112
ECM *see* educative curriculum materials (ECM)
ecological knowledge 193
EC-PSTs *see* early childhood preservice teachers (EC-PSTs)
educational reform *see* reform, educational
educational surveys 16–27; background and importance of 16; data access and analysis software **23**; exemplar data resources 17, 19; High School Longitudinal Study of 2009 (HSLS:2009) 21; in mixed methods research 46; National Assessment of Educational Progress (NAEP) 20–21; National Survey of Science and Mathematics Education (NSSME) 21–22; National Teacher and Principal Survey (NTPS) 20; summary 25–26; TIMSS data from South Africa, example of analysis 22–25; topics and questionnaire items **18–19**; training on using large datasets 26; Trends in International Mathematics and Science Surveys (TIMSS) 19–20
educative curriculum materials (ECM) 388–398; article search process 389–390, **390**; background 388–389; changing teacher beliefs 392–393; changing teacher PCK 390–392; changing teacher pedagogical design capacity 393; design features and conditions of use 393–395; summary 395
educative materials, for teaching science to emergent bilinguals 378–379
educative mentoring 133–134, 138, 139, 141
educator preparation providers (EPPs), and informal science learning environments (ISLEs) 190–191
effective science instruction (ESI), professional development for mentors 139
elementary teachers 83–96; article search process 84; background, preparation for rigorous, consequential, just, and equitable science teaching 83; content courses and content-focused experiences 84–85, **92**; field experiences 88–90, **92**; next-generation science teaching 83, 91; science methods courses 85–88, **92**; summary and recommendations 91; teacher education programs 90–91, **92**

embodied, situated, and distributed cognition (ESDC) 344
embodied cultural capital 261–262
emergent bilinguals, and role of teacher education 376–387; academic language and translanguaging 380–381; article search process 376–377; assessing for science and language learning 381; background 376–377; bridging communities of practice 383; contextualizing science instruction 381–382, 443; developing empathy in teachers 382; foundations for teaching: integration of language, literacy, and science 377–378; hegemonic language ideologies 383; professional learning approaches 378–380; recommendations 382–384; shifts in teacher knowledge and practice 380–382; summary 384; theories of change 383–384
emerging technologies 218–230; access, equity, and global perspectives 224–226, **225**, 227; affordances 219, 222–224, **223**; article search process 219–221; background 218–219; creative thinking **223**, 224; definitions and examples 219; descriptive statistics and categories of technologies 221–222; framing 221; recommendations 226–227; safety and convenience **223**, 224, 227
emotions, and science teacher education 426–438; article search process 427–428; background and conceptualization of 426–427; career-change scientists 429–431; and development of professional identity 418–419, 422; identity and work 428–431; and informal reasoning 433, 435; and science inquiry 431–433; and socioscientific issues 433–435; summary and recommendations 435–436
empathy in teachers, in teaching emergent bilinguals 382
enacted curriculum 388
enacted PCK (ePCK) 331, 333, 335
engineering, and integrated STEM 472
Engineering for Sustainable Communities (EfSC) 58–59, 60
England: emerging technologies research 222; high-quality science instruction research 330; PST education 164, **165**, 166, 167, *168*, 169, **170**, 172; teacher preparation policy 232, 236; *see also* United Kingdom
English learners 376, 384n1; *see also* emergent bilinguals, and role of teacher education
enterprise education 190–191
entrance exams 235–236
environmental education 193
environmental racism, community partnership 183, 185
environmental science 290
epistemic criterion of controversial issues 404
epistemology 204, 205, *206*, 207, 408–409, 460
equitable and just, elementary science teaching 83, 91

equitable assessment for science and language
learning, in emergent bilinguals 381, 382
equitable science learning environments, for students
with disabilities 367–369
equity: addressing in science teacher preparation
237–238; focus on, for PST preparation 74–75,
76; as inclusion in rightful presence 53; and
social justice, promotion of, with action research
357–358
Estonia: professional learning communities 305
ethical issues: controversial topics 408; with emergent
technologies 227; environmental 121
ethnography: community ethnography 58–60, 62; as
qualitative research 34–35
Europe: call for culturally relevant education
288, 289, 296; Digital Education Action
Plan 218; Science Education for Responsible
Citizenship 190
European Credit Transfer and Accumulation System
(ECTS) 164
evolution: as controversial topic, teaching 405,
409–410; secondary PSTs' knowledge on 98, 110
Exceptional Graduates as Rural Teachers, China 147
expansive learning 452, **453**, 454, 457, 459, 460

face-to-face tools for mentoring, sentence
stems 135
family science nights 123, 183
field experiences for inservice teachers: and
development of professional identity 418–419,
422; for elementary teachers 88–90, **92**;
methods courses for early childhood PSTs 74;
as opportunities to learn for new hires 247; for
secondary PSTs 109–110
field experiences in PST preparation 119–131; in
1970s 120–122; article search process 119; data
collection and analysis 124–125, **125**, **126**; defined
119–120; helping PSTs change internally and
externally 125–127; location and duration **122**,
122–123, 128; summary and recommendations
127–129; theoretical and methodological framing
123–124, 128
field trips 120, 191, 368; virtual reality field trips
(VRFTs) 222
Finland: collaborative researcher-teacher learning
460; emerging technologies research 222; informal
science learning environments (ISLEs) 190; PST
education 164, **165**, 166, *168*, 169, 174; teacher
preparation policy 232, 234, 235, 236, 237
floating science teachers 250
food unit, and healthy snacks 55–58
Framework for K-12 Teacher Education, USA 190
France: PST education 164, **165**, 166, 167, 168,
168, 174; teacher preparation policy 232, 235

Galileo 42
gender issues: and development of professional
identity 417–418; focus on gender-aware teaching

for PST preparation 74–75; gender inclusion in
science teaching 357–358
general pedagogical knowledge (GPK): in curricular
aspects of PST education internationally 167, *168*,
174–175; as type of teacher knowledge 331
general qualitative research 31–32
general (integrated) science teacher education for
secondary PSTs 111
generation gap in PLCs 306
generative partnership arrangement 181
genetic engineering 433–434
genetics literacy 98
geospatial technologies (GPS and GIS) 319
Germany: high-quality science instruction research
332, 334; inclusive science teacher education 369;
PST education 164, **165**, 166, 168, *168*, **170**,
172, 174
Ghana: action research 355; emerging technologies
research 222
GIS technology 319
global warming 434; *see also* climate change
glocalization in science education 343
Government-Sponsored Normal Students Program,
China 237–238
GPS technology 319
Graduate Australian Professional Teaching
Standards 182
graduation requirements for science teacher
education **165**, 166–167
Greece: emerging technologies research 222
grounded theory, as qualitative research 33–34

hearing impaired 368; *see also* inclusive education for
students with disabilities
hegemonic language ideologies 382, 383
high-quality science instruction 329–339;
argumentation skills 335–336; article search
process 329–330; background 329; defined
330–331; knowledge-practice-learning 334–335;
museums and informal science education (ISE)
336; summary and recommendations 336–337;
teacher improvement via long-term PD 333–334;
teacher professional knowledge, and student
learning 331–333; teacher professional knowledge,
defined 331; teacher-scientist partnerships 336
High School Longitudinal Study of 2009
(HSLS:2009), USA **18**, 21, **23**, 26
holistic nature of indigenous knowledge 341,
342, 343
Hong Kong: high-quality science instruction
research 335

identity, professional, of science teachers 414–425;
background and importance of 414–415; defined,
concept of 415–417; factors that shape identity
417–420; field experiences 418–419, 422;
how scholars study identity 420–421; identity
development inherent to learning processes 421;

identity dimensions 421–422; multidimensional view of 416–417; in PD 419–420, 422; personal schooling histories and individual variables 417–418; preservice preparation 418–419; recommendations 422–423; school socialization and PD 419–420; science identity *vs.* teacher-of-science identity 416, 419, 421

identity development of science teachers: as area of research 9; and classroom-based opportunities to learn 251–252; in early childhood education 77; emotion and science teacher education 428–431; learning to teach in ISLEs 190–193, 194; of secondary PSTs 108; supporting, in science methods courses 85–86

inclusive education for students with disabilities 363–375; article search process 364–365, 371; background 363–364; content knowledge **364**, 365–366; content pedagogy **364**, 366–367; equitable impact on student learning **364**, 369–370; learning environments and safety **364**, 367–369; science teachers with disabilities 370–371; standardized assessments 370; strengths-based instruction and assessments 370; summary and recommendations 371–372

inclusiveness: focus on, for PST preparation 74–75; language-inclusion ideology 383; of large-scale data sets 19

inclusive science content knowledge: conceptual change 365; disciplinary literacy 365–366

inclusive science content pedagogy: co-teaching 366; differentiated instruction 366–367; Universal Design for Learning (UDL) 367

inclusive science learning environments 367–369; assistive technology (AT) 369; safe and equitable lab experiences and field trips 368; social-emotional learning (SEL) in classrooms 369

Inclusive Science Teacher Education (ISTE) 364

India: alternative pathways to teaching **148**, 154

indigenous knowledge (IK) 340–351; article search process 345; background 340; and culturally responsive science teaching 292, 294, 443; defined 341; empowerment of learners 346; examples of 343, 344, 347; holistic nature of 341, 342, 343; implementation in classroom 346; indigenous artifacts in instruction 347; infusion of, into science education 344–345; intersecting domain view 342–343, 346; and place-based education 193, 292; relationship with western science 341, 342; and science education 343–344; and science knowledge 342–343; and science teacher education 345–347; science teacher pedagogical skills 345–346; summary 347–348; support of science teacher learning 346

Indonesia: PST education **165**, 166

inequalities in science education: in early childhood education 69; learning to teach in justice-oriented ways 52; in South Africa 23–25

informal reasoning 433, 435

informal science education (ISE) 336, 419, 420

informal science learning environments (ISLEs) 189–202; article search process 189–190; defined 189; diverse learners and museums 196; gaps in research 194–196; place-based education (PBE) 193–194; scalability and sustainability 197; science teacher identity and self-efficacy 190–193, 194; summary and recommendations 197–199

information and communication technologies (ICT) 313–314

infrastructuring, in collaborative researcher-teacher learning 458–459, 460

inquiry: early childhood PSTs preparation 76–77; scientific, implementation with action research 355–356

inquiry-based science teaching: defined 273; development of inquiry lessons in PD 278–279, 281–282; emotion, and science teacher education 431–433; in ethnography qualitative research 34; examples of 313; and high-quality science instruction 336; identity dimensions 416; professional development for *see* professional development (PD) for inquiry-based instruction

insect repellants, as indigenous knowledge 343

inservice teachers: career phases in teachers' professional life cycle 301–304, *303*, 309; PD for teaching science to emergent bilinguals 378–379; *see also* teachers

institutional cultural capital 262

institutions of training programs, and policy in science teacher preparation 236–237

instructional coaching 394

instructional design and planning: through onsite workshops 316, **317**, 318; using TPACK 316, **317**

instructional guidance infrastructure 458–459

integrated (general) science teacher education for secondary PSTs 111

integrated STEM teacher education 465–476; background 465–466; factors for successful adoption 471; implementation challenges 470; model-eliciting activities 471; partnerships 469–470; primary level preservice teacher programs 466–468; professional development at secondary level 471–472; recommendations by in-service teachers 468–469; recommendations for future research 473; secondary level preservice teacher programs 468; students' motivation by STEM instruction 470–471, 472; summary and recommendations 472–473

integrative *vs.* transformative development of PCK 320

intelligent design 409

intended curriculum 388

interactive whiteboard (IWB) **318**, 319, 321

Interconnected Model of Professional Growth (IMPG) 318

International Association for the Evaluation of Educational Achievement (IEA) 26

International Handbook of Science Education 132, 140
International Mathematics and Science Survey 19
internships, as student teaching in partnerships 179
interpretivist approach in qualitative research **31**, 37
interviews, in mixed methods research 46
Investigating and Questioning Our World Through Science and Technology (IQWST) 279
Iran: professional learning communities 308
Ireland: Teacher's Research Exchange (T-Rex) 12
isolation, professional, of teachers 251
Israel: action research 357; alternative pathways to teaching 147, **148**, 149, 151, 153; emerging technologies research 222; evolution as controversial topic 410; and informal science learning environments (ISLEs) 194; professional identity 416; professional learning communities 304, 307; PST education **165**, 166, *168*, 173
IWB (interactive whiteboard) **318**, 319, 321

Japan: PST education 164, **165**, 166, 167, *168*, **172**, 173, 174
Jordan: action research 355
journaling process, in reflective triadic partnerships 180
Journal of Science Teacher Education: on international science teacher education 234, 238
just and equitable elementary science teaching 83, 91
justice 52; environmental racism and partnerships in PST education 183, 185; *see also* rightful presence

karrikins, and seed germination of indigenous knowledge 347
Kenya: contextualized instruction 444
Kirby-Bauer technique 344, 346
kit-based curriculum materials, for elementary teachers 89
knowledge: and classroom-based opportunities to learn 251–252; of content, as development component for science teacher leaders 263, 268; pedagogy supportive of secondary PST learning 112–113; professional, and high-quality science instruction 331–335; relationship between knowledge, attitudes, and beliefs 72–74; supporting, in science methods courses 86; teaching science to emergent bilinguals 380–382; types of 331
Knowledge Forum 313
knowledge of assessment (KA) 331
knowledge of context (CxK) 331, 335
knowledge of students (KS) 331, 335
knowledge of students' misconceptions (KOSM) 332
knowledge-practice-learning connections 334–335

laboratories: inclusive and safe science learning environments 368; inequalities in science education 25; undergraduate laboratory courses, as PST field experiences 123
landscape, as type of research 8

language diversity: academic language 380, 382; cultural diversity of students and culturally responsive science teaching 294; elementary teacher experiences 88, 89; equitable assessment for science and language learning 381, 382; integration of language, literacy, and science in teaching emergent bilinguals 377–378; proficiency in, and inequalities in science education 24; secondary PSTs core practices with linguistically diverse students 111; *see also* emergent bilinguals
language-exclusion ideology 382–383
language-inclusion ideology 383
leadership *see* science teacher leadership
leadership skills, as development component 263, 268
learning activity types (LAT) 321
learning and knowledge building (LKB), in professional learning communities 305
learning opportunities of newly hired science teachers *see* opportunities to learn (OTL)
learning theories **453**, 453–454; learning as acquisition **453**, 454; learning as expansion 452, **453**, 454, 457, 459, 460; learning as participation **453**, 454
lesson and unit design: in PD of culturally responsive science teachers 293–294; using TPACK 316, **317**, 320–321
life cycle of teachers' careers 301–304, *303*, 309
lightning and electrostatics, in indigenous knowledge 344
linguistic hegemony 382, 383
literacy, language, and science, integration of, in teaching emergent bilinguals 377–378
Looking at Student Work (LaSW) PD program 334
Luxembourg: preparation of EC professionals 71, *71*
Lyell, Charles 42

Macau: PST education 164, **165**, 166, 167, *168*, 169
macroteaching 114
maker activities, and STEM 467, 468
Malaysia: action research 355
Māori culture, and culturally responsive science teaching 294
Mathematics-Science Partnership (MSP) 469
Matrix Method 346
Mauritius: PST education 173
mentoring: in alternative pathways to science teaching 150; and culturally responsive science teaching 294; instructional coaching 394; onsite TPACK-based workshop **317**, 318; and opportunities to learn for new hires 248; in PLCs 308, 309; for student success, qualitative case study 33; *see also* partnerships in PST education
mentoring preservice teachers 132–144; alternative models 136–137, 141; article search process 132–133; background 132; importance of context on mentoring relationships 137–138, 141; professional development 138–140, 141–142;

recommendations 140–142; summary 142; tools to support mentoring work 134–136, 140, 141; traditional and educative mentoring 133–134, 138, 139, 141

mentoring triads 136

mentor teachers: and development of professional identity 418; for elementary PSTs 88–89; and integrated STEM 469; in practicums of PST education internationally **170**, 172; for PSTs in field experiences 127; for secondary PSTs 109–110; teaching science to emergent bilinguals 379

metacognition 6, 7, 432, 433

Metacognitive Analysis (MA) PD program 334

meta-strategic knowledge (MSK) 7

methods courses: in curricular aspects of PST education internationally 168; for early childhood PST education 73; for elementary teachers in science 85–88, **92**; influence of field experiences 74; integrated STEM 467, 468; and partnerships in PST education 180–181

microteaching 114

misconceptions of students 332, 394

mixed methods research 41–51; approaches 45–46; background 41; benefits of 43, 45, 48; defined 42, 46; history of 42; models resulting from 46–48; purposes and research questions 43–45; summary 48–49; surveys and interviews 46

model-eliciting activities, and integrated STEM 471

modeling of scientific discourse, as discursive practice 211

moral principles 405, 411, 434

multilinguals *see* emergent bilinguals, and role of teacher education

museums: and development of professional identity 419; and high-quality science instruction 336; as ISLEs 190, 196; as OTL 247

mutuality, in partnerships in PST education 184

narrative, as qualitative research 35–36

National Assessment of Educational Progress (NAEP), USA **18**, 20–21, **23**, 26

National Board of Professional Standards of Teaching 237

National Center for Education Statistics (NCES), USA 20, 26

National Council for Accreditation of Teacher Education (NCATE), USA 178, 233, 237

National Education Association, USA 218

National Science Foundation, USA 356

National Science Teachers Association (NSTA), USA 233; NSTA/ASTE Standards for Science Teacher Preparation 364, **364**

National Survey of Science and Mathematics Education (NSSME), USA **18**, 21–22, **23**, 26

National Teacher and Principal Survey (NTPS), USA **18**, 20, **23**, 26

nature of science (NOS): action research implementation 355–356; and controversial topics 406–407; in early childhood PST methods courses 73–74; and educative curriculum materials 391–392; in elementary teacher education programs 90; emotion and science teacher education 430; explicit *versus* implicit instruction in science methods courses 86; as keyword in journal search 72; PST understanding of 113, 126

Netherlands: inclusive science teacher education 367; PST education **165**, 166, *168*, **170**, 172; science teacher leadership 260

networking: in leadership development 264, 268; and opportunities to learn for new hires 249

newly hired teachers of science (NHTS), learning opportunities *see* opportunities to learn (OTL)

New Zealand: CoRes tools to support PCK in mentoring 135; culturally responsive science teaching (CRST) 289, 294; informal science learning environments (ISLEs) 190; partnerships in PST education 181; science teacher leadership 260; self-study qualitative research 37

Next Generation Science Standards (NGSS), USA: curriculum reform 345; and development of professional identity 420; effect on mentoring views 132; and equity as inclusion 53; integrated STEM 465; reform-minded science teacher identity and ISLEs 190; Science and Engineering Practices 367; and teacher education 163

next-generation science teaching 83, 91

Nigeria: emerging technologies research 222; PST education 173; secondary PST research 108

No Child Left Behind (NCLB) 44–45

norms and values shared among teachers, as feature of PLCs 300

Norway: handbook tool for mentoring 136

NOS *see* nature of science (NOS)

noticing *see* teacher noticing

Noyce Program, USA 238

nuclear power, as controversial topic 406–407

objectified cultural capital 262

Ohio State Teacher Sense of Efficacy Scale 152

opportunities to learn (OTL) 245–256; article search process 246; background 245; policies in context 250; preparation programs 246–248; professional learning programs 248–250; resources from school and community 251; socialized contexts 251; summary and recommendations 253–254; teacher attributes 251–252; teacher resilience and agency 252

Organisation for Economic Co-operation and Development (OECD): on high-quality science instruction 329

organizational tensions, in collaborative researcher-teacher learning 458, 459

orientations, as type of research 8

OTL *see* opportunities to learn (OTL)

outdoor science 121, 193
out-of-class experiences (OOC), as approach to
  contextualization of science instruction 440–442,
  441, **442**, 443, 445, 446

Palestine: educative curriculum materials 391
paper circuit mistakes video 60, 61
participatory action research (PAR) 354
Partnership for 21st Century Learning 465
partnerships: between ISLEs and EPPS *see* informal
  science learning environments (ISLEs); with
  scientists *see* scientist partnership; for STEM
  integration 469–470
partnerships in PST education 178–188;
  article search process 179; background 178;
  community organization partnerships 183,
  185; connecting methods courses to school
  contexts 180–181; definitions 179; need
  for science-focused partnerships 178–179;
  research scientist partnerships 184, 186;
  school-university partnerships 181–183, 184;
  summary and recommendations 184–186; types of
  arrangements 181
PCK *see* pedagogical content knowledge (PCK)
PD *see* professional development (PD)
PDS (professional development school), in
  university-school partnerships 179, 182
pedagogical content knowledge (PCK) 6; CoRes
  tools to support mentoring 135; in curricular
  aspects of PST education internationally
  167–169, *168*, 174–175; defined 314–315; as
  development component for science teacher
  leaders 263, 268; in early childhood PST methods
  courses 74; and educative curriculum materials
  390–392; and high-quality science instruction
  331, 332, 333, 334, 336, 337; and informal
  science learning environments (ISLEs) 195;
  integrative *vs.* transformative development 320;
  and opportunities to learn for new hires 248;
  as origin of TPACK 314–315, 321; in science
  methods courses 86; secondary PSTs, reading and
  knowledge 111, 112
pedagogical design capacity (PDC) 390, 393, 395
pedagogical knowledge (PK) 315, 321, 334
pedagogical preparation and teacher retention 151
pedagogical resources, as discursive practice 210–211
pedagogical skills, and indigenous knowledge
  345–346
pedagogies of community ethnography (PCEs) 62
pedagogies supportive of secondary PST learning
  112–115, 116; approximations of practice
  114; reflective practice 113–114; secondary
  PST knowledge 112–113; supporting diverse
  learners 115
pedagogy and science in design of teacher training
  programs 234–235
pedagogy of listening 76–77
pedagogy of place 193

pedagogy of teacher education 9–10
peer discussions, as discursive practice 208
Perceptions of Success Inventory for Beginning
  Teachers 152
performance, supporting, in science methods
  courses 86
personal PCK (pPCK) 331
phenomenology, as qualitative research 35
Philadelphia Negro, The (Du Bois) 42
Philippines: indigenous knowledge in 347
physics, secondary PST challenges and knowledge of
  111, 112–113
place-based education (PBE) 193–194, 292
place-based teaching 467
place conscious 193
place identity 193–194
planning practices, of secondary PSTs 109–110
planning tools for mentoring 135
plants, antimicrobial properties of, as indigenous
  knowledge 344, 346, 347
PLC *see* professional learning communities (PLCs)
podcasts 222
Poland: PST education **165**, 166, *168*, 169, 174
policy, local and national, impact on opportunities to
  learn for new hires 250
policy implications of science teacher
  leadership 268
policy in science teacher preparation 231–241;
  admission and attraction to training programs
  235–236; background and defined 231–232;
  design of training programs 234–235; equity
  issues 237–238; institutions of training programs
  236–237; standards 231, 233–234, 237; summary
  238–239; teacher qualification 232–233
political allies *see* allied political stuggle
Portugal: knowledge in science methods courses
  86; professional learning communities 305; PST
  education 164, **165**, 166, 167, 168, *168*, **170**,
  172, 174
practice-based teacher education, for elementary
  teachers 87, 89–90
practices of secondary PSTs 108–112
practicum experiences: in PST education
  internationally 169–172, **170–172**; of secondary
  PSTs in science classrooms 109–110
practitioner research 28–29
pragmatic approach, in mixed methods research
  42, 45
presence *see* rightful presence
preservice science teacher education (PSTE),
  international research 163–177; background
  163–164; curricular aspects 167–169, *168*;
  practicum experiences 169–172, **170–172**;
  research experience in PSTE 173–174; structure
  of PSTE 164–169, **165**; summary 174–175
preservice science teachers (PSTs): PD for teaching
  science to emergent bilinguals 379–380;
  self-efficacy, in mixed methods research 43–44;

see also field experiences in PST preparation; partnerships in PST education; teachers

principals *see* administrators in schools

privacy, with emergent technologies 227

procedural knowledge 7

procedural neutrality approach, teaching controversial topics 406

professional development (PD): with action research 356–357; and contextualized instruction 444–447, *445*; and development of professional identity 419–420, 422; and educative curriculum materials 391; goals of 287; integrated STEM at secondary level 471–472; long-term, and teacher improvement in high-quality science instruction 333–334; mentoring preservice teachers 138–140, 141–142; and opportunities to learn for new hires 248–250; of teacher educators 10–11; teaching science to emergent bilinguals 378–380; and TPACK 316; training on using large datasets 26

professional development (PD) for inquiry-based instruction 273–286; article search process 273–275; authentic inquiry experiences 278, 281; background 273–274; blended learning 275, 279–280, 282; collaborative community 275, 279, 282; collaborative community and reflection 280–281; defined 273; development of inquiry lessons 278–279, 281–282; features studied 275, **276–277**; research experience for teachers (RETs) 278, 281, 282; summary 282–283; teacher content knowledge and student achievement 275, 282; time and collaborative learning 280

professional development (PD) of culturally responsive science teachers 287–299; article search process 289, **290, 291**; background 287–288; critical reflection 294–295; CRST (culturally responsive science teaching) 288; CRST, cultural exposure in **291**, 291–292; culturally relevant pedagogy and culturally responsive teaching 288; lesson and unit design 293–294; partnerships with scientists and community experts 292; science topics 290, 291–292; student information gathering 293; summary and recommendations 295–296

professional development school (PDS), in university-school partnerships 179, 182

professional knowledge *see* teacher professional knowledge, and high-quality science instruction

professional learning communities (PLCs) 300–312; action research program 357; also known as 301, 305; article search process 301; background 300–301; benefits to new teachers 304–306; benefits to teachers in all phases 306–309; characteristics of 300; phases of teachers' careers 301–304, *303*; summary and recommendations 309–310

Professional Learning Environments (PLEs) 34

Professional Standards for Accreditation of Teacher Preparation Institutions 233

project-based instruction (PBI) 110

Project for Enhancing Effective Learning (PEEL) 355

Promoting Science among English Language Learners (P-SELL) Project 379

PST *see* preservice science teachers (PSTs)

PSTE *see* preservice science teacher education (PSTE)

purpose statements, in mixed methods research 43–45

qualifications for teaching, policy in science teacher preparation 232–233, 238

qualitative research 28–40; approaches 29; article search process 29–31; characteristics 29, *30*; conducting 31; defined 28; expanding 38; summary 37–39

qualitative research, spotlight studies: action research 36–37; case study 32–33; ethnography 34–35; general qualitative 31–32; grounded theory 33–34; narrative 35–36; phenomenology 35; self-study 37

questioning techniques 281–282

questionnaire items in large educational surveys **18–19**

randomised control trial (RCT) 7

Rapid Survey of Student Thinking document 135

reasoning, informal 433, 435

reauthoring rights, in rightful presence 54, 59–60

reciprocity, in partnerships in PST education 184

Reconceptualising Maths and Science Teacher Education Programs, Australia 184

reflection: and collaborative community in PD for inquiry-based instruction 280–281; critical, of culturally responsive science teachers 294–295; on discursive practices 211

reflection tools for mentoring 135–136

reflective dialogue, as feature of PLCs 300, 301

reflective practice, as pedagogy supportive of secondary PST learning 113–114

reflective triadic partnerships and reflective teaching process 180

reform, educational: emotion and science teacher education 431; reform-minded science teachers and professional identity 416, 418, 420; science teacher identity and ISLEs 190

rehearsals 114

re-mediating relations, in collaborative researcher-teacher learning 459–460

research: questions, in mixed methods research 43, 44–45; by students on controversial topics 407–408; *see also* educational surveys; mixed methods research; qualitative research

researcher-teacher collaboration *see* collaborative researcher-teacher learning

research experience: in design of teacher training programs 235; and development of professional

identity 419; in PST education internationally
173–174
research experience for teachers (RETs) 278,
281, 282
research in science teacher education 5–15;
areas of research 7–11; background 5–6; key
constructs in 6–7; pedagogy of teacher education
9–10; summary 12; teacher beliefs, attitudes,
dispositions, and identities 8–9; teacher education
communities, institutions, and accountability 11;
teacher educators' professional development 10–11
Research on Science Education Survey (ROSES) 9
research-practice partnerships 181; *see also*
partnerships in PST education
research scientist partnerships in PST education 184,
186; *see also* scientist partnerships
resilience of teachers 252
resources: digital, collaboration in PLCs 308, 309;
for integrated STEM 469, 470; from school
and community, and opportunities to learn for
new hires 251; science teacher leaders (STL)
responsibilities for resources, materials, and safety
267; *see also* educative curriculum materials
(ECM)
rhetoric-practice gap 109
rightfulness claimed through presence 54, 56–57
rightful presence 52–63; defined 52; designing for,
with community ethnography 58–60; equity
as inclusion 53; framework and tenets 53–55;
noticing student bids for 55–58, 61; pedagogies of
community ethnography (PCEs) 62; summary 62
rigorous and consequential elementary science
teaching 83, 91
Rittel, Horst 403
robotics 222
role-playing, as discursive practice 207, 208, 211
Romania: emerging technologies research 222
Rowe, M. B. 121
Russia: PST education 164, **165**, 166, **171**, 172, 174
Rwanda: PST education 173

safety: and convenience, with emerging technologies
223, 224, 227; safe science learning environments,
for students with disabilities 367–369; science
teacher leaders (STL) responsible for 267
Salamanca Statement and Framework for Action on
Special Needs Education 363
sample weighting 19
satisfaction, and teacher retention 152
Saudi Arabia: emerging technologies research 222;
inclusive science teacher education 366
scenarios for teaching, as discursive practice 210
school culture: and development of professional
identity 419–420; preschool culture *vs.* culture
of science 75; support of leadership development
264–265
schools: context importance for mentoring 137–138;
departmental organization of secondary schools,

and STEM instruction 470; influences by science
teacher leaders 261, 266; as PST field experiences
122, **122**; rural or high-need schools, incentive
programs for teachers 147, 150–151, 237–238
Schools and Staffing Survey 20
school-university partnerships 181–183, 184
science, technology, and society (STS) 107
Science and IK Project (SIKSP), South Africa 346
Science Education for Responsible Citizenship,
Europe 190
science fairs 430
science-focused partnerships, need for 178–179; *see
also* partnerships in PST education
science methods courses for elementary teachers
85–88, **92**
Science Teacher Education Partnership with Schools
(STEPS), Australia 180–181
Science Teacher Efficacy Beliefs Instrument 152, 180
science teacher leaders (STL): defined 257, *258*,
266–267; descriptions of 260; impacts on
educational systems 266; impacts on peers and
colleagues 265–266; impacts on student learning
266; impacts on themselves (confidence) 265;
influence on schools 261; influence on teachers
260–261; influencing capital (social, symbolic,
and cultural) 261–262, 268; responsibilities
for advocacy 260, 266, 267; responsibilities for
resources, materials, and safety 267
science teacher leadership 257–272; article
search process 258–259; background 257–258;
defined 259–260, 262; development, supportive
conditions for 264–265; development components
263–264; development models 262–263;
recommendations 267–270; summary 266–267,
267, 270
scientific discourse *see* discursive practices, in science
education (SEDP)
scientific literacy, defined 408
scientist partnerships: for culturally responsive science
teachers 292; and high-quality science instruction
336; in PST education 184, 186; TPACK
community approach 319
scientists, career-change 429–431
Scope, Sequence and Coordination (SS&C),
USA 356
secondary preservice science teachers (S-PSTs)
97–118; article search process 97–98; background
97; characteristics of, cognitive and non-cognitive
98, *99–102*, 102, 107–108, 116; deficit
perspective 108, 116; pedagogies supportive of
S-PST learning *104–107*, 112–115, 116; *see also*
pedagogies supportive of secondary PST learning;
practices of S-PSTs *103–104*, 108–112, 116;
summary 115–117
Secondary Science Teaching with English
Language and Literacy Acquisition (SSTELLA)
Project 379
seed germination, and indigenous knowledge 347

self-efficacy of teachers: and educative curriculum materials 392–393; elementary PSTs 84, 90; and informal science learning environments (ISLEs) 192; in mixed methods research 43–44, 47; in PLCs 308; of PSTs in partnerships 180, 182, 183; teacher retention and perceptions of preparation 152

self-study, as qualitative research 8, 37

Senegal: PST education 173

sense of place 193

SENSE rating system 179

sensitive issues, controversial topics as 408–409

sequential model of teacher education **165**, 166, 174

service learning 33

Sheltered Instruction Observation Protocol (SIOP) 377

Shulman, Lee 6

simulations, as discursive practice 207, 211

simulation software 313

Singapore: educative curriculum materials 391; high-quality science instruction research 335; PST education 173; teacher preparation policy 236

Slovenia: PST education **165**, 166, 167, 168, *168*, 169, 174

Smart Science Initiative, Australia 319

SMK *see* subject matter knowledge (SMK)

social capital of science teacher leaders 261, 262, 268

social-emotional learning (SEL) for inclusive classrooms 369

socialized contexts and opportunities to learn for new hires 251

social justice: and equity, promotion of, with action research 357–358; as identity dimension 416, 418

social media 222

sociocultural learning theory perspectives, on PSTs in field experience research 124, 128

socioscientific inquiry (SSI): as approach to contextualization of science instruction 440, **441**, 442, *442*, 443, 445–446, 447

socioscientific issues (SSI): as controversial topics 405; emotion and informal reasoning 433–435; interactive action research 355; secondary PST beliefs in 107

South Africa: argumentation in curriculum reform 5; culturally responsive science teaching (CRST) 289, 292; emerging technologies research 222; indigenous knowledge in 343, 344, 346, 347; intrinsic and extrinsic factors in implementation of inquiry-based learning 45, 47; opportunities to learn for new hires 250; partnerships in PST education 178; PST education **165**, 166, 169, 173; teacher preparation policy 232; teaching science to emergent bilinguals 380–381, 382; using TIMSS data as example of analysis 22–25

South Korea: action research 355; cultural diversity in early childhood PST studies 75; culturally responsive science teaching (CRST) 289; emotion

and science teacher education 434; PST education 164, **165**, *168*, 173, 174

Spain: preparation of EC professionals 71, *71*

special needs education *see* inclusive education for students with disabilities

spreadsheets 313, 319

S-PSTs *see* secondary preservice science teachers (S-PSTs)

standardized tests: effect on mentoring relationships 138; impact on opportunities to learn for new hires 250; student achievement and ACP-prepared teachers 152–153; and students with disabilities 370

Standards for Professional Development for Teachers of Science 233

Standards for Science Teacher Preparation 233

standards for teacher education: accountability for 11; in Australia 182; international 164; and policy 231, 233–234, 237; and students with disabilities (SWD) 364; in United States *see* Next Generation Science Standards (NGSS)

STEBI-B (Science Teaching Efficacy Belief Instrument-B) 73

STEM (science, technology, engineering, and mathematics): in action research, qualitative study 36; and culturally responsive science teachers 294; curriculum reform 5; *see also* integrated STEM teacher education

stem cell research 434

STIP approach 367

STL *see* science teacher leaders

Stoplight Model for Reflection, mentoring tool 135

strategies, as type of research 8

strengths-based instruction and assessments 370

structured science teaching 88

student achievement and learning: and ACP-prepared teachers 152–153; cognition of science, and action research 355; and high-quality science instruction 331–335; impact of science teacher leaders 266; with inclusive science teacher education 369–370; relationship to teacher certification 231, 233; STEM instruction as motivation 470–471, 472; teacher content knowledge and PD for inquiry-based instruction 275, 282; teachers' beliefs about, and educative curriculum materials 393; teachers' collective responsibility for, as feature of PLCs 300

student-centered learning: in contextualizing instruction 444; and integrated STEM 471

student content knowledge (SCK) 334

student research and argumentation on controversial topics 407–408

students' lived experiences: and student information gathering 293; understanding by PSTs in field experiences 127

students with disabilities (SWD) *see* inclusive education for students with disabilities

student teaching 119, 120; *see also* practicum experiences
subject matter knowledge (SMK): and classroom-based opportunities to learn 252; in curricular aspects of PST education internationally 167, *168*, 174–175; in early childhood PST education 73; and educative curriculum materials 391; for elementary teachers 84–85, 86; and high-quality science instruction 331, 335, 337
summer camps 35, 123
surfacing different perspectives, in collaborative researcher-teacher learning 456–457, 459
surveys *see* educational surveys
Sweden: action research 357; and informal science learning environments (ISLEs) 192; PST education *168*, **171**, 173
Switzerland: high-quality science instruction research 334
symbolic capital, of science teacher leaders 261, 262, 268

Taiwan: general qualitative study 32; PST education 164, **165**, 166
Tanzania: contextualized instruction 444, 447; digital technologies **317**
teacher education communities and institutions 11
teacher education programs: for elementary teachers 90–91, **92**; opportunities to learn as newly hired teachers 246–248; policy and training programs *see* policy in science teacher preparation
teacher noticing: mixed noticing 113; student bids for rightful presence 55, 61–62
teacher professional knowledge, and high-quality science instruction: defined 331; and student learning 331–333; and teacher practices, and student learning 333–335
Teacher Professional Knowledge Bases (TPKB) 6
teachers: attrition and shortages of 147, 151, 153–154; career phases in professional life cycle 301–304, *303*, 309; as co-learners with paper circuit mistakes video 60, 61; with disabilities 370–371; influences by science teacher leaders 260–261; lived experiences and informal science learning environments (ISLEs) 194, *198*; measures of effectiveness of ACPs 150–153; recruitment of 147, 149, 237–238; retention of 151–152, 415; *see also* attitudes of teachers; beliefs of teachers; early childhood preservice teachers (EC-PSTs); elementary teachers; inservice teachers; mentor teachers; preservice science teachers (PSTs); secondary preservice science teachers (S-PSTs)
Teach for All (other countries) 146, 147, 149
Teach for America (TFA) 146
Teaching Academies Partnerships Program, Australia 181
Teaching Cases (TC) PD program 334
teaching licenses 232–233, 238

teaching practice groups (TPG), as professional learning communities 305
teaching practices: simulations, as discursive practice 207; willingness to examine, as feature of PLCs 300
teaching rehearsals, as discursive practice 207
Teaching Science Inquiry (TSI) 280
Tech Clubs 123
Technological Acceptance Model (TAM) 219
technological content knowledge (TCK) 315
technological knowledge (TK) 315
technological pedagogical content knowledge *see* TPACK
technological pedagogical content knowledge (TPCK) 315
technological pedagogical knowledge (TPK) 315, 321
technological pedagogical science knowledge (TPASK) 316, **317**
technologies *see* emerging technologies
textbooks, inequalities in science education 25
Thailand: partnerships in PST education 185
theoretical and methodological framing, of field experience research on PSTs 123–124
theories of change, in teaching emergent bilinguals 383–384
theories of learning **453**, 453–454; learning as acquisition **453**, 454; learning as expansion 452, **453**, 454, 457, 459, 460; learning as participation **453**, 454
theory-to-practice 108–109, 234
time, and collaborative learning in PD for inquiry-based instruction 280
tools: data analysis tools 20, **23**; for opportunities to learn for new hires 249; to support mentoring work 134–136, 140, 141; *see also* resources
Topic Specific Professional Knowledge (TSPK) 6
toxicology, in ethnography qualitative research 34
TPACK (technological pedagogical content knowledge) 313–324; article search process 314; background 313–314; community approach 319; defined, and origins of 314–315; of early childhood PSTs 73; emerging technologies 219; instructional design and planning 316, **317**, 318; methodological approaches 320; PD approaches 315–316; PD with specific technologies **318**, 319; recommendations 321–322; strengths of, for PD 319–320; summary 322; theories in action 320–321
TPACK-COIR (TPACK comprehension, observation, instruction, and reflection) 319
traditional certification program (TCP), compared with alternative pathways to teaching 147–154
Traditional Ecological Knowledge 292
transformative partnership arrangement 181
transformative *vs.* integrative development of PCK 320
translanguaging 380–381

Trends in International Mathematics and Science Surveys (TIMSS) **18–19**, 19–20, **23**, 26; analysis example from South Africa 22–25; on professional development and cultural diversity 287

triadic partnerships 180

Trinidad and Tobago: contextualized instruction 446; culturally responsive science teaching (CRST) 289

trust, in partnerships in PST education 184

Turkey: action research 357; content courses for elementary teachers 84; emerging technologies research 222; emotion and science teacher education 433; and informal science learning environments (ISLEs) 192; integrated STEM 468, 470; PST education **165**, 166, 167, 168, *168*, 169, 173; secondary PST research 108

Uganda: PST education 173

undergraduate laboratory courses, as PST field experiences 123

United Kingdom: Ofsted (Office for Standards in Education, Children's Services and Skills) 11; partnerships in PST education 178; *see also* England

United Nations, Sustainable Development Goal 6 329

United States: action research 356, 358; alternative pathways to teaching **148**, 150; content courses for elementary teachers 85; cultural diversity in early childhood PST studies 75; culturally responsive science teaching (CRST) 288, 289, 291–292, 293; educational surveys *see* educational surveys; emerging technologies research 222; Hawaiian traditional practices 292, 443; high-quality science instruction research 332, 333, 334, 335–336; incentive programs for teachers in high-need schools 238; indigenous knowledge in 345; and informal science learning environments (ISLEs) 192; integrated STEM 467, 469–470; mentoring tools 135; opportunities to learn for new hires 250; partnerships in PST education 178, 181, 182, 183; preparation of EC professionals 71, *71*; professional identity 420; PST education 164, **165**, 166, 168, *168*; science methods courses for elementary teachers 87; science teacher leadership 260; secondary PST research 108, 116;

standards *see* Next Generation Science Standards (NGSS); standards for teacher education; teacher preparation policy 232, 233, 234, 236, 237; teaching science to emergent bilinguals 379, 382; Virginia, Alternate Routes to Licensure 150

Universal Design for Learning (UDL) 367

universities: as institutions of training programs, and policy in science teacher preparation 236–237; resources for integrated STEM 469

University of Florida: PSTs' science content knowledge 121

University of Georgia (UGA): portal schools 120–121

University of Iowa: field-based clinical experiences 121

vaccines, as controversial topic 411–412

vertical professional learning community (V-PLC) 33

video, for PST education 10, 74, 113

video clubs 113–114

videoconference, in PST field experience 123

virtual laboratories 222

virtual reality field trips (VRFTs) 222

visually impaired 368; *see also* inclusive education for students with disabilities

vocabulary instruction 365–366

vocational schools, as institutions of training programs, and policy in science teacher preparation 236–237

Web-based Inquiry Science Environment (WISE) 313

well-started beginners 83

western science, relationship with indigenous knowledge 341, 342

Whiteness: and development of professional identity 418; and heteropatriarchy and equity 53, 54; and linguistic hegemony 382, 383

wicked problem, controversial topics as 403

wildlife sanctuaries, as ISLEs 190–191

Wiley Handbook of Educational Policy, The 231

written curriculum 388

Zambia: PST education 173

Zimbabwe: emerging technologies research 222